PEARSON

Margaret L. Lial • John Hornsby • Terry McGinnis

Intermediate Algebra

Custom Edition for Moberly Area Community College

Taken from:
Intermediate Algebra, Fifth Edition
by Margaret L. Lial, John Hornsby, and Terry McGinnis

Cover Art: Courtesy of Digital Vision/Getty Images.

Taken from:

Intermediate Algebra, Fifth Edition
by Margaret L. Lial, John Hornsby, and Terry McGinnis
Copyright © 2012, 2008, 2004, 2000 by Pearson Education, Inc.
Published by Addison-Wesley
San Francisco, California 94111

This special edition published in cooperation with Pearson Learning Solutions.

Pearson Learning Solutions, 501 Boylston Street, Suite 900, Boston, MA 02116
A Pearson Education Company
www.pearsoned.com

Printed in the United States of America

7 8 9 10 11 12 13 14 15 16 V092 18 17 16 15 14

000200010270666593

SW

ISBN 10: 1-256-39856-X
ISBN 13: 978-1-256-39856-1

To Callie, Kurt, Clayton, and Grady—
Welcome to our family.

Marge, John, and Terry

Contents

5 Factoring and Applications 295

5.1 The Greatest Common Factor; Factoring by Grouping 296
5.2 Factoring Trinomials 304
5.3 More on Factoring Trinomials 309
5.4 Special Factoring Techniques 317
SUMMARY EXERCISES on Factoring 325
STUDY SKILLS Preparing for Your Math Final Exam 328
5.5 Solving Quadratic Equations by Factoring 329
5.6 Applications of Quadratic Equations 337
Chapter 5 Summary 347
Chapter 5 Review Exercises 350
Chapter 5 Test 353
Chapter 1-5 Cumulative Review Exercises 354

6 Rational Expressions and Applications 357

6.1 The Fundamental Property of Rational Expressions 358
6.2 Multiplying and Dividing Rational Expressions 367
6.3 Least Common Denominators 373
6.4 Adding and Subtracting Rational Expressions 378
6.5 Complex Fractions 386
6.6 Solving Equations with Rational Expressions 395
SUMMARY EXERCISES on Rational Expressions and Equations 404
6.7 Applications of Rational Expressions 406
Chapter 6 Summary 415
Chapter 6 Review Exercises 419
Chapter 6 Test 422
Chapters 1–6 Cumulative Review Exercises 423

Graphs, Linear Equations, and Functions   425

7.1 Review of Graphs and Slopes of Lines   426
7.2 Review of Equations of Lines; Linear Models   444
SUMMARY EXERCISES on Slopes and Equations of Lines   456
7.3 Introduction to Relations and Functions   456
7.4 Function Notation and Linear Functions   464
7.5 Operations on Functions and Composition   472
7.6 Variation   480
Chapter 7 Summary   489
Chapter 7 Review Exercises   493
Chapter 7 Test   496
Chapters 1–7 Cumulative Review Exercises   498

Systems of Linear Equations   501

8.1 Solving Systems of Linear Equations by Graphing   502
8.2 Solving Systems of Linear Equations by Substitution   511
8.3 Solving Systems of Linear Equations by Elimination   518
SUMMARY EXERCISES on Solving Systems of Linear Equations   524
8.4 Solving Systems of Linear Equations in Three Variables   526
8.5 Applications of Systems of Linear Equations   533
8.6 Solving Systems of Linear Equations by Matrix Methods   547
Chapter 8 Summary   553
Chapter 8 Review Exercises   557
Chapter 8 Test   560
Chapters 1–8 Cumulative Review Exercises   561

Inequalities and Absolute Value   565

9.1 Set Operations and Compound Inequalities   566
9.2 Absolute Value Equations and Inequalities   574
SUMMARY EXERCISES on Solving Linear and Absolute Value Equations
and Inequalities   583
9.3 Linear Inequalities in Two Variables   584
Chapter 9 Summary   592
Chapter 9 Review Exercises   594
Chapter 9 Test   596
Chapters 1–9 Cumulative Review Exercises   596

10 Roots, Radicals, and Root Functions   599

10.1 Radical Expressions and Graphs   600
10.2 Rational Exponents   611
10.3 Simplifying Radical Expressions   619
10.4 Adding and Subtracting Radical Expressions   629
10.5 Multiplying and Dividing Radical Expressions   634
SUMMARY EXERCISES on Operations with Radicals and Rational Exponents   642
10.6 Solving Equations with Radicals   644
10.7 Complex Numbers   650
Chapter 10 Summary   658
Chapter 10 Review Exercises   662
Chapter 10 Test   665
Chapters 1–10 Cumulative Review Exercises   667

11 Quadratic Equations, Inequalities, and Functions   669

11.1 Solving Quadratic Equations by the Square Root Property   670
11.2 Solving Quadratic Equations by Completing the Square   676
11.3 Solving Quadratic Equations by the Quadratic Formula   683
11.4 Equations Quadratic in Form   690
SUMMARY EXERCISES on Solving Quadratic Equations   700
11.5 Formulas and Further Applications   701
11.6 Graphs of Quadratic Functions   709
11.7 More about Parabolas and Their Applications   719
11.8 Polynomial and Rational Inequalities   730
Chapter 11 Summary   737
Chapter 11 Review Exercises   740
Chapter 11 Test   744
Chapters 1–11 Cumulative Review Exercises   746

12 Inverse, Exponential, and Logarithmic Functions   749

12.1 Inverse Functions   750
12.2 Exponential Functions   758
12.3 Logarithmic Functions   766
12.4 Properties of Logarithms   773
12.5 Common and Natural Logarithms   782
12.6 Exponential and Logarithmic Equations; Further Applications   791
Chapter 12 Summary   801
Chapter 12 Review Exercises   804
Chapter 12 Test   808
Chapters 1–12 Cumulative Review Exercises   810

Nonlinear Functions, Conic Sections, and Nonlinear Systems   813

13.1   Additional Graphs of Functions   814
13.2   The Circle and the Ellipse   820
13.3   The Hyperbola and Functions Defined by Radicals   828
13.4   Nonlinear Systems of Equations   835
13.5   Second-Degree Inequalities and Systems of Inequalities   842
       Chapter 13 Summary   847
       Chapter 13 Review Exercises   850
       Chapter 13 Test   852
       Chapters 1–13 Cumulative Review Exercises   853

Sequences and Series   855

14.1   Sequences and Series   856
14.2   Arithmetic Sequences   862
14.3   Geometric Sequences   869
14.4   The Binomial Theorem   879
       Chapter 14 Summary   884
       Chapter 14 Review Exercises   887
       Chapter 14 Test   889
       Chapters 1–14 Cumulative Review Exercises   890

Answers to Selected Exercises   A-1
Glossary   G-1
Credits   C-1
Index   I-1

CHAPTER 5

Factoring and Applications

5.1 The Greatest Common Factor; Factoring by Grouping

5.2 Factoring Trinomials

5.3 More on Factoring Trinomials

5.4 Special Factoring Techniques

Summary Exercises on Factoring

5.5 Solving Quadratic Equations by Factoring

5.6 Applications of Quadratic Equations

Wireless communication uses radio waves to carry signals and messages across distances. Cellular phones, one of the most popular forms of wireless communication, have become an invaluable tool for people to stay connected to family, friends, and work while on the go. In 2007, there were about 243 million cell phone subscribers in the United States, with 81% of the population having cell phone service. Total revenue from this service was about $133 billion. (*Source:* CITA—The Wireless Association.)

In **Exercise 37** of **Section 5.6,** we use a *quadratic equation* to model the number of cell phone subscribers in the United States.

The Greatest Common Factor; Factoring by Grouping

OBJECTIVES

1 Find the greatest common factor of a list of terms.

2 Factor out the greatest common factor.

3 Factor by grouping.

Recall from **Section 1.1** that to **factor** means "to write a quantity as a product." That is, factoring is the opposite of multiplying.

Multiplying	*Factoring*
$6 \cdot 2 = 12$	$12 = 6 \cdot 2$
↑ ↑ ↑	↑ ↑ ↑
Factors Product	Product Factors

Other **factored forms** of 12 are

$$-6(-2), \quad 3 \cdot 4, \quad -3(-4), \quad 12 \cdot 1, \quad \text{and} \quad -12(-1).$$

More than two factors may be used, so another factored form of 12 is $2 \cdot 2 \cdot 3$.

OBJECTIVE 1 **Find the greatest common factor of a list of terms.** An integer that is a factor of two or more integers is a **common factor** of those integers. For example, 6 is a common factor of 18 and 24, since 6 is a factor of both 18 and 24. Other common factors of 18 and 24 are 1, 2, and 3.

The **greatest common factor (GCF)** of a list of integers is the largest common factor of those integers. Thus, 6 is the greatest common factor of 18 and 24, since it is the largest of their common factors.

NOTE *Factors* of a number are also *divisors* of the number. The *greatest common factor* is actually the same as the *greatest common divisor*. Here are some useful divisibility rules for deciding what numbers divide into a given number.

A Whole Number Divisible by	Must Have the Following Property:
2	Ends in 0, 2, 4, 6, or 8
3	Sum of digits divisible by 3
4	Last two digits form a number divisible by 4
5	Ends in 0 or 5
6	Divisible by both 2 and 3
8	Last three digits form a number divisible by 8
9	Sum of digits divisible by 9
10	Ends in 0

Finding the Greatest Common Factor (GCF)

Step 1 **Factor.** Write each number in prime factored form.

Step 2 **List common factors.** List each prime number or each variable that is a factor of every term in the list. (If a prime does not appear in one of the prime factored forms, it cannot appear in the greatest common factor.)

Step 3 **Choose least exponents.** Use as exponents on the common prime factors the *least* exponents from the prime factored forms.

Step 4 **Multiply** the primes from Step 3. If there are no primes left after Step 3, the greatest common factor is 1.

**NOW TRY
EXERCISE 1**

Find the greatest common factor for each list of numbers.

(a) 24, 36

(b) 54, 90, 108

(c) 15, 19, 25

EXAMPLE 1   Finding the Greatest Common Factor for Numbers

Find the greatest common factor for each list of numbers.

(a) 30, 45

$$30 = 2 \cdot 3 \cdot 5$$
$$45 = 3 \cdot 3 \cdot 5$$

Write the prime factored form of each number.

Use each prime the least number of times it appears in all the factored forms. There is no 2 in the prime factored form of 45, so there will be no 2 in the greatest common factor. The least number of times 3 appears in all the factored forms is 1, and the least number of times 5 appears is also 1.

$$\text{GCF} = 3^1 \cdot 5^1 = 15$$

(b) 72, 120, 432

$$72 = 2 \cdot 2 \cdot 2 \cdot 3 \cdot 3$$
$$120 = 2 \cdot 2 \cdot 2 \cdot 3 \cdot 5$$
$$432 = 2 \cdot 2 \cdot 2 \cdot 2 \cdot 3 \cdot 3 \cdot 3$$

Write the prime factored form of each number.

The least number of times 2 appears in all the factored forms is 3, and the least number of times 3 appears is 1. There is no 5 in the prime factored form of either 72 or 432.

$$\text{GCF} = 2^3 \cdot 3^1 = 24$$

(c) 10, 11, 14

$$10 = 2 \cdot 5$$
$$11 = 11$$
$$14 = 2 \cdot 7$$

Write the prime factored form of each number.

There are no primes common to all three numbers, so the GCF is 1.   NOW TRY

The greatest common factor can also be found for a list of variable terms. For example, the terms x^4, x^5, x^6, and x^7 have x^4 as the greatest common factor because each of these terms can be written with x^4 as a factor.

$$x^4 = 1 \cdot x^4, \quad x^5 = x \cdot x^4, \quad x^6 = x^2 \cdot x^4, \quad x^7 = x^3 \cdot x^4$$

NOTE   *The exponent on a variable in the GCF is the least exponent that appears in all the common factors.*

EXAMPLE 2   Finding the Greatest Common Factor for Variable Terms

Find the greatest common factor for each list of terms.

(a) $21m^7, 18m^6, 45m^8, 24m^5$

$$21m^7 = 3 \cdot 7 \cdot m^7$$
$$18m^6 = 2 \cdot 3 \cdot 3 \cdot m^6$$
$$45m^8 = 3 \cdot 3 \cdot 5 \cdot m^8$$
$$24m^5 = 2 \cdot 2 \cdot 2 \cdot 3 \cdot m^5$$

Here, 3 is the greatest common factor of the coefficients 21, 18, 45, and 24. The least exponent on m is 5.

$$\text{GCF} = 3m^5$$

NOW TRY ANSWERS
1. (a) 12   **(b)** 18   **(c)** 1

⤷ NOW TRY
⤷ EXERCISE 2

Find the greatest common factor for each list of terms.

(a) $25k^3, 15k^2, 35k^5$

(b) m^3n^5, m^4n^4, m^5n^2

(b) $x^4y^2, \quad x^7y^5, \quad x^3y^7, \quad y^{15}$

$x^4y^2 = x^4 \cdot y^2$

$x^7y^5 = x^7 \cdot y^5$

$x^3y^7 = x^3 \cdot y^7$

$y^{15} = y^{15}$

There is no x in the last term, y^{15}, so x will not appear in the greatest common factor. There is a y in each term, however, and 2 is the least exponent on y.

$$\text{GCF} = y^2$$

NOW TRY ⤸

OBJECTIVE 2 **Factor out the greatest common factor.** Writing a polynomial (a sum) in factored form as a product is called **factoring.** For example, the polynomial

$$3m + 12$$

has two terms: $3m$ and 12. The greatest common factor of these two terms is 3. We can write $3m + 12$ so that each term is a product with 3 as one factor.

$$3m + 12$$

$$= 3 \cdot m + 3 \cdot 4 \quad \text{GCF} = 3$$

$$= 3(m + 4) \quad \text{Distributive property}$$

The factored form of $3m + 12$ is $3(m + 4)$. This process is called **factoring out the greatest common factor.**

⚠ **CAUTION** The polynomial $3m + 12$ is *not* in factored form when written as

$$3 \cdot m + 3 \cdot 4. \quad \text{Not in factored form}$$

The *terms* are factored, but the polynomial is not. The factored form of $3m + 12$ is the *product*

$$3(m + 4). \quad \text{In factored form}$$

EXAMPLE 3 Factoring Out the Greatest Common Factor

Write in factored form by factoring out the greatest common factor.

(a) $5y^2 + 10y$

$$= 5y(y) + 5y(2) \quad \text{GCF} = 5y$$

$$= 5y(y + 2) \quad \text{Distributive property}$$

CHECK Multiply the factored form.

$$5y(y + 2)$$

$$= 5y(y) + 5y(2) \quad \text{Distributive property}$$

$$= 5y^2 + 10y \ \checkmark \quad \text{Original polynomial}$$

(b) $20m^5 + 10m^4 + 15m^3$

$$= 5m^3(4m^2) + 5m^3(2m) + 5m^3(3) \quad \text{GCF} = 5m^3$$

$$= 5m^3(4m^2 + 2m + 3) \quad \text{Factor out } 5m^3.$$

CHECK $5m^3(4m^2 + 2m + 3)$

$$= 20m^5 + 10m^4 + 15m^3 \ \checkmark \quad \text{Original polynomial}$$

NOW TRY ANSWERS
2. (a) $5k^2$ (b) m^3n^2

NOW TRY
EXERCISE 3

Write in factored form by factoring out the greatest common factor.

(a) $7t^4 - 14t^3$

(b) $8x^6 - 20x^5 + 28x^4$

(c) $30m^4n^3 - 42m^2n^2$

(c) $x^5 + x^3$

$= x^3(x^2) + x^3(1)$ GCF $= x^3$

$= x^3(x^2 + 1)$ ⟵ Don't forget the 1.

Check mentally by distributing x^3 over each term inside the parentheses.

(d) $20m^7p^2 - 36m^3p^4$

$= 4m^3p^2(5m^4) - 4m^3p^2(9p^2)$ GCF $= 4m^3p^2$

$= 4m^3p^2(5m^4 - 9p^2)$ Factor out $4m^3p^2$.   NOW TRY

⚠ **CAUTION**   Be sure to include the 1 in a problem like **Example 3(c).** *Check that the factored form can be multiplied out to give the original polynomial.*

NOW TRY
EXERCISE 4

Write in factored form by factoring out the greatest common factor.

(a) $x(x + 2) + 5(x + 2)$

(b) $a(t + 10) - b(t + 10)$

EXAMPLE 4   Factoring Out the Greatest Common Factor

Write in factored form by factoring out the greatest common factor.

        Same

(a) $a(a + 3) + 4(a + 3)$ The binomial $a + 3$ is the greatest common factor.

$= (a + 3)(a + 4)$ Factor out $a + 3$.

(b) $x^2(x + 1) - 5(x + 1)$

$= (x + 1)(x^2 - 5)$ Factor out $x + 1$.   NOW TRY

NOTE   In factored forms like those in **Example 4,** the order of the factors does not matter because of the commutative property of multiplication.

$(a + 3)(a + 4)$ can also be written $(a + 4)(a + 3).$

OBJECTIVE 3   **Factor by grouping.** *When a polynomial has four terms, common factors can sometimes be used to factor by grouping.*

EXAMPLE 5   Factoring by Grouping

Factor by grouping.

(a) $2x + 6 + ax + 3a$

Group the first two terms and the last two terms, since the first two terms have a common factor of 2 and the last two terms have a common factor of a.

$2x + 6 + ax + 3a$

$= (2x + 6) + (ax + 3a)$ Group the terms.

$= 2(x + 3) + a(x + 3)$ Factor each group.

The expression is still not in factored form because it is the *sum* of two terms. Now, however, $x + 3$ is a common factor and can be factored out.

$= 2(x + 3) + a(x + 3)$ $x + 3$ is a common factor.

$(2 + a)(x + 3)$ is also correct. — $= (x + 3)(2 + a)$ Factor out $x + 3$.

NOW TRY ANSWERS

3. (a) $7t^3(t - 2)$

(b) $4x^4(2x^2 - 5x + 7)$

(c) $6m^2n^2(5m^2n - 7)$

4. (a) $(x + 2)(x + 5)$

(b) $(t + 10)(a - b)$

NOW TRY
EXERCISE 5

Factor by grouping.

(a) $ab + 3a + 5b + 15$

(b) $12xy + 3x + 4y + 1$

(c) $x^3 + 5x^2 - 8x - 40$

The final result $(x + 3)(2 + a)$ is in factored form because it is a *product.*

CHECK $(x + 3)(2 + a)$

$\qquad = 2x + ax + 6 + 3a$ FOIL (Section 5.5)

$\qquad = 2x + 6 + ax + 3a$ ✓ Rearrange terms to obtain the original polynomial.

(b) $6ax + 24x + a + 4$

$\qquad = (6ax + 24x) + (a + 4)$ Group the terms.

$\qquad = 6x(a + 4) + 1(a + 4)$ Factor each group.

Remember the 1.

$\qquad = (a + 4)(6x + 1)$ Factor out $a + 4$.

CHECK $(a + 4)(6x + 1)$

$\qquad = 6ax + a + 24x + 4$ FOIL

$\qquad = 6ax + 24x + a + 4$ ✓ Rearrange terms to obtain the original polynomial.

(c) $2x^2 - 10x + 3xy - 15y$

$\qquad = (2x^2 - 10x) + (3xy - 15y)$ Group the terms.

$\qquad = 2x(x - 5) + 3y(x - 5)$ Factor each group.

$\qquad = (x - 5)(2x + 3y)$ Factor out $x - 5$.

CHECK $(x - 5)(2x + 3y)$

$\qquad = 2x^2 + 3xy - 10x - 15y$ FOIL

$\qquad = 2x^2 - 10x + 3xy - 15y$ ✓ Original polynomial

(d) $t^3 + 2t^2 - 3t - 6$

Write a + sign between the groups.

$\qquad = (t^3 + 2t^2) + (-3t - 6)$ Group the terms.

$\qquad = t^2(t + 2) - 3(t + 2)$ Factor out -3 so there is a common factor, $t + 2$; $-3(t + 2) = -3t - 6$.

Be careful with signs.

$\qquad = (t + 2)(t^2 - 3)$ Factor out $t + 2$.

Check by multiplying.

NOW TRY

⚠ CAUTION   *Be careful with signs when grouping* in a problem like **Example 5(d).** It is wise to check the factoring in the second step, as shown in the side comment in that example, before continuing.

Factoring a Polynomial with Four Terms by Grouping

Step 1   **Group terms.** Collect the terms into two groups so that each group has a common factor.

Step 2   **Factor within groups.** Factor out the greatest common factor from each group.

Step 3   **Factor the entire polynomial.** Factor out a common binomial factor from the results of Step 2.

Step 4   **If necessary, rearrange terms.** If Step 2 does not result in a common binomial factor, try a different grouping.

NOW TRY ANSWERS
5. (a) $(b + 3)(a + 5)$
   (b) $(4y + 1)(3x + 1)$
   (c) $(x + 5)(x^2 - 8)$

NOW TRY
EXERCISE 6

Factor by grouping.

(a) $12p^2 - 28q - 16pq + 21p$

(b) $5xy - 6 - 15x + 2y$

EXAMPLE 6   Rearranging Terms before Factoring by Grouping

Factor by grouping.

(a) $10x^2 - 12y + 15x - 8xy$

Factoring out the common factor of 2 from the first two terms and the common factor of x from the last two terms gives the following.

$$10x^2 - 12y + 15x - 8xy$$
$$= 2(5x^2 - 6y) + x(15 - 8y)$$

This does not lead to a common factor, so we try rearranging the terms.

$$10x^2 - 12y + 15x - 8xy$$

$= 10x^2 - 8xy - 12y + 15x$	Commutative property
$= (10x^2 - 8xy) + (-12y + 15x)$	Group the terms.
$= 2x(5x - 4y) + 3(-4y + 5x)$	Factor each group.
$= 2x(5x - 4y) + 3(5x - 4y)$	Rewrite $-4y + 5x$.
$= (5x - 4y)(2x + 3)$	Factor out $5x - 4y$.

CHECK $(5x - 4y)(2x + 3)$

$= 10x^2 + 15x - 8xy - 12y$	FOIL
$= 10x^2 - 12y + 15x - 8xy$ ✓	Original polynomial

(b) $2xy + 12 - 3y - 8x$

We need to rearrange these terms to get two groups that each have a common factor. Trial and error suggests the following grouping.

$$2xy + 12 - 3y - 8x$$

Write a + sign between the groups.

$= (2xy - 3y) + (-8x + 12)$	Group the terms.
$= y(2x - 3) - 4(2x - 3)$	Factor each group; $-4(2x - 3) = -8x + 12$.
$= (2x - 3)(y - 4)$	Factor out $2x - 3$.

Be careful with signs

NOW TRY ANSWERS

6. **(a)** $(3p - 4q)(4p + 7)$
   (b) $(5x + 2)(y - 3)$

Since the quantities in parentheses in the second step must be the same, we factored out -4 rather than 4. *Check* by multiplying.

NOW TRY

5.1 EXERCISES

MyMathLab | Math XL PRACTICE | WATCH | DOWNLOAD | READ | REVIEW

🌐 *Complete solution available on the Video Resources on DVD*

*Find the greatest common factor for each list of numbers. **See Example 1.***

🌐 **1.** 40, 20, 4   **2.** 50, 30, 5   **3.** 18, 24, 36, 48

4. 15, 30, 45, 75   **5.** 6, 8, 9   **6.** 20, 22, 23

*Find the greatest common factor for each list of terms. **See Examples 1 and 2.***

7. $16y, 24$ **8.** $18w, 27$

9. $30x^3, 40x^6, 50x^7$ **10.** $60z^4, 70z^8, 90z^9$

11. x^4y^3, xy^2 **12.** a^4b^5, a^3b

13. $12m^3n^2, 18m^5n^4, 36m^8n^3$ **14.** $25p^5r^7, 30p^7r^8, 50p^5r^3$

Concept Check *An expression is factored when it is written as a product, not a sum. Which of the following are not factored?*

15. $2k^2(5k)$ **16.** $2k^2(5k + 1)$

17. $2k^2 + (5k + 1)$ **18.** $(2k^2 + 5k) + 1$

Complete each factoring by writing each polynomial as the product of two factors.

19. $9m^4$
$= 3m^2(\underline{\quad})$

20. $12p^5$
$= 6p^3(\underline{\quad})$

21. $-8z^9$
$= -4z^5(\underline{\quad})$

22. $-15k^{11}$
$= -5k^8(\underline{\quad})$

23. $6m^4n^5$
$= 3m^3n(\underline{\quad})$

24. $27a^3b^2$
$= 9a^2b(\underline{\quad})$

25. $12y + 24$
$= 12(\underline{\quad})$

26. $18p + 36$
$= 18(\underline{\quad})$

27. $10a^2 - 20a$
$= 10a(\underline{\quad})$

28. $15x^2 - 30x$
$= 15x(\underline{\quad})$

29. $8x^2y + 12x^3y^2$
$= 4x^2y(\underline{\quad})$

30. $18s^3t^2 + 10st$
$= 2st(\underline{\quad})$

31. How can you check your answer when you factor a polynomial?

32. *Concept Check* A student factored $18x^3y^2 + 9xy$ as $9xy(2x^2y)$. **WHAT WENT WRONG?** Factor correctly.

Write in factored form by factoring out the greatest common factor. **See Examples 3 and 4.**

33. $x^2 - 4x$ **34.** $m^2 - 7m$ **35.** $6t^2 + 15t$ **36.** $8x^2 + 6x$

37. $27m^3 - 9m$ **38.** $36p^3 - 24p$ **39.** $16z^4 + 24z^2$ **40.** $25k^4 + 15k^2$

41. $12x^3 + 6x^2$ **42.** $21b^3 + 7b^2$ **43.** $65y^{10} + 35y^6$ **44.** $100a^5 + 16a^3$

45. $11w^3 - 100$ **46.** $13z^5 - 80$ **47.** $8mn^3 + 24m^2n^3$ **48.** $19p^2y + 38p^2y^3$

49. $13y^8 + 26y^4 - 39y^2$ **50.** $5x^5 + 25x^4 - 20x^3$

51. $36p^6q + 45p^5q^4 + 81p^3q^2$ **52.** $125a^3z^5 + 60a^4z^4 + 85a^5z^2$

53. $a^5 + 2a^3b^2 - 3a^5b^2 + 4a^4b^3$ **54.** $x^6 + 5x^4y^3 - 6xy^4 + 10xy$

55. $c(x + 2) - d(x + 2)$ **56.** $r(x + 5) - t(x + 5)$

57. $m(m + 2n) + n(m + 2n)$ **58.** $q(q + 4p) + p(q + 4p)$

59. $q^2(p - 4) + 1(p - 4)$ **60.** $y^2(x - 9) + 1(x - 9)$

Students often have difficulty when factoring by grouping because they are not able to tell when the polynomial is completely factored. For example,

$$5y(2x - 3) + 8t(2x - 3) \qquad \text{Not in factored form}$$

is not in factored form, because it is the *sum* of two terms: $5y(2x - 3)$ and $8t(2x - 3)$. However, because $2x - 3$ is a common factor of these two terms, the expression can now be factored.

$$(2x - 3)(5y + 8t) \qquad \text{In factored form}$$

The factored form is a *product* of two factors: $2x - 3$ and $5y + 8t$.

Concept Check *Determine whether each expression is in factored form or is not in factored form. If it is not in factored form, factor it if possible.*

61. $8(7t + 4) + x(7t + 4)$ **62.** $3r(5x - 1) + 7(5x - 1)$

63. $(8 + x)(7t + 4)$ **64.** $(3r + 7)(5x - 1)$

65. $18x^2(y + 4) + 7(y - 4)$ **66.** $12k^3(s - 3) + 7(s + 3)$

67. *Concept Check* Why is it not possible to factor the expression in **Exercise 65?**

68. *Concept Check*   A student factored $x^3 + 4x^2 - 2x - 8$ as follows.

$$x^3 + 4x^2 - 2x - 8$$
$$= (x^3 + 4x^2) + (-2x - 8)$$
$$= x^2(x + 4) + 2(-x - 4)$$

The student could not find a common factor of the two terms. *WHAT WENT WRONG?* Complete the factoring.

*Factor by grouping. **See Examples 5 and 6.***

69. $p^2 + 4p + pq + 4q$

70. $m^2 + 2m + mn + 2n$

71. $a^2 - 2a + ab - 2b$

72. $y^2 - 6y + yw - 6w$

73. $7z^2 + 14z - az - 2a$

74. $5m^2 + 15mp - 2mr - 6pr$

75. $18r^2 + 12ry - 3xr - 2xy$

76. $8s^2 - 4st + 6sy - 3yt$

77. $3a^3 + 3ab^2 + 2a^2b + 2b^3$

78. $4x^3 + 3x^2y + 4xy^2 + 3y^3$

79. $12 - 4a - 3b + ab$

80. $6 - 3x - 2y + xy$

81. $16m^3 - 4m^2p^2 - 4mp + p^3$

82. $10t^3 - 2t^2s^2 - 5ts + s^3$

83. $y^2 + 3x + 3y + xy$

84. $m^2 + 14p + 7m + 2mp$

85. $5m - 6p - 2mp + 15$

86. $7y - 9x - 3xy + 21$

87. $18r^2 - 2ty + 12ry - 3rt$

88. $12a^2 - 4bc + 16ac - 3ab$

89. $a^5 - 3 + 2a^5b - 6b$

90. $b^3 - 2 + 5ab^3 - 10a$

RELATING CONCEPTS   EXERCISES 91–94

FOR INDIVIDUAL OR GROUP WORK

*In many cases, the choice of which pairs of terms to group when factoring by grouping can be made in different ways. To see this for **Example 6 (b)**, work Exercises 91–94 in order.*

91. Start with the polynomial from **Example 6(b)**, $2xy + 12 - 3y - 8x$, and rearrange the terms as follows:

$$2xy - 8x - 3y + 12.$$

What property from **Section 1.7** allows this?

92. Group the first two terms and the last two terms of the rearranged polynomial in **Exercise 91.** Then factor each group.

93. Is your result from **Exercise 92** in factored form? Explain your answer.

94. If your answer to **Exercise 93** is *no,* factor the polynomial. Is the result the same as that shown for **Example 6(b)?**

PREVIEW EXERCISES

*Find each product. **See Section 4.5.***

95. $(x + 6)(x - 9)$

96. $(x - 3)(x - 6)$

97. $(x + 2)(x + 7)$

98. $2x(x + 5)(x - 1)$

99. $2x^2(x^2 + 3x + 5)$

100. $-5x^2(2x^2 - 4x - 9)$

5.2 Factoring Trinomials

OBJECTIVES

1. Factor trinomials with a coefficient of 1 for the second-degree term.

2. Factor such trinomials after factoring out the greatest common factor.

Using the FOIL method, we can find the product of the binomials $k - 3$ and $k + 1$.

$$(k - 3)(k + 1) = k^2 - 2k - 3 \quad \text{Multiplying}$$

Suppose instead that we are given the polynomial $k^2 - 2k - 3$ and want to rewrite it as the product $(k - 3)(k + 1)$.

$$k^2 - 2k - 3 = (k - 3)(k + 1) \quad \text{Factoring}$$

Recall from **Section 5.1** that this process is called factoring the polynomial. Factoring reverses or "undoes" multiplying.

OBJECTIVE 1 Factor trinomials with a coefficient of 1 for the second-degree term. When factoring polynomials with integer coefficients, we use only integers in the factors. For example, we can factor $x^2 + 5x + 6$ by finding integers m and n such that

$$x^2 + 5x + 6 \quad \text{is written as} \quad (x + m)(x + n).$$

To find these integers m and n, we multiply the two binomials on the right.

$$(x + m)(x + n)$$
$$= x^2 + nx + mx + mn \quad \text{FOIL}$$
$$= x^2 + (n + m)x + mn \quad \text{Distributive property}$$

Comparing this result with $x^2 + 5x + 6$ shows that we must find integers m and n having a sum of 5 and a product of 6.

Product of m and n is 6.
$$\downarrow$$
$$x^2 + 5x + 6 = x^2 + (n + m)x + mn$$
$$\uparrow$$
Sum of m and n is 5.

Since many pairs of integers have a sum of 5, it is best to begin by listing those pairs of integers whose product is 6. Both 5 and 6 are positive, so we consider only pairs in which both integers are positive.

Factors of 6	Sums of Factors
6, 1	6 + 1 = 7
3, 2	3 + 2 = 5

Sum is 5.

Both pairs have a product of 6, but only the pair 3 and 2 has a sum of 5. So 3 and 2 are the required integers.

$$x^2 + 5x + 6 \quad \text{factors as} \quad (x + 3)(x + 2).$$

Check by using the FOIL method to multiply the binomials. *Make sure that the sum of the outer and inner products produces the correct middle term.*

CHECK $\quad (x + 3)(x + 2) = x^2 + 5x + 6 \quad \checkmark \quad$ Correct

$3x$
$2x$
$5x \quad$ Add.

NOW TRY
EXERCISE 1
Factor $p^2 + 7p + 10$.

EXAMPLE 1 Factoring a Trinomial with All Positive Terms

Factor $m^2 + 9m + 14$.

Look for two integers whose product is 14 and whose sum is 9. List pairs of integers whose product is 14, and examine the sums. Again, only positive integers are needed because all signs in $m^2 + 9m + 14$ are positive.

Factors of 14	Sums of Factors
14, 1	14 + 1 = 15
7, 2	7 + 2 = 9

Sum is 9.

From the list, 7 and 2 are the required integers, since $7 \cdot 2 = 14$ and $7 + 2 = 9$.

$m^2 + 9m + 14$ factors as $(m + 7)(m + 2)$. $(m + 2)(m + 7)$ is also correct.

CHECK $(m + 7)(m + 2)$

$= m^2 + 2m + 7m + 14$ FOIL

$= m^2 + 9m + 14$ ✓   Original polynomial   NOW TRY

NOW TRY
EXERCISE 2
Factor $t^2 - 9t + 18$.

EXAMPLE 2 Factoring a Trinomial with a Negative Middle Term

Factor $x^2 - 9x + 20$.

We must find two integers whose product is 20 and whose sum is -9. Since the numbers we are looking for have a *positive product* and a *negative sum,* we consider only pairs of negative integers.

Factors of 20	Sums of Factors
−20, −1	−20 + (−1) = −21
−10, −2	−10 + (−2) = −12
−5, −4	−5 + (−4) = −9

Sum is −9.

The required integers are -5 and -4.

$x^2 - 9x + 20$ factors as $(x - 5)(x - 4)$. The order of the factors does not matter.

CHECK $(x - 5)(x - 4)$

$= x^2 - 4x - 5x + 20$ FOIL

$= x^2 - 9x + 20$ ✓   Original polynomial   NOW TRY

NOW TRY
EXERCISE 3
Factor $x^2 + x - 42$.

EXAMPLE 3 Factoring a Trinomial with a Negative Last (Constant) Term

Factor $x^2 + x - 6$.

We must find two integers whose product is -6 and whose sum is 1 (since the coefficient of x, or $1x$, is 1). To get a *negative product,* the pairs of integers must have different signs.

Once we find the required pair, we can stop listing factors.

Factors of −6	Sums of Factors
6, −1	6 + (−1) = 5
−6, 1	−6 + 1 = −5
3, −2	3 + (−2) = 1

Sum is 1.

NOW TRY ANSWERS
1. $(p + 2)(p + 5)$
2. $(t - 3)(t - 6)$
3. $(x + 7)(x - 6)$

The required integers are 3 and -2.   To check, multiply the factored form.

$x^2 + x - 6$ factors as $(x + 3)(x - 2)$.   NOW TRY

> NOW TRY
> EXERCISE 4
>
> Factor $x^2 - 4x - 21$.

EXAMPLE 4 Factoring a Trinomial with Two Negative Terms

Factor $p^2 - 2p - 15$.

Find two integers whose product is -15 and whose sum is -2. Because the constant term, -15, is negative, list pairs of integers with different signs.

Factors of -15	Sums of Factors
15, -1	$15 + (-1) = 14$
-15, 1	$-15 + 1 = -14$
5, -3	$5 + (-3) = 2$
-5, 3	$-5 + 3 = -2$ ← Sum is -2.

The required integers are -5 and 3.

$$p^2 - 2p - 15 \quad \text{factors as} \quad (p - 5)(p + 3).$$

To check, multiply the factored form. NOW TRY

NOTE In **Examples 1–4**, notice that we listed factors in descending order (disregarding their signs) when we were looking for the required pair of integers. This helps avoid skipping the correct combination.

Some trinomials cannot be factored by using only integers. We call such trinomials **prime polynomials.**

> NOW TRY
> EXERCISE 5
>
> Factor each trinomial if possible.
> **(a)** $m^2 + 5m + 8$
> **(b)** $t^2 + 11t - 24$

EXAMPLE 5 Deciding Whether Polynomials Are Prime

Factor each trinomial if possible.

(a) $x^2 - 5x + 12$

As in **Example 2,** both factors must be negative to give a positive product and a negative sum. List pairs of negative integers whose product is 12, and examine the sums.

Factors of 12	Sums of Factors
-12, -1	$-12 + (-1) = -13$
-6, -2	$-6 + (-2) = -8$
-4, -3	$-4 + (-3) = -7$

No sum is -5.

None of the pairs of integers has a sum of -5. Therefore, the trinomial $x^2 - 5x + 12$ *cannot be factored by using only integers.* It is a *prime polynomial.*

(b) $k^2 - 8k + 11$

There is no pair of integers whose product is 11 and whose sum is -8, so $k^2 - 8k + 11$ is a prime polynomial. NOW TRY

Guidelines for Factoring $x^2 + bx + c$

Find two integers whose product is c and whose sum is b.

1. Both integers must be positive if b and c are positive. (See **Example 1.**)

2. Both integers must be negative if c is positive and b is negative. (See **Example 2.**)

3. One integer must be positive and one must be negative if c is negative. (See **Examples 3 and 4.**)

NOW TRY ANSWERS
4. $(x + 3)(x - 7)$
5. **(a)** prime **(b)** prime

NOW TRY
EXERCISE 6

Factor $a^2 + 2ab - 15b^2$.

EXAMPLE 6 Factoring a Trinomial with Two Variables

Factor $z^2 - 2bz - 3b^2$.

Here, the coefficient of z in the middle term is $-2b$, so we need to find two expressions whose product is $-3b^2$ and whose sum is $-2b$.

Factors of $-3b^2$	Sums of Factors
$3b, -b$	$3b + (-b) = 2b$
$-3b, b$	$-3b + b = -2b$

Sum is $-2b$.

$z^2 - 2bz - 3b^2$ factors as $(z - 3b)(z + b)$.

CHECK $(z - 3b)(z + b)$

$= z^2 + zb - 3bz - 3b^2$ FOIL

$= z^2 + 1bz - 3bz - 3b^2$ Identity and commutative properties

$= z^2 - 2bz - 3b^2$ ✓   Combine like terms.   NOW TRY

OBJECTIVE 2 **Factor such trinomials after factoring out the greatest common factor.** If a trinomial has a common factor, first factor it out.

NOW TRY
EXERCISE 7

Factor $3y^4 - 27y^3 + 60y^2$.

EXAMPLE 7 Factoring a Trinomial with a Common Factor

Factor $4x^5 - 28x^4 + 40x^3$.

$4x^5 - 28x^4 + 40x^3$

$= 4x^3(x^2 - 7x + 10)$ Factor out the greatest common factor, $4x^3$.

Factor $x^2 - 7x + 10$. The integers -5 and -2 have a product of 10 and a sum of -7.

Include $4x^3$. $= 4x^3(x - 5)(x - 2)$ Completely factored form

CHECK $4x^3(x - 5)(x - 2)$

$= 4x^3(x^2 - 7x + 10)$ FOIL; Combine like terms.

$= 4x^5 - 28x^4 + 40x^3$ ✓   Distributive property   NOW TRY

NOW TRY ANSWERS
6. $(a + 5b)(a - 3b)$
7. $3y^2(y - 5)(y - 4)$

⚠ **CAUTION** *When factoring, always look for a common factor first.* Remember to include the common factor as part of the answer. Always check by multiplying.

5.2 EXERCISES

🌐 *Complete solution available on the Video Resources on DVD*

In Exercises 1–4, list all pairs of integers with the given product. Then find the pair whose sum is given. ***See the tables in Examples 1–4.***

1. Product: 48;   Sum: -19 **2.** Product: 18;   Sum: 9

3. Product: -24;   Sum: -5 **4.** Product: -36;   Sum: -16

5. *Concept Check* If a trinomial in x is factored as $(x + a)(x + b)$, what must be true of a and b if the coefficient of the constant term of the trinomial is negative?

6. *Concept Check* In **Exercise 5,** what must be true of a and b if the coefficient of the constant term is positive?

7. What is meant by a *prime polynomial*?

8. How can you check your work when factoring a trinomial? Does the check ensure that the trinomial is completely factored?

9. *Concept Check* Which is the correct factored form of $x^2 - 12x + 32$?

   A. $(x - 8)(x + 4)$ **B.** $(x + 8)(x - 4)$

   C. $(x - 8)(x - 4)$ **D.** $(x + 8)(x + 4)$

10. *Concept Check* What is the suggested first step in factoring $2x^3 + 8x^2 - 10x$? (See **Example 7.**)

11. *Concept Check* What polynomial can be factored as $(a + 9)(a + 4)$?

12. *Concept Check* What polynomial can be factored as $(y - 7)(y + 3)$?

Complete each factoring. See Examples 1–4.

13. $p^2 + 11p + 30$
    $= (p + 5)(\underline{\quad})$

14. $x^2 + 10x + 21$
    $= (x + 7)(\underline{\quad})$

15. $x^2 + 15x + 44$
    $= (x + 4)(\underline{\quad})$

16. $r^2 + 15r + 56$
    $= (r + 7)(\underline{\quad})$

17. $x^2 - 9x + 8$
    $= (x - 1)(\underline{\quad})$

18. $t^2 - 14t + 24$
    $= (t - 2)(\underline{\quad})$

19. $y^2 - 2y - 15$
    $= (y + 3)(\underline{\quad})$

20. $t^2 - t - 42$
    $= (t + 6)(\underline{\quad})$

21. $x^2 + 9x - 22$
    $= (x - 2)(\underline{\quad})$

22. $x^2 + 6x - 27$
    $= (x - 3)(\underline{\quad})$

23. $y^2 - 7y - 18$
    $= (y + 2)(\underline{\quad})$

24. $y^2 - 2y - 24$
    $= (y + 4)(\underline{\quad})$

Factor completely. If the polynomial cannot be factored, write prime. *See Examples 1–5.* (Hint: *In Exercises 43 and 44, first write the trinomial in descending powers and then factor.*)

25. $y^2 + 9y + 8$

26. $a^2 + 9a + 20$

27. $b^2 + 8b + 15$

28. $x^2 + 6x + 8$

29. $m^2 + m - 20$

30. $p^2 + 4p - 5$

31. $y^2 - 8y + 15$

32. $y^2 - 6y + 8$

33. $x^2 + 4x + 5$

34. $t^2 + 11t + 12$

35. $z^2 - 15z + 56$

36. $x^2 - 13x + 36$

37. $r^2 - r - 30$

38. $q^2 - q - 42$

39. $a^2 - 8a - 48$

40. $d^2 - 4d - 45$

41. $x^2 + 3x - 39$

42. $m^2 + 10m - 30$

43. $-32 + 14x + x^2$

44. $-39 + 10x + x^2$

Factor completely. See Example 6.

45. $r^2 + 3ra + 2a^2$

46. $x^2 + 5xa + 4a^2$

47. $t^2 - tz - 6z^2$

48. $a^2 - ab - 12b^2$

49. $x^2 + 4xy + 3y^2$

50. $p^2 + 9pq + 8q^2$

51. $v^2 - 11vw + 30w^2$

52. $v^2 - 11vx + 24x^2$

Factor completely. See Example 7.

53. $4x^2 + 12x - 40$

54. $5y^2 - 5y - 30$

55. $2t^3 + 8t^2 + 6t$

56. $3t^3 + 27t^2 + 24t$ **57.** $2x^6 + 8x^5 - 42x^4$ **58.** $4y^5 + 12y^4 - 40y^3$

59. $5m^5 + 25m^4 - 40m^2$ **60.** $12k^5 - 6k^3 + 10k^2$

61. $m^3n - 10m^2n^2 + 24mn^3$ **62.** $y^3z + 3y^2z^2 - 54yz^3$

Brain Busters   *Factor each polynomial.*

63. $a^5 + 3a^4b - 4a^3b^2$ **64.** $m^3n - 2m^2n^2 - 3mn^3$ **65.** $y^3z + y^2z^2 - 6yz^3$

66. $k^7 - 2k^6m - 15k^5m^2$ **67.** $z^{10} - 4z^9y - 21z^8y^2$ **68.** $x^9 + 5x^8w - 24x^7w^2$

69. $(a + b)x^2 + (a + b)x - 12(a + b)$

70. $(x + y)n^2 + (x + y)n - 20(x + y)$

71. $(2p + q)r^2 - 12(2p + q)r + 27(2p + q)$

72. $(3m - n)k^2 - 13(3m - n)k + 40(3m - n)$

PREVIEW EXERCISES

*Find each product. **See Section 4.5.***

73. $(2y - 7)(y + 4)$ **74.** $(3a + 2)(2a + 1)$ **75.** $(5z + 2)(3z - 2)$

5.3   More on Factoring Trinomials

OBJECTIVES

1 Factor trinomials by grouping when the coefficient of the second-degree term is not 1.

2 Factor trinomials by using the FOIL method.

Trinomials such as $2x^2 + 7x + 6$, in which the coefficient of the second-degree term is *not* 1, are factored with extensions of the methods from the previous sections.

OBJECTIVE 1   **Factor trinomials by grouping when the coefficient of the second-degree term is not 1.**   A trinomial such as $m^2 + 3m + 2$ is factored by finding two numbers whose product is 2 and whose sum is 3. To factor $2x^2 + 7x + 6$, we look for two integers whose product is $2 \cdot 6 = 12$ and whose sum is 7.

Sum is 7.

$$2x^2 + 7x + 6$$

Product is $2 \cdot 6 = 12$.

By considering pairs of positive integers whose product is 12, we find the required integers, 3 and 4. We use these integers to write the middle term, $7x$, as $7x = 3x + 4x$.

$$2x^2 + 7x + 6$$

$$= 2x^2 + \underbrace{3x + 4x}_{7x} + 6$$

$$= (2x^2 + 3x) + (4x + 6) \qquad \text{Group the terms.}$$

$$= x(2x + 3) + 2(2x + 3) \qquad \text{Factor each group.}$$

Must be the same factor

$$= (2x + 3)(x + 2) \qquad \text{Factor out } 2x + 3.$$

CHECK   Multiply $(2x + 3)(x + 2)$ to obtain $2x^2 + 7x + 6$. ✓

NOTE In the preceding example, we could have written $7x$ as $4x + 3x$, rather than as $3x + 4x$. Factoring by grouping would give the same answer. Try this.

⌇NOW TRY
 ↳EXERCISE 1

Factor.

(a) $2z^2 + 5z + 3$

(b) $15m^2 + m - 2$

(c) $8x^2 - 2xy - 3y^2$

EXAMPLE 1   Factoring Trinomials by Grouping

Factor each trinomial.

(a) $6r^2 + r - 1$

We must find two integers with a product of $6(-1) = -6$ and a sum of 1.

$$\text{Sum is 1.}$$
$$\downarrow$$
$$6r^2 + 1r - 1$$
$$\text{Product is } 6(-1) = -6.$$

The integers are -2 and 3. We write the middle term, r, as $-2r + 3r$.

$$6r^2 + r - 1$$
$$= 6r^2 - 2r + 3r - 1 \qquad r = -2r + 3r$$
$$= (6r^2 - 2r) + (3r - 1) \qquad \text{Group the terms.}$$
$$= 2r(3r - 1) + 1(3r - 1) \qquad \text{The binomials must be the same.}$$
$$\boxed{\text{Remember the 1.}}$$
$$= (3r - 1)(2r + 1) \qquad \text{Factor out } 3r - 1.$$

CHECK   Multiply $(3r - 1)(2r + 1)$ to obtain $6r^2 + r - 1.$ ✓

(b) $12z^2 - 5z - 2$

Look for two integers whose product is $12(-2) = -24$ and whose sum is -5. The required integers are 3 and -8.

$$12z^2 - 5z - 2$$
$$= 12z^2 + 3z - 8z - 2 \qquad -5z = 3z - 8z$$
$$= (12z^2 + 3z) + (-8z - 2) \qquad \text{Group the terms.}$$
$$= 3z(4z + 1) - 2(4z + 1) \qquad \text{Factor each group.}$$
$$\boxed{\text{Be careful with signs.}}$$
$$= (4z + 1)(3z - 2) \qquad \text{Factor out } 4z + 1.$$

CHECK   Multiply $(4z + 1)(3z - 2)$ to obtain $12z^2 - 5z - 2.$ ✓

(c) $10m^2 + mn - 3n^2$

Two integers whose product is $10(-3) = -30$ and whose sum is 1 are -5 and 6.

$$10m^2 + mn - 3n^2$$
$$= 10m^2 - 5mn + 6mn - 3n^2 \qquad mn = -5mn + 6mn$$
$$= (10m^2 - 5mn) + (6mn - 3n^2) \qquad \text{Group the terms.}$$
$$= 5m(2m - n) + 3n(2m - n) \qquad \text{Factor each group.}$$
$$= (2m - n)(5m + 3n) \qquad \text{Factor out } 2m - n.$$

CHECK   Multiply $(2m - n)(5m + 3n)$ to obtain $10m^2 + mn - 3n^2.$ ✓

NOW TRY ↻

NOW TRY ANSWERS

1. (a) $(2z + 3)(z + 1)$

    (b) $(3m - 1)(5m + 2)$

    (c) $(4x - 3y)(2x + y)$

NOW TRY
EXERCISE 2
Factor $15z^6 + 18z^5 - 24z^4$.

EXAMPLE 2 Factoring a Trinomial with a Common Factor by Grouping

Factor $28x^5 - 58x^4 - 30x^3$.

$$28x^5 - 58x^4 - 30x^3$$
$$= 2x^3(14x^2 - 29x - 15)$$ Factor out the greatest common factor, $2x^3$.

To factor $14x^2 - 29x - 15$, find two integers whose product is $14(-15) = -210$ and whose sum is -29. Factoring 210 into prime factors helps find these integers.

$$210 = 2 \cdot 3 \cdot 5 \cdot 7$$

Combine the prime factors of $210 = 2 \cdot 3 \cdot 5 \cdot 7$ into pairs in different ways, using one positive and one negative (to get -210). The factors 6 and -35 have the correct sum, -29.

$$28x^5 - 58x^4 - 30x^3$$
$$= 2x^3(14x^2 - 29x - 15)$$

Remember the common factor.
$$= 2x^3(14x^2 + 6x - 35x - 15)$$ $-29x = 6x - 35x$
$$= 2x^3[(14x^2 + 6x) + (-35x - 15)]$$ Group the terms.
$$= 2x^3[2x(7x + 3) - 5(7x + 3)]$$ Factor each group.
$$= 2x^3[(7x + 3)(2x - 5)]$$ Factor out $7x + 3$.
$$= 2x^3(7x + 3)(2x - 5)$$ Check by multiplying.   NOW TRY

OBJECTIVE 2 Factor trinomials by using the FOIL method. There is an alternative method of factoring trinomials that uses trial and error.

To factor $2x^2 + 7x + 6$ (the trinomial factored at the beginning of this section) by trial and error, we use the FOIL method in reverse. We want to write $2x^2 + 7x + 6$ as the product of two binomials.

$$2x^2 + 7x + 6$$
$$= (\underline{\qquad})(\underline{\qquad})$$

The product of the two first terms of the binomials is $2x^2$. The possible factors of $2x^2$ are $2x$ and x or $-2x$ and $-x$. Since all terms of the trinomial are positive, we consider only positive factors. Thus, we have the following.

$$2x^2 + 7x + 6$$
$$= (2x\underline{\qquad})(x\underline{\qquad})$$

The product of the two last terms, 6, can be factored as $1 \cdot 6$, $6 \cdot 1$, $2 \cdot 3$, or $3 \cdot 2$. Try each pair to find the pair that gives the correct middle term, $7x$.

$(2x + 1)(x + 6)$ Incorrect
x
$12x$
$13x$ Add.

$(2x + 6)(x + 1)$ Incorrect
$6x$
$2x$
$8x$ Add.

Since $2x + 6 = 2(x + 3)$, the binomial $2x + 6$ has a common factor of 2, while $2x^2 + 7x + 6$ has no common factor other than 1. The product $(2x + 6)(x + 1)$ cannot be correct.

NOTE If the terms of the original polynomial have greatest common factor 1, then each factor of that polynomial will also have terms with GCF 1.

NOW TRY ANSWER
2. $3z^4(5z - 4)(z + 2)$

Now try the numbers 2 and 3 as factors of 6. Because of the common factor 2 in $2x + 2$, the product $(2x + 2)(x + 3)$ will not work, so we try $(2x + 3)(x + 2)$.

$$(2x + 3)(x + 2) = 2x^2 + 7x + 6 \quad \text{Correct}$$

$3x$
$4x$
$7x$ Add.

Thus, $2x^2 + 7x + 6$ factors as $(2x + 3)(x + 2)$.

NOW TRY
EXERCISE 3
Factor $8y^2 + 22y + 5$.

EXAMPLE 3   Factoring a Trinomial with All Positive Terms by Using FOIL

Factor $8p^2 + 14p + 5$.

The number 8 has several possible pairs of factors, but 5 has only 1 and 5 or -1 and -5, so begin by considering the factors of 5. Ignore the negative factors, since all coefficients in the trinomial are positive. The factors will have this form.

$$(\underline{\quad} + 5)(\underline{\quad} + 1)$$

The possible pairs of factors of $8p^2$ are $8p$ and p, or $4p$ and $2p$. Try various combinations, checking in each case to see if the middle term is $14p$.

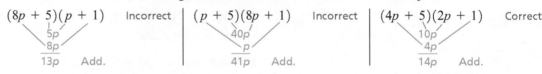

$(8p + 5)(p + 1)$ Incorrect $\quad$ $(p + 5)(8p + 1)$ Incorrect $\quad$ $(4p + 5)(2p + 1)$ Correct

$5p$ $40p$ $10p$
$8p$ p $4p$
$13p$ Add. $\quad\quad$ $41p$ Add. $\quad\quad$ $14p$ Add.

Since the combination on the right produces $14p$, the correct middle term,

$$8p^2 + 14p + 5 \quad \text{factors as} \quad (4p + 5)(2p + 1).$$

CHECK   Multiply $(4p + 5)(2p + 1)$ to obtain $8p^2 + 14p + 5$ ✓ NOW TRY

NOW TRY
EXERCISE 4
Factor $10x^2 - 9x + 2$.

EXAMPLE 4   Factoring a Trinomial with a Negative Middle Term by Using FOIL

Factor $6x^2 - 11x + 3$.

Since 3 has only 1 and 3 or -1 and -3 as factors, it is better here to begin by factoring 3. The last (constant) term of the trinomial $6x^2 - 11x + 3$ is positive and the middle term has a negative coefficient, so we consider only negative factors. We need two negative factors, because the *product* of two negative factors is positive and their *sum* is negative, as required. Try -3 and -1 as factors of 3.

$$(\underline{\quad} - 3)(\underline{\quad} - 1)$$

The factors of $6x^2$ may be either $6x$ and x or $2x$ and $3x$.

$(6x - 3)(x - 1)$ Incorrect $\quad$ $(2x - 3)(3x - 1)$ Correct

$-3x$ $-9x$
$-6x$ $-2x$
$-9x$ Add. $\quad\quad$ $-11x$ Add.

The factors $2x$ and $3x$ produce $-11x$, the correct middle term.   *Check by multiplying.*

$$6x^2 - 11x + 3 \quad \text{factors as} \quad (2x - 3)(3x - 1).$$ NOW TRY

NOTE In **Example 4,** we might also realize that our initial attempt to factor $6x^2 - 11x + 3$ as $(6x - 3)(x - 1)$ *cannot* be correct, since the terms of $6x - 3$ have a common factor of 3, while those of the original polynomial do not.

NOW TRY ANSWERS
3. $(4y + 1)(2y + 5)$
4. $(5x - 2)(2x - 1)$

NOW TRY
EXERCISE 5
Factor $10a^2 + 31a - 14$.

EXAMPLE 5 **Factoring a Trinomial with a Negative Constant Term by Using FOIL**

Factor $8x^2 + 6x - 9$.

The integer 8 has several possible pairs of factors, as does -9. Since the constant term is negative, one positive factor and one negative factor of -9 are needed. Since the coefficient of the middle term is relatively small, it is wise to avoid large factors such as 8 or 9. We try $4x$ and $2x$ as factors of $8x^2$, and 3 and -3 as factors of -9.

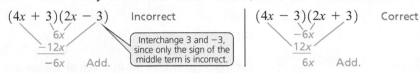

The combination on the right produces the correct middle term.

$$8x^2 + 6x - 9 \quad \text{factors as} \quad (4x - 3)(2x + 3).$$

NOW TRY

NOW TRY
EXERCISE 6
Factor $8z^2 + 2wz - 15w^2$.

EXAMPLE 6 **Factoring a Trinomial with Two Variables**

Factor $12a^2 - ab - 20b^2$.

There are several pairs of factors of $12a^2$, including

$$12a \text{ and } a, \quad 6a \text{ and } 2a, \quad \text{and} \quad 3a \text{ and } 4a.$$

There are also many pairs of factors of $-20b^2$, including

$$20b \text{ and } -b, \quad -20b \text{ and } b, \quad 10b \text{ and } -2b, \quad -10b \text{ and } 2b,$$
$$4b \text{ and } -5b, \quad \text{and} \quad -4b \text{ and } 5b.$$

Once again, since the coefficient of the desired middle term is relatively small, avoid the larger factors. Try the factors $6a$ and $2a$, and $4b$ and $-5b$.

$$(6a + 4b)(2a - 5b)$$

This cannot be correct, since there is a factor of 2 in $6a + 4b$, while 2 is not a factor of the given trinomial. Try $3a$ and $4a$ with $4b$ and $-5b$.

$$(3a + 4b)(4a - 5b)$$
$$= 12a^2 + ab - 20b^2 \quad \text{Incorrect}$$

Here the middle term is ab rather than $-ab$, so we interchange the signs of the last two terms in the factors.

$$12a^2 - ab - 20b^2 \quad \text{factors as} \quad (3a - 4b)(4a + 5b).$$

Check by multiplying.

NOW TRY

EXAMPLE 7 **Factoring Trinomials with Common Factors**

Factor each trinomial.

(a) $15y^3 + 55y^2 + 30y$

$$= 5y(3y^2 + 11y + 6) \quad \text{Factor out the greatest common factor, } 5y.$$

To factor $3y^2 + 11y + 6$, try $3y$ and y as factors of $3y^2$, and 2 and 3 as factors of 6.

$$(3y + 2)(y + 3)$$
$$= 3y^2 + 11y + 6 \quad \text{Correct}$$

NOW TRY ANSWERS
5. $(5a - 2)(2a + 7)$
6. $(4z - 5w)(2z + 3w)$

NOW TRY
EXERCISE 7
Factor $-10x^3 - 45x^2 + 90x$.

This leads to the completely factored form.

$$15y^3 + 55y^2 + 30y$$

Remember the common factor.

$$= 5y(3y + 2)(y + 3)$$

CHECK $5y(3y + 2)(y + 3)$

$$= 5y(3y^2 + 11y + 6) \qquad \text{FOIL; Combine like terms.}$$

$$= 15y^3 + 55y^2 + 30y \quad \checkmark \qquad \text{Distributive property}$$

(b) $-24a^3 - 42a^2 + 45a$

The common factor could be $3a$ or $-3a$. If we factor out $-3a$, the first term of the trinomial will be positive, which makes it easier to factor the remaining trinomial.

$$-24a^3 - 42a^2 + 45a$$

$$= -3a(8a^2 + 14a - 15) \qquad \text{Factor out } -3a.$$

$$= -3a(4a - 3)(2a + 5) \qquad \text{Factor the trinomial.}$$

Check by multiplying.

NOW TRY

NOW TRY ANSWER
7. $-5x(2x - 3)(x + 6)$

⚠ **CAUTION** *Include the common factor in the final factored form.*

5.3 EXERCISES

MyMathLab | Math XL PRACTICE | WATCH | DOWNLOAD | READ | REVIEW

🌐 *Complete solution available on the Video Resources on DVD*

Concept Check   The middle term of each trinomial has been rewritten. Now factor by grouping.

1. $10t^2 + 9t + 2$
$= 10t^2 + 5t + 4t + 2$

2. $6x^2 + 13x + 6$
$= 6x^2 + 9x + 4x + 6$

3. $15z^2 - 19z + 6$
$= 15z^2 - 10z - 9z + 6$

4. $12p^2 - 17p + 6$
$= 12p^2 - 9p - 8p + 6$

5. $8s^2 + 2st - 3t^2$
$= 8s^2 - 4st + 6st - 3t^2$

6. $3x^2 - xy - 14y^2$
$= 3x^2 - 7xy + 6xy - 14y^2$

Concept Check   Complete the steps to factor each trinomial by grouping.

7. $2m^2 + 11m + 12$

(a) Find two integers whose product is

_____ · _____ = _____

and whose sum is _____.

(b) The required integers are _____ and _____.

(c) Write the middle term, $11m$, as _____ + _____.

(d) Rewrite the given trinomial as _____.

(e) Factor the polynomial in part (d) by grouping.

(f) Check by multiplying.

8. $6y^2 - 19y + 10$

(a) Find two integers whose product is

_____ · _____ = _____

and whose sum is _____.

(b) The required integers are _____ and _____.

(c) Write the middle term, $-19y$, as _____ + _____.

(d) Rewrite the given trinomial as _____.

(e) Factor the polynomial in part (d) by grouping.

(f) Check by multiplying.

9. *Concept Check*   Which pair of integers would be used to rewrite the middle term when one is factoring $12y^2 + 5y - 2$ by grouping?

A. $-8, 3$ **B.** $8, -3$

C. $-6, 4$ **D.** $6, -4$

10. *Concept Check*   Which pair of integers would be used to rewrite the middle term when one is factoring $20b^2 - 13b + 2$ by grouping?

A. $10, 3$ **B.** $-10, -3$

C. $8, 5$ **D.** $-8, -5$

Concept Check   Which is the correct factored form of the given polynomial?

11. $2x^2 - x - 1$

   A. $(2x - 1)(x + 1)$

   B. $(2x + 1)(x - 1)$

13. $4y^2 + 17y - 15$

   A. $(y + 5)(4y - 3)$

   B. $(2y - 5)(2y + 3)$

12. $3a^2 - 5a - 2$

   A. $(3a + 1)(a - 2)$

   B. $(3a - 1)(a + 2)$

14. $12c^2 - 7c - 12$

   A. $(6c - 2)(2c + 6)$

   B. $(4c + 3)(3c - 4)$

Complete each factoring. **See Examples 1–7.**

15. $6a^2 + 7ab - 20b^2$
$= (3a - 4b)(\underline{\qquad})$

17. $2x^2 + 6x - 8$
$= 2(\underline{\qquad})$
$= 2(\underline{\quad})(\underline{\quad})$

19. $4z^3 - 10z^2 - 6z$
$= 2z(\underline{\qquad})$
$= 2z(\underline{\quad})(\underline{\quad})$

16. $9m^2 + 6mn - 8n^2$
$= (3m - 2n)(\underline{\qquad})$

18. $3x^2 + 9x - 30$
$= 3(\underline{\qquad})$
$= 3(\underline{\quad})(\underline{\quad})$

20. $15r^3 - 39r^2 - 18r$
$= 3r(\underline{\qquad})$
$= 3r(\underline{\quad})(\underline{\quad})$

21. The polynomial $12x^2 + 7x - 12$ does not have 2 as a factor. Explain why the binomial $2x - 6$, then, cannot be a factor of the polynomial.

22. *Concept Check*   On a quiz, a student factored $3k^3 - 12k^2 - 15k$ by first factoring out the common factor $3k$ to get $3k(k^2 - 4k - 5)$. Then the student wrote the following.

$$k^2 - 4k - 5$$
$$= k^2 - 5k + k - 5$$
$$= k(k - 5) + 1(k - 5)$$
$$= (k - 5)(k + 1) \qquad \text{Her answer}$$

WHAT WENT WRONG?   What is the correct factored form?

Factor each trinomial completely. **See Examples 1–7.** *(Hint: In Exercises 55–58, first write the trinomial in descending powers and then factor.)*

23. $3a^2 + 10a + 7$

25. $2y^2 + 7y + 6$

27. $15m^2 + m - 2$

29. $12s^2 + 11s - 5$

31. $10m^2 - 23m + 12$

33. $8w^2 - 14w + 3$

35. $20y^2 - 39y - 11$

37. $3x^2 - 15x + 16$

39. $20x^2 + 22x + 6$

41. $24x^2 - 42x + 9$

24. $7r^2 + 8r + 1$

26. $5z^2 + 12z + 4$

28. $6x^2 + x - 1$

30. $20x^2 + 11x - 3$

32. $6x^2 - 17x + 12$

34. $9p^2 - 18p + 8$

36. $10x^2 - 11x - 6$

38. $2t^2 - 14t + 15$

40. $36y^2 + 81y + 45$

42. $48b^2 - 74b - 10$

43. $40m^2q + mq - 6q$

44. $15a^2b + 22ab + 8b$

45. $15n^4 - 39n^3 + 18n^2$

46. $24a^4 + 10a^3 - 4a^2$

47. $15x^2y^2 - 7xy^2 - 4y^2$

48. $14a^2b^3 + 15ab^3 - 9b^3$

49. $5a^2 - 7ab - 6b^2$

50. $6x^2 - 5xy - y^2$

51. $12s^2 + 11st - 5t^2$

52. $25a^2 + 25ab + 6b^2$

53. $6m^6n + 7m^5n^2 + 2m^4n^3$

54. $12k^3q^4 - 4k^2q^5 - kq^6$

55. $5 - 6x + x^2$

56. $7 - 8x + x^2$

57. $16 + 16x + 3x^2$

58. $18 + 65x + 7x^2$

59. $-10x^3 + 5x^2 + 140x$

60. $-18k^3 - 48k^2 + 66k$

61. $12x^2 - 47x - 4$

62. $12x^2 - 19x - 10$

63. $24y^2 - 41xy - 14x^2$

64. $24x^2 + 19xy - 5y^2$

65. $36x^4 - 64x^2y + 15y^2$

66. $36x^4 + 59x^2y + 24y^2$

67. $48a^2 - 94ab - 4b^2$

68. $48t^2 - 147ts + 9s^2$

69. $10x^4y^5 + 39x^3y^5 - 4x^2y^5$

70. $14x^7y^4 - 31x^6y^4 + 6x^5y^4$

71. $36a^3b^2 - 104a^2b^2 - 12ab^2$

72. $36p^4q + 129p^3q - 60p^2q$

73. $24x^2 - 46x + 15$

74. $24x^2 - 94x + 35$

75. $24x^4 + 55x^2 - 24$

76. $24x^4 + 17x^2 - 20$

77. $24x^2 + 38xy + 15y^2$

78. $24x^2 + 62xy + 33y^2$

If a trinomial has a negative coefficient for the squared term, as in $-2x^2 + 11x - 12$, it is usually easier to factor by first factoring out the common factor -1.

$$-2x^2 + 11x - 12$$
$$= -1(2x^2 - 11x + 12)$$
$$= -1(2x - 3)(x - 4)$$

Use this method to factor each trinomial. **See Example 7(b).**

79. $-x^2 - 4x + 21$

80. $-x^2 + x + 72$

81. $-3x^2 - x + 4$

82. $-5x^2 + 2x + 16$

83. $-2a^2 - 5ab - 2b^2$

84. $-3p^2 + 13pq - 4q^2$

Brain Busters *Factor each polynomial. (Hint: As the first step, factor out the greatest common factor.)*

85. $25q^2(m + 1)^3 - 5q(m + 1)^3 - 2(m + 1)^3$

86. $18x^2(y - 3)^2 - 21x(y - 3)^2 - 4(y - 3)^2$

87. $9x^2(r + 3)^3 + 12xy(r + 3)^3 + 4y^2(r + 3)^3$

88. $4t^2(k + 9)^7 + 20ts(k + 9)^7 + 25s^2(k + 9)^7$

Brain Busters *Find all integers k so that the trinomial can be factored by the methods of this section.*

89. $5x^2 + kx - 1$

90. $2x^2 + kx - 3$

91. $2m^2 + km + 5$

92. $3y^2 + ky + 4$

PREVIEW EXERCISES

Find each product. **See Section 4.6.**

93. $(7p + 3)(7p - 3)$

94. $(3h + 5k)(3h - 5k)$

95. $(x + 6)^2$

96. $(3t + 4)^2$

5.4 Special Factoring Techniques

By reversing the rules for multiplication of binomials from **Section 4.6,** we get rules for factoring polynomials in certain forms.

OBJECTIVE 1 **Factor a difference of squares.** The formula for the product of the sum and difference of the same two terms is

$$(x + y)(x - y) = x^2 - y^2.$$

Reversing this rule leads to the following special factoring rule.

Factoring a Difference of Squares

$$x^2 - y^2 = (x + y)(x - y)$$

For example,

$$m^2 - 16$$
$$= m^2 - 4^2$$
$$= (m + 4)(m - 4).$$

The following conditions must be true for a binomial to be a difference of squares.

1. Both terms of the binomial must be squares, such as

$$x^2, \quad 9y^2 = (3y)^2, \quad 25 = 5^2, \quad 1 = 1^2, \quad m^4 = (m^2)^2.$$

2. The terms of the binomial must have different signs (one positive and one negative).

EXAMPLE 1 Factoring Differences of Squares

Factor each binomial if possible.

$$x^2 - y^2 = (x + y)(x - y)$$

(a) $a^2 - 49 = a^2 - 7^2 = (a + 7)(a - 7)$ **(b)** $y^2 - m^2 = (y + m)(y - m)$

(c) $x^2 - 8$

Because 8 is not the square of an integer, this binomial does not satisfy the conditions above. It is a prime polynomial.

(d) $p^2 + 16$

Since $p^2 + 16$ is a *sum* of squares, it is not equal to $(p + 4)(p - 4)$. Also, we use FOIL and try the following.

$$(p - 4)(p - 4)$$
$$= p^2 - 8p + 16, \quad \text{not} \quad p^2 + 16.$$
$$(p + 4)(p + 4)$$
$$= p^2 + 8p + 16, \quad \text{not} \quad p^2 + 16.$$

Thus, $p^2 + 16$ is a prime polynomial.   NOW TRY

> *NOW TRY*
> *EXERCISE 1*
> Factor each binomial if possible.
> **(a)** $x^2 - 100$ **(b)** $x^2 + 49$

> **⚠ CAUTION** *As Example 1(d) suggests, after any common factor is removed, a sum of squares cannot be factored.*

NOW TRY
EXERCISE 2

Factor each difference of squares.

(a) $9t^2 - 100$

(b) $36a^2 - 49b^2$

EXAMPLE 2 Factoring Differences of Squares

Factor each difference of squares.

$$x^2 \ - \ y^2 \ = \ (x \ + \ y) \ (x \ - \ y)$$

(a) $25m^2 - 16 = (5m)^2 - 4^2 = (5m + 4)(5m - 4)$

(b) $49z^2 - 64t^2$

$\quad = (7z)^2 - (8t)^2$ Write each term as a square.

$\quad = (7z + 8t)(7z - 8t)$ Factor the difference of squares.   NOW TRY

NOTE *Always check a factored form by multiplying.*

NOW TRY
EXERCISE 3

Factor completely.

(a) $16k^2 - 64$

(b) $m^4 - 144$

(c) $v^4 - 625$

EXAMPLE 3 Factoring More Complex Differences of Squares

Factor completely.

(a) $81y^2 - 36$

$\quad = 9(9y^2 - 4)$ Factor out the GCF, 9.

$\quad = 9[(3y)^2 - 2^2]$ Write each term as a square.

$\quad = 9(3y + 2)(3y - 2)$ Factor the difference of squares.

(b) $\qquad\qquad p^4 - 36$

$\qquad\qquad = (p^2)^2 - 6^2$ Write each term as a square.

Neither binomial can be factored further. $= (p^2 + 6)(p^2 - 6)$ Factor the difference of squares.

(c) $\qquad m^4 - 16$

$\qquad = (m^2)^2 - 4^2$

$\qquad = (m^2 + 4)(m^2 - 4)$ Factor the difference of squares.

Don't stop here. $= (m^2 + 4)(m + 2)(m - 2)$ Factor the difference of squares again.

NOW TRY

⚠ **CAUTION** *Factor again when any of the factors is a difference of squares,* as in **Example 3(c).** Check by multiplying.

OBJECTIVE 2 **Factor a perfect square trinomial.** The expressions 144, $4x^2$, and $81m^6$ are called **perfect squares** because

$$144 = 12^2, \quad 4x^2 = (2x)^2, \quad \text{and} \quad 81m^6 = (9m^3)^2.$$

A **perfect square trinomial** is a trinomial that is the square of a binomial. For example, $x^2 + 8x + 16$ is a perfect square trinomial because it is the square of the binomial $x + 4$.

$$x^2 + 8x + 16$$

$$= (x + 4)(x + 4)$$

$$= (x + 4)^2$$

On the one hand, a necessary condition for a trinomial to be a perfect square is that *two of its terms be perfect squares*. For this reason, $16x^2 + 4x + 15$ is not a perfect square trinomial, because only the term $16x^2$ is a perfect square.

On the other hand, even if two of the terms are perfect squares, the trinomial may not be a perfect square trinomial. For example, $x^2 + 6x + 36$ has two perfect square terms, x^2 and 36, but it is not a perfect square trinomial.

Factoring Perfect Square Trinomials

$$x^2 + 2xy + y^2 = (x + y)^2$$
$$x^2 - 2xy + y^2 = (x - y)^2$$

The middle term of a perfect square trinomial is always twice the product of the two terms in the squared binomial (as shown in Section 4.6). Use this rule to check any attempt to factor a trinomial that appears to be a perfect square.

NOW TRY
EXERCISE 4
Factor $y^2 + 14y + 49$.

EXAMPLE 4 Factoring a Perfect Square Trinomial

Factor $x^2 + 10x + 25$.
   The x^2-term is a perfect square, and so is 25.

$$\text{Try to factor} \quad x^2 + 10x + 25 \quad \text{as} \quad (x + 5)^2.$$

To check, take twice the product of the two terms in the squared binomial.

$$2 \cdot x \cdot 5 = 10x \leftarrow \text{Middle term of } x^2 + 10x + 25$$

Twice   First term   Last term
         of binomial   of binomial

Since $10x$ is the middle term of the trinomial, the trinomial is a perfect square.

$$x^2 + 10x + 25 \quad \text{factors as} \quad (x + 5)^2.$$

NOW TRY

EXAMPLE 5 Factoring Perfect Square Trinomials

Factor each trinomial.

(a) $x^2 - 22x + 121$
   The first and last terms are perfect squares ($121 = 11^2$ or $(-11)^2$). Check to see whether the middle term of $x^2 - 22x + 121$ is twice the product of the first and last terms of the binomial $x - 11$.

$$2 \cdot x \cdot (-11) = -22x \leftarrow \text{Middle term of } x^2 - 22x + 121$$

Twice   First   Last
         term   term

Thus, $x^2 - 22x + 121$ is a perfect square trinomial.

$$x^2 - 22x + 121 \quad \text{factors as} \quad (x - 11)^2.$$

Same sign

NOW TRY ANSWER
4. $(y + 7)^2$

Notice that the sign of the second term in the squared binomial is the same as the sign of the middle term in the trinomial.

NOW TRY
EXERCISE 5

Factor each trinomial.

(a) $t^2 - 18t + 81$

(b) $4p^2 - 28p + 49$

(c) $9x^2 + 6x + 4$

(d) $80x^3 + 120x^2 + 45x$

(b) $9m^2 - 24m + 16 = (3m)^2 + 2(3m)(-4) + (-4)^2 = (3m - 4)^2$

Twice —— First —— Last
term   term

(c) $25y^2 + 20y + 16$

The first and last terms are perfect squares.

$$25y^2 = (5y)^2 \quad \text{and} \quad 16 = 4^2$$

Twice the product of the first and last terms of the binomial $5y + 4$ is

$$2 \cdot 5y \cdot 4 = 40y,$$

which is *not* the middle term of

$$25y^2 + 20y + 16.$$

This trinomial is not a perfect square. In fact, the trinomial cannot be factored even with the methods of the previous sections. It is a prime polynomial.

(d) $12z^3 + 60z^2 + 75z$

$= 3z(4z^2 + 20z + 25)$ Factor out the common factor, $3z$.

$= 3z[(2z)^2 + 2(2z)(5) + 5^2]$ $4z^2 + 20z + 25$ is a perfect square trinomial.

$= 3z(2z + 5)^2$ Factor.   *NOW TRY*

NOTE

1. The sign of the second term in the squared binomial is always the same as the sign of the middle term in the trinomial.

2. The first and last terms of a perfect square trinomial must be *positive,* because they are squares. For example, the polynomial $x^2 - 2x - 1$ cannot be a perfect square, because the last term is negative.

3. Perfect square trinomials can also be factored by using grouping or the FOIL method, although using the method of this section is often easier.

OBJECTIVE 3 **Factor a difference of cubes.** We can factor a **difference of cubes** by using the following pattern.

Factoring a Difference of Cubes

$$x^3 - y^3 = (x - y)(x^2 + xy + y^2)$$

This pattern for factoring a difference of cubes should be memorized. To see that the pattern is correct, multiply $(x - y)(x^2 + xy + y^2)$.

$$\begin{array}{r} x^2 + xy + y^2 \\ x - y \\ \hline -x^2y - xy^2 - y^3 \\ x^3 + x^2y + xy^2 \\ \hline x^3 \qquad\qquad - y^3 \end{array}$$

Multiply vertically. (Section 4.5)

$-y(x^2 + xy + y^2)$
$x(x^2 + xy + y^2)$
Add.

NOW TRY ANSWERS
5. **(a)** $(t - 9)^2$
   (b) $(2p - 7)^2$
   (c) prime
   (d) $5x(4x + 3)^2$

Notice the pattern of the terms in the factored form of $x^3 - y^3$.

- $x^3 - y^3 = $ (a binomial factor)(a trinomial factor)
- The binomial factor has the difference of the cube roots of the given terms.
- The terms in the trinomial factor are all positive.
- The terms in the binomial factor help to determine the trinomial factor.

$$x^3 - y^3 = (x - y)(\underset{\substack{\text{First term} \\ \text{squared}}}{x^2} + \underset{\substack{\text{positive} \\ \text{product of} \\ \text{the terms}}}{xy} + \underset{\substack{\text{second term} \\ \text{squared}}}{y^2})$$

> ⚠ **CAUTION** The polynomial $x^3 - y^3$ is not equivalent to $(x - y)^3$.
>
> | $x^3 - y^3$ | $(x - y)^3$ |
> |---|---|
> | $= (x - y)(x^2 + xy + y^2)$ | $= (x - y)(x - y)(x - y)$ |
> | | $= (x - y)(x^2 - 2xy + y^2)$ |

**NOW TRY
EXERCISE 6**

Factor each polynomial.

(a) $a^3 - 27$

(b) $8t^3 - 125$

(c) $3k^3 - 192$

(d) $125x^3 - 343y^6$

EXAMPLE 6 Factoring Differences of Cubes

Factor each polynomial.

(a) $m^3 - 125$

Let $x = m$ and $y = 5$ in the pattern for the difference of cubes.

$$x^3 - y^3 = (x - y)(x^2 + xy + y^2)$$

$$m^3 - 125 = m^3 - 5^3 = (m - 5)(m^2 + 5m + 5^2) \qquad \text{Let } x = m, y = 5.$$
$$= (m - 5)(m^2 + 5m + 25) \qquad 5^2 = 25$$

(b) $8p^3 - 27$

$$= (2p)^3 - 3^3 \qquad 8p^3 = (2p)^3 \text{ and } 27 = 3^3.$$
$$= (2p - 3)[(2p)^2 + (2p)3 + 3^2] \qquad \text{Let } x = 2p, y = 3.$$
$$= (2p - 3)(4p^2 + 6p + 9) \qquad \text{Apply the exponents. Multiply.}$$

> $(2p)^2 = 2^2 p^2 = 4p^2$, NOT $2p^2$.

(c) $4m^3 - 32$

$$= 4(m^3 - 8) \qquad \text{Factor out the common factor, 4.}$$
$$= 4(m^3 - 2^3) \qquad 8 = 2^3$$
$$= 4(m - 2)(m^2 + 2m + 4) \qquad \text{Factor the difference of cubes.}$$

(d) $125t^3 - 216s^6$

$$= (5t)^3 - (6s^2)^3 \qquad \text{Write each term as a cube.}$$
$$= (5t - 6s^2)[(5t)^2 + 5t(6s^2) + (6s^2)^2] \qquad \text{Factor the difference of cubes.}$$
$$= (5t - 6s^2)(25t^2 + 30ts^2 + 36s^4) \qquad \text{Apply the exponents. Multiply.}$$

NOW TRY

NOW TRY ANSWERS
6. (a) $(a - 3)(a^2 + 3a + 9)$
   (b) $(2t - 5)(4t^2 + 10t + 25)$
   (c) $3(k - 4)(k^2 + 4k + 16)$
   (d) $(5x - 7y^2) \cdot$
       $(25x^2 + 35xy^2 + 49y^4)$

⚠️ **CAUTION** A common error in factoring a difference of cubes, such as $x^3 - y^3 = (x - y)(x^2 + xy + y^2)$, is to try to factor $x^2 + xy + y^2$. This is usually not possible.

OBJECTIVE 4 **Factor a sum of cubes.** A sum of squares, such as $m^2 + 25$, cannot be factored by using real numbers, but a **sum of cubes** can.

Factoring a Sum of Cubes

$$x^3 + y^3 = (x + y)(x^2 - xy + y^2)$$

Compare the pattern for the *sum* of cubes with that for the *difference* of cubes.

$$x^3 - y^3 = (x - y)(x^2 + xy + y^2) \quad \text{Difference of cubes}$$

Same sign — Opposite sign — Positive

The only difference between the patterns is the positive and negative signs.

$$x^3 + y^3 = (x + y)(x^2 - xy + y^2) \quad \text{Sum of cubes}$$

Same sign — Opposite sign — Positive

NOW TRY
EXERCISE 7
Factor each polynomial.
(a) $x^3 + 125$
(b) $27a^3 + 8b^3$

EXAMPLE 7 Factoring Sums of Cubes

Factor each polynomial.

(a) $k^3 + 27$

$= k^3 + 3^3$ $27 = 3^3$

$= (k + 3)(k^2 - 3k + 3^2)$ Factor the sum of cubes.

$= (k + 3)(k^2 - 3k + 9)$ Apply the exponent.

(b) $8m^3 + 125n^3$

$= (2m)^3 + (5n)^3$ $8m^3 = (2m)^3$ and $125n^3 = (5n)^3$.

$= (2m + 5n)[(2m)^2 - 2m(5n) + (5n)^2]$ Factor the sum of cubes.

$= (2m + 5n)(4m^2 - 10mn + 25n^2)$ Be careful: $(2m)^2 = 2^2m^2$ and $(5n)^2 = 5^2n^2$.

(c) $1000a^6 + 27b^3$

$= (10a^2)^3 + (3b)^3$

$= (10a^2 + 3b)[(10a^2)^2 - (10a^2)(3b) + (3b)^2]$ Factor the sum of cubes.

$= (10a^2 + 3b)(100a^4 - 30a^2b + 9b^2)$ $(10a^2)^2 = 10^2(a^2)^2 = 100a^4$

NOW TRY ANSWERS
7. (a) $(x + 5)(x^2 - 5x + 25)$
(b) $(3a + 2b)(9a^2 - 6ab + 4b^2)$

NOW TRY

The methods of factoring discussed in this section are summarized here.

Special Factorizations	
Difference of squares	$x^2 - y^2 = (x + y)(x - y)$
Perfect square trinomials	$x^2 + 2xy + y^2 = (x + y)^2$
	$x^2 - 2xy + y^2 = (x - y)^2$
Difference of cubes	$x^3 - y^3 = (x - y)(x^2 + xy + y^2)$
Sum of cubes	$x^3 + y^3 = (x + y)(x^2 - xy + y^2)$

The sum of squares can be factored only if the terms have a common factor.

5.4 EXERCISES

MyMathLab | Math XL PRACTICE | WATCH | DOWNLOAD | READ | REVIEW

Complete solution available on the Video Resources on DVD

1. *Concept Check*   To help you factor the difference of squares, complete the following list of squares.

$1^2 =$ _____ $2^2 =$ _____ $3^2 =$ _____ $4^2 =$ _____ $5^2 =$ _____

$6^2 =$ _____ $7^2 =$ _____ $8^2 =$ _____ $9^2 =$ _____ $10^2 =$ _____

$11^2 =$ _____ $12^2 =$ _____ $13^2 =$ _____ $14^2 =$ _____ $15^2 =$ _____

$16^2 =$ _____ $17^2 =$ _____ $18^2 =$ _____ $19^2 =$ _____ $20^2 =$ _____

2. *Concept Check*   The following powers of x are all perfect squares: $x^2, x^4, x^6, x^8, x^{10}$. On the basis of this observation, we may make a conjecture (an educated guess) that if the power of a variable is divisible by _____ (with 0 remainder), then we have a perfect square.

3. *Concept Check*   To help you factor the sum or difference of cubes, complete the following list of cubes.

$1^3 =$ _____ $2^3 =$ _____ $3^3 =$ _____ $4^3 =$ _____ $5^3 =$ _____

$6^3 =$ _____ $7^3 =$ _____ $8^3 =$ _____ $9^3 =$ _____ $10^3 =$ _____

4. *Concept Check*   The following powers of x are all perfect cubes: $x^3, x^6, x^9, x^{12}, x^{15}$. On the basis of this observation, we may make a conjecture that if the power of a variable is divisible by _____ (with 0 remainder), then we have a perfect cube.

5. *Concept Check*   Identify each monomial as a *perfect square*, a *perfect cube*, *both of these*, or *neither of these*.

(a) $64x^6y^{12}$ (b) $125t^6$ (c) $49x^{12}$ (d) $81r^{10}$

6. *Concept Check*   What must be true for x^n to be both a perfect square and a perfect cube?

Factor each binomial completely. If the binomial is prime, say so. Use your answers from Exercises 1 and 2 as necessary. See Examples 1–3.

 7. $y^2 - 25$ **8.** $t^2 - 16$ **9.** $x^2 - 144$

10. $x^2 - 400$ **11.** $m^2 + 64$ **12.** $k^2 + 49$

13. $4m^2 + 16$ **14.** $9x^2 + 81$ **15.** $9r^2 - 4$

16. $4x^2 - 9$ **17.** $36x^2 - 16$ **18.** $32a^2 - 8$

19. $196p^2 - 225$ **20.** $361q^2 - 400$ **21.** $16r^2 - 25a^2$

22. $49m^2 - 100p^2$ **23.** $100x^2 + 49$ **24.** $81w^2 + 16$

25. $p^4 - 49$ **26.** $r^4 - 25$ **27.** $x^4 - 1$

28. $y^4 - 10{,}000$ **29.** $p^4 - 256$ **30.** $k^4 - 81$

31. *Concept Check*   When a student was directed to factor $k^4 - 81$ from **Exercise 30** completely, his teacher did not give him full credit for the answer

$$(k^2 + 9)(k^2 - 9).$$

The student argued that since his answer does indeed give $k^4 - 81$ when multiplied out, he should be given full credit. *WHAT WENT WRONG?* Give the correct factored form.

32. *Concept Check*   The binomial $4x^2 + 36$ is a sum of squares that *can* be factored. How is this binomial factored? When can the sum of squares be factored?

Concept Check   *Find the value of the indicated variable.*

33. Find b so that $x^2 + bx + 25$ factors as $(x + 5)^2$.

34. Find c so that $4m^2 - 12m + c$ factors as $(2m - 3)^2$.

35. Find a so that $ay^2 - 12y + 4$ factors as $(3y - 2)^2$.

36. Find b so that $100a^2 + ba + 9$ factors as $(10a + 3)^2$.

Factor each trinomial completely. **See Examples 4 and 5.**

🌐 **37.** $w^2 + 2w + 1$ **38.** $p^2 + 4p + 4$

🌐 **39.** $x^2 - 8x + 16$ **40.** $x^2 - 10x + 25$

    41. $2x^2 + 24x + 72$ **42.** $3y^2 + 48y + 192$

    43. $16x^2 - 40x + 25$ **44.** $36y^2 - 60y + 25$

    45. $49x^2 - 28xy + 4y^2$ **46.** $4z^2 - 12zw + 9w^2$

    47. $64x^2 + 48xy + 9y^2$ **48.** $9t^2 + 24tr + 16r^2$

    49. $50h^2 - 40hy + 8y^2$ **50.** $18x^2 - 48xy + 32y^2$

    51. $4k^3 - 4k^2 + 9k$ **52.** $9r^3 - 6r^2 + 16r$

    53. $25z^4 + 5z^3 + z^2$ **54.** $4x^4 + 2x^3 + x^2$

Factor each binomial completely. Use your answers from **Exercises 3 and 4** *as necessary.* **See Examples 6 and 7.**

🌐 **55.** $a^3 - 1$ **56.** $m^3 - 8$ 🌐 **57.** $m^3 + 8$

    58. $b^3 + 1$ **59.** $k^3 + 1000$ **60.** $p^3 + 512$

    61. $27x^3 - 64$ **62.** $64y^3 - 27$ **63.** $6p^3 + 6$

    64. $81x^3 + 3$ **65.** $5x^3 + 40$ **66.** $128y^3 + 54$

    67. $y^3 - 8x^3$ **68.** $w^3 - 216z^3$

    69. $2x^3 - 16y^3$ **70.** $27w^3 - 216z^3$

    71. $8p^3 + 729q^3$ **72.** $64x^3 + 125y^3$

    73. $27a^3 + 64b^3$ **74.** $125m^3 + 8p^3$

    75. $125t^3 + 8s^3$ **76.** $27r^3 + 1000s^3$

    77. $8x^3 - 125y^6$ **78.** $27t^3 - 64s^6$

    79. $27m^6 + 8n^3$ **80.** $1000r^6 + 27s^3$

    81. $x^9 + y^9$ **82.** $x^9 - y^9$

Although we usually factor polynomials using integers, we can apply the same concepts to factoring using fractions and decimals.

$$z^2 - \frac{9}{16}$$

$$= z^2 - \left(\frac{3}{4}\right)^2 \qquad \frac{9}{16} = \left(\frac{3}{4}\right)^2$$

$$= \left(z + \frac{3}{4}\right)\left(z - \frac{3}{4}\right) \qquad \text{Factor the difference of squares.}$$

Apply the special factoring rules of this section to factor each binomial or trinomial.

83. $p^2 - \frac{1}{9}$ **84.** $q^2 - \frac{1}{4}$ **85.** $36m^2 - \frac{16}{25}$

86. $100b^2 - \frac{4}{49}$ **87.** $x^2 - 0.64$ **88.** $y^2 - 0.36$

89. $t^2 + t + \frac{1}{4}$ **90.** $m^2 + \frac{2}{3}m + \frac{1}{9}$ **91.** $x^2 - 1.0x + 0.25$

92. $y^2 - 1.4y + 0.49$ **93.** $x^3 + \frac{1}{8}$ **94.** $x^3 + \frac{1}{64}$

Brain Busters *Factor each polynomial completely.*

95. $(m + n)^2 - (m - n)^2$ **96.** $(a - b)^3 - (a + b)^3$

97. $m^2 - p^2 + 2m + 2p$ **98.** $3r - 3k + 3r^2 - 3k^2$

PREVIEW EXERCISES

Solve each equation. See Sections 2.1 and 2.2.

99. $m - 4 = 0$ **100.** $3t + 2 = 0$ **101.** $2t + 10 = 0$ **102.** $7x = 0$

SUMMARY EXERCISES on Factoring

As you factor a polynomial, ask yourself these questions to decide on a suitable factoring technique.

Factoring a Polynomial

1. **Is there a common factor?** If so, factor it out.

2. **How many terms are in the polynomial?**

   Two terms: Check to see whether it is a difference of squares or a sum or difference of cubes. If so, factor as in **Section 5.4.**

   Three terms: Is it a perfect square trinomial? If the trinomial is not a perfect square, check to see whether the coefficient of the second-degree term is 1. If so, use the method of **Section 5.2.** If the coefficient of the second-degree term of the trinomial is not 1, use the general factoring methods of **Section 5.3.**

   Four terms: Try to factor the polynomial by grouping, as in **Section 5.1.**

3. **Can any factors be factored further?** If so, factor them.

(continued)

Match each polynomial in Column I with the best choice for factoring it in Column II. The choices in Column II may be used once, more than once, or not at all.

I

1. $12x^2 + 20x + 8$

2. $x^2 - 17x + 72$

3. $16m^2n + 24mn - 40mn^2$

4. $64a^2 - 121b^2$

5. $36p^2 - 60pq + 25q^2$

6. $z^2 - 4z + 6$

7. $8r^3 - 125$

8. $x^6 + 4x^4 - 3x^2 - 12$

9. $4w^2 + 49$

10. $z^2 - 24z + 144$

II

A. Factor out the GCF. No further factoring is possible.

B. Factor a difference of squares.

C. Factor a difference of cubes.

D. Factor a sum of cubes.

E. Factor a perfect square trinomial.

F. Factor by grouping.

G. Factor out the GCF. Then factor a trinomial by grouping or trial and error.

H. Factor into two binomials by finding two integers whose product is the constant in the trinomial and whose sum is the coefficient of the middle term.

I. The polynomial is prime.

Factor each polynomial completely.

11. $a^2 - 4a - 12$

12. $a^2 + 17a + 72$

13. $6y^2 - 6y - 12$

14. $7y^6 + 14y^5 - 168y^4$

15. $6a + 12b + 18c$

16. $m^2 - 3mn - 4n^2$

17. $p^2 - 17p + 66$

18. $z^2 - 6z + 7z - 42$

19. $10z^2 - 7z - 6$

20. $2m^2 - 10m - 48$

21. $17x^3y^2 + 51xy$

22. $15y + 5$

23. $8a^5 - 8a^4 - 48a^3$

24. $8k^2 - 10k - 3$

25. $z^2 - 3za - 10a^2$

26. $50z^2 - 100$

27. $x^2 - 4x - 5x + 20$

28. $100n^2r^2 + 30nr^3 - 50n^2r$

29. $6n^2 - 19n + 10$

30. $9y^2 + 12y - 5$

31. $16x + 20$

32. $m^2 + 2m - 15$

33. $6y^2 - 5y - 4$

34. $m^2 - 81$

35. $6z^2 + 31z + 5$

36. $12x^2 + 47x - 4$

37. $4k^2 - 12k + 9$

38. $8p^2 + 23p - 3$

39. $54m^2 - 24z^2$

40. $8m^2 - 2m - 3$

41. $3k^2 + 4k - 4$

42. $45a^3b^5 - 60a^4b^2 + 75a^6b^4$

43. $14k^3 + 7k^2 - 70k$

44. $5 + r - 5s - rs$

45. $y^4 - 16$

46. $20y^5 - 30y^4$

47. $8m - 16m^2$

48. $k^2 - 16$

49. $z^3 - 8$

50. $y^2 - y - 56$

51. $k^2 + 9$

52. $27p^{10} - 45p^9 - 252p^8$

53. $32m^9 + 16m^5 + 24m^3$

54. $8m^3 + 125$

55. $16r^2 + 24rm + 9m^2$

56. $z^2 - 12z + 36$

57. $15h^2 + 11hg - 14g^2$

58. $5z^3 - 45z^2 + 70z$

59. $k^2 - 11k + 30$

60. $64p^2 - 100m^2$

61. $3k^3 - 12k^2 - 15k$

62. $y^2 - 4yk - 12k^2$

63. $1000p^3 + 27$

64. $64r^3 - 343$

65. $6 + 3m + 2p + mp$

66. $2m^2 + 7mn - 15n^2$

67. $16z^2 - 8z + 1$

68. $125m^4 - 400m^3n + 195m^2n^2$

69. $108m^2 - 36m + 3$

70. $100a^2 - 81y^2$

71. $x^2 - xy + y^2$

72. $4y^2 - 25$

73. $32z^3 + 56z^2 - 16z$

74. $10m^2 + 25m - 60$

75. $20 + 5m + 12n + 3mn$

76. $4 - 2q - 6p + 3pq$

77. $6a^2 + 10a - 4$

78. $36y^6 - 42y^5 - 120y^4$

79. $a^3 - b^3 + 2a - 2b$

80. $16k^2 - 48k + 36$

81. $64m^2 - 80mn + 25n^2$

82. $72y^3z^2 + 12y^2 - 24y^4z^2$

83. $8k^2 - 2kh - 3h^2$

84. $2a^2 - 7a - 30$

85. $2x^3 + 128$

86. $8a^3 - 27$

87. $10y^2 - 7yz - 6z^2$

88. $m^2 - 4m + 4$

89. $8a^2 + 23ab - 3b^2$

90. $a^4 - 625$

RELATING CONCEPTS   EXERCISES 91–98

FOR INDIVIDUAL OR GROUP WORK

*A binomial may be both a difference of squares and a difference of cubes. One example of such a binomial is $x^6 - 1$. With the techniques of **Section 5.4,** one factoring method will give the completely factored form, while the other will not. **Work Exercises 91–98 in order** to determine the method to use if you have to make such a decision.*

91. Factor $x^6 - 1$ as the difference of squares.

92. The factored form obtained in **Exercise 91** consists of a difference of cubes multiplied by a sum of cubes. Factor each binomial further.

93. Now start over and factor $x^6 - 1$ as the difference of cubes.

94. The factored form obtained in **Exercise 93** consists of a binomial that is a difference of squares and a trinomial. Factor the binomial further.

95. Compare your results in **Exercises 92 and 94.** Which one of these is factored completely?

96. Verify that the trinomial in the factored form in **Exercise 94** is the product of the two trinomials in the factored form in **Exercise 92.**

97. Use the results of **Exercises 91–96** to complete the following statement: In general, if I must choose between factoring first with the method for the difference of squares or the method for the difference of cubes, I should choose the _____ method to eventually obtain the completely factored form.

98. Find the *completely* factored form of $x^6 - 729$ by using the knowledge you gained in **Exercises 91–97.**

STUDY SKILLS

Preparing for Your Math Final Exam

Your math final exam is likely to be a comprehensive exam, which means it will cover material from the entire term.

1. **Figure out the grade you need to earn on the final exam to get the course grade you want.** Check your course syllabus for grading policies, or ask your instructor if you are not sure.

   How many points do you need to earn on your math final exam to get the grade you want?

2. **Create a final exam week plan.** Set priorities that allow you to spend extra time studying. This may mean making adjustments, in advance, in your work schedule or enlisting extra help with family responsibilities.

   What adjustments do you need to make for final exam week?

3. **Use the following suggestions to guide your studying and reviewing.**

   ▶ **Begin reviewing several days before the final exam.** DON'T wait until the last minute.

   ▶ **Know exactly which chapters and sections will be covered on the exam.**

   ▶ **Divide up the chapters.** Decide how much you will review each day.

   ▶ **Use returned quizzes and tests to review earlier material.**

   ▶ **Practice all types of problems. Use the Cumulative Reviews** that are at the end of each chapter in your textbook. All answers, with section references, are given in the answer section.

   ▶ **Review or rewrite your notes** to create summaries of important information.

   ▶ **Make study cards for all types of problems.** Carry the cards with you, and review them whenever you have a few minutes.

   ▶ **Take plenty of short breaks to reduce physical and mental stress.** Exercising, listening to music, and enjoying a favorite activity are effective stress busters.

   Finally, *DON'T* stay up all night the night before an exam—*get a good night's sleep.*

   Select several suggestions to use as you study for your math final exam.

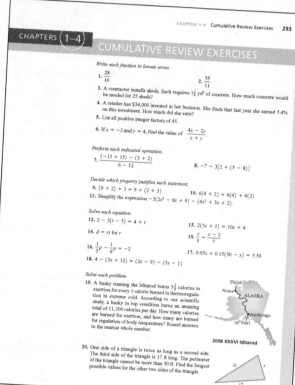

5.5 Solving Quadratic Equations by Factoring

OBJECTIVES

1 Solve quadratic equations by factoring.

2 Solve other equations by factoring.

Galileo Galilei (1564–1642)

Galileo Galilei developed theories to explain physical phenomena and set up experiments to test his ideas. According to legend, Galileo dropped objects of different weights from the Leaning Tower of Pisa to disprove the belief that heavier objects fall faster than lighter objects. He developed the formula

$$d = 16t^2$$

describing the motion of freely falling objects. In this formula, d is the distance in feet that an object falls (disregarding air resistance) in t seconds, regardless of weight.

The equation $d = 16t^2$ is a *quadratic equation*. A quadratic equation contains a second-degree term and no terms of greater degree.

Quadratic Equation

A **quadratic equation** is an equation that can be written in the form

$$ax^2 + bx + c = 0,$$

where a, b, and c are real numbers, with $a \neq 0$.

The form $ax^2 + bx + c = 0$ is the **standard form** of a quadratic equation.

$$x^2 + 5x + 6 = 0, \quad 2x^2 - 5x = 3, \quad x^2 = 4 \qquad \text{Quadratic equations}$$

Of these quadratic equations, only $x^2 + 5x + 6 = 0$ is in standard form.

We have factored many quadratic *expressions* of the form $ax^2 + bx + c$. In this section, we use factored quadratic expressions to solve quadratic *equations*.

OBJECTIVE 1 Solve quadratic equations by factoring. We use the **zero-factor property** to solve a quadratic equation by factoring.

Zero-Factor Property

If a and b are real numbers and if $ab = 0$, then $a = 0$ or $b = 0$.

That is, if the product of two numbers is 0, then at least one of the numbers must be 0. One number *must* be 0, but both *may* be 0.

EXAMPLE 1 Using the Zero-Factor Property

Solve each equation.

(a) $(x + 3)(2x - 1) = 0$

The product $(x + 3)(2x - 1)$ is equal to 0. By the zero-factor property, the only way that the product of these two factors can be 0 is if at least one of the factors equals 0. Therefore, either $x + 3 = 0$ or $2x - 1 = 0$.

$$x + 3 = 0 \qquad \text{or} \quad 2x - 1 = 0 \qquad \text{Zero-factor property}$$

$$x = -3 \qquad\qquad 2x = 1 \qquad \text{Solve each equation.}$$

$$x = \frac{1}{2} \qquad \text{Divide each side by 2.}$$

NOW TRY
EXERCISE 1
Solve each equation.

(a) $(x - 4)(3x + 1) = 0$

(b) $y(4y - 5) = 0$

The original equation, $(x + 3)(2x - 1) = 0$, has two solutions, -3 and $\frac{1}{2}$. Check these solutions by substituting -3 for x in this equation. *Then start over* and substitute $\frac{1}{2}$ for x.

CHECK   Let $x = -3$.

$$(x + 3)(2x - 1) = 0$$

$$(-3 + 3)[2(-3) - 1] \overset{?}{=} 0$$

$$0(-7) = 0 \; ✓ \; \text{True}$$

Let $x = \dfrac{1}{2}$.

$$(x + 3)(2x - 1) = 0$$

$$\left(\frac{1}{2} + 3\right)\left(2 \cdot \frac{1}{2} - 1\right) \overset{?}{=} 0$$

$$\frac{7}{2}(1 - 1) \overset{?}{=} 0$$

$$\frac{7}{2} \cdot 0 = 0 \; ✓ \; \text{True}$$

Both -3 and $\frac{1}{2}$ result in true equations, so the solution set is $\left\{-3, \frac{1}{2}\right\}$.

(b) $$y(3y - 4) = 0$$

$$y = 0 \quad \text{or} \quad 3y - 4 = 0 \qquad \text{Zero-factor property}$$

Don't forget that 0 is a solution.

$$3y = 4$$

$$y = \frac{4}{3}$$

Check these solutions by substituting each one into the original equation. The solution set is $\left\{0, \frac{4}{3}\right\}$.

NOW TRY

NOTE The word *or* as used in **Example 1** means "one or the other or both."

If the polynomial in an equation is not already factored, first make sure that the equation is in standard form. Then factor.

EXAMPLE 2   Solving Quadratic Equations

Solve each equation.

(a) $x^2 - 5x = -6$

First, rewrite the equation in standard form by adding 6 to each side.

Don't factor x out at this step.

$$x^2 - 5x = -6$$

$$x^2 - 5x + 6 = 0 \qquad \text{Add 6.}$$

Now factor $x^2 - 5x + 6$. Find two numbers whose product is 6 and whose sum is -5. These two numbers are -2 and -3, so we factor as follows.

$$(x - 2)(x - 3) = 0 \qquad \text{Factor.}$$

$$x - 2 = 0 \quad \text{or} \quad x - 3 = 0 \qquad \text{Zero-factor property}$$

$$x = 2 \quad \text{or} \qquad x = 3 \qquad \text{Solve each equation.}$$

NOW TRY ANSWERS

1. (a) $\left\{-\frac{1}{3}, 4\right\}$ **(b)** $\left\{0, \frac{5}{4}\right\}$

NOW TRY
EXERCISE 2
Solve $t^2 = -3t + 18$.

CHECK   Let $x = 2$.

$$x^2 - 5x = -6$$
$$2^2 - 5(2) \stackrel{?}{=} -6$$
$$4 - 10 \stackrel{?}{=} -6$$
$$-6 = -6 \checkmark \text{ True}$$

Let $x = 3$.

$$x^2 - 5x = -6$$
$$3^2 - 5(3) \stackrel{?}{=} -6$$
$$9 - 15 \stackrel{?}{=} -6$$
$$-6 = -6 \checkmark \text{ True}$$

Both solutions check, so the solution set is $\{2, 3\}$.

(b)
$$y^2 = y + 20 \quad \text{Write this equation in standard form.}$$

Standard form $\rightarrow$ $y^2 - y - 20 = 0$ Subtract y and 20.

$$(y - 5)(y + 4) = 0 \quad \text{Factor.}$$
$$y - 5 = 0 \quad \text{or} \quad y + 4 = 0 \quad \text{Zero-factor property}$$
$$y = 5 \quad \text{or} \quad y = -4 \quad \text{Solve each equation.}$$

Check each solution to verify that the solution set is $\{-4, 5\}$.   NOW TRY

Solving a Quadratic Equation by Factoring

Step 1 **Write the equation in standard form**—that is, with all terms on one side of the equals symbol in descending powers of the variable and 0 on the other side.

Step 2 **Factor** completely.

Step 3 **Use the zero-factor property** to set each factor with a variable equal to 0.

Step 4 **Solve** the resulting equations.

Step 5 **Check** each solution in the original equation.

NOTE Not all quadratic equations can be solved by factoring. A more general method for solving such equations is given in **Chapter 11**.

NOW TRY
EXERCISE 3
Solve $10p^2 + 65p = 35$.

EXAMPLE 3 Solving a Quadratic Equation with a Common Factor

Solve $4p^2 + 40 = 26p$.

$$4p^2 + 40 = 26p$$
$$4p^2 - 26p + 40 = 0 \quad \text{Standard form}$$
$$2(2p^2 - 13p + 20) = 0 \quad \text{Factor out 2.}$$

This 2 is *not* a solution of the equation.

$$2p^2 - 13p + 20 = 0 \quad \text{Divide each side by 2.}$$
$$(2p - 5)(p - 4) = 0 \quad \text{Factor.}$$
$$2p - 5 = 0 \quad \text{or} \quad p - 4 = 0 \quad \text{Zero-factor property}$$
$$2p = 5 \quad\quad p = 4 \quad \text{Solve each equation.}$$
$$p = \frac{5}{2}$$

NOW TRY ANSWERS
2. $\{-6, 3\}$ 3. $\{-7, \frac{1}{2}\}$

Check each solution to verify that the solution set is $\{\frac{5}{2}, 4\}$.   NOW TRY

⚠ **CAUTION** A common error is to include the common factor 2 as a solution in **Example 3**. *Only factors containing variables lead to solutions,* such as the factor y in the equation $y(3y - 4) = 0$ in **Example 1(b)**.

⤸ *NOW TRY*
EXERCISE 4

Solve each equation.

(a) $9x^2 - 64 = 0$

(b) $m^2 = 5m$

(c) $p(6p - 1) = 2$

EXAMPLE 4 Solving Quadratic Equations

Solve each equation.

(a)
$$16m^2 - 25 = 0$$
$$(4m + 5)(4m - 5) = 0 \qquad \text{Factor the difference of squares. (Section 6.4)}$$
$$4m + 5 = 0 \quad \text{or} \quad 4m - 5 = 0 \qquad \text{Zero-factor property}$$
$$4m = -5 \quad \text{or} \qquad 4m = 5 \qquad \text{Solve each equation.}$$
$$m = -\frac{5}{4} \quad \text{or} \qquad m = \frac{5}{4}$$

Check the solutions, $-\frac{5}{4}$ and $\frac{5}{4}$, in the original equation. The solution set is $\left\{-\frac{5}{4}, \frac{5}{4}\right\}$.

(b)
$$y^2 = 2y$$
$$y^2 - 2y = 0 \qquad \text{Standard form}$$
$$y(y - 2) = 0 \qquad \text{Factor.}$$

> Don't forget to set the variable factor y equal to 0.

$$y = 0 \quad \text{or} \quad y - 2 = 0 \qquad \text{Zero-factor property}$$
$$y = 2 \qquad \text{Solve.}$$

The solution set is $\{0, 2\}$.

(c)

> To be in standard form, 0 must be on the right side.

$$k(2k + 1) = 3$$
$$2k^2 + k = 3 \qquad \text{Distributive property}$$
$$\text{Standard form} \longrightarrow 2k^2 + k - 3 = 0 \qquad \text{Subtract 3.}$$
$$(2k + 3)(k - 1) = 0 \qquad \text{Factor.}$$
$$2k + 3 = 0 \quad \text{or} \quad k - 1 = 0 \qquad \text{Zero-factor property}$$
$$2k = -3 \qquad \qquad k = 1 \qquad \text{Solve each equation.}$$
$$k = -\frac{3}{2}$$

The solution set is $\left\{-\frac{3}{2}, 1\right\}$.

NOW TRY ↻

⚠ **CAUTION** In **Example 4(b)**, it is tempting to begin by dividing both sides of
$$y^2 = 2y$$
by y to get $y = 2$. Note, however, that we do not get the other solution, 0, if we divide by a variable. (We *may* divide each side of an equation by a *nonzero* real number, however. For instance, in **Example 3** we divided each side by 2.)

In **Example 4(c)**, we could not use the zero-factor property to solve the equation
$$k(2k + 1) = 3$$
in its given form because of the 3 on the right. *The zero-factor property applies only to a product that equals 0.*

NOW TRY ANSWERS

4. (a) $\left\{-\frac{8}{3}, \frac{8}{3}\right\}$ **(b)** $\{0, 5\}$

(c) $\left\{-\frac{1}{2}, \frac{2}{3}\right\}$

NOW TRY
EXERCISE 5
Solve.

$$4x^2 - 4x + 1 = 0$$

EXAMPLE 5   Solving Quadratic Equations with Double Solutions

Solve each equation.

(a)

$$z^2 - 22z + 121 = 0$$

$$(z - 11)^2 = 0 \qquad \text{Factor the perfect square trinomial.}$$

$$(z - 11)(z - 11) = 0 \qquad a^2 = a \cdot a$$

$$z - 11 = 0 \quad \text{or} \quad z - 11 = 0 \qquad \text{Zero-factor property}$$

Because the two factors are identical, they both lead to the same solution. (This is called a **double solution.**)

$$z = 11 \qquad \text{Add 11.}$$

CHECK
$$z^2 - 22z + 121 = 0$$

$$11^2 - 22(11) + 121 \overset{?}{=} 0 \qquad \text{Let } z = 11.$$

$$121 - 242 + 121 \overset{?}{=} 0$$

$$0 = 0 \ \checkmark \ \text{True}$$

The solution set is $\{11\}$.

(b)

$$9t^2 - 30t = -25$$

$$9t^2 - 30t + 25 = 0 \qquad \text{Standard form}$$

$$(3t - 5)^2 = 0 \qquad \text{Factor the perfect square trinomial.}$$

$$3t - 5 = 0 \quad \text{or} \quad 3t - 5 = 0 \qquad \text{Zero-factor property}$$

$$3t = 5 \qquad \text{Solve the equation.}$$

$$t = \frac{5}{3} \qquad \tfrac{5}{3} \text{ is a double solution.}$$

Check by substituting $\frac{5}{3}$ in the original equation. The solution set is $\left\{\frac{5}{3}\right\}$.

NOW TRY

⚠ **CAUTION**   Each of the equations in **Example 5** has only *one* distinct solution. *There is no need to write the same number more than once in a solution set.*

OBJECTIVE 2   **Solve other equations by factoring.**   We can also use the zero-factor property to solve equations that involve more than two factors with variables. (These equations are *not* quadratic equations. Why not?)

EXAMPLE 6   Solving Equations with More Than Two Variable Factors

Solve each equation.

(a)

$$6z^3 - 6z = 0$$

$$6z(z^2 - 1) = 0 \qquad \text{Factor out } 6z.$$

$$6z(z + 1)(z - 1) = 0 \qquad \text{Factor } z^2 - 1.$$

By an extension of the zero-factor property, this product can equal 0 only if at least one of the factors is 0. Write and solve three equations, one for each factor with a variable.

NOW TRY ANSWER
5. $\left\{\frac{1}{2}\right\}$

NOW TRY
EXERCISE 6

Solve each equation.

(a) $3x^3 - 27x = 0$

(b) $(3a - 1) \cdot$
$(2a^2 - 5a - 12) = 0$

$6z = 0$ or $z + 1 = 0$ or $z - 1 = 0$

$z = 0$ or $z = -1$ or $z = 1$

Check by substituting, in turn, 0, -1, and 1 into the original equation. The solution set is $\{-1, 0, 1\}$.

(b)
$(3x - 1)(x^2 - 9x + 20) = 0$

$(3x - 1)(x - 5)(x - 4) = 0$ Factor $x^2 - 9x + 20$.

$3x - 1 = 0$ or $x - 5 = 0$ or $x - 4 = 0$ Zero-factor property

$x = \dfrac{1}{3}$ or $x = 5$ or $x = 4$ Solve each equation.

Check each solution to verify that the solution set is $\left\{\frac{1}{3}, 4, 5\right\}$.   NOW TRY

⚠ **CAUTION** In **Example 6(b),** it would be unproductive to begin by multiplying the two factors together. The zero-factor property requires the *product* of two or more factors to equal 0. *Always consider first whether an equation is given in an appropriate form for the zero-factor property to apply.*

NOW TRY
EXERCISE 7

Solve.

$x(4x - 9) = (x - 2)^2 + 24$

EXAMPLE 7 Solving an Equation Requiring Multiplication before Factoring

Solve $(3x + 1)x = (x + 1)^2 + 5$.

The zero-factor property requires the *product* of two or more factors to equal 0.

$(3x + 1)x = (x + 1)^2 + 5$ $(x + 1)^2 = (x + 1)(x + 1)$

$3x^2 + x = x^2 + 2x + 1 + 5$ Multiply.

$3x^2 + x = x^2 + 2x + 6$ Combine like terms.

$2x^2 - x - 6 = 0$ Standard form

$(2x + 3)(x - 2) = 0$ Factor.

$2x + 3 = 0$ or $x - 2 = 0$ Zero-factor property

$x = -\dfrac{3}{2}$ or $x = 2$ Solve each equation.

NOW TRY ANSWERS

6. (a) $\{-3, 0, 3\}$ (b) $\left\{-\frac{3}{2}, \frac{1}{3}, 4\right\}$

7. $\left\{-\frac{7}{3}, 4\right\}$

Check that the solution set is $\left\{-\frac{3}{2}, 2\right\}$.   NOW TRY

5.5 EXERCISES

  PRACTICE   WATCH   DOWNLOAD   READ   REVIEW

🌐 *Complete solution available on the Video Resources on DVD*

Concept Check In Exercises 1–5, fill in the blank with the correct response.

1. A quadratic equation in x is an equation that can be put into the form _____ = 0.

2. The form $ax^2 + bx + c = 0$ is called _____ form.

3. If a quadratic equation is in standard form, to solve the equation we should begin by attempting to _____ the polynomial.

4. The equation $x^3 + x^2 + x = 0$ is not a quadratic equation, because _____.

5. If a quadratic equation $ax^2 + bx + c = 0$ has $c = 0$, then _____ *must* be a solution because _____ is a factor of the polynomial.

6. *Concept Check* Identify each equation as *linear* or *quadratic*.

(a) $2x - 5 = 6$

(b) $x^2 - 5 = -4$

(c) $x^2 + 2x - 3 = 2x^2 - 2$

(d) $5^2x + 2 = 0$

7. Students often become confused as to how to handle a constant, such as 2 in the equation $2x(3x - 4) = 0$. How would you explain to someone how to solve this equation and how to handle the constant 2?

8. *Concept Check* The number 9 is a *double solution* of the equation $(x - 9)^2 = 0$. Why is this so?

9. *Concept Check* Look at this "solution."   **WHAT WENT WRONG?**

$$x(7x - 1) = 0$$

$7x - 1 = 0$ Zero-factor property

$$x = \frac{1}{7}$$

The solution set is $\left\{\frac{1}{7}\right\}$.

10. *Concept Check* Look at this "solution."   **WHAT WENT WRONG?**

$$3x(5x - 4) = 0$$

$x = 3$ or $x = 0$ or $5x - 4 = 0$

$$x = \frac{4}{5}$$

The solution set is $\left\{3, 0, \frac{4}{5}\right\}$.

Solve each equation, and check your solutions. **See Example 1.**

11. $(x + 5)(x - 2) = 0$

12. $(x - 1)(x + 8) = 0$

13. $(2m - 7)(m - 3) = 0$

14. $(6x + 5)(x + 4) = 0$

15. $(2x + 1)(6x - 1) = 0$

16. $(3x + 2)(10x - 1) = 0$

17. $t(6t + 5) = 0$

18. $w(4w + 1) = 0$

19. $2x(3x - 4) = 0$

20. $6y(4y + 9) = 0$

21. $(x - 6)(x - 6) = 0$

22. $(y + 1)(y + 1) = 0$

Solve each equation, and check your solutions. **See Examples 2–7.**

23. $y^2 + 3y + 2 = 0$

24. $p^2 + 8p + 7 = 0$

25. $y^2 - 3y + 2 = 0$

26. $r^2 - 4r + 3 = 0$

27. $x^2 = 24 - 5x$

28. $t^2 = 2t + 15$

29. $x^2 = 3 + 2x$

30. $x^2 = 4 + 3x$

31. $z^2 + 3z = -2$

32. $p^2 - 2p = 3$

33. $m^2 + 8m + 16 = 0$

34. $x^2 - 6x + 9 = 0$

35. $3x^2 + 5x - 2 = 0$

36. $6r^2 - r - 2 = 0$

37. $12p^2 = 8 - 10p$

38. $18x^2 = 12 + 15x$

39. $9s^2 + 12s = -4$

40. $36x^2 + 60x = -25$

41. $y^2 - 9 = 0$

42. $m^2 - 100 = 0$

43. $16x^2 - 49 = 0$

44. $4w^2 - 9 = 0$

45. $n^2 = 121$

46. $x^2 = 400$

47. $x^2 = 7x$

48. $t^2 = 9t$

49. $6r^2 = 3r$

50. $10y^2 = -5y$

51. $x(x - 7) = -10$

52. $r(r - 5) = -6$

53. $3z(2z + 7) = 12$

54. $4x(2x + 3) = 36$

55. $2y(y + 13) = 136$

56. $t(3t - 20) = -12$

57. $(2r + 5)(3r^2 - 16r + 5) = 0$

58. $(3m + 4)(6m^2 + m - 2) = 0$

59. $(2x + 7)(x^2 + 2x - 3) = 0$

60. $(x + 1)(6x^2 + x - 12) = 0$

61. $9y^3 - 49y = 0$

62. $16r^3 - 9r = 0$

63. $r^3 - 2r^2 - 8r = 0$

64. $x^3 - x^2 - 6x = 0$

65. $x^3 + x^2 - 20x = 0$

66. $y^3 - 6y^2 + 8y = 0$

67. $r^4 = 2r^3 + 15r^2$

68. $x^3 = 3x + 2x^2$

69. $3x(x + 1) = (2x + 3)(x + 1)$ **70.** $2x(x + 3) = (3x + 1)(x + 3)$

🌐 **71.** $x^2 + (x + 1)^2 = (x + 2)^2$ **72.** $(x - 7)^2 + x^2 = (x + 1)^2$

Brain Busters   *Solve each equation, and check your solutions.*

73. $(2x)^2 = (2x + 4)^2 - (x + 5)^2$ **74.** $5 - (x - 1)^2 = (x - 2)^2$

75. $(x + 3)^2 - (2x - 1)^2 = 0$ **76.** $(4y - 3)^3 - 9(4y - 3) = 0$

77. $6p^2(p + 1) = 4(p + 1) - 5p(p + 1)$

78. $6x^2(2x + 3) = 4(2x + 3) + 5x(2x + 3)$

Galileo's formula describing the motion of freely falling objects is

$$d = 16t^2.$$

*The distance d in feet an object falls depends on the time t elapsed, in seconds. (This is an example of an important mathematical concept, the **function**.)*

79. (a) Use Galileo's formula and complete the following table. (*Hint:* Substitute each given value into the formula and solve for the unknown value.)

t in seconds	0	1	2	3		
d in feet	0	16			256	576

📝 **(b)** When $t = 0$, $d = 0$. Explain this in the context of the problem.

📝 **80.** When you substituted 256 for d and solved the formula for t in **Exercise 79,** you should have found two solutions: 4 and -4. Why doesn't -4 make sense as an answer?

TECHNOLOGY INSIGHTS   EXERCISES 81–82

*In **Section 3.2,** we showed how an equation in one variable can be solved with a graphing calculator by getting 0 on one side and then replacing 0 with y to get a corresponding equation in two variables. The x-values of the x-intercepts of the graph of the two-variable equation then give the solutions of the original equation.*

   Use the calculator screens to determine the solution set of each quadratic equation. Verify your answers by substitution.

81. $x^2 + 0.4x - 0.05 = 0$

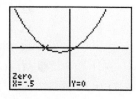   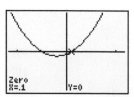

82. $2x^2 - 7.2x + 6.3 = 0$

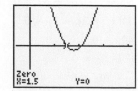   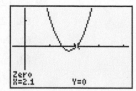

*Solve each problem. **See Sections 2.4 and 2.5.***

83. If a number is doubled and 6 is subtracted from this result, the answer is 3684. The unknown number is the year that Texas was admitted to the Union. What year was Texas admitted?

84. The length of the rectangle is 3 m more than its width. The perimeter of the rectangle is 34 m. Find the width of the rectangle.

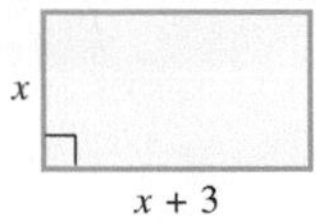

x

$x + 3$

85. Twice the sum of two consecutive integers is 28 more than the greater integer. Find the integers.

86. The area of a triangle with base 12 in. is 48 in.^{2}. Find the height of the triangle.

5.6 Applications of Quadratic Equations

OBJECTIVES

1 Solve problems involving geometric figures.

2 Solve problems involving consecutive integers.

3 Solve problems by applying the Pythagorean theorem.

4 Solve problems by using given quadratic models.

We use factoring to solve quadratic equations that arise in application problems. We follow the same six problem-solving steps given in **Section 2.4.**

Solving an Applied Problem

Step 1 **Read** the problem carefully. What information is given? What are you asked to find?

Step 2 **Assign a variable** to represent the unknown value. Use a sketch, diagram, or table, as needed. If necessary, express any other unknown values in terms of the variable.

Step 3 **Write an equation,** using the variable expression(s).

Step 4 **Solve** the equation.

Step 5 **State the answer.** Label it appropriately. Does it seem reasonable?

Step 6 **Check** the answer in the words of the original problem.

OBJECTIVE 1 **Solve problems involving geometric figures.** Refer to the formulas given on the inside covers of the text, if necessary.

EXAMPLE 1 Solving an Area Problem

Abe Biggs wants to plant a triangular flower bed in a corner of his garden. One leg of the right-triangular flower bed will be 2 m shorter than the other leg. He wants the bed to have an area of 24 m^2. See **FIGURE 1**. Find the lengths of the legs.

Step 1 **Read** the problem. We need to find the lengths of the legs of a right triangle with area 24 m^2.

Step 2 **Assign a variable.**

Let $\quad x =$ the length of one leg.

Then $\quad x - 2 =$ the length of the other leg.

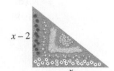

$x - 2$

x

FIGURE 1

NOW TRY
EXERCISE 1

A right triangle has one leg that is 4 ft shorter than the other leg. The area of the triangle is 6 ft². Determine the lengths of the legs.

Step 3 **Write an equation.** The area of a right triangle is given by the formula

$$\text{area} = \frac{1}{2} \times \text{base} \times \text{height}.$$

In a right triangle, the legs are the base and height, so we substitute 24 for the area, x for the base, and $x - 2$ for the height in the formula.

$$\mathcal{A} = \frac{1}{2}bh \qquad \text{Formula for the area of a triangle}$$

$$24 = \frac{1}{2}x(x - 2) \qquad \text{Let } \mathcal{A} = 24, b = x, h = x - 2.$$

Step 4 **Solve.**

$$48 = x(x - 2) \qquad \text{Multiply by 2.}$$

$$48 = x^2 - 2x \qquad \text{Distributive property}$$

$$x^2 - 2x - 48 = 0 \qquad \text{Standard form}$$

$$(x + 6)(x - 8) = 0 \qquad \text{Factor.}$$

$$x + 6 = 0 \quad \text{or} \quad x - 8 = 0 \qquad \text{Zero-factor property}$$

$$x = -6 \quad \text{or} \qquad x = 8 \qquad \text{Solve each equation.}$$

Step 5 **State the answer.** The solutions are -6 and 8. Because a triangle cannot have a side of negative length, we discard the solution -6. Then the lengths of the legs will be 8 m and $8 - 2 = 6$ m.

Step 6 **Check.** The length of one leg is 2 m less than the length of the other leg, and the area is

$$\frac{1}{2}(8)(6) = 24 \text{ m}^2, \quad \text{as required.} \qquad \text{NOW TRY}$$

⚠ **CAUTION** *In solving applied problems, always check solutions against physical facts* and discard any answers that are not appropriate.

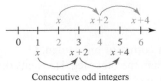

Consecutive integers

(a)

Consecutive even integers

Consecutive odd integers

(b)

FIGURE 2

OBJECTIVE 2 **Solve problems involving consecutive integers.** Recall from our work in **Section 2.4** that **consecutive integers** are integers that are next to each other on a number line, such as 3 and 4, or -11 and -10. See **FIGURE 2(a)**.

Consecutive odd integers are *odd* integers that are next to each other, such as 3 and 5, or -13 and -11. **Consecutive even integers** are defined similarly—for example, 4 and 6 are consecutive even integers, as are -10 and -8. See **FIGURE 2(b)**.

PROBLEM-SOLVING HINT

If x represents the lesser integer, then, for any

two consecutive integers, use	$x,\ x + 1;$
three consecutive integers, use	$x,\ x + 1,\ x + 2;$
two consecutive even or odd integers, use	$x,\ x + 2;$
three consecutive even or odd integers, use	$x,\ x + 2,\ x + 4.$

As a general rule in this book, we list consecutive integers in increasing order when solving applications.

NOW TRY ANSWER
1. 2 ft, 6 ft

NOW TRY
EXERCISE 2

The product of the first and second of three consecutive integers is 2 more than 8 times the third integer. Find the integers.

EXAMPLE 2 Solving a Consecutive Integer Problem

The product of the second and third of three consecutive integers is 2 more than 7 times the first integer. Find the integers.

Step 1 **Read** the problem. Note that the integers are consecutive.

Step 2 **Assign a variable.**

Let x = the first integer.

Then $x + 1$ = the second integer,

and $x + 2$ = the third integer.

Step 3 **Write an equation.**

The product of the second and third $\quad$ is $\quad$ 2 more than 7 times the first.
$$\downarrow \qquad\qquad\qquad\qquad \downarrow \qquad\qquad \downarrow$$
$$(x + 1)(x + 2) \qquad\qquad = \qquad\qquad 7x + 2$$

Step 4 **Solve.**

$x^2 + 3x + 2 = 7x + 2$	Multiply.
$x^2 - 4x = 0$	Standard form
$x(x - 4) = 0$	Factor.
$x = 0$ or $x = 4$	Zero-factor property

Step 5 **State the answer.** The solutions 0 and 4 each lead to a correct answer.

$$0, 1, 2 \qquad \text{or} \qquad 4, 5, 6$$

Step 6 **Check.** The product of the second and third integers must equal 2 more than 7 times the first. Since $1 \cdot 2 = 7 \cdot 0 + 2$ and $5 \cdot 6 = 7 \cdot 4 + 2$, both sets of consecutive integers satisfy the statement of the problem.

NOW TRY

OBJECTIVE 3 **Solve problems by applying the Pythagorean theorem.**

Pythagorean Theorem

If a right triangle has longest side of length c and two other sides of lengths a and b, then

$$a^2 + b^2 = c^2.$$

The longest side, the **hypotenuse,** is opposite the right angle. The two shorter sides are the **legs** of the triangle.

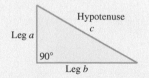

EXAMPLE 3 Applying the Pythagorean Theorem

Patricia Walker and Ali Ulku leave their office, Patricia traveling north and Ali traveling east. When Ali is 1 mi farther than Patricia from the office, the distance between them is 2 mi more than Patricia's distance from the office. Find their distances from the office and the distance between them.

Step 1 **Read** the problem again. There will be three answers to this problem.

NOW TRY
EXERCISE 3
The longer leg of a right triangle is 7 ft longer than the shorter leg and the hypotenuse is 8 ft longer than the shorter leg. Find the lengths of the sides of the triangle.

Step 2 **Assign a variable.**

Let x = Patricia's distance from the office.

Then $x + 1$ = Ali's distance from the office,

and $x + 2$ = the distance between them.

Place these expressions on a right triangle, as in **FIGURE 3**.

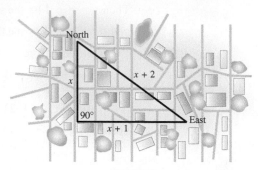

FIGURE 3

Step 3 **Write an equation.** Use the Pythagorean theorem.

$$a^2 + b^2 = c^2$$

$$x^2 + (x + 1)^2 = (x + 2)^2$$

⟵ Be careful to substitute properly.

Step 4 **Solve.**

$x^2 + x^2 + 2x + 1 = x^2 + 4x + 4$	Square each binomial.
$x^2 - 2x - 3 = 0$	Standard form
$(x - 3)(x + 1) = 0$	Factor.
$x - 3 = 0$ or $x + 1 = 0$	Zero-factor property
$x = 3$ or $x = -1$	Solve each equation.

Step 5 **State the answer.** Since -1 cannot represent a distance, 3 is the only possible answer. Patricia's distance is 3 mi, Ali's distance is $3 + 1 = 4$ mi, and the distance between them is $3 + 2 = 5$ mi.

Step 6 **Check.** Since $3^2 + 4^2 = 5^2$, the answers are correct.

NOW TRY

PROBLEM-SOLVING HINT

In solving a problem involving the Pythagorean theorem, be sure that the expressions for the sides are properly placed.

$$(\textbf{one leg})^2 + (\textbf{other leg})^2 = \textbf{hypotenuse}^2$$

OBJECTIVE 4 **Solve problems by using given quadratic models.** In **Examples 1–3**, we wrote quadratic equations to model, or mathematically describe, various situations and then solved the equations. In the last two examples of this section, we are given the quadratic models and must use them to determine data.

NOW TRY ANSWER
3. 5 ft, 12 ft, 13 ft

NOW TRY
EXERCISE 4

Refer to **Example 4.** How long will it take for the ball to reach a height of 50 ft?

EXAMPLE 4 Finding the Height of a Ball

A tennis player's serve travels 180 ft per sec (123 mph). If she hits the ball directly upward, the height h of the ball in feet at time t in seconds is modeled by the quadratic equation

$$h = -16t^2 + 180t + 6.$$

How long will it take for the ball to reach a height of 206 ft?

A height of 206 ft means that $h = 206$, so we substitute 206 for h in the equation.

$$h = -16t^2 + 180t + 6$$

$$206 = -16t^2 + 180t + 6 \qquad \text{Let } h = 206.$$

$$-16t^2 + 180t + 6 = 206 \qquad \text{Interchange sides.}$$

$$16t^2 + 180t - 200 - 0 \qquad \text{Standard form}$$

$$4t^2 - 45t + 50 = 0 \qquad \text{Divide by } -4.$$

$$(4t - 5)(t - 10) = 0 \qquad \text{Factor.}$$

$$4t - 5 = 0 \quad \text{or} \quad t - 10 = 0 \qquad \text{Zero-factor property}$$

$$4t = 5 \quad \text{or} \qquad t = 10 \qquad \text{Solve each equation.}$$

$$t = \frac{5}{4}$$

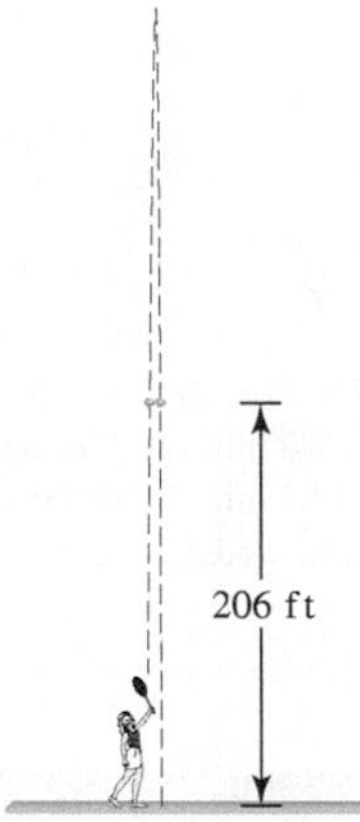

Since we found two acceptable answers, the ball will be 206 ft above the ground twice, once on its way up and once on its way down, at $\frac{5}{4}$ sec and at 10 sec. See **FIGURE 4**.

206 ft

FIGURE 4

NOW TRY

EXAMPLE 5 Modeling the Foreign-Born Population of the United States

The foreign-born population of the United States over the years 1930–2007 can be modeled by the quadratic equation

$$y = 0.01048x^2 - 0.5400x + 15.43,$$

where $x = 0$ represents 1930, $x = 10$ represents 1940, and so on, and y is the number of people in millions. (*Source:* U.S. Census Bureau.)

(a) Use the model to find the foreign-born population in 1980 to the nearest tenth of a million.

Since $x = 0$ represents 1930, $x = 50$ represents 1980. Substitute 50 for x in the equation.

$$y = 0.01048\,(50)^2 - 0.5400\,(50) + 15.43 \qquad \text{Let } x = 50.$$

$$y = 14.6 \qquad\qquad\qquad\qquad\qquad \text{Round to the nearest tenth.}$$

In 1980, the foreign-born population of the United States was about 14.6 million.

(b) Repeat part (a) for 2007.

$$y = 0.01048\,(77)^2 - 0.5400\,(77) + 15.43 \qquad \text{For 2007, let } x = 77.$$

$$y = 36.0 \qquad\qquad\qquad\qquad\qquad \text{Round to the nearest tenth.}$$

In 2007, the foreign-born population of the United States was about 36.0 million.

NOW TRY ANSWER
4. $\frac{1}{4}$ sec and 11 sec

*NOW TRY
EXERCISE 5*

Use the model in **Example 5** to find the foreign-born population of the United States in the year 2000. Give your answer to the nearest tenth of a million. How does it compare to the actual value from the table?

(c) The model used in parts (a) and (b) was developed using the data in the table below. How do the results in parts (a) and (b) compare to the actual data from the table?

Year	Foreign-Born Population (millions)
1930	14.2
1940	11.6
1950	10.3
1960	9.7
1970	9.6
1980	14.1
1990	19.8
2000	28.4
2007	37.3

NOW TRY ANSWER

5. 29.0 million; The actual value is 28.4 million, so the answer using the model is slightly high.

From the table, the actual value for 1980 is 14.1 million. Our answer in part (a), 14.6 million, is slightly high. For 2007, the actual value is 37.3 million, so our answer of 36.0 million in part (b) is somewhat low.   *NOW TRY*

5.6 EXERCISES

🌐 *Complete solution available on the Video Resources on DVD*

1. *Concept Check*   To review the six problem-solving steps first introduced in **Section 2.4,** complete each statement.

   Step 1: _____ the problem carefully.

   Step 2: Assign a _____ to represent the unknown value.

   Step 3: Write a(n) _____ using the variable expression(s).

   Step 4: _____ the equation.

   Step 5: State the _____.

   Step 6: _____ the answer in the words of the _____ problem.

📝 **2.** A student solves an applied problem and gets 6 or −3 for the length of the side of a square. Which of these answers is reasonable? Explain.

*In Exercises 3–6, a figure and a corresponding geometric formula are given. Using x as the variable, complete Steps 3–6 for each problem. (Refer to the steps in **Exercise 1** as needed.)*

3.

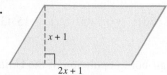
x + 1
2*x* + 1

Area of a parallelogram: $\mathcal{A} = bh$

The area of this parallelogram is 45 sq. units. Find its base and height.

4.

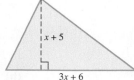
x + 5
3*x* + 6

Area of a triangle: $\mathcal{A} = \frac{1}{2}bh$

The area of this triangle is 60 sq. units. Find its base and height.

5.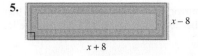

Area of a rectangular rug: $\mathcal{A} = LW$

The area of this rug is 80 sq. units. Find its length and width.

6.

Volume of a rectangular Chinese box: $V = LWH$

The volume of this box is 192 cu. units. Find its length and width.

Solve each problem. Check your answers to be sure that they are reasonable. Refer to the formulas on the inside covers. ***See Example 1.***

🌐 **7.** The length of a standard jewel case is 2 cm more than its width. The area of the rectangular top of the case is 168 cm². Find the length and width of the jewel case.

8. A standard DVD case is 6 cm longer than it is wide. The area of the rectangular top of the case is 247 cm². Find the length and width of the case.

9. The area of a triangle is 30 in.². The base of the triangle measures 2 in. more than twice the height of the triangle. Find the measures of the base and the height.

10. A certain triangle has its base equal in measure to its height. The area of the triangle is 72 m². Find the equal base and height measure.

11. A 10-gal aquarium is 3 in. higher than it is wide. Its length is 21 in., and its volume is 2730 in.³. What are the height and width of the aquarium?

12. A toolbox is 2 ft high, and its width is 3 ft less than its length. If its volume is 80 ft³, find the length and width of the box.

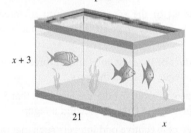

13. The dimensions of an HPf1905 flat-panel monitor are such that its length is 3 in. more than its width. If the length were doubled and if the width were decreased by 1 in., the area would be increased by 150 in.². What are the length and width of the flat panel?

14. The keyboard that accompanies the monitor in **Exercise 13** is 11 in. longer than it is wide. If the length were doubled and if 2 in. were added to the width, the area would be increased by 198 in.². What are the length and width of the keyboard? (*Source:* Author's computer.)

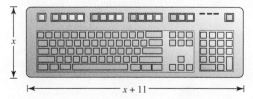

15. A square mirror has sides measuring 2 ft less than the sides of a square painting. If the difference between their areas is 32 ft^2, find the lengths of the sides of the mirror and the painting.

16. The sides of one square have length 3 m more than the sides of a second square. If the area of the larger square is subtracted from 4 times the area of the smaller square, the result is 36 m^2. What are the lengths of the sides of each square?

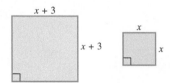

*Solve each problem. **See Example 2.***

17. The product of the numbers on two consecutive volumes of research data is 420. Find the volume numbers. See the figure.

18. The product of the page numbers on two facing pages of a book is 600. Find the page numbers.

🌐 **19.** The product of the second and third of three consecutive integers is 2 more than 10 times the first integer. Find the integers.

20. The product of the first and third of three consecutive integers is 3 more than 3 times the second integer. Find the integers.

21. Find three consecutive odd integers such that 3 times the sum of all three is 18 more than the product of the first and second integers.

22. Find three consecutive odd integers such that the sum of all three is 42 less than the product of the second and third integers.

23. Find three consecutive even integers such that the sum of the squares of the first and second integers is equal to the square of the third integer.

24. Find three consecutive even integers such that the square of the sum of the first and second integers is equal to twice the third integer.

*Solve each problem. **See Example 3.***

🌐 **25.** The hypotenuse of a right triangle is 1 cm longer than the longer leg. The shorter leg is 7 cm shorter than the longer leg. Find the length of the longer leg of the triangle.

26. The longer leg of a right triangle is 1 m longer than the shorter leg. The hypotenuse is 1 m shorter than twice the shorter leg. Find the length of the shorter leg of the triangle.

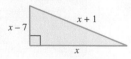

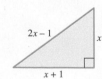

27. Tram works due north of home. Her husband Alan works due east. They leave for work at the same time. By the time Tram is 5 mi from home, the distance between them is 1 mi more than Alan's distance from home. How far from home is Alan?

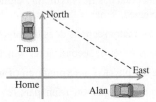

28. Two cars left an intersection at the same time. One traveled north. The other traveled 14 mi farther, but to the east. How far apart were they at that time if the distance between them was 4 mi more than the distance traveled east?

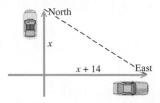

29. A ladder is leaning against a building. The distance from the bottom of the ladder to the building is 4 ft less than the length of the ladder. How high up the side of the building is the top of the ladder if that distance is 2 ft less than the length of the ladder?

30. A lot has the shape of a right triangle with one leg 2 m longer than the other. The hypotenuse is 2 m less than twice the length of the shorter leg. Find the length of the shorter leg.

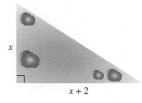

If an object is projected upward with an initial velocity of 128 *ft per sec, its height h after t seconds is*

$$h = -16t^2 + 128t.$$

Find the height of the object after each time listed. ***See Example 4.***

31. 1 sec   **32.** 2 sec   **33.** 4 sec

34. How long does it take the object just described to return to the ground? (*Hint:* When the object hits the ground, $h = 0$.)

Solve each problem. ***See Examples 4 and 5.***

🌐 **35.** An object projected from a height of 48 ft with an initial velocity of 32 ft per sec after t seconds has height

$$h = -16t^2 + 32t + 48.$$

(a) After how many seconds is the height 64 ft? (*Hint:* Let $h = 64$ and solve.)

(b) After how many seconds is the height 60 ft?

(c) After how many seconds does the object hit the ground?

✏ **(d)** The quadratic equation from part (c) has two solutions, yet only one of them is appropriate for answering the question. Why is this so?

36. If an object is projected upward from ground level with an initial velocity of 64 ft per sec, its height h in feet t seconds later is

$$h = -16t^2 + 64t.$$

(a) After how many seconds is the height 48 ft?

(b) The object reaches its maximum height 2 sec after it is projected. What is this maximum height?

(c) After how many seconds does the object hit the ground?

(d) Find the number of seconds after which the height is 60 ft.

✎ **(e)** What is the physical interpretation of why part (d) has two answers?

✎ **(f)** The quadratic equation from part (c) has two solutions, yet only one of them is appropriate for answering the question. Why is this so?

37. The table shows the number of cellular phone subscribers (in millions) in the United States.

Year	Subscribers (in millions)
1990	5
1992	11
1994	24
1996	44
1998	69
2000	109
2002	141
2004	182
2006	233
2008	263

Source: CTIA—The Wireless Association.

We used the preceding data to develop the quadratic equation

$$y = 0.590x^2 + 4.523x + 0.136,$$

which models the number y of cellular phone subscribers (in millions) in the year x, where $x = 0$ represents 1990, $x = 2$ represents 1992, and so on.

(a) Use the model to find the number of subscribers in 2000, to the nearest tenth. How does the result compare with the actual data in the table?

(b) What value of x corresponds to 2008?

(c) Use the model to find the number of cellular phone subscribers in 2008, to the nearest tenth. How does the result compare with the actual data in the table?

(d) Assuming that the trend in the data continues, use the quadratic equation to estimate the number of cellular phone subscribers in 2010, to the nearest tenth.

38. Annual revenue in billions of dollars for eBay is shown in the table.

Year	Annual Revenue (in billions of dollars)
2002	1.21
2003	2.17
2004	3.27
2005	4.55
2006	5.97
2007	7.67

Source: eBay.

Using the data, we developed the quadratic equation

$$y = 0.089x^2 + 0.841x + 1.224$$

to model eBay revenues y in year x, where $x = 0$ represents 2002, $x = 1$ represents 2003, and so on.

(a) Use the model to find annual revenue for eBay in 2005 and 2007, to the nearest hundredth. How do the results compare with the actual data in the table?

(b) Use the model to estimate annual revenue for eBay in 2009, to the nearest hundredth.

(c) Actual revenue for eBay in 2009 was $8.73 billion. How does the result from part (b) compare with the actual revenue in 2009?

(d) Should the quadratic equation be used to estimate eBay revenue for years after 2007? Explain.

PREVIEW EXERCISES

Write each fraction in lowest terms. *See Section 1.1.*

39. $\dfrac{50}{72}$ **40.** $\dfrac{-26}{156}$ **41.** $\dfrac{48}{-27}$ **42.** $\dfrac{-35}{-21}$

CHAPTER 5 SUMMARY

KEY TERMS

5.1
factor
factored form
common factor
greatest common
   factor (GCF)

5.2
prime polynomial

5.4
perfect square
perfect square trinomial

5.5
quadratic equation
standard form
double solution

5.6
hypotenuse
legs

TEST YOUR WORD POWER

See how well you have learned the vocabulary in this chapter.

1. Factoring is
   A. a method of multiplying polynomials
   B. the process of writing a polynomial as a product
   C. the answer in a multiplication problem
   D. a way to add the terms of a polynomial.

2. A polynomial is in **factored form** when
   A. it is prime
   B. it is written as a sum
   C. the squared term has a coefficient of 1
   D. it is written as a product.

3. A **perfect square trinomial** is a trinomial
   A. that can be factored as the square of a binomial
   B. that cannot be factored
   C. that is multiplied by a binomial
   D. all of whose terms are perfect squares.

4. A **quadratic equation** is an equation that can be written in the form
   A. $y = mx + b$
   B. $ax^2 + bx + c = 0$ $(a \neq 0)$
   C. $Ax + By = C$
   D. $x = k$.

5. A **hypotenuse** is
   A. either of the two shorter sides of a triangle
   B. the shortest side of a triangle
   C. the side opposite the right angle in a triangle
   D. the longest side in any triangle.

ANSWERS
1. B; *Example:* $x^2 - 5x - 14$ factors as $(x - 7)(x + 2)$. **2.** D; *Example:* The factored form of $x^2 - 5x - 14$ is $(x - 7)(x + 2)$. **3.** A; *Example:* $a^2 + 2a + 1$ is a perfect square trinomial. Its factored form is $(a + 1)^2$. **4.** B; *Examples:* $y^2 - 3y + 2 = 0, x^2 - 9 = 0, 2m^2 = 6m + 8$
5. C; *Example:* In **FIGURE 3** of **Section 5.6**, the hypotenuse is the side labeled $x + 2$.

QUICK REVIEW

CONCEPTS	EXAMPLES

5.1 The Greatest Common Factor; Factoring by Grouping

Finding the Greatest Common Factor (GCF)

Step 1 Write each number in prime factored form.

Step 2 List each prime number or each variable that is a factor of every term in the list.

Step 3 Use as exponents on the common prime factors the *least* exponents from the prime factored forms.

Step 4 Multiply the primes from Step 3.

Find the greatest common factor of $4x^2y$, $6x^2y^3$, and $2xy^2$.

$$4x^2y = 2 \cdot 2 \cdot x^2 \cdot y$$
$$6x^2y^3 = 2 \cdot 3 \cdot x^2 \cdot y^3$$
$$2xy^2 = 2 \cdot x \cdot y^2$$

The greatest common factor is $2xy$.

Factoring by Grouping

Step 1 Group the terms.

Step 2 Factor out the greatest common factor in each group.

Step 3 Factor out a common binomial factor from the results of Step 2.

Step 4 If necessary, try a different grouping.

Factor by grouping.

$3x^2 + 5x - 24xy - 40y$

$= (3x^2 + 5x) + (-24xy - 40y)$ Group the terms.

$= x(3x + 5) - 8y(3x + 5)$ Factor each group.

$= (3x + 5)(x - 8y)$ Factor out $3x + 5$.

5.2 Factoring Trinomials

To factor $x^2 + bx + c$, find m and n such that $mn = c$ and $m + n = b$.

$$mn = c$$
$$x^2 + bx + c$$
$$m + n = b$$

Then $x^2 + bx + c$ factors as $(x + m)(x + n)$.

Check by multiplying.

Factor $x^2 + 6x + 8$.

$$mn = 8$$
$$x^2 + 6x + 8 \quad m = 2 \text{ and } n = 4$$
$$m + n = 6$$

$x^2 + 6x + 8$ factors as $(x + 2)(x + 4)$.

CHECK $(x + 2)(x + 4)$

$= x^2 + 4x + 2x + 8$

$= x^2 + 6x + 8$ ✓

5.3 More on Factoring Trinomials

To factor $ax^2 + bx + c$, use one of the following methods.

Grouping

Find m and n.

$$mn = ac$$
$$ax^2 + bx + c$$
$$m + n = b$$

Trial and Error

Use FOIL in reverse.

Factor $3x^2 + 14x - 5$.

$$-15$$

$mn = -15, m + n = 14$

The required integers are $m = -1$ and $n = 15$.

By trial and error or by grouping,

$$3x^2 + 14x - 5 \quad \text{factors as} \quad (3x - 1)(x + 5).$$

(continued)

CONCEPTS	EXAMPLES

5.4 Special Factoring Techniques

Difference of Squares

$$x^2 - y^2 = (x + y)(x - y)$$

Perfect Square Trinomials

$$x^2 + 2xy + y^2 = (x + y)^2$$
$$x^2 - 2xy + y^2 = (x - y)^2$$

Difference of Cubes

$$x^3 - y^3 = (x - y)(x^2 + xy + y^2)$$

Sum of Cubes

$$x^3 + y^3 = (x + y)(x^2 - xy + y^2)$$

Factor.

$$4x^2 - 9$$
$$= (2x + 3)(2x - 3)$$

$$9x^2 + 6x + 1 \qquad 4x^2 - 20x + 25$$
$$= (3x + 1)^2 \qquad = (2x - 5)^2$$

$$m^3 - 8 \qquad\qquad z^3 + 27$$
$$- m^3 - 2^3 \qquad\qquad = z^3 + 3^3$$
$$= (m - 2)(m^2 + 2m + 4) \qquad = (z + 3)(z^2 - 3z + 9)$$

5.5 Solving Quadratic Equations by Factoring

Zero-Factor Property

If a and b are real numbers and if $ab = 0$, then $a = 0$ or $b = 0$.

Solving a Quadratic Equation by Factoring

Step 1 Write the equation in standard form.

Step 2 Factor.

Step 3 Use the zero-factor property.

Step 4 Solve the resulting equations.

Step 5 Check.

If $(x - 2)(x + 3) = 0$, then $x - 2 = 0$ or $x + 3 = 0$.

Solve $2x^2 = 7x + 15$.

$$2x^2 - 7x - 15 = 0$$
$$(2x + 3)(x - 5) = 0$$
$$2x + 3 = 0 \quad \text{or} \quad x - 5 = 0$$
$$2x = -3 \qquad\qquad x = 5$$
$$x = -\frac{3}{2}$$

Both solutions satisfy the original equation. The solution set is $\left\{ -\frac{3}{2}, 5 \right\}$.

5.6 Applications of Quadratic Equations

Pythagorean Theorem

In a right triangle, the square of the hypotenuse equals the sum of the squares of the legs.

$$a^2 + b^2 = c^2$$

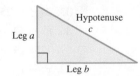

In a right triangle, one leg measures 2 ft longer than the other. The hypotenuse measures 4 ft longer than the shorter leg. Find the lengths of the three sides of the triangle.

Let $x =$ the length of the shorter leg. Then

$$x^2 + (x + 2)^2 = (x + 4)^2.$$

Verify that the solutions of this equation are -2 and 6. Discard -2 as a solution. Check that the sides have lengths

$$6 \text{ ft}, \quad 6 + 2 = 8 \text{ ft}, \quad \text{and} \quad 6 + 4 = 10 \text{ ft}.$$

CHAPTER (5)

REVIEW EXERCISES

5.1 *Factor out the greatest common factor, or factor by grouping.*

1. $7t + 14$

2. $60z^3 + 30z$

3. $2xy - 8y + 3x - 12$

4. $6y^2 + 9y + 4xy + 6x$

5.2 *Factor completely.*

5. $x^2 + 5x + 6$

6. $y^2 - 13y + 40$

7. $q^2 + 6q - 27$

8. $r^2 - r - 56$

9. $r^2 - 4rs - 96s^2$

10. $p^2 + 2pq - 120q^2$

11. $8p^3 - 24p^2 - 80p$

12. $3x^4 + 30x^3 + 48x^2$

13. $p^7 - p^6q - 2p^5q^2$

14. $3r^5 - 6r^4s - 45r^3s^2$

15. $9x^4y - 9x^3y - 54x^2y$

16. $2x^7 + 2x^6y - 12x^5y^2$

5.3

17. *Concept Check* To begin factoring $6r^2 - 5r - 6$, what are the possible first terms of the two binomial factors if we consider only positive integer coefficients?

18. *Concept Check* What is the first step you would use to factor $2z^3 + 9z^2 - 5z$?

Factor completely.

19. $2k^2 - 5k + 2$

20. $3r^2 + 11r - 4$

21. $6r^2 - 5r - 6$

22. $10z^2 - 3z - 1$

23. $8v^2 + 17v - 21$

24. $24x^5 - 20x^4 + 4x^3$

25. $-6x^2 + 3x + 30$

26. $10r^3s + 17r^2s^2 + 6rs^3$

27. $48x^4y + 4x^3y^2 - 4x^2y^3$

28. *Concept Check* On a quiz, a student factored $16x^2 - 24x + 5$ by grouping as follows.

$$16x^2 - 24x + 5$$
$$= 16x^2 - 4x - 20x + 5$$
$$= 4x(4x - 1) - 5(4x - 1) \qquad \text{His answer}$$

He thought his answer was correct, since it checked by multiplication. *WHAT WENT WRONG?* Give the correct factored form.

5.4

29. *Concept Check* Which one of the following is the difference of squares?

A. $32x^2 - 1$ **B.** $4x^2y^2 - 25z^2$ **C.** $x^2 + 36$ **D.** $25y^3 - 1$

30. *Concept Check* Which one of the following is a perfect square trinomial?

A. $x^2 + x + 1$ **B.** $y^2 - 4y + 9$ **C.** $4x^2 + 10x + 25$ **D.** $x^2 - 20x + 100$

Factor completely.

31. $n^2 - 49$

32. $25b^2 - 121$

33. $49y^2 - 25w^2$

34. $144p^2 - 36q^2$

35. $x^2 + 100$

36. $r^2 - 12r + 36$

37. $9t^2 - 42t + 49$

38. $m^3 + 1000$

39. $125k^3 + 64x^3$

40. $343x^3 - 64$

41. $1000 - 27x^6$

42. $x^6 - y^6$

5.5 *Solve each equation, and check your solutions.*

43. $(4t + 3)(t - 1) = 0$

44. $(x + 7)(x - 4)(x + 3) = 0$

45. $x(2x - 5) = 0$

46. $z^2 + 4z + 3 = 0$

47. $m^2 - 5m + 4 = 0$ **48.** $x^2 = -15 + 8x$

49. $3z^2 - 11z - 20 = 0$ **50.** $81t^2 - 64 = 0$

51. $y^2 = 8y$ **52.** $n(n - 5) = 6$

53. $t^2 - 14t + 49 = 0$ **54.** $t^2 = 12(t - 3)$

55. $(5z + 2)(z^2 + 3z + 2) = 0$ **56.** $x^2 = 9$

5.6 *Solve each problem.*

57. The length of a rug is 6 ft more than the width. The area is 40 ft². Find the length and width of the rug.

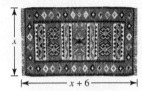

58. The surface area S of a box is given by
$$S = 2WH + 2WL + 2LH.$$
A treasure chest from a sunken galleon has the dimensions shown in the figure. Its surface area is 650 ft². Find its width.

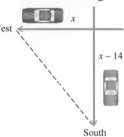

59. The product of two consecutive integers is 29 more than their sum. What are the integers?

60. Two cars left an intersection at the same time. One traveled west, and the other traveled 14 mi less, but to the south. How far apart were they at that time, if the distance between them was 16 mi more than the distance traveled south?

61. If an object is dropped, the distance d in feet it falls in t seconds (disregarding air resistance) is given by the quadratic equation
$$d = 16t^2.$$
Find the distance an object would fall in **(a)** 4 sec and **(b)** 8 sec.

62. The numbers of alternative-fueled vehicles in use in the United States, in thousands, for the years 2001–2006 are given in the table.

Year	Number (in thousands)
2001	425
2002	471
2003	534
2004	565
2005	592
2006	635

Source: Energy Information Administration.

Using statistical methods, we developed the quadratic equation
$$y = -2.84x^2 + 61.1x + 366$$
to model the number of vehicles y in year x. Here, we used $x = 1$ for 2001, $x = 2$ for 2002, and so on.

(a) Use the model to find the number of alternative-fueled vehicles in 2005, to the nearest thousand. How does the result compare with the actual data in the table?

(b) Use the model to estimate the number of alternative-fueled vehicles in 2007, to the nearest thousand.

✏ **(c)** Why might the estimate for 2007 be unreliable?

MIXED REVIEW EXERCISES

63. *Concept Check* Which of the following is *not* factored completely?

A. $3(7t)$ **B.** $3x(7t + 4)$ **C.** $(3 + x)(7t + 4)$ **D.** $3(7t + 4) + x(7t + 4)$

✏ **64.** A student factored $6x^2 + 16x - 32$ as $(2x + 8)(3x - 4)$. Explain why the polynomial is not factored completely, and give the completely factored form.

Factor completely.

65. $3k^2 + 11k + 10$ **66.** $z^2 - 11zx + 10x^2$

67. $y^4 - 625$ **68.** $15m^2 + 20m - 12mp - 16p$

69. $24ab^3c^2 - 56a^2bc^3 + 72a^2b^2c$ **70.** $6m^3 - 21m^2 - 45m$

71. $12x^2yz^3 + 12xy^2z - 30x^3y^2z^4$ **72.** $25a^2 + 15ab + 9b^2$

73. $12r^2 + 18rq - 10r - 15q$ **74.** $2a^5 - 8a^4 - 24a^3$

75. $49t^2 + 56t + 16$ **76.** $1000a^3 + 27$

Solve.

77. $t(t - 7) = 0$ **78.** $x^2 + 3x = 10$ **79.** $25x^2 + 20x + 4 = 0$

80. The product of the first and second of three consecutive integers is equal to 23 plus the third. Find the integers.

81. A pyramid has a rectangular base with a length that is 2 m more than its width. The height of the pyramid is 6 m, and its volume is 48 m³. Find the length and width of the base.

82. A lot is in the shape of a right triangle. The hypotenuse is 3 m longer than the longer leg. The longer leg is 6 m longer than twice the length of the shorter leg. Find the lengths of the sides of the lot.

83. The triangular sail of a schooner has an area of 30 m². The height of the sail is 4 m more than the base. Find the base of the sail.

84. The floor plan for a house is a rectangle with length 7 m more than its width. The area is 170 m². Find the width and length of the house.

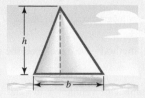

CHAPTER (5)

TEST

CHAPTER
Test Prep
VIDEOS
Step-by-step test solutions are found on the Chapter Test Prep Videos available via the Video Resources on DVD, in *MyMathLab* , or on YouTube (search "LialCombinedAlgebra").

View the complete solutions to all Chapter Test exercises on the Video Resources on DVD.

1. *Concept Check*   Which one of the following is the correct completely factored form of $2x^2 - 2x - 24$?

   A. $(2x + 6)(x - 4)$ **B.** $(x + 3)(2x - 8)$
   C. $2(x + 4)(x - 3)$ **D.** $2(x + 3)(x - 4)$

Factor each polynomial completely. If the polynomial is prime, say so.

2. $12x^2 - 30x$ **3.** $2m^3n^2 + 3m^3n - 5m^2n^2$ **4.** $2ax - 2bx + ay - by$

5. $x^2 - 5x - 24$ **6.** $2x^2 + x - 3$ **7.** $10z^2 - 17z + 3$

8. $t^2 + 2t + 3$ **9.** $x^2 + 36$ **10.** $12 - 6a + 2b - ab$

11. $9y^2 - 64$ **12.** $4x^2 - 28xy + 49y^2$ **13.** $-2x^2 - 4x - 2$

14. $6t^4 + 3t^3 - 108t^2$ **15.** $r^3 - 125$ **16.** $8k^3 + 64$

17. $x^4 - 81$ **18.** $81x^4 - 16y^4$ **19.** $9x^6y^4 + 12x^3y^2 + 4$

Solve each equation.

20. $2r^2 - 13r + 6 = 0$ **21.** $25x^2 - 4 = 0$ **22.** $t^2 = 9t$

23. $x(x - 20) = -100$ **24.** $(s + 8)(6s^2 + 13s - 5) = 0$

Solve each problem.

25. The length of a rectangular flower bed is 3 ft less than twice its width. The area of the bed is 54 ft². Find the dimensions of the flower bed.

26. Find two consecutive integers such that the square of the sum of the two integers is 11 more than the first integer.

27. A carpenter needs to cut a brace to support a wall stud, as shown in the figure. The brace should be 7 ft less than three times the length of the stud. If the brace will be anchored on the floor 15 ft away from the stud, how long should the brace be?

28. The public debt y (in billions of dollars) of the United States from 2000 through 2008 can be approximated by the quadratic equation

$$y = 29.92x^2 + 305.8x + 5581,$$

where $x = 0$ represents 2000, $x = 1$ represents 2001, and so on. (*Source:* Bureau of Public Debt.) Use the model to estimate the public debt, to the nearest billion dollars, in the year 2006.

CHAPTERS (1–5)

CUMULATIVE REVIEW EXERCISES

Solve each equation.

1. $3x + 2(x - 4) = 4(x - 2)$

2. $0.3x + 0.9x = 0.06$

3. $\dfrac{2}{3}m - \dfrac{1}{2}(m - 4) = 3$

4. Solve for P: $A = P + Prt$.

5. Find the measures of the marked angles.

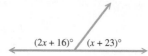

$(2x + 16)°$ $(x + 23)°$

Solve each problem.

6. At the 2006 Winter Olympics in Torino, Italy, the top medal winner was Germany, which won a total of 29 medals. Germany won 1 more silver medal than gold and 5 more gold medals than bronze. Find the number of each type of medal won. (*Source:* www.infoplease.com.)

7. From a list of "technology-related items," adults were recently surveyed as to those items they couldn't live without. Complete the results shown in the table if 500 adults were surveyed.

Item	Percent That Couldn't Live Without	Number That Couldn't Live Without
Personal computer	46%	
Cell phone	41%	
High-speed Internet		190
MP3 player		60

(Other items included digital cable, HDTV, and electronic gaming console.)
Source: Ipsos for AP.

8. Fill in each blank with *positive* or *negative*. The point with coordinates (a, b) is in

   (a) quadrant II if a is _____ and b is _____.

   (b) quadrant III if a is _____ and b is _____.

9. Consider the equation $y = 12x + 3$. Find the following.

   (a) The x- and y-intercepts   **(b)** The slope   **(c)** The graph

10. The points on the graph show the total retail sales of prescription drugs in the United States in the years 2001–2007, along with a graph of a linear equation that models the data.

   (a) Use the ordered pairs shown on the graph to find the slope of the line to the nearest whole number. Interpret the slope.

   (b) Use the graph to estimate sales in the year 2005. Write your answer as an ordered pair of the form (year, sales in billions of dollars).

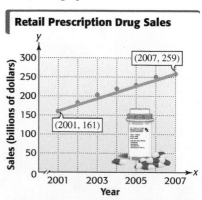

Retail Prescription Drug Sales

(2007, 259)

(2001, 161)

Source: National Association of Chain Drug Stores.

Evaluate each expression.

11. $\left(\dfrac{3}{4}\right)^{-2}$

12. $\left(\dfrac{4^{-3} \cdot 4^4}{4^5}\right)^{-1}$

Simplify each expression, and write the answer with only positive exponents. Assume that no denominators are 0.

13. $\dfrac{(p^2)^3 p^{-4}}{(p^{-3})^{-1} p}$

14. $\dfrac{(m^{-2})^3 m}{m^5 m^{-4}}$

Perform each indicated operation.

15. $(2k^2 + 4k) - (5k^2 - 2) - (k^2 + 8k - 6)$ **16.** $(9x + 6)(5x - 3)$

17. $(3p + 2)^2$

18. $\dfrac{8x^4 + 12x^3 - 6x^2 + 20x}{2x}$

19. To make a pound of honey, bees may travel 55,000 mi and visit more than 2,000,000 flowers. (*Source: Home & Garden.*) Write the two given numbers in scientific notation.

Factor completely.

20. $2a^2 + 7a - 4$

21. $10m^2 + 19m + 6$

22. $8t^2 + 10tv + 3v^2$

23. $4p^2 - 12p + 9$

24. $25r^2 - 81t^2$

25. $2pq + 6p^3q + 8p^2q$

Solve each equation.

26. $6m^2 + m - 2 = 0$

27. $8x^2 = 64x$

28. The length of the hypotenuse of a right triangle is twice the length of the shorter leg, plus 3 m. The longer leg is 7 m longer than the shorter leg. Find the lengths of the sides.

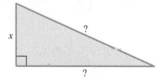

Rational Expressions and Applications

6.1 The Fundamental Property of Rational Expressions

6.2 Multiplying and Dividing Rational Expressions

6.3 Least Common Denominators

6.4 Adding and Subtracting Rational Expressions

6.5 Complex Fractions

6.6 Solving Equations with Rational Expressions

Summary Exercises on Rational Expressions and Equations

6.7 Applications of Rational Expressions

In 2006, Earth's temperature was within 1.8°F of its highest level in 12,000 years. This temperature increase is causing ocean levels to rise as ice fields in Greenland and elsewhere melt. To demonstrate the effects that such global warming is having, British adventurer and endurance swimmer Lewis Gordon Pugh swam at the North Pole in July 2007 in waters that were completely frozen 10 years ago. The swim, in a water hole where polar ice had melted, was in 28.8°F waters, the coldest ever endured by a human. Pugh, who has also swum in the waters of Antarctica, hopes his efforts will inspire world leaders to take climate change seriously. (*Source:* www.breitbart.com, IPCC.)

In **Exercise 11** of **Section 6.7,** we use a *rational expression* to determine the time Pugh swam at the North Pole.

6.1 The Fundamental Property of Rational Expressions

OBJECTIVES

1. Find the numerical value of a rational expression.
2. Find the values of the variable for which a rational expression is undefined.
3. Write rational expressions in lowest terms.
4. Recognize equivalent forms of rational expressions.

The quotient of two integers (with denominator not 0), such as $\frac{2}{3}$ or $-\frac{3}{4}$, is called a *rational number.* In the same way, the quotient of two polynomials with denominator not equal to 0 is called a *rational expression.*

Rational Expression

A **rational expression** is an expression of the form $\frac{P}{Q}$, where P and Q are polynomials and $Q \neq 0$.

$$\frac{-6x}{x^3 + 8}, \quad \frac{9x}{y + 3}, \quad \text{and} \quad \frac{2m^3}{8} \qquad \text{Rational expressions}$$

Our work with rational expressions requires much of what we learned in **Chapters 4 and 5** on polynomials and factoring, as well as the rules for fractions from **Section 1.1.**

OBJECTIVE 1 **Find the numerical value of a rational expression.** We use substitution to evaluate a rational expression for a given value of the variable.

NOW TRY EXERCISE 1

Find the value of the following rational expression for $x = -3$.

$$\frac{2x - 1}{x + 4}$$

EXAMPLE 1 Evaluating Rational Expressions

Find the numerical value of $\frac{3x + 6}{2x - 4}$ for the given value of x.

(a) $x = 1$

$$\frac{3x + 6}{2x - 4}$$

$$= \frac{3(1) + 6}{2(1) - 4} \qquad \text{Let } x = 1.$$

$$= \frac{9}{-2} \qquad \text{Simplify.}$$

$$= -\frac{9}{2} \qquad \frac{a}{-b} = -\frac{a}{b}$$

(b) $x = -2$

> Use parentheses around negative numbers to avoid errors.

$$\frac{3x + 6}{2x - 4}$$

$$= \frac{3(-2) + 6}{2(-2) - 4} \qquad \text{Let } x = -2.$$

$$= \frac{0}{-8} \qquad \text{Simplify.}$$

$$= 0 \qquad \frac{0}{b} = 0$$

NOW TRY

OBJECTIVE 2 **Find the values of the variable for which a rational expression is undefined.** In the definition of a rational expression $\frac{P}{Q}$, Q cannot equal 0. *The denominator of a rational expression cannot equal 0 because division by 0 is undefined.*

For instance, in the rational expression

$$\frac{3x + 6}{2x - 4} \leftarrow \text{Denominator cannot equal 0.}$$

from **Example 1,** the variable x can take on any real number value except 2. If x is 2, then the denominator becomes $2(2) - 4 = 0$, making the expression undefined. Thus, x cannot equal 2. We indicate this restriction by writing $x \neq 2$.

NOW TRY ANSWER
1. -7

NOTE *The numerator of a rational expression may be any real number.* If the numerator equals 0 and the denominator does not equal 0, then the rational expression equals 0. See **Example 1(b).**

Determining When a Rational Expression Is Undefined

Step 1   Set the denominator of the rational expression equal to 0.

Step 2   Solve this equation.

Step 3   The solutions of the equation are the values that make the rational expression undefined. The variable *cannot* equal these values.

NOW TRY
EXERCISE 2

Find any values of the variable for which each rational expression is undefined.

(a) $\dfrac{k - 4}{2k - 1}$

(b) $\dfrac{2x}{x^2 + 5x - 14}$

(c) $\dfrac{y + 10}{y^2 + 10}$

EXAMPLE 2   Finding Values That Make Rational Expressions Undefined

Find any values of the variable for which each rational expression is undefined.

(a) $\dfrac{x + 5}{3x + 2}$ We must find any value of x that makes the *denominator* equal to 0, since division by 0 is undefined.

Step 1   Set the denominator equal to 0.

$$3x + 2 = 0$$

Step 2   Solve. $3x = -2$ Subtract 2.

$$x = -\frac{2}{3}$$ Divide by 3.

Step 3   The given expression is undefined for $-\frac{2}{3}$, so $x \neq -\frac{2}{3}$.

(b) $\dfrac{8x^2 + 1}{x - 3}$ The denominator $x - 3 = 0$ when x is 3. The given expression is undefined for 3, so $x \neq 3$.

(c) $\dfrac{9m^2}{m^2 - 5m + 6}$

$$m^2 - 5m + 6 = 0 \qquad \text{Set the denominator equal to 0.}$$
$$(m - 2)(m - 3) = 0 \qquad \text{Factor.}$$
$$m - 2 = 0 \quad \text{or} \quad m - 3 = 0 \qquad \text{Zero-factor property}$$
$$m = 2 \quad \text{or} \qquad m = 3 \qquad \text{Solve for } m.$$

The given expression is undefined for 2 and 3, so $m \neq 2$, $m \neq 3$.

(d) $\dfrac{2r}{r^2 + 1}$ This denominator will not equal 0 for any value of r, because r^2 is always greater than or equal to 0, and adding 1 makes the sum greater than or equal to 1. There are no values for which this expression is undefined.

NOW TRY

OBJECTIVE 3   **Write rational expressions in lowest terms.** A fraction such as $\frac{2}{3}$ is said to be in *lowest terms.*

Lowest Terms

A rational expression $\dfrac{P}{Q}$ $(Q \neq 0)$ is in **lowest terms** if the greatest common factor of its numerator and denominator is 1.

NOW TRY ANSWERS
2. (a) $k \neq \frac{1}{2}$ **(b)** $x \neq -7, x \neq 2$
   (c) never undefined

We use the **fundamental property of rational expressions** to write a rational expression in lowest terms.

Fundamental Property of Rational Expressions

If $\frac{P}{Q}$ $(Q \neq 0)$ is a rational expression and if K represents any polynomial, where $K \neq 0$, then the following is true.

$$\frac{PK}{QK} = \frac{P}{Q}$$

This property is based on the identity property of multiplication.

$$\frac{PK}{QK} = \frac{P}{Q} \cdot \frac{K}{K} = \frac{P}{Q} \cdot 1 = \frac{P}{Q}$$

NOW TRY
EXERCISE 3
Write the rational expression in lowest terms.

$$\frac{21y^5}{7y^2}$$

EXAMPLE 3   Writing in Lowest Terms

Write each rational expression in lowest terms.

(a) $\dfrac{30}{72}$

Begin by factoring.

$$\frac{30}{72} = \frac{2 \cdot 3 \cdot 5}{2 \cdot 2 \cdot 2 \cdot 3 \cdot 3}$$

(b) $\dfrac{14k^2}{2k^3}$

Write k^2 as $k \cdot k$ and k^3 as $k \cdot k \cdot k$.

$$\frac{14k^2}{2k^3} = \frac{2 \cdot 7 \cdot k \cdot k}{2 \cdot k \cdot k \cdot k}$$

Group any factors common to the numerator and denominator.

$$\frac{30}{72} = \frac{5 \cdot (2 \cdot 3)}{2 \cdot 2 \cdot 3 \cdot (2 \cdot 3)}$$

$$\frac{14k^2}{2k^3} = \frac{7(2 \cdot k \cdot k)}{k(2 \cdot k \cdot k)}$$

Use the fundamental property.

$$\frac{30}{72} = \frac{5}{2 \cdot 2 \cdot 3} = \frac{5}{12}$$

$$\frac{14k^2}{2k^3} = \frac{7}{k}$$ NOW TRY

Writing a Rational Expression in Lowest Terms

Step 1   **Factor** the numerator and denominator completely.

Step 2   **Use the fundamental property** to divide out any common factors.

EXAMPLE 4   Writing in Lowest Terms

Write each rational expression in lowest terms.

(a) $\dfrac{3x - 12}{5x - 20}$ [$x \neq 4$, since the denominator is 0 for this value.]

$$= \frac{3(x - 4)}{5(x - 4)}$$ Factor. (Step 1)

$$= \frac{3}{5}$$ Fundamental property (Step 2)

NOW TRY ANSWER
3. $3y^3$

The given expression is equal to $\frac{3}{5}$ for all values of x, where $x \neq 4$ (since the denominator of the original rational expression is 0 when x is 4).

NOW TRY
EXERCISE 4

Write each rational expression in lowest terms.

(a) $\dfrac{3x + 15}{5x + 25}$

(b) $\dfrac{k^2 - 36}{k^2 + 8k + 12}$

(b) $\dfrac{2y^2 - 8}{2y + 4}$ $\boxed{y \neq -2,\text{ since the denominator is 0 for this value.}}$

$= \dfrac{2(y^2 - 4)}{2(y + 2)}$ Factor. (Step 1)

$= \dfrac{2(y + 2)(y - 2)}{2(y + 2)}$ Factor the numerator completely.

$= y - 2$ Fundamental property (Step 2)

(c) $\dfrac{m^2 + 2m - 8}{2m^2 - m - 6}$

$= \dfrac{(m + 4)(m - 2)}{(2m + 3)(m - 2)}$ $\boxed{m \neq -\frac{3}{2}, m \neq 2}$ Factor. (Step 1)

$= \dfrac{m + 4}{2m + 3}$ Fundamental property (Step 2)   *NOW TRY*

We write statements of equality of rational expressions with the understanding that they apply only to real numbers that make neither denominator equal to 0.

⚠ **CAUTION** *Rational expressions cannot be written in lowest terms until after the numerator and denominator have been factored.*

$$\dfrac{6x + 9}{4x + 6} = \dfrac{3(2x + 3)}{2(2x + 3)} = \dfrac{3}{2} \qquad \dfrac{6 + x}{4x} \leftarrow \text{Numerator cannot be factored.}$$

Divide out the common factor.   Already in lowest terms

NOW TRY
EXERCISE 5

Write in lowest terms.

$$\dfrac{10 - a^2}{a^2 - 10}$$

EXAMPLE 5   Writing in Lowest Terms (Factors Are Opposites)

Write $\dfrac{x - y}{y - x}$ in lowest terms.

To get a common factor, the denominator $y - x$ can be factored as follows.

$y - x$ $\boxed{\text{We are factoring out } -1, \textbf{ NOT} \text{ multiplying by it.}}$

$= -1(-y + x)$ Factor out -1.

$= -1(x - y)$ Commutative property

With this result in mind, we simplify.

$\dfrac{x - y}{y - x}$

$= \dfrac{1(x - y)}{-1(x - y)}$ $y - x = -1(x - y)$ from above.

$= \dfrac{1}{-1}$,   or -1 Fundamental property   *NOW TRY*

NOW TRY ANSWERS
4. (a) $\frac{3}{5}$ (b) $\frac{k - 6}{k + 2}$

5. -1

NOTE The numerator *or* the denominator could have been factored in the first step in **Example 5.** Factor -1 from the numerator, and confirm that the result is the same.

In **Example 5,** notice that $y - x$ is the **opposite** (or **additive inverse**) of $x - y$.

Quotient of Opposites

If the numerator and the denominator of a rational expression are opposites, as in $\frac{x - y}{y - x}$, then the rational expression is equal to -1.

Based on this result, the following are true.

Numerator and denominator are opposites. → $\dfrac{q - 7}{7 - q} = -1$ and $\dfrac{-5a + 2b}{5a - 2b} = -1$

However, the following expression cannot be simplified further.

$$\frac{x - 2}{x + 2}$$ ← Numerator and denominator are *not* opposites.

NOW TRY
EXERCISE 6

Write each rational expression in lowest terms.

(a) $\dfrac{p - 4}{4 - p}$ **(b)** $\dfrac{4m^2 - n^2}{2n - 4m}$

(c) $\dfrac{x + y}{x - y}$

EXAMPLE 6   Writing in Lowest Terms (Factors Are Opposites)

Write each rational expression in lowest terms.

(a) $\dfrac{2 - m}{m - 2}$ Since $2 - m$ and $m - 2$ are opposites, this expression equals -1.

(b) $\dfrac{4x^2 - 9}{6 - 4x}$

$= \dfrac{(2x + 3)(2x - 3)}{2(3 - 2x)}$ Factor the numerator and denominator.

$= \dfrac{(2x + 3)(2x - 3)}{2(-1)(2x - 3)}$ Write $3 - 2x$ in the denominator as $-1(2x - 3)$.

$= \dfrac{2x + 3}{2(-1)}$ Fundamental property

$= \dfrac{2x + 3}{-2}$,   or $-\dfrac{2x + 3}{2}$ $\frac{a}{-b} = -\frac{a}{b}$

(c) $\dfrac{3 + r}{3 - r}$ $3 - r$ is *not* the opposite of $3 + r$.

This rational expression is already in lowest terms.   *NOW TRY*

OBJECTIVE 4   **Recognize equivalent forms of rational expressions.** The common fraction $-\frac{5}{6}$ can also be written $\frac{-5}{6}$ and $\frac{5}{-6}$.

Consider the final rational expression from **Example 6(b).**

$$-\frac{2x + 3}{2}$$

The $-$ sign representing the factor -1 is in front of the expression, even with the fraction bar. The factor -1 may instead be placed in the numerator or denominator.

Use parentheses.

$$\frac{-(2x + 3)}{2}$$ and $$\frac{2x + 3}{-2}$$

NOW TRY ANSWERS
6. (a) -1
(b) $\frac{2m + n}{-2}$,   or $-\frac{2m + n}{2}$
(c) already in lowest terms

The distributive property can also be applied.

$$-\frac{(2x + 3)}{2} \quad \text{can also be written} \quad \frac{-2x - 3}{2}.$$

> Multiply *each* term in the numerator by -1.

⚠ **CAUTION** $\frac{-2x + 3}{2}$ is *not* an equivalent form of $\frac{-(2x + 3)}{2}$. The sign preceding 3 in the numerator of $\frac{-2x + 3}{2}$ should be $-$ rather than $+$. *Be careful to apply the distributive property correctly.*

↱ NOW TRY
→ EXERCISE 7

Write four equivalent forms of the rational expression.

$$-\frac{4k - 9}{k + 3}$$

EXAMPLE 7 Writing Equivalent Forms of a Rational Expression

Write four equivalent forms of the rational expression.

$$-\frac{3x + 2}{x - 6}$$

If we apply the negative sign to the numerator, we obtain these equivalent forms.

$$① \rightarrow \frac{-(3x + 2)}{x - 6} \quad \text{and, by the distributive property,} \quad \frac{-3x - 2}{x - 6} \leftarrow ②$$

If we apply the negative sign to the denominator, we obtain two more forms.

$$③ \rightarrow \frac{3x + 2}{-(x - 6)} \quad \text{or, distributing once again,} \quad \frac{3x + 2}{-x + 6} \leftarrow ④$$

NOW TRY ↵

⚠ **CAUTION** Recall that $-\frac{5}{6} \neq \frac{-5}{-6}$. Thus, in **Example 7,** it would be incorrect to distribute the negative sign in $-\frac{3x + 2}{x - 6}$ to *both* the numerator *and* the denominator. (Doing this would actually lead to the *opposite* of the original expression.)

CONNECTIONS

In **Section 4.7,** we used long division to find the quotient of two polynomials such as $(2x^2 + 5x - 12) \div (2x - 3)$, as shown on the left. The quotient is $x + 4$. We get the same quotient by expressing the division problem as a rational expression (fraction) and writing this rational expression in lowest terms, as shown on the right.

$$2x - 3\overline{)2x^2 + 5x - 12} \qquad \frac{2x^2 + 5x - 12}{2x - 3}$$
$$\begin{array}{r} x + 4 \\ \underline{2x^2 - 3x} \\ 8x - 12 \\ \underline{8x - 12} \\ 0 \end{array} \qquad \begin{aligned} &= \frac{(2x - 3)(x + 4)}{2x - 3} \quad \text{Factor.} \\ &= x + 4 \quad \text{Fundamental property} \end{aligned}$$

For Discussion or Writing

What kind of division problem has a quotient that cannot be found by writing a fraction in lowest terms? Try using rational expressions to solve each division problem. Then use long division and compare.

1. $(3x^2 + 11x + 8) \div (x + 2)$ **2.** $(x^3 - 8) \div (x^2 + 2x + 4)$

NOW TRY ANSWER

7. $\frac{-(4k - 9)}{k + 3}$, $\frac{-4k + 9}{k + 3}$, $\frac{4k - 9}{-(k + 3)}$, $\frac{4k - 9}{-k - 3}$

6.1 EXERCISES *MyMathLab*   PRACTICE   WATCH   DOWNLOAD   READ   REVIEW

⊕ *Complete solution available on the Video Resources on DVD*

Find the numerical value of each rational expression for **(a)** $x = 2$ *and* **(b)** $x = -3$. ***See Example 1.***

⊕ **1.** $\dfrac{3x + 1}{5x}$

2. $\dfrac{5x - 2}{4x}$

3. $\dfrac{x^2 - 4}{2x + 1}$

4. $\dfrac{2x^2 - 4x}{3x - 1}$

5. $\dfrac{(-2x)^3}{3x + 9}$

6. $\dfrac{(-3x)^2}{4x + 12}$

7. $\dfrac{7 - 3x}{3x^2 - 7x + 2}$

8. $\dfrac{5x + 2}{4x^2 - 5x - 6}$

9. $\dfrac{(x + 3)(x - 2)}{500x}$

10. $\dfrac{(x - 2)(x + 3)}{1000x}$

11. $\dfrac{x^2 - 4}{x^2 - 9}$

12. $\dfrac{x^2 - 9}{x^2 - 4}$

✎ **13.** Define *rational expression* in your own words, and give an example.

14. *Concept Check*   Fill in each blank with the correct response: The rational expression $\frac{x + 5}{x - 3}$ is undefined when x is _____, so $x \neq$ _____. This rational expression is equal to 0 when $x =$ _____.

✎ **15.** Why can't the denominator of a rational expression equal 0?

✎ **16.** If 2 is substituted for x in the rational expression $\frac{x - 2}{x^2 - 4}$, the result is $\frac{0}{0}$. An often-heard statement is "Any number divided by itself is 1." Does this mean that this expression is equal to 1 for $x = 2$? If not, explain.

Find any values of the variable for which each rational expression is undefined. Write answers with the symbol $\neq$. ***See Example 2.***

17. $\dfrac{12}{5y}$

18. $\dfrac{-7}{3z}$

19. $\dfrac{x + 1}{x - 6}$

20. $\dfrac{m - 2}{m - 5}$

⊕ **21.** $\dfrac{4x^2}{3x + 5}$

22. $\dfrac{2x^3}{3x + 4}$

23. $\dfrac{5m + 2}{m^2 + m - 6}$

24. $\dfrac{2r - 5}{r^2 - 5r + 4}$

25. $\dfrac{x^2 + 3x}{4}$

26. $\dfrac{x^2 - 4x}{6}$

27. $\dfrac{3x - 1}{x^2 + 2}$

28. $\dfrac{4q + 2}{q^2 + 9}$

29. (a) Identify the two *terms* in the numerator and the two *terms* in the denominator of the rational expression $\frac{x^2 + 4x}{x + 4}$.

✎ **(b)** Describe the steps you would use to write the rational expression in part (a) in lowest terms. (*Hint:* It simplifies to x.)

30. *Concept Check*   Which one of these rational expressions can be simplified?

A. $\dfrac{x^2 + 2}{x^2}$ **B.** $\dfrac{x^2 + 2}{2}$ **C.** $\dfrac{x^2 + y^2}{y^2}$ **D.** $\dfrac{x^2 - 5x}{x}$

Write each rational expression in lowest terms. ***See Examples 3 and 4.***

⊕ **31.** $\dfrac{18r^3}{6r}$

32. $\dfrac{27p^4}{3p}$

33. $\dfrac{4(y - 2)}{10(y - 2)}$

34. $\dfrac{15(m - 1)}{9(m - 1)}$

35. $\dfrac{(x + 1)(x - 1)}{(x + 1)^2}$

36. $\dfrac{(t + 5)(t - 3)}{(t + 5)^2}$

⊕ **37.** $\dfrac{7m + 14}{5m + 10}$

38. $\dfrac{16x + 8}{14x + 7}$

39. $\dfrac{6m - 18}{7m - 21}$

40. $\dfrac{5r + 20}{3r + 12}$

41. $\dfrac{m^2 - n^2}{m + n}$

42. $\dfrac{a^2 - b^2}{a - b}$

43. $\dfrac{2t + 6}{t^2 - 9}$

44. $\dfrac{5s - 25}{s^2 - 25}$

45. $\dfrac{12m^2 - 3}{8m - 4}$

46. $\dfrac{20p^2 - 45}{6p - 9}$

47. $\dfrac{3m^2 - 3m}{5m - 5}$

48. $\dfrac{6t^2 - 6t}{5t - 5}$

49. $\dfrac{9r^2 - 4s^2}{9r + 6s}$

50. $\dfrac{16x^2 - 9y^2}{12x - 9y}$

51. $\dfrac{5k^2 - 13k - 6}{5k + 2}$

52. $\dfrac{7t^2 - 31t - 20}{7t + 4}$

53. $\dfrac{x^2 + 2x - 15}{x^2 + 6x + 5}$

54. $\dfrac{y^2 - 5y - 14}{y^2 + y - 2}$

55. $\dfrac{2x^2 - 3x - 5}{2x^2 - 7x + 5}$

56. $\dfrac{3x^2 + 8x + 4}{3x^2 - 4x - 4}$

57. $\dfrac{3x^3 + 13x^2 + 14x}{3x^3 - 5x^2 - 28x}$

58. $\dfrac{2x^3 + 7x^2 - 30x}{2x^3 - 11x^2 + 15x}$

59. $\dfrac{-3t + 6t^2 - 3t^3}{7t^2 - 14t^3 + 7t^4}$

60. $\dfrac{-20r - 20r^2 - 5r^3}{24r^2 + 24r^3 + 6r^4}$

*Exercises 61–82 involve factoring by grouping **(Section 5.1)** and factoring sums and differences of cubes **(Section 5.4)**. Write each rational expression in lowest terms.*

61. $\dfrac{zw + 4z - 3w - 12}{zw + 4z + 5w + 20}$

62. $\dfrac{km + 4k - 4m - 16}{km + 4k + 5m + 20}$

63. $\dfrac{pr + qr + ps + qs}{pr + qr - ps - qs}$

64. $\dfrac{wt + ws + xt + xs}{wt - xs - xt + ws}$

65. $\dfrac{ac - ad + bc - bd}{ac - ad - bc + bd}$

66. $\dfrac{ac - bc - ad + bd}{ac - ad - bd + bc}$

67. $\dfrac{m^2 - n^2 - 4m - 4n}{2m - 2n - 8}$

68. $\dfrac{x^2 - y^2 - 7y - 7x}{3x - 3y - 21}$

69. $\dfrac{x^2y + y + x^2z + z}{xy + xz}$

70. $\dfrac{y^2k + pk - y^2z - pz}{yk - yz}$

71. $\dfrac{1 + p^3}{1 + p}$

72. $\dfrac{8 + x^3}{2 + x}$

73. $\dfrac{x^3 - 27}{x - 3}$

74. $\dfrac{r^3 - 1000}{r - 10}$

75. $\dfrac{b^3 - a^3}{a^2 - b^2}$

76. $\dfrac{8y^3 - 27z^3}{9z^2 - 4y^2}$

77. $\dfrac{k^3 + 8}{k^2 - 4}$

78. $\dfrac{r^3 + 27}{r^2 - 9}$

79. $\dfrac{z^3 + 27}{z^3 - 3z^2 + 9z}$

80. $\dfrac{t^3 + 64}{t^3 - 4t^2 + 16t}$

81. $\dfrac{1 - 8r^3}{8r^2 + 4r + 2}$

82. $\dfrac{8 - 27x^3}{27x^2 + 18x + 12}$

83. *Concept Check*   Which two of the following rational expressions equal -1?

A. $\dfrac{2x + 3}{2x - 3}$ **B.** $\dfrac{2x - 3}{3 - 2x}$ **C.** $\dfrac{2x + 3}{3 + 2x}$ **D.** $\dfrac{2x + 3}{-2x - 3}$

84. *Concept Check*   Make the correct choice for the blank: $\dfrac{4 - r^2}{4 + r^2}$ _____ equal to -1.
(is/is not)

*Write each rational expression in lowest terms. **See Examples 5 and 6.***

🌐 **85.** $\dfrac{6 - t}{t - 6}$

86. $\dfrac{2 - k}{k - 2}$

🌐 **87.** $\dfrac{m^2 - 1}{1 - m}$

88. $\dfrac{a^2 - b^2}{b - a}$

89. $\dfrac{q^2 - 4q}{4q - q^2}$

90. $\dfrac{z^2 - 5z}{5z - z^2}$

91. $\dfrac{p + 6}{p - 6}$

92. $\dfrac{5 - x}{5 + x}$

93. *Concept Check*   Which one of these rational expressions is *not* equivalent to $\frac{x-3}{4-x}$?

A. $\dfrac{3-x}{x-4}$ **B.** $\dfrac{x+3}{4+x}$ **C.** $-\dfrac{3-x}{4-x}$ **D.** $-\dfrac{x-3}{x-4}$

94. *Concept Check*   Make the correct choice for the blank: $\frac{5+2x}{3-x}$ and $\frac{-5-2x}{x-3}$ _____ equivalent rational expressions.   (are/are not)

*Write four equivalent forms for each rational expression. **See Example 7.***

95. $-\dfrac{x+4}{x-3}$

96. $-\dfrac{x+6}{x-1}$

97. $-\dfrac{2x-3}{x+3}$

98. $-\dfrac{5x-6}{x+4}$

99. $-\dfrac{3x-1}{5x-6}$

100. $-\dfrac{2x-9}{7x-1}$

101. The area of the rectangle is represented by
$$x^4 + 10x^2 + 21.$$
What is the width? $\left(Hint:\ \text{Use } W = \frac{\mathscr{A}}{L}.\right)$

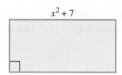

$x^2 + 7$

102. The volume of the box is represented by
$$(x^2 + 8x + 15)(x + 4).$$
Find the polynomial that represents the area of the bottom of the box.

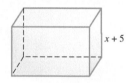

$x + 5$

Solve each problem.

103. The average number of vehicles waiting in line to enter a sports arena parking area is approximated by the rational expression
$$\frac{x^2}{2(1-x)},$$
where x is a quantity between 0 and 1 known as the **traffic intensity.** (*Source:* Mannering, F., and W. Kilareski, *Principles of Highway Engineering and Traffic Control,* John Wiley and Sons.) To the nearest tenth, find the average number of vehicles waiting if the traffic intensity is the given number.

(a) 0.1   **(b)** 0.8   **(c)** 0.9

(d) What happens to waiting time as traffic intensity increases?

104. The percent of deaths caused by smoking is modeled by the rational expression
$$\frac{x-1}{x},$$
where x is the number of times a smoker is more likely than a nonsmoker to die of lung cancer. This is called the **incidence rate.** (*Source:* Walker, A., *Observation and Inference: An Introduction to the Methods of Epidemiology,* Epidemiology Resources Inc.) For example, $x = 10$ means that a smoker is 10 times more likely than a nonsmoker to die of lung cancer. Find the percent of deaths if the incidence rate is the given number.

(a) 5   **(b)** 10   **(c)** 20

(d) Can the incidence rate equal 0? Explain.

PREVIEW EXERCISES

*Multiply or divide as indicated. Write each answer in lowest terms. **See Section 1.1.***

105. $\dfrac{2}{3} \cdot \dfrac{5}{6}$

106. $\dfrac{3}{7} \cdot \dfrac{4}{5}$

107. $\dfrac{10}{3} \div \dfrac{5}{6}$

108. $\dfrac{7}{12} \div \dfrac{15}{4}$

Multiplying and Dividing Rational Expressions

OBJECTIVES

1 Multiply rational expressions.

2 Divide rational expressions.

OBJECTIVE 1 Multiply rational expressions. The product of two fractions is found by multiplying the numerators and multiplying the denominators. Rational expressions are multiplied in the same way.

Multiplying Rational Expressions

The product of the rational expressions $\frac{P}{Q}$ and $\frac{R}{S}$ is defined as follows.

$$\frac{P}{Q} \cdot \frac{R}{S} = \frac{PR}{QS}$$

That is, to multiply rational expressions, multiply the numerators and multiply the denominators.

NOW TRY
EXERCISE 1

Multiply. Write the answer in lowest terms.

$$\frac{4k^2}{7} \cdot \frac{14}{11k}$$

EXAMPLE 1 Multiplying Rational Expressions

Multiply. Write each answer in lowest terms.

(a) $\dfrac{3}{10} \cdot \dfrac{5}{9}$ **(b)** $\dfrac{6}{x} \cdot \dfrac{x^2}{12}$

Indicate the product of the numerators and the product of the denominators.

$$= \frac{3 \cdot 5}{10 \cdot 9} \qquad\qquad = \frac{6 \cdot x^2}{x \cdot 12}$$

Leave the products in factored form because common factors are needed to write the product in lowest terms. Factor the numerator and denominator to further identify any common factors. Then use the fundamental property to write each product in lowest terms.

$$= \frac{3 \cdot 5}{2 \cdot 5 \cdot 3 \cdot 3} \qquad\qquad = \frac{6 \cdot x \cdot x}{2 \cdot 6 \cdot x}$$

$$= \frac{1}{6} \quad\text{Remember to write 1 in the numerator.} \qquad = \frac{x}{2}$$

NOW TRY

NOTE It is also possible to divide out common factors in the numerator and denominator *before* multiplying the rational expressions. Consider this example.

$$\frac{6}{5} \cdot \frac{35}{22}$$

$$= \frac{2 \cdot 3}{5} \cdot \frac{5 \cdot 7}{2 \cdot 11} \qquad \text{Identify the common factors.}$$

$$= \frac{3}{1} \cdot \frac{7}{11} \qquad \text{Divide out the common factors.}$$

$$= \frac{21}{11} \qquad \text{Multiply.}$$

NOW TRY ANSWER
1. $\frac{8k}{11}$

NOW TRY
EXERCISE 2

Multiply. Write the answer in lowest terms.

$$\frac{m-3}{3m} \cdot \frac{9m^2}{8(m-3)^2}$$

EXAMPLE 2 Multiplying Rational Expressions

Multiply. Write the answer in lowest terms.

$$\frac{x+y}{2x} \cdot \frac{x^2}{(x+y)^2}$$

Use parentheses here around $x + y$.

$$= \frac{(x+y)x^2}{2x(x+y)^2}$$ Multiply numerators.
Multiply denominators.

$$= \frac{(x+y)x \cdot x}{2x(x+y)(x+y)}$$ Factor. Identify the common factors.

$$= \frac{x}{2(x+y)}$$ $\frac{(x+y)x}{x(x+y)} = 1$; Write in lowest terms.

NOW TRY

NOW TRY
EXERCISE 3

Multiply. Write the answer in lowest terms.

$$\frac{y^2-3y-28}{y^2-9y+14} \cdot \frac{y^2-7y+10}{y^2+4y}$$

EXAMPLE 3 Multiplying Rational Expressions

Multiply. Write the answer in lowest terms.

$$\frac{x^2+3x}{x^2-3x-4} \cdot \frac{x^2-5x+4}{x^2+2x-3}$$

$$= \frac{(x^2+3x)(x^2-5x+4)}{(x^2-3x-4)(x^2+2x-3)}$$ Definition of multiplication

$$= \frac{x(x+3)(x-4)(x-1)}{(x-4)(x+1)(x+3)(x-1)}$$ Factor.

$$= \frac{x}{x+1}$$ Divide out the common factors.

The quotients $\frac{x+3}{x+3}, \frac{x-4}{x-4},$ and $\frac{x-1}{x-1}$ all equal 1, justifying the final product $\frac{x}{x+1}$.

NOW TRY

OBJECTIVE 2 **Divide rational expressions.** Suppose we have $\frac{7}{8}$ gal of milk and want to find how many quarts we have. Since 1 qt is $\frac{1}{4}$ gal, we ask, "How many $\frac{1}{4}$s are there in $\frac{7}{8}$?" This would be interpreted as follows.

$$\frac{7}{8} \div \frac{1}{4}, \quad \text{or} \quad \frac{\frac{7}{8}}{\frac{1}{4}} \leftarrow \text{The fraction bar means division.}$$

The fundamental property of rational expressions discussed earlier can be applied to rational number values of P, Q, and K.

$$\frac{P}{Q} = \frac{P \cdot K}{Q \cdot K} = \frac{\frac{7}{8} \cdot 4}{\frac{1}{4} \cdot 4} = \frac{\frac{7}{8} \cdot 4}{1} = \frac{7}{8} \cdot \frac{4}{1}$$ Let $P = \frac{7}{8}$, $Q = \frac{1}{4}$, and $K = 4$.
(K is the reciprocal of $Q = \frac{1}{4}$.)

So, to divide $\frac{7}{8}$ by $\frac{1}{4}$, we multiply $\frac{7}{8}$ by the reciprocal of $\frac{1}{4}$, namely, 4. Since $\frac{7}{8}(4) = \frac{7}{2}$, there are $\frac{7}{2}$, or $3\frac{1}{2}$, qt in $\frac{7}{8}$ gal.

NOW TRY ANSWERS
2. $\frac{3m}{8(m-3)}$
3. $\frac{y-5}{y}$

The preceding discussion illustrates dividing common fractions. Division of rational expressions is defined in the same way.

Dividing Rational Expressions

If $\frac{P}{Q}$ and $\frac{R}{S}$ are any two rational expressions with $\frac{R}{S} \neq 0$, then their quotient is defined as follows.

$$\frac{P}{Q} \div \frac{R}{S} = \frac{P}{Q} \cdot \frac{S}{R} = \frac{PS}{QR}$$

That is, to divide one rational expression by another rational expression, multiply the first rational expression (dividend) by the reciprocal of the second rational expression (divisor).

NOW TRY
EXERCISE 4

Divide. Write the answer in lowest terms.

$$\frac{2x - 5}{3x^2} \div \frac{2x - 5}{12x}$$

EXAMPLE 4   Dividing Rational Expressions

Divide. Write each answer in lowest terms.

(a) $\dfrac{5}{8} \div \dfrac{7}{16}$

(b) $\dfrac{y}{y + 3} \div \dfrac{4y}{y + 5}$

Multiply the dividend by the reciprocal of the divisor.

$= \dfrac{5}{8} \cdot \dfrac{16}{7}$ ← Reciprocal of $\frac{7}{16}$

$= \dfrac{5 \cdot 16}{8 \cdot 7}$

$= \dfrac{5 \cdot 8 \cdot 2}{8 \cdot 7}$

$= \dfrac{10}{7}$

$= \dfrac{y}{y + 3} \cdot \dfrac{y + 5}{4y}$ ← Reciprocal of $\frac{4y}{y + 5}$

$= \dfrac{y(y + 5)}{(y + 3)(4y)}$

$= \dfrac{y + 5}{4(y + 3)}$

NOW TRY

NOW TRY
EXERCISE 5

Divide. Write the answer in lowest terms.

$$\frac{(3k)^3}{2j^4} \div \frac{9k^2}{6j}$$

EXAMPLE 5   Dividing Rational Expressions

Divide. Write the answer in lowest terms.

$$\frac{(3m)^2}{(2p)^3} \div \frac{6m^3}{16p^2}$$

$= \dfrac{(3m)^2}{(2p)^3} \cdot \dfrac{16p^2}{6m^3}$ Multiply by the reciprocal.

$(3m)^2 = 3^2m^2;$
$(2p)^3 = 2^3p^3$
$= \dfrac{9m^2}{8p^3} \cdot \dfrac{16p^2}{6m^3}$ Power rule for exponents

$= \dfrac{9 \cdot 16m^2p^2}{8 \cdot 6p^3m^3}$ Multiply numerators.
Multiply denominators.

$= \dfrac{3}{mp}$ Lowest terms

NOW TRY

NOW TRY ANSWERS
4. $\dfrac{4}{x}$ **5.** $\dfrac{9k}{j^3}$

NOW TRY
EXERCISE 6

Divide. Write the answer in lowest terms.

$$\frac{(t + 2)(t - 5)}{-4t} \div \frac{t^2 - 25}{(t + 5)(t + 2)}$$

EXAMPLE 6 Dividing Rational Expressions

Divide. Write the answer in lowest terms.

$$\frac{x^2 - 4}{(x + 3)(x - 2)} \div \frac{(x + 2)(x + 3)}{-2x}$$

$$= \frac{x^2 - 4}{(x + 3)(x - 2)} \cdot \frac{-2x}{(x + 2)(x + 3)} \qquad \text{Multiply by the reciprocal.}$$

$$= \frac{-2x(x^2 - 4)}{(x + 3)(x - 2)(x + 2)(x + 3)} \qquad \begin{array}{l}\text{Multiply numerators.}\\ \text{Multiply denominators.}\end{array}$$

$$= \frac{-2x(x + 2)(x - 2)}{(x + 3)(x - 2)(x + 2)(x + 3)} \qquad \text{Factor the numerator.}$$

$$= \frac{-2x}{(x + 3)^2}, \quad \text{or} \quad -\frac{2x}{(x + 3)^2} \qquad \text{Lowest terms; } \frac{-a}{b} = -\frac{a}{b}$$

NOW TRY

NOW TRY
EXERCISE 7

Divide. Write the answer in lowest terms.

$$\frac{7 - x}{2x + 6} \div \frac{x^2 - 49}{x^2 + 6x + 9}$$

EXAMPLE 7 Dividing Rational Expressions (Factors Are Opposites)

Divide. Write the answer in lowest terms.

$$\frac{m^2 - 4}{m^2 - 1} \div \frac{2m^2 + 4m}{1 - m}$$

$$= \frac{m^2 - 4}{m^2 - 1} \cdot \frac{1 - m}{2m^2 + 4m} \qquad \text{Multiply by the reciprocal.}$$

$$= \frac{(m^2 - 4)(1 - m)}{(m^2 - 1)(2m^2 + 4m)} \qquad \begin{array}{l}\text{Multiply numerators.}\\ \text{Multiply denominators.}\end{array}$$

$$= \frac{(m + 2)(m - 2)(1 - m)}{(m + 1)(m - 1)(2m)(m + 2)} \qquad \text{Factor; } 1 - m \text{ and } m - 1 \text{ are opposites.}$$

$$= \frac{-1(m - 2)}{2m(m + 1)} \qquad \text{From Section 6.1, } \frac{1 - m}{m - 1} = -1.$$

$$= \frac{-m + 2}{2m(m + 1)}, \quad \text{or} \quad \frac{2 - m}{2m(m + 1)} \qquad \begin{array}{l}\text{Distribute } -1 \text{ in the numerator.}\\ \text{Rewrite } -m + 2 \text{ as } 2 - m.\end{array}$$

NOW TRY

In summary, use the following steps to multiply or divide rational expressions.

Multiplying or Dividing Rational Expressions

Step 1 **Note the operation.** If the operation is division, use the definition of division to rewrite it as multiplication.

Step 2 **Multiply** numerators and multiply denominators.

Step 3 **Factor** all numerators and denominators completely.

Step 4 **Write in lowest terms** using the fundamental property.

Note: Steps 2 and 3 may be interchanged based on personal preference.

NOW TRY ANSWERS

6. $\frac{(t + 2)^2}{-4t}$, or $-\frac{(t + 2)^2}{4t}$

7. $\frac{-x - 3}{2(x + 7)}$, or $-\frac{x + 3}{2(x + 7)}$

6.2 EXERCISES

 MyMathLab Math XL PRACTICE WATCH DOWNLOAD READ REVIEW

🌐 *Complete solution available on the Video Resources on DVD*

1. *Concept Check* Match each multiplication problem in Column I with the correct product in Column II.

I	II
(a) $\dfrac{5x^3}{10x^4} \cdot \dfrac{10x^7}{4x}$	**A.** $\dfrac{4}{5x^5}$
(b) $\dfrac{10x^4}{5x^3} \cdot \dfrac{10x^7}{4x}$	**B.** $\dfrac{5x^5}{4}$
(c) $\dfrac{5x^3}{10x^4} \cdot \dfrac{4x}{10x^7}$	**C.** $\dfrac{1}{5x^7}$
(d) $\dfrac{10x^4}{5x^3} \cdot \dfrac{4x}{10x^7}$	**D.** $5x^7$

2. *Concept Check* Match each division problem in Column I with the correct quotient in Column II.

I	II
(a) $\dfrac{5x^3}{10x^4} \div \dfrac{10x^7}{4x}$	**A.** $\dfrac{5x^5}{4}$
(b) $\dfrac{10x^4}{5x^3} \div \dfrac{10x^7}{4x}$	**B.** $5x^7$
(c) $\dfrac{5x^3}{10x^4} \div \dfrac{4x}{10x^7}$	**C.** $\dfrac{4}{5x^5}$
(d) $\dfrac{10x^4}{5x^3} \div \dfrac{4x}{10x^7}$	**D.** $\dfrac{1}{5x^7}$

Multiply. Write each answer in lowest terms. **See Examples 1 and 2.**

🌐 **3.** $\dfrac{15a^2}{14} \cdot \dfrac{7}{5a}$

4. $\dfrac{21b^6}{18} \cdot \dfrac{9}{7b^4}$

5. $\dfrac{12x^4}{18x^3} \cdot \dfrac{-8x^5}{4x^2}$

6. $\dfrac{12m^5}{-2m^2} \cdot \dfrac{6m^6}{28m^3}$

7. $\dfrac{2(c+d)}{3} \cdot \dfrac{18}{6(c+d)^2}$

8. $\dfrac{4(y-2)}{x} \cdot \dfrac{3x}{6(y-2)^2}$

🌐 **9.** $\dfrac{(x-y)^2}{2} \cdot \dfrac{24}{3(x-y)}$

10. $\dfrac{(a+b)^2}{5} \cdot \dfrac{30}{2(a+b)}$

11. $\dfrac{t-4}{8} \cdot \dfrac{4t^2}{t-4}$

12. $\dfrac{z+9}{12} \cdot \dfrac{3z^2}{z+9}$

13. $\dfrac{3x}{x+3} \cdot \dfrac{(x+3)^2}{6x^2}$

14. $\dfrac{(t-2)^2}{4t^2} \cdot \dfrac{2t}{t-2}$

Divide. Write each answer in lowest terms. **See Examples 4 and 5.**

15. $\dfrac{9z^4}{3z^5} \div \dfrac{3z^2}{5z^3}$

16. $\dfrac{35x^8}{7x^9} \div \dfrac{5x^5}{9x^6}$

🌐 **17.** $\dfrac{4t^4}{2t^5} \div \dfrac{(2t)^3}{-6}$

18. $\dfrac{-12u^6}{3a^2} \div \dfrac{(2a)^3}{27a}$

🌐 **19.** $\dfrac{3}{2y-6} \div \dfrac{6}{y-3}$

20. $\dfrac{4m+16}{10} \div \dfrac{3m+12}{18}$

21. $\dfrac{7t+7}{-6} \div \dfrac{4t+4}{15}$

22. $\dfrac{8z-16}{-20} \div \dfrac{3z-6}{40}$

23. $\dfrac{2x}{x-1} \div \dfrac{x^2}{x+2}$

24. $\dfrac{y^2}{y+1} \div \dfrac{3y}{y-3}$

25. $\dfrac{(x-3)^2}{6x} \div \dfrac{x-3}{x^2}$

26. $\dfrac{2a}{a+4} \div \dfrac{a^2}{(a+4)^2}$

Multiply or divide. Write each answer in lowest terms. **See Examples 3, 6, and 7.**

27. $\dfrac{5x-15}{3x+9} \cdot \dfrac{4x+12}{6x-18}$

28. $\dfrac{8r+16}{24r-24} \cdot \dfrac{6r-6}{3r+6}$

29. $\dfrac{2-t}{8} \div \dfrac{t-2}{6}$

30. $\dfrac{m-2}{4} \div \dfrac{2-m}{6}$

31. $\dfrac{27-3z}{4} \cdot \dfrac{12}{2z-18}$

32. $\dfrac{35-5x}{6} \cdot \dfrac{12}{3x-21}$

🌐 **33.** $\dfrac{p^2+4p-5}{p^2+7p+10} \div \dfrac{p-1}{p+4}$

34. $\dfrac{z^2-3z+2}{z^2+4z+3} \div \dfrac{z-1}{z+1}$

🌐 **35.** $\dfrac{m^2-4}{16-8m} \div \dfrac{m+2}{8}$

36. $\dfrac{r^2-36}{54-9r} \div \dfrac{r+6}{9}$

37. $\dfrac{2x^2-7x+3}{x-3} \cdot \dfrac{x+2}{x-1}$

38. $\dfrac{3x^2-5x-2}{x-2} \cdot \dfrac{x-3}{x+1}$

39. $\dfrac{2k^2-k-1}{2k^2+5k+3} \div \dfrac{4k^2-1}{2k^2+k-3}$

40. $\dfrac{3t^2-4t-4}{3t^2+10t+8} \div \dfrac{9t^2+21t+10}{3t^2+14t+15}$

41. $\dfrac{2k^2 + 3k - 2}{6k^2 - 7k + 2} \cdot \dfrac{4k^2 - 5k + 1}{k^2 + k - 2}$

42. $\dfrac{2m^2 - 5m - 12}{m^2 - 10m + 24} \cdot \dfrac{m^2 - 9m + 18}{4m^2 - 9}$

43. $\dfrac{m^2 + 2mp - 3p^2}{m^2 - 3mp + 2p^2} \div \dfrac{m^2 + 4mp + 3p^2}{m^2 + 2mp - 8p^2}$

44. $\dfrac{r^2 + rs - 12s^2}{r^2 - rs - 20s^2} \div \dfrac{r^2 - 2rs - 3s^2}{r^2 + rs - 30s^2}$

45. $\dfrac{m^2 + 3m + 2}{m^2 + 5m + 4} \cdot \dfrac{m^2 + 10m + 24}{m^2 + 5m + 6}$

46. $\dfrac{z^2 - z - 6}{z^2 - 2z - 8} \cdot \dfrac{z^2 + 7z + 12}{z^2 - 9}$

47. $\dfrac{y^2 + y - 2}{y^2 + 3y - 4} \div \dfrac{y + 2}{y + 3}$

48. $\dfrac{r^2 + r - 6}{r^2 + 4r - 12} \div \dfrac{r + 3}{r - 1}$

49. $\dfrac{2m^2 + 7m + 3}{m^2 - 9} \cdot \dfrac{m^2 - 3m}{2m^2 + 11m + 5}$

50. $\dfrac{6s^2 + 17s + 10}{s^2 - 4} \cdot \dfrac{s^2 - 2s}{6s^2 + 29s + 20}$

51. $\dfrac{r^2 + rs - 12s^2}{r^2 - rs - 20s^2} \div \dfrac{r^2 - 2rs - 3s^2}{r^2 + rs - 30s^2}$

52. $\dfrac{m^2 + 8mn + 7n^2}{m^2 + mn - 42n^2} \div \dfrac{m^2 - 3mn - 4n^2}{m^2 - mn - 30n^2}$

53. $\dfrac{(q - 3)^4(q + 2)}{q^2 + 3q + 2} \div \dfrac{q^2 - 6q + 9}{q^2 + 4q + 4}$

54. $\dfrac{(x + 4)^3(x - 3)}{x^2 - 9} \div \dfrac{x^2 + 8x + 16}{x^2 + 6x + 9}$

Brain Busters *Exercises 55–60 involve grouping symbols **(Section 1.2)**, factoring by grouping **(Section 5.1)**, and factoring sums and differences of cubes **(Section 5.4)**. Multiply or divide as indicated. Write each answer in lowest terms.*

55. $\dfrac{x + 5}{x + 10} \div \left(\dfrac{x^2 + 10x + 25}{x^2 + 10x} \cdot \dfrac{10x}{x^2 + 15x + 50} \right)$

56. $\dfrac{m - 8}{m - 4} \div \left(\dfrac{m^2 - 12m + 32}{8m} \cdot \dfrac{m^2 - 8m}{m^2 - 8m + 16} \right)$

57. $\dfrac{3a - 3b - a^2 + b^2}{4a^2 - 4ab + b^2} \cdot \dfrac{4a^2 - b^2}{2a^2 - ab - b^2}$

58. $\dfrac{4r^2 - t^2 + 10r - 5t}{2r^2 + rt + 5r} \cdot \dfrac{4r^3 + 4r^2t + rt^2}{2r + t}$

59. $\dfrac{-x^3 - y^3}{x^2 - 2xy + y^2} \div \dfrac{3y^2 - 3xy}{x^2 - y^2}$

60. $\dfrac{b^3 - 8a^3}{4a^3 + 4a^2b + ab^2} \div \dfrac{4a^2 + 2ab + b^2}{-a^3 - ab^3}$

61. If the rational expression $\frac{5x^2y^3}{2pq}$ represents the area of a rectangle and $\frac{2xy}{p}$ represents the length, what rational expression represents the width?

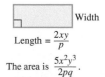

Width

Length $= \dfrac{2xy}{p}$

The area is $\dfrac{5x^2y^3}{2pq}$.

62. *Concept Check* If you are given the following problem, what must be the polynomial that is represented by the question mark?

$$\dfrac{4y + 12}{2y - 10} \div \dfrac{?}{y^2 - y - 20} = \dfrac{2(y + 4)}{y - 3}$$

PREVIEW EXERCISES

*Write the prime factored form of each number. **See Section 1.1.***

63. 18   **64.** 48   **65.** 108   **66.** 60

*Find the greatest common factor of each group of terms. **See Section 5.1.***

67. $24m, 18m^2, 6$ **68.** $14t^2, 28t, 7$ **69.** $84q^3, 90q^6$ **70.** $54k^3, 36k^4$

Least Common Denominators

OBJECTIVES

1 Find the least common denominator for a group of fractions.

2 Write equivalent rational expressions.

OBJECTIVE 1 **Find the least common denominator for a group of fractions.** Adding or subtracting rational expressions often requires a **least common denominator (LCD).** The LCD is the simplest expression that is divisible by all of the denominators in all of the expressions. For example, the fractions

$$\frac{2}{9} \quad \text{and} \quad \frac{5}{12} \quad \text{have LCD 36,}$$

because 36 is the least positive number divisible by both 9 and 12.

We can often find least common denominators by inspection. In other cases, we find the LCD by a procedure similar to that used in **Section 5.1** for finding the greatest common factor.

Finding the Least Common Denominator (LCD)

Step 1 **Factor** each denominator into prime factors.

Step 2 **List each different denominator factor** the *greatest* number of times it appears in any of the denominators.

Step 3 **Multiply** the denominator factors from Step 2 to get the LCD.

When each denominator is factored into prime factors, every prime factor must be a factor of the least common denominator.

NOW TRY
EXERCISE 1

Find the LCD for each pair of fractions.

(a) $\dfrac{5}{48}, \dfrac{1}{30}$ (b) $\dfrac{3}{10y}, \dfrac{1}{6y}$

EXAMPLE 1 Finding the LCD

Find the LCD for each pair of fractions.

(a) $\dfrac{1}{24}, \dfrac{7}{15}$ (b) $\dfrac{1}{8x}, \dfrac{3}{10x}$

Step 1 Write each denominator in factored form with numerical coefficients in prime factored form.

$$24 = 2 \cdot 2 \cdot 2 \cdot 3 = 2^3 \cdot 3 \qquad\qquad 8x = 2 \cdot 2 \cdot 2 \cdot x = 2^3 \cdot x$$
$$15 = 3 \cdot 5 \qquad\qquad\qquad\qquad 10x = 2 \cdot 5 \cdot x$$

Step 2 Find the LCD by taking each different factor the *greatest* number of times it appears as a factor in any of the denominators.

The factor 2 appears three times in one product and not at all in the other, so the greatest number of times 2 appears is three. The greatest number of times both 3 and 5 appear is one.

Here, 2 appears three times in one product and once in the other, so the greatest number of times 2 appears is three. The greatest number of times 5 appears is one, and the greatest number of times x appears in either product is one.

Step 3 $\text{LCD} = 2 \cdot 2 \cdot 2 \cdot 3 \cdot 5$
$$= 2^3 \cdot 3 \cdot 5$$
$$= 120$$

$\text{LCD} = 2 \cdot 2 \cdot 2 \cdot 5 \cdot x$
$$= 2^3 \cdot 5 \cdot x$$
$$= 40x \qquad \text{NOW TRY}$$

NOW TRY ANSWERS
1. (a) 240 **(b)** 30y

NOW TRY
EXERCISE 2

Find the LCD for the pair of fractions.

$$\frac{5}{6x^4} \quad \text{and} \quad \frac{7}{8x^3}$$

EXAMPLE 2 Finding the LCD

Find the LCD for $\dfrac{5}{6r^2}$ and $\dfrac{3}{4r^3}$.

Step 1 Factor each denominator.

$$6r^2 = 2 \cdot 3 \cdot r^2$$
$$4r^3 = 2 \cdot 2 \cdot r^3 = 2^2 \cdot r^3$$

Step 2 The greatest number of times 2 appears is two, the greatest number of times 3 appears is one, and the greatest number of times r appears is three.

Step 3 $\qquad\qquad$ LCD $= 2^2 \cdot 3 \cdot r^3 = 12r^3$ $\qquad$ NOW TRY

⚠ **CAUTION** When finding the LCD, use each factor the *greatest* number of times it appears in any *single* denominator, not the *total* number of times it appears. For instance, the greatest number of times r appears as a factor in one denominator in **Example 2** is 3, *not* 5.

NOW TRY
EXERCISE 3

Find the LCD for the fractions in each list.

(a) $\dfrac{3t}{2t^2 - 10t}, \dfrac{t + 4}{t^2 - 25}$

(b) $\dfrac{1}{x^2 + 7x + 12}$,

$\dfrac{2}{x^2 + 6x + 9}, \dfrac{5}{x^2 + 2x - 8}$

(c) $\dfrac{2}{a - 4}, \dfrac{1}{4 - a}$

EXAMPLE 3 Finding LCDs

Find the LCD for the fractions in each list.

(a) $\dfrac{6}{5m}, \dfrac{4}{m^2 - 3m}$

$$\left.\begin{array}{l} 5m = 5 \cdot m \\ m^2 - 3m = m(m - 3) \end{array}\right\} \text{Factor each denominator.}$$

Use each different factor the greatest number of times it appears.

$$\text{LCD} = 5 \cdot m \cdot (m - 3) = 5m(m - 3)$$

Be sure to include m as a factor in the LCD.

Because m is not a *factor* of $m - 3$, both m and $m - 3$ must appear in the LCD.

(b) $\dfrac{1}{r^2 - 4r - 5}, \dfrac{3}{r^2 - r - 20}, \dfrac{1}{r^2 - 10r + 25}$

$$\left.\begin{array}{l} r^2 - 4r - 5 = (r - 5)(r + 1) \\ r^2 - r - 20 = (r - 5)(r + 4) \\ r^2 - 10r + 25 = (r - 5)^2 \end{array}\right\} \text{Factor each denominator.}$$

Use each different factor the greatest number of times it appears as a factor.

$$\text{LCD} = (r - 5)^2(r + 1)(r + 4)$$

Be sure to include the exponent 2.

(c) $\dfrac{1}{q - 5}, \dfrac{3}{5 - q}$

The expressions $q - 5$ and $5 - q$ are opposites of each other. This means that if we multiply $q - 5$ by -1, we will get $5 - q$.

$$-(q - 5) = -q + 5 = 5 - q$$

Therefore, either $q - 5$ or $5 - q$ can be used as the LCD. $\qquad$ NOW TRY

NOW TRY ANSWERS
2. $24x^4$
3. (a) $2t(t - 5)(t + 5)$
  (b) $(x + 3)^2(x + 4)(x - 2)$
  (c) either $a - 4$ or $4 - a$

OBJECTIVE 2 **Write equivalent rational expressions.** Once the LCD has been found, the next step in preparing to add or subtract two rational expressions is to use the fundamental property to write equivalent rational expressions.

Writing a Rational Expression with a Specified Denominator

Step 1 **Factor** both denominators.

Step 2 **Decide what factor(s) the denominator must be multiplied by** in order to equal the specified denominator.

Step 3 **Multiply** the rational expression by that factor divided by itself. (That is, multiply by 1.)

NOW TRY
EXERCISE 4

Rewrite each rational expression with the indicated denominator.

(a) $\dfrac{2}{9} = \dfrac{?}{27}$ (b) $\dfrac{4t}{11} = \dfrac{?}{33t}$

EXAMPLE 4 Writing Equivalent Rational Expressions

Rewrite each rational expression with the indicated denominator.

(a) $\dfrac{3}{8} = \dfrac{?}{40}$ (b) $\dfrac{9k}{25} = \dfrac{?}{50k}$

Step 1 For each example, first factor the denominator on the right. Then compare the denominator on the left with the one on the right to decide what factors are missing. (It may sometimes be necessary to factor both denominators.)

$$\frac{3}{8} = \frac{?}{5 \cdot 8} \qquad\qquad \frac{9k}{25} = \frac{?}{25 \cdot 2k}$$

Step 2 A factor of 5 is missing. Factors of 2 and k are missing.

Step 3 Multiply $\frac{3}{8}$ by $\frac{5}{5}$. Multiply $\frac{9k}{25}$ by $\frac{2k}{2k}$.

$$\frac{3}{8} = \frac{3}{8} \cdot \frac{5}{5} = \frac{15}{40} \qquad\qquad \frac{9k}{25} = \frac{9k}{25} \cdot \frac{2k}{2k} = \frac{18k^2}{50k}$$

$$\frac{5}{5} = 1 \uparrow \qquad\qquad\qquad\qquad \frac{2k}{2k} = 1 \uparrow$$

NOW TRY

EXAMPLE 5 Writing Equivalent Rational Expressions

Rewrite each rational expression with the indicated denominator.

(a)
$$\frac{8}{3x + 1} = \frac{?}{12x + 4}$$

$$\frac{8}{3x + 1} = \frac{?}{4(3x + 1)} \leftarrow \text{Factor the denominator on the right.}$$

The missing factor is 4, so multiply the fraction on the left by $\frac{4}{4}$.

$$\frac{8}{3x + 1} \cdot \frac{4}{4} = \frac{32}{12x + 4} \qquad \text{Fundamental property}$$

NOW TRY ANSWERS

4. (a) $\dfrac{6}{27}$ (b) $\dfrac{12t^2}{33t}$

NOW TRY
EXERCISE 5

Rewrite each rational expression with the indicated denominator.

(a) $\dfrac{8k}{5k - 2} = \dfrac{?}{25k - 10}$

(b) $\dfrac{2t - 1}{t^2 + 4t} = \dfrac{?}{t^3 + 12t^2 + 32t}$

(b) $\dfrac{12p}{p^2 + 8p} = \dfrac{?}{p^3 + 4p^2 - 32p}$

Factor the denominator in each rational expression.

$$\frac{12p}{p(p + 8)} = \frac{?}{p(p + 8)(p - 4)}$$

$$\boxed{\begin{aligned} p^3 + 4p^2 - 32p \\ = p(p^2 + 4p - 32) \\ = p(p + 8)(p - 4) \end{aligned}}$$

The factor $p - 4$ is missing, so multiply $\dfrac{12p}{p(p + 8)}$ by $\dfrac{p - 4}{p - 4}$.

$$\frac{12p}{p^2 + 8p} = \frac{12p}{p(p + 8)} \cdot \frac{p - 4}{p - 4} \qquad \text{Fundamental property}$$

$$= \frac{12p(p - 4)}{p(p + 8)(p - 4)} \qquad \begin{array}{l}\text{Multiply numerators.}\\ \text{Multiply denominators.}\end{array}$$

$$= \frac{12p^2 - 48p}{p^3 + 4p^2 - 32p} \qquad \text{Multiply the factors.} \qquad \textit{NOW TRY}$$

NOW TRY ANSWERS

5. (a) $\dfrac{40k}{25k - 10}$

(b) $\dfrac{2t^2 + 15t - 8}{t^3 + 12t^2 + 32t}$

NOTE While it is beneficial to leave the denominator in factored form, we multiplied the factors in the denominator in **Example 5** to give the answer in the same form as the original problem.

6.3 EXERCISES

MyMathLab | Math XL PRACTICE | WATCH | DOWNLOAD | READ | REVIEW

⊕ *Complete solution available on the Video Resources on DVD*

Concept Check   Choose the correct response in Exercises 1–4.

1. Suppose that the greatest common factor of x and y is 1. What is the least common denominator for $\frac{1}{x}$ and $\frac{1}{y}$?

    A. x **B.** y **C.** xy **D.** 1

2. If x is a factor of y, what is the least common denominator for $\frac{1}{x}$ and $\frac{1}{y}$?

    A. x **B.** y **C.** xy **D.** 1

3. What is the least common denominator for $\frac{9}{20}$ and $\frac{1}{2}$?

    A. 40   **B.** 2   **C.** 20   **D.** none of these

4. Suppose that we wish to write the fraction $\dfrac{1}{(x - 4)^2(y - 3)}$ with denominator $(x - 4)^3(y - 3)^2$. By what must we multiply both the numerator and the denominator?

    A. $(x - 4)(y - 3)$ **B.** $(x - 4)^2$ **C.** $x - 4$ **D.** $(x - 4)^2(y - 3)$

Find the LCD for the fractions in each list. See Examples 1–3.

⊕ 5. $\dfrac{7}{15}, \dfrac{21}{20}$

6. $\dfrac{9}{10}, \dfrac{13}{25}$

7. $\dfrac{17}{100}, \dfrac{23}{120}, \dfrac{43}{180}$

8. $\dfrac{17}{250}, \dfrac{21}{300}, \dfrac{1}{360}$

9. $\dfrac{9}{x^2}, \dfrac{8}{x^5}$

10. $\dfrac{12}{m^7}, \dfrac{14}{m^8}$

11. $\dfrac{-2}{5p}, \dfrac{13}{6p}$

12. $\dfrac{-14}{15k}, \dfrac{11}{4k}$

⊕ 13. $\dfrac{17}{15y^2}, \dfrac{55}{36y^4}$

14. $\dfrac{4}{25m^3}, \dfrac{7}{10m^4}$

15. $\dfrac{5}{21r^3}, \dfrac{7}{12r^5}$

16. $\dfrac{6}{35t^2}, \dfrac{5}{49t^6}$

17. $\dfrac{13}{5a^2b^3}, \dfrac{29}{15a^5b}$

18. $\dfrac{7}{3r^4s^5}, \dfrac{23}{9r^6s^8}$

🌐 19. $\dfrac{7}{6p}, \dfrac{15}{4p - 8}$

20. $\dfrac{7}{8k}, \dfrac{28}{12k - 24}$

21. $\dfrac{9}{28m^2}, \dfrac{3}{12m - 20}$

22. $\dfrac{14}{27a^3}, \dfrac{7}{9a - 45}$

23. $\dfrac{7}{5b - 10}, \dfrac{11}{6b - 12}$

24. $\dfrac{3}{7x^2 + 21x}, \dfrac{2}{5x^2 + 15x}$

25. $\dfrac{37}{6r - 12}, \dfrac{25}{9r - 18}$

26. $\dfrac{14}{5p - 30}, \dfrac{11}{6p - 36}$

27. $\dfrac{5}{12p + 60}, \dfrac{-17}{p^2 + 5p}, \dfrac{-16}{p^2 + 10p + 25}$

28. $\dfrac{13}{r^2 + 7r}, \dfrac{-3}{5r + 35}, \dfrac{-4}{r^2 + 14r + 49}$

29. $\dfrac{-3}{8y + 16}, \dfrac{-22}{y^2 + 3y + 2}$

30. $\dfrac{-2}{9m - 18}, \dfrac{-6}{m^2 - 7m + 10}$

31. $\dfrac{5}{c - d}, \dfrac{8}{d - c}$

32. $\dfrac{4}{y - x}, \dfrac{8}{x - y}$

33. $\dfrac{12}{m - 3}, \dfrac{-4}{3 - m}$

34. $\dfrac{3}{a - 8}, \dfrac{-17}{8 - a}$

35. $\dfrac{29}{p - q}, \dfrac{18}{q - p}$

36. $\dfrac{16}{z - x}, \dfrac{9}{x - z}$

37. $\dfrac{3}{k^2 + 5k}, \dfrac{2}{k^2 + 3k - 10}$

38. $\dfrac{1}{z^2 - 4z}, \dfrac{9}{z^2 - 3z - 4}$

39. $\dfrac{6}{a^2 + 6a}, \dfrac{-5}{a^2 + 3a - 18}$

40. $\dfrac{8}{y^2 - 5y}, \dfrac{-5}{y^2 - 2y - 15}$

41. $\dfrac{5}{p^2 + 8p + 15}, \dfrac{3}{p^2 - 3p - 18}, \dfrac{12}{p^2 - p - 30}$

42. $\dfrac{10}{y^2 - 10y + 21}, \dfrac{2}{y^2 - 2y - 3}, \dfrac{15}{y^2 - 6y - 7}$

43. $\dfrac{-5}{k^2 + 2k - 35}, \dfrac{-8}{k^2 + 3k - 40}, \dfrac{19}{k^2 - 2k - 15}$

44. $\dfrac{-19}{z^2 + 4z - 12}, \dfrac{-16}{z^2 + z - 30}, \dfrac{16}{z^2 + 2z - 24}$

RELATING CONCEPTS   EXERCISES 45–50

FOR INDIVIDUAL OR GROUP WORK

Work Exercises 45–50 in order.

45. Suppose that you want to write $\frac{3}{4}$ as an equivalent fraction with denominator 28. By what number must you multiply both the numerator and the denominator?

46. If you write $\frac{3}{4}$ as an equivalent fraction with denominator 28, by what number are you actually multiplying the fraction?

47. What property of multiplication is being used when we write a common fraction as an equivalent one with a larger denominator? (See **Section 1.7.**)

48. Suppose that you want to write $\frac{2x + 5}{x - 4}$ as an equivalent fraction with denominator $7x - 28$. By what number must you multiply both the numerator and the denominator?

49. If you write $\frac{2x + 5}{x - 4}$ as an equivalent fraction with denominator $7x - 28$, by what number are you actually multiplying the fraction?

50. Repeat **Exercise 47,** changing "a common" to "an algebraic."

Rewrite each rational expression with the indicated denominator. See Examples 4 and 5.

51. $\dfrac{4}{11} = \dfrac{?}{55}$ 　　　　　 **52.** $\dfrac{8}{7} = \dfrac{?}{42}$ 　　　　　 **53.** $\dfrac{-5}{k} = \dfrac{?}{9k}$

54. $\dfrac{-4}{q} = \dfrac{?}{6q}$ 　　　　　 **55.** $\dfrac{15m^2}{8k} = \dfrac{?}{32k^4}$ 　　　　　 **56.** $\dfrac{7t^2}{3y} = \dfrac{?}{9y^2}$

57. $\dfrac{19z}{2z - 6} = \dfrac{?}{6z - 18}$ 　　　　　 **58.** $\dfrac{3r}{5r - 5} = \dfrac{?}{15r - 15}$

59. $\dfrac{-2a}{9a - 18} = \dfrac{?}{18a - 36}$ 　　　　　 **60.** $\dfrac{-7y}{6y + 18} = \dfrac{?}{24y + 72}$

61. $\dfrac{6}{k^2 - 4k} = \dfrac{?}{k(k - 4)(k + 1)}$ 　　　　　 **62.** $\dfrac{25}{m^2 - 9m} = \dfrac{?}{m(m - 9)(m + 8)}$

63. $\dfrac{36r}{r^2 - r - 6} = \dfrac{?}{(r - 3)(r + 2)(r + 1)}$

64. $\dfrac{4m}{m^2 + m - 2} = \dfrac{?}{(m - 1)(m - 3)(m + 2)}$

65. $\dfrac{a + 2b}{2a^2 + ab - b^2} = \dfrac{?}{2a^3b + a^2b^2 - ab^3}$

66. $\dfrac{m - 4}{6m^2 + 7m - 3} = \dfrac{?}{12m^3 + 14m^2 - 6m}$

67. $\dfrac{4r - t}{r^2 + rt + t^2} = \dfrac{?}{t^3 - r^3}$ 　　　　　 **68.** $\dfrac{3x - 1}{x^2 + 2x + 4} = \dfrac{?}{x^3 - 8}$

69. $\dfrac{2(z - y)}{y^2 + yz + z^2} = \dfrac{?}{y^4 - z^3y}$ 　　　　　 **70.** $\dfrac{2p + 3q}{p^2 + 2pq + q^2} = \dfrac{?}{(p + q)(p^3 + q^3)}$

PREVIEW EXERCISES

Add or subtract as indicated. Write each answer in lowest terms. See Section 1.1.

71. $\dfrac{1}{2} + \dfrac{7}{8}$ 　　　 **72.** $\dfrac{2}{3} + \dfrac{8}{27}$ 　　　 **73.** $\dfrac{7}{5} - \dfrac{3}{4}$ 　　　 **74.** $\dfrac{11}{6} - \dfrac{2}{5}$

6.4 Adding and Subtracting Rational Expressions

OBJECTIVES

1 Add rational expressions having the same denominator.

2 Add rational expressions having different denominators.

3 Subtract rational expressions.

OBJECTIVE 1 **Add rational expressions having the same denominator.**
We find the sum of two rational expressions with the same denominator using the same procedure that we used in **Section 1.1** for adding two common fractions.

Adding Rational Expressions (Same Denominator)

The rational expressions $\dfrac{P}{Q}$ and $\dfrac{R}{Q}$ ($Q \neq 0$) are added as follows.

$$\frac{P}{Q} + \frac{R}{Q} = \frac{P + R}{Q}$$

That is, to add rational expressions with the same denominator, add the numerators and keep the same denominator.

**NOW TRY
EXERCISE 1**
Add. Write each answer in
lowest terms.

(a) $\dfrac{2}{7k} + \dfrac{4}{7k}$

(b) $\dfrac{4y}{y+3} + \dfrac{12}{y+3}$

EXAMPLE 1 Adding Rational Expressions (Same Denominator)

Add. Write each answer in lowest terms.

(a) $\dfrac{4}{9} + \dfrac{2}{9}$ (b) $\dfrac{3x}{x+1} + \dfrac{3}{x+1}$

The denominators are the same, so the sum is found by adding the two numerators and keeping the same (common) denominator.

$= \dfrac{4+2}{9}$ Add.

$= \dfrac{6}{9}$

$= \dfrac{2 \cdot 3}{3 \cdot 3}$ Factor.

$= \dfrac{2}{3}$ Lowest terms

$= \dfrac{3x+3}{x+1}$ Add.

$= \dfrac{3(x+1)}{x+1}$ Factor.

$= 3$ Lowest terms

NOW TRY

OBJECTIVE 2 **Add rational expressions having different denominators.**
As in **Section 1.1,** we use the following steps to add fractions having different denominators.

Adding Rational Expressions (Different Denominators)

Step 1   **Find the least common denominator (LCD).**

Step 2   **Rewrite each rational expression** as an equivalent rational expression with the LCD as the denominator.

Step 3   **Add** the numerators to get the numerator of the sum. The LCD is the denominator of the sum.

Step 4   **Write in lowest terms** using the fundamental property.

EXAMPLE 2 Adding Rational Expressions (Different Denominators)

Add. Write each answer in lowest terms.

(a) $\dfrac{1}{12} + \dfrac{7}{15}$ (b) $\dfrac{2}{3y} + \dfrac{1}{4y}$

Step 1   First find the LCD, using the methods of the previous section.

$12 = 2 \cdot 2 \cdot 3 = 2^2 \cdot 3$ $3y = 3 \cdot y$

$15 = 3 \cdot 5$ $4y = 2 \cdot 2 \cdot y = 2^2 \cdot y$

$LCD = 2^2 \cdot 3 \cdot 5 = 60$ $LCD = 2^2 \cdot 3 \cdot y = 12y$

Step 2   Now rewrite each rational expression as a fraction with the LCD (60 and 12y, respectively) as the denominator.

$\dfrac{1}{12} + \dfrac{7}{15} = \dfrac{1(5)}{12(5)} + \dfrac{7(4)}{15(4)}$ $\dfrac{2}{3y} + \dfrac{1}{4y} = \dfrac{2(4)}{3y(4)} + \dfrac{1(3)}{4y(3)}$

$= \dfrac{5}{60} + \dfrac{28}{60}$ $= \dfrac{8}{12y} + \dfrac{3}{12y}$

NOW TRY ANSWERS
1. (a) $\frac{6}{7k}$ (b) 4

Add. Write each answer in lowest terms.

(a) $\dfrac{5}{12} + \dfrac{3}{20}$ (b) $\dfrac{3}{5x} + \dfrac{2}{7x}$

Step 3 Add the numerators. The LCD is the denominator.

Step 4 Write in lowest terms if necessary.

$$= \frac{5 + 28}{60} \qquad\qquad = \frac{8 + 3}{12y}$$

$$= \frac{33}{60}, \quad \text{or} \quad \frac{11}{20} \qquad = \frac{11}{12y}$$

NOW TRY

Add. Write the answer in lowest terms.

$$\frac{6t}{t^2 - 9} + \frac{-3}{t + 3}$$

EXAMPLE 3 Adding Rational Expressions

Add. Write the answer in lowest terms.

$$\frac{2x}{x^2 - 1} + \frac{-1}{x + 1}$$

Step 1 Since the denominators are different, find the LCD.

$$\left. \begin{array}{l} x^2 - 1 = (x + 1)(x - 1) \\ x + 1 \text{ is prime.} \end{array} \right\} \text{ The LCD is } (x + 1)(x - 1).$$

Step 2 Rewrite each rational expression with the LCD as the denominator.

$$\frac{2x}{x^2 - 1} + \frac{-1}{x + 1} \qquad\qquad \text{LCD} = (x + 1)(x - 1)$$

$$= \frac{2x}{(x + 1)(x - 1)} + \frac{-1(x - 1)}{(x + 1)(x - 1)} \qquad \text{Multiply the second fraction by } \frac{x - 1}{x - 1}.$$

$$= \frac{2x}{(x + 1)(x - 1)} + \frac{-x + 1}{(x + 1)(x - 1)} \qquad \text{Distributive property}$$

Step 3 $$= \frac{2x - x + 1}{(x + 1)(x - 1)} \qquad\qquad \begin{array}{l} \text{Add numerators.} \\ \text{Keep the same denominator.} \end{array}$$

$$= \frac{x + 1}{(x + 1)(x - 1)} \qquad\qquad \text{Combine like terms.}$$

Step 4 $$= \frac{1(x + 1)}{(x + 1)(x - 1)} \qquad\qquad \begin{array}{l} \text{Identity property of} \\ \text{multiplication} \end{array}$$

Remember to write 1 in the numerator. $$= \frac{1}{x - 1} \qquad\qquad \begin{array}{l} \text{Divide out the common} \\ \text{factors.} \end{array}$$

NOW TRY

EXAMPLE 4 Adding Rational Expressions

Add. Write the answer in lowest terms.

$$\frac{2x}{x^2 + 5x + 6} + \frac{x + 1}{x^2 + 2x - 3}$$

$$= \frac{2x}{(x + 2)(x + 3)} + \frac{x + 1}{(x + 3)(x - 1)} \qquad \begin{array}{l} \text{Factor the} \\ \text{denominators.} \end{array}$$

$$= \frac{2x(x - 1)}{(x + 2)(x + 3)(x - 1)} + \frac{(x + 1)(x + 2)}{(x + 2)(x + 3)(x - 1)} \qquad \begin{array}{l} \text{The LCD is} \\ (x + 2)(x + 3)(x - 1). \end{array}$$

NOW TRY ANSWERS

2. (a) $\frac{17}{30}$ (b) $\frac{31}{35x}$

3. $\frac{3}{t - 3}$

NOW TRY
EXERCISE 4

Add. Write the answer in lowest terms.

$$\frac{x - 1}{x^2 + 6x + 8} + \frac{4x}{x^2 + x - 12}$$

$$= \frac{2x(x - 1) + (x + 1)(x + 2)}{(x + 2)(x + 3)(x - 1)}$$ Add numerators.
Keep the same denominator.

$$= \frac{2x^2 - 2x + x^2 + 3x + 2}{(x + 2)(x + 3)(x - 1)}$$ Multiply.

$$= \frac{3x^2 + x + 2}{(x + 2)(x + 3)(x - 1)}$$ Combine like terms.

The numerator cannot be factored here, so the expression is in lowest terms.

NOW TRY

NOTE If the final expression in **Example 4** could be written in lower terms, the numerator would have a factor of $x + 2$, $x + 3$, or $x - 1$. Therefore, it is only necessary to check for possible factored forms of the numerator that would contain one of these binomials.

NOW TRY
EXERCISE 5

Add. Write the answer in lowest terms.

$$\frac{2k}{k - 7} + \frac{5}{7 - k}$$

EXAMPLE 5 Adding Rational Expressions (Denominators Are Opposites)

Add. Write the answer in lowest terms.

$$\frac{y}{y - 2} + \frac{8}{2 - y}$$

The denominators are opposites. Use the process of multiplying one of the fractions by 1 in the form $\frac{-1}{-1}$ to get the same denominator for both fractions.

$$= \frac{y}{y - 2} + \frac{8(-1)}{(2 - y)(-1)}$$ Multiply $\frac{8}{2 - y}$ by $\frac{-1}{-1}$.

$$= \frac{y}{y - 2} + \frac{-8}{-2 + y}$$ Distributive property

$$= \frac{y}{y - 2} + \frac{-8}{y - 2}$$ Rewrite $-2 + y$ as $y - 2$.

$$= \frac{y - 8}{y - 2}$$ Add numerators.
Keep the same denominator.

If we had chosen $2 - y$ as the common denominator, the final answer would be $\frac{8 - y}{2 - y}$, which is equivalent to $\frac{y - 8}{y - 2}$.

NOW TRY

OBJECTIVE 3 Subtract rational expressions.

Subtracting Rational Expressions (Same Denominator)

The rational expressions $\frac{P}{Q}$ and $\frac{R}{Q}$ ($Q \neq 0$) are subtracted as follows.

$$\frac{P}{Q} - \frac{R}{Q} = \frac{P - R}{Q}$$

That is, to subtract rational expressions with the same denominator, subtract the numerators and keep the same denominator.

NOW TRY ANSWERS

4. $\dfrac{5x^2 + 4x + 3}{(x + 4)(x + 2)(x - 3)}$

5. $\dfrac{2k - 5}{k - 7}$, or $\dfrac{5 - 2k}{7 - k}$

NOW TRY
EXERCISE 6
Subtract. Write the answer in lowest terms.

$$\frac{2x}{x+5} - \frac{x+1}{x+5}$$

EXAMPLE 6 Subtracting Rational Expressions (Same Denominator)

Subtract. Write the answer in lowest terms.

$$\frac{2m}{m-1} - \frac{m+3}{m-1}$$

> Use parentheses around the numerator of the subtrahend.

$$= \frac{2m - (m+3)}{m-1}$$ Subtract numerators. Keep the same denominator.

> Be careful with signs.

$$= \frac{2m - m - 3}{m-1}$$ Distributive property

$$= \frac{m-3}{m-1}$$ Combine like terms.   NOW TRY

⚠ **CAUTION** Sign errors often occur in subtraction problems like the one in **Example 6.** The numerator of the fraction being subtracted must be treated as a single quantity. ***Be sure to use parentheses after the subtraction symbol.***

NOW TRY
EXERCISE 7
Subtract. Write the answer in lowest terms.

$$\frac{6}{y-6} - \frac{2}{y}$$

EXAMPLE 7 Subtracting Rational Expressions (Different Denominators)

Subtract. Write the answer in lowest terms.

$$\frac{9}{x-2} - \frac{3}{x}$$ The LCD is $x(x-2)$.

$$= \frac{9x}{x(x-2)} - \frac{3(x-2)}{x(x-2)}$$ Write each expression with the LCD.

$$= \frac{9x - 3(x-2)}{x(x-2)}$$ Subtract numerators. Keep the same denominator.

> Be careful with signs.

$$= \frac{9x - 3x + 6}{x(x-2)}$$ Distributive property

$$= \frac{6x+6}{x(x-2)}, \quad \text{or} \quad \frac{6(x+1)}{x(x-2)}$$ Combine like terms. Factor the numerator.   NOW TRY

NOTE We factored the final numerator in **Example 7** to get $\frac{6(x+1)}{x(x-2)}$. The fundamental property does not apply, however since there are no common factors to divide out. The answer is in lowest terms.

EXAMPLE 8 Subtracting Rational Expressions (Denominators Are Opposites)

Subtract. Write the answer in lowest terms.

$$\frac{3x}{x-5} - \frac{2x-25}{5-x}$$ The denominators are opposites. We choose $x-5$ as the common denominator.

$$= \frac{3x}{x-5} - \frac{(2x-25)(-1)}{(5-x)(-1)}$$ Multiply $\frac{2x-25}{5-x}$ by $\frac{-1}{-1}$ to get a common denominator.

$$= \frac{3x}{x-5} - \frac{-2x+25}{x-5}$$ $(5-x)(-1) = -5 + x = x - 5$

NOW TRY ANSWERS
6. $\frac{x-1}{x+5}$
7. $\frac{4(y+3)}{y(y-6)}$

NOW TRY
EXERCISE 8

Subtract. Write the answer in lowest terms.

$$\frac{2m}{m-4} - \frac{m-12}{4-m}$$

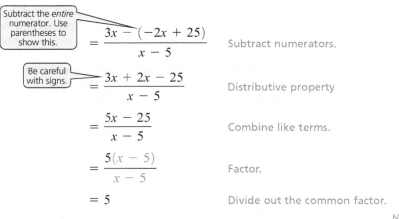

Subtract the *entire* numerator. Use parentheses to show this.

$$= \frac{3x - (-2x + 25)}{x - 5}$$ Subtract numerators.

Be careful with signs.

$$= \frac{3x + 2x - 25}{x - 5}$$ Distributive property

$$= \frac{5x - 25}{x - 5}$$ Combine like terms.

$$= \frac{5(x-5)}{x-5}$$ Factor.

$$= 5$$ Divide out the common factor.

NOW TRY

NOW TRY
EXERCISE 9

Subtract. Write the answer in lowest terms.

$$\frac{5}{t^2 - 6t + 9} - \frac{2t}{t^2 - 9}$$

EXAMPLE 9   **Subtracting Rational Expressions**

Subtract. Write the answer in lowest terms.

$$\frac{6x}{x^2 - 2x + 1} - \frac{1}{x^2 - 1}$$

$$= \frac{6x}{(x-1)^2} - \frac{1}{(x-1)(x+1)}$$ Factor the denominators. LCD = $(x-1)(x-1)(x+1)$, or $(x-1)^2(x+1)$

$$= \frac{6x(x+1)}{(x-1)^2(x+1)} - \frac{1(x-1)}{(x-1)(x-1)(x+1)}$$ Fundamental property

$$= \frac{6x(x+1) - 1(x-1)}{(x-1)^2(x+1)}$$ Subtract numerators.

$$= \frac{6x^2 + 6x - x + 1}{(x-1)^2(x+1)}$$ Distributive property

$$= \frac{6x^2 + 5x + 1}{(x-1)^2(x+1)}, \quad \text{or} \quad \frac{(2x+1)(3x+1)}{(x-1)^2(x+1)}$$ Combine like terms. Factor the numerator.

NOW TRY

NOW TRY ANSWERS
8. 3
9. $\dfrac{-2t^2 + 11t + 15}{(t-3)^2(t+3)}$

6.4 EXERCISES   **MyMathLab**   **Math XL** PRACTICE   WATCH   DOWNLOAD   READ   REVIEW

🌐 Complete solution available on the Video Resources on DVD

Concept Check   *Match each expression in Column I with the correct sum or difference in Column II.*

I

1. $\dfrac{x}{x+8} + \dfrac{8}{x+8}$ **2.** $\dfrac{2x}{x-8} - \dfrac{16}{x-8}$

3. $\dfrac{8}{x-8} - \dfrac{x}{x-8}$ **4.** $\dfrac{8}{x+8} - \dfrac{x}{x+8}$

5. $\dfrac{x}{x+8} - \dfrac{8}{x+8}$ **6.** $\dfrac{1}{x} + \dfrac{1}{8}$

7. $\dfrac{1}{8} - \dfrac{1}{x}$ **8.** $\dfrac{1}{8x} - \dfrac{1}{8x}$

II

A. 2   **B.** $\dfrac{x-8}{x+8}$

C. -1 **D.** $\dfrac{8+x}{8x}$

E. 1   **F.** 0

G. $\dfrac{x-8}{8x}$ **H.** $\dfrac{8-x}{x+8}$

PREVIEW EXERCISES

Perform the indicated operations, using the order of operations as necessary. ***See Section 1.1.***

77. $\dfrac{\frac{5}{6}}{\frac{2}{3}}$ **78.** $\dfrac{\frac{3}{8}}{\frac{1}{4}}$ **79.** $\dfrac{\frac{3}{2}}{\frac{7}{4}}$ **80.** $\dfrac{\frac{5}{7}}{\frac{5}{3}}$

6.5 Complex Fractions

OBJECTIVES

1 Simplify a complex fraction by writing it as a division problem (Method 1).

2 Simplify a complex fraction by multiplying numerator and denominator by the least common denominator (Method 2).

3 Simplify rational expressions with negative exponents.

The quotient of two mixed numbers in arithmetic, such as $2\frac{1}{2} \div 3\frac{1}{4}$, can be written as a fraction.

$$2\frac{1}{2} \div 3\frac{1}{4} = \frac{2\frac{1}{2}}{3\frac{1}{4}} = \frac{2 + \frac{1}{2}}{3 + \frac{1}{4}}$$

We do this to illustrate a *complex fraction.*

In algebra, some rational expressions have fractions in the numerator, or denominator, or both.

Complex Fraction

A quotient with one or more fractions in the numerator, or denominator, or both, is called a **complex fraction.**

$$\frac{2 + \frac{1}{2}}{3 + \frac{1}{4}}, \quad \frac{\frac{3x^2 - 5x}{6x^2}}{2x - \frac{1}{x}}, \quad \text{and} \quad \frac{3 + x}{5 - \frac{2}{x}} \qquad \text{Complex fractions}$$

The parts of a complex fraction are named as follows.

$$\left.\frac{\frac{2}{p} - \frac{1}{q}}{\frac{3}{p} + \frac{5}{q}}\right\}$$

$\leftarrow$ Numerator of complex fraction
$\leftarrow$ Main fraction bar
$\leftarrow$ Denominator of complex fraction

OBJECTIVE 1 **Simplify a complex fraction by writing it as a division problem (Method 1).** Since the main fraction bar represents division in a complex fraction, one method of simplifying a complex fraction involves division.

Method 1 for Simplifying a Complex Fraction

Step 1 Write both the numerator and denominator as single fractions.

Step 2 Change the complex fraction to a division problem.

Step 3 Perform the indicated division.

NOW TRY
EXERCISE 1

Simplify each complex fraction.

(a) $\dfrac{\dfrac{2}{5}+\dfrac{1}{4}}{\dfrac{1}{6}+\dfrac{3}{8}}$ **(b)** $\dfrac{2+\dfrac{4}{x}}{\dfrac{5}{6}+\dfrac{5x}{12}}$

EXAMPLE 1 Simplifying Complex Fractions (Method 1)

Simplify each complex fraction.

(a) $\dfrac{\dfrac{2}{3}+\dfrac{5}{9}}{\dfrac{1}{4}+\dfrac{1}{12}}$ **(b)** $\dfrac{6+\dfrac{3}{x}}{\dfrac{x}{4}+\dfrac{1}{8}}$

Step 1 First, write each numerator as a single fraction.

$$\frac{2}{3}+\frac{5}{9}=\frac{2(3)}{3(3)}+\frac{5}{9}$$
$$=\frac{6}{9}+\frac{5}{9}=\frac{11}{9}$$

$$6+\frac{3}{x}=\frac{6}{1}+\frac{3}{x}$$
$$=\frac{6x}{x}+\frac{3}{x}=\frac{6x+3}{x}$$

Now, write each denominator as a single fraction.

$$\frac{1}{4}+\frac{1}{12}=\frac{1(3)}{4(3)}+\frac{1}{12}$$
$$=\frac{3}{12}+\frac{1}{12}=\frac{4}{12}$$

$$\frac{x}{4}+\frac{1}{8}=\frac{x(2)}{4(2)}+\frac{1}{8}$$
$$=\frac{2x}{8}+\frac{1}{8}=\frac{2x+1}{8}$$

Step 2 Write the equivalent complex fraction as a division problem.

$$\frac{\dfrac{11}{9}}{\dfrac{4}{12}}=\frac{11}{9}\div\frac{4}{12}$$

$$\frac{\dfrac{6x+3}{x}}{\dfrac{2x+1}{8}}=\frac{6x+3}{x}\div\frac{2x+1}{8}$$

Step 3 Use the rule for division and the fundamental property.

Multiply by the reciprocal.

$$\frac{11}{9}\div\frac{4}{12}=\frac{11}{9}\cdot\frac{12}{4}$$
$$=\frac{11\cdot3\cdot4}{3\cdot3\cdot4}$$
$$=\frac{11}{3}$$

Multiply by the reciprocal.

$$\frac{6x+3}{x}\div\frac{2x+1}{8}=\frac{6x+3}{x}\cdot\frac{8}{2x+1}$$
$$=\frac{3(2x+1)}{x}\cdot\frac{8}{2x+1}$$
$$=\frac{24}{x}$$

NOW TRY

NOW TRY
EXERCISE 2

Simplify the complex fraction.

$$\frac{\dfrac{a^2b}{c}}{\dfrac{ab^2}{c^3}}$$

NOW TRY ANSWERS

1. (a) $\dfrac{6}{5}$ **(b)** $\dfrac{24}{5x}$

2. $\dfrac{ac^2}{b}$

EXAMPLE 2 Simplifying a Complex Fraction (Method 1)

Simplify the complex fraction.

$$\frac{\dfrac{xp}{q^3}}{\dfrac{p^2}{qx^2}}$$

The numerator and denominator are single fractions, so use the definition of division and then the fundamental property.

$$\frac{xp}{q^3}\div\frac{p^2}{qx^2}$$
$$=\frac{xp}{q^3}\cdot\frac{qx^2}{p^2}$$
$$=\frac{x^3}{q^2p}$$

NOW TRY

NOW TRY
EXERCISE 3

Simplify the complex fraction.

$$\dfrac{5 + \dfrac{2}{a - 3}}{\dfrac{1}{a - 3} - 2}$$

EXAMPLE 3 Simplifying a Complex Fraction (Method 1)

Simplify the complex fraction.

$$\dfrac{\dfrac{3}{x + 2} - 4}{\dfrac{2}{x + 2} + 1}$$

$$= \dfrac{\dfrac{3}{x + 2} - \dfrac{4(x + 2)}{x + 2}}{\dfrac{2}{x + 2} + \dfrac{1(x + 2)}{x + 2}} \qquad \text{Write both second terms with a denominator of } x + 2.$$

$$= \dfrac{\dfrac{3 - 4(x + 2)}{x + 2}}{\dfrac{2 + 1(x + 2)}{x + 2}} \qquad \begin{array}{l} \text{Subtract in the numerator.} \\[6pt] \text{Add in the denominator.} \end{array}$$

$$= \dfrac{\dfrac{3 - 4x - 8}{x + 2}}{\dfrac{2 + x + 2}{x + 2}} \qquad \text{Distributive property}$$

Be careful with signs.

$$= \dfrac{\dfrac{-5 - 4x}{x + 2}}{\dfrac{4 + x}{x + 2}} \qquad \text{Combine like terms.}$$

$$= \dfrac{-5 - 4x}{x + 2} \cdot \dfrac{x + 2}{4 + x} \qquad \text{Multiply by the reciprocal of the denominator (divisor).}$$

$$= \dfrac{-5 - 4x}{4 + x} \qquad \text{Divide out the common factor.}$$

NOW TRY

OBJECTIVE 2 **Simplify a complex fraction by multiplying numerator and denominator by the least common denominator (Method 2).** Any expression can be multiplied by a form of 1 to get an equivalent expression. Thus we can multiply both the numerator and the denominator of a complex fraction by the same nonzero expression to get an equivalent rational expression. If we choose the expression to be the LCD of all the fractions within the complex fraction, the complex fraction can then be simplified. This is Method 2.

Method 2 for Simplifying a Complex Fraction

Step 1 Find the LCD of all fractions within the complex fraction.

Step 2 Multiply both the numerator and the denominator of the complex fraction by this LCD using the distributive property as necessary. Write in lowest terms.

NOW TRY ANSWER
3. $\frac{5a - 13}{7 - 2a}$

NOW TRY
EXERCISE 4
Simplify each complex fraction.

(a) $\dfrac{\dfrac{3}{5} - \dfrac{1}{4}}{\dfrac{1}{8} + \dfrac{3}{20}}$ (b) $\dfrac{\dfrac{2}{x} - 3}{7 + \dfrac{x}{5}}$

EXAMPLE 4 Simplifying Complex Fractions (Method 2)

Simplify each complex fraction.

(a) $\dfrac{\dfrac{2}{3} + \dfrac{5}{9}}{\dfrac{1}{4} + \dfrac{1}{12}}$

(b) $\dfrac{6 + \dfrac{3}{x}}{\dfrac{x}{4} + \dfrac{1}{8}}$ (In **Example 1,** we simplified these same fractions using Method 1.)

Step 1 Find the LCD for all denominators in the complex fraction.

The LCD for 3, 9, 4, and 12 is 36. | The LCD for x, 4, and 8 is $8x$.

Step 2 $\dfrac{\dfrac{2}{3} + \dfrac{5}{9}}{\dfrac{1}{4} + \dfrac{1}{12}}$ $\dfrac{6 + \dfrac{3}{x}}{\dfrac{x}{4} + \dfrac{1}{8}}$ Multiply numerator and denominator of the complex fraction by the LCD.

$$= \frac{36\left(\dfrac{2}{3} + \dfrac{5}{9}\right)}{36\left(\dfrac{1}{4} + \dfrac{1}{12}\right)}$$ $$= \frac{8x\left(6 + \dfrac{3}{x}\right)}{8x\left(\dfrac{x}{4} + \dfrac{1}{8}\right)}$$

Multiply each term by 36. $$= \frac{36\left(\dfrac{2}{3}\right) + 36\left(\dfrac{5}{9}\right)}{36\left(\dfrac{1}{4}\right) + 36\left(\dfrac{1}{12}\right)}$$ Multiply each term by $8x$. $$= \frac{8x(6) + 8x\left(\dfrac{3}{x}\right)}{8x\left(\dfrac{x}{4}\right) + 8x\left(\dfrac{1}{8}\right)}$$ Distributive property

$$= \frac{24 + 20}{9 + 3}$$ $$= \frac{48x + 24}{2x^2 + x}$$ Multiply

$$= \frac{44}{12} = \frac{4 \cdot 11}{4 \cdot 3}, \text{ or } \frac{11}{3}$$ $$= \frac{24(2x + 1)}{x(2x + 1)}, \text{ or } \frac{24}{x}$$ NOW TRY

NOW TRY
EXERCISE 5
Simplify the complex fraction.

$$\frac{\dfrac{1}{y} + \dfrac{2}{3y^2}}{\dfrac{5}{4y^2} - \dfrac{3}{2y^3}}$$

EXAMPLE 5 Simplifying a Complex Fraction (Method 2)

Simplify the complex fraction.

$$\frac{\dfrac{3}{5m} - \dfrac{2}{m^2}}{\dfrac{9}{2m} + \dfrac{3}{4m^2}}$$ The LCD for $5m$, m^2, $2m$, and $4m^2$ is $20m^2$.

$$= \frac{20m^2\left(\dfrac{3}{5m} - \dfrac{2}{m^2}\right)}{20m^2\left(\dfrac{9}{2m} + \dfrac{3}{4m^2}\right)}$$ Multiply numerator and denominator by $20m^2$.

$$= \frac{20m^2\left(\dfrac{3}{5m}\right) - 20m^2\left(\dfrac{2}{m^2}\right)}{20m^2\left(\dfrac{9}{2m}\right) + 20m^2\left(\dfrac{3}{4m^2}\right)}$$ Distributive property.

$$= \frac{12m - 40}{90m + 15}$$ Multiply and simplify.   NOW TRY

NOW TRY ANSWERS

4. (a) $\dfrac{14}{11}$ (b) $\dfrac{10 - 15x}{x^2 + 35x}$

5. $\dfrac{12y^2 + 8y}{15y - 18}$

Some students prefer Method 1 for problems like **Example 2,** which is the quotient of two fractions. They will use Method 2 for problems like **Examples 1, 3, 4, and 5,** which have sums or differences in the numerators, or denominators, or both.

EXAMPLE 6 Deciding on a Method and Simplifying Complex Fractions

Simplify each complex fraction.

(a) $\dfrac{\dfrac{1}{y} + \dfrac{2}{y+2}}{\dfrac{4}{y} - \dfrac{3}{y+2}}$ There are sums and differences in the numerator and denominator. Use Method 2.

$= \dfrac{\left(\dfrac{1}{y} + \dfrac{2}{y+2}\right) \cdot y(y+2)}{\left(\dfrac{4}{y} - \dfrac{3}{y+2}\right) \cdot y(y+2)}$ Multiply numerator and denominator by the LCD, $y(y+2)$.

$= \dfrac{\left(\dfrac{1}{y}\right)y(y+2) + \left(\dfrac{2}{y+2}\right)y(y+2)}{\left(\dfrac{4}{y}\right)y(y+2) - \left(\dfrac{3}{y+2}\right)y(y+2)}$ Distributive property

$= \dfrac{1(y+2) + 2y}{4(y+2) - 3y}$ Fundamental property

$= \dfrac{y+2+2y}{4y+8-3y}$ Distributive property

$= \dfrac{3y+2}{y+8}$ Combine like terms.

Be careful not to use $y+2$ as the LCD. Because y appears in two denominators, it must be a factor in the LCD.

(b) $\dfrac{1 - \dfrac{2}{x} - \dfrac{3}{x^2}}{1 - \dfrac{5}{x} + \dfrac{6}{x^2}}$ There are sums and differences in the numerator and denominator. Use Method 2.

$= \dfrac{\left(1 - \dfrac{2}{x} - \dfrac{3}{x^2}\right)x^2}{\left(1 - \dfrac{5}{x} + \dfrac{6}{x^2}\right)x^2}$ Multiply numerator and denominator by the LCD, x^2.

$= \dfrac{x^2 - 2x - 3}{x^2 - 5x + 6}$ Distributive property

$= \dfrac{(x-3)(x+1)}{(x-3)(x-2)}$ Factor.

$= \dfrac{x+1}{x-2}$ Divide out the common factor.

NOW TRY
EXERCISE 6

Simplify each complex fraction.

(a) $\dfrac{1 - \dfrac{2}{x} - \dfrac{15}{x^2}}{1 + \dfrac{5}{x} + \dfrac{6}{x^2}}$

(b) $\dfrac{\dfrac{9y^2 - 16}{y^2 - 100}}{\dfrac{3y - 4}{y + 10}}$

(c) $\dfrac{\dfrac{x + 2}{x - 3}}{\dfrac{x^2 - 4}{x^2 - 9}}$ This is a quotient of two rational expressions. Use Method 1.

$= \dfrac{x + 2}{x - 3} \div \dfrac{x^2 - 4}{x^2 - 9}$ Write as a division problem.

$= \dfrac{x + 2}{x - 3} \cdot \dfrac{x^2 - 9}{x^2 - 4}$ Multiply by the reciprocal.

$= \dfrac{(x + 2)(x + 3)(x - 3)}{(x - 3)(x + 2)(x - 2)}$ Multiply and then factor.

$= \dfrac{x + 3}{x - 2}$ Divide out the common factors.   *NOW TRY*

OBJECTIVE 3 **Simplify rational expressions with negative exponents.** To simplify, we begin by rewriting the expressions with only positive exponents. Recall from **Section 4.2** that for any nonzero real number a and any integer n,

$$a^{-n} = \frac{1}{a^n}.$$ Definition of negative exponent

⚠ **CAUTION** $a^{-1} + b^{-1} = \dfrac{1}{a} + \dfrac{1}{b}$, **not** $\dfrac{1}{a + b}$.   Avoid this common error.

EXAMPLE 7 **Simplifying Rational Expressions with Negative Exponents**

Simplify each expression, using only positive exponents in the answer.

(a) $\dfrac{m^{-1} + p^{-2}}{2m^{-2} - p^{-1}}$ $a^{-n} = \frac{1}{a^n}$

$= \dfrac{\dfrac{1}{m} + \dfrac{1}{p^2}}{\dfrac{2}{m^2} - \dfrac{1}{p}}$ Write with positive exponents.

The base of $2m^{-2}$ is m, not $2m$: $2m^{-2} = \frac{2}{m^2}$.

$2m^{-2} = 2 \cdot m^{-2} = \frac{2}{1} \cdot \frac{1}{m^2} = \frac{2}{m^2}$

$= \dfrac{m^2 p^2 \left(\dfrac{1}{m} + \dfrac{1}{p^2}\right)}{m^2 p^2 \left(\dfrac{2}{m^2} - \dfrac{1}{p}\right)}$ Simplify by Method 2, multiplying the numerator and denominator by the LCD, $m^2 p^2$.

$= \dfrac{m^2 p^2 \cdot \dfrac{1}{m} + m^2 p^2 \cdot \dfrac{1}{p^2}}{m^2 p^2 \cdot \dfrac{2}{m^2} - m^2 p^2 \cdot \dfrac{1}{p}}$ Distributive property

$= \dfrac{mp^2 + m^2}{2p^2 - m^2 p}$ Lowest terms

NOW TRY ANSWERS

6. (a) $\dfrac{x - 5}{x + 2}$ (b) $\dfrac{3y + 4}{y - 10}$

NOW TRY
EXERCISE 7

Simplify the expression, using only positive exponents in the answer.

$$\frac{2y^{-1} - 3y^{-2}}{y^{-2} + 3x^{-1}}$$

(b) $\dfrac{x^{-2} - 2y^{-1}}{y - 2x^2}$

> The 2 does *not* go in the denominator of this fraction.

$$= \frac{\dfrac{1}{x^2} - \dfrac{2}{y}}{y - 2x^2}$$ Write with positive exponents.

$$= \frac{\left(\dfrac{1}{x^2} - \dfrac{2}{y}\right)x^2 y}{(y - 2x^2)x^2 y}$$ Use Method 2. Multiply by the LCD, $x^2 y$.

$$= \frac{y - 2x^2}{(y - 2x^2)x^2 y}$$ Use the distributive property in the numerator.

$$= \frac{1}{x^2 y}$$
> Remember to write 1 in the numerator.

Lowest terms

NOW TRY

NOW TRY ANSWER

7. $\dfrac{2xy - 3x}{x + 3y^2}$

6.5 EXERCISES

MyMathLab | Math XL PRACTICE | WATCH | DOWNLOAD | READ | REVIEW

🌐 *Complete solution available on the Video Resources on DVD*

1. *Concept Check* Consider the complex fraction . Answer each part, outlining Method 1 for simplifying this complex fraction.

(a) To combine the terms in the numerator, we must find the LCD of $\frac{3}{2}$ and $\frac{4}{3}$. What is this LCD? Determine the simplified form of the numerator of the complex fraction.

(b) To combine the terms in the denominator, we must find the LCD of $\frac{1}{6}$ and $\frac{5}{12}$. What is this LCD? Determine the simplified form of the denominator of the complex fraction.

(c) Now use the results from parts (a) and (b) to write the complex fraction as a division problem using the symbol $\div$.

(d) Perform the operation from part (c) to obtain the final simplification.

2. *Concept Check* Consider the complex fraction given in **Exercise 1:** $\dfrac{\frac{3}{2} - \frac{4}{3}}{\frac{1}{6} - \frac{5}{12}}$. Answer each part, outlining Method 2 for simplifying this complex fraction.

(a) We must determine the LCD of all the fractions within the complex fraction. What is this LCD?

(b) Multiply every term in the complex fraction by the LCD found in part (a), but do not yet combine the terms in the numerator and the denominator.

(c) Combine the terms from part (b) to obtain the simplified form of the complex fraction.

3. Which complex fraction is equivalent to $\dfrac{2 - \frac{1}{4}}{3 - \frac{1}{2}}$? Answer this question without showing any work, and explain your reasoning.

A. $\dfrac{2 + \frac{1}{4}}{3 + \frac{1}{2}}$ **B.** $\dfrac{2 - \frac{1}{4}}{-3 + \frac{1}{2}}$ **C.** $\dfrac{-2 - \frac{1}{4}}{-3 - \frac{1}{2}}$ **D.** $\dfrac{-2 + \frac{1}{4}}{-3 + \frac{1}{2}}$

4. Only one of these choices is equal to $\dfrac{\frac{1}{3} + \frac{1}{12}}{\frac{1}{2} + \frac{1}{4}}$. Which one is it? Answer this question without showing any work, and explain your reasoning.

A. $\dfrac{5}{9}$ **B.** $-\dfrac{5}{9}$ **C.** $-\dfrac{9}{5}$ **D.** $-\dfrac{1}{12}$

Simplify each complex fraction. Use either method. ***See Examples 1–6.***

5. $\dfrac{-\dfrac{4}{3}}{\dfrac{2}{9}}$

6. $\dfrac{-\dfrac{5}{6}}{\dfrac{5}{4}}$

7. $\dfrac{\dfrac{x}{y^2}}{\dfrac{x^2}{y}}$

8. $\dfrac{\dfrac{p^4}{r}}{\dfrac{p^2}{r^2}}$

9. $\dfrac{\dfrac{4a^4b^3}{3a}}{\dfrac{2ab^4}{b^2}}$

10. $\dfrac{\dfrac{2r^4t^2}{3t}}{\dfrac{5r^2t^5}{3r}}$

11. $\dfrac{\dfrac{m+2}{3}}{\dfrac{m-4}{m}}$

12. $\dfrac{\dfrac{q-5}{q}}{\dfrac{q+5}{3}}$

13. $\dfrac{\dfrac{2}{x}-3}{\dfrac{2-3x}{2}}$

14. $\dfrac{6+\dfrac{2}{r}}{\dfrac{3r+1}{4}}$

15. $\dfrac{\dfrac{1}{x}+x}{\dfrac{x^2+1}{8}}$

16. $\dfrac{\dfrac{3}{m}-m}{\dfrac{3-m^2}{4}}$

17. $\dfrac{a-\dfrac{5}{a}}{a+\dfrac{1}{a}}$

18. $\dfrac{q+\dfrac{1}{q}}{q+\dfrac{4}{q}}$

19. $\dfrac{\dfrac{5}{8}+\dfrac{2}{3}}{\dfrac{7}{3}-\dfrac{1}{4}}$

20. $\dfrac{\dfrac{6}{5}-\dfrac{1}{9}}{\dfrac{2}{5}+\dfrac{5}{3}}$

21. $\dfrac{\dfrac{1}{x^2}+\dfrac{1}{y^2}}{\dfrac{1}{x}-\dfrac{1}{y}}$

22. $\dfrac{\dfrac{1}{a^2}-\dfrac{1}{b^2}}{\dfrac{1}{a}-\dfrac{1}{b}}$

23. $\dfrac{\dfrac{2}{p^2}-\dfrac{3}{5p}}{\dfrac{4}{p}+\dfrac{1}{4p}}$

24. $\dfrac{\dfrac{2}{m^2}-\dfrac{3}{m}}{\dfrac{2}{5m^2}+\dfrac{1}{3m}}$

25. $\dfrac{\dfrac{5}{x^2y}-\dfrac{2}{xy^2}}{\dfrac{3}{x^2y^2}+\dfrac{4}{xy}}$

26. $\dfrac{\dfrac{1}{m^3p}+\dfrac{2}{mp^2}}{\dfrac{4}{mp}+\dfrac{1}{m^2p}}$

27. $\dfrac{\dfrac{1}{4}-\dfrac{1}{a^2}}{\dfrac{1}{2}+\dfrac{1}{a}}$

28. $\dfrac{\dfrac{1}{9}-\dfrac{1}{m^2}}{\dfrac{1}{3}+\dfrac{1}{m}}$

29. $\dfrac{\dfrac{1}{z+5}}{\dfrac{4}{z^2-25}}$

30. $\dfrac{\dfrac{1}{a+1}}{\dfrac{2}{a^2-1}}$

31. $\dfrac{\dfrac{1}{m+1}-1}{\dfrac{1}{m+1}+1}$

32. $\dfrac{\dfrac{2}{x-1}+2}{\dfrac{2}{x-1}-2}$

33. $\dfrac{\dfrac{1}{m-1}+\dfrac{2}{m+2}}{\dfrac{2}{m+2}-\dfrac{1}{m-3}}$

34. $\dfrac{\dfrac{5}{r+3}-\dfrac{1}{r-1}}{\dfrac{2}{r+2}+\dfrac{3}{r+3}}$

35. $\dfrac{2+\dfrac{1}{x}-\dfrac{28}{x^2}}{3+\dfrac{13}{x}+\dfrac{4}{x^2}}$

36. $\dfrac{4-\dfrac{11}{x}-\dfrac{3}{x^2}}{2-\dfrac{1}{x}-\dfrac{15}{x^2}}$

37. $\dfrac{\dfrac{y+8}{y-4}}{\dfrac{y^2-64}{y^2-16}}$

38. $\dfrac{\dfrac{t+5}{t-8}}{\dfrac{t^2-25}{t^2-64}}$

Simplify each expression, using only positive exponents in the answer. ***See Example 7.***

39. $\dfrac{1}{x^{-2} + y^{-2}}$

40. $\dfrac{1}{p^{-2} - q^{-2}}$

 41. $\dfrac{x^{-2} + y^{-2}}{x^{-1} + y^{-1}}$

42. $\dfrac{x^{-1} - y^{-1}}{x^{-2} - y^{-2}}$

43. $\dfrac{x^{-1} + 2y^{-1}}{2y + 4x}$

44. $\dfrac{a^{-2} - 4b^{-2}}{3b - 6a}$

Brain Busters *Simplify each fraction.*

45. $\dfrac{1 + x^{-1} - 12x^{-2}}{1 - x^{-1} - 20x^{-2}}$

46. $\dfrac{1 + t^{-1} - 56t^{-2}}{1 - t^{-1} - 72t^{-2}}$

47. *Concept Check* In a fraction, what operation does the fraction bar represent?

48. *Concept Check* What property of real numbers justifies Method 2 of simplifying complex fractions?

RELATING CONCEPTS EXERCISES 49–52

FOR INDIVIDUAL OR GROUP WORK

To find the average of two numbers, we add them and divide by 2. Suppose that we wish to find the average of $\frac{3}{8}$ and $\frac{5}{6}$. ***Work Exercises 49–52 in order,*** *to see how a complex fraction occurs in a problem like this.*

49. Write in symbols: The sum of $\frac{3}{8}$ and $\frac{5}{6}$, divided by 2. Your result should be a complex fraction.

50. Use Method 1 to simplify the complex fraction from **Exercise 49.**

51. Use Method 2 to simplify the complex fraction from **Exercise 49.**

52. Your answers in **Exercises 50 and 51** should be the same. Which method did you prefer? Why?

Brain Busters *The fractions in Exercises 53–58 are called* **continued fractions.** *Simplify by starting at "the bottom" and working upward.*

53. $1 + \dfrac{1}{1 + \dfrac{1}{1 + 1}}$

54. $5 + \dfrac{5}{5 + \dfrac{5}{5 + 5}}$

55. $7 - \dfrac{3}{5 + \dfrac{2}{4 - 2}}$

56. $3 - \dfrac{2}{4 + \dfrac{2}{4 - 2}}$

57. $r + \dfrac{r}{4 - \dfrac{2}{6 + 2}}$

58. $\dfrac{2q}{7} - \dfrac{q}{6 + \dfrac{8}{4 + 4}}$

PREVIEW EXERCISES

Simplify. ***See Section 1.8.***

59. $9\left(\dfrac{4x}{3} + \dfrac{2}{9}\right)$

60. $8\left(\dfrac{3r}{4} + \dfrac{9}{8}\right)$

61. $-12\left(\dfrac{11p^2}{3} - \dfrac{9p}{4}\right)$

62. $6\left(\dfrac{5z^2}{2} - \dfrac{8z}{3}\right)$

Solve each equation. ***See Sections 2.3 and 5.5.***

63. $3x + 5 = 7x + 3$

64. $9z + 2 = 7z + 6$

65. $6(z - 3) + 5 = 8z - 3$

66. $k^2 + 3k - 4 = 0$

6.6 Solving Equations with Rational Expressions

OBJECTIVES

1 Distinguish between operations with rational expressions and equations with terms that are rational expressions.

2 Solve equations with rational expressions.

3 Solve a formula for a specified variable.

OBJECTIVE 1 Distinguish between operations with rational expressions and equations with terms that are rational expressions. Before solving equations with rational expressions, you must understand the difference between sums and differences of terms with rational coefficients, or rational *expressions*, and *equations* with terms that are rational expressions.

Sums and differences are expressions to simplify. Equations are solved.

EXAMPLE 1 Distinguishing between Expressions and Equations

Identify each of the following as an *expression* or an *equation*. Then simplify the expression or solve the equation.

(a) $\dfrac{3}{4}x - \dfrac{2}{3}x$

This is a difference of two terms. It represents an *expression* to simplify since there is no equals symbol.

$= \dfrac{3 \cdot 3}{3 \cdot 4}x - \dfrac{4 \cdot 2}{4 \cdot 3}x$ The LCD is 12. Write each coefficient with this LCD.

$= \dfrac{9}{12}x - \dfrac{8}{12}x$ Multiply.

$= \dfrac{1}{12}x$ Combine like terms, using the distributive property: $\frac{9}{12}x - \frac{8}{12}x = \left(\frac{9}{12} - \frac{8}{12}\right)x$.

(b) $\dfrac{3}{4}x - \dfrac{2}{3}x = \dfrac{1}{2}$ Because there is an equals symbol, this is an **equation** to be solved.

$12\left(\dfrac{3}{4}x - \dfrac{2}{3}x\right) = 12\left(\dfrac{1}{2}\right)$ Use the multiplication property of equality to clear fractions. Multiply by 12, the LCD.

$12\left(\dfrac{3}{4}x\right) - 12\left(\dfrac{2}{3}x\right) = 12\left(\dfrac{1}{2}\right)$ Distributive property (Multiply each term by 12.)

$9x - 8x = 6$ Multiply.

$x = 6$ Combine like terms.

CHECK $\dfrac{3}{4}x - \dfrac{2}{3}x = \dfrac{1}{2}$ Original equation

$\dfrac{3}{4}(6) - \dfrac{2}{3}(6) \stackrel{?}{=} \dfrac{1}{2}$ Let x = 6.

$\dfrac{9}{2} - 4 \stackrel{?}{=} \dfrac{1}{2}$ Multiply.

$\dfrac{1}{2} = \dfrac{1}{2}$ ✓ True

Since a true statement results, {6} is the solution set of the equation. NOW TRY

**NOW TRY
EXERCISE 1**

Identify each of the following as an *expression* or an *equation*. Then simplify the expression or solve the equation.

(a) $\dfrac{3}{2}t - \dfrac{5}{7}t - \dfrac{11}{7}$

(b) $\dfrac{3}{2}t - \dfrac{5}{7}t$

NOW TRY ANSWERS
1. **(a)** equation; {2}
   (b) expression; $\frac{11}{14}t$

The ideas of **Example 1** can be summarized as follows.

Uses of the LCD

When adding or subtracting rational expressions, keep the LCD throughout the simplification. (See **Example 1(a).**)

When solving an equation, multiply each side by the LCD so that denominators are eliminated. (See **Example 1(b).**)

OBJECTIVE 2   **Solve equations with rational expressions.** When an equation involves fractions, as in **Example 1(b),** we use the multiplication property of equality to clear the fractions. Choose as multiplier the LCD of all denominators in the fractions of the equation.

⟲ *NOW TRY*
EXERCISE 2

Solve, and check the solution.

$$\frac{x + 5}{5} - \frac{x}{7} = \frac{3}{7}$$

EXAMPLE 2   Solving an Equation with Rational Expressions

Solve, and check the solution.

$$\frac{p}{2} - \frac{p - 1}{3} = 1$$

$$6\left(\frac{p}{2} - \frac{p - 1}{3}\right) = 6(1) \qquad \text{Multiply each side by the LCD, 6.}$$

$$6\left(\frac{p}{2}\right) - 6\left(\frac{p - 1}{3}\right) = 6(1) \qquad \text{Distributive property}$$

$$3p - 2(p - 1) = 6 \qquad \boxed{\text{Use parentheses around } p - 1 \text{ to avoid errors.}}$$

$$\boxed{\text{Be careful with signs.}} \quad 3p - 2(p) - 2(-1) = 6 \qquad \text{Distributive property}$$

$$3p - 2p + 2 = 6 \qquad \text{Multiply.}$$

$$p + 2 = 6 \qquad \text{Combine like terms.}$$

$$p = 4 \qquad \text{Subtract 2.}$$

Check to see that $\{4\}$ is the solution set by replacing p with 4 in the original equation.

NOW TRY ⟳

⚠ **CAUTION**   In **Example 2,** we used the multiplication property of equality to multiply each side of an *equation* by the LCD. In **Section 6.5,** we used the fundamental property to multiply a *fraction* by another fraction that had the LCD as both its numerator and denominator. Be careful not to confuse these procedures.

Recall from **Section 6.1** that the denominator of a rational expression cannot equal 0, since division by 0 is undefined. ***Therefore, when solving an equation with rational expressions that have variables in the denominator, the solution cannot be a number that makes the denominator equal 0.***

A value of the variable that appears to be a solution after both sides of a rational equation are multiplied by a variable expression is called a **proposed solution.** *All proposed solutions must be checked in the original equation.*

NOW TRY ANSWER
2. $\{-10\}$

NOW TRY
EXERCISE 3

Solve, and check the proposed solution.

$$4 + \frac{6}{x-3} = \frac{2x}{x-3}$$

EXAMPLE 3 Solving an Equation with Rational Expressions

Solve, and check the proposed solution.

$$\frac{x}{x-2} = \frac{2}{x-2} + 2$$ *x cannot* equal 2, since 2 causes both denominators to equal 0.

$$(x-2)\left(\frac{x}{x-2}\right) = (x-2)\left(\frac{2}{x-2} + 2\right)$$ Multiply each side by the LCD, $x-2$.

$$(x-2)\left(\frac{x}{x-2}\right) = (x-2)\left(\frac{2}{x-2}\right) + (x-2)(2)$$ Distributive property

$$x = 2 + 2x - 4$$ Simplify.

$$x = -2 + 2x$$ Combine like terms.

$$-x = -2$$ Subtract $2x$.

$$x = 2$$ Multiply by -1.

As noted, x cannot equal 2, since replacing x with 2 in the original equation causes the denominators to equal 0.

CHECK $$\frac{x}{x-2} = \frac{2}{x-2} + 2$$ Original equation

$$\frac{2}{2-2} \stackrel{?}{=} \frac{2}{2-2} + 2$$ Let $x = 2$.

Division by 0 is undefined. $$\frac{2}{0} \stackrel{?}{=} \frac{2}{0} + 2$$ Subtract in the denominators.

Thus, 2 must be rejected as a solution, and the solution set is $\emptyset$.   NOW TRY

A proposed solution that is not an actual solution of the original equation, such as 2 in **Example 3**, is called an **extraneous solution,** or **extraneous value.** Some students like to determine which numbers cannot be solutions *before* solving the equation, as we did in **Example 3.**

Solving an Equation with Rational Expressions

Step 1 **Multiply each side of the equation by the LCD** to clear the equation of fractions. Be sure to distribute to *every* term on *both* sides.

Step 2 **Solve** the resulting equation.

Step 3 **Check** each proposed solution by substituting it into the original equation. Reject any that cause a denominator to equal 0.

EXAMPLE 4 Solving an Equation with Rational Expressions

Solve, and check the proposed solution.

$$\frac{2}{x^2 - x} = \frac{1}{x^2 - 1}$$

NOW TRY ANSWER
3. $\emptyset$

Step 1 $$\frac{2}{x(x-1)} = \frac{1}{(x+1)(x-1)}$$ Factor the denominators to find the LCD, $x(x+1)(x-1)$.

NOW TRY
EXERCISE 4

Solve, and check the proposed solution.

$$\frac{3}{2x^2 - 8x} = \frac{1}{x^2 - 16}$$

Notice that 0, 1, and -1 cannot be solutions. Otherwise a denominator will equal 0.

$$\frac{2}{x(x - 1)} = \frac{1}{(x + 1)(x - 1)} \qquad \text{The LCD is } x(x + 1)(x - 1).$$

$$x(x + 1)(x - 1)\frac{2}{x(x - 1)} = x(x + 1)(x - 1)\frac{1}{(x + 1)(x - 1)} \qquad \begin{array}{l}\text{Multiply by}\\\text{the LCD.}\end{array}$$

Step 2

$$2(x + 1) = x \qquad \text{Divide out the common factors.}$$

$$2x + 2 = x \qquad \text{Distributive property}$$

$$x + 2 = 0 \qquad \text{Subtract } x.$$

$$x = -2 \qquad \text{Subtract 2.}$$

Step 3 The proposed solution is -2, which does not make any denominator equal 0.

CHECK

$$\frac{2}{x^2 - x} = \frac{1}{x^2 - 1} \qquad \text{Original equation}$$

$$\frac{2}{(-2)^2 - (-2)} \overset{?}{=} \frac{1}{(-2)^2 - 1} \qquad \text{Let } x = -2.$$

$$\frac{2}{4 + 2} \overset{?}{=} \frac{1}{4 - 1} \qquad \text{Apply the exponents.}$$

$$\frac{1}{3} = \frac{1}{3} \checkmark \qquad \text{True}$$

The solution set is $\{-2\}$.

NOW TRY

NOW TRY
EXERCISE 5

Solve, and check the proposed solution.

$$\frac{2y}{y^2 - 25} = \frac{8}{y + 5} - \frac{1}{y - 5}$$

EXAMPLE 5 Solving an Equation with Rational Expressions

Solve, and check the proposed solution.

$$\frac{2m}{m^2 - 4} + \frac{1}{m - 2} = \frac{2}{m + 2}$$

$$\frac{2m}{(m + 2)(m - 2)} + \frac{1}{m - 2} = \frac{2}{m + 2} \qquad \begin{array}{l}\text{Factor the first denominator}\\\text{on the left to find the LCD,}\\(m + 2)(m - 2).\end{array}$$

Notice that -2 and 2 cannot be solutions of this equation.

$$(m + 2)(m - 2)\left(\frac{2m}{(m + 2)(m - 2)} + \frac{1}{m - 2}\right) \qquad \text{Multiply by the LCD.}$$

$$= (m + 2)(m - 2)\frac{2}{m + 2}$$

$$(m + 2)(m - 2)\frac{2m}{(m + 2)(m - 2)} + (m + 2)(m - 2)\frac{1}{m - 2}$$

$$= (m + 2)(m - 2)\frac{2}{m + 2} \qquad \text{Distributive property}$$

$$2m + m + 2 = 2(m - 2) \qquad \text{Divide out the common factors.}$$

$$3m + 2 = 2m - 4 \qquad \text{Combine like terms; distributive property}$$

$$m + 2 = -4 \qquad \text{Subtract } 2m.$$

$$m = -6 \qquad \text{Subtract 2.}$$

NOW TRY ANSWERS
4. $\{-12\}$ 5. $\{9\}$

A check verifies that $\{-6\}$ is the solution set.

NOW TRY

NOW TRY
EXERCISE 6

Solve, and check the proposed solution(s).

$$\frac{3}{m^2 - 9} = \frac{1}{2(m - 3)} - \frac{1}{4}$$

EXAMPLE 6 Solving an Equation with Rational Expressions

Solve, and check the proposed solution(s).

$$\frac{1}{x - 1} + \frac{1}{2} = \frac{2}{x^2 - 1}$$

$\boxed{x \neq 1, -1 \text{ or a denominator is 0.}}$ $\frac{1}{x - 1} + \frac{1}{2} = \frac{2}{(x + 1)(x - 1)}$

Factor the denominator on the right. The LCD is $2(x + 1)(x - 1)$.

$$2(x + 1)(x - 1)\left(\frac{1}{x - 1} + \frac{1}{2}\right) = 2(x + 1)(x - 1)\frac{2}{(x + 1)(x - 1)}$$

Multiply by the LCD.

$$2(x + 1)(x - 1)\frac{1}{x - 1} + 2(x + 1)(x - 1)\frac{1}{2} = 2(x + 1)(x - 1)\frac{2}{(x + 1)(x - 1)}$$

Distributive property

$$2(x + 1) + (x + 1)(x - 1) = 4$$ Divide out the common factors.

$$2x + 2 + x^2 - 1 = 4$$ Distributive property

$\boxed{\text{Write in standard form.}}$ $x^2 + 2x - 3 = 0$ Subtract 4. Combine like terms.

$$(x + 3)(x - 1) = 0$$ Factor.

$$x + 3 = 0 \quad \text{or} \quad x - 1 = 0$$ Zero-factor property

$$x = -3 \quad \text{or} \quad x = 1 \leftarrow \text{Proposed solutions}$$

Since 1 makes a denominator equal 0, 1 is *not* a solution. Check that -3 is a solution.

CHECK $$\frac{1}{x - 1} + \frac{1}{2} = \frac{2}{x^2 - 1}$$ Original equation

$$\frac{1}{-3 - 1} + \frac{1}{2} \stackrel{?}{=} \frac{2}{(-3)^2 - 1}$$ Let $x = -3$.

$$\frac{1}{-4} + \frac{1}{2} \stackrel{?}{=} \frac{2}{9 - 1}$$ Simplify.

$$\frac{1}{4} = \frac{1}{4} \checkmark$$ True

The solution set is $\{-3\}$.   NOW TRY

EXAMPLE 7 Solving an Equation with Rational Expressions

Solve, and check the proposed solution.

$$\frac{1}{k^2 + 4k + 3} + \frac{1}{2k + 2} = \frac{3}{4k + 12}$$

$$\frac{1}{(k + 1)(k + 3)} + \frac{1}{2(k + 1)} = \frac{3}{4(k + 3)}$$

Factor each denominator. The LCD is $4(k + 1)(k + 3)$.

$\boxed{k \neq -1, -3}$ $4(k + 1)(k + 3)\left(\frac{1}{(k + 1)(k + 3)} + \frac{1}{2(k + 1)}\right)$

$$= 4(k + 1)(k + 3)\frac{3}{4(k + 3)}$$

Multiply by the LCD.

NOW TRY ANSWER
6. $\{-1\}$

NOW TRY
EXERCISE 7
Solve, and check the proposed solution.

$$\frac{5}{k^2 + k - 2} = \frac{1}{3k - 3} - \frac{1}{k + 2}$$

$$4(k + 1)(k + 3)\frac{1}{(k + 1)(k + 3)} + 2 \cdot 2(k + 1)(k + 3)\frac{1}{2(k + 1)}$$

$$= 4(k + 1)(k + 3)\frac{3}{4(k + 3)} \qquad \text{Distributive property}$$

> Do *not* add 4 + 2 here.

$$4 + 2(k + 3) = 3(k + 1) \qquad \text{Simplify.}$$
$$4 + 2k + 6 = 3k + 3 \qquad \text{Distributive property}$$
$$2k + 10 = 3k + 3 \qquad \text{Combine like terms.}$$
$$10 = k + 3 \qquad \text{Subtract } 2k.$$
$$7 = k \qquad \text{Subtract 3.}$$

The proposed solution, 7, does not make an original denominator equal 0. A check shows that the algebra is correct (see **Exercise 78**), so {7} is the solution set. NOW TRY

OBJECTIVE 3 **Solve a formula for a specified variable.** When solving a formula for a specified variable, *remember to treat the variable for which you are solving as if it were the only variable, and all others as if they were constants.*

NOW TRY
EXERCISE 8
Solve each formula for the specified variable.

(a) $p = \dfrac{x - y}{z}$ for x

(b) $a = \dfrac{b}{c + d}$ for d

EXAMPLE 8 Solving for a Specified Variable

Solve each formula for the specified variable.

(a) $a = \dfrac{v - w}{t}$ for v

$$a = \frac{v - w}{t} \qquad \text{Our goal is to isolate } v.$$

$$at = v - w \qquad \text{Multiply by } t.$$
$$at + w = v, \quad \text{or} \quad v = at + w \qquad \text{Add } w.$$

(b) $F = \dfrac{k}{d - D}$ for d

$$F = \frac{k}{d - D} \qquad \text{Given equation}$$

> We must isolate d.

$$F(d - D) = \frac{k}{d - D}(d - D) \qquad \text{Multiply by } d - D \text{ to clear the fraction.}$$

$$F(d - D) = k \qquad \text{Simplify.}$$
$$Fd - FD = k \qquad \text{Distributive property}$$
$$Fd = k + FD \qquad \text{Add } FD.$$
$$d = \frac{k + FD}{F} \qquad \text{Divide by } F.$$

We can write an equivalent form of this answer as follows.

$$d = \frac{k + FD}{F} \qquad \text{Answer from above}$$

$$d = \frac{k}{F} + \frac{FD}{F} \qquad \text{Definition of addition of fractions: } \frac{a + b}{c} = \frac{a}{c} + \frac{b}{c}$$

$$d = \frac{k}{F} + D \qquad \text{Divide out the common factor from } \frac{FD}{F}.$$

Either answer is correct. NOW TRY

NOW TRY ANSWERS
7. {−5}
8. (a) $x = pz + y$
  (b) $d = \dfrac{b - ac}{a}$

NOW TRY
EXERCISE 9
Solve the following formula for x.

$$\frac{2}{w} = \frac{1}{x} - \frac{3}{y}$$

EXAMPLE 9 Solving for a Specified Variable

Solve the following formula for c.

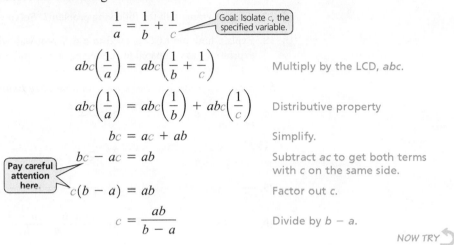

$\dfrac{1}{a} = \dfrac{1}{b} + \dfrac{1}{c}$ — Goal: Isolate c, the specified variable.	
$abc\left(\dfrac{1}{a}\right) = abc\left(\dfrac{1}{b} + \dfrac{1}{c}\right)$	Multiply by the LCD, abc.
$abc\left(\dfrac{1}{a}\right) = abc\left(\dfrac{1}{b}\right) + abc\left(\dfrac{1}{c}\right)$	Distributive property
$bc = ac + ab$	Simplify.
$bc - ac = ab$	Subtract ac to get both terms with c on the same side.
$c(b - a) = ab$ — Pay careful attention here.	Factor out c.
$c = \dfrac{ab}{b - a}$	Divide by $b - a$.

NOW TRY

⚠ **CAUTION** Students often have trouble in the step that involves factoring out the variable for which they are solving. In **Example 9,** we needed to get both terms with c on the same side of the equation. This allowed us to factor out c on the left, and then isolate it by dividing each side by $b - a$.

When solving an equation for a specified variable, be sure that the specified variable appears alone on only one side of the equals symbol in the final equation.

NOW TRY ANSWER
9. $x = \dfrac{wy}{2y + 3w}$

6.6 EXERCISES

MyMathLab Math XL PRACTICE WATCH DOWNLOAD READ REVIEW

🌐 *Complete solution available on the Video Resources on DVD*

Identify each of the following as an expression *or an* equation. *Then simplify the expression or solve the equation.* **See Example 1.**

🌐 **1.** $\dfrac{7}{8}x + \dfrac{1}{5}x$

2. $\dfrac{4}{7}x + \dfrac{4}{5}x$

3. $\dfrac{7}{8}x + \dfrac{1}{5}x = 1$

4. $\dfrac{4}{7}x + \dfrac{4}{5}x = 1$

5. $\dfrac{3}{5}x - \dfrac{7}{10}x$

6. $\dfrac{2}{3}x - \dfrac{9}{4}x$

7. $\dfrac{3}{5}x - \dfrac{7}{10}x = 1$

8. $\dfrac{2}{3}x - \dfrac{9}{4}x = -19$

9. $\dfrac{3}{4}x - \dfrac{1}{2}x = 0$

📝 **10.** Explain why the equation in **Exercise 9** is easy to check.

When solving an equation with variables in denominators, we must determine the values that cause these denominators to equal 0, so that we can reject these extraneous values if they appear as potential solutions. Find all values for which at least one denominator is equal to 0. Write answers using the symbol ≠. Do not solve. **See Examples 3–7.**

11. $\dfrac{3}{x + 2} - \dfrac{5}{x} = 1$

12. $\dfrac{7}{x} + \dfrac{9}{x - 4} = 5$

13. $\dfrac{-1}{(x + 3)(x - 4)} = \dfrac{1}{2x + 1}$

14. $\dfrac{8}{(x - 7)(x + 3)} = \dfrac{7}{3x - 10}$

15. $\dfrac{4}{x^2 + 8x - 9} + \dfrac{1}{x^2 - 4} = 0$

16. $\dfrac{-3}{x^2 + 9x - 10} - \dfrac{12}{x^2 - 49} = 0$

17. What is wrong with the following problem? "Solve $\frac{2}{3x} + \frac{1}{5x}$."

18. Explain how the LCD is used in a different way when adding and subtracting rational expressions as compared to solving equations with rational expressions.

*Solve each equation, and check your solutions. **See Examples 1(b), 2, and 3.***

19. $\dfrac{5}{m} - \dfrac{3}{m} = 8$

20. $\dfrac{4}{y} + \dfrac{1}{y} = 2$

21. $\dfrac{5}{y} + 4 = \dfrac{2}{y}$

22. $\dfrac{11}{q} - 3 = \dfrac{1}{q}$

23. $\dfrac{3x}{5} - 6 = x$

24. $\dfrac{5t}{4} + t = 9$

25. $\dfrac{4m}{7} + m = 11$

26. $a - \dfrac{3a}{2} = 1$

27. $\dfrac{z - 1}{4} = \dfrac{z + 3}{3}$

28. $\dfrac{r - 5}{2} = \dfrac{r + 2}{3}$

29. $\dfrac{3p + 6}{8} = \dfrac{3p - 3}{16}$

30. $\dfrac{2z + 1}{5} = \dfrac{7z + 5}{15}$

31. $\dfrac{2x + 3}{x} = \dfrac{3}{2}$

32. $\dfrac{7 - 2x}{x} = \dfrac{-17}{5}$

33. $\dfrac{k}{k - 4} - 5 = \dfrac{4}{k - 4}$

34. $\dfrac{-5}{a + 5} - 2 = \dfrac{a}{a + 5}$

35. $\dfrac{q + 2}{3} + \dfrac{q - 5}{5} = \dfrac{7}{3}$

36. $\dfrac{x - 6}{6} + \dfrac{x + 2}{8} = \dfrac{11}{4}$

37. $\dfrac{x}{2} = \dfrac{5}{4} + \dfrac{x - 1}{4}$

38. $\dfrac{8p}{5} = \dfrac{3p - 4}{2} + \dfrac{5}{2}$

39. $x + \dfrac{17}{2} = \dfrac{x}{2} + x + 6$

40. $t + \dfrac{8}{3} = \dfrac{t}{3} + t + \dfrac{14}{3}$

41. $\dfrac{9}{3x + 4} = \dfrac{36 - 27x}{16 - 9x^2}$

42. $\dfrac{25}{5x - 6} = \dfrac{-150 - 125x}{36 - 25x^2}$

*Solve each equation, and check your solutions. **Be careful with signs. See Example 2.***

43. $\dfrac{a + 7}{8} - \dfrac{a - 2}{3} = \dfrac{4}{3}$

44. $\dfrac{x + 3}{7} - \dfrac{x + 2}{6} = \dfrac{1}{6}$

45. $\dfrac{p}{2} - \dfrac{p - 1}{4} = \dfrac{5}{4}$

46. $\dfrac{r}{6} - \dfrac{r - 2}{3} = -\dfrac{4}{3}$

47. $\dfrac{3x}{5} - \dfrac{x - 5}{7} = 3$

48. $\dfrac{8k}{5} - \dfrac{3k - 4}{2} = \dfrac{5}{2}$

*Solve each equation, and check your solutions. **See Examples 3–7.***

49. $\dfrac{4}{x^2 - 3x} = \dfrac{1}{x^2 - 9}$

50. $\dfrac{2}{t^2 - 4} = \dfrac{3}{t^2 - 2t}$

51. $\dfrac{2}{m} = \dfrac{m}{5m + 12}$

52. $\dfrac{x}{4 - x} = \dfrac{2}{x}$

53. $\dfrac{-2}{z + 5} + \dfrac{3}{z - 5} = \dfrac{20}{z^2 - 25}$

54. $\dfrac{3}{r + 3} - \dfrac{2}{r - 3} = \dfrac{-12}{r^2 - 9}$

55. $\dfrac{3}{x - 1} + \dfrac{2}{4x - 4} = \dfrac{7}{4}$

56. $\dfrac{2}{p + 3} + \dfrac{3}{8} = \dfrac{5}{4p + 12}$

57. $\dfrac{x}{3x+3} = \dfrac{2x-3}{x+1} - \dfrac{2x}{3x+3}$

58. $\dfrac{2k+3}{k+1} - \dfrac{3k}{2k+2} = \dfrac{-2k}{2k+2}$

59. $\dfrac{2p}{p^2-1} = \dfrac{2}{p+1} - \dfrac{1}{p-1}$

60. $\dfrac{2x}{x^2-16} - \dfrac{2}{x-4} = \dfrac{4}{x+4}$

61. $\dfrac{5x}{14x+3} = \dfrac{1}{x}$

62. $\dfrac{m}{8m+3} = \dfrac{1}{3m}$

63. $\dfrac{2}{x-1} - \dfrac{2}{3} = \dfrac{-1}{x+1}$

64. $\dfrac{5}{p-2} = 7 - \dfrac{10}{p+2}$

65. $\dfrac{x}{2x+2} = \dfrac{-2x}{4x+4} + \dfrac{2x-3}{x+1}$

66. $\dfrac{5t+1}{3t+3} = \dfrac{5t-5}{5t+5} + \dfrac{3t-1}{t+1}$

67. $\dfrac{8x+3}{x} = 3x$

68. $\dfrac{10x-24}{x} = x$

69. $\dfrac{1}{x+4} + \dfrac{x}{x-4} = \dfrac{-8}{x^2-16}$

70. $\dfrac{x}{x-3} + \dfrac{4}{x+3} = \dfrac{18}{x^2-9}$

71. $\dfrac{4}{3x+6} - \dfrac{3}{x+3} = \dfrac{8}{x^2+5x+6}$

72. $\dfrac{-13}{t^2+6t+8} + \dfrac{4}{t+2} = \dfrac{3}{2t+8}$

73. $\dfrac{3x}{x^2+5x+6} = \dfrac{5x}{x^2+2x-3} - \dfrac{2}{x^2+x-2}$

74. $\dfrac{m}{m^2+m-2} + \dfrac{m}{m^2-1} = \dfrac{m}{m^2+3m+2}$

75. $\dfrac{x+4}{x^2-3x+2} - \dfrac{5}{x^2-4x+3} = \dfrac{x-4}{x^2-5x+6}$

76. $\dfrac{3}{r^2+r-2} - \dfrac{1}{r^2-1} = \dfrac{7}{2(r^2+3r+2)}$

77. *Concept Check* If you are solving a formula for the letter k, and your steps lead to the equation $kr - mr = km$, what would be your next step?

78. Refer to **Example 7,** and show that 7 is a solution.

*Solve each formula for the specified variable. **See Examples 8 and 9.***

79. $m = \dfrac{kF}{a}$ for F

80. $I = \dfrac{kE}{R}$ for E

81. $m = \dfrac{kF}{a}$ for a

82. $I = \dfrac{kE}{R}$ for R

83. $I = \dfrac{E}{R+r}$ for R

84. $I = \dfrac{E}{R+r}$ for r

85. $h = \dfrac{2\mathcal{A}}{B+b}$ for $\mathcal{A}$

86. $d = \dfrac{2S}{n(a+L)}$ for S

87. $d = \dfrac{2S}{n(a+L)}$ for a

88. $h = \dfrac{2\mathcal{A}}{B+b}$ for B

89. $\dfrac{1}{x} = \dfrac{1}{y} - \dfrac{1}{z}$ for y

90. $\dfrac{3}{k} = \dfrac{1}{p} + \dfrac{1}{q}$ for q

91. $\dfrac{2}{r} + \dfrac{3}{s} + \dfrac{1}{t} = 1$ for t

92. $\dfrac{5}{p} + \dfrac{2}{q} + \dfrac{3}{r} = 1$ for r

93. $9x + \dfrac{3}{z} = \dfrac{5}{y}$ for z

94. $-3t - \dfrac{4}{p} = \dfrac{6}{s}$ for p

95. $\dfrac{t}{x-1} - \dfrac{2}{x+1} = \dfrac{1}{x^2-1}$ for t

96. $\dfrac{5}{y+2} - \dfrac{r}{y-2} = \dfrac{3}{y^2-4}$ for r

Write a mathematical expression for each exercise. See Section 2.7.

97. Andrew drives from Pittsburgh to Philadelphia, a distance of 288 mi, in *t* hours. Find his rate in miles per hour.

98. Tyler drives for 20 hr, traveling from City *A* to City *B*, a distance of *d* kilometers. Find his rate in kilometers per hour.

99. Jack flies his small plane from St. Louis to Chicago, a distance of 289 mi, at *z* miles per hour. Find his time in hours.

100. Joshua can do a job in *r* hours. What portion of the job is done in 1 hr?

SUMMARY EXERCISES on Rational Expressions and Equations

Students often confuse *simplifying expressions* with *solving equations*. We review the four operations to simplify the rational expressions $\frac{1}{x}$ and $\frac{1}{x-2}$ as follows.

Add: $\dfrac{1}{x} + \dfrac{1}{x-2}$

$= \dfrac{1(x-2)}{x(x-2)} + \dfrac{x(1)}{x(x-2)}$ Write with a common denominator.

$= \dfrac{x-2+x}{x(x-2)}$ Add numerators.
Keep the same denominator.

$= \dfrac{2x-2}{x(x-2)}$ Combine like terms.

Subtract: $\dfrac{1}{x} - \dfrac{1}{x-2}$

$= \dfrac{1(x-2)}{x(x-2)} - \dfrac{x(1)}{x(x-2)}$ Write with a common denominator.

$= \dfrac{x-2-x}{x(x-2)}$ Subtract numerators.
Keep the same denominator.

$= \dfrac{-2}{x(x-2)}$ Combine like terms.

Multiply: $\dfrac{1}{x} \cdot \dfrac{1}{x-2}$

$= \dfrac{1}{x(x-2)}$ Multiply numerators and multiply denominators.

Divide: $\dfrac{1}{x} \div \dfrac{1}{x-2}$

$= \dfrac{1}{x} \cdot \dfrac{x-2}{1}$ Multiply by the reciprocal of the divisor.

$= \dfrac{x-2}{x}$ Multiply numerators and multiply denominators.

(continued)

By contrast, consider the following *equation*.

$$\frac{1}{x} + \frac{1}{x-2} = \frac{3}{4} \quad \boxed{\begin{array}{l} x \neq 0 \text{ and } x \neq 2 \\ \text{since a denominator} \\ \text{is 0 for these values.} \end{array}}$$

$$4x(x-2)\frac{1}{x} + 4x(x-2)\frac{1}{x-2} = 4x(x-2)\frac{3}{4} \qquad \begin{array}{l}\text{Multiply each side by the LCD,} \\ 4x(x-2), \text{ to clear fractions.}\end{array}$$

$$4(x-2) + 4x = 3x(x-2) \qquad \text{Divide out common factors.}$$

$$4x - 8 + 4x = 3x^2 - 6x \qquad \text{Distributive property}$$

$$3x^2 - 14x + 8 = 0 \qquad \text{Get 0 on one side.}$$

$$(3x - 2)(x - 4) = 0 \qquad \text{Factor.}$$

$$3x - 2 = 0 \quad \text{or} \quad x - 4 = 0 \qquad \text{Zero-factor property}$$

$$x = \frac{2}{3} \quad \text{or} \qquad x = 4 \qquad \text{Solve for } x.$$

Both $\frac{2}{3}$ and 4 are solutions, since neither makes a denominator equal 0. Check to confirm that the solution set is $\left\{\frac{2}{3}, 4\right\}$.

Points to Remember When Working with Rational Expressions and Equations

1. When simplifying rational expressions, the fundamental property is applied only after numerators and denominators have been *factored*.

2. When adding and subtracting rational expressions, the common denominator must be kept throughout the problem and in the final result.

3. When simplifying rational expressions, always check to see if the answer is in lowest terms. If it is not, use the fundamental property.

4. When solving equations with rational expressions, the LCD is used to clear the equation of fractions. Multiply each side by the LCD. (Notice how this use differs from that of the LCD in Point 2.)

5. When solving equations with rational expressions, reject any proposed solution that causes an original denominator to equal 0.

For each exercise, indicate "expression" if an expression is to be simplified or "equation" if an equation is to be solved. Then simplify the expression or solve the equation.

1. $\dfrac{4}{p} + \dfrac{6}{p}$

2. $\dfrac{x^3 y^2}{x^2 y^4} \cdot \dfrac{y^5}{x^4}$

3. $\dfrac{1}{x^2 + x - 2} \div \dfrac{4x^2}{2x - 2}$

4. $\dfrac{8}{t - 5} = 2$

5. $\dfrac{2y^2 + y - 6}{2y^2 - 9y + 9} \cdot \dfrac{y^2 - 2y - 3}{y^2 - 1}$

6. $\dfrac{2}{k^2 - 4k} + \dfrac{3}{k^2 - 16}$

7. $\dfrac{x - 4}{5} = \dfrac{x + 3}{6}$

8. $\dfrac{3t^2 - t}{6t^2 + 15t} \div \dfrac{6t^2 + t - 1}{2t^2 - 5t - 25}$

9. $\dfrac{4}{p + 2} + \dfrac{1}{3p + 6}$

10. $\dfrac{1}{x} + \dfrac{1}{x - 3} = -\dfrac{5}{4}$

11. $\dfrac{3}{t-1} + \dfrac{1}{t} = \dfrac{7}{2}$

12. $\dfrac{6}{k} - \dfrac{2}{3k}$

13. $\dfrac{5}{4z} - \dfrac{2}{3z}$

14. $\dfrac{x+2}{3} = \dfrac{2x-1}{5}$

15. $\dfrac{1}{m^2 + 5m + 6} + \dfrac{2}{m^2 + 4m + 3}$

16. $\dfrac{2k^2 - 3k}{20k^2 - 5k} \div \dfrac{2k^2 - 5k + 3}{4k^2 + 11k - 3}$

17. $\dfrac{2}{x+1} + \dfrac{5}{x-1} = \dfrac{10}{x^2 - 1}$

18. $\dfrac{3}{x+3} + \dfrac{4}{x+6} = \dfrac{9}{x^2 + 9x + 18}$

19. $\dfrac{4t^2 - t}{6t^2 + 10t} \div \dfrac{8t^2 + 2t - 1}{3t^2 + 11t + 10}$

20. $\dfrac{x}{x-2} + \dfrac{3}{x+2} = \dfrac{8}{x^2 - 4}$

6.7 Applications of Rational Expressions

OBJECTIVES

1 Solve problems about numbers.

2 Solve problems about distance, rate, and time.

3 Solve problems about work.

For applications that lead to rational equations, the six-step problem-solving method of **Section 2.4** still applies.

OBJECTIVE 1 Solve problems about numbers.

EXAMPLE 1 Solving a Problem about an Unknown Number

If the same number is added to both the numerator and the denominator of the fraction $\frac{2}{5}$, the result is equivalent to $\frac{2}{3}$. Find the number.

Step 1 **Read** the problem carefully. We are trying to find a number.

Step 2 **Assign a variable.**

Let $x =$ the number added to the numerator and the denominator.

NOW TRY
EXERCISE 1

In a certain fraction, the numerator is 4 less than the denominator. If 7 is added to both the numerator and denominator, the resulting fraction is equivalent to $\frac{7}{8}$. What is the original fraction?

Step 3 **Write an equation.** The fraction $\frac{2+x}{5+x}$ represents the result of adding the same number to both the numerator and the denominator. Since this result is equivalent to $\frac{2}{3}$, the equation is written as follows.

$$\frac{2+x}{5+x} = \frac{2}{3}$$

Step 4 **Solve** this equation.

$$3(5+x)\frac{2+x}{5+x} = 3(5+x)\frac{2}{3} \qquad \text{Multiply by the LCD, } 3(5+x).$$

$$3(2+x) = 2(5+x) \qquad \text{Divide out common factors.}$$

$$6 + 3x = 10 + 2x \qquad \text{Distributive property}$$

$$x = 4 \qquad \text{Subtract } 2x. \text{ Subtract } 6.$$

Step 5 **State the answer.** The number is 4.

Step 6 **Check** the solution in the words of the original problem. If 4 is added to both the numerator and the denominator of $\frac{2}{5}$, the result is $\frac{6}{9} = \frac{2}{3}$, as required.

NOW TRY ANSWER
1. $\frac{21}{25}$

NOW TRY

OBJECTIVE 2 **Solve problems about distance, rate, and time.** Recall from **Chapter 2** the following formulas relating distance, rate, and time. You may wish to refer to **Example 5** in **Section 2.7** to review the basic use of these formulas.

Distance, Rate, and Time Relationship

$$d = rt \qquad r = \frac{d}{t} \qquad t = \frac{d}{r}$$

EXAMPLE 2 Solving a Problem about Distance, Rate, and Time

The Tickfaw River has a current of 3 mph. A motorboat takes as long to go 12 mi downstream as to go 8 mi upstream. What is the rate of the boat in still water?

Step 1 **Read** the problem again. We must find the rate (speed) of the boat in still water.

Step 2 **Assign a variable.** Let x = the rate of the boat in still water.

Because the current pushes the boat when the boat is going downstream, the rate of the boat downstream will be the *sum* of the rate of the boat and the rate of the current, $(x + 3)$ mph.

Because the current slows down the boat when the boat is going upstream, the boat's rate going upstream is given by the *difference* between the rate of the boat and the rate of the current, $(x - 3)$ mph. See **FIGURE 1**.

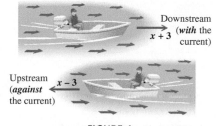

FIGURE 1

This information is summarized in the following table.

	d	r	t
Downstream	12	x + 3	
Upstream	8	x − 3	

Fill in the times by using the formula $t = \frac{d}{r}$.

The time downstream is the distance divided by the rate.

$$t = \frac{d}{r} = \frac{12}{x + 3} \qquad \text{Time downstream}$$

The time upstream is that distance divided by that rate.

$$t = \frac{d}{r} = \frac{8}{x - 3} \qquad \text{Time upstream}$$

	d	r	t
Downstream	12	x + 3	$\frac{12}{x + 3}$
Upstream	8	x − 3	$\frac{8}{x - 3}$

Times are equal.

NOW TRY
EXERCISE 2

In her small boat, Jennifer can travel 12 mi downstream in the same amount of time that she can travel 4 mi upstream. The rate of the current is 2 mph. Find the rate of Jennifer's boat in still water.

Step 3 **Write an equation.**

$$\frac{12}{x + 3} = \frac{8}{x - 3}$$

The time downstream equals the time upstream, so the two times from the table must be equal.

Step 4 **Solve.**

$$(x + 3)(x - 3)\frac{12}{x + 3} = (x + 3)(x - 3)\frac{8}{x - 3}$$

Multiply by the LCD, $(x + 3)(x - 3)$.

$$12(x - 3) = 8(x + 3)$$

Divide out the common factors.

$$12x - 36 = 8x + 24$$

Distributive property

$$4x = 60$$

Subtract 8x and add 36.

$$x = 15$$

Divide by 4.

Step 5 **State the answer.** The rate of the boat in still water is 15 mph.

Step 6 **Check.** First we find the rate of the boat going downstream, which is $15 + 3 = 18$ mph. Divide 12 mi by 18 mph to find the time.

$$t = \frac{d}{r} = \frac{12}{18} = \frac{2}{3} \text{ hr}$$

The rate of the boat going upstream is $15 - 3 = 12$ mph. Divide 8 mi by 12 mph to find the time.

$$t = \frac{d}{r} = \frac{8}{12} = \frac{2}{3} \text{ hr}$$

The time upstream equals the time downstream, as required.

NOW TRY

OBJECTIVE 3 **Solve problems about work.** Suppose that you can mow your lawn in 4 hr. Then after 1 hr, you will have mowed $\frac{1}{4}$ of the lawn. After 2 hr, you will have mowed $\frac{2}{4}$, or $\frac{1}{2}$, of the lawn, and so on. This idea is generalized as follows.

Rate of Work

If a job can be completed in t units of time, then the rate of work is

$$\frac{1}{t} \text{ job per unit of time.}$$

PROBLEM-SOLVING HINT

Recall that the formula $d = rt$ says that distance traveled is equal to rate of travel multiplied by time traveled. Similarly, the fractional part of a job accomplished is equal to the rate of work multiplied by the time worked. In the lawn-mowing example, after 3 hr, the fractional part of the job done is as follows.

$$\underset{\substack{\text{Rate of} \\ \text{work}}}{\frac{1}{4}} \cdot \underset{\substack{\text{Time} \\ \text{worked}}}{3} = \underset{\substack{\text{Fractional part} \\ \text{of job done}}}{\frac{3}{4}}$$

After 4 hr, $\frac{1}{4}(4) = 1$ whole job has been done.

NOW TRY ANSWER
2. 4 mph

From *Little Big League*

NOW TRY EXERCISE 3

Sarah can proofread a manuscript in 10 hr, while Joyce can proofread the same manuscript in 12 hr. How long will it take them to proofread the manuscript if they work together?

EXAMPLE 3 Solving a Problem about Work Rates

"If Joe can paint a house in 3 hr and Sam can paint the same house in 5 hr, how long does it take for them to do it together?" (*Source*: The movie *Little Big League*.)

Step 1 **Read** the problem again. We are looking for time working together.

Step 2 **Assign a variable.** Let x = the number of hours it takes Joe and Sam to paint the house, working together.

Certainly, x will be less than 3, since Joe alone can complete the job in 3 hr. We begin by making a table. Based on the preceding discussion, Joe's rate alone is $\frac{1}{3}$ job per hour, and Sam's rate is $\frac{1}{5}$ job per hour.

	Rate	Time Working Together	Fractional Part of the Job Done When Working Together
Joe	$\frac{1}{3}$	x	$\frac{1}{3}x$
Sam	$\frac{1}{5}$	x	$\frac{1}{5}x$

Sum is 1 whole job.

Step 3 **Write an equation.**

$$\underbrace{\frac{1}{3}x}_{\substack{\text{Fractional part} \\ \text{done by Joe}}} + \underbrace{\frac{1}{5}x}_{\substack{\text{Fractional part} \\ \text{done by Sam}}} = \underbrace{1}_{\text{1 whole job.}}$$

Together, Joe and Sam complete 1 whole job. Add their individual fractional parts and set the sum equal to 1.

Step 4 **Solve.**

$$15\left(\frac{1}{3}x + \frac{1}{5}x\right) = 15(1) \qquad \text{Multiply by the LCD, 15.}$$

$$15\left(\frac{1}{3}x\right) + 15\left(\frac{1}{5}x\right) = 15(1) \qquad \text{Distributive property}$$

$$5x + 3x = 15$$

$$8x = 15 \qquad \text{Combine like terms.}$$

$$x = \frac{15}{8} \qquad \text{Divide by 8.}$$

Step 5 **State the answer.** Working together, Joe and Sam can paint the house in $\frac{15}{8}$ hr, or $1\frac{7}{8}$ hr.

Step 6 **Check** to be sure the answer is correct.

NOW TRY

NOTE An alternative approach in work problems is to consider the part of the job that can be done in 1 hr. For instance, in **Example 3** Joe can do the entire job in 3 hr and Sam can do it in 5 hr. Thus, their work rates, as we saw in **Example 3,** are $\frac{1}{3}$ and $\frac{1}{5}$, respectively. Since it takes them x hours to complete the job working together, in 1 hr they can paint $\frac{1}{x}$ of the house.

(continued)

The amount painted by Joe in 1 hr plus the amount painted by Sam in 1 hr must equal the amount they can do together. This relationship leads to the equation

Amount by Sam
↓

Amount by Joe → $\dfrac{1}{3} + \dfrac{1}{5} = \dfrac{1}{x}$. ← Amount together

Compare this equation with the one in **Example 3.** Multiplying each side by $15x$ leads to

$$5x + 3x = 15,$$

the same equation found in the third line of Step 4 in the example. The same solution results.

PROBLEM-SOLVING HINT

A common error students make when solving a work problem like that in **Example 3** is to add the two times, 3 hr and 5 hr, to get an answer of 8 hr. We reason, however, that x, the time it will take Joe and Sam working together, must be *less than* 3 hr, since Joe can complete the job by himself in 3 hr.

Another common error students make is to try to split the job in half between the two workers so that Joe would work $\frac{1}{2}(3)$, or $1\frac{1}{2}$ hr, and Sam would work $\frac{1}{2}(5)$, or $2\frac{1}{2}$ hr. In this case, Joe finishes 1 hr before Sam and they have not worked together to get the entire job done as quickly as possible. If Joe, when he finishes, helps Sam, the job should actually be completed in a time between $1\frac{1}{2}$ hr and $2\frac{1}{2}$ hr.

Based on this reasoning, does our answer of $1\frac{7}{8}$ hr in **Example 3** hold up?

6.7 EXERCISES

🌐 *Complete solution available on the Video Resources on DVD*

Concept Check   Use Steps 2 and 3 of the six-step method to set up the equation you would use to solve each problem. (Remember that Step 1 is to read the problem carefully.) Do not actually solve the equation. ***See Example 1.***

1. The numerator of the fraction $\frac{5}{6}$ is increased by an amount so that the value of the resulting fraction is equivalent to $\frac{13}{3}$. By what amount was the numerator increased?

   (a) Let $x =$ _____ . (*Step 2*)

   (b) Write an expression for "the numerator of the fraction $\frac{5}{6}$ is increased by an amount."

   (c) Set up an equation to solve the problem. (*Step 3*)

2. If the same number is added to the numerator and subtracted from the denominator of $\frac{23}{12}$, the resulting fraction is equivalent to $\frac{3}{2}$. What is the number?

   (a) Let $x =$ _____ . (*Step 2*)

   (b) Write an expression for "a number is added to the numerator of $\frac{23}{12}$." Then write an expression for "the same number is subtracted from the denominator of $\frac{23}{12}$."

   (c) Set up an equation to solve the problem. (*Step 3*)

*Solve each problem. **See Example 1.***

3. In a certain fraction, the denominator is 6 more than the numerator. If 3 is added to both the numerator and the denominator, the resulting fraction is equivalent to $\frac{5}{7}$. What was the original fraction (*not* written in lowest terms)?

4. In a certain fraction, the denominator is 4 less than the numerator. If 3 is added to both the numerator and the denominator, the resulting fraction is equivalent to $\frac{3}{2}$. What was the original fraction?

5. The numerator of a certain fraction is four times the denominator. If 6 is added to both the numerator and the denominator, the resulting fraction is equivalent to 2. What was the original fraction (*not* written in lowest terms)?

6. The denominator of a certain fraction is three times the numerator. If 2 is added to the numerator and subtracted from the denominator, the resulting fraction is equivalent to 1. What was the original fraction (*not* written in lowest terms)?

7. One-third of a number is 2 greater than one-sixth of the same number. What is the number?

8. One-seventh of a number is 6 greater than the same number. What is the number?

9. A quantity, $\frac{2}{3}$ of it, $\frac{1}{2}$ of it, and $\frac{1}{7}$ of it, added together, equals 33. What is the quantity? (*Source:* Rhind Mathematical Papyrus.)

10. A quantity, $\frac{3}{4}$ of it, $\frac{1}{2}$ of it, and $\frac{1}{3}$ of it, added together, equals 93. What is the quantity? (*Source:* Rhind Mathematical Papyrus.)

*Solve each problem. **See Example 5** in **Section 2.7 (pages 143 and 144).***

11. In 2007, British explorer and endurance swimmer Lewis Gordon Pugh became the first person to swim at the North Pole. He swam 0.6 mi at 0.0319 mi per min in waters created by melted sea ice. What was his time (to three decimal places)? (*Source: The Gazette.*)

12. In the 2008 Summer Olympics, Britta Steffen of Germany won the women's 100-m freestyle swimming event. Her rate was 1.8825 m per sec. What was her time (to two decimal places)? (*Source: World Almanac and Book of Facts.*)

13. Tirunesh Dibaba of Ethiopia won the women's 5000-m race in the 2008 Olympics with a time of 15.911 min. What was her rate (to three decimal places)? (*Source: World Almanac and Book of Facts.*)

14. The winner of the women's 1500-m run in the 2008 Olympics was Nancy Jebet Langat of Kenya with a time of 4.004 min. What was her rate (to three decimal places)? (*Source: World Almanac and Book of Facts.*)

15. The winner of the 2008 Daytona 500 (mile) race was Ryan Newman, who drove his Dodge to victory with a rate of 152.672 mph. What was his time (to the nearest thousandth of an hour)? (*Source: World Almanac and Book of Facts.*)

16. In 2008, Kasey Kahne drove his Dodge to victory in the Coca-Cola 600 (mile) race. His rate was 135.722 mph. What was his time (to the nearest thousandth of an hour)? (*Source: World Almanac and Book of Facts.*)

Concept Check *Solve each problem.*

17. Suppose Stephanie walks D miles at R mph in the same time that Wally walks d miles at r mph. Give an equation relating D, R, d, and r.

18. If a migrating hawk travels m mph in still air, what is its rate when it flies into a steady headwind of 6 mph?   What is its rate with a tailwind of 6 mph?

Set up the equation you would use to solve each problem. Do not actually solve the equation. ***See Example 2.***

19. Mitch Levy flew his airplane 500 mi against the wind in the same time it took him to fly 600 mi with the wind. If the speed of the wind was 10 mph, what was the rate of his plane in still air? (Let x = rate of the plane in still air.)

	d	r	t
Against the Wind	500	x − 10	
With the Wind	600	x + 10	

20. Janet Sturdy can row 4 mph in still water. She takes as long to row 8 mi upstream as 24 mi downstream. How fast is the current? (Let x = rate of the current.)

	d	r	t
Upstream	8	4 − x	
Downstream	24	4 + x	

Solve each problem. ***See Example 2.***

21. A boat can go 20 mi against a current in the same time that it can go 60 mi with the current. The current is 4 mph. Find the rate of the boat in still water.

22. Vince Grosso can fly his plane 200 mi against the wind in the same time it takes him to fly 300 mi with the wind. The wind blows at 30 mph. Find the rate of his plane in still air.

23. The sanderling is a small shorebird about 6.5 in. long, with a thin, dark bill and a wide, white wing stripe. If a sanderling can fly 30 mi with the wind in the same time it can fly 18 mi against the wind when the wind speed is 8 mph, what is the rate of the bird in still air? (*Source: U.S. Geological Survey.*)

24. Airplanes usually fly faster from west to east than from east to west because the prevailing winds go from west to east. The air distance between Chicago and London is about 4000 mi, while the air distance between New York and London is about 3500 mi. If a jet can fly eastbound from Chicago to London in the same time it can fly westbound from London to New York in a 35-mph wind, what is the rate of the plane in still air? (*Source. Encyclopaedia Britannica.*)

25. An airplane maintaining a constant airspeed takes as long to go 450 mi with the wind as it does to go 375 mi against the wind. If the wind is blowing at 15 mph, what is the rate of the plane in still air?

26. A river has a current of 4 km per hr. Find the rate of Jai Singh's boat in still water if it goes 40 km downstream in the same time that it takes to go 24 km upstream.

27. Connie McNair's boat goes 12 mph. Find the rate of the current of the river if she can go 6 mi upstream in the same amount of time she can go 10 mi downstream.

28. Howie Sorkin can travel 8 mi upstream in the same time it takes him to go 12 mi downstream. His boat goes 15 mph in still water. What is the rate of the current?

29. The distance from Seattle, Washington, to Victoria, British Columbia, is about 148 mi by ferry. It takes about 4 hr less to travel by the same ferry from Victoria to Vancouver, British Columbia, a distance of about 74 mi. What is the average rate of the ferry?

30. Driving from Tulsa to Detroit, Dean Loring averaged 50 mph. He figured that if he had averaged 60 mph, his driving time would have decreased 3 hr. How far is it from Tulsa to Detroit?

Concept Check *Solve each problem.*

31. If it takes Elayn 10 hr to do a job, what is her rate?

32. If it takes Clay 12 hr to do a job, how much of the job does he do in 8 hr?

In Exercises 33 and 34, set up the equation you would use to solve each problem. Do not actually solve the equation. ***See Example 3.***

33. Working alone, Edward Good can paint a room in 8 hr. Abdalla Elusta can paint the same room working alone in 6 hr. How long will it take them if they work together? (Let t represent the time they work together.)

	r	t	w
Edward		t	
Abdalla		t	

34. Donald Bridgewater can tune up his Chevy in 2 hr working alone. Jeff Bresner can do the job in 3 hr working alone. How long would it take them if they worked together? (Let t represent the time they work together.)

	r	t	w
Donald		t	
Jeff		t	

Solve each problem. ***See Example 3.***

🌐 **35.** Heather Schaefer, a high school mathematics teacher, gave a test on perimeter, area, and volume to her geometry classes. Working alone, it would take her 4 hr to grade the tests. Her student teacher, Courtney Slade, would take 6 hr to grade the same tests. How long would it take them to grade these tests if they work together?

36. Zachary and Samuel are brothers who share a bedroom. By himself, Zachary can completely mess up their room in 20 min, while it would take Samuel only 12 min to do the same thing. How long would it take them to mess up the room together?

37. A pump can pump the water out of a flooded basement in 10 hr. A smaller pump takes 12 hr. How long would it take to pump the water from the basement with both pumps?

38. Lou Viggiano's copier can do a printing job in 7 hr. Nora Demosthenes' copier can do the same job in 12 hr. How long would it take to do the job with both copiers?

39. An experienced employee can enter tax data into a computer twice as fast as a new employee. Working together, it takes the employees 2 hr. How long would it take the experienced employee working alone?

40. One roofer can put a new roof on a house three times faster than another. Working together, they can roof a house in 4 days. How long would it take the faster roofer working alone?

41. One pipe can fill a swimming pool in 6 hr, and another pipe can do it in 9 hr. How long will it take the two pipes working together to fill the pool $\frac{3}{4}$ full?

42. An inlet pipe can fill a swimming pool in 9 hr, and an outlet pipe can empty the pool in 12 hr. Through an error, both pipes are left open. How long will it take to fill the pool?

Brain Busters *Extend the concepts of* ***Example 3*** *to solve each problem.*

43. A cold-water faucet can fill a sink in 12 min, and a hot-water faucet can fill it in 15 min. The drain can empty the sink in 25 min. If both faucets are on and the drain is open, how long will it take to fill the sink?

44. Refer to **Exercise 42.** Assume that the error was discovered after both pipes had been running for 3 hr and the outlet pipe was then closed. How much more time would then be required to fill the pool? (*Hint:* Consider how much of the job had been done when the error was discovered.)

PREVIEW EXERCISES

Find each quotient. ***See Section 1.6.***

45. $\dfrac{6 - 2}{5 - 3}$

46. $\dfrac{5 - 7}{-4 - 2}$

47. $\dfrac{4 - (-1)}{-3 - (-5)}$

48. $\dfrac{-6 - 0}{0 - (-3)}$

49. $\dfrac{-5 - (-5)}{3 - 2}$

50. $\dfrac{7 - (-2)}{-3 - (-3)}$

Solve each equation for y. ***See Section 2.5.***

51. $3x + 2y = 8$

52. $4x + 3y = 0$

CHAPTER (6)

SUMMARY

KEY TERMS

6.1
rational expression
lowest terms

6.3
least common
  denominator (LCD)

6.5
complex fraction

6.6
proposed solution
extraneous solution (value)

TEST YOUR WORD POWER

See how well you have learned the vocabulary in this chapter.

1. A **rational expression** is
   A. an algebraic expression made up of a term or the sum of a finite number of terms with real coefficients and whole number exponents
   B. a polynomial equation of degree 2
   C. an expression with one or more fractions in the numerator, or denominator, or both
   D. the quotient of two polynomials with denominator not 0.

2. In a given set of fractions, the **least common denominator** is
   A. the smallest denominator of all the denominators
   B. the smallest expression that is divisible by all the denominators
   C. the largest integer that evenly divides the numerator and denominator of all the fractions
   D. the largest denominator of all the denominators.

3. A **complex fraction** is
   A. an algebraic expression made up of a term or the sum of a finite number of terms with real coefficients and whole number exponents
   B. a polynomial equation of degree 2
   C. a quotient with one or more fractions in the numerator, or denominator, or both
   D. the quotient of two polynomials with denominator not 0

ANSWERS

1. D; *Examples:* $-\dfrac{3}{4y}, \dfrac{5x^3}{x+2}, \dfrac{a+3}{a^2-4a-5}$ 2. B; *Example:* The LCD of $\dfrac{1}{x}, \dfrac{2}{3}$, and $\dfrac{5}{x+1}$ is $3x(x+1)$.   3. C; *Examples:* $\dfrac{\frac{2}{3}}{\frac{4}{7}}, \dfrac{x-\frac{1}{y}}{x+\frac{1}{y}}, \dfrac{\frac{2}{a+1}}{a^2-1}$

QUICK REVIEW

CONCEPTS	EXAMPLES
6.1 The Fundamental Property of Rational Expressions To find the value(s) for which a rational expression is undefined, set the denominator equal to 0 and solve the equation.	Find the values for which the expression $\dfrac{x-4}{x^2-16}$ is undefined. $x^2 - 16 = 0$ $(x-4)(x+4) = 0$ Factor. $x - 4 = 0$ or $x + 4 = 0$ Zero-factor property $x = 4$ or $x = -4$ Solve for x. The rational expression is undefined for 4 and -4, so $x \neq 4$ and $x \neq -4$.

(continued)

CONCEPTS	EXAMPLES

Writing a Rational Expression in Lowest Terms

Step 1 Factor the numerator and denominator.

Step 2 Use the fundamental property to divide out common factors.

Write in lowest terms. $\dfrac{x^2 - 1}{(x - 1)^2}$

$$= \frac{(x - 1)(x + 1)}{(x - 1)(x - 1)}$$

$$= \frac{x + 1}{x - 1}$$

6.2 Multiplying and Dividing Rational Expressions

Multiplying or Dividing Rational Expressions

Step 1 Note the operation. If the operation is division, use the definition of division to rewrite as multiplication.

Step 2 Multiply numerators and multiply denominators.

Step 3 Factor numerators and denominators completely.

Step 4 Write in lowest terms, using the fundamental property.

Note: Steps 2 and 3 may be interchanged based on personal preference.

Multiply. $\dfrac{3x + 9}{x - 5} \cdot \dfrac{x^2 - 3x - 10}{x^2 - 9}$

$$= \frac{(3x + 9)(x^2 - 3x - 10)}{(x - 5)(x^2 - 9)} \quad \text{Multiply numerators and denominators.}$$

$$= \frac{3(x + 3)(x - 5)(x + 2)}{(x - 5)(x + 3)(x - 3)} \quad \text{Factor.}$$

$$= \frac{3(x + 2)}{x - 3} \quad \text{Lowest terms}$$

Divide. $\dfrac{2x + 1}{x + 5} \div \dfrac{6x^2 - x - 2}{x^2 - 25}$

$$= \frac{2x + 1}{x + 5} \cdot \frac{x^2 - 25}{6x^2 - x - 2} \quad \text{Multiply by the reciprocal of the divisor.}$$

$$= \frac{(2x + 1)(x^2 - 25)}{(x + 5)(6x^2 - x - 2)} \quad \text{Multiply numerators and denominators.}$$

$$= \frac{(2x + 1)(x + 5)(x - 5)}{(x + 5)(2x + 1)(3x - 2)} \quad \text{Factor.}$$

$$= \frac{x - 5}{3x - 2} \quad \text{Lowest terms}$$

6.3 Least Common Denominators

Finding the LCD

Step 1 Factor each denominator into prime factors.

Step 2 List each different factor the greatest number of times it appears.

Step 3 Multiply the factors from Step 2 to get the LCD.

Writing a Rational Expression with a Specified Denominator

Step 1 Factor both denominators.

Step 2 Decide what factor(s) the denominator must be multiplied by in order to equal the specified denominator.

Step 3 Multiply the rational expression by that factor divided by itself. (That is, multiply by 1.)

Find the LCD for $\dfrac{3}{k^2 - 8k + 16}$ and $\dfrac{1}{4k^2 - 16k}$.

$$\begin{aligned} k^2 - 8k + 16 &= (k - 4)^2 \\ 4k^2 - 16k &= 4k(k - 4) \end{aligned} \Big\} \text{ Factor each denominator.}$$

$$\begin{aligned} \text{LCD} &= (k - 4)^2 \cdot 4 \cdot k \\ &= 4k(k - 4)^2 \end{aligned}$$

Find the numerator. $\dfrac{5}{2z^2 - 6z} = \dfrac{?}{4z^3 - 12z^2}$

$$\frac{5}{2z(z - 3)} = \frac{?}{4z^2(z - 3)}$$

$2z(z - 3)$ must be multiplied by $2z$ in order to obtain $4z^2(z - 3)$.

$$\frac{5}{2z(z - 3)} \cdot \frac{2z}{2z} = \frac{10z}{4z^2(z - 3)} = \frac{10z}{4z^3 - 12z^2}$$

(continued)

CONCEPTS	EXAMPLES
6.4 **Adding and Subtracting Rational Expressions** **Adding Rational Expressions** *Step 1* Find the LCD. *Step 2* Rewrite each rational expression with the LCD as denominator. *Step 3* Add the numerators to get the numerator of the sum. The LCD is the denominator of the sum. *Step 4* Write in lowest terms.	Add. $\dfrac{2}{3m + 6} + \dfrac{m}{m^2 - 4}$ $\left.\begin{array}{l} 3m + 6 = 3(m + 2) \\ m^2 - 4 = (m + 2)(m - 2) \end{array}\right\}$ The LCD is $3(m + 2)(m - 2)$. $= \dfrac{2(m - 2)}{3(m + 2)(m - 2)} + \dfrac{3m}{3(m + 2)(m - 2)}$ Write with the LCD. $= \dfrac{2m - 4 + 3m}{3(m + 2)(m - 2)}$ Add numerators and keep the same denominator. $= \dfrac{5m - 4}{3(m + 2)(m - 2)}$ Combine like terms.
Subtracting Rational Expressions Follow the same steps as for addition, but subtract in Step 3.	Subtract. $\dfrac{6}{k + 4} - \dfrac{2}{k}$ The LCD is $k(k + 4)$. $= \dfrac{6k}{(k + 4)k} - \dfrac{2(k + 4)}{k(k + 4)}$ Write with the LCD. $= \dfrac{6k - 2(k + 4)}{k(k + 4)}$ Subtract numerators and keep the same denominator. $= \dfrac{6k - 2k - 8}{k(k + 4)}$ Distributive property $= \dfrac{4k - 8}{k(k + 4)}$ Combine like terms.
6.5 **Complex Fractions** **Simplifying Complex Fractions** *Method 1* Simplify the numerator and denominator separately. Then divide the simplified numerator by the simplified denominator.	Simplify. *Method 1* $\dfrac{\dfrac{1}{a} - a}{1 - a} = \dfrac{\dfrac{1}{a} - \dfrac{a^2}{a}}{1 - a} = \dfrac{\dfrac{1 - a^2}{a}}{1 - a}$ $= \dfrac{1 - a^2}{a} \div (1 - a)$ $= \dfrac{1 - a^2}{a} \cdot \dfrac{1}{1 - a}$ Multiply by the reciprocal of the divisor. $= \dfrac{(1 - a)(1 + a)}{a(1 - a)} = \dfrac{1 + a}{a}$
Method 2 Multiply the numerator and denominator of the complex fraction by the LCD of all the denominators in the complex fraction. Write in lowest terms.	*Method 2* $\dfrac{\dfrac{1}{a} - a}{1 - a} = \dfrac{\left(\dfrac{1}{a} - a\right)a}{(1 - a)a} = \dfrac{\dfrac{a}{a} - a^2}{(1 - a)a}$ $= \dfrac{1 - a^2}{(1 - a)a} = \dfrac{(1 + a)(1 - a)}{(1 - a)a}$ $= \dfrac{1 + a}{a}$

(continued)

CONCEPTS	EXAMPLES

6.6 Solving Equations with Rational Expressions

Solving Equations with Rational Expressions

Step 1 Multiply each side of the equation by the LCD to clear the equation of fractions. Be sure to distribute to *every* term on *both* sides.

Solve.

$$\frac{x}{x-3} + \frac{4}{x+3} = \frac{18}{x^2-9}$$

$$\frac{x}{x-3} + \frac{4}{x+3} = \frac{18}{(x-3)(x+3)} \qquad \text{Factor.}$$

The LCD is $(x-3)(x+3)$. Note that 3 and -3 cannot be solutions, as they cause a denominator to equal 0.

$$(x-3)(x+3)\left(\frac{x}{x-3} + \frac{4}{x+3}\right)$$

$$= (x-3)(x+3)\frac{18}{(x-3)(x+3)} \qquad \text{Multiply by the LCD.}$$

Step 2 Solve the resulting equation.

$$x(x+3) + 4(x-3) = 18 \qquad \text{Distributive property}$$

$$x^2 + 3x + 4x - 12 = 18 \qquad \text{Distributive property}$$

$$x^2 + 7x - 30 = 0 \qquad \text{Standard form}$$

$$(x-3)(x+10) = 0 \qquad \text{Factor.}$$

$$x - 3 = 0 \quad \text{or} \quad x + 10 = 0 \qquad \text{Zero-factor property}$$

$$\text{Reject} \longrightarrow x = 3 \quad \text{or} \qquad x = -10 \qquad \text{Solve for } x.$$

Step 3 Check each proposed solution.

Since 3 causes denominators to equal 0, the only solution is -10. Thus, $\{-10\}$ is the solution set.

6.7 Applications of Rational Expressions

Solving Problems about Distance, Rate, and Time

Use the formulas relating d, r, and t.

$$d = rt, \quad r = \frac{d}{t}, \quad t = \frac{d}{r}$$

Solving Problems about Work

Step 1 Read the problem carefully.

Step 2 Assign a variable. State what the variable represents. Put the information from the problem into a table. If a job is done in t units of time, the rate is $\frac{1}{t}$.

It takes the regular mail carrier 6 hr to cover her route. A substitute takes 8 hr to cover the same route. How long would it take them to cover the route together?

Let $x =$ the number of hours required to cover the route together.

	Rate	Time	Part of the Job Done
Regular	$\frac{1}{6}$	x	$\frac{1}{6}x$
Substitute	$\frac{1}{8}$	x	$\frac{1}{8}x$

Step 3 Write an equation. The sum of the fractional parts should equal 1 (whole job).

Step 4 Solve the equation.

$$\frac{1}{6}x + \frac{1}{8}x = 1$$

$$24\left(\frac{1}{6}x + \frac{1}{8}x\right) = 24(1) \qquad \text{The LCD is 24.}$$

$$4x + 3x = 24 \qquad \text{Distributive property}$$

$$7x = 24 \qquad \text{Combine like terms.}$$

$$x = \frac{24}{7} \qquad \text{Divide by 7.}$$

Steps 5 and 6 State the answer and check the solution.

It would take them $\frac{24}{7}$ hr, or $3\frac{3}{7}$ hr, to cover the route together.

The solution checks because $\frac{1}{6}\left(\frac{24}{7}\right) + \frac{1}{8}\left(\frac{24}{7}\right) = 1$.

CHAPTER 6 REVIEW EXERCISES

6.1 *Find the numerical value of each rational expression for **(a)** and **(b)**.*

1. $\dfrac{4x - 3}{5x + 2}$

2. $\dfrac{3x}{x^2 - 4}$

Find any values of the variable for which each rational expression is undefined. Write answers with the symbol $\neq$.

3. $\dfrac{4}{x - 3}$

4. $\dfrac{y + 3}{2y}$

5. $\dfrac{2k + 1}{3k^2 + 17k + 10}$

6. How do you determine the values of the variable for which a rational expression is undefined?

Write each rational expression in lowest terms.

7. $\dfrac{5a^3b^3}{15a^4b^2}$

8. $\dfrac{m - 4}{4 - m}$

9. $\dfrac{4x^2 - 9}{6 - 4x}$

10. $\dfrac{4p^2 + 8pq - 5q^2}{10p^2 - 3pq - q^2}$

Write four equivalent forms for each rational expression.

11. $-\dfrac{4x - 9}{2x + 3}$

12. $-\dfrac{8 - 3x}{3 - 6x}$

6.2 *Multiply or divide, and write each answer in lowest terms.*

13. $\dfrac{18p^3}{6} \cdot \dfrac{24}{p^4}$

14. $\dfrac{8x^2}{12x^5} \cdot \dfrac{6x^4}{2x}$

15. $\dfrac{x - 3}{4} \cdot \dfrac{5}{2x - 6}$

16. $\dfrac{2r + 3}{r - 4} \cdot \dfrac{r^2 - 16}{6r + 9}$

17. $\dfrac{6a^2 + 7a - 3}{2a^2 - a - 6} \div \dfrac{a + 5}{a - 2}$

18. $\dfrac{y^2 - 6y + 8}{y^2 + 3y - 18} \div \dfrac{y - 4}{y + 6}$

19. $\dfrac{2p^2 + 13p + 20}{p^2 + p - 12} \cdot \dfrac{p^2 + 2p - 15}{2p^2 + 7p + 5}$

20. $\dfrac{3z^2 + 5z - 2}{9z^2 - 1} \cdot \dfrac{9z^2 + 6z + 1}{z^2 + 5z + 6}$

6.3 *Find the least common denominator for the fractions in each list.*

21. $\dfrac{4}{9y}, \dfrac{7}{12y^2}, \dfrac{5}{27y^4}$

22. $\dfrac{3}{x^2 + 4x + 3}, \dfrac{5}{x^2 + 5x + 4}$

Rewrite each rational expression with the given denominator.

23. $\dfrac{3}{2a^3} = \dfrac{?}{10a^4}$

24. $\dfrac{9}{x - 3} = \dfrac{?}{18 - 6x}$

25. $\dfrac{-3y}{2y - 10} = \dfrac{?}{50 - 10y}$

26. $\dfrac{4b}{b^2 + 2b - 3} = \dfrac{?}{(b + 3)(b - 1)(b + 2)}$

6.4 *Add or subtract, and write each answer in lowest terms.*

27. $\dfrac{10}{x} + \dfrac{5}{x}$

28. $\dfrac{6}{3p} - \dfrac{12}{3p}$

29. $\dfrac{9}{k} - \dfrac{5}{k-5}$

30. $\dfrac{4}{y} + \dfrac{7}{7+y}$

31. $\dfrac{m}{3} - \dfrac{2+5m}{6}$

32. $\dfrac{12}{x^2} - \dfrac{3}{4x}$

33. $\dfrac{5}{a-2b} + \dfrac{2}{a+2b}$

34. $\dfrac{4}{k^2-9} - \dfrac{k+3}{3k-9}$

35. $\dfrac{8}{z^2+6z} - \dfrac{3}{z^2+4z-12}$

36. $\dfrac{11}{2p-p^2} - \dfrac{2}{p^2-5p+6}$

6.5 *Simplify each complex fraction.*

37. $\dfrac{\frac{y-3}{y}}{\frac{y+3}{4y}}$

38. $\dfrac{\frac{2}{3} - \frac{1}{6}}{\frac{1}{4} + \frac{2}{5}}$

39. $\dfrac{x + \frac{1}{w}}{x - \frac{1}{w}}$

40. $\dfrac{\frac{1}{p} - \frac{1}{q}}{\frac{1}{q-p}}$

41. $\dfrac{\frac{x^2-25}{x+3}}{\frac{x+5}{x^2-9}}$

42. $\dfrac{x^{-2} - y^{-2}}{x^{-1} - y^{-1}}$

6.6 *Solve each equation, and check your solutions.*

43. $\dfrac{3x-1}{x-2} = \dfrac{5}{x-2} + 1$

44. $\dfrac{4-z}{z} + \dfrac{3}{2} = \dfrac{-4}{z}$

45. $\dfrac{3}{x+4} - \dfrac{2x}{5} = \dfrac{3}{x+4}$

46. $\dfrac{3}{m-2} + \dfrac{1}{m-1} = \dfrac{7}{m^2-3m+2}$

Solve each formula for the specified variable.

47. $m = \dfrac{Ry}{t}$ for t

48. $x = \dfrac{3y-5}{4}$ for y

49. $p^2 = \dfrac{4}{3m-q}$ for m

6.7 *Solve each problem.*

50. In a certain fraction, the denominator is 5 less than the numerator. If 5 is added to both the numerator and the denominator, the resulting fraction is equivalent to $\frac{5}{4}$. Find the original fraction (*not* written in lowest terms).

51. The denominator of a certain fraction is six times the numerator. If 3 is added to the numerator and subtracted from the denominator, the resulting fraction is equivalent to $\frac{2}{5}$. Find the original fraction (*not* written in lowest terms).

52. A plane flies 350 mi with the wind in the same time that it can fly 310 mi against the wind. The plane has a speed of 165 mph in still air. Find the speed of the wind.

53. Susan Costa can plant her garden in 5 hr working alone. A friend can do the same job in 8 hr. How long would it take them if they worked together?

54. The head gardener can mow the lawns in the city park twice as fast as his assistant. Working together, they can complete the job in $1\frac{1}{3}$ hr. How long would it take the head gardener working alone?

MIXED REVIEW EXERCISES

Perform each indicated operation.

55. $\dfrac{4}{m-1} - \dfrac{3}{m+1}$

56. $\dfrac{8p^5}{5} \div \dfrac{2p^3}{10}$

57. $\dfrac{r-3}{8} \div \dfrac{3r-9}{4}$

58. $\dfrac{t^{-2}+s^{-2}}{t^{-1}-s^{-1}}$

59. $\dfrac{\dfrac{5}{x}-1}{\dfrac{5-x}{3x}}$

60. $\dfrac{4}{z^2-2z+1} - \dfrac{3}{z^2-1}$

61. $\dfrac{1}{t^2-4} + \dfrac{1}{2-t}$

Solve.

62. $\dfrac{2}{z} - \dfrac{z}{z+3} = \dfrac{1}{z+3}$

63. $a = \dfrac{v-w}{t}$ for v

64. Rob Fusco flew his plane 400 km with the wind in the same time it took him to go 200 km against the wind. The speed of the wind is 50 km per hr. Find the rate of the plane in still air.

65. With spraying equipment, Lizette Foley can paint the woodwork in a small house in 8 hr. Seyed Sadati needs 14 hr to complete the same job painting by hand. If Lizette and Seyed work together, how long will it take them to paint the woodwork?

RELATING CONCEPTS   EXERCISES 66–75

FOR INDIVIDUAL OR GROUP WORK

In these exercises, we summarize the various concepts involving rational expressions.
Work Exercises 66–75 in order.

Let P, Q, and R be rational expressions defined as follows:

$$P = \frac{6}{x+3}, \qquad Q = \frac{5}{x+1}, \qquad R = \frac{4x}{x^2+4x+3}.$$

66. Find the value or values for which the expression is undefined.

    (a) P **(b)** Q **(c)** R

67. Find and express $(P \cdot Q) \div R$ in lowest terms.

68. Why is $(P \cdot Q) \div R$ not defined if $x = 0$?

69. Find the LCD for P, Q, and R.

70. Perform the operations and express $P + Q - R$ in lowest terms.

71. Simplify the complex fraction $\dfrac{P+Q}{R}$.

72. Solve the equation $P + Q = R$.

73. How does your answer to **Exercise 66** help you work **Exercise 72?**

74. Suppose that a car travels 6 miles in $(x + 3)$ minutes. Explain why P represents the rate of the car (in miles per minute).

75. For what value or values of x is $R = \frac{40}{77}$?

CHAPTER **6**

TEST

CHAPTER Test Prep

Step-by-step test solutions are found on the Chapter Test Prep Videos available via the Video Resources on DVD, in *MyMathLab*, or on YouTube (search "LialCombinedAlgebra").

View the complete solutions to all Chapter Test exercises on the Video Resources on DVD.

1. Find the numerical value of $\dfrac{6r + 1}{2r^2 - 3r - 20}$ for **(a)** $r = -2$ and **(b)** $r = 4$.

2. Find any values for which $\dfrac{3x - 1}{x^2 - 2x - 8}$ is undefined. Write your answer with the symbol $\neq$.

3. Write four rational expressions equivalent to $-\dfrac{6x - 5}{2x + 3}$.

Write each rational expression in lowest terms.

4. $\dfrac{-15x^6 y^4}{5x^4 y}$

5. $\dfrac{6a^2 + a - 2}{2a^2 - 3a + 1}$

Multiply or divide. Write each answer in lowest terms.

6. $\dfrac{5(d - 2)}{9} \div \dfrac{3(d - 2)}{5}$

7. $\dfrac{6k^2 - k - 2}{8k^2 + 10k + 3} \cdot \dfrac{4k^2 + 7k + 3}{3k^2 + 5k + 2}$

8. $\dfrac{4a^2 + 9a + 2}{3a^2 + 11a + 10} \div \dfrac{4a^2 + 17a + 4}{3a^2 + 2a - 5}$

9. $\dfrac{x^2 - 10x + 25}{9 - 6x + x^2} \cdot \dfrac{x - 3}{5 - x}$

Find the least common denominator for the fractions in each list.

10. $\dfrac{-3}{10p^2}, \dfrac{21}{25p^3}, \dfrac{-7}{30p^5}$

11. $\dfrac{r + 1}{2r^2 + 7r + 6}, \dfrac{-2r + 1}{2r^2 - 7r - 15}$

Rewrite each rational expression with the given denominator.

12. $\dfrac{15}{4p} = \dfrac{?}{64p^3}$

13. $\dfrac{3}{6m - 12} = \dfrac{?}{42m - 84}$

Add or subtract. Write each answer in lowest terms.

14. $\dfrac{4x + 2}{x + 5} + \dfrac{-2x + 8}{x + 5}$

15. $\dfrac{-4}{y + 2} + \dfrac{6}{5y + 10}$

16. $\dfrac{x + 1}{3 - x} + \dfrac{x^2}{x - 3}$

17. $\dfrac{3}{2m^2 - 9m - 5} - \dfrac{m + 1}{2m^2 - m - 1}$

Simplify each complex fraction.

18. $\dfrac{\dfrac{2p}{k^2}}{\dfrac{3p^2}{k^3}}$

19. $\dfrac{\dfrac{1}{x + 3} - 1}{1 + \dfrac{1}{x + 3}}$

20. $\dfrac{2x^{-2} + y^{-2}}{x^{-1} - y^{-1}}$

Solve.

21. $\dfrac{3x}{x + 1} = \dfrac{3}{2x}$

22. $\dfrac{2x}{x - 3} + \dfrac{1}{x + 3} = \dfrac{-6}{x^2 - 9}$

23. $F = \dfrac{k}{d - D}$ for D

Solve each problem.

24. A boat goes 7 mph in still water. It takes as long to go 20 mi upstream as 50 mi downstream. Find the rate of the current.

25. Sanford Geraci can paint a room in his house, working alone, in 5 hr. His neighbor can do the job in 4 hr. How long will it take them to paint the room if they work together?

CHAPTERS (1–6) CUMULATIVE REVIEW EXERCISES

1. Use the order of operations to evaluate $3 + 4\left(\frac{1}{2} - \frac{3}{4}\right)$.

Solve.

2. $3(2y - 5) = 2 + 5y$

3. $\mathcal{A} = \frac{1}{2}bh$ for b

4. $\dfrac{2 + m}{2 - m} = \dfrac{3}{4}$

5. $5y \le 6y + 8$

6. Consider the graph of $4x + 3y = -12$.

   (a) What is the x-intercept? (b) What is the y-intercept?

Sketch each graph.

7. $y = -3x + 2$

8. $y = -x^2 + 1$

Simplify each expression. Write with only positive exponents.

9. $\dfrac{(2x^3)^{-1} \cdot x}{2^3 x^5}$

10. $\dfrac{(m^{-2})^3 m}{m^5 m^{-4}}$

Perform each indicated operation.

11. $(2k^2 + 3k) - (k^2 + k - 1)$

12. $(2a - b)^2$

13. $(y^2 + 3y + 5)(3y - 1)$

14. $\dfrac{12p^3 + 2p^2 - 12p + 4}{2p - 2}$

Factor completely.

15. $8t^2 + 10tv + 3v^2$

16. $8r^2 - 9rs + 12s^2$

17. $16x^4 - 1$

Solve each equation.

18. $r^2 = 2r + 15$

19. $(r - 5)(2r + 1)(3r - 2) = 0$

Solve each problem.

20. One number is 4 greater than another. The product of the numbers is 2 less than the lesser number. Find the lesser number.

21. The length of a rectangle is 2 m less than twice the width. The area is 60 m². Find the width of the rectangle.

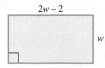

2w – 2

w

22. Which one of the following is equal to 1 for *all* real numbers?

   A. $\dfrac{k^2 + 2}{k^2 + 2}$ B. $\dfrac{4 - m}{4 - m}$ C. $\dfrac{2x + 9}{2x + 9}$ D. $\dfrac{x^2 - 1}{x^2 - 1}$

23. Which one of the following rational expressions is *not* equivalent to $\dfrac{4 - 3x}{7}$?

   A. $-\dfrac{-4 + 3x}{7}$ B. $-\dfrac{4 - 3x}{-7}$ C. $\dfrac{-4 + 3x}{-7}$ D. $\dfrac{-(3x + 4)}{7}$

Perform each operation and write the answer in lowest terms.

24. $\dfrac{5}{q} - \dfrac{1}{q}$

25. $\dfrac{3}{7} + \dfrac{4}{r}$

26. $\dfrac{4}{5q - 20} - \dfrac{1}{3q - 12}$

27. $\dfrac{2}{k^2 + k} - \dfrac{3}{k^2 - k}$

28. $\dfrac{7z^2 + 49z + 70}{16z^2 + 72z - 40} \div \dfrac{3z + 6}{4z^2 - 1}$

29. $\dfrac{\dfrac{4}{a} + \dfrac{5}{2a}}{\dfrac{7}{6a} - \dfrac{1}{5a}}$

Solve each equation. Check your solutions.

30. $\dfrac{r + 2}{5} = \dfrac{r - 3}{3}$

31. $\dfrac{1}{x} = \dfrac{1}{x + 1} + \dfrac{1}{2}$

32. Jody Harris can weed the yard in 3 hr. Pat Tabler can weed the same yard in 2 hr. How long will it take them if they work together?

Graphs, Linear Equations, and Functions

7.1 Review of Graphs and Slopes of Lines

7.2 Review of Equations of Lines; Linear Models

Summary Exercises on Slopes and Equations of Lines

7.3 Introduction to Relations and Functions

7.4 Function Notation and Linear Functions

7.5 Operations on Functions and Composition

7.6 Variation

The two most common measures of temperature are Fahrenheit (F) and Celsius (C). It is fairly common knowledge that water freezes at 32°F, or 0°C, and boils at 212°F, or 100°C. Because there is a *linear* relationship between the Fahrenheit and Celsius temperature scales, using these two equivalences we can derive the familiar formulas for converting from one temperature scale to the other, as seen in **Section 7.2, Exercises 93–100.**

Graphs are widely used in the media because they present a great deal of information in a concise form. In this chapter, we see how information such as the relationship between the two temperature scales can be depicted by graphs.

7.1   Review of Graphs and Slopes of Lines

OBJECTIVES

1. Plot ordered pairs.
2. Graph lines and find intercepts.
3. Recognize equations of horizontal and vertical lines and lines passing through the origin.
4. Use the midpoint formula.
5. Find the slope of a line.
6. Graph a line, given its slope and a point on the line.
7. Use slopes to determine whether two lines are parallel, perpendicular, or neither.
8. Solve problems involving average rate of change.

This section and the next review and extend some of the main topics of linear equations in two variables, first introduced in **Chapter 3.**

OBJECTIVE 1   **Plot ordered pairs.** Each of the pairs of numbers

$$(3, 2), \quad (-5, 6), \quad \text{and} \quad (4, -1)$$

is an example of an **ordered pair**—that is, a pair of numbers written within parentheses, consisting of a **first component** and a **second component.** We graph an ordered pair by using two perpendicular number lines that intersect at their 0 points, as shown in the plane in **FIGURE 1.** The common 0 point is called the **origin.**

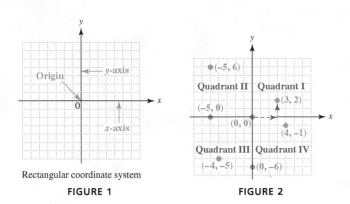

Rectangular coordinate system

FIGURE 1

FIGURE 2

The position of any point in this plane is determined by referring to the horizontal number line, or **x-axis,** and the vertical number line, or **y-axis.** The x-axis and y-axis make up a **rectangular coordinate system,** also called a **Cartesian coordinate system** after René Descartes, the French mathematician credited with its invention.

In an ordered pair, the first component indicates position relative to the x-axis, and the second component indicates position relative to the y-axis. For example, to locate, or **plot,** the point on the graph that corresponds to the ordered pair $(3, 2)$, we move three units from 0 to the right along the x-axis and then two units up parallel to the y-axis. See **FIGURE 2.** The numbers in an ordered pair are called the **coordinates** of the corresponding point.

The four regions of the graph, shown in **FIGURE 2,** are called **quadrants I, II, III, and IV,** reading counterclockwise from the upper right quadrant. *The points on the x-axis and y-axis do not belong to any quadrant.*

OBJECTIVE 2   **Graph lines and find intercepts.** Each solution of an equation with two variables, such as

$$2x + 3y = 6,$$

includes two numbers, one for each variable. To keep track of which number goes with which variable, we write the solutions as ordered pairs. *(If x and y are used as the variables, the x-value is given first.)*

For example, we can show that $(6, -2)$ is a solution of the equation $2x + 3y = 6$ by substitution.

$$2x + 3y = 6$$

$$2(6) + 3(-2) \overset{?}{=} 6 \qquad \text{Let } x = 6, y = -2.$$

Use parentheses to avoid errors.

$$12 - 6 \overset{?}{=} 6 \qquad \text{Multiply.}$$

$$6 = 6 \quad \checkmark \quad \text{True}$$

Because the ordered pair $(6, -2)$ makes the equation true, it is a solution. On the other hand, $(5, 1)$ is *not* a solution of the equation $2x + 3y = 6$.

$$2x + 3y = 6$$

$$2(5) + 3(1) \overset{?}{=} 6 \qquad \text{Let } x = 5, y = 1.$$

$$10 + 3 \overset{?}{=} 6 \qquad \text{Multiply.}$$

$$13 = 6 \qquad \text{False}$$

To find ordered pairs that satisfy an equation, select a number for one of the variables, substitute it into the equation for that variable, and solve for the other variable. Two other ordered pairs satisfying $2x + 3y = 6$ are $(0, 2)$ and $(3, 0)$.

Since any real number could be selected for one variable and would lead to a real number for the other variable, linear equations in two variables have an infinite number of solutions.

The **graph of an equation** is the set of points corresponding to *all* ordered pairs that satisfy the equation. It gives a "picture" of the equation. The graph of the equation $2x + 3y = 6$ is shown in **FIGURE 3** along with a table of ordered pairs.

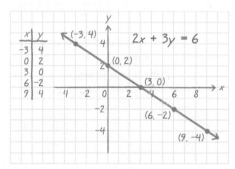

FIGURE 3

The equation $2x + 3y = 6$ is called a **first-degree equation,** because it has no term with a variable to a power greater than 1.

The graph of any first-degree equation in two variables is a straight line.

Since first-degree equations with two variables have straight-line graphs, they are called *linear equations in two variables.*

Linear Equation in Two Variables

A **linear equation in two variables** can be written in the form

$$Ax + By = C,$$

where A, B, and C are real numbers and A and B are not both 0. This form is called **standard form.**

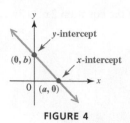

FIGURE 4

A straight line is determined if any two different points on the line are known. Two useful points for graphing are the *x*- and *y*-intercepts. The ***x*-intercept** is the point (if any) where the line intersects the *x*-axis. The ***y*-intercept** is the point (if any) where the line intersects the *y*-axis.* See **FIGURE 4**.

The *y*-value of the point where the line intersects the *x*-axis is 0. Similarly, the *x*-value of the point where the line intersects the *y*-axis is 0. This suggests a method for finding the *x*- and *y*-intercepts.

Finding Intercepts

When graphing the equation of a line, find the intercepts as follows.

Let $y = 0$ to find the *x*-intercept.

Let $x = 0$ to find the *y*-intercept.

NOW TRY
EXERCISE 1

Find the *x*- and *y*-intercepts, and graph the equation.

$$x - 2y = 4$$

EXAMPLE 1 Finding Intercepts

Find the *x*- and *y*-intercepts of $4x - y = -3$ and graph the equation.

To find the *x*-intercept, let $y = 0$.

$$4x - y = -3$$
$$4x - 0 = -3 \quad \text{Let } y = 0.$$
$$4x = -3$$
$$x = -\frac{3}{4} \quad \text{x-intercept is } \left(-\frac{3}{4}, 0\right).$$

To find the *y*-intercept, let $x = 0$.

$$4x - y = -3$$
$$4(0) - y = -3 \quad \text{Let } x = 0.$$
$$-y = -3$$
$$y = 3 \quad \text{y-intercept is } (0, 3).$$

The intercepts of $4x - y = -3$ are the points $\left(-\frac{3}{4}, 0\right)$ and $(0, 3)$. Verify by substitution that $(-2, -5)$ also satisfies the equation. We use these ordered pairs to draw the graph in **FIGURE 5**.

x	y
$-\frac{3}{4}$	0
0	3
-2	-5

Use a third point as a check.

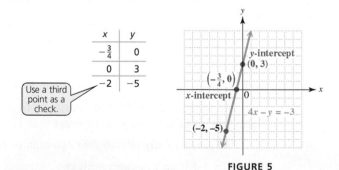

FIGURE 5

NOW TRY

NOW TRY ANSWER

1. *x*-intercept: $(4, 0)$;
   y-intercept: $(0, -2)$

NOTE While two points, such as the two intercepts in **FIGURE 5**, are sufficient to graph a straight line, *it is a good idea to use a third point to guard against errors.*

---

*Some texts define an intercept as a number, not a point. For example, "*y*-intercept $(0, 4)$" would be given as "*y*-intercept 4."

OBJECTIVE 3 **Recognize equations of horizontal and vertical lines and lines passing through the origin.** A line parallel to the *x*-axis will not have an *x*-intercept. Similarly, a line parallel to the *y*-axis will not have a *y*-intercept. We graph these types of lines in the next two examples.

NOW TRY
EXERCISE 2
Graph $y = -2$.

EXAMPLE 2 Graphing a Horizontal Line

Graph $y = 2$.

Writing $y = 2$ as $0x + 1y = 2$ shows that any value of *x*, including $x = 0$, gives $y = 2$. Thus, the *y*-intercept is $(0, 2)$. Since *y* is always 2, there is no value of *x* corresponding to $y = 0$, so the graph has no *x*-intercept. The graph is shown with a table of ordered pairs in **FIGURE 6**. It is a horizontal line.

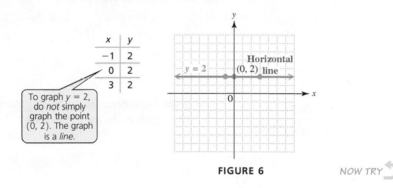

x	y
−1	2
0	2
3	2

To graph $y = 2$, do *not* simply graph the point $(0, 2)$. The graph is a *line*.

FIGURE 6 *NOW TRY*

NOTE The horizontal line $y = 0$ is the *x*-axis.

NOW TRY
EXERCISE 3
Graph $x + 3 = 0$.

EXAMPLE 3 Graphing a Vertical Line

Graph $x + 1 = 0$.

The form $1x + 0y = -1$ shows that every value of *y* leads to $x = -1$, making the *x*-intercept $(-1, 0)$. No value of *y* makes $x = 0$, so the graph has no *y*-intercept. A straight line that has no *y*-intercept is vertical. See **FIGURE 7**.

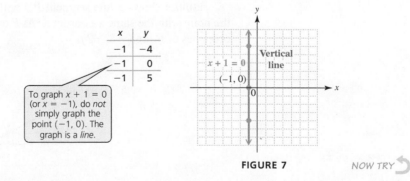

x	y
−1	−4
−1	0
−1	5

To graph $x + 1 = 0$ (or $x = -1$), do *not* simply graph the point $(-1, 0)$. The graph is a *line*.

FIGURE 7 *NOW TRY*

NOW TRY ANSWERS

2. 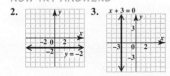 3.

NOTE The vertical line $x = 0$ is the *y*-axis.

NOW TRY
EXERCISE 4
Graph $2x + 3y = 0$.

EXAMPLE 4 Graphing a Line That Passes through the Origin

Graph $x + 2y = 0$.

Find the x-intercept.

$$x + 2y = 0$$
$$x + 2(0) = 0 \quad \text{Let } y = 0.$$
$$x + 0 = 0 \quad \text{Multiply.}$$
$$x = 0 \quad \text{x-intercept is } (0, 0).$$

Find the y-intercept.

$$x + 2y = 0$$
$$0 + 2y = 0 \quad \text{Let } x = 0.$$
$$2y = 0 \quad \text{Add.}$$
$$y = 0 \quad \text{y-intercept is } (0, 0).$$

Both intercepts are the same point, $(0, 0)$, which means that the graph passes through the origin. To find another point, choose any nonzero number for x or y and solve for the other variable. We choose $x = 4$.

$$x + 2y = 0$$
$$4 + 2y = 0 \quad \text{Let } x = 4.$$
$$2y = -4 \quad \text{Subtract 4.}$$
$$y = -2 \quad \text{Divide by 2.}$$

This gives the ordered pair $(4, -2)$. As a check, verify that $(-2, 1)$ also lies on the line. The graph is shown in **FIGURE 8**.

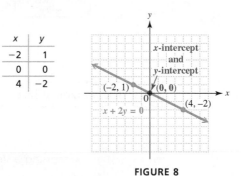

x	y
-2	1
0	0
4	-2

FIGURE 8

NOW TRY

OBJECTIVE 4 **Use the midpoint formula.** If the coordinates of the endpoints of a line segment are known, then the coordinates of the *midpoint* of the segment can be found.

FIGURE 9 shows a line segment PQ with endpoints $P(-8, 4)$ and $Q(3, -2)$. R is the point with the same x-coordinate as P and the same y-coordinate as Q. So the coordinates of R are $(-8, -2)$.

NOW TRY ANSWER
4.

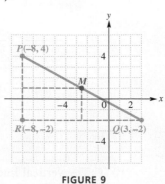

FIGURE 9

The x-coordinate of the midpoint M of PQ is the same as the x-coordinate of the midpoint of RQ. Since RQ is horizontal, the x-coordinate of its midpoint is the *average* of the x-coordinates of its endpoints.

$$\frac{1}{2}(-8 + 3) = -2.5$$

The y-coordinate of M is the average of the y-coordinates of the midpoint of PR.

$$\frac{1}{2}(4 + (-2)) = 1$$

The midpoint of PQ is $M(-2.5, 1)$. This discussion leads to the *midpoint formula*.

Midpoint Formula

If the endpoints of a line segment PQ are (x_1, y_1) and (x_2, y_2), its midpoint M is

$$\left(\frac{x_1 + x_2}{2}, \frac{y_1 + y_2}{2} \right).$$

Recall that the small numbers 1 and 2 in the ordered pairs above are called **subscripts**. Read (x_1, y_1) as "***x*-sub-one, *y*-sub-one**."

NOW TRY
EXERCISE 5

Find the coordinates of the midpoint of the line segment PQ with endpoints $P(2, -5)$ and $Q(-4, 7)$.

EXAMPLE 5   Finding the Coordinates of a Midpoint

Find the coordinates of the midpoint of line segment PQ with endpoints $P(4, -3)$ and $Q(6, -1)$.

Use the midpoint formula with $x_1 = 4$, $x_2 = 6$, $y_1 = -3$, and $y_2 = -1$.

$$\left(\frac{4 + 6}{2}, \frac{-3 + (-1)}{2} \right) = \left(\frac{10}{2}, \frac{-4}{2} \right) = (5, -2) \longleftarrow \text{Midpoint}$$

NOW TRY

NOTE   When finding the coordinates of the midpoint of a line segment, we are finding the *average* of the x-coordinates and the *average* of the y-coordinates of the endpoints of the segment. In both cases, add the corresponding coordinates and divide the sum by 2.

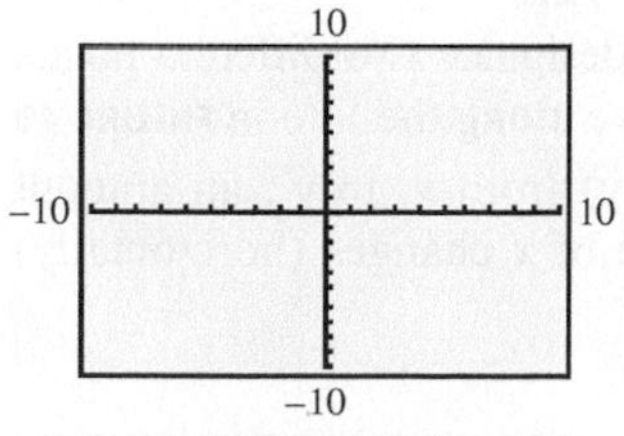

Standard viewing window
FIGURE 10

CONNECTIONS

When graphing with a graphing calculator, we must tell the calculator how to set up a rectangular coordinate system. In the screen in **FIGURE 10**, we chose minimum x- and y-values of -10 and maximum x- and y-values of 10. The **scale** on each axis determines the distance between the tick marks. In the screen shown, the scale is 1 for both axes. We refer to this screen as the **standard viewing window**.

To graph an equation such as $4x - y = 3$, we must solve the equation for y to enter it into the calculator.

$$4x - y = 3$$

$$-y = -4x + 3 \qquad \text{Subtract } 4x.$$

$$y = 4x - 3 \qquad \text{Multiply by } -1.$$

NOW TRY ANSWER
5. $(-1, 1)$

The graph of $y = 4x - 3$ in **FIGURE 11** also gives the intercepts at the bottoms of the screens. Some calculators have the capability of locating the x-intercept (called "Root" or "Zero").

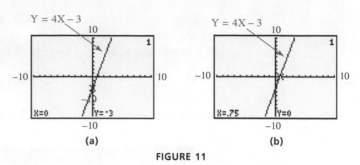

(a)   (b)

FIGURE 11

For Discussion or Writing

1. The graphing calculator screens in **Exercise 39** on **page 439** show the graph of a linear equation. What are the intercepts?

Graph each equation with a graphing calculator. Use the standard viewing window.

2. $4x - y = -3$ **(Example 1)**   3. $x + 2y = 0$ **(Example 4)**

OBJECTIVE 5 **Find the slope of a line.** Slope (steepness) is used in many practical ways. The slope of a highway (sometimes called the *grade*) is often given as a percent. For example, a 10% $\left(\text{or } \frac{10}{100} = \frac{1}{10}\right)$ slope means that the highway rises 1 unit for every 10 horizontal units. Stairs and roofs have slopes too, as shown in **FIGURE 12**.

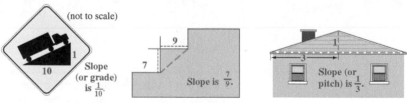

FIGURE 12

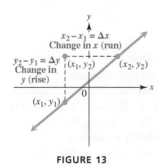

FIGURE 13

Slope is the ratio of vertical change, or **rise,** to horizontal change, or **run.** A simple way to remember this is to think, ***"Slope is rise over run."***

To get a formal definition of the slope of a line, we designate two different points (x_1, y_1) and (x_2, y_2) on the line. See **FIGURE 13.** As we move along the line in **FIGURE 13** from (x_1, y_1) to (x_2, y_2), the y-value changes (vertically) from y_1 to y_2, an amount equal to $y_2 - y_1$. As y changes from y_1 to y_2, the value of x changes (horizontally) from x_1 to x_2 by the amount $x_2 - x_1$.

NOTE The Greek letter **delta,** Δ, is used in mathematics to denote "change in," so Δy and Δx represent the change in y and the change in x, respectively.

The ratio of the change in y to the change in x (the rise over the run) is called the *slope* of the line, with the letter m traditionally used for slope.

Slope Formula

The **slope** m of the line through the distinct points (x_1, y_1) and (x_2, y_2) is

$$m = \frac{\text{rise}}{\text{run}} = \frac{\text{change in } y}{\text{change in } x} = \frac{\Delta y}{\Delta x} = \frac{y_2 - y_1}{x_2 - x_1} \quad (x_1 \neq x_2).$$

◠ NOW TRY
↳ EXERCISE 6
Find the slope of the line through the points $(2, -6)$ and $(-3, 5)$.

EXAMPLE 6 Finding the Slope of a Line

Find the slope of the line through the points $(2, -1)$ and $(-5, 3)$.

We let $(2, -1) = (x_1, y_1)$ and $(-5, 3) = (x_2, y_2)$ in the slope formula.

$$m = \frac{y_2 - y_1}{x_2 - x_1} = \frac{3 - (-1)}{-5 - 2} = \frac{4}{-7} = -\frac{4}{7}$$

Thus, the slope is $-\frac{4}{7}$. See **FIGURE 14**.

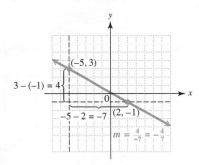

FIGURE 14

If we interchange the ordered pairs so that $(-5, 3) = (x_1, y_1)$ and $(2, -1) = (x_2, y_2)$ in the slope formula, the slope is the same.

y-values are in the *numerator*, x-values in the *denominator*.

$$m = \frac{-1 - 3}{2 - (-5)} = \frac{-4}{7} = -\frac{4}{7}$$

NOW TRY ↻

Example 6 suggests the following important ideas regarding slope:

1. The slope is the same no matter which point we consider first.

2. Using similar triangles from geometry, we can show that the slope is the same no matter which two different points on the line we choose.

⚠ **CAUTION** *In calculating slope, be careful to subtract the y-values and the x-values in the same order.*

Correct	Incorrect
$\dfrac{y_2 - y_1}{x_2 - x_1}$ or $\dfrac{y_1 - y_2}{x_1 - x_2}$	$\dfrac{y_2 - y_1}{x_1 - x_2}$ or $\dfrac{y_1 - y_2}{x_2 - x_1}$

The change in y is the numerator and the change in x is the denominator.

NOW TRY ANSWER
6. $-\frac{11}{5}$

NOW TRY
EXERCISE 7
Find the slope of the line
$3x - 7y = 21$.

EXAMPLE 7 Finding the Slope of a Line

Find the slope of the line $4x - y = -8$.

The intercepts can be used as the two different points needed to find the slope. Let $y = 0$ to find that the x-intercept is $(-2, 0)$. Then let $x = 0$ to find that the y-intercept is $(0, 8)$. Use these two points in the slope formula.

$$m = \frac{\text{rise}}{\text{run}} = \frac{8 - 0}{0 - (-2)} = \frac{8}{2} = 4$$

NOW TRY

We review the following special cases of slope.

Horizontal and Vertical Lines

- An equation of the form $y = b$ always intersects the y-axis at the point $(0, b)$. The line with that equation is horizontal and has slope 0. See **FIGURE 15**.

- An equation of the form $x = a$ always intersects the x-axis at the point $(a, 0)$. The line with that equation is vertical and has undefined slope. See **FIGURE 16**.

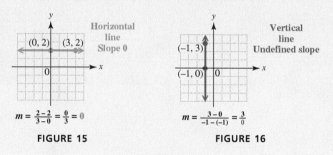

FIGURE 15   FIGURE 16

The slope of a line can also be found directly from its equation. Look again at the equation $4x - y = -8$ from **Example 7**. Solve this equation for y.

$$4x - y = -8 \qquad \text{Equation from \textbf{Example 7}}$$
$$-y = -4x - 8 \qquad \text{Subtract } 4x.$$
$$y = 4x + 8 \qquad \text{Multiply by } -1.$$

Notice that the slope, 4, found with the slope formula in **Example 7** is the same number as the coefficient of x in the equation $y = 4x + 8$. We will see in the next section that this always happens, *as long as the equation is solved for y.*

NOW TRY
EXERCISE 8
Find the slope of the graph
of $5x - 4y = 7$.

EXAMPLE 8 Finding the Slope from an Equation

Find the slope of the graph of $3x - 5y = 8$.

Solve the equation for y.

$$3x - 5y = 8$$
$$-5y = -3x + 8 \qquad \text{Subtract } 3x.$$
$$\boxed{\frac{-3x}{-5} = \frac{-3}{-5} \cdot \frac{x}{1} = \frac{3}{5}x} \qquad y = \frac{3}{5}x - \frac{8}{5} \qquad \text{Divide \textit{each} term by } -5.$$

NOW TRY ANSWERS

7. $\frac{3}{7}$ **8.** $\frac{5}{4}$

The slope is given by the coefficient of x, so the slope is $\frac{3}{5}$.   NOW TRY

OBJECTIVE 6 **Graph a line, given its slope and a point on the line.**

NOW TRY
EXERCISE 9

Graph the line passing through $(-4, 1)$ that has slope $-\frac{2}{3}$.

EXAMPLE 9 Using the Slope and a Point to Graph Lines

Graph each line described.

(a) With slope $\frac{2}{3}$ and y-intercept $(0, -4)$

Begin by plotting the point $P(0, -4)$, as shown in **FIGURE 17**. Then use the slope to find a second point.

$$m = \frac{\text{change in } y}{\text{change in } x} = \frac{2}{3}$$

We move 2 units *up* from $(0, -4)$ and then 3 units to the *right* to locate another point on the graph, $R(3, -2)$. The line through $P(0, -4)$ and R is the required graph.

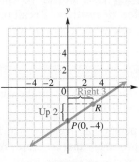
FIGURE 17

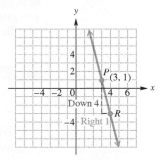
FIGURE 18

(b) Through $(3, 1)$ with slope -4

Start by locating the point $P(3, 1)$, as shown in **FIGURE 18**. Find a second point R on the line by writing the slope -4 as $\frac{-4}{1}$ and using the slope formula.

$$m = \frac{\text{change in } y}{\text{change in } x} = \frac{-4}{1}$$

We move 4 units *down* from $(3, 1)$ and then 1 unit to the *right* to locate this second point $R(4, -3)$. The line through $P(3, 1)$ and R is the required graph.

The slope also could be written as

$$m = \frac{\text{change in } y}{\text{change in } x} = \frac{4}{-1}.$$

In this case, the second point R is located 4 units *up* and 1 unit to the *left*. Verify that this approach also produces the line in **FIGURE 18**. NOW TRY

In **Example 9(a),** the slope of the line is the *positive* number $\frac{2}{3}$. The graph of the line in **FIGURE 17** slants up (rises) from left to right. The line in **Example 9(b)** has *negative* slope -4. As **FIGURE 18** shows, its graph slants down (falls) from left to right. These facts illustrate the following generalization.

Orientation of a Line in the Plane

A positive slope indicates that the line slants *up* (rises) from left to right.

A negative slope indicates that the line slants *down* (falls) from left to right.

NOW TRY ANSWER
9.

FIGURE 19 shows lines of positive, 0, negative, and undefined slopes.

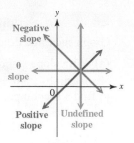

FIGURE 19

OBJECTIVE 7 **Use slopes to determine whether two lines are parallel, perpendicular, or neither.** Recall that the slopes of a pair of parallel or perpendicular lines are related in a special way.

Slopes of Parallel Lines and Perpendicular Lines

- Two nonvertical lines with the same slope are parallel. Two nonvertical parallel lines have the same slope.

- Two perpendicular lines, neither of which is vertical, have slopes that are negative reciprocals— that is, their product is -1. Also, lines with slopes that are negative reciprocals are perpendicular.

- A line with 0 slope is perpendicular to a line with undefined slope.

EXAMPLE 10   **Determining Whether Two Lines Are Parallel, Perpendicular, or Neither**

Determine whether the two lines described are *parallel, perpendicular,* or *neither*.

(a) Line L_1, through $(-2, 1)$ and $(4, 5)$, and line L_2, through $(3, 0)$ and $(0, -2)$

Find the slope of L_1.

$$m_1 = \frac{5 - 1}{4 - (-2)} = \frac{4}{6} = \frac{2}{3}$$

Find the slope of L_2.

$$m_2 = \frac{-2 - 0}{0 - 3} = \frac{-2}{-3} = \frac{2}{3}$$

Because the slopes are equal, the two lines are parallel.

(b) The lines with equations $2y = 3x - 6$ and $2x + 3y = -6$

Find the slope of each line by solving each equation for y.

$2y = 3x - 6$

$y = \dfrac{3}{2}x - 3$ Divide by 2.

↑
Slope

$2x + 3y = -6$

$3y = -2x - 6$ Subtract 2x.

$y = -\dfrac{2}{3}x - 2$ Divide by 3.

↑
Slope

Since the product of the slopes is $\frac{3}{2}\left(-\frac{2}{3}\right) = -1$, the lines are perpendicular.

NOW TRY
EXERCISE 10

Determine whether the two lines described are *parallel, perpendicular,* or *neither.*

(a) Line L_1 through $(2, 5)$ and $(4, 8)$, and line L_2 through $(2, 0)$ and $(-1, -2)$

(b) The lines with equations

$$x + 2y = 7$$
and $\quad 2x = y - 4$

(c) The lines with equations

$$2x - y = 4$$
and $\quad -2x + y = 6$

(c) The lines with equations $2x - 5y = 8$ and $2x + 5y = 8$

Find the slope of each line by solving each equation for y.

$$2x - 5y = 8$$
$$-5y = -2x + 8 \qquad \text{Subtract } 2x.$$
$$y = \frac{2}{5}x - \frac{8}{5} \qquad \text{Divide by } -5.$$
↑
Slope

$$2x + 5y = 8$$
$$5y = -2x + 8 \qquad \text{Subtract } 2x.$$
$$y = -\frac{2}{5}x + \frac{8}{5} \qquad \text{Divide by } 5.$$
↑
Slope

The slopes, $\frac{2}{5}$ and $-\frac{2}{5}$, are not equal, and they are not negative reciprocals because their product is $-\frac{4}{25}$, not -1. Thus, the two lines are neither parallel nor perpendicular.

NOW TRY

OBJECTIVE 8 **Solve problems involving average rate of change.** The slope formula applied to any two points on a line gives the **average rate of change** in y per unit change in x, where the value of y depends on the value of x.

For example, suppose the height of a boy increased from 60 to 68 in. between the ages of 12 and 16, as shown in **FIGURE 20**.

$$\begin{array}{l} \text{Change in height } y \longrightarrow \\ \text{Change in age } x \longrightarrow \end{array} \frac{68 - 60}{16 - 12} = \frac{8}{4} = 2 \text{ in.} \qquad \begin{array}{l} \text{Boy's average growth rate (or average} \\ \text{change in height) } per \ year \end{array}$$

The boy may actually have grown more than 2 in. during some years and less than 2 in. during other years. If we plotted ordered pairs (age, height) for those years and drew a line connecting any two of the points, the average rate of change would likely be slightly different than that found above. However using the data for ages 12 and 16, the boy's *average* change in height was 2 in. per year over these years.

Growth Rate

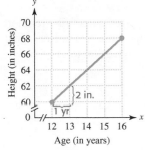

FIGURE 20

EXAMPLE 11 Interpreting Slope as Average Rate of Change

The graph in **FIGURE 21** approximates the average number of hours per year spent watching cable and satellite TV for each person in the United States from 2000 to 2005. Find the average rate of change in number of hours per year.

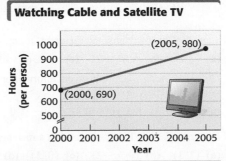

Source: Veronis Suhler Stevenson.

FIGURE 21

NOW TRY ANSWERS
10. (a) neither **(b)** perpendicular
(c) parallel

Americans spent an average of 828 hr in 2002 watching cable and satellite TV. Using this number for 2002 and the number for 2000 from the graph in **FIGURE 21**, find the average rate of change from 2000 to 2002. How does it compare with the average rate of change found in **Example 11?**

In 2000, sales of digital camcorders in the United States totaled $2838 million. In 2008, sales totaled $1885 million. Find the average rate of change in sales of digital camcorders per year, to the nearest million dollars. (*Source:* Consumer Electronics Association.)

To find the average rate of change, we need two pairs of data. From the graph, we have the ordered pairs (2000, 690) and (2005, 980). We use the slope formula.

$$\text{average rate of change} = \frac{980 - 690}{2005 - 2000} = \frac{290}{5} = 58 \quad \boxed{\text{A positive slope indicates an increase.}}$$

This means that the average time per person spent watching cable and satellite TV *increased* by 58 hr per year from 2000 to 2005.

NOW TRY

EXAMPLE 12 Interpreting Slope as Average Rate of Change

During the year 2000, the average person in the United States spent 812 hr watching broadcast TV. In 2005, the average number of hours per person spent watching broadcast TV was 679. Find the average rate of change in number of hours per year. (*Source:* Veronis Suhler Stevenson.)

To use the slope formula, we let one ordered pair be (2000, 812) and the other be (2005, 679).

$$\text{average rate of change} = \frac{679 - 812}{2005 - 2000} = \frac{-133}{5} = -26.6 \quad \boxed{\text{A negative slope indicates a decrease.}}$$

The graph in **FIGURE 22** confirms that the line through the ordered pairs falls from left to right and therefore has negative slope. Thus, the average time per person spent watching broadcast TV *decreased* by about 27 hr per year from 2000 to 2005.

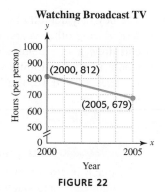

Watching Broadcast TV

FIGURE 22

NOW TRY

NOW TRY ANSWERS
11. 69 hr per yr; It is greater than the average rate of change from 2000 to 2005.
12. −$119 million per yr

7.1 EXERCISES

MyMathLab | Math XL PRACTICE | WATCH | DOWNLOAD | READ | REVIEW

🌐 *Complete solution available on the Video Resources on DVD*

1. *Concept Check* Name the quadrant, if any, in which each point is located.
   (a) $(1, 6)$ (b) $(-4, -2)$ (c) $(-3, 6)$ (d) $(7, -5)$ (e) $(-3, 0)$ (f) $(0, -0.5)$

2. *Concept Check* Use the given information to determine the quadrants in which the point (x, y) may lie.
   (a) $xy > 0$ (b) $xy < 0$ (c) $\dfrac{x}{y} < 0$ (d) $\dfrac{x}{y} > 0$

3. *Concept Check* Plot each point in a rectangular coordinate system.
   (a) $(2, 3)$ (b) $(-3, -2)$ (c) $(0, 5)$ (d) $(-2, 4)$ (e) $(-2, 0)$ (f) $(3, -3)$

4. *Concept Check* What must be true about the value of at least one of the coordinates of any point that lies along an axis?

*In Exercises 5–8, **(a)** complete the given table for each equation and then **(b)** graph the equation. **See** FIGURE 3.*

5. $x - y = 3$

x	y
0	
	0
5	
2	

6. $x + 2y = 5$

x	y
0	
	0
2	
2	

7. $y = -2x + 3$

x	y
0	
	1
2	
	-3

8. $4x - 5y = 20$

x	y
0	
	0
2	
	-3

*Find the x- and y-intercepts. Then graph each equation. **See Examples 1–4.***

9. $2x + 3y = 12$ **10.** $5x + 2y = 10$ **11.** $x - 3y = 6$

12. $x - 2y = -4$ **13.** $5x + 6y = -10$ **14.** $3x - 7y = 9$

15. $y = 5$ **16.** $y = -3$ **17.** $x = 2$

18. $x = -3$ **19.** $x + 4 = 0$ **20.** $x - 4 = 0$

21. $y + 2 = 0$ **22.** $y - 5 = 0$ **23.** $x + 5y = 0$

24. $x - 3y = 0$ **25.** $2x = 3y$ **26.** $4y = 3x$

*Find the midpoint of each segment with the given endpoints. **See Example 5.***

27. $(-8, 4)$ and $(-2, -6)$ **28.** $(5, 2)$ and $(-1, 8)$

29. $(3, -6)$ and $(6, 3)$ **30.** $(-10, 4)$ and $(7, 1)$

31. $(-9, 3)$ and $(9, 8)$ **32.** $(4, -3)$ and $(-1, 3)$

33. $(2.5, 3.1)$ and $(1.7, -1.3)$ **34.** $(6.2, 5.8)$ and $(1.4, -0.6)$

Brain Busters *Find the midpoint of each segment with the given endpoints.*

35. $\left(\dfrac{1}{2}, \dfrac{1}{3}\right)$ and $\left(\dfrac{3}{2}, \dfrac{5}{3}\right)$ **36.** $\left(\dfrac{21}{4}, \dfrac{2}{5}\right)$ and $\left(\dfrac{7}{4}, \dfrac{3}{5}\right)$

37. $\left(-\dfrac{1}{3}, \dfrac{2}{7}\right)$ and $\left(-\dfrac{1}{2}, \dfrac{1}{14}\right)$ **38.** $\left(\dfrac{3}{5}, -\dfrac{1}{3}\right)$ and $\left(\dfrac{1}{2}, -\dfrac{7}{2}\right)$

TECHNOLOGY INSIGHTS   EXERCISES 39 AND 40

39. The screens show the graph of one of the equations in A–D. Which equation is it?

   A. $3x + 2y = 6$ **B.** $-3x + 2y = 6$ **C.** $-3x - 2y = 6$ **D.** $3x - 2y = 6$

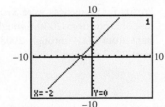

40. The table of ordered pairs was generated by a graphing calculator.

   (a) What is the x-intercept?   **(b)** What is the y-intercept?

   (c) Which equation corresponds to this table of values?

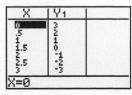

   A. $Y_1 = 2X - 3$ **B.** $Y_1 = -2X - 3$

   C. $Y_1 = 2X + 3$ **D.** $Y_1 = -2X + 3$

Concept Check *Answer each question about slope in Exercises 41 and 42.*

41. A hill rises 30 ft for every horizontal 100 ft. Which of the following express its slope (or grade)? (There are several correct choices.)

A. 0.3   B. $\frac{3}{10}$ C. $3\frac{1}{3}$ D. $\frac{30}{100}$

E. $\frac{10}{3}$ F. 30   G. 30%   H. $-\frac{10}{3}$

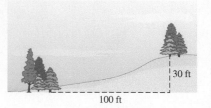
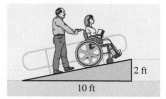

42. If a walkway rises 2 ft for every 10 ft on the horizontal, which of the following express its slope (or grade)? (There are several correct choices.)

A. 0.2   B. $\frac{2}{10}$ C. $\frac{1}{5}$ D. 20%

E. 5   F. $\frac{20}{100}$ G. $\frac{10}{2}$ H. -5

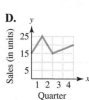

43. *Concept Check* Match each situation in (a)–(d) with the most appropriate graph in A–D.

(a) Sales rose sharply during the first quarter, leveled off during the second quarter, and then rose slowly for the rest of the year.

(b) Sales fell sharply during the first quarter and then rose slowly during the second and third quarters before leveling off for the rest of the year.

(c) Sales rose sharply during the first quarter and then fell to the original level during the second quarter before rising steadily for the rest of the year.

(d) Sales fell during the first two quarters of the year, leveled off during the third quarter, and rose during the fourth quarter.

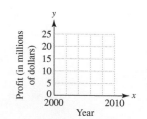

44. *Concept Check* Using the given axes, draw a graph that illustrates the following description:

Profits for a business were $10 million in 2000. They rose sharply from 2000 through 2004, remained constant from 2004 through 2008, and then fell slowly from 2008 through 2010.

45. *Concept Check* Determine the slope of each line segment in the given figure.

(a) *AB*   **(b)** *BC*   **(c)** *CD*

(d) *DE*   **(e)** *EF*   **(f)** *FG*

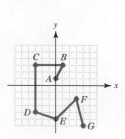

46. *Concept Check*   On the basis of the figure shown here, determine which line satisfies the given description.

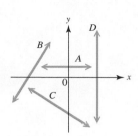

(a) The line has positive slope.

(b) The line has negative slope.

(c) The line has slope 0.

(d) The line has undefined slope.

For Exercises 47–58, **(a)** *find the slope of the line through each pair of points, if possible, and* **(b)** *based on the slope, indicate whether the line through the points* rises *from left to right,* falls *from left to right, is* horizontal, *or is* vertical. ***See Example 6 and* FIGURE 19**.

47. $(-2, -3)$ and $(-1, 5)$ **48.** $(-4, 1)$ and $(-3, 4)$ ● **49.** $(-4, 1)$ and $(2, 6)$

50. $(-3, -3)$ and $(5, 6)$ **51.** $(2, 4)$ and $(-4, 4)$ **52.** $(-6, 3)$ and $(2, 3)$

53. $(-2, 2)$ and $(4, -1)$ **54.** $(-3, 1)$ and $(6, -2)$ **55.** $(5, -3)$ and $(5, 2)$

56. $(4, -1)$ and $(4, 3)$ **57.** $(1.5, 2.6)$ and $(0.5, 3.6)$ **58.** $(3.4, 4.2)$ and $(1.4, 10.2)$

Brain Busters   *Find the slope of the line through each pair of points.* $\left(Hint: \dfrac{\frac{a}{b}}{\frac{c}{d}} = \dfrac{a}{b} \div \dfrac{c}{d} \right)$

59. $\left(\dfrac{1}{6}, \dfrac{1}{2} \right)$ and $\left(\dfrac{5}{6}, \dfrac{9}{2} \right)$ **60.** $\left(\dfrac{3}{4}, \dfrac{1}{3} \right)$ and $\left(\dfrac{5}{4}, \dfrac{10}{3} \right)$

61. $\left(-\dfrac{2}{9}, \dfrac{5}{18} \right)$ and $\left(\dfrac{1}{18}, -\dfrac{5}{9} \right)$ **62.** $\left(-\dfrac{4}{5}, \dfrac{9}{10} \right)$ and $\left(-\dfrac{3}{10}, \dfrac{1}{5} \right)$

Find the slope of each line.

63.   **64.**   **65.**

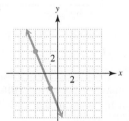   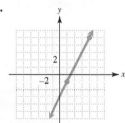   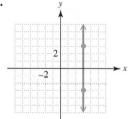

66. *Concept Check*   Let k be the number of letters in your last name. Sketch the graph of $y = k$. What is the slope of this line?

Find the slope of the line and sketch the graph. ***See Examples 6–8.***

● **67.** $x + 2y = 4$ **68.** $x + 3y = -6$ ● **69.** $5x - 2y = 10$

70. $4x - y = 4$ **71.** $y = 4x$ **72.** $y = -3x$

● **73.** $x - 3 = 0$ **74.** $x + 2 = 0$ ● **75.** $y = -5$ **76.** $y = -4$

Graph each line described. ***See Example 9.***

77. Through $(-4, 2)$; $m = \dfrac{1}{2}$ **78.** Through $(-2, -3)$; $m = \dfrac{5}{4}$

● **79.** y-intercept $(0, -2)$; $m = -\dfrac{2}{3}$ **80.** y-intercept $(0, -4)$; $m = -\dfrac{3}{2}$

81. Through $(-1, -2)$; $m = 3$ **82.** Through $(-2, -4)$; $m = 4$

83. $m = 0$; through $(2, -5)$ **84.** $m = 0$; through $(5, 3)$

85. Undefined slope; through $(-3, 1)$ **86.** Undefined slope; through $(-4, 1)$

87. *Concept Check* If a line has slope $-\frac{4}{9}$, then any line parallel to it has slope _____, and any line perpendicular to it has slope _____.

88. *Concept Check* If a line has slope 0.2, then any line parallel to it has slope _____, and any line perpendicular to it has slope _____.

Decide whether each pair of lines is parallel, perpendicular, *or* neither. **See Example 10.**

89. The line through $(15, 9)$ and $(12, -7)$ and the line through $(8, -4)$ and $(5, -20)$

90. The line through $(4, 6)$ and $(-8, 7)$ and the line through $(-5, 5)$ and $(7, 4)$

91. $x + 4y = 7$ and $4x - y = 3$

92. $2x + 5y = -7$ and $5x - 2y = 1$

93. $4x - 3y = 6$ and $3x - 4y = 2$

94. $2x + y = 6$ and $x - y = 4$

95. $x = 6$ and $6 - x = 8$

96. $3x = y$ and $2y - 6x = 5$

97. $4x + y = 0$ and $5x - 8 = 2y$

98. $2x + 5y = -8$ and $6 + 2x = 5y$

99. $2x = y + 3$ and $2y + x = 3$

100. $4x - 3y = 8$ and $4y + 3x = 12$

Concept Check *Find and interpret the average rate of change illustrated in each graph.*

101.
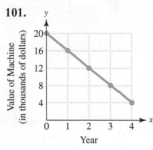
Year

102.
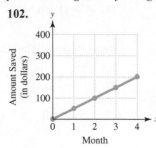
Month

103.
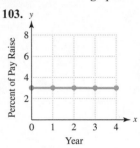
Year

104. *Concept Check* If the graph of a linear equation rises from left to right, then the average rate of change is _____ . If the graph of a linear equation falls from

(positive/negative)

left to right, then the average rate of change is _____ .

(positive/negative)

Solve each problem. **See Examples 11 and 12.**

105. The graph shows the number of cellular phone subscribers (in millions) in the United States from 2005 to 2008.

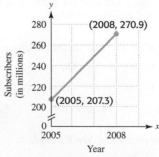

Cellular Phone Subscribers

Source: CTIA: The Wireless Association.

(a) Use the given ordered pairs to find the slope of the line.

(b) Interpret the slope in the context of this problem.

106. The graph shows spending on personal care products (in billions of dollars) in the United States from 2005 to 2008.

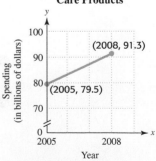

Spending on Personal Care Products

Source: U.S. Department of Commerce.

(a) Use the given ordered pairs to find the slope of the line to the nearest tenth.

(b) Interpret the slope in the context of this problem.

107. The graph provides a good approximation of the number of drive-in theaters in the United States from 2000 through 2007.

(a) Use the given ordered pairs to find the average rate of change in the number of drive-in theaters per year during this period. Round your answer to the nearest whole number.

✎ (b) Explain how a negative slope is interpreted in this situation.

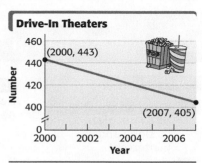

Drive-In Theaters

Source: www.drive-ins.com

108. The graph provides a good approximation of the number of mobile homes (in thousands) placed in use in the United States from 2000 through 2008.

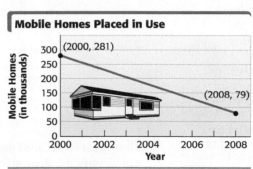

Mobile Homes Placed in Use

Source: U.S. Census Bureau.

(a) Use the given ordered pairs to find the average rate of change in the number of mobile homes per year during this period.

✎ (b) Explain how a negative slope is interpreted in this situation.

✎ **109.** The total amount spent on plasma TVs in the United States changed from $1590 million in 2003 to $5705 million in 2006. Find and interpret the average rate of change in sales, in millions of dollars per year. Round your answer to the nearest hundredth. (*Source:* Consumer Electronics Association.)

✎ **110.** The total amount spent on analog TVs in the United States changed from $5836 million in 2003 to $1424 million in 2006. Find and interpret the average rate of change in sales, in millions of dollars per year. Round your answer to the nearest hundredth. (*Source:* Consumer Electronics Association.)

PREVIEW EXERCISES

Write each equation in the form $Ax + By = C$. *See Section 3.4.*

111. $y - (-2) = \dfrac{3}{2}(x - 5)$

112. $y - (-1) = -\dfrac{1}{2}[x - (-2)]$

7.2 Review of Equations of Lines; Linear Models

OBJECTIVES

1. Write an equation of a line, given its slope and y-intercept.

2. Graph a line, using its slope and y-intercept.

3. Write an equation of a line, given its slope and a point on the line.

4. Write equations of horizontal and vertical lines.

5. Write an equation of a line, given two points on the line.

6. Write an equation of a line parallel or perpendicular to a given line.

7. Write an equation of a line that models real data.

OBJECTIVE 1 **Write an equation of a line, given its slope and y-intercept.** Recall that we can find the slope of a line from its equation by solving the equation for y. For example, we found that the slope of the line with equation

$$y = 4x + 8$$

is 4, the coefficient of x. What does the number 8 represent?

To find out, suppose a line has slope m and y-intercept $(0, b)$. We can find an equation of this line by choosing another point (x, y) on the line, as shown in **FIGURE 23**, and using the slope formula.

$$m = \frac{y - b}{x - 0} \quad \longleftarrow \text{Change in } y\text{-values}$$
$$\qquad\qquad \longleftarrow \text{Change in } x\text{-values}$$

$$m = \frac{y - b}{x} \qquad \text{Subtract in the denominator.}$$

$$mx = y - b \qquad \text{Multiply by } x.$$

$$mx + b = y \qquad \text{Add } b.$$

$$y = mx + b \qquad \text{Rewrite.}$$

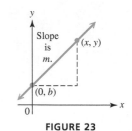

FIGURE 23

This last equation is called the *slope-intercept form* of the equation of a line, because we can identify the slope m and y-intercept $(0, b)$ at a glance. Thus, in the line with equation $y = 4x + 8$, the number 8 indicates that the y-intercept is $(0, 8)$.

Slope-Intercept Form

The **slope-intercept form** of the equation of a line with slope m and y-intercept $(0, b)$ is

$$y = mx + b.$$

Slope ↑   ↑ y-intercept is $(0, b)$.

**NOW TRY
EXERCISE 1**

Write an equation of the line with slope $\frac{2}{3}$ and y-intercept $(0, 1)$.

EXAMPLE 1 Writing an Equation of a Line

Write an equation of the line with slope $-\frac{4}{5}$ and y-intercept $(0, -2)$.

Here, $m = -\frac{4}{5}$ and $b = -2$. Substitute these values into the slope-intercept form.

$$y = mx + b \qquad \text{Slope-intercept form}$$

$$y = -\frac{4}{5}x - 2 \qquad m = -\tfrac{4}{5}; b = -2 \qquad \text{NOW TRY}$$

NOTE Every linear equation (of a nonvertical line) has a *unique* (one and only one) slope-intercept form. In **Section 7.4**, we study *linear functions,* which are defined using slope-intercept form. Also, this is the form we use when graphing a line with a graphing calculator.

NOW TRY ANSWER
1. $y = \frac{2}{3}x + 1$

OBJECTIVE 2 **Graph a line, using its slope and y-intercept.** We first saw this approach in **Example 9(a)** of **Section 7.1**.

◠ *NOW TRY*
EXERCISE 2
Graph the line, using the slope and y-intercept.

$$4x + 3y = 6$$

EXAMPLE 2 Graphing Lines Using Slope and y-Intercept

Graph each line, using the slope and y-intercept.

(a) $y = 3x - 6$

Here, $m = 3$ and $b = -6$. Plot the y-intercept $(0, -6)$. The slope 3 can be interpreted as

$$m = \frac{\text{rise}}{\text{run}} = \frac{\text{change in } y}{\text{change in } x} = \frac{3}{1}.$$

From $(0, -6)$, move 3 units *up* and 1 unit to the *right*, and plot a second point at $(1, -3)$. Join the two points with a straight line. See **FIGURE 24.**

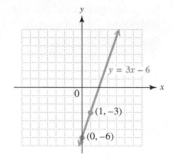

FIGURE 24

(b) $3y + 2x = 9$

Write the equation in slope-intercept form by solving for y.

$$3y + 2x = 9$$

$$3y = -2x + 9 \qquad \text{Subtract } 2x.$$

$$y = -\frac{2}{3}x + 3 \qquad \text{Divide by 3.}$$

Slope ⬑   ⬑ y-intercept is $(0, 3)$.

Plot the y-intercept $(0, 3)$. The slope can be interpreted as either $\frac{-2}{3}$ or $\frac{2}{-3}$. Using $\frac{-2}{3}$, begin at $(0, 3)$ and move 2 units *down* and 3 units to the *right* to locate the point $(3, 1)$. The line through these two points is the required graph. See **FIGURE 25.** (Verify that the point obtained with $\frac{2}{-3}$ as the slope is also on this line.)

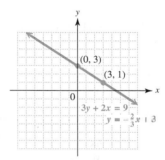

FIGURE 25

NOW TRY ↻

OBJECTIVE 3 **Write an equation of a line, given its slope and a point on the line.** Let m represent the slope of a line and (x_1, y_1) represent a given point on the line. Let (x, y) represent any other point on the line. See **FIGURE 26.**

$$m = \frac{y - y_1}{x - x_1} \qquad \text{Slope formula}$$

$$m(x - x_1) = y - y_1 \qquad \text{Multiply each side by } x - x_1.$$

$$y - y_1 = m(x - x_1) \qquad \text{Rewrite.}$$

This last equation is the *point-slope form* of the equation of a line.

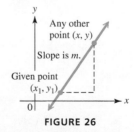

FIGURE 26

Point-Slope Form

The **point-slope form** of the equation of a line with slope m passing through the point (x_1, y_1) is

Slope
↓
$$y - y_1 = m(x - x_1).$$
⬑ Given point ⬏

NOW TRY ANSWER
2.
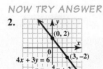

NOW TRY
EXERCISE 3

Write an equation of the line with slope $-\frac{1}{5}$ and passing through the point $(5, -3)$.

EXAMPLE 3 Writing an Equation of a Line, Given the Slope and a Point

Write an equation of the line with slope $\frac{1}{3}$ and passing through the point $(-2, 5)$.

Method 1 Use the point-slope form of the equation of a line, with $(x_1, y_1) = (-2, 5)$ and $m = \frac{1}{3}$.

$$y - y_1 = m(x - x_1) \qquad \text{Point-slope form}$$

$$y - 5 = \frac{1}{3}[x - (-2)] \qquad \text{Substitute for } y_1, m, \text{ and } x_1.$$

$$y - 5 = \frac{1}{3}(x + 2) \qquad \text{Definition of subtraction}$$

$$3y - 15 = x + 2 \qquad \text{(*) Multiply by 3.}$$

$$3y = x + 17 \qquad \text{Add 15.}$$

Slope-intercept form $\longrightarrow y = \frac{1}{3}x + \frac{17}{3} \qquad \text{Divide by 3.}$

Method 2 An alternative method for finding this equation uses slope-intercept form, with $(x, y) = (-2, 5)$ and $m = \frac{1}{3}$.

$$y = mx + b \qquad \text{Slope-intercept form}$$

$$5 = \frac{1}{3}(-2) + b \qquad \text{Substitute for } y, m, \text{ and } x.$$

Solve for b. $\longrightarrow 5 = -\frac{2}{3} + b \qquad \text{Multiply.}$

$$\frac{17}{3} = b, \quad \text{or} \quad b = \frac{17}{3} \qquad 5 = \frac{15}{3}; \text{ Add } \frac{2}{3}.$$

Since $m = \frac{1}{3}$ and $b = \frac{17}{3}$, the equation is

$$y = \frac{1}{3}x + \frac{17}{3}. \quad \boxed{\text{Same equation found in Method 1}} \qquad NOW \ TRY$$

OBJECTIVE 4 Write equations of horizontal and vertical lines. A horizontal line has slope 0. Using point-slope form, we can find the equation of a horizontal line through the point (a, b).

$$y - y_1 = m(x - x_1) \qquad \text{Point-slope form}$$

$$y - b = 0(x - a) \qquad y_1 = b, m = 0, x_1 = a$$

$$y - b = 0 \qquad \text{Multiplication property of 0}$$

$$y = b \qquad \text{Add } b.$$

Point-slope form does not apply to a vertical line, since the slope of a vertical line is undefined. A vertical line through the point (a, b) has equation $x = a$.

Equations of Horizontal and Vertical Lines

The horizontal line through the point (a, b) has equation **$y = b$**.

The vertical line through the point (a, b) has equation **$x = a$**.

NOW TRY ANSWER
3. $y = -\frac{1}{5}x - 2$

NOW TRY
EXERCISE 4

Write an equation of the line passing through the point $(4, -4)$ that satisfies the given condition.

(a) Undefined slope

(b) Slope 0

EXAMPLE 4 Writing Equations of Horizontal and Vertical Lines

Write an equation of the line passing through the point $(-3, 3)$ that satisfies the given condition.

(a) Slope 0

Since the slope is 0, this is a horizontal line. A horizontal line through the point (a, b) has equation $y = b$. Here the y-coordinate is 3, so the equation is $y = 3$.

(b) Undefined slope

This is a vertical line, since the slope is undefined. A vertical line through the point (a, b) has equation $x = a$. Here the x-coordinate is -3, so the equation is $x = -3$. Both lines are graphed in **FIGURE 27**.

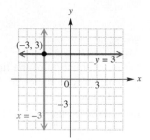

FIGURE 27

NOW TRY

OBJECTIVE 5 **Write an equation of a line, given two points on the line.** Recall that we defined *standard form* for a linear equation as

$$Ax + By = C, \quad \text{Standard form}$$

where A, B, and C are real numbers and A and B are not both 0. (In most cases, A, B, and C are rational numbers.) We give answers so that A, B, and C are integers with greatest common factor 1, and $A \geq 0$. For example, the equation in **Example 3** is written in standard form as follows.

$$3y - 15 = x + 2 \qquad \text{Equation (*) from Example 3}$$

$$-x + 3y = 17 \qquad \text{Subtract } x \text{ and add 15.}$$

$$\text{Standard form} \longrightarrow x - 3y = -17 \qquad \text{Multiply by } -1.$$

NOW TRY
EXERCISE 5

Write an equation of the line passing through the points $(3, -4)$ and $(-2, -1)$. Give the final answer in standard form.

EXAMPLE 5 Writing an Equation of a Line, Given Two Points

Write an equation of the line passing through the points $(-4, 3)$ and $(5, -7)$. Give the final answer in standard form.

First find the slope by the slope formula.

$$m = \frac{-7 - 3}{5 - (-4)} = -\frac{10}{9}$$

Use either $(-4, 3)$ or $(5, -7)$ as (x_1, y_1) in the point-slope form of the equation of a line. We choose $(-4, 3)$, so $-4 = x_1$ and $3 = y_1$.

$$y - y_1 = m(x - x_1) \qquad \text{Point-slope form}$$

$$y - 3 = -\frac{10}{9}[x - (-4)] \qquad y_1 = 3, m = -\tfrac{10}{9}, x_1 = -4$$

$$y - 3 = -\frac{10}{9}(x + 4) \qquad \text{Definition of subtraction}$$

$$9y - 27 = -10(x + 4) \qquad \text{Multiply by 9 to clear the fraction.}$$

$$9y - 27 = -10x - 40 \qquad \text{Distributive property}$$

$$\begin{array}{l}\text{Standard} \\ \text{form}\end{array} \longrightarrow 10x + 9y = -13 \qquad \text{Add 10}x. \text{ Add 27.}$$

NOW TRY ANSWERS
4. **(a)** $x = 4$ **(b)** $y = -4$
5. $3x + 5y = -11$

Verify that if $(5, -7)$ were used, the same equation would result. NOW TRY

OBJECTIVE 6 **Write an equation of a line parallel or perpendicular to a given line.** Recall that parallel lines have the same slope and perpendicular lines have slopes that are negative reciprocals of each other.

NOW TRY
EXERCISE 6

Write an equation of the line passing through the point $(6, -1)$ and

(a) parallel to the line
$3x - 5y = 7$;

(b) perpendicular to the line
$3x - 5y = 7$.

Give final answers in slope-intercept form.

EXAMPLE 6 Writing Equations of Parallel or Perpendicular Lines

Write an equation of the line passing through the point $(-3, 6)$ and **(a)** parallel to the line $2x + 3y = 6$; **(b)** perpendicular to the line $2x + 3y = 6$. Give final answers in slope-intercept form.

(a) We find the slope of the line $2x + 3y = 6$ by solving for y.

$$2x + 3y = 6$$
$$3y = -2x + 6 \qquad \text{Subtract } 2x.$$
$$y = -\frac{2}{3}x + 2 \qquad \text{Divide by 3.}$$
$$\underset{\text{Slope}}{\uparrow}$$

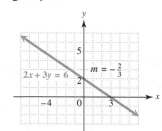

FIGURE 28

The slope of the line is given by the coefficient of x, so $m = -\frac{2}{3}$. See **FIGURE 28**.

The required equation of the line through $(-3, 6)$ and parallel to $2x + 3y = 6$ must also have slope $-\frac{2}{3}$. To find this equation, we use the point-slope form, with $(x_1, y_1) = (-3, 6)$ and $m = -\frac{2}{3}$.

$$y - 6 = -\frac{2}{3}[x - (-3)] \qquad y_1 = 6, \, m = -\frac{2}{3}, \, x_1 = -3$$

$$y - 6 = -\frac{2}{3}(x + 3) \qquad \text{Definition of subtraction}$$

$$y - 6 = -\frac{2}{3}x - 2 \qquad \text{Distributive property}$$

$$y = -\frac{2}{3}x + 4 \qquad \text{Add 6.}$$

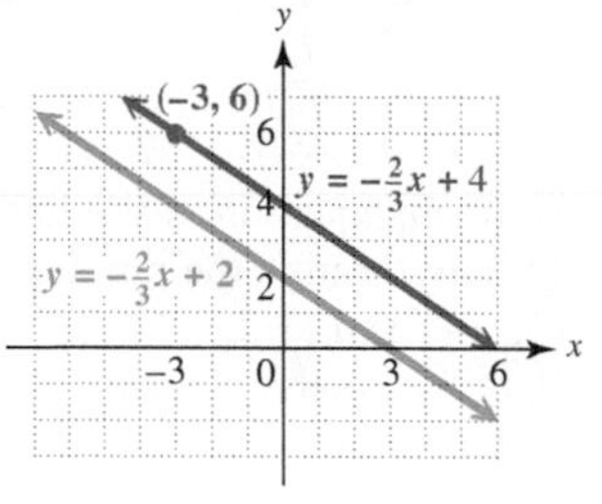

We did not clear the fraction here because we want the equation in slope-intercept form—that is, solved for y. Both lines are shown in **FIGURE 29**.

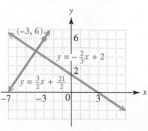

FIGURE 29

(b) To be perpendicular to the line $2x + 3y = 6$, a line must have a slope that is the negative reciprocal of $-\frac{2}{3}$, which is $\frac{3}{2}$. We use $(-3, 6)$ and slope $\frac{3}{2}$ in the point-slope form to find the equation of the perpendicular line shown in **FIGURE 30**.

$$y - 6 = \frac{3}{2}[x - (-3)] \qquad y_1 = 6, \, m = \frac{3}{2}, \, x_1 = -3$$

$$y - 6 = \frac{3}{2}(x + 3) \qquad \text{Definition of subtraction}$$

$$y - 6 = \frac{3}{2}x + \frac{9}{2} \qquad \text{Distributive property}$$

$$y = \frac{3}{2}x + \frac{21}{2} \qquad \text{Add } 6 = \frac{12}{2}.$$

FIGURE 30

NOW TRY

NOW TRY ANSWERS
6. (a) $y = \frac{3}{5}x - \frac{23}{5}$

(b) $y = -\frac{5}{3}x + 9$

A summary of the various forms of linear equations follows.

Forms of Linear Equations

Equation	Description	When to Use
$y = mx + b$	**Slope-Intercept Form** Slope is m. y-intercept is $(0, b)$.	The slope and y-intercept can be easily identified and used to quickly graph the equation.
$y - y_1 = m(x - x_1)$	**Point-Slope Form** Slope is m. Line passes through (x_1, y_1).	This form is ideal for finding the equation of a line if the slope and a point on the line or two points on the line are known.
$Ax + By = C$	**Standard Form** (A, B, and C integers, $A \geq 0$) Slope is $-\frac{A}{B}$ ($B \neq 0$). x-intercept is $\left(\frac{C}{A}, 0\right)$ ($A \neq 0$). y-intercept is $\left(0, \frac{C}{B}\right)$ ($B \neq 0$).	The x- and y-intercepts can be found quickly and used to graph the equation. The slope must be calculated.
$y = b$	**Horizontal Line** Slope is 0. y-intercept is $(0, b)$.	If the graph intersects only the y-axis, then y is the only variable in the equation.
$x = a$	**Vertical Line** Slope is undefined. x-intercept is $(a, 0)$.	If the graph intersects only the x-axis, then x is the only variable in the equation.

OBJECTIVE 7 **Write an equation of a line that models real data.** If a given set of data changes at a fairly constant rate, the data may fit a linear pattern, where the rate of change is the slope of the line.

EXAMPLE 7   Determining a Linear Equation to Describe Real Data

A local gasoline station is selling 89-octane gas for $3.20 per gal.

(a) Write an equation that describes the cost y to buy x gallons of gas.

The total cost is determined by the number of gallons we buy multiplied by the price per gallon (in this case, $3.20). As the gas is pumped, two sets of numbers spin by: the number of gallons pumped and the cost of that number of gallons. The table illustrates this situation.

If we let x denote the number of gallons pumped, then the total cost y in dollars can be found using the following linear equation.

Number of Gallons Pumped	Cost of This Number of Gallons
0	0($3.20) = $ 0.00
1	1($3.20) = $ 3.20
2	2($3.20) = $ 6.40
3	3($3.20) = $ 9.60
4	4($3.20) = $12.80

Total cost $\longrightarrow$ $\longleftarrow$ Number of gallons
$$y = 3.20x$$

Theoretically, there are infinitely many ordered pairs (x, y) that satisfy this equation, but here we are limited to nonnegative values for x, since we cannot have a negative number of gallons. In this situation, there is also a practical maximum value for x that varies from one car to another. What determines this maximum value?

(b) A car wash at this gas station costs an additional $3.00. Write an equation that defines the cost of gas and a car wash.

The cost will be $3.20x + 3.00$ dollars for x gallons of gas and a car wash.

$$y = 3.2x + 3 \qquad \text{Delete unnecessary zeros.}$$

A cell phone plan costs $100 for the telephone plus $85 per month for service. Write an equation that gives the cost y in dollars for x months of cell phone service using this plan.

(c) Interpret the ordered pairs $(5, 19)$ and $(10, 35)$ in relation to the equation from part (b).

The ordered pair $(5, 19)$ indicates that 5 gal of gas and a car wash costs $19.00. Similarly, $(10, 35)$ indicates that 10 gal of gas and a car wash costs $35.00.

NOW TRY

NOTE In **Example 7(a),** the ordered pair $(0, 0)$ satisfied the equation, so the linear equation has the form $y = mx$, where $b = 0$. If a realistic situation involves an initial charge plus a charge per unit, as in **Example 7(b),** the equation has the form $y = mx + b$, where $b \neq 0$.

Refer to **Example 8.**

(a) Use the ordered pairs $(2, 183)$ and $(6, 251)$ to write an equation that models the data.

(b) Use the equation from part (a) to estimate retail spending on prescription drugs in 2011.

EXAMPLE 8 Writing an Equation of a Line That Models Data

Retail spending (in billions of dollars) on prescription drugs in the United States is shown in the graph in **FIGURE 31**.

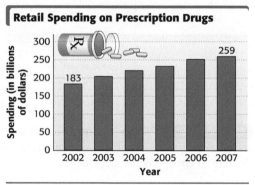

Retail Spending on Prescription Drugs

Source: National Association of Chain Drug Stores.

FIGURE 31

(a) Write an equation that models the data.

The data increase linearly—that is, a straight line through the tops of any two bars in the graph would be close to the top of each bar. To model the relationship between year x and spending on prescription drugs y, we let $x = 2$ represent 2002, $x = 3$ represent 2003, and so on. The given data for 2002 and 2007 can be written as the ordered pairs $(2, 183)$ and $(7, 259)$.

$$m = \frac{259 - 183}{7 - 2} = \frac{76}{5} = 15.2 \qquad \text{Find the slope of the line through } (2, 183) \text{ and } (7, 259).$$

Thus, spending increased by about $15.2 billion per year. To write an equation, we substitute this slope and one of the points, say, $(2, 183)$, into the point-slope form.

$$y - y_1 = m(x - x_1) \qquad \text{Point-slope form}$$
$$y - 183 = 15.2(x - 2) \qquad (x_1, y_1) = (2, 183); m = 15.2$$

Either point can be used here. $(7, 259)$ provides the same answer.

$$y - 183 = 15.2x - 30.4 \qquad \text{Distributive property}$$
$$y = 15.2x + 152.6 \qquad \text{Add 183.}$$

NOW TRY ANSWERS
7. $y = 85x + 100$
8. (a) $y = 17x + 149$
(b) $336 billion

Retail spending y (in billions of dollars) on prescription drugs in the United States in year x can be approximated by the equation $y = 15.2x + 152.6$.

(b) Use the equation from part (a) to estimate retail spending on prescription drugs in the United States in 2010. (Assume a constant rate of change.)

Since $x = 2$ represents 2002 and 2010 is 8 yr after 2002, $x = 10$ represents 2010.

$$y = 15.2x + 152.6 \qquad \text{Equation from part (a)}$$
$$y = 15.2(10) + 152.6 \qquad \text{Substitute 10 for } x.$$
$$y = 304.6 \qquad \text{Multiply, and then add.}$$

About \$305 billion was spent on prescription drugs in 2010.   *NOW TRY*

7.2 EXERCISES

 MyMathLab | Math XL PRACTICE | WATCH | DOWNLOAD | READ | REVIEW

Complete solution available on the Video Resources on DVD

Concept Check   In Exercises 1–6, provide the appropriate response.

1. The following equations all represent the same line. Which one is in standard form as defined in the text?

A. $3x - 2y = 5$ **B.** $2y = 3x - 5$ **C.** $\frac{3}{5}x - \frac{2}{5}y = 1$ **D.** $3x = 2y + 5$

2. Which equation is in point-slope form?

A. $y = 6x + 2$ **B.** $4x + y = 9$ **C.** $y - 3 = 2(x - 1)$ **D.** $2y = 3x - 7$

3. Which equation in **Exercise 2** is in slope-intercept form?

4. Write the equation $y + 2 = -3(x - 4)$ in slope-intercept form.

5. Write the equation from **Exercise 4** in standard form.

6. Write the equation $10x - 7y = 70$ in slope-intercept form.

Concept Check   Match each equation with the graph that it most closely resembles. (Hint. Determine the signs of m and b to help you make your decision.)

7. $y = 2x + 3$

8. $y = -2x + 3$

9. $y = -2x - 3$

10. $y = 2x - 3$

11. $y = 2x$

12. $y = -2x$

13. $y = 3$

14. $y = -3$

    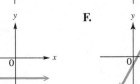

Write the equation in slope-intercept form of the line satisfying the given conditions. ***See Example 1.***

15. $m = 5; b = 15$

16. $m = 2; b = 12$

17. $m = -\frac{2}{3}; b = \frac{4}{5}$

18. $m = -\frac{5}{8}; b = -\frac{1}{3}$

19. Slope 1; y-intercept $(0, -1)$

20. Slope -1; y-intercept $(0, -3)$

21. Slope $\frac{2}{5}$; y-intercept $(0, 5)$

22. Slope $-\frac{3}{4}$; y-intercept $(0, 7)$

Concept Check Write an equation in slope-intercept form of the line shown in each graph. (Hint: Use the indicated points to find the slope.)

23.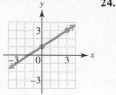

24.

25.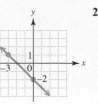

26.

*For each equation, **(a)** write it in slope-intercept form, **(b)** give the slope of the line, **(c)** give the y-intercept, and **(d)** graph the line. See Example 2.*

27. $-x + y = 4$ **28.** $-x + y = 6$ **29.** $6x + 5y = 30$ **30.** $3x + 4y = 12$

31. $4x - 5y = 20$ **32.** $7x - 3y = 3$ **33.** $x + 2y = -4$ **34.** $x + 3y = -9$

*Find an equation of the line that satisfies the given conditions. **(a)** Write the equation in standard form. **(b)** Write the equation in slope-intercept form. See Example 3.*

35. Through $(5, 8)$; slope -2

36. Through $(12, 10)$; slope 1

37. Through $(-2, 4)$; slope $-\frac{3}{4}$

38. Through $(-1, 6)$; slope $-\frac{5}{6}$

39. Through $(-5, 4)$; slope $\frac{1}{2}$

40. Through $(7, -2)$; slope $\frac{1}{4}$

41. x-intercept $(3, 0)$; slope 4

42. x-intercept $(-2, 0)$; slope -5

43. Through $(2, 6.8)$; slope 1.4

44. Through $(6, -1.2)$; slope 0.8

Find an equation of the line that satisfies the given conditions. See Example 4.

45. Through $(9, 5)$; slope 0

46. Through $(-4, -2)$; slope 0

47. Through $(9, 10)$; undefined slope

48. Through $(-2, 8)$; undefined slope

49. Through $\left(-\frac{3}{4}, -\frac{3}{2}\right)$; slope 0

50. Through $\left(-\frac{5}{8}, -\frac{9}{2}\right)$; slope 0

51. Through $(-7, 8)$; horizontal

52. Through $(2, -7)$; horizontal

53. Through $(0.5, 0.2)$; vertical

54. Through $(0.1, 0.4)$; vertical

*Find an equation of the line passing through the given points. **(a)** Write the equation in standard form. **(b)** Write the equation in slope-intercept form if possible. See Example 5.*

55. $(3, 4)$ and $(5, 8)$

56. $(5, -2)$ and $(-3, 14)$

57. $(6, 1)$ and $(-2, 5)$

58. $(-2, 5)$ and $(-8, 1)$

59. $(2, 5)$ and $(1, 5)$

60. $(-2, 2)$ and $(4, 2)$

61. $(7, 6)$ and $(7, -8)$

62. $(13, 5)$ and $(13, -1)$

63. $\left(\frac{1}{2}, -3\right)$ and $\left(-\frac{2}{3}, -3\right)$

64. $\left(-\frac{4}{9}, -6\right)$ and $\left(\frac{12}{7}, -6\right)$

65. $\left(-\frac{2}{5}, \frac{2}{5}\right)$ and $\left(\frac{4}{3}, \frac{2}{3}\right)$

66. $\left(\frac{3}{4}, \frac{8}{3}\right)$ and $\left(\frac{2}{5}, \frac{2}{3}\right)$

*Find an equation of the line that satisfies the given conditions. **(a)** Write the equation in slope-intercept form. **(b)** Write the equation in standard form. See Example 6.*

67. Through $(7, 2)$; parallel to $3x - y = 8$

68. Through $(4, 1)$; parallel to $2x + 5y = 10$

69. Through $(-2, -2)$; parallel to $-x + 2y = 10$

70. Through $(-1, 3)$; parallel to $-x + 3y = 12$

71. Through $(8, 5)$; perpendicular to $2x - y = 7$

72. Through $(2, -7)$; perpendicular to $5x + 2y = 18$

73. Through $(-2, 7)$; perpendicular to $x = 9$

74. Through $(8, 4)$; perpendicular to $x = -3$

*Write an equation in the form $y = mx$ for each situation. Then give the three ordered pairs associated with the equation for x-values 0, 5, and 10. **See Example 7(a).***

75. x represents the number of hours traveling at 45 mph, and y represents the distance traveled (in miles).

76. x represents the number of t-shirts sold at $26 each, and y represents the total cost of the t-shirts (in dollars).

77. x represents the number of gallons of gas sold at $3.10 per gal, and y represents the total cost of the gasoline (in dollars).

78. x represents the number of days a DVD movie is rented at $4.50 per day, and y represents the total charge for the rental (in dollars).

79. x represents the number of credit hours taken at Kirkwood Community College at $111 per credit hour, and y represents the total tuition paid for the credit hours (in dollars). (*Source:* www.kirkwood.edu)

80. x represents the number of tickets to a performance of *Jersey Boys* at the Des Moines Civic Center purchased at $125 per ticket, and y represents the total paid for the tickets (in dollars). (*Source:* Ticketmaster.)

*For each situation, **(a)** write an equation in the form $y = mx + b$, **(b)** find and interpret the ordered pair associated with the equation for $x = 5$, and **(c)** answer the question. **See Examples 7(b) and 7(c).***

81. A ticket for the 2010 Troubadour Reunion, featuring James Taylor and Carole King, costs $112.50. A parking pass costs $12. (*Source:* Ticketmaster.) Let x represent the number of tickets and y represent the cost. How much does it cost for 2 tickets and a parking pass?

82. Resident tuition at Broward College is $87.95 per credit hour. There is also a $20 health science application fee. (*Source:* www.broward.edu) Let x represent the number of credit hours and y represent the cost. How much does it cost for a student in health science to take 15 credit hours?

83. A membership in the Midwest Athletic Club costs $99, plus $41 per month. (*Source:* Midwest Athletic Club.) Let x represent the number of months and y represent the cost. How much does the first year's membership cost?

84. For a family membership, the athletic club in **Exercise 83** charges a membership fee of $159, plus $60 for each additional family member after the first. Let x represent the number of additional family members and y represent the cost. What is the membership fee for a four-person family?

85. A cell phone plan includes 900 anytime minutes for $60 per month, plus a one-time activation fee of $36. A Nokia 6650 cell phone is included at no additional charge. (*Source:* AT&T.) Let x represent the number of months of service and y represent the cost. If you sign a 1-yr contract, how much will this cell phone plan cost? (Assume that you never use more than the allotted number of minutes.)

86. Another cell phone plan includes 450 anytime minutes for $40 per month, plus $50 for a Nokia 2320 cell phone and $36 for a one-time activation fee. (*Source:* AT&T.) Let x represent the number of months of service and y represent the cost. If you sign a 1-yr contract, how much will this cell phone plan cost? (Assume that you never use more than the allotted number of minutes.)

87. There is a $30 fee to rent a chain saw, plus $6 per day. Let x represent the number of days the saw is rented and y represent the charge to the user in dollars. If the total charge is $138, for how many days is the saw rented?

88. A rental car costs $50 plus $0.20 per mile. Let x represent the number of miles driven and y represent the total charge to the renter. How many miles was the car driven if the renter paid $84.60?

Solve each problem. In part (a), give equations in slope-intercept form. (Round the slope to the nearest tenth.) **See Example 8.**

89. Total sales of digital cameras in the United States (in millions of dollars) are shown in the graph, where the year 2003 corresponds to $x = 0$.

(a) Use the ordered pairs from the graph to write an equation that models the data. What does the slope tell us in the context of this problem?

(b) Use the equation from part (a) to approximate the sales of digital cameras in the United States in 2007.

Digital Camera Sales

Source: Consumer Electronics Association.

90. Total sales of fax machines in the United States (in millions of dollars) are shown in the graph, where the year 2003 corresponds to $x = 0$.

(a) Use the ordered pairs from the graph to write an equation that models the data. What does the slope tell us in the context of this problem?

(b) Use the equation from part (a) to approximate the sales of fax machines in the United States in 2007.

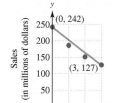

Fax Machine Sales

Source: Consumer Electronics Association.

91. Expenditures for home health care in the United States are shown in the graph.

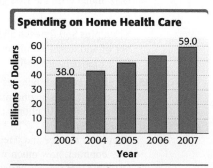

Spending on Home Health Care

Source: U.S. Centers for Medicare & Medicaid Services.

(a) Use the information given for the years 2003 and 2007, letting $x = 3$ represent 2003, $x = 7$ represent 2007, and y represent the amount (in billions of dollars) to write an equation that models home health care spending.

(b) Use the equation from part (a) to approximate the amount spent on home health care in 2005. How does your result compare with the actual value, $48.1 billion?

92. The number of post offices in the United States is shown in the graph.

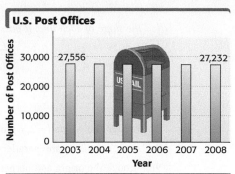

U.S. Post Offices

Source: U.S. Postal Service.

(a) Use the information given for the years 2003 and 2008, letting $x = 3$ represent 2003, $x = 8$ represent 2008, and y represent the number of post offices, to write an equation that models the data.

(b) Use the equation to approximate the number of post offices in 2006. How does this result compare with the actual value, 27,318?

RELATING CONCEPTS   EXERCISES 93–100

FOR INDIVIDUAL OR GROUP WORK

*In **Section 2.5,** we worked with formulas. **Work Exercises 93–100 in order,** to see how the formula that relates Celsius and Fahrenheit temperatures is derived.*

93. There is a linear relationship between Celsius and Fahrenheit temperatures. When $C = 0°$, $F = \_\_\_\_°$, and when $C = 100°$, $F = \_\_\_\_°$.

94. Think of ordered pairs of temperatures (C, F), where C and F represent corresponding Celsius and Fahrenheit temperatures. The equation that relates the two scales has a straight-line graph that contains the two points determined in **Exercise 93.** What are these two points?

95. Find the slope of the line described in **Exercise 94.**

96. Use the slope found in **Exercise 95** and one of the two points determined earlier, and write an equation that gives F in terms of C. (*Hint:* Use the point-slope form, with C replacing x and F replacing y.)

97. To obtain another form of the formula, use the equation found in **Exercise 96** and solve for C in terms of F.

98. Use the equation from **Exercise 96** to find the Fahrenheit temperature when $C = 30$.

99. Use the equation from **Exercise 97** to find the Celsius temperature when $F = 50$.

100. For what temperature is $F = C$? (Use the photo to confirm your answer.)

PREVIEW EXERCISES

*Write each inequality using interval notation. **See Section 2.8.***

101. $x \geq 0$ **102.** $x \leq 0$ **103.** $-4 \leq x \leq 4$

104. Express the set of all real numbers using interval notation. **See Section 2.8.**

SUMMARY EXERCISES on Slopes and Equations of Lines

Find the slope of each line, if possible.

1. $3x + 5y = 9$ **2.** $4x + 7y = 3$ **3.** $y = 2x - 5$

4. $5x - 2y = 4$ **5.** $x - 4 = 0$ **6.** $y = 0.5$

*For each line described, write an equation of the line **(a)** in slope-intercept form and **(b)** in standard form.*

7. Through the points $(-2, 6)$ and $(4, 1)$

8. Through $(-2, 5)$ and parallel to the graph of $3x - y = 4$

9. Through the origin and perpendicular to the graph of $2x - 5y = 6$

10. Through $(5, -8)$ and parallel to the graph of $y = 4$

11. Through $\left(\frac{3}{4}, -\frac{7}{9}\right)$ and perpendicular to the graph of $x = \frac{2}{3}$

12. Through $(4, -2)$ with slope -3

13. Through $(-4, 2)$ and parallel to the line through $(3, 9)$ and $(6, 11)$

14. Through $(4, -2)$ and perpendicular to the line through $(3, 7)$ and $(5, 6)$

15. Through the points $(4, -8)$ and $(-4, 12)$

16. Through $(-3, 6)$ with slope $\frac{2}{3}$

17. Through $(0, 3)$ and the midpoint of the segment with endpoints $(2, 8)$ and $(-4, 12)$

18. *Concept Check* Match the description in Column I with its equation in Column II.

I	**II**
(a) Slope -0.5, $b = -2$	**A.** $y = -\frac{1}{2}x$
(b) x-intercept $(4, 0)$, y-intercept $(0, 2)$	**B.** $y = -\frac{1}{2}x - 2$
(c) Passes through $(4, -2)$ and $(0, 0)$	**C.** $x - 2y = 2$
(d) $m = \frac{1}{2}$, passes through $(-2, -2)$	**D.** $x + 2y = 4$
(e) $m = \frac{1}{2}$, passes through the origin	**E.** $x = 2y$

7.3   Introduction to Relations and Functions

OBJECTIVES

1. Distinguish between independent and dependent variables.
2. Define and identify relations and functions.
3. Find the domain and range.
4. Identify functions defined by graphs and equations.

OBJECTIVE 1 Distinguish between independent and dependent variables.
We often describe one quantity in terms of another. Consider the following:

- The amount of a paycheck for an hourly employee depends on the number of hours worked.
- The cost at a gas station depends on the number of gallons of gas pumped.
- The distance traveled by a car moving at a constant rate depends on the time traveled.

We can use ordered pairs to represent these corresponding quantities. We indicate the relationship between hours worked and paycheck amount as follows.

$(5, 40)$ Working 5 hr results in a \$40 paycheck.

Number of hours worked   Paycheck amount in dollars

Similarly, the ordered pair $(10, 80)$ indicates that working 10 hr results in an \$80 paycheck. In this example, what would the ordered pair $(20, 160)$ indicate?

Since paycheck amount *depends* on number of hours worked, paycheck amount is called the *dependent variable,* and number of hours worked is called the *independent variable.* Generalizing, if the value of the variable y depends on the value of the variable x, then y is the **dependent variable** and x is the **independent variable.**

Independent variable ⌐ ⌐ Dependent variable
$$(x, y)$$

OBJECTIVE 2 **Define and identify relations and functions.** Since we can write related quantities as ordered pairs, a set of ordered pairs such as

$$\{(5, 40), (10, 80), (20, 160), (40, 320)\}$$

is called a *relation.*

Relation

A **relation** is any set of ordered pairs.

A *function* is a special kind of relation.

Function

A **function** is a relation in which, for each value of the first component of the ordered pairs, there is *exactly one value* of the second component.

NOW TRY
EXERCISE 1
Determine whether each relation defines a function.
(a) $\{(1, 5), (3, 5), (5, 5)\}$
(b) $\{(-1, -3), (0, 2), (-1, 6)\}$

EXAMPLE 1 Determining Whether Relations Are Functions

Determine whether each relation defines a function.

(a) $F = \{(1, 2), (-2, 4), (3, -1)\}$

For $x = 1$, there is only one value of y, 2.

For $x = -2$, there is only one value of y, 4.

For $x = 3$, there is only one value of y, -1.

Thus, relation F is a function, because for each different x-value, there is exactly one y-value.

(b) $G = \{(-2, -1), (-1, 0), (0, 1), (1, 2), (2, 2)\}$

Relation G is also a function. Although the last two ordered pairs have the same y-value (1 is paired with 2 and 2 is paired with 2), this does not violate the definition of a function. The first components (x-values) are different, and each is paired with only one second component (y-value).

(c) $H = \{(-4, 1), (-2, 1), (-2, 0)\}$

In relation H, the last two ordered pairs have the *same* x-value paired with *two different* y-values (-2 is paired with both 1 and 0), so H is a relation, but *not* a function.

Different y-values
$$H = \{(-4, 1), (-2, 1), (-2, 0)\} \qquad \text{Not a function}$$
Same x-value

In a function, no two ordered pairs can have the same first component and different second components.

NOW TRY

Relations and functions can be defined in several different ways.

- **As a set of ordered pairs** (See Example 1.)
- **As a correspondence or *mapping***

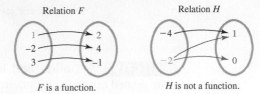

Relation *F*   Relation *H*

F is a function.   *H* is not a function.

FIGURE 32

See **FIGURE 32**. In the mapping for relation *F* from **Example 1(a),** 1 is mapped to 2, -2 is mapped to 4, and 3 is mapped to -1. Thus, *F* is a function, since each first component is paired with exactly one second component. In the mapping for relation *H* from **Example 1(c),** which is not a function, the first component -2 is paired with two different second components.

- **As a table**
- **As a graph**

  FIGURE 33 includes a table and graph for relation *F* from **Example 1(a).**

x	y
1	2
-2	4
3	-1

Table for relation *F*

Graph of relation *F*

FIGURE 33

- **As an equation (or rule)**

  An equation (or rule) can tell how to determine the dependent variable for a specific value of the independent variable. For example, if the value of *y* is twice the value of *x*, the equation is

  $$y = 2x.$$

  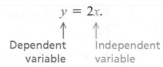

  Dependent variable   Independent variable

  The solutions of this equation define an infinite set of ordered pairs that can be represented by the graph in **FIGURE 34**.

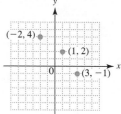

Graph of the relation defined by $y = 2x$

FIGURE 34

NOTE Another way to think of a function relationship is to think of the independent variable as an input and the dependent variable as an output. This is illustrated by the input-output (function) machine for the function defined by

$$y = 2x.$$

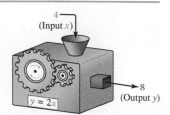

Function machine

In a function, there is exactly one value of the dependent variable, the second component, for each value of the independent variable, the first component.

OBJECTIVE 3 **Find the domain and range.** For every relation, there are two important sets of elements called the *domain* and *range*.

Domain and Range

In a relation, the set of all values of the independent variable (x) is the **domain.** The set of all values of the dependent variable (y) is the **range.**

NOW TRY
EXERCISE 2
Give the domain and range of each relation. Tell whether the relation defines a function.
(a) $\{(2, 2), (2, 5), (4, 8), (6, 5)\}$
(b)

x	y
1	$ 1.39
10	$10.39
15	$20.85

EXAMPLE 2 Finding Domains and Ranges of Relations

Give the domain and range of each relation. Tell whether the relation defines a function.

(a) $\{(3, -1), (4, 2), (4, 5), (6, 8)\}$

The domain, the set of x-values, is $\{3, 4, 6\}$. The range, the set of y-values, is $\{-1, 2, 5, 8\}$. This relation is not a function because the same x-value 4 is paired with two different y-values, 2 and 5.

(b)

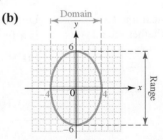

The domain of the relation represented by this mapping is $\{95, 89, 88, 78\}$, and the range is $\{A, B, C\}$. The mapping defines a function—each domain value corresponds to exactly one range value.

(c)

x	y
-5	2
0	2
5	2

In this table, the domain is the set of x-values $\{-5, 0, 5\}$ and the range is the set of y-values $\{2\}$. The table defines a function—each x-value corresponds to exactly one y-value (even though it is the same y-value).

NOW TRY

A graph gives a "picture" of a relation and can be used to determine its domain and range.

EXAMPLE 3 Finding Domains and Ranges from Graphs

Give the domain and range of each relation.

(a)

(b)

This relation includes the four ordered pairs that are graphed. The domain is the set of x-values,

$$\{-1, 0, 1, 4\}.$$

The range is the set of y-values,

$$\{-3, -1, 1, 2\}.$$

The x-values of the points on the graph include all numbers between -4 and 4, inclusive. The y-values include all numbers between -6 and 6, inclusive.

The domain is $[-4, 4]$.   Use interval
The range is $[-6, 6]$.   notation.

NOW TRY ANSWERS
2. **(a)** domain: $\{2, 4, 6\}$;
    range: $\{2, 5, 8\}$;
    not a function
  (b) domain: $\{1, 10, 15\}$;
    range: $\{\$1.39, \$10.39, \$20.85\}$;
    function

NOW TRY
EXERCISE 3
Give the domain and range of
the relation.

(c)

The arrowheads indicate that the
line extends indefinitely left and right,
as well as up and down. Therefore, both
the domain and the range include all real
numbers, written $(-\infty, \infty)$.

(d)

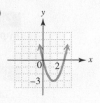

The graph extends indefinitely left and
right, as well as upward. The domain is
$(-\infty, \infty)$. Because there is a least y-value,
-3, the range includes all numbers greater
than or equal to -3, written $[-3, \infty)$.

NOW TRY

OBJECTIVE 4 **Identify functions defined by graphs and equations.** Since
each value of x in a function corresponds to only one value of y, any vertical line
drawn through the graph of a function must intersect the graph in at most one point.

Vertical Line Test

If every vertical line intersects the graph of a relation in no more than one point,
then the relation is a function.

FIGURE 35 illustrates the vertical line test with the graphs of two relations.

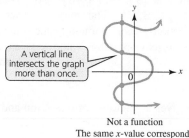

A vertical line
intersects the graph
more than once.

Not a function
The same x-value corresponds
to four different y-values.

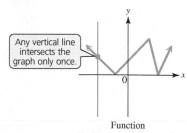

Any vertical line
intersects the
graph only once.

Function
Each x-value corresponds
to only one y-value.

FIGURE 35

NOW TRY
EXERCISE 4
Use the vertical line test to
determine whether the relation is a function.

EXAMPLE 4 Using the Vertical Line Test

Use the vertical line test to determine whether each relation graphed in **Example 3**
is a function. (We repeat the graphs here.)

(a)

$(-1, 1)$ $(1, 2)$

$(0, -1)$

$(4, -3)$

Function

(b)

Not a function

(c)

Function

(d)

Function

The graphs in (a), (c), and (d) satisfy the vertical line test and represent functions.
The graph in (b) fails the vertical line test, since the same x-value corresponds to two
different y-values, and is not the graph of a function.

NOW TRY

NOW TRY ANSWERS
3. domain: $(-\infty, \infty)$;
  range: $[-2, \infty)$
4. not a function

NOTE Graphs that do not represent functions are still relations. *All equations and graphs represent relations, and all relations have a domain and range.*

Relations are often defined by equations. If a relation is defined by an equation, keep the following in mind when finding its domain.

> **Exclude from the domain any values that make the denominator of a fraction equal to 0.**

For example, the function defined by $y = \frac{1}{x}$ has all real numbers except 0 as its domain, since division by 0 is undefined.

NOTE As we will see in **Section 10.1,** we must also **exclude from the domain any values that result in an even root of a negative number.**

In this book, we assume the following agreement on the domain of a relation.

Agreement on Domain

Unless specified otherwise, the domain of a relation is assumed to be all real numbers that produce real numbers when substituted for the independent variable.

NOW TRY
EXERCISE 5

Decide whether each relation defines y as a function of x, and give the domain.

(a) $y = 4x - 3$

(b) $y = \dfrac{1}{x - 8}$

EXAMPLE 5 Identifying Functions from Their Equations

Decide whether each relation defines y as a function of x, and give the domain.

(a) $y = x + 4$

In the defining equation (or rule) $y = x + 4$, y is always found by adding 4 to x. Thus, each value of x corresponds to just one value of y, and the relation defines a function. Since x can be any real number, the domain is

$$\{x \mid x \text{ is a real number}\}, \quad \text{or} \quad (-\infty, \infty).$$

(b) $y^2 = x$

The ordered pairs $(16, 4)$ and $(16, -4)$ both satisfy this equation. Since one value of x, 16, corresponds to two values of y, 4 and -4, this equation does not define a function. Because x is equal to the square of y, the values of x must always be nonnegative. The domain of the relation is $[0, \infty)$.

(c) $y = \dfrac{5}{x - 1}$

Given any value of x in the domain, we find y by subtracting 1 and then dividing the result into 5. This process produces exactly one value of y for each value in the domain, so the given equation defines a function.

The domain includes all real numbers except those which make the denominator 0. We find these numbers by setting the denominator equal to 0 and solving for x.

$$x - 1 = 0$$

$$x = 1 \quad \text{Add 1.}$$

The domain includes all real numbers *except* 1, written $(-\infty, 1) \cup (1, \infty)$.*

NOW TRY

NOW TRY ANSWERS

5. (a) yes; $(-\infty, \infty)$
   (b) yes; $(-\infty, 8) \cup (8, \infty)$

In summary, we give three variations of the definition of a function.

Variations of the Definition of a Function

1. A **function** is a relation in which, for each value of the first component of the ordered pairs, there is exactly one value of the second component.

2. A **function** is a set of distinct ordered pairs in which no first component is repeated.

3. A **function** is a correspondence or rule that assigns exactly one range value to each domain value.

7.3 EXERCISES

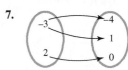

Complete solution available on the Video Resources on DVD

1. In your own words, define a function and give an example.

2. In your own words, define the domain of a function and give an example.

3. *Concept Check*   In an ordered pair of a relation, is the first element the independent or the dependent variable?

4. *Concept Check*   Give an example of a relation that is not a function and that has domain $\{-3, 2, 6\}$ and range $\{4, 6\}$. (There are many possible correct answers.)

Concept Check   *Express each relation using a different form. There is more than one correct way to do this.* **See Objective 2.**

5. $\{(0, 2), (2, 4), (4, 6)\}$

6.
x	y
−1	−3
0	−1
1	1
3	3

7.

8. *Concept Check*   Does the relation given in **Exercise 7** define a function? Why or why not?

Decide whether each relation defines a function, and give the domain and range. **See Examples 1–4.**

9. $\{(5, 1), (3, 2), (4, 9), (7, 6)\}$

10. $\{(8, 0), (5, 4), (9, 3), (3, 8)\}$

11. $\{(2, 4), (0, 2), (2, 5)\}$

12. $\{(9, -2), (-3, 5), (9, 2)\}$

13. $\{(-3, 1), (4, 1), (-2, 7)\}$

14. $\{(-12, 5), (-10, 3), (8, 3)\}$

15. $\{(1, 1), (1, -1), (0, 0), (2, 4), (2, -4)\}$

16. $\{(2, 5), (3, 7), (4, 9), (5, 11)\}$

17.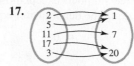

18.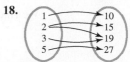

19.
x	y
1	5
1	2
1	−1
1	−4

20.
x	y
−4	−4
−4	0
−4	4
−4	8

21.
x	y
4	−3
2	−3
0	−3
−2	−3

22.
x	y
−3	−6
−1	−6
1	−6
3	−6

23.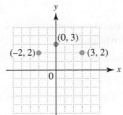

24.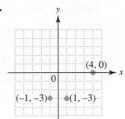

🌐 **25.**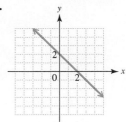

26.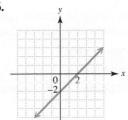

27.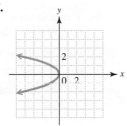

28.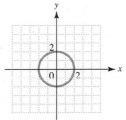

🌐 **29.**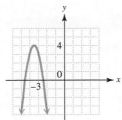

30.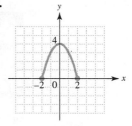

🌐 **31.**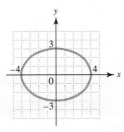

32.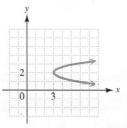

Decide whether each relation defines y as a function of x. Give the domain. ***See Example 5.***

33. $y = -6x$

34. $y = -9x$

🌐 **35.** $y = 2x - 6$

36. $y = 6x + 8$

37. $y = x^2$

38. $y = x^3$

39. $x = y^6$

40. $x = y^4$

41. $y = \dfrac{x + 4}{5}$

42. $y = \dfrac{x - 3}{2}$

43. $y = -\dfrac{2}{x}$

44. $y = -\dfrac{6}{x}$

45. $y = \dfrac{2}{x - 4}$

46. $y = \dfrac{7}{x - 2}$

47. $y = \dfrac{1}{4x + 3}$

48. $y = \dfrac{1}{2x + 9}$

49. $x = y^2 + 1$

50. $x = y^2 - 3$

51. $xy = 1$

52. $xy = 3$

Solve each problem.

53. The table shows the percentage of students at 4-year public colleges who graduated within 5 years.

  (a) Does the table define a function?

  (b) What are the domain and range?

  (c) Call this function f. Give two ordered pairs that belong to f.

Year	Percentage
2004	42.3
2005	42.3
2006	42.8
2007	43.7
2008	43.8

Source: ACT.

54. The table shows the percentage of full-time college freshmen who said they had discussed politics in election years.

  (a) Does the table define a function?

  (b) What are the domain and range?

  (c) Call this function g. Give two ordered pairs that belong to g.

Year	Percentage
1992	83.7
1996	73.0
2000	69.6
2004	77.4
2008	85.9

Source: Cooperative Institutional Research Program.

PREVIEW EXERCISES

*Evaluate y for x = 3. **See Section 3.1.***

55. $y = -7x + 12$ **56.** $y = -5x - 4$ **57.** $y = 3x - 8$

*Solve for y. **See Section 2.5.***

58. $3x - 7y = 8$ **59.** $2x - 4y = 7$ **60.** $\dfrac{3}{4}x + 2y = 9$

7.4 Function Notation and Linear Functions

OBJECTIVES

1 Use function notation.

2 Graph linear and constant functions.

OBJECTIVE 1 **Use function notation.** When a function f is defined with a rule or an equation using x and y for the independent and dependent variables, we say, "*y is a function of x*" to emphasize that y *depends on* x. We use the notation

$$y = f(x),$$

> The parentheses here do *not* indicate multiplication.

called **function notation,** to express this and read $f(x)$ as **"f of x."** The letter f is a name for this particular function. For example, if $y = 9x - 5$, we can name this function f and write

$$f(x) = 9x - 5.$$

f is the name of the function.
x is a value from the domain.
$f(x)$ is the function value (or y-value) that corresponds to x.

$f(x)$ *is just another name for the dependent variable* y.

  We can evaluate a function at different values of x by substituting x-values from the domain into the function.

NOW TRY
EXERCISE 1

Let $f(x) = 4x + 3$. Find the value of the function f for $x = -2$.

EXAMPLE 1 Evaluating a Function

Let $f(x) = 9x - 5$. Find the value of the function f for $x = 2$.

$$f(x) = 9x - 5$$

Read $f(2)$ as "f of 2" or "f at 2." $f(2) = 9 \cdot 2 - 5$ Replace x with 2.

$$f(2) = 18 - 5$$ Multiply.

$$f(2) = 13$$ Add.

Thus, for $x = 2$, the corresponding function value (or y-value) is 13. $f(2) = 13$ is an abbreviation for the statement

"If $x = 2$ in the function f, then $y = 13$"

and is represented by the ordered pair $(2, 13)$.   NOW TRY

⚠ **CAUTION** The symbol $f(x)$ *does not* indicate "f times x," but represents the y-value associated with the indicated x-value. As just shown, $f(2)$ is the y-value that corresponds to the x-value 2 in the function.

These ideas can be illustrated as follows.

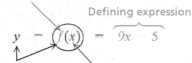

NOW TRY
EXERCISE 2

Let $f(x) = 2x^2 - 4x + 1$. Find the following.

(a) $f(-2)$ (b) $f(a)$

EXAMPLE 2 Evaluating a Function

Let $f(x) = -x^2 + 5x - 3$. Find the following.

(a) $f(4)$

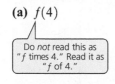

$$f(x) = -x^2 + 5x - 3$$ The base in $-x^2$ is x, *not* $(-x)$.

Do *not* read this as "f times 4." Read it as "f of 4." $f(4) = -4^2 + 5 \cdot 4 - 3$ Replace x with 4.

$$f(4) = -16 + 20 - 3$$ Apply the exponent. Multiply.

$$f(4) = 1$$ Add and subtract.

Thus, $f(4) = 1$, and the ordered pair $(4, 1)$ belongs to f.

(b) $f(q)$

$$f(x) = -x^2 + 5x - 3$$

$$f(q) = -q^2 + 5q - 3$$ Replace x with q.

The replacement of one variable with another is important in later courses.

NOW TRY

NOW TRY ANSWERS
1. -5
2. (a) 17 (b) $2a^2 - 4a + 1$

Sometimes letters other than f, such as g, h, or capital letters F, G, and H are used to name functions.

NOW TRY
EXERCISE 3
Let $g(x) = 8x - 5$. Find and simplify $g(a - 2)$.

EXAMPLE 3 Evaluating a Function

Let $g(x) = 2x + 3$. Find and simplify $g(a + 1)$.

$$g(x) = 2x + 3$$
$$g(a + 1) = 2(a + 1) + 3 \quad \text{Replace } x \text{ with } a + 1.$$
$$g(a + 1) = 2a + 2 + 3 \quad \text{Distributive property}$$
$$g(a + 1) = 2a + 5 \quad \text{Add.} \qquad \text{NOW TRY}$$

NOW TRY
EXERCISE 4
Find $f(-1)$ for each function.
(a) $f = \{(-5, -1), (-3, 2), (-1, 4)\}$
(b) $f(x) = x^2 - 12$

EXAMPLE 4 Evaluating Functions

For each function, find $f(3)$.

(a) $f(x) = 3x - 7$
$$f(3) = 3(3) - 7 \quad \text{Replace } x \text{ with 3.}$$
$$f(3) = 9 - 7 \quad \text{Multiply.}$$
$$f(3) = 2 \quad \text{Subtract.}$$

(b)
x	$y = f(x)$
6	−12
3	−6
0	0
−3	6

← Here, $f(3) = -6$.

(c) $f = \{(-3, 5), (0, 3), (3, 1), (6, -1)\}$
We want $f(3)$, the y-value of the ordered pair whose first component is $x = 3$. As indicated by the ordered pair $(3, 1)$, for $x = 3$, $y = 1$. Thus, $f(3) = 1$.

(d)
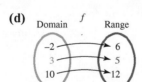

The domain element 3 is paired with 5 in the range, so $f(3) = 5$.

NOW TRY

EXAMPLE 5 Finding Function Values from a Graph

Refer to the function graphed in FIGURE 36.

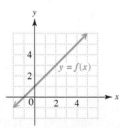

FIGURE 36

(a) Find $f(3)$.
Locate 3 on the x-axis. See FIGURE 37. Moving up to the graph of f and over to the y-axis gives 4 for the corresponding y-value. Thus, $f(3) = 4$, which corresponds to the ordered pair $(3, 4)$.

(b) Find $f(0)$.
Refer to FIGURE 37 to see that $f(0) = 1$.

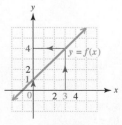

FIGURE 37

NOW TRY ANSWERS
3. $8a - 21$
4. (a) 4   (b) −11

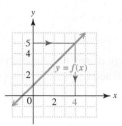

FIGURE 38

NOW TRY
EXERCISE 5

Refer to the function graphed in **FIGURE 36** on the previous page.

(a) Find $f(-1)$.

(b) For what value of x is $f(x) = 2$?

NOW TRY
EXERCISE 6

Rewrite the equation using function notation $f(x)$. Then find $f(-3)$ and $f(h)$.

$$-4x^2 + y = 5$$

(c) For what value of x is $f(x) = 5$?

Since $f(x) = y$, we want the value of x that corresponds to $y = 5$. Locate 5 on the y-axis. See **FIGURE 38**. Moving across to the graph of f and down to the x-axis gives $x = 4$. Thus, $f(4) = 5$, which corresponds to the ordered pair $(4, 5)$.   NOW TRY

If a function f is defined by an equation with x and y, and y is not solved for x, use the following steps to find $f(x)$.

Finding an Expression for $f(x)$

Step 1   Solve the equation for y.

Step 2   Replace y with $f(x)$.

EXAMPLE 6   Writing Equations Using Function Notation

Rewrite each equation using function notation $f(x)$. Then find $f(-2)$ and $f(a)$.

(a) $y = x^2 + 1$

This equation is already solved for y, so we replace y with $f(x)$.

$$f(x) = x^2 + 1 \qquad y = f(x)$$

To find $f(-2)$, let $x = -2$.

$$f(x) = x^2 + 1$$
$$f(-2) = (-2)^2 + 1 \qquad \text{Let } x = -2.$$
$$f(-2) = 4 + 1 \qquad (-2)^2 = -2(-2)$$
$$f(-2) = 5 \qquad \text{Add.}$$

Find $f(a)$ by letting $x = a$: $f(a) = a^2 + 1$.

(b) $x - 4y = 5$ Solve for y. (Step 1)

$x - 5 = 4y$ Add 4y. Subtract 5.

$$y = \frac{x - 5}{4}, \quad \text{so} \quad f(x) = \frac{1}{4}x - \frac{5}{4} \qquad \boxed{\frac{a-b}{c} = \frac{a}{c} - \frac{b}{c}}$$

$y = f(x)$ (Step 2)

Now find $f(-2)$ and $f(a)$.

$$f(-2) = \frac{1}{4}(-2) - \frac{5}{4} = -\frac{7}{4} \qquad \text{Let } x = -2.$$

$$f(a) = \frac{1}{4}a - \frac{5}{4} \qquad \text{Let } x = a. \qquad \text{NOW TRY}$$

OBJECTIVE 2   **Graph linear and constant functions.**   Linear equations (except for vertical lines with equations $x = a$) define *linear functions*.

Linear Function

A function that can be defined by

$$f(x) = ax + b$$

for real numbers a and b is a **linear function.** The value of a is the slope m of the graph of the function. The domain of any linear function is $(-\infty, \infty)$.

NOW TRY ANSWERS
5. (a) 0   **(b)** 1
6. $f(x) = 4x^2 + 5$; $f(-3) = 41$; $f(h) = 4h^2 + 5$

A linear function whose graph is a horizontal line is defined by

$$f(x) = b \qquad \text{Constant function}$$

and is sometimes called a **constant function.** While the range of any nonconstant linear function is $(-\infty, \infty)$, the range of a constant function defined by $f(x) = b$ is $\{b\}$.

NOW TRY
EXERCISE 7
Graph the function. Give the domain and range.

$$g(x) = \frac{1}{3}x - 2$$

EXAMPLE 7 Graphing Linear and Constant Functions

Graph each function. Give the domain and range.

(a) $f(x) = \dfrac{1}{4}x - \dfrac{5}{4}$ (from **Example 6(b)**)

Slope⤴   ⤴ y-intercept is $\left(0, -\frac{5}{4}\right)$.

The graph of $y = \frac{1}{4}x - \frac{5}{4}$ has slope $m = \frac{1}{4}$ and y-intercept $\left(0, -\frac{5}{4}\right)$. To graph this function, plot the y-intercept $\left(0, -\frac{5}{4}\right)$ and use the definition of slope as $\frac{\text{rise}}{\text{run}}$ to find a second point on the line. Since the slope is $\frac{1}{4}$, move 1 unit up from $\left(0, -\frac{5}{4}\right)$ and 4 units to the right to find this second point. Draw the straight line through the points to obtain the graph shown in **FIGURE 39**. The domain and range are both $(-\infty, \infty)$.

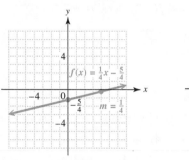

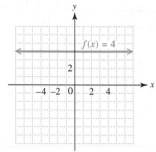

FIGURE 39   **FIGURE 40**

(b) $f(x) = 4$

The graph of this constant function is the horizontal line containing all points with y-coordinate 4. See **FIGURE 40**. The domain is $(-\infty, \infty)$ and the range is $\{4\}$.

NOW TRY⤴

NOW TRY ANSWER
7.

domain: $(-\infty, \infty)$;
range: $(-\infty, \infty)$

7.4 EXERCISES

PRACTICE   WATCH   DOWNLOAD   READ   REVIEW

🌐 *Complete solution available on the Video Resources on DVD*

1. *Concept Check*   Choose the correct response: The notation $f(3)$ means

A. the variable f times 3, or $3f$.

B. the value of the dependent variable when the independent variable is 3.

C. the value of the independent variable when the dependent variable is 3.

D. f equals 3.

2. *Concept Check*   Give an example of a function from everyday life. (*Hint:* Fill in the blanks: _____ depends on _____, so _____ is a function of _____.)

Let $f(x) = -3x + 4$ and $g(x) = -x^2 + 4x + 1$. Find the following. *See Examples 1–3.*

 3. $f(0)$ **4.** $f(-3)$ **5.** $g(-2)$ **6.** $g(10)$

7. $f\left(\dfrac{1}{3}\right)$ **8.** $f\left(\dfrac{7}{3}\right)$ **9.** $g(0.5)$ **10.** $g(1.5)$

11. $f(p)$ **12.** $g(k)$ **13.** $f(-x)$ **14.** $g(-x)$

 15. $f(x + 2)$ **16.** $f(x - 2)$ **17.** $g(\pi)$ **18.** $g(e)$

19. $f(x + h)$ **20.** $f(x + h) - f(x)$ **21.** $f(4) - g(4)$ **22.** $f(10) - g(10)$

For each function, find **(a)** $f(2)$ and **(b)** $f(-1)$. *See Examples 4 and 5.*

23. $f = \{(-2, 2), (-1, -1), (2, -1)\}$ **24.** $f = \{(-1, -5), (0, 5), (2, -5)\}$

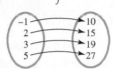 **25.** $f = \{(-1, 3), (4, 7), (0, 6), (2, 2)\}$ **26.** $f = \{(2, 5), (3, 9), (-1, 11), (5, 3)\}$

27.

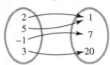

28.

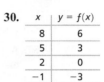

29.

x	$y = f(x)$
2	4
1	1
0	0
−1	1
−2	4

30.

x	$y = f(x)$
8	6
5	3
2	0
−1	−3
−4	−6

31.

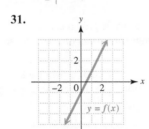

32.

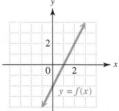

33.

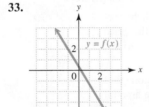

34.

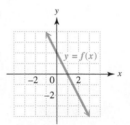

35. Refer to **Exercise 31.** Find the value of x for each value of $f(x)$. *See Example 5(c).*

     (a) $f(x) = 3$ **(b)** $f(x) = -1$ **(c)** $f(x) = -3$

36. Refer to **Exercise 32.** Find the value of x for each value of $f(x)$. *See Example 5(c).*

     (a) $f(x) = 4$ **(b)** $f(x) = -2$ **(c)** $f(x) = 0$

An equation that defines y as a function f of x is given. **(a)** Solve for y in terms of x, and replace y with the function notation $f(x)$. **(b)** Find $f(3)$. *See Example 6.*

37. $x + 3y = 12$ **38.** $x - 4y = 8$ **39.** $y + 2x^2 = 3$

40. $y - 3x^2 = 2$ **41.** $4x - 3y = 8$ **42.** $-2x + 5y = 9$

43. *Concept Check* Fill in each blank with the correct response.

The equation $2x + y = 4$ has a straight _____ as its graph. One point that lies on the graph is $(3, $ _____ $)$. If we solve the equation for y and use function notation, we obtain $f(x) = $ _____. For this function, $f(3) = $ _____, meaning that the point ($_____ , _____$) lies on the graph of the function.

44. *Concept Check* Which of the following defines y as a linear function of x?

A. $y = \dfrac{1}{4}x - \dfrac{5}{4}$ **B.** $y = \dfrac{1}{x}$ **C.** $y = x^2$ **D.** $y = \sqrt{x}$

*Graph each linear function. Give the domain and range. **See Example 7.***

45. $f(x) = -2x + 5$ **46.** $g(x) = 4x - 1$ **47.** $h(x) = \dfrac{1}{2}x + 2$

48. $F(x) = -\dfrac{1}{4}x + 1$ **49.** $G(x) = 2x$ **50.** $H(x) = -3x$

51. $g(x) = -4$ **52.** $f(x) = 5$ **53.** $f(x) = 0$ **54.** $f(x) = -2.5$

55. *Concept Check* What is the name that is usually given to the graph in **Exercise 53?**

56. Can the graph of a linear function have an undefined slope? Explain.

Solve each problem.

57. A package weighing x pounds costs $f(x)$ dollars to mail to a given location, where

$$f(x) = 3.75x.$$

(a) Evaluate $f(3)$.

(b) Describe what 3 and the value $f(3)$ mean in part (a), using the terminology *independent variable* and *dependent variable*.

(c) How much would it cost to mail a 5-lb package? Interpret this question and its answer, using function notation.

58. A taxicab driver charges $2.50 per mile.

(a) Fill in the table with the correct response for the price $f(x)$ he charges for a trip of x miles.

x	$f(x)$
0	
1	
2	
3	

(b) The linear function that gives a rule for the amount charged is $f(x) = $ _____.

(c) Graph this function for the domain $\{0, 1, 2, 3\}$.

59. Forensic scientists use the lengths of certain bones to calculate the height of a person. Two bones often used are the tibia (t), the bone from the ankle to the knee, and the femur (r), the bone from the knee to the hip socket. A person's height (h) in centimeters is determined from the lengths of these bones by using functions defined by the following formulas.

For men: $h(r) = 69.09 + 2.24r$ or $h(t) = 81.69 + 2.39t$

For women: $h(r) = 61.41 + 2.32r$ or $h(t) = 72.57 + 2.53t$

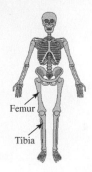

Femur

Tibia

(a) Find the height of a man with a femur measuring 56 cm.

(b) Find the height of a man with a tibia measuring 40 cm.

(c) Find the height of a woman with a femur measuring 50 cm.

(d) Find the height of a woman with a tibia measuring 36 cm.

60. Federal regulations set standards for the size of the quarters of marine mammals. A pool to house sea otters must have a volume of "the square of the sea otter's average adult length (in meters) multiplied by 3.14 and by 0.91 meter." If x represents the sea otter's average adult length and $f(x)$ represents the volume (in cubic meters) of the corresponding pool size, this formula can be written as

$$f(x) = 0.91(3.14)x^2.$$

Find the volume of the pool for each adult sea otter length (in meters). Round answers to the nearest hundredth.

(a) 0.8   (b) 1.0   (c) 1.2   (d) 1.5

61. To print t-shirts, there is a $100 set-up fee, plus a $12 charge per t-shirt. Let x represent the number of t-shirts printed and $f(x)$ represent the total charge.

(a) Write a linear function that models this situation.

(b) Find $f(125)$. Interpret your answer in the context of this problem.

(c) Find the value of x if $f(x) = 1000$. Express this situation using function notation, and interpret it in the context of this problem.

62. Rental on a car is $150, plus $0.20 per mile. Let x represent the number of miles driven and $f(x)$ represent the total cost to rent the car.

(a) Write a linear function that models this situation.

(b) How much would it cost to drive 250 mi? Interpret this question and answer, using function notation.

(c) Find the value of x if $f(x) = 230$. Interpret your answer in the context of this problem.

63. The table represents a linear function.

(a) What is $f(2)$?

(b) If $f(x) = -2.5$, what is the value of x?

(c) What is the slope of the line?

(d) What is the y-intercept of the line?

(e) Using your answers from parts (c) and (d), write an equation for $f(x)$.

x	$y = f(x)$
0	3.5
1	2.3
2	1.1
3	-0.1
4	-1.3
5	-2.5

64. The table represents a linear function.

(a) What is $f(2)$?

(b) If $f(x) = 2.1$, what is the value of x?

(c) What is the slope of the line?

(d) What is the y-intercept of the line?

(e) Using your answers from parts (c) and (d), write an equation for $f(x)$.

x	$y = f(x)$
-1	-3.9
0	-2.4
1	-0.9
2	0.6
3	2.1

65. Refer to the graph to answer each of the questions.

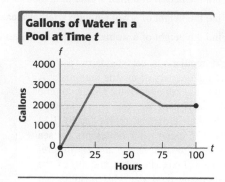

Gallons of Water in a Pool at Time t

(a) What numbers are possible values of the independent variable? The dependent variable?

(b) For how long is the water level increasing? Decreasing?

(c) How many gallons of water are in the pool after 90 hr?

(d) Call this function f. What is $f(0)$? What does it mean?

(e) What is $f(25)$? What does it mean?

66. The graph shows megawatts of electricity used on a summer day.

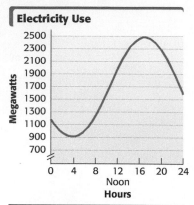

Electricity Use

Source: Sacramento Municipal Utility District.

(a) Why is this the graph of a function?

(b) What is the domain?

(c) Estimate the number of megawatts used at 8 A.M.

(d) At what time was the most electricity used? The least electricity?

(e) Call this function f. What is $f(12)$? What does it mean?

PREVIEW EXERCISES

Perform each indicated operation. See Sections 4.4, 4.5, and 4.7.

67. $(15x^2 - 2x) + (x - 4)$ **68.** $(3r + 8) - (2r - 5)$ **69.** $(4x - 5)(3x + 1)$

70. $(3x - 4)(2x^2 + x)$ **71.** $\dfrac{27x^3 - 18x^2}{9x}$ **72.** $\dfrac{q^2 + 2q - 35}{q - 5}$

7.5   Operations on Functions and Composition

OBJECTIVES

1. Recognize and evaluate polynomial functions.

2. Perform operations on polynomial functions.

3. Find the composition of functions.

OBJECTIVE 1   Recognize and evaluate polynomial functions. In **Section 7.4,** we studied linear (first-degree polynomial) functions, defined as $f(x) = ax + b$. Now we consider more general polynomial functions.

Polynomial Function

A **polynomial function of degree** n is defined by

$$f(x) = a_n x^n + a_{n-1}x^{n-1} + \cdots + a_1 x + a_0,$$

for real numbers $a_n, a_{n-1}, \ldots, a_1$, and a_0, where $a_n \neq 0$ and n is a whole number.

Another way of describing a polynomial function is to say that it is a function defined by a polynomial in one variable, consisting of one or more terms. It is usually written in descending powers of the variable, and its degree is the degree of the polynomial that defines it.

We can evaluate a polynomial function $f(x)$ at different values of the variable x.

NOW TRY
EXERCISE 1
Let $f(x) = x^3 - 2x^2 + 7$.
Find $f(-3)$.

EXAMPLE 1 Evaluating Polynomial Functions

Let $f(x) = 4x^3 - x^2 + 5$. Find each value.

(a) $f(3)$

Read this as "f of 3," not "f times 3."

$$f(x) = 4x^3 - x^2 + 5 \qquad \text{Given function}$$
$$f(3) = 4(3)^3 - 3^2 + 5 \qquad \text{Substitute 3 for } x.$$
$$f(3) = 4(27) - 9 + 5 \qquad \text{Apply the exponents.}$$
$$f(3) = 108 - 9 + 5 \qquad \text{Multiply.}$$
$$f(3) = 104 \qquad \text{Subtract, and then add.}$$

Thus, $f(3) = 104$ and the ordered pair $(3, 104)$ belongs to f.

(b) $f(-4)$

$$f(x) = 4x^3 - x^2 + 5 \qquad \text{Use parentheses.}$$
$$f(-4) = 4 \cdot (-4)^3 - (-4)^2 + 5 \qquad \text{Let } x = -4.$$
$$f(-4) = 4 \cdot (-64) - 16 + 5 \qquad \text{Be careful with signs.}$$
$$f(-4) = -256 - 16 + 5 \qquad \text{Multiply.}$$
$$f(-4) = -267 \qquad \text{Subtract, and then add.}$$

So, $f(-4) = -267$. The ordered pair $(-4, -267)$ belongs to f.   **NOW TRY**

While f is the most common letter used to represent functions, recall that other letters, such as g and h, are also used. ***The capital letter P is often used for polynomial functions.*** The function defined as

$$P(x) = 4x^3 - x^2 + 5$$

yields the same ordered pairs as the function f in **Example 1.**

OBJECTIVE 2 **Perform operations on polynomial functions.** The operations of addition, subtraction, multiplication, and division are also defined for functions. For example, businesses use the equation "profit equals revenue minus cost," which can be written in function notation.

$$P(x) \;=\; R(x) \;-\; C(x) \qquad \text{x is the number of items produced and sold.}$$

    ↑   ↑   ↑
  Profit Revenue   Cost
function function function

NOW TRY ANSWER
1. -38

The profit function is found by subtracting the cost function from the revenue function.

We define the following **operations on functions.**

Operations on Functions

If $f(x)$ and $g(x)$ define functions, then

$$(f + g)(x) = f(x) + g(x), \qquad \text{Sum function}$$

$$(f - g)(x) = f(x) - g(x), \qquad \text{Difference function}$$

$$(fg)(x) = f(x) \cdot g(x), \qquad \text{Product function}$$

and

$$\left(\frac{f}{g}\right)x = \frac{f(x)}{g(x)}, \quad g(x) \neq 0. \qquad \text{Quotient function}$$

In each case, the domain of the new function is the intersection of the domains of $f(x)$ and $g(x)$. Additionally, the domain of the quotient function must exclude any values of x for which $g(x) = 0$.

NOW TRY
EXERCISE 2

For $f(x) = x^3 - 3x^2 + 4$ and $g(x) = -2x^3 + x^2 - 12$, find each of the following.

(a) $(f + g)(x)$

(b) $(f - g)(x)$

EXAMPLE 2   Adding and Subtracting Polynomial Functions

Find each of the following for the polynomial functions defined by

$$f(x) = x^2 - 3x + 7 \quad \text{and} \quad g(x) = -3x^2 - 7x + 7.$$

(a) $(f + g)(x)$ ⟵ This notation does *not* indicate the distributive property.

$= f(x) + g(x)$ Use the definition.

$= (x^2 - 3x + 7) + (-3x^2 - 7x + 7)$ Substitute.

$= -2x^2 - 10x + 14$ Add the polynomials.

(b) $(f - g)(x)$

$= f(x) - g(x)$ Use the definition.

$= (x^2 - 3x + 7) - (-3x^2 - 7x + 7)$ Substitute.

$= (x^2 - 3x + 7) + (3x^2 + 7x - 7)$ Change subtraction to addition.

$= 4x^2 + 4x$ Add.   NOW TRY

EXAMPLE 3   Adding and Subtracting Polynomial Functions

Find each of the following for the functions defined by

$$f(x) = 10x^2 - 2x \quad \text{and} \quad g(x) = 2x.$$

(a) $(f + g)(2)$

$= f(2) + g(2)$ Use the definition.

$\overbrace{f(x) = 10x^2 - 2x}\qquad \overbrace{g(x) = 2x}$

$= [10(2)^2 - 2(2)] + 2(2)$ Substitute.

This is a key step. $= [40 - 4] + 4$ Order of operations

$= 40$ Subtract, and then add.

NOW TRY ANSWERS
2. (a) $-x^3 - 2x^2 - 8$
    (b) $3x^3 - 4x^2 + 16$

NOW TRY
EXERCISE 3

For $f(x) = x^2 - 4$
and $g(x) = -6x^2$,
find each of the following.

(a) $(f + g)(x)$

(b) $(f - g)(-4)$

Alternatively, we could first find $(f + g)(x)$.

$$(f + g)(x)$$
$$= f(x) + g(x) \qquad \text{Use the definition.}$$
$$= (10x^2 - 2x) + 2x \qquad \text{Substitute.}$$
$$= 10x^2 \qquad \text{Combine like terms.}$$

Then,

$$(f + g)(2)$$
$$= 10(2)^2 \qquad \text{Substitute.}$$
$$= 40. \qquad \text{The result is the same.}$$

(b) $(f - g)(x)$ and $(f - g)(1)$

$$(f - g)(x)$$
$$= f(x) - g(x) \qquad \text{Use the definition.}$$
$$= (10x^2 - 2x) - 2x \qquad \text{Substitute.}$$
$$= 10x^2 - 4x \qquad \text{Combine like terms.}$$

Then,

$$(f - g)(1)$$
$$= 10(1)^2 - 4(1) \qquad \text{Substitute.}$$
$$= 6. \qquad \text{Simplify.}$$

Confirm that $f(1) - g(1)$ gives the same result. NOW TRY

NOW TRY
EXERCISE 4

For $f(x) = 3x^2 - 1$
and $g(x) = 8x + 7$,
find $(fg)(x)$ and $(fg)(-2)$.

EXAMPLE 4 Multiplying Polynomial Functions

For $f(x) = 3x + 4$ and $g(x) = 2x^2 + x$, find $(fg)(x)$ and $(fg)(-1)$.

$$(fg)(x)$$
$$= f(x) \cdot g(x) \qquad \text{Use the definition.}$$
$$= (3x + 4)(2x^2 + x) \qquad \text{Substitute.}$$
$$= 6x^3 + 3x^2 + 8x^2 + 4x \qquad \text{FOIL}$$
$$= 6x^3 + 11x^2 + 4x \qquad \text{Combine like terms.}$$

$$(fg)(-1)$$
$$= 6(-1)^3 + 11(-1)^2 + 4(-1) \qquad \text{Let } x = -1 \text{ in } (fg)(x).$$
$$= -6 + 11 - 4 \quad \boxed{\text{Be careful with signs.}}$$
$$= 1 \qquad \text{Add and subtract.}$$

Confirm that $f(-1) \cdot g(-1)$ is equal to $(fg)(-1)$. NOW TRY

EXAMPLE 5 Dividing Polynomial Functions

For $f(x) = 2x^2 + x - 10$ and $g(x) = x - 2$, find $\left(\frac{f}{g}\right)(x)$ and $\left(\frac{f}{g}\right)(-3)$. What value of x is not in the domain of the quotient function?

$$\left(\frac{f}{g}\right)(x) = \frac{f(x)}{g(x)} = \frac{2x^2 + x - 10}{x - 2}$$

NOW TRY ANSWERS
3. (a) $-5x^2 - 4$ **(b)** 108
4. $24x^3 + 21x^2 - 8x - 7$; -99

NOW TRY
EXERCISE 5

For $f(x) = 8x^2 + 2x - 3$
and $g(x) = 2x - 1$,
find $\left(\frac{f}{g}\right)(x)$ and $\left(\frac{f}{g}\right)(8)$.

To find the quotient, divide as in **Section 4.7.**

$$
\begin{array}{r}
2x + 5 \\
x - 2\overline{)2x^2 + x - 10} \\
\end{array}
$$

To subtract, add the opposite.
$\quad 2x^2 - 4x \quad\quad 2x(x-2)$
$\quad\quad\quad 5x - 10 \quad$ Subtract.
$\quad\quad\quad \underline{5x - 10} \quad 5(x-2)$
$\quad\quad\quad\quad\quad 0$

The quotient here is $2x + 5$, so

$$\left(\frac{f}{g}\right)(x) = 2x + 5, \quad x \neq 2.$$

The number 2 is not in the domain because it causes the denominator $g(x) = x - 2$ to equal 0. Then

$$\left(\frac{f}{g}\right)(-3) = 2(-3) + 5 = -1. \quad \text{Let } x = -3.$$

Verify that the same value is found by evaluating $\frac{f(-3)}{g(-3)}$.   NOW TRY

OBJECTIVE 3 **Find the composition of functions.** The diagram in **FIGURE 41** shows a function f that assigns, to each element x of set X, some element y of set Y. Suppose that a function g takes each element of set Y and assigns a value z of set Z. Then f and g together assign an element x in X to an element z in Z. The result of this process is a new function h that takes an element x in X and assigns it an element z in Z.

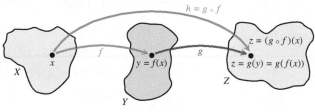

FIGURE 41

This function h is called the *composition* of functions g and f, written $\boldsymbol{g \circ f}$.

Composition of Functions
If f and g are functions, then the **composite function,** or **composition,** of g and f is defined by $$(g \circ f)(x) = g(f(x))$$ for all x in the domain of f such that $f(x)$ is in the domain of g.

Read $g \circ f$ as "g of f".

As a real-life example of how composite functions occur, consider the following retail situation.

A $40 pair of blue jeans is on sale for 25% off. If you purchase the jeans before noon, the retailer offers an additional 10% off. What is the final sale price of the blue jeans?

NOW TRY ANSWER
5. $4x + 3, \quad x \neq \frac{1}{2}; 35$

You might be tempted to say that the blue jeans are $25\% + 10\% = 35\%$ off and calculate $\$40(0.35) = \$14$, giving a final sale price of

$$\$40 - \$14 = \$26. \quad \text{This is not correct.}$$

To find the correct final sale price, we must first find the price after taking 25% off, and then take an additional 10% off that price.

$$\$40(0.25) = \$10, \text{ giving a sale price of } \$40 - \$10 = \$30. \quad \text{Take 25\% off original price.}$$

$$\$30(0.10) = \$3, \text{ giving a } \textit{final sale price} \text{ of } \$30 - \$3 = \$27. \quad \text{Take additional 10\% off.}$$

This is the idea behind composition of functions.

NOW TRY
EXERCISE 6

Let $f(x) = 3x + 7$
and $g(x) = x - 2$.
Find $(f \circ g)(7)$.

EXAMPLE 6 Evaluating a Composite Function

Let $f(x) = x^2$ and $g(x) = x + 3$. Find $(f \circ g)(4)$.

$$(f \circ g)(4) \quad \boxed{\text{Evaluate the "inside" function value first.}}$$

$$= f(g(4)) \qquad \text{Definition}$$

$$= f(4 + 3) \qquad \text{Use the rule for } g(x); g(4) = 4 + 3.$$

$$= f(7) \qquad \text{Add.}$$

$\boxed{\text{Now evaluate the "outside" function.}}$ $= 7^2 \qquad \text{Use the rule for } f(x); f(7) = 7^2.$

$$= 49 \qquad \text{Square 7.} \qquad \text{NOW TRY}$$

If we interchange the order of the functions in **Example 6,** the composition of g and f is defined by $g(f(x))$. To find $(g \circ f)(4)$, we let $x = 4$.

$$(g \circ f)(4)$$

$$= g(f(4)) \qquad \text{Definition}$$

$$= g(4^2) \qquad \text{Use the rule for } f(x); f(4) = 4^2.$$

$$= g(16) \qquad \text{Square 4.}$$

$$= 16 + 3 \qquad \text{Use the rule for } g(x); g(16) = 16 + 3.$$

$$= 19 \qquad \text{Add.}$$

Here we see that $(f \circ g)(4) \neq (g \circ f)(4)$ because $49 \neq 19$. In general,

$$(\boldsymbol{f \circ g})(\boldsymbol{x}) \neq (\boldsymbol{g \circ f})(\boldsymbol{x}).$$

EXAMPLE 7 Finding Composite Functions

Let $f(x) = 4x - 1$ and $g(x) = x^2 + 5$. Find the following.

(a) $(f \circ g)(2)$

$$= f(g(2))$$

$$= f(2^2 + 5) \qquad g(x) = x^2 + 5$$

$$= f(9) \qquad \text{Work inside the parentheses.}$$

$$= 4(9) - 1 \qquad f(x) = 4x - 1$$

$$= 35 \qquad \text{Multiply, and then subtract.}$$

NOW TRY ANSWER
6. 22

NOW TRY
EXERCISE 7

Let $f(x) = x - 5$
and $g(x) = -x^2 + 2$.
Find the following.
(a) $(g \circ f)(-1)$
(b) $(f \circ g)(x)$

(b) $(f \circ g)(x)$

$= f(g(x))$ Use $g(x)$ as the input for the function f.

$= 4(g(x)) - 1$ Use the rule for $f(x)$; $f(x) = 4x - 1$.

$= 4(x^2 + 5) - 1$ $g(x) = x^2 + 5$

$= 4x^2 + 20 - 1$ Distributive property

$= 4x^2 + 19$ Combine like terms.

(c) Find $(f \circ g)(2)$ again, this time using the rule obtained in part (b).

$$(f \circ g)(x) = 4x^2 + 19 \quad \text{From part (b)}$$

$$(f \circ g)(2) = 4(2)^2 + 19 \quad \text{Let } x = 2.$$

$$= 4(4) + 19 \quad \text{Square 2.}$$

$$= 16 + 19 \quad \text{Multiply.}$$

NOW TRY ANSWERS
7. **(a)** -34 **(b)** $-x^2 - 3$

Same result as in part (a) $\longrightarrow$ $= 35$ Add.   NOW TRY

7.5 EXERCISES

MyMathLab   Math XL PRACTICE   WATCH   DOWNLOAD   READ   REVIEW

🔵 *Complete solution available on the Video Resources on DVD*

*For each polynomial function, find **(a)** $f(-1)$ and **(b)** $f(2)$. See Example 1.*

1. $f(x) = 6x - 4$ **2.** $f(x) = -2x + 5$ **3.** $f(x) = x^2 - 3x + 4$

4. $f(x) = 3x^2 + x - 5$ **5.** $f(x) = 5x^4 - 3x^2 + 6$ **6.** $f(x) = -4x^4 + 2x^2 - 1$

 7. $f(x) = -x^2 + 2x^3 - 8$ **8.** $f(x) = -x^2 - x^3 + 11x$

*For each pair of functions, find **(a)** $(f + g)(x)$ and **(b)** $(f - g)(x)$. See Example 2.*

9. $f(x) = 5x - 10$, $g(x) = 3x + 7$

10. $f(x) = -4x + 1$, $g(x) = 6x + 2$

🔵 **11.** $f(x) = 4x^2 + 8x - 3$, $g(x) = -5x^2 + 4x - 9$

12. $f(x) = 3x^2 - 9x + 10$, $g(x) = -4x^2 + 2x + 12$

Let $f(x) = x^2 - 9$, $g(x) = 2x$, and $h(x) = x - 3$. Find each of the following. See Example 3.

🔵 **13.** $(f + g)(x)$ **14.** $(f - g)(x)$ **15.** $(f + g)(3)$ **16.** $(f - g)(-3)$

17. $(f - h)(x)$ **18.** $(f + h)(x)$ **19.** $(f - h)(-3)$

20. $(f + h)(-2)$ **21.** $(g + h)(-10)$ **22.** $(g - h)(10)$

23. $(g - h)(-3)$ **24.** $(g + h)(1)$ **25.** $(g + h)\left(\dfrac{1}{4}\right)$

26. $(g + h)\left(\dfrac{1}{3}\right)$ **27.** $(g + h)\left(-\dfrac{1}{2}\right)$ **28.** $(g + h)\left(-\dfrac{1}{4}\right)$

📝 **29.** Construct two functions defined by $f(x)$, a polynomial of degree 3, and $g(x)$, a polynomial of degree 4. Find $(f - g)(x)$ and $(g - f)(x)$. Use your answers to decide whether subtraction of functions is a commutative operation. Explain.

30. *Concept Check*   Find two polynomial functions defined by $f(x)$ and $g(x)$ such that

$$(f + g)(x) = 3x^3 - x + 3.$$

For each pair of functions, find the product $(fg)(x)$. ***See Example 4.***

31. $f(x) = 2x$, $g(x) = 5x - 1$ **32.** $f(x) = 3x$, $g(x) = 6x - 8$

33. $f(x) = x + 1$, $g(x) = 2x - 3$ **34.** $f(x) = x - 7$, $g(x) = 4x + 5$

35. $f(x) = 2x - 3$, $g(x) = 4x^2 + 6x + 9$

36. $f(x) = 3x + 4$, $g(x) = 9x^2 - 12x + 16$

Let $f(x) = x^2 - 9, g(x) = 2x,$ *and* $h(x) = x - 3.$ *Find each of the following.* ***See Example 4.***

◑ **37.** $(fg)(x)$ **38.** $(fh)(x)$ **39.** $(fg)(2)$

40. $(fh)(1)$ **41.** $(gh)(x)$ **42.** $(fh)(-1)$

43. $(gh)(-3)$ **44.** $(fg)(-2)$ **45.** $(fg)\left(-\dfrac{1}{2}\right)$

46. $(fg)\left(-\dfrac{1}{3}\right)$ **47.** $(fh)\left(-\dfrac{1}{4}\right)$ **48.** $(fh)\left(-\dfrac{1}{5}\right)$

For each pair of functions, find the quotient $\left(\dfrac{f}{g}\right)(x)$ *and give any x-values that are not in the domain of the quotient function.* ***See Example 5.***

49. $f(x) = 10x^2 - 2x$, $g(x) = 2x$ **50.** $f(x) = 18x^2 - 24x$, $g(x) = 3x$

51. $f(x) = 2x^2 - x - 3$, $g(x) = x + 1$ **52.** $f(x) = 4x^2 - 23x - 35$, $g(x) = x - 7$

53. $f(x) = 8x^3 - 27$, $g(x) = 2x - 3$ **54.** $f(x) = 27x^3 + 64$, $g(x) = 3x + 4$

Let $f(x) = x^2 - 9, g(x) = 2x,$ *and* $h(x) = x - 3.$ *Find each of the following.* ***See Example 5.***

◑ **55.** $\left(\dfrac{f}{g}\right)(x)$ **56.** $\left(\dfrac{f}{h}\right)(x)$ **57.** $\left(\dfrac{f}{g}\right)(2)$ **58.** $\left(\dfrac{f}{h}\right)(1)$

59. $\left(\dfrac{h}{g}\right)(x)$ **60.** $\left(\dfrac{g}{h}\right)(x)$ **61.** $\left(\dfrac{h}{g}\right)(3)$ **62.** $\left(\dfrac{g}{h}\right)(-1)$

63. $\left(\dfrac{f}{g}\right)\left(\dfrac{1}{2}\right)$ **64.** $\left(\dfrac{f}{g}\right)\left(\dfrac{3}{2}\right)$ **65.** $\left(\dfrac{h}{g}\right)\left(-\dfrac{1}{2}\right)$ **66.** $\left(\dfrac{h}{g}\right)\left(-\dfrac{3}{2}\right)$

Let $f(x) = x^2 + 4, g(x) = 2x + 3,$ *and* $h(x) = x - 5.$ *Find each value or expression.* ***See Examples 6 and 7.***

67. $(h \circ g)(4)$ **68.** $(f \circ g)(4)$ **69.** $(g \circ f)(6)$ **70.** $(h \circ f)(6)$

71. $(f \circ h)(-2)$ **72.** $(h \circ g)(-2)$ **73.** $(f \circ g)(0)$ **74.** $(f \circ h)(0)$

75. $(g \circ f)(x)$ **76.** $(g \circ h)(x)$ **77.** $(h \circ g)(x)$ **78.** $(h \circ f)(x)$

79. $(f \circ h)\left(\dfrac{1}{2}\right)$ **80.** $(h \circ f)\left(\dfrac{1}{2}\right)$ **81.** $(f \circ g)\left(-\dfrac{1}{2}\right)$ **82.** $(g \circ f)\left(-\dfrac{1}{2}\right)$

Solve each problem.

83. The function defined by $f(x) = 12x$ computes the number of inches in x feet, and the function defined by $g(x) = 5280x$ computes the number of feet in x miles. What is $(f \circ g)(x)$ and what does it compute?

84. The perimeter x of a square with sides of length s is given by the formula $x = 4s$.

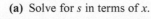

   (a) Solve for s in terms of x.

   (b) If y represents the area of this square, write y as a function of the perimeter x.

   (c) Use the composite function of part (b) to find the area of a square with perimeter 6.

85. When a thermal inversion layer is over a city (as happens often in Los Angeles), pollutants cannot rise vertically, but are trapped below the layer and must disperse horizontally. Assume that a factory smokestack begins emitting a pollutant at 8 A.M. Assume that the pollutant disperses horizontally over a circular area. Suppose that t represents the time, in hours, since the factory began emitting pollutants ($t = 0$ represents 8 A.M.), and assume that the radius of the circle of pollution is $r(t) = 2t$ miles. Let $\mathcal{A}(r) = \pi r^2$ represent the area of a circle of radius r. Find and interpret $(\mathcal{A} \circ r)(t)$.

86. An oil well is leaking, with the leak spreading oil over the surface as a circle. At any time t, in minutes, after the beginning of the leak, the radius of the circular oil slick on the surface is $r(t) = 4t$ feet. Let $\mathcal{A}(r) = \pi r^2$ represent the area of a circle of radius r. Find and interpret $(\mathcal{A} \circ r)(t)$.

PREVIEW EXERCISES

Find k, given that y = 1 and x = 3. See Sections 2.3 and 2.5.

87. $y = kx$ **88.** $y = kx^2$ **89.** $y = \dfrac{k}{x}$ **90.** $y = \dfrac{k}{x^2}$

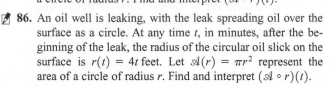

7.6 Variation

OBJECTIVES

1. Write an equation expressing direct variation.
2. Find the constant of variation, and solve direct variation problems.
3. Solve inverse variation problems.
4. Solve joint variation problems.
5. Solve combined variation problems.

Functions in which *y depends on a multiple of x* or *y depends on a number divided by x* are common in business and the physical sciences.

OBJECTIVE 1 **Write an equation expressing direct variation.** The circumference of a circle is given by the formula $C = 2\pi r$, where r is the radius of the circle. See **FIGURE 42**. The circumference is always a constant multiple of the radius. (C is always found by multiplying r by the constant 2π.)

> As the *radius increases*, the *circumference increases.*
>
> As the *radius decreases*, the *circumference decreases.*

Because of these relationships, the circumference is said to *vary directly* as the radius.

$C = 2\pi r$

FIGURE 42

Direct Variation

y **varies directly as** *x* if there exists a real number k such that
$$y = kx.$$
y is said to be **proportional to** *x.* The number k is called the **constant of variation.**

In direct variation, for k > 0, as the value of x increases, the value of y increases. Similarly, as x decreases, y decreases.

OBJECTIVE 2 **Find the constant of variation, and solve direct variation problems.** *The direct variation equation y = kx defines a linear function, where the constant of variation k is the slope of the line.* For example, we wrote the following equation to describe the cost y to buy x gallons of gasoline.

$$y = 3.20x \qquad \text{See } \textbf{Section 7.2, Example 7.}$$

The cost varies directly as, or is proportional to, the number of gallons of gasoline purchased.

> As the *number of gallons* of gasoline *increases,* the *cost increases.*

> As the *number of gallons* of gasoline *decreases,* the *cost decreases.*

The constant of variation k is 3.20, the cost of 1 gal of gasoline.

⟡ *NOW TRY*
↪ *EXERCISE 1*
One week Morgan sold 8 dozen eggs for $20. How much does she charge for one dozen eggs?

EXAMPLE 1   Finding the Constant of Variation and the Variation Equation

Eva Lutchman is paid an hourly wage. One week she worked 43 hr and was paid $795.50. How much does she earn per hour?

Let h represent the number of hours she works and P represent her corresponding pay. Write the variation equation.

$$P = kh \qquad P \text{ varies directly as } h.$$

Here, k represents Eva's hourly wage.

$$P = kh \qquad\qquad P \text{ varies directly as } h.$$

$$795.50 = 43k \qquad \text{Substitute 795.50 for } P \text{ and 43 for } h.$$

This is the constant of variation. ⟶ $\quad k = 18.50 \qquad \text{Use a calculator.}$

Her hourly wage is $18.50, and P and h are related by

$$P = 18.50h.$$

We can use this equation to find her pay for any number of hours worked.

NOW TRY ↻

EXAMPLE 2   Solving a Direct Variation Problem

Hooke's law for an elastic spring states that the distance a spring stretches is directly proportional to the force applied. If a force of 150 newtons* stretches a certain spring 8 cm, how much will a force of 400 newtons stretch the spring? See **FIGURE 43**.

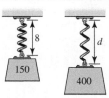

If d is the distance the spring stretches and f is the force applied, then $d = kf$ for some constant k. Since a force of 150 newtons stretches the spring 8 cm, we use these values to find k.

FIGURE 43

$$d = kf \qquad \text{Variation equation}$$

$$8 = k \cdot 150 \qquad \text{Let } d = 8 \text{ and } f = 150.$$

$$k = \frac{8}{150} \qquad \text{Solve for } k.$$

$$k = \frac{4}{75} \qquad \text{Lowest terms}$$

NOW TRY ANSWER
1. $2.50

———————————————

*A newton is a unit of measure of force used in physics.

NOW TRY
EXERCISE 2

For a constant height, the area of a parallelogram is directly proportional to its base. If the area is 20 cm² when the base is 4 cm, find the area when the base is 7 cm.

Substitute $\frac{4}{75}$ for k in the variation equation $d = kf$.

$$d = \frac{4}{75}f \qquad \text{Here, } k = \frac{4}{75}.$$

For a force of 400 newtons, substitute 400 for f.

$$d = \frac{4}{75}(400) = \frac{64}{3} \qquad \text{Let } f = 400.$$

The spring will stretch $\frac{64}{3}$ cm, or $21\frac{1}{3}$ cm, if a force of 400 newtons is applied.

NOW TRY

Solving a Variation Problem

Step 1   Write the variation equation.

Step 2   Substitute the initial values and solve for k.

Step 3   Rewrite the variation equation with the value of k from Step 2.

Step 4   Substitute the remaining values, solve for the unknown, and find the required answer.

One variable can be proportional to a power of another variable.

Direct Variation as a Power

y **varies directly as the** *n***th power of** *x* if there exists a real number k such that

$$y = kx^n.$$

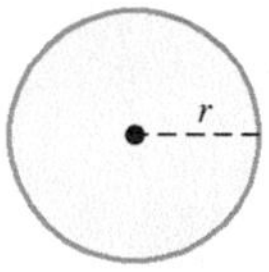

$\mathcal{A} = \pi r^2$

FIGURE 44

The formula for the area of a circle, $\mathcal{A} = \pi r^2$, is an example. See **FIGURE 44**. Here, π is the constant of variation, and the area varies directly as the *square* of the radius.

NOW TRY
EXERCISE 3

Suppose y varies directly as the square of x, and $y = 200$ when $x = 5$. Find y when $x = 7$.

EXAMPLE 3   Solving a Direct Variation Problem

The distance a body falls from rest varies directly as the square of the time it falls (disregarding air resistance). If a skydiver falls 64 ft in 2 sec, how far will she fall in 8 sec?

Step 1   If d represents the distance the skydiver falls and t the time it takes to fall, then d is a function of t for some constant k.

$$d = kt^2 \qquad \textit{d varies directly as the square of t.}$$

Step 2   To find the value of k, use the fact that the skydiver falls 64 ft in 2 sec.

$$d = kt^2 \qquad \text{Variation equation}$$
$$64 = k(2)^2 \qquad \text{Let } d = 64 \text{ and } t = 2.$$
$$k = 16 \qquad \text{Find } k.$$

Step 3   Now we rewrite the variation equation $d = kt^2$ using 16 for k.

$$d = 16t^2 \qquad \text{Here, } k = 16.$$

Step 4   Let $t = 8$ to find the number of feet the skydiver will fall in 8 sec.

$$d = 16(8)^2 = 1024 \qquad \text{Let } t = 8.$$

The skydiver will fall 1024 ft in 8 sec.

NOW TRY

NOW TRY ANSWERS
2. 35 cm²   **3.** 392

As pressure
on trash
increases,
volume of
trash
decreases.

FIGURE 45

OBJECTIVE 3   **Solve inverse variation problems.**   Another type of variation is *inverse variation*. **With inverse variation, where $k > 0$, as one variable increases, the other variable decreases.**

For example, in a closed space, volume decreases as pressure increases, which can be illustrated by a trash compactor. See **FIGURE 45**. As the compactor presses down, the pressure on the trash increases, and in turn, the trash occupies a smaller space.

Inverse Variation

y **varies inversely as** *x* if there exists a real number k such that

$$y = \frac{k}{x}.$$

Also, *y* **varies inversely as the** *n*th **power of** *x* if there exists a real number k such that

$$y = \frac{k}{x^n}.$$

The inverse variation equation defines a rational function. Another example of inverse variation comes from the distance formula.

$$d = rt \qquad \text{Distance formula}$$

$$t = \frac{d}{r} \qquad \text{Divide each side by } r.$$

Here, t (time) varies inversely as r (rate or speed), with d (distance) serving as the constant of variation. For example, if the distance between Chicago and Des Moines is 300 mi, then

$$t = \frac{300}{r},$$

and the values of r and t might be any of the following.

$$\left. \begin{array}{l} r = 50, t = 6 \\ r = 60, t = 5 \\ r = 75, t = 4 \end{array} \right\} \begin{array}{l} \text{As } r \text{ increases,} \\ t \text{ decreases.} \end{array} \qquad \left. \begin{array}{l} r = 30, t = 10 \\ r = 25, t = 12 \\ r = 20, t = 15 \end{array} \right\} \begin{array}{l} \text{As } r \text{ decreases,} \\ t \text{ increases.} \end{array}$$

If we *increase* the rate (speed) at which we drive, time *decreases*. If we *decrease* the rate (speed) at which we drive, time *increases*.

EXAMPLE 4   Solving an Inverse Variation Problem

In the manufacture of a certain medical syringe, the cost of producing the syringe varies inversely as the number produced. If 10,000 syringes are produced, the cost is \$2 per syringe. Find the cost per syringe of producing 25,000 syringes.

$$\text{Let} \qquad x = \text{the number of syringes produced,}$$

$$\text{and} \qquad c = \text{the cost per syringe.}$$

Here, as production increases, cost decreases, and as production decreases, cost increases. We write a variation equation using the variables c and x and the constant k.

$$c = \frac{k}{x} \qquad c \text{ varies inversely as } x.$$

NOW TRY
EXERCISE 4

For a constant area, the height of a triangle varies inversely as the base. If the height is 7 cm when the base is 8 cm, find the height when the base is 14 cm.

To find k, we replace c with 2 and x with 10,000 in the variation equation $c = \frac{k}{x}$.

$$2 = \frac{k}{10,000} \qquad \text{Substitute in the variation equation.}$$

$$20,000 = k \qquad \text{Multiply by 10,000.}$$

Since $c = \frac{k}{x}$,

$$c = \frac{20,000}{25,000} = 0.80. \qquad \text{Here, } k = 20,000. \text{ Let } x = 25,000.$$

The cost per syringe to make 25,000 syringes is \$0.80.

NOW TRY
EXERCISE 5

The weight of an object above Earth varies inversely as the square of its distance from the center of Earth. If an object weighs 150 lb on the surface of Earth, and the radius of Earth is about 3960 mi, how much does it weigh when it is 1000 mi above Earth's surface?

EXAMPLE 5 Solving an Inverse Variation Problem

The weight of an object above Earth varies inversely as the square of its distance from the center of Earth. A space shuttle in an elliptical orbit has a maximum distance from the center of Earth (*apogee*) of 6700 mi. Its minimum distance from the center of Earth (*perigee*) is 4090 mi. See **FIGURE 46**. If an astronaut in the shuttle weighs 57 lb at its apogee, what does the astronaut weigh at its perigee?

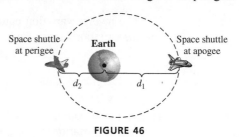

FIGURE 46

Let $w =$ the weight and $d =$ the distance from the center of Earth, for some constant k.

$$w = \frac{k}{d^2} \qquad w \text{ varies inversely as the square of } d.$$

At the apogee, the astronaut weighs 57 lb, and the distance from the center of Earth is 6700 mi. Use these values to find k.

$$57 = \frac{k}{(6700)^2} \qquad \text{Let } w = 57 \text{ and } d = 6700.$$

$$k = 57(6700)^2 \qquad \text{Solve for } k.$$

Substitute $k = 57(6700)^2$ and $d = 4090$ to find the weight at the perigee.

$$w = \frac{57(6700)^2}{(4090)^2} \approx 153 \text{ lb} \qquad \text{Use a calculator.} \qquad \text{NOW TRY}$$

OBJECTIVE 4 Solve joint variation problems. If one variable varies directly as the *product* of several other variables (perhaps raised to powers), the first variable is said to *vary jointly* as the others.

Joint Variation

y **varies jointly as x and z** if there exists a real number k such that

$$y = kxz.$$

NOW TRY ANSWERS
4. 4 cm   **5.** about 96 lb

NOW TRY
EXERCISE 6

The volume of a right pyramid varies jointly as the height and the area of the base. If the volume is 100 ft^3 when the area of the base is 30 ft^2 and the height is 10 ft, find the volume when the area of the base is 90 ft^2 and the height is 20 ft.

EXAMPLE 6 Solving a Joint Variation Problem

The interest on a loan or an investment is given by the formula $I = prt$. Here, for a given principal p, the interest earned, I, varies jointly as the interest rate r and the time t the principal is left earning interest. If an investment earns $100 interest at 5% for 2 yr, how much interest will the same principal earn at 4.5% for 3 yr?

We use the formula $I = prt$, where p is the constant of variation because it is the same for both investments.

$$I = prt$$
$$100 = p(0.05)(2) \quad \text{Let } I = 100, r = 0.05, \text{ and } t = 2.$$
$$100 = 0.1p$$
$$p = 1000 \quad \text{Divide by 0.1. Rewrite.}$$

Now we find I when $p = 1000$, $r = 0.045$, and $t = 3$.

$$I = 1000(0.045)(3) = 135 \quad \text{Here, } p = 1000. \text{ Let } r = 0.045 \text{ and } t = 3.$$

The interest will be $135.   *NOW TRY*

⚠ **CAUTION** Note that *and* in the expression "*y* varies directly as *x and z*" translates as a product in $y = kxz$. The word *and* does not indicate addition here.

OBJECTIVE 5 **Solve combined variation problems.** There are many combinations of direct and inverse variation, typically called **combined variation.**

NOW TRY
EXERCISE 7

In statistics, the sample size used to estimate a population mean varies directly as the variance and inversely as the square of the maximum error of the estimate. If the sample size is 200 when the variance is 25 m^2 and the maximum error of the estimate is 0.5 m, find the sample size when the variance is 25 m^2 and the maximum error of the estimate is 0.1 m.

EXAMPLE 7 Solving a Combined Variation Problem

Body mass index, or BMI, is used to assess a person's level of fatness. A BMI from 19 through 25 is considered desirable. BMI varies directly as an individual's weight in pounds and inversely as the square of the individual's height in inches.

A person who weighs 116.5 lb and is 64 in. tall has a BMI of 20. (The BMI is rounded to the nearest whole number.) Find the BMI of a man who weighs 165 lb and is 70 in. tall. (*Source: Washington Post.*)

Let B represent the BMI, w the weight, and h the height.

$$B = \frac{kw}{h^2} \quad \longleftarrow \text{ BMI varies directly as the weight.}$$
$$\longleftarrow \text{ BMI varies inversely as the square of the height.}$$

To find k, let $B = 20$, $w = 116.5$, and $h = 64$.

$$20 = \frac{k(116.5)}{64^2} \qquad B = \frac{kw}{h^2}$$

$$k = \frac{20(64^2)}{116.5} \qquad \text{Multiply by } 64^2. \text{ Divide by } 116.5.$$

$$k \approx 703 \qquad \text{Use a calculator.}$$

Now find B when $k = 703$, $w = 165$, and $h = 70$.

$$B = \frac{703(165)}{70^2} \approx 24 \qquad \text{Nearest whole number}$$

The man's BMI is 24.   *NOW TRY*

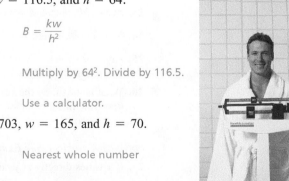

NOW TRY ANSWERS
6. 600 ft^3 **7.** 5000

7.6 EXERCISES

MyMathLab PRACTICE   WATCH   DOWNLOAD   READ   REVIEW

🌐 *Complete solution available on the Video Resources on DVD*

Concept Check   Use personal experience or intuition to determine whether the situation suggests direct *or* inverse *variation.*

1. The number of lottery tickets you buy and your probability of winning that lottery

2. The rate and the distance traveled by a pickup truck in 3 hr

3. The amount of pressure put on the accelerator of a car and the speed of the car

4. The number of days from now until December 25 and the magnitude of the frenzy of Christmas shopping

5. Your age and the probability that you believe in Santa Claus

6. The surface area of a balloon and its diameter

7. The number of days until the end of the baseball season and the number of home runs that Albert Pujols has

8. The amount of gasoline you pump and the amount you pay

Concept Check   Determine whether each equation represents direct, inverse, joint, *or* combined *variation.*

9. $y = \dfrac{3}{x}$
10. $y = \dfrac{8}{x}$
11. $y = 10x^2$
12. $y = 2x^3$

13. $y = 3xz^4$
14. $y = 6x^3z^2$
15. $y = \dfrac{4x}{wz}$
16. $y = \dfrac{6x}{st}$

17. *Concept Check*   For $k > 0$, if y varies directly as x, then when x increases, y _____, and when x decreases, y _____.

18. *Concept Check*   For $k > 0$, if y varies inversely as x, then when x increases, y _____, and when x decreases, y _____.

Concept Check   Write each formula using the "language" of variation. For example, the formula for the circumference of a circle, $C = 2\pi r$, can be written as

   "The circumference of a circle varies directly as the length of its radius."

19. $P = 4s$, where P is the perimeter of a square with side of length s

20. $d = 2r$, where d is the diameter of a circle with radius r

21. $S = 4\pi r^2$, where S is the surface area of a sphere with radius r

22. $V = \frac{4}{3}\pi r^3$, where V is the volume of a sphere with radius r

23. $\mathcal{A} = \frac{1}{2}bh$, where $\mathcal{A}$ is the area of a triangle with base b and height h

24. $V = \frac{1}{3}\pi r^2h$, where V is the volume of a cone with radius r and height h

25. *Concept Check*   What is the constant of variation in each of the variation equations in **Exercises 19–24?**

26. What is meant by the constant of variation in a direct variation problem? If you were to graph the linear equation $y = kx$ for some nonnegative constant k, what role would k play in the graph?

*Solve each problem. **See Examples 1–7.***

27. If x varies directly as y, and $x = 9$ when $y = 3$, find x when $y = 12$.

28. If x varies directly as y, and $x = 10$ when $y = 7$, find y when $x = 50$.

29. If a varies directly as the square of b, and $a = 4$ when $b = 3$, find a when $b = 2$.

30. If h varies directly as the square of m, and $h = 15$ when $m = 5$, find h when $m = 7$.

31. If z varies inversely as w, and $z = 10$ when $w = 0.5$, find z when $w = 8$.

32. If t varies inversely as s, and $t = 3$ when $s = 5$, find s when $t = 5$.

33. If m varies inversely as p^2, and $m = 20$ when $p = 2$, find m when $p = 5$.

34. If a varies inversely as b^2, and $a = 48$ when $b = 4$, find a when $b = 7$.

35. p varies jointly as q and r^2, and $p = 200$ when $q = 2$ and $r = 3$. Find p when $q = 5$ and $r = 2$.

36. f varies jointly as g^2 and h, and $f = 50$ when $g = 4$ and $h = 2$. Find f when $g = 3$ and $h = 6$.

Solve each problem. ***See Examples 1–7.***

37. Ben bought 15 gal of gasoline and paid $43.79. To the nearest tenth of a cent, what is the price of gasoline per gallon?

38. Sara gives horseback rides at Shadow Mountain Ranch. A 2.5-hr ride costs $50.00. What is the price per hour?

39. The weight of an object on Earth is directly proportional to the weight of that same object on the moon. A 200-lb astronaut would weigh 32 lb on the moon. How much would a 50-lb dog weigh on the moon?

40. The pressure exerted by a certain liquid at a given point is directly proportional to the depth of the point beneath the surface of the liquid. The pressure at 30 m is 80 newtons. What pressure is exerted at 50 m?

41. The volume of a can of tomatoes is directly proportional to the height of the can. If the volume of the can is 300 cm³ when its height is 10.62 cm, find the volume of a can with height 15.92 cm.

42. The force required to compress a spring is directly proportional to the change in length of the spring. If a force of 20 newtons is required to compress a certain spring 2 cm, how much force is required to compress the spring from 20 cm to 8 cm?

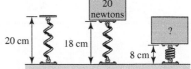

43. For a body falling freely from rest (disregarding air resistance), the distance the body falls varies directly as the square of the time. If an object is dropped from the top of a tower 576 ft high and hits the ground in 6 sec, how far did it fall in the first 4 sec?

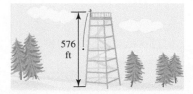

44. The amount of water emptied by a pipe varies directly as the square of the diameter of the pipe. For a certain constant water flow, a pipe emptying into a canal will allow 200 gal of water to escape in an hour. The diameter of the pipe is 6 in. How much water would a 12-in. pipe empty into the canal in an hour, assuming the same water flow?

45. Over a specified distance, rate varies inversely with time. If a Dodge Viper on a test track goes a certain distance in one-half minute at 160 mph, what rate is needed to go the same distance in three-fourths minute?

46. For a constant area, the length of a rectangle varies inversely as the width. The length of a rectangle is 27 ft when the width is 10 ft. Find the width of a rectangle with the same area if the length is 18 ft.

47. The frequency of a vibrating string varies inversely as its length. That is, a longer string vibrates fewer times in a second than a shorter string. Suppose a piano string 2 ft long vibrates 250 cycles per sec. What frequency would a string 5 ft long have?

48. The current in a simple electrical circuit varies inversely as the resistance. If the current is 20 amps when the resistance is 5 ohms, find the current when the resistance is 7.5 ohms.

49. The amount of light (measured in foot-candles) produced by a light source varies inversely as the square of the distance from the source. If the illumination produced 1 m from a light source is 768 foot-candles, find the illumination produced 6 m from the same source.

50. The force with which Earth attracts an object above Earth's surface varies inversely as the square of the distance of the object from the center of Earth. If an object 4000 mi from the center of Earth is attracted with a force of 160 lb, find the force of attraction if the object were 6000 mi from the center of Earth.

51. For a given interest rate, simple interest varies jointly as principal and time. If $2000 left in an account for 4 yr earned interest of $280, how much interest would be earned in 6 yr?

52. The collision impact of an automobile varies jointly as its mass and the square of its speed. Suppose a 2000-lb car traveling at 55 mph has a collision impact of 6.1. What is the collision impact of the same car at 65 mph?

53. The weight of a bass varies jointly as its girth and the square of its length. (**Girth** is the distance around the body of the fish.) A prize-winning bass weighed in at 22.7 lb and measured 36 in. long with a 21-in. girth. How much would a bass 28 in. long with an 18-in. girth weigh?

54. The weight of a trout varies jointly as its length and the square of its girth. One angler caught a trout that weighed 10.5 lb and measured 26 in. long with an 18-in. girth. Find the weight of a trout that is 22 in. long with a 15-in. girth.

55. The force needed to keep a car from skidding on a curve varies inversely as the radius of the curve and jointly as the weight of the car and the square of the speed. If 242 lb of force keeps a 2000-lb car from skidding on a curve of radius 500 ft at 30 mph, what force would keep the same car from skidding on a curve of radius 750 ft at 50 mph?

56. The maximum load that a cylindrical column with a circular cross section can hold varies directly as the fourth power of the diameter of the cross section and inversely as the square of the height. A 9-m column 1 m in diameter will support 8 metric tons. How many metric tons can be supported by a column 12 m high and $\frac{2}{3}$ m in diameter?

Load = 8 metric tons

57. The number of long-distance phone calls between two cities during a certain period varies jointly as the populations of the cities, p_1 and p_2, and inversely as the distance between them. If 80,000 calls are made between two cities 400 mi apart, with populations of 70,000 and 100,000, how many calls are made between cities with populations of 50,000 and 75,000 that are 250 mi apart?

58. In 2007, 51.2% of the homes in the United States used natural gas as the primary heating fuel. (*Source:* U.S. Census Bureau.) The volume of gas varies inversely as the pressure and directly as the temperature. (Temperature must be measured in *Kelvin* (K), a unit of measurement used in physics.) If a certain gas occupies a volume of 1.3 L at 300 K and a pressure of 18 newtons, find the volume at 340 K and a pressure of 24 newtons.

59. A body mass index from 27 through 29 carries a slight risk of weight-related health problems, while one of 30 or more indicates a great increase in risk. Use your own height and weight and the information in **Example 7** to determine your BMI and whether you are at risk.

60. The maximum load of a horizontal beam that is supported at both ends varies directly as the width and the square of the height and inversely as the length between the supports. A beam 6 m long, 0.1 m wide, and 0.06 m high supports a load of 360 kg. What is the maximum load supported by a beam 16 m long, 0.2 m wide, and 0.08 m high?

PREVIEW EXERCISES

Graph each pair of equations on the same coordinate axes. ***See Sections 3.2 and 7.1.***

61. $2x + 3y = 12$
$4x - 2y = 8$

62. $x + y = 4$
$2x = 8 - 2y$

63. $-5x + 2y = 10$
$2y = -4 + 5x$

64. $2y = -3x$
$-2x + 3y = 0$

CHAPTER 7 SUMMARY

KEY TERMS

7.1
ordered pair
components
origin
x-axis
y-axis
rectangular (Cartesian) coordinate system
plot
coordinate
quadrant
graph of an equation
first-degree equation

linear equation in two variables
standard form
x-intercept
y-intercept
rise
run
slope

7.2
slope-intercept form
point-slope form

7.3
dependent variable
independent variable
relation
function
domain
range

7.4
function notation
linear function
constant function

7.5
polynomial function
composition of functions

7.6
vary directly
proportional
constant of variation
vary inversely
vary jointly
combined variation

NEW SYMBOLS

(a, b) ordered pair
x_1 a specific value of x (read "x-sub-one")

Δ Greek letter delta
m slope

$f(x)$ function of x (read "f of x")

$(f \circ g)(x) = f(g(x))$ composite function

TEST YOUR WORD POWER

See how well you have learned the vocabulary in this chapter.

1. A **linear equation in two variables** is an equation that can be written in the form
   A. $Ax + By < C$
   B. $ax = b$
   C. $y = x^2$
   D. $Ax + By = C$.

2. The **slope** of a line is
   A. the measure of the run over the rise of the line
   B. the distance between two points on the line
   C. the ratio of the change in y to the change in x along the line
   D. the horizontal change compared with the vertical change between two points on the line.

3. A **relation** is
   A. a set of ordered pairs
   B. the ratio of the change in y to the change in x along a line
   C. the set of all possible values of the independent variable
   D. all the second components of a set of ordered pairs.

4. A **function** is
   A. the pair of numbers in an ordered pair
   B. a set of ordered pairs in which each x-value corresponds to exactly one y-value
   C. a pair of numbers written between parentheses
   D. the set of all ordered pairs that satisfy an equation.

5. The **domain** of a function is
   A. the set of all possible values of the dependent variable y
   B. a set of ordered pairs
   C. the difference between the x-values
   D. the set of all possible values of the independent variable x.

6. The **range** of a function is
   A. the set of all possible values of the dependent variable y
   B. a set of ordered pairs
   C. the difference between the y-values
   D. the set of all possible values of the independent variable x.

ANSWERS

1. D; *Examples:* $3x + 2y = 6$, $x = y - 7$ 2. C; *Example:* The line through $(3, 6)$ and $(5, 4)$ has slope $\frac{4 - 6}{5 - 3} = \frac{-2}{2} = -1$.   3. A; *Example:* The set $\{(2, 0), (4, 3), (6, 6)\}$ defines a relation.   4. B; The relation given in Answer 3 is a function.   5. D; *Example:* In the function in Answer 3, the domain is the set of x-values, $\{2, 4, 6\}$.   6. A; *Example:* In the function in Answer 3, the range is the set of y-values, $\{0, 3, 6\}$.

QUICK REVIEW

CONCEPTS	EXAMPLES

7.1   Review of Graphs and Slopes of Lines

Finding Intercepts

To find the *x*-intercept, let $y = 0$ and solve for x.

To find the *y*-intercept, let $x = 0$ and solve for y.

Find the intercepts of the graph of $2x + 3y = 12$.

$$2x + 3(0) = 12 \qquad\qquad 2(0) + 3y = 12$$
$$2x = 12 \qquad\qquad\qquad 3y = 12$$
$$x = 6 \qquad\qquad\qquad\quad y = 4$$

The *x*-intercept is $(6, 0)$. | The *y*-intercept is $(0, 4)$.

Midpoint Formula

If the endpoints of a line segment PQ are $P(x_1, y_1)$ and $Q(x_2, y_2)$, then its midpoint M is

$$\left(\frac{x_1 + x_2}{2}, \frac{y_1 + y_2}{2} \right).$$

Find the midpoint of the segment with endpoints $(4, -7)$ and $(-10, -13)$.

$$\left(\frac{4 + (-10)}{2}, \frac{-7 + (-13)}{2} \right) = (-3, -10)$$

Slope Formula

If $x_2 \neq x_1$, then

$$\text{slope } m = \frac{\text{rise}}{\text{run}} = \frac{\text{change in } y}{\text{change in } x} = \frac{\Delta y}{\Delta x} = \frac{y_2 - y_1}{x_2 - x_1}.$$

Find the slope of the graph of $2x + 3y = 12$.
   Use the intercepts $(6, 0)$ and $(0, 4)$ and the slope formula.

$$m = \frac{4 - 0}{0 - 6} = \frac{4}{-6} = -\frac{2}{3} \qquad x_1 = 6,\ y_1 = 0,\ x_2 = 0,\ y_2 = 4$$

(continued)

CONCEPTS	EXAMPLES
A vertical line has undefined slope.	The graph of the line $x = 3$ has undefined slope.
A horizontal line has 0 slope.	The graph of the line $y = -5$ has slope $m = 0$.
Parallel lines have equal slopes.	The lines $y = 2x + 3$ and $4x - 2y = 6$ are parallel—both have $m = 2$.

$$y = 2x + 3 \qquad\qquad 4x - 2y = 6$$
$$m = 2 \qquad\qquad\qquad -2y = -4x + 6$$
$$y = 2x - 3$$
$$m = 2$$

CONCEPTS	EXAMPLES
The slopes of perpendicular lines, neither of which is vertical, are negative reciprocals with a product of -1.	The lines $y = 3x - 1$ and $x + 3y = 4$ are perpendicular—their slopes are negative reciprocals.

$$y = 3x - 1 \qquad\qquad x + 3y = 4$$
$$m = 3 \qquad\qquad\qquad 3y = -x + 4$$
$$y = -\frac{1}{3}x + \frac{4}{3}$$
$$m = -\frac{1}{3}$$

7.2 Review of Equations of Lines; Linear Models

Slope-Intercept Form
$$y = mx + b$$

Point-Slope Form
$$y - y_1 = m(x - x_1)$$

Standard Form
$$Ax + By = C$$

Horizontal Line
$$y = b$$

Vertical Line
$$x = a$$

$y = 2x + 3$	$m = 2$, y-intercept is $(0, 3)$.
$y - 3 = 4(x - 5)$	$(5, 3)$ is on the line, $m = 4$.
$2x - 5y = 8$	Standard form
$y = 4$	Horizontal line
$x = -1$	Vertical line

7.3 Introduction to Relations and Functions

A **function** is a set of ordered pairs such that, for each first component, there is one and only one second component. The set of first components is called the **domain,** and the set of second components is called the **range.**

$f = \{(-1, 4), (0, 6), (1, 4)\}$ defines a function f with domain, the set of x-values, $\{-1, 0, 1\}$ and range, the set of y-values, $\{4, 6\}$.

$y = x^2$ defines a function with domain $(-\infty, \infty)$ and range $[0, \infty)$.

7.4 Function Notation and Linear Functions

To evaluate a function f, where $f(x)$ defines the range value for a given value of x in the domain, substitute the value wherever x appears.

If $f(x) = x^2 - 7x + 12$, then
$$f(1) = 1^2 - 7(1) + 12 = 6.$$

(continued)

CONCEPTS	EXAMPLES
To write an equation that defines a function f in function notation, follow these steps.	Write $2x + 3y = 12$ using notation for a function f.

Step 1 Solve the equation for y.

$$3y = -2x + 12 \qquad \text{Subtract } 2x.$$

$$y = -\frac{2}{3}x + 4 \qquad \text{Divide by 3.}$$

Step 2 Replace y with $f(x)$.

$$f(x) = -\frac{2}{3}x + 4 \qquad y = f(x)$$

7.5 Operations on Functions and Composition

Operations on Functions

If $f(x)$ and $g(x)$ define functions, then

$$(f + g)(x) = f(x) + g(x),$$
$$(f - g)(x) = f(x) - g(x),$$
$$(fg)(x) = f(x) \cdot g(x),$$

and

$$\left(\frac{f}{g}\right)(x) = \frac{f(x)}{g(x)}, \quad g(x) \neq 0.$$

Let $f(x) = x^2$ and $g(x) = 2x + 1$.

$(f + g)(x)$
$= f(x) + g(x)$
$= x^2 + 2x + 1$

$(f - g)(x)$
$= f(x) - g(x)$
$= x^2 - (2x + 1)$
$= x^2 - 2x - 1$

$(fg)(x)$
$= f(x) \cdot g(x)$
$= x^2(2x + 1)$
$= 2x^3 + x^2$

$\left(\dfrac{f}{g}\right)(x)$
$= \dfrac{f(x)}{g(x)}$
$= \dfrac{x^2}{2x + 1}, \quad x \neq -\dfrac{1}{2}$

Composition of f and g

$$(f \circ g)(x) = f(g(x))$$

Let $f(x) = x^2$ and $g(x) = 2x + 1$.

$(f \circ g)(x) = f(g(x))$
$= f(2x + 1)$
$= (2x + 1)^2$

$(g \circ f)(x) = g(f(x))$
$= g(x^2)$
$= 2x^2 + 1$

7.6 Variation

Let k be a real number.

If $y = kx^n$, then y varies directly as x^n.

If $y = \dfrac{k}{x^n}$, then y varies inversely as x^n.

If $y = kxz$, then y varies jointly as x and z.

The area of a circle varies directly as the square of the radius.

$$\mathcal{A} = kr^2 \qquad \text{Here, } k = \pi.$$

Pressure varies inversely as volume.

$$p = \frac{k}{V}$$

For a given principal, interest varies jointly as interest rate and time.

$$I = krt \qquad k \text{ is the given principal.}$$

CHAPTER (7)   REVIEW EXERCISES

7.1 *Complete the table of ordered pairs for each equation. Then graph the equation.*

1. $3x + 2y = 10$

x	y
0	
	0
2	
	-2

2. $x - y = 8$

x	y
2	
	-3
3	
	-2

Find the x- and y-intercepts and then graph each equation.

3. $4x - 3y = 12$

4. $5x + 7y = 28$

5. $2x + 5y = 20$

6. $x - 4y = 8$

Use the midpoint formula to find the midpoint of each segment with the given endpoints.

7. $(-8, -12)$ and $(8, 16)$

8. $(0, -5)$ and $(-9, 8)$

Find the slope of each line.

9. Through $(-1, 2)$ and $(4, -5)$

10. Through $(0, 3)$ and $(-2, 4)$

11. $y = 2x + 3$

12. $3x - 4y = 5$

13. $x = 5$

14. Parallel to $3y = 2x + 5$

15. Perpendicular to $3x - y = 4$

16. Through $(-1, 5)$ and $(-1, -4)$

17.
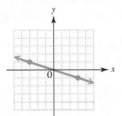

18.
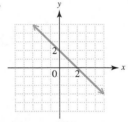

Tell whether each line has positive, negative, 0, *or* undefined *slope.*

19.

20.

21.

22.

23. *Concept Check*   If the pitch of a roof is $\frac{1}{4}$, how many feet in the horizontal direction correspond to a rise of 3 ft?

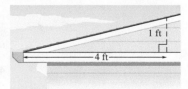

24. Family income in the United States has increased steadily for many years (primarily due to inflation). In 1980, the median family income was about $21,000 per year. In 2007, it was about $61,400 per year. Find the average rate of change of median family income to the nearest dollar over that period. (*Source:* U.S. Census Bureau.)

7.2 *Find an equation for each line.* **(a)** *Write the equation in slope-intercept form.* **(b)** *Write the equation in standard form.*

25. Slope $-\frac{1}{3}$; y-intercept $(0, -1)$

26. Slope 0; y-intercept $(0, -2)$

27. Slope $-\frac{4}{3}$; through $(2, 7)$

28. Slope 3; through $(-1, 4)$

29. Vertical; through $(2, 5)$

30. Through $(2, -5)$ and $(1, 4)$

31. Through $(-3, -1)$ and $(2, 6)$

32. The line pictured in **Exercise 18**

33. Parallel to $4x - y = 3$ and through $(7, -1)$

34. Perpendicular to $2x - 5y = 7$ and through $(4, 3)$

35. The Midwest Athletic Club offers two special membership plans. (*Source:* Midwest Athletic Club.) For each plan, write a linear equation in slope-intercept form and give the cost y in dollars of a 1-yr membership. Let x represent the number of months.

(a) Executive VIP/Gold membership: $159 fee, plus $57 per month

(b) Executive Regular/Silver membership: $159 fee, plus $47 per month

36. Revenue for skiing facilities in the United States is shown in the graph.

(a) Use the information given for the years 2003 and 2007, letting $x = 3$ represent 2003, $x = 7$ represent 2007, and y represent revenue (in millions of dollars) to find a linear equation that models the data. Write the equation in slope-intercept form. Interpret the slope.

(b) Use your equation from part (a) to estimate revenue for skiing facilities in 2008, to the nearest million.

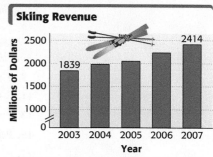

Skiing Revenue

Source: U.S. Census Bureau.

7.3 *In Exercises 37–40, give the domain and range of each relation. Identify any functions.*

37. $\{(-4, 2), (-4, -2), (1, 5), (1, -5)\}$

38.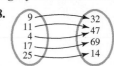

39.

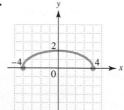

40.

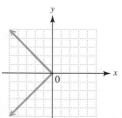

7.3–7.4 *Determine whether each equation defines y as a function of x. Give the domain in each case. Identify any linear functions.*

41. $y = 3x - 3$

42. $x = y^2$

43. $y = \dfrac{7}{x - 6}$

7.4 *Given $f(x) = -2x^2 + 3x - 6$, find each function value or expression.*

44. $f(0)$

45. $f(2.1)$

46. $f\left(-\dfrac{1}{2}\right)$

47. $f(k)$

48. The equation $2x^2 - y = 0$ defines y as a function f of x. Write it using function notation, and find $f(3)$.

49. *Concept Check* Suppose that $2x - 5y = 7$ defines y as a function f of x. If $y = f(x)$, which one of the following defines the same function?

A. $f(x) = -\dfrac{2}{5}x + \dfrac{7}{5}$ **B.** $f(x) = -\dfrac{2}{5}x - \dfrac{7}{5}$

C. $f(x) = \dfrac{2}{5}x - \dfrac{7}{5}$ **D.** $f(x) = \dfrac{2}{5}x + \dfrac{7}{5}$

50. The table shows life expectancy at birth in the United States for selected years.

(a) Does the table define a function?

(b) What are the domain and range?

(c) Call this function f. Give two ordered pairs that belong to f.

(d) Find $f(1980)$. What does this mean?

(e) If $f(x) = 76.8$, what does x equal?

Year	Life Expectancy at Birth (years)
1960	69.7
1970	70.8
1980	73.7
1990	75.4
2000	76.8
2009	78.1

Source: National Center for Health Statistics.

7.5

51. Find each of the following for the polynomial function defined by

$$f(x) = -2x^2 + 5x + 7.$$

(a) $f(-2)$ (b) $f(3)$

52. Find each of the following for the polynomial functions defined by

$$f(x) = 2x + 3 \quad \text{and} \quad g(x) = 5x^2 - 3x + 2.$$

(a) $(f + g)(x)$ (b) $(f - g)(x)$ (c) $(f + g)(-1)$ (d) $(f - g)(-1)$

53. Find each of the following for the polynomial functions defined by

$$f(x) = 12x^2 - 3x \quad \text{and} \quad g(x) = 3x.$$

(a) $(fg)(x)$ (b) $\left(\dfrac{f}{g}\right)(x)$ (c) $(fg)(-1)$ (d) $\left(\dfrac{f}{g}\right)(2)$

54. Find each of the following for the polynomial functions defined by

$$f(x) = 3x^2 + 2x - 1 \quad \text{and} \quad g(x) = 5x + 7.$$

(a) $(g \circ f)(3)$ (b) $(f \circ g)(3)$ (c) $(f \circ g)(-2)$

(d) $(g \circ f)(-2)$ (e) $(f \circ g)(x)$ (f) $(g \circ f)(x)$

7.6

55. *Concept Check* In which one of the following does y vary inversely as x?

A. $y = 2x$ **B.** $y = \dfrac{x}{3}$ **C.** $y = \dfrac{3}{x}$ **D.** $y = x^2$

Solve each problem.

56. For the subject in a photograph to appear in the same perspective in the photograph as in real life, the viewing distance must be properly related to the amount of enlargement. For a particular camera, the viewing distance varies directly as the amount of enlargement. A picture that is taken with this camera and enlarged 5 times should be viewed from a distance of 250 mm. Suppose a print 8.6 times the size of the negative is made. From what distance should it be viewed?

57. The frequency (number of vibrations per second) of a vibrating guitar string varies inversely as its length. That is, a longer string vibrates fewer times in a second than a shorter string. Suppose a guitar string 0.65 m long vibrates 4.3 times per sec. What frequency would a string 0.5 m long have?

58. The volume of a rectangular box of a given height is proportional to its width and length. A box with width 2 ft and length 4 ft has volume 12 ft^3. Find the volume of a box with the same height, but that is 3 ft wide and 5 ft long.

CHAPTER 7

TEST

Step-by-step test solutions are found on the Chapter Test Prep Videos available via the Video Resources on DVD, in *MyMathLab*, or on YouTube (search "LialCombinedAlgebra").

🌐 *View the complete solutions to all Chapter Test exercises on the Video Resources on DVD.*

1. Complete the table of ordered pairs for the equation $2x - 3y = 12$.

x	y
1	
3	
	−4

Find the x- and y-intercepts, and graph each equation.

2. $3x - 2y = 20$ **3.** $y = 5$ **4.** $x = 2$

5. Find the slope of the line through the points $(6, 4)$ and $(-4, -1)$.

📝 **6.** Describe how the graph of a line with undefined slope is situated in a rectangular coordinate system.

Determine whether each pair of lines is parallel, perpendicular, *or* neither.

7. $5x - y = 8$ and $5y = -x + 3$

8. $2y = 3x + 12$ and $3y = 2x - 5$

📝 **9.** In 1980, there were 119,000 farms in Iowa. As of 2008, there were 93,000. Find and interpret the average rate of change in the number of farms per year, to the nearest whole number. (*Source:* U.S. Department of Agriculture.)

Find an equation of each line, and write it in **(a)** *slope-intercept form if possible and* **(b)** *standard form.*

10. Through $(4, -1)$; $m = -5$ **11.** Through $(-3, 14)$; horizontal

12. Through $(-2, 3)$ and $(6, -1)$ **13.** Through $(5, -6)$; vertical

14. Through $(-7, 2)$ and parallel to $3x + 5y = 6$

15. Through $(-7, 2)$ and perpendicular to $y = 2x$

16. *Concept Check* Which line has positive slope and negative y-coordinate for its y-intercept?

A.

B.

C.

D.

17. The bar graph shows median household income for Asians and Pacific Islanders in the United States.

    (a) Use the information for the years 2001 and 2007 to find an equation that models the data. Let $x = 1$ represent 2001, $x = 7$ represent 2007, and y represent the median income. Write the equation in slope-intercept form.

    (b) Use the equation from part (a) to approximate median household income for 2005 to the nearest dollar. How does your result compare against the actual value, $61,094?

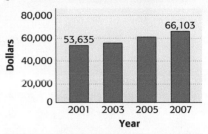

Median Household Income for Asians and Pacific Islanders

Source: U.S. Census Bureau.

18. Which one of the following is the graph of a function?

    A.   **B.** 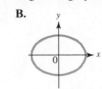   **C.**   **D.**

19. Which of the following does not define y as a function of x?

    A. $\{(0, 1), (-2, 3), (4, 8)\}$ **B.** $y = 2x - 6$ **C.** $y = \sqrt{x + 2}$ **D.**

x	y
0	1
3	2
0	2
6	3

20. Give the domain and range of the relation shown in each of the following.

    (a) Choice A of **Exercise 18**   **(b)** Choice A of **Exercise 19**

21. For $f(x) = -x^2 + 2x - 1$, find **(a)** $f(1)$, and **(b)** $f(a)$.

22. Graph the linear function defined by $f(x) = \frac{2}{3}x - 1$. What is its domain and range?

23. Find each of the following for the functions defined by

    $$f(x) = -2x^2 + 5x - 6 \quad \text{and} \quad g(x) = 7x - 3.$$

    (a) $f(4)$ **(b)** $(f + g)(x)$ **(c)** $(f - g)(x)$ **(d)** $(f - g)(-2)$

24. If $f(x) = x^2 + 3x + 2$ and $g(x) = x + 1$, find each of the following.

    (a) $(fg)(x)$ **(b)** $(fg)(-2)$

25. Use $f(x)$ and $g(x)$ from **Exercise 24** to find each of the following.

    (a) $\left(\dfrac{f}{g}\right)(x)$ **(b)** $\left(\dfrac{f}{g}\right)(-2)$

26. Find each of the following for the functions defined by

    $$f(x) = 3x + 5 \quad \text{and} \quad g(x) = x^2 + 2.$$

    (a) $(f \circ g)(-2)$ **(b)** $(f \circ g)(x)$ **(c)** $(g \circ f)(x)$

27. The current in a simple electrical circuit is inversely proportional to the resistance. If the current is 80 amps when the resistance is 30 ohms, find the current when the resistance is 12 ohms.

28. The force of the wind blowing on a vertical surface varies jointly as the area of the surface and the square of the velocity. If a wind blowing at 40 mph exerts a force of 50 lb on a surface of 500 ft², how much force will a wind of 80 mph place on a surface of 2 ft²?

CHAPTERS $\left(1–7\right)$ CUMULATIVE REVIEW EXERCISES

Decide whether each statement is always true, sometimes true, *or* never true. *If the statement is* sometimes true, *give examples in which it is true and in which it is false.*

1. The absolute value of a negative number equals the additive inverse of the number.

2. The sum of two negative numbers is positive.

3. The sum of a positive number and a negative number is 0.

Simplify.

4. $-|-2| - 4 + |-3| + 7$ 5. $-(-4m + 3)$

6. $\dfrac{(4^2 - 4) - (-1)7}{4 + (-6)}$

Evaluate each expression for $p = -4$, $q = \frac{1}{2}$, and $r = 16$.

7. $-3(2q - 3p)$

8. $\dfrac{r}{8p + 2r}$

Solve.

9. $2z - 5 + 3z = 2 - z$

10. $\dfrac{3x - 1}{5} + \dfrac{x + 2}{2} = -\dfrac{3}{10}$

Solve each problem.

11. If each side of a square were increased by 4 in., the perimeter would be 8 in. less than twice the perimeter of the original square. Find the length of a side of the original square.

x $x + 4$

Original square   New square

12. Two planes leave the Dallas-Fort Worth airport at the same time. One travels east at 550 mph, and the other travels west at 500 mph. Assuming no wind, how long will it take for the planes to be 2100 mi apart?

West Airport East

Solve. Write each solution set in interval notation and graph it.

13. $-4 < 3 - 2k < 9$

14. $-0.3x + 2.1(x - 4) \le -6.6$

15. Find the x- and y-intercepts of the line with equation $3x + 5y = 12$, and graph the line.

16. Consider the points $A(-2, 1)$ and $B(3, -5)$.

    (a) Find the slope of the line AB.

    (b) Find the slope of a line perpendicular to line AB.

Write an equation for each line. Express the equation (a) in slope-intercept form if possible and (b) in standard form.

17. Slope $-\dfrac{3}{4}$; y-intercept $(0, -1)$

18. Through $(4, -3)$ and $(1, 1)$

Perform the indicated operations. In Exercise 22, assume that variables represent nonzero real numbers.

19. $(3x^2y^{-1})^{-2}(2x^{-3}y)^{-1}$

20. $(7x + 3y)^2$

21. $(3x^3 + 4x^2 - 7) - (2x^3 - 8x^2 + 3x)$

22. $\dfrac{m^3 - 3m^2 + 5m - 3}{m - 1}$

Factor.

23. $16w^2 + 50wz - 21z^2$ **24.** $4x^2 - 4x + 1 - y^2$ **25.** $8p^3 + 27$

26. Solve $9x^2 = 6x - 1$.

Solve each problem.

27. A sign is to have the shape of a triangle with a height 3 ft greater than the length of the base. How long should the base be if the area is to be 14 ft²?

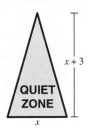

28. A game board has the shape of a rectangle. The longer sides are each 2 in. longer than the distance between them. The area of the board is 288 in.². Find the length of the longer sides and the distance between them.

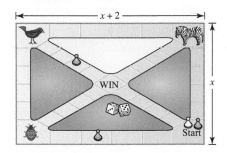

Perform each indicated operation. Write the answer in lowest terms.

29. $\dfrac{8}{x + 1} - \dfrac{2}{x + 3}$

30. $\dfrac{x^2 + 5x + 6}{3x} \div \dfrac{x^2 - 4}{x^2 + x - 6}$

31. Simplify $\dfrac{\dfrac{12}{x + 6}}{\dfrac{4}{2x + 12}}$.

32. Solve $\dfrac{2}{x - 1} = \dfrac{5}{x - 1} - \dfrac{3}{4}$.

33. Give the domain and range of the relation. Does it define a function? Explain.

34. Consider the function defined by
$$f(x) = -4x + 10.$$

(a) Find the domain and range.

(b) Evaluate $f(-3)$.

(c) If $f(x) = 6$, find the value of x.

35. Use the information in the graph to find and interpret the average rate of change in the per capita consumption of potatoes in the United States from 2003 to 2008.

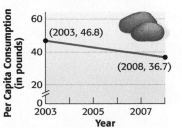

Source: U.S. Department of Agriculture.

Systems of Linear Equations

8.1 Solving Systems of Linear Equations by Graphing

8.2 Solving Systems of Linear Equations by Substitution

8.3 Solving Systems of Linear Equations by Elimination

Summary Exercises on Solving Systems of Linear Equations

8.4 Solving Systems of Linear Equations in Three Variables

8.5 Applications of Systems of Linear Equations

8.6 Solving Systems of Linear Equations by Matrix Methods

In the early 1970s, the NBC television network presented *The Bill Cosby Show*, in which the popular comedian played Chet Kincaid, a Los Angeles high school physical education teacher. In the episode "Let *x* Equal a Lousy Weekend," Chet must substitute for the algebra teacher. He and the entire class are stumped by the following problem:

> *How many pounds of candy that sells for $0.75 per lb must be mixed with candy that sells for $1.25 per lb to obtain 9 lb of a mixture that should sell for $0.96 per lb?*

The smartest student in the class eventually helps Chet solve this problem. In **Exercise 31** of **Section 8.5**, we ask you to use a *system of linear equations,* the topic of this chapter, to do so.

8.1 Solving Systems of Linear Equations by Graphing

OBJECTIVES

1 Decide whether a given ordered pair is a solution of a system.
2 Solve linear systems by graphing.
3 Solve special systems by graphing.
4 Identify special systems without graphing.

A **system of linear equations,** often called a **linear system,** consists of two or more linear equations with the same variables.

$$2x + 3y = 4 \qquad\qquad x + 3y = 1 \qquad\qquad x - y = 1$$
$$3x - y = -5 \qquad -y = 4 - 2x \qquad y = 3$$

Linear systems

NOTE In the system on the right, think of $y = 3$ as an equation in two variables by writing it as $0x + y = 3$.

OBJECTIVE 1 **Decide whether a given ordered pair is a solution of a system.** A **solution of a system** of linear equations is an ordered pair that makes both equations true at the same time. A solution of an equation is said to *satisfy* the equation.

NOW TRY
EXERCISE 1

Decide whether the ordered pair $(5, 2)$ is a solution of each system.

(a) $2x + 5y = 20$
$x - y = 7$

(b) $3x - y = 13$
$2x + y = 12$

EXAMPLE 1 Determining Whether an Ordered Pair Is a Solution

Decide whether the ordered pair $(4, -3)$ is a solution of each system.

(a) $x + 4y = -8$
$3x + 2y = 6$

To decide whether $(4, -3)$ is a solution of the system, substitute 4 for x and -3 for y in each equation.

$x + 4y = -8$		$3x + 2y = 6$	
$4 + 4(-3) \stackrel{?}{=} -8$	Substitute.	$3(4) + 2(-3) \stackrel{?}{=} 6$	Substitute.
$4 + (-12) \stackrel{?}{=} -8$	Multiply.	$12 + (-6) \stackrel{?}{=} 6$	Multiply.
$-8 = -8$ ✓	True	$6 = 6$ ✓	True

Because $(4, -3)$ satisfies both equations, it is a solution of the system.

(b) $2x + 5y = -7$
$3x + 4y = 2$

Again, substitute 4 for x and -3 for y in both equations.

$2x + 5y = -7$		$3x + 4y = 2$	
$2(4) + 5(-3) \stackrel{?}{=} -7$	Substitute.	$3(4) + 4(-3) \stackrel{?}{=} 2$	Substitute.
$8 + (-15) \stackrel{?}{=} -7$	Multiply.	$12 + (-12) \stackrel{?}{=} 2$	Multiply.
$-7 = -7$ ✓	True	$0 = 2$	False

The ordered pair $(4, -3)$ is not a solution of this system because it does not satisfy the second equation.

NOW TRY

NOW TRY ANSWERS
1. (a) no **(b)** yes

OBJECTIVE 2 **Solve linear systems by graphing.** The set of all ordered pairs that are solutions of a system is its **solution set.** One way to find the solution set of a system of two linear equations is to graph both equations on the same axes.

Any intersection point would be on both lines and would therefore be a solution of *both* equations. ***Thus, the coordinates of any point at which the lines intersect give a solution of the system.***

The graph in **FIGURE 1** shows that the solution of the system in **Example 1(a)** is the intersection point $(4, -3)$. Because two *different* straight lines can intersect at no more than one point, there can never be more than one solution for such a system.

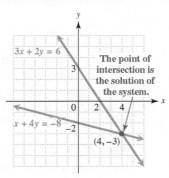

FIGURE 1

NOW TRY
EXERCISE 2

Solve the system by graphing.

$$x - 2y = 4$$
$$2x + y = 3$$

EXAMPLE 2   Solving a System by Graphing

Solve the system of equations by graphing both equations on the same axes.

$$2x + 3y = 4$$
$$3x - y = -5$$

We graph these two lines by plotting several points for each line. Recall from **Section 3.2** that the intercepts are often convenient choices.

$$2x + 3y = 4 \qquad\qquad 3x - y = -5$$

x	y
0	$\frac{4}{3}$
2	0
-2	$\frac{8}{3}$

Find a third ordered pair as a check.

x	y
0	5
$-\frac{5}{3}$	0
-2	-1

The lines in **FIGURE 2** suggest that the graphs intersect at the point $(-1, 2)$. We check this by substituting -1 for x and 2 for y in both equations.

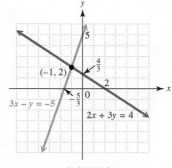

FIGURE 2

CHECK

$$2x + 3y = 4 \qquad \text{First equation}$$
$$2(-1) + 3(2) \stackrel{?}{=} 4 \qquad \text{Substitute.}$$
$$4 = 4 \;\checkmark \qquad \text{True}$$
$$3x - y = -5 \qquad \text{Second equation}$$
$$3(-1) - 2 \stackrel{?}{=} -5 \qquad \text{Substitute.}$$
$$-5 = -5 \;\checkmark \qquad \text{True}$$

NOW TRY ANSWER
2. $\{(2, -1)\}$

Because $(-1, 2)$ satisfies both equations, the solution set of this system is $\{(-1, 2)\}$.

NOW TRY

Solving a Linear System by Graphing

Step 1 **Graph each equation** of the system on the same coordinate axes.

Step 2 **Find the coordinates of the point of intersection** of the graphs if possible. This is the solution of the system.

Step 3 **Check** the solution in *both* of the original equations. Then write the solution set.

⚠ **CAUTION** With the graphing method, it may not be possible to determine the exact coordinates of the point that represents the solution, particularly if those coordinates are not integers. The graphing method does, however, show geometrically how solutions are found and is useful when approximate answers will do.

OBJECTIVE 3 **Solve special systems by graphing.** Sometimes the graphs of the two equations in a system either do not intersect at all or are the same line.

⤸ NOW TRY
EXERCISE 3

Solve each system by graphing.

(a) $5x - 3y = 2$
  $10x - 6y = 4$

(b) $4x + y = 7$
  $12x + 3y = 10$

EXAMPLE 3 Solving Special Systems by Graphing

Solve each system by graphing.

(a) $2x + y = 2$
  $2x + y = 8$

The graphs of these lines are shown in **FIGURE 3**. The two lines are parallel and have no points in common. For such a system, there is no solution. We write the solution set as ∅.

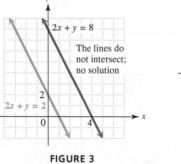

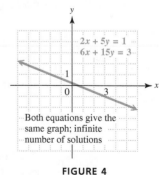

FIGURE 3   FIGURE 4

(b) $2x + 5y = 1$
  $6x + 15y = 3$

The graphs of these two equations are the same line. See **FIGURE 4**. We can obtain the second equation by multiplying each side of the first equation by 3. In this case, every point on the line is a solution of the system, and the solution set contains an infinite number of ordered pairs, each of which satisfies both equations of the system. We write the solution set as

$$\{(x, y) \mid 2x + 5y = 1\},$$

This is the first equation in the system. See the Note on the next page.

read "the set of ordered pairs (x, y) such that $2x + 5y = 1$." Recall from **Section 1.4** that this notation is called **set-builder notation.**   NOW TRY ⤸

NOW TRY ANSWERS

3. (a) $\{(x, y) \mid 5x - 3y = 2\}$
  (b) ∅

NOTE When a system has an infinite number of solutions, as in **Example 3(b),** either equation of the system could be used to write the solution set. *We prefer to use the equation in standard form with integer coefficients that have greatest common factor 1.* If neither of the given equations is in this form, we will use an *equivalent* equation that is in standard form with integer coefficients that have greatest common factor 1.

The system in **Example 2** has exactly one solution. A system with at least one solution is called a **consistent system.** A system with no solution, such as the one in **Example 3(a),** is called an **inconsistent system.**

The equations in **Example 2** are **independent equations** with different graphs. The equations of the system in **Example 3(b)** have the same graph and are equivalent. Because they are different forms of the same equation, these equations are called **dependent equations.**

Examples 2 and 3 show the three cases that may occur when solving a system of equations with two variables.

Three Cases for Solutions of Systems

1. The graphs intersect at exactly one point, which gives the (single) ordered-pair solution of the system. The **system is consistent** and the **equations are independent.** See **FIGURE 5(a).**

2. The graphs are parallel lines, so there is no solution and the solution set is $\emptyset$. The **system is inconsistent** and the **equations are independent.** See **FIGURE 5(b).**

3. The graphs are the same line. There is an infinite number of solutions, and the solution set is written in set-builder notation as

$$\{(x,y)\ |\ \underline{\qquad\qquad}\},$$

where one of the equations is written after the $|$ symbol. The **system is consistent** and the **equations are dependent.** See **FIGURE 5(c).**

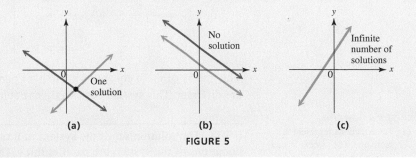

(a)   (b)   (c)

FIGURE 5

OBJECTIVE 4 **Identify special systems without graphing. Example 3** showed that the graphs of an inconsistent system are parallel lines and the graphs of a system of dependent equations are the same line. We can recognize these special kinds of systems without graphing by using slopes.

NOW TRY
EXERCISE 4

Describe each system without graphing. State the number of solutions.

(a) $5x - 8y = 4$

$\quad x - \frac{8}{5}y = \frac{4}{5}$

(b) $2x + y = 7$

$\quad 3y = -6x - 12$

(c) $y - 3x = 7$

$\quad 3y - x = 0$

EXAMPLE 4 Identifying the Three Cases by Using Slopes

Describe each system without graphing. State the number of solutions.

(a) $3x + 2y = 6$

$\quad -2y = 3x - 5$

Write each equation in slope-intercept form, $y = mx + b$, by solving for y.

$3x + 2y = 6$		$-2y = 3x - 5$	
$2y = -3x + 6$	Subtract 3x.	$y = -\frac{3}{2}x + \frac{5}{2}$	Divide by −2.
$y = -\frac{3}{2}x + 3$	Divide by 2.		

Both equations have slope $-\frac{3}{2}$ but they have different y-intercepts, 3 and $\frac{5}{2}$. Recall that lines with the same slope are parallel, so these equations have graphs that are parallel lines. Thus, the system has no solution.

(b) $2x - y = 4$

$\quad x = \frac{y}{2} + 2$

Again, write the equations in slope-intercept form.

$2x - y = 4$		$x = \frac{y}{2} + 2$	
$-y = -2x + 4$	Subtract 2x.	$\frac{y}{2} + 2 = x$	Interchange sides.
$y = 2x - 4$	Multiply by −1.	$\frac{y}{2} = x - 2$	Subtract 2.
		$y = 2x - 4$	Multiply by 2.

The equations are exactly the same—their graphs are the same line. Thus, the system has an infinite number of solutions.

(c) $x - 3y = 5$

$\quad 2x + y = 8$

In slope-intercept form, the equations are as follows.

$x - 3y = 5$		$2x + y = 8$	
$-3y = -x + 5$	Subtract x.	$y = -2x + 8$	Subtract 2x.
$y = \frac{1}{3}x - \frac{5}{3}$	Divide by −3.		

The graphs of these equations are neither parallel nor the same line, since the slopes are different. This system has exactly one solution. NOW TRY

NOW TRY ANSWERS

4. (a) The equations represent the same line. The system has an infinite number of solutions.
(b) The equations represent parallel lines. The system has no solution.
(c) The equations represent lines that are neither parallel nor the same line. The system has exactly one solution.

NOTE The solution set of the system in **Example 4(a)** is $\emptyset$, since the graphs of the equations of the system are parallel lines. The solution set of the system in **Example 4(b)**, written using set-builder notation and the first equation, is

$$\{(x, y) \mid 2x - y = 4\}.$$

If we try to solve the system in **Example 4(c)** by graphing, we will have difficulty identifying the point of intersection of the graphs. We introduce an algebraic method for solving systems like this in **Section 8.2.**

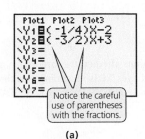

Notice the careful use of parentheses with the fractions.

(a)

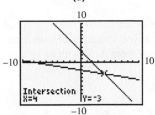

The display at the bottom of the screen indicates that the solution set is $\{(4, -3)\}$.

(b)

FIGURE 6

CONNECTIONS

We can solve the system from **Example 1(a)** by graphing with a calculator.

$$x + 4y = -8$$
$$3x + 2y = 6$$

To enter the equations in a graphing calculator, first solve each equation for y.

$$x + 4y = -8 \qquad\qquad 3x + 2y = 6$$

$$4y = -x - 8 \quad \text{Subtract } x. \qquad 2y = -3x + 6 \quad \text{Subtract } 3x.$$

$$y = -\frac{1}{4}x - 2 \quad \text{Divide by 4.} \qquad y = -\frac{3}{2}x + 3 \quad \text{Divide by 2.}$$

We designate the first equation Y_1 and the second equation Y_2. See **FIGURE 6(a)**. We graph the two equations using a standard window and then use the capability of the calculator to find the coordinates of the point of intersection of the graphs. See **FIGURE 6(b)**.

For Discussion or Writing

Use a graphing calculator to solve each system.

1. $3x + y = 2$
$\quad 2x - y = -7$

2. $8x + 4y = 0$
$\quad 4x - 2y = 2$

3. $3x + 3y = 0$
$\quad 4x + 2y = 3$

8.1 EXERCISES

MyMathLab **Math XL** PRACTICE WATCH DOWNLOAD READ REVIEW

⊕ *Complete solution available on the Video Resources on DVD*

1. *Concept Check* Which ordered pair could not be a solution of the system graphed? Why is it the only valid choice?

 A. $(-4, -4)$ **B.** $(-2, 2)$
 C. $(-4, 4)$ **D.** $(-3, 3)$

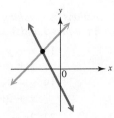

2. *Concept Check* Which ordered pair could be a solution of the system graphed? Why is it the only valid choice?

 A. $(2, 0)$ **B.** $(0, 2)$
 C. $(-2, 0)$ **D.** $(0, -2)$

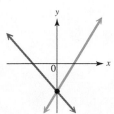

Decide whether the given ordered pair is a solution of the given system. See Example 1.

⊕ **3.** $(2, -3)$
$\quad x + y = -1$
$\quad 2x + 5y = 19$

4. $(4, 3)$
$\quad x + 2y = 10$
$\quad 3x + 5y = 3$

5. $(-1, -3)$
$\quad 3x + 5y = -18$
$\quad 4x + 2y = -10$

6. $(-9, -2)$
$\quad 2x - 5y = -8$
$\quad 3x + 6y = -39$

7. $(7, -2)$
$\quad 4x = 26 - y$
$\quad 3x = 29 + 4y$

8. $(9, 1)$
$\quad 2x = 23 - 5y$
$\quad 3x = 24 + 3y$

9. $(6, -8)$
$-2y = x + 10$
$3y = 2x + 30$

10. $(-5, 2)$
$5y = 3x + 20$
$3y = -2x - 4$

11. $(0, 0)$
$4x + 2y = 0$
$x + y = 0$

12. *Concept Check*   When a student was asked to determine whether the ordered pair $(1, -2)$ is a solution of the following system, he answered "yes." His reasoning was that the ordered pair satisfies the equation $x + y = -1$, since $1 + (-2) = -1$. **WHAT WENT WRONG?**

$$x + y = -1$$
$$2x + y = 4$$

13. *Concept Check*   Each ordered pair in (a)–(d) is a solution of one of the systems graphed in A–D. Because of the location of the point of intersection, you should be able to determine the correct system for each solution. Match each system from A–D with its solution from (a)–(d).

(a) $(3, 4)$ **A.**

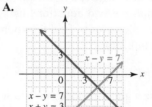

B.

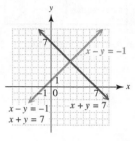

(b) $(-2, 3)$

(c) $(-3, 2)$ **C.**

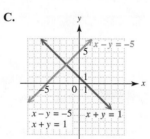

D.

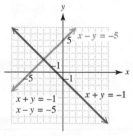

(d) $(5, -2)$

14. *Concept Check*   The following system has infinitely many solutions. Write its solution set, using set-builder notation as described in **Example 3(b).**

$$6x - 4y = 8$$
$$3x - 2y = 4$$

Solve each system of equations by graphing. If the system is inconsistent or the equations are dependent, say so. ***See Examples 2 and 3.***

15. $x - y = 2$
$x + y = 6$

16. $x - y = 3$
$x + y = -1$

17. $x + y = 4$
$y - x = 4$

18. $x + y = -5$
$y - x = -5$

19. $x - 2y = 6$
$x + 2y = 2$

20. $2x - y = 4$
$4x + y = 2$

21. $3x - 2y = -3$
$-3x - y = -6$

22. $2x - y = 4$
$2x + 3y = 12$

23. $2x - 3y = -6$
$y = -3x + 2$

24. $-3x + y = -3$
$y = x - 3$

25. $2x - y = 6$
$4x - 2y = 8$

26. $x + 2y = 4$
$2x + 4y = 12$

27. $3x + y = 5$
$6x + 2y = 10$

28. $2x - y = 4$
$4x - 2y = 8$

29. $3x - 4y = 24$
$y = -\dfrac{3}{2}x + 3$

30. $4x + y = 5$
$y = \dfrac{3}{2}x - 6$

31. $2x = y - 4$
$4x + 4 = 2y$

32. $3x = y + 5$
$6x - 5 = 2y$

33. Solve the system by graphing. Can you check your solution? Why or why not?

$$2x + 3y = 6$$
$$x - 3y = 5$$

34. Explain one of the drawbacks of solving a system of equations graphically.

Without graphing, answer the following questions for each linear system. ***See Example 4.***

(a) Is the system inconsistent, are the equations dependent, or neither?
(b) Is the graph a pair of intersecting lines, a pair of parallel lines, or one line?
(c) Does the system have one solution, no solution, or an infinite number of solutions?

35. $y - x = -5$
$x + y = 1$

36. $y + 2x = 6$
$x - 3y = -4$

37. $x + 2y = 0$
$4y = -2x$

38. $2x - y = 4$
$y + 4 = 2x$

39. $x - 3y = 5$
$2x + y = 8$

40. $2x + 3y = 12$
$2x - y = 4$

41. $5x + 4y = 7$
$10x + 8y = 4$

42. $3x + 2y = 5$
$6x + 4y = 3$

Work each problem using the graph provided.

43. The numbers of daily morning and evening newspapers in the United States in selected years over the period 1980–2008 are shown in the graph.

(a) For which years were there more evening dailies than morning dailies?

(b) Estimate the year in which the number of evening and morning dailies was closest to the same. About how many newspapers of each type were there in that year?

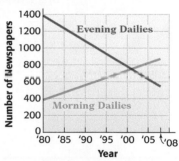

Source: Editor & Publisher
International Year Book.

44. The graph shows how sales of music CDs and digital downloads of single songs (in millions) in the United States have changed over the years 2004 through 2007.

(a) In what year did Americans purchase about the same number of CDs as single digital downloads? How many units was this?

(b) Express the point of intersection of the two graphs as an ordered pair of the form (year, units in millions).

(c) Describe the trend in sales of music CDs over the years 2004 to 2007. If a straight line were used to approximate its graph, would the line have positive, negative, or zero slope? Explain.

(d) If a straight line were used to approximate the graph of sales of digital downloads over the years 2004 to 2007, would the line have positive, negative, or zero slope? Explain.

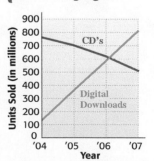

Source: Recording Industry
Association of America.

45. The graph shows how college students managed their money during the years 1997 through 2004.

(a) During what period did ATM use dominate both credit card *and* debit card use?

(b) In what year did debit card use overtake credit card use?

(c) In what year did debit card use overtake ATM use?

(d) Write an ordered pair for the debit card use data in the year 1998.

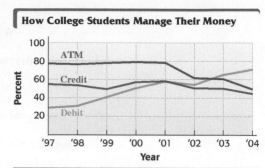

How College Students Manage Their Money

Source: Georgetown University Credit Research Center.

An application of mathematics in economics deals with **supply and demand.** *Typically, as the price of an item increases, the demand for the item decreases while the supply increases. If supply and demand can be described by straight-line equations, the point at which the lines intersect determines the* **equilibrium supply** *and* **equilibrium demand.**

The price per unit, p, and the demand, x, for a particular aluminum siding are related by the linear equation $p = 60 - \frac{3}{4}x$, *while the supply is given by the linear equation* $p = \frac{3}{4}x$, *as shown in the figure.*

Use the graph to answer the questions in Exercises 46–48.

SUPPLY AND DEMAND

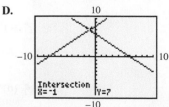

$p = 60 - \frac{3}{4}x$ (demand)

$p = \frac{3}{4}x$ (supply)

46. At what value of x does supply equal demand?

47. At what value of p does supply equal demand?

48. When $x > 40$, does demand exceed supply or does supply exceed demand?

TECHNOLOGY INSIGHTS EXERCISES 49–52

Match the graphing calculator screens in choices A–D with the appropriate system in Exercises 49–52. **See the Connections box.**

A.

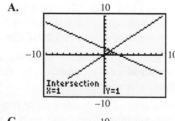

B.

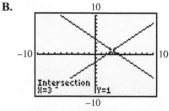

C.

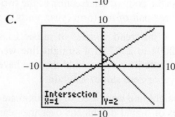

D.

49. $x + y = 4$
$x - y = 2$

50. $x + y = 6$
$x - y = -8$

51. $2x + 3y = 5$
$x - y = 0$

52. $3x + 2y = 7$
$-x + y = 1$

*Solve each equation for y. **See Sections 2.5, 3.3, and 7.1.***

53. $3x + y = 4$ **54.** $-2x + y = 9$ **55.** $9x - 2y = 4$ **56.** $5x - 3y = 12$

*Solve each equation. Check the solution. **See Section 2.3.***

57. $-2(x - 2) + 5x = 10$ **58.** $4(3 - 2k) + 3k = 12$

59. $4x - 2(1 - 3x) = 6$ **60.** $t + 3(2t - 4) = -13$

8.2 Solving Systems of Linear Equations by Substitution

OBJECTIVES

1 Solve linear systems by substitution.
2 Solve special systems by substitution.
3 Solve linear systems with fractions and decimals by substitution.

OBJECTIVE 1 Solve linear systems by substitution. Graphing to solve a system of equations has a serious drawback. For example, consider the system graphed in **FIGURE 7**. It is difficult to determine an accurate solution of the system from the graph.

As a result, there are algebraic methods for solving systems of equations. The **substitution method,** which gets its name from the fact that an expression in one variable is *substituted* for the other variable, is one such method.

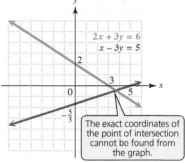

The exact coordinates of the point of intersection cannot be found from the graph.

$2x + 3y = 6$
$x - 3y = 5$

FIGURE 7

EXAMPLE 1 Using the Substitution Method

Solve the system by the substitution method.

$$3x + 5y = 26 \quad (1)$$
$$y = 2x \quad (2)$$

We number the equations for reference in our discussion.

Equation (2), $y = 2x$, is already solved for y, so we substitute $2x$ for y in equation (1).

$$3x + 5y = 26 \quad (1)$$
$$3x + 5(2x) = 26 \quad \text{Let } y = 2x.$$
$$3x + 10x = 26 \quad \text{Multiply.}$$
$$13x = 26 \quad \text{Combine like terms.}$$
$$x = 2 \quad \text{Divide by 13.}$$

Don't stop here.

Now we can find the value of y by substituting 2 for x in either equation. We choose equation (2).

$$y = 2x \quad (2)$$
$$y = 2(2) \quad \text{Let } x = 2.$$
$$y = 4 \quad \text{Multiply.}$$

NOW TRY
EXERCISE 1

Solve the system by the substitution method.

$$2x - 4y = 28$$
$$y = -3x$$

We check the solution $(2, 4)$ by substituting 2 for x and 4 for y in *both* equations.

CHECK

$3x + 5y = 26$ (1)

$3(2) + 5(4) \stackrel{?}{=} 26$ Substitute.

$6 + 20 \stackrel{?}{=} 26$ Multiply.

$26 = 26$ ✓ True

$y = 2x$ (2)

$4 \stackrel{?}{=} 2(2)$ Substitute.

$4 = 4$ ✓ True

Since $(2, 4)$ satisfies both equations, the solution set is $\{(2, 4)\}$.   NOW TRY

> **⚠ CAUTION** *A system is not completely solved until values for both x and y are found.* Write the solution set as a set containing an ordered pair.

EXAMPLE 2   Using the Substitution Method

Solve the system by the substitution method.

$$2x + 5y = 7 \quad (1)$$
$$x = -1 - y \quad (2)$$

NOW TRY
EXERCISE 2

Solve the system by the substitution method.

$$4x + 9y = 1$$
$$x = y - 3$$

Equation (2) gives x in terms of y. Substitute $-1 - y$ for x in equation (1).

$2x + 5y = 7$ (1)

$2(-1 - y) + 5y = 7$ Let $x = -1 - y$.

$-2 - 2y + 5y = 7$ Distributive property   [Distribute 2 to both −1 and −y.]

$-2 + 3y = 7$ Combine like terms.

$3y = 9$ Add 2.

$y = 3$ Divide by 3.

To find x, substitute 3 for y in equation (2), $x = -1 - y$, to get

$$x = -1 - 3 = -4.$$ [Write the x-coordinate first.]

Check that the solution set of the given system is $\{(-4, 3)\}$.   NOW TRY

> **⚠ CAUTION** Even though we found y first in **Example 2**, *the x-coordinate is always written first in the ordered-pair solution of a system.*

Solving a Linear System by Substitution

Step 1   **Solve one equation for either variable.** If one of the variables has coefficient 1 or −1, choose it, since it usually makes the substitution method easier.

Step 2   **Substitute** for that variable in the other equation. The result should be an equation with just one variable.

Step 3   **Solve** the equation from Step 2.

Step 4   **Substitute** the result from Step 3 into the equation from Step 1 to find the value of the other variable.

Step 5   **Check** the solution in both of the original equations. Then write the solution set.

NOW TRY ANSWERS
1. $\{(2, -6)\}$ 2. $\{(-2, 1)\}$

NOW TRY
EXERCISE 3
Use substitution to solve the
system.
$$2y = x - 2$$
$$4x - 5y = -4$$

EXAMPLE 3   Using the Substitution Method

Use substitution to solve the system.

$$2x = 4 - y \qquad (1)$$
$$5x + 3y = 10 \qquad (2)$$

Step 1   We must solve one of the equations for either x or y. Because the coefficient of y in equation (1) is -1, we avoid fractions by solving this equation for y.

$$2x = 4 - y \qquad (1)$$
$$y + 2x = 4 \qquad \text{Add } y.$$
$$y = -2x + 4 \qquad \text{Subtract } 2x.$$

Step 2   Now substitute $-2x + 4$ for y in equation (2).

$$5x + 3y = 10 \qquad (2)$$
$$5x + 3(-2x + 4) = 10 \qquad \text{Let } y = -2x + 4.$$

Step 3   Solve the equation from Step 2.

$$5x - 6x + 12 = 10 \qquad \text{Distributive property}$$

> Distribute 3 to
> both $-2x$ and 4.

$$-x + 12 = 10 \qquad \text{Combine like terms.}$$
$$-x = -2 \qquad \text{Subtract 12.}$$
$$x = 2 \qquad \text{Multiply by } -1.$$

Step 4   Equation (1) solved for y is $y = -2x + 4$. Since $x = 2$,

$$y = -2(2) + 4 = 0.$$

Step 5   Check that $(2, 0)$ is the solution.

CHECK $\quad 2x = 4 - y \quad (1) \qquad\qquad 5x + 3y = 10 \qquad (2)$

$\qquad 2(2) \overset{?}{=} 4 - 0 \quad \text{Substitute.} \quad\;\; 5(2) + 3(0) \overset{?}{=} 10 \qquad \text{Substitute.}$

$\qquad\quad 4 = 4 \;\checkmark \quad \text{True} \qquad\qquad\qquad 10 = 10 \;\checkmark \;\; \text{True}$

Since both results are true, the solution set of the system is $\{(2, 0)\}$.   *NOW TRY*

OBJECTIVE 2   **Solve special systems by substitution.** Recall from **Section 8.1** that systems of equations with graphs that are parallel lines have no solution. Systems of equations with graphs that are the same line have an infinite number of solutions.

EXAMPLE 4   Solving an Inconsistent System by Substitution

Use substitution to solve the system.

$$x = 5 - 2y \qquad (1)$$
$$2x + 4y = 6 \qquad (2)$$

Equation (1) is already solved for x, so substitute $5 - 2y$ for x in equation (2).

$$2x + 4y = 6 \qquad (2)$$
$$2(5 - 2y) + 4y = 6 \qquad \text{Let } x = 5 - 2y \text{ from equation (1).}$$
$$10 - 4y + 4y = 6 \qquad \text{Distributive property}$$
$$10 = 6 \qquad \text{False}$$

NOW TRY ANSWER
3. $\{(-6, -4)\}$

NOW TRY
EXERCISE 4

Use substitution to solve the system.

$$8x - 2y = 1$$
$$y = 4x - 8$$

The false result $10 = 6$ means that the equations in the system have graphs that are parallel lines. The system is inconsistent and has no solution, so the solution set is $\emptyset$. See **FIGURE 8**.

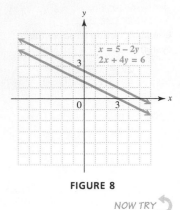

FIGURE 8

NOW TRY

⚠ **CAUTION** It is a common error to give "false" as the solution of an inconsistent system. The correct response is $\emptyset$.

NOW TRY
EXERCISE 5

Solve the system by the substitution method.

$$5x - y = 6$$
$$-10x + 2y = -12$$

EXAMPLE 5 Solving a System with Dependent Equations by Substitution

Solve the system by the substitution method.

$$3x - y = 4 \qquad (1)$$
$$-9x + 3y = -12 \qquad (2)$$

Begin by solving equation (1) for y to get $y = 3x - 4$. Substitute $3x - 4$ for y in equation (2) and solve the resulting equation.

$$-9x + 3y = -12 \qquad \text{(2)}$$
$$-9x + 3(3x - 4) = -12 \qquad \text{Let } y = 3x - 4 \text{ from equation (1).}$$
$$-9x + 9x - 12 = -12 \qquad \text{Distributive property}$$
$$0 = 0 \qquad \text{Add 12. Combine like terms.}$$

This true result means that every solution of one equation is also a solution of the other, so the system has an infinite number of solutions. The solution set is

$$\{(x, y) \mid 3x - y = 4\}.$$

A graph of the equations of this system is shown in **FIGURE 9**.

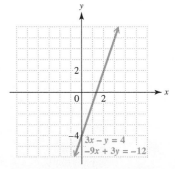

FIGURE 9

NOW TRY

⚠ **CAUTION** It is a common error to give "true" as the solution of a system of dependent equations. Write the solution set in set-builder notation using the equation in the system (or an equivalent equation) that is in standard form, with integer coefficients that have greatest common factor 1.

NOW TRY ANSWERS
4. $\emptyset$ **5.** $\{(x, y) \mid 5x - y = 6\}$

OBJECTIVE 3 Solve linear systems with fractions and decimals by substitution.

NOW TRY
EXERCISE 6
Solve the system by the substitution method.

$$x + \tfrac{1}{2}y = \tfrac{1}{2}$$
$$\tfrac{1}{6}x - \tfrac{1}{3}y = \tfrac{4}{3}$$

EXAMPLE 6 Using the Substitution Method with Fractions as Coefficients

Solve the system by the substitution method.

$$3x + \frac{1}{4}y = 2 \qquad (1)$$

$$\frac{1}{2}x + \frac{3}{4}y = -\frac{5}{2} \qquad (2)$$

Clear equation (1) of fractions by multiplying each side by 4.

$$4\left(3x + \frac{1}{4}y\right) = 4(2) \qquad \text{Multiply by 4.}$$

$$4(3x) + 4\left(\frac{1}{4}y\right) = 4(2) \qquad \text{Distributive property}$$

$$12x + y = 8 \qquad (3)$$

Now clear equation (2) of fractions by multiplying each side by 4.

$$4\left(\frac{1}{2}x + \frac{3}{4}y\right) = 4\left(-\frac{5}{2}\right) \qquad \text{Multiply by 4, the common denominator.}$$

$$4\left(\frac{1}{2}x\right) + 4\left(\frac{3}{4}y\right) = 4\left(-\frac{5}{2}\right) \qquad \text{Distributive property}$$

$$2x + 3y = -10 \qquad (4)$$

The given system of equations has been simplified to an equivalent system.

$$12x + y = 8 \qquad (3)$$
$$2x + 3y = -10 \qquad (4)$$

To solve this system by substitution, solve equation (3) for y.

$$12x + y = 8 \qquad (3)$$
$$y = -12x + 8 \qquad \text{Subtract } 12x.$$

Now substitute this result for y in equation (4).

$$2x + 3y = -10 \qquad (4)$$
$$2x + 3(-12x + 8) = -10 \qquad \text{Let } y = -12x + 8.$$
$$2x - 36x + 24 = -10 \qquad \text{Distributive property}$$

Distribute 3 to both $-12x$ and 8.

$$-34x = -34 \qquad \text{Combine like terms. Subtract 24.}$$
$$x = 1 \qquad \text{Divide by } -34.$$

Since equation (3) solved for y is $y = -12x + 8$, substitute 1 for x to get

$$y = -12(1) + 8 = -4.$$

Check by substituting 1 for x and -4 for y in both of the original equations. The solution set is $\{(1, -4)\}$.

NOW TRY ANSWER
6. $\{(2, -3)\}$

NOW TRY

**NOW TRY
EXERCISE 7**

Solve the system by the substitution method.

$$0.2x + 0.3y = 0.5$$
$$0.3x - 0.1y = 1.3$$

EXAMPLE 7 Using the Substitution Method with Decimals as Coefficients

Solve the system by the substitution method.

$$0.5x + 2.4y = 4.2 \quad (1)$$
$$-0.1x + 1.5y = 5.1 \quad (2)$$

Clear each equation of decimals by multiplying by 10.

$10(0.5x + 2.4y) = 10(4.2)$	Multiply equation (1) by 10.
$10(0.5x) + 10(2.4y) = 10(4.2)$	Distributive property
$5x + 24y = 42$	(3)
$10(-0.1x + 1.5y) = 10(5.1)$	Multiply equation (2) by 10.
$10(-0.1x) + 10(1.5y) = 10(5.1)$	Distributive property

$$\boxed{10(-0.1x) = -1x = -x} \longrightarrow -x + 15y = 51 \quad (4)$$

Now solve the equivalent system of equations by substitution.

$$5x + 24y = 42 \quad (3)$$
$$-x + 15y = 51 \quad (4)$$

Equation (4) can be solved for x.

$$x = 15y - 51 \qquad \text{Equation (4) solved for } x$$

Substitute this result for x in equation (3).

$5x + 24y = 42$	(3)
$5(15y - 51) + 24y = 42$	Let $x = 15y - 51$.
$75y - 255 + 24y = 42$	Distributive property
$99y = 297$	Combine like terms. Add 255.
$y = 3$	Divide by 99.

Since equation (4) solved for x is $x = 15y - 51$, substitute 3 for y to get

$$x = 15(3) - 51 = -6.$$

**NOW TRY ANSWER
7.** $\{(4, -1)\}$

Check $(-6, 3)$ in both of the original equations. The solution set is $\{(-6, 3)\}$.

NOW TRY

8.2 EXERCISES

🌐 *Complete solution available
on the Video Resources on DVD*

1. *Concept Check*   A student solves the following system and finds that $x = 3$, which is correct. The student gives the solution set as $\{3\}$. *WHAT WENT WRONG?*

$$5x - y = 15$$
$$7x + y = 21$$

2. *Concept Check*   A student solves the following system and obtains the equation $0 = 0$. The student gives the solution set as $\{(0, 0)\}$. *WHAT WENT WRONG?*

$$x + y = 4$$
$$2x + 2y = 8$$

Solve each system by the substitution method. Check each solution. ***See Examples 1–5.***

3. $x + y = 12$
$y = 3x$

4. $x + 3y = -28$
$y = -5x$

5. $3x + 2y = 27$
$x = y + 4$

6. $4x + 3y = -5$
$x = y - 3$

7. $3x + 4 = -y$
$2x + y = 0$

8. $2x - 5 = -y$
$x + 3y = 0$

9. $7x + 4y = 13$
$x + y = 1$

10. $3x - 2y = 19$
$x + y = 8$

11. $3x + 5y = 25$
$x - 2y = -10$

12. $5x + 2y = -15$
$2x - y = -6$

13. $3x - y = 5$
$y = 3x - 5$

14. $4x - y = -3$
$y = 4x + 3$

15. $2x + y = 0$
$4x - 2y = 2$

16. $x + y = 0$
$4x + 2y = 3$

17. $2x + 8y = 3$
$x = 8 - 4y$

18. $2x + 10y = 3$
$x = 1 - 5y$

19. $2y = 4x + 24$
$2x - y = -12$

20. $2y = 14 - 6x$
$3x + y = 7$

Solve each system by the substitution method. Check each solution. ***See Examples 6 and 7.***

21. $\frac{1}{2}x + \frac{1}{3}y = 3$
$y = 3x$

22. $\frac{1}{4}x - \frac{1}{5}y = 9$
$y = 5x$

23. $\frac{1}{2}x + \frac{1}{3}y = -\frac{1}{3}$
$\frac{1}{2}x + 2y = -7$

24. $\frac{1}{6}x + \frac{1}{6}y = 1$
$-\frac{1}{2}x - \frac{1}{3}y = -5$

25. $\frac{x}{5} + 2y = \frac{8}{5}$
$\frac{3x}{5} + \frac{y}{2} = -\frac{7}{10}$

26. $\frac{x}{2} + \frac{y}{3} = \frac{7}{6}$
$\frac{x}{4} - \frac{3y}{2} = \frac{9}{4}$

27. $\frac{1}{6}x + \frac{1}{3}y = 8$
$\frac{1}{4}x + \frac{1}{2}y = 12$

28. $\frac{1}{2}x - \frac{1}{8}y = -\frac{1}{4}$
$\frac{1}{3}x - \frac{1}{12}y = -\frac{1}{6}$

29. $0.2x - 1.3y = -3.2$
$-0.1x + 2.7y = 9.8$

30. $0.1x + 0.9y = -2$
$0.5x - 0.2y = 4.1$

31. $0.3x - 0.1y = 2.1$
$0.6x + 0.3y = -0.3$

32. $0.8x - 0.1y = 1.3$
$2.2x + 1.5y = 8.9$

RELATING CONCEPTS   EXERCISES 33–36

FOR INDIVIDUAL OR GROUP WORK

A system of linear equations can be used to model the cost and the revenue of a business.
Work Exercises 33–36 in order.

 33. Suppose that you start a business manufacturing and selling bicycles, and it costs you $5000 to get started. Each bicycle will cost $400 to manufacture. Explain why the linear equation

$$y_1 = 400x + 5000 \quad (y_1 \text{ in dollars})$$

gives your *total* cost of manufacturing x bicycles.

34. You decide to sell each bike for $600. Write an equation using y_2 (in dollars) to express your revenue when you sell x bikes.

35. Form a system from the two equations in **Exercises 33 and 34.** Solve the system.

36. The value of x from **Exercise 35** is the number of bikes it takes to *break even*. Fill in the blanks: When _____ bikes are sold, the break-even point is reached. At that point, you have spent _____ dollars and taken in _____ dollars.

Solve each system by substitution. Then graph both lines in the standard viewing window of a graphing calculator, and use the intersection feature to support your answer. See the Connections box in **Section 8.1.** *(In Exercises 41 and 42, solve each equation for y before graphing.)*

37. $y = 6 - x$
$y = 2x$

38. $y = 4x - 4$
$y = -3x - 11$

39. $y = -\dfrac{4}{3}x + \dfrac{19}{3}$
$y = \dfrac{15}{2}x - \dfrac{5}{2}$

40. $y = -\dfrac{15}{2}x + 10$
$y = \dfrac{25}{3}x - \dfrac{65}{3}$

41. $4x + 5y = 5$
$2x + 3y = 1$

42. $6x + 5y = 13$
$3x + 3y = 4$

PREVIEW EXERCISES

Simplify. **See Section 1.8.**

43. $(14x - 3y) + (2x + 3y)$

44. $(-6x + 8y) + (6x + 2y)$

45. $(-x + 7y) + (3y + x)$

46. $(3x - 4y) + (4y - 3x)$

47. What must be added to $-4x$ to get a sum of 0?

48. What must be added to $6y$ to get a sum of 0?

49. What must $4y$ be multiplied by so that when the product is added to $8y$, the sum is 0?

50. What must $-3x$ be multiplied by so that when the product is added to $-12x$, the result is 0?

8.3 Solving Systems of Linear Equations by Elimination

OBJECTIVES

1 Solve linear systems by elimination.

2 Multiply when using the elimination method.

3 Use an alternative method to find the second value in a solution.

4 Solve special systems by elimination.

OBJECTIVE 1 **Solve linear systems by elimination.** Recall that adding the same quantity to each side of an equation results in equal sums.

$$\text{If } A = B, \text{ then } A + C = B + C.$$

We can take this addition a step further. Adding *equal* quantities, rather than the *same* quantity, to each side of an equation also results in equal sums.

$$\text{If } A = B \text{ and } C = D, \text{ then } A + C = B + D.$$

Using the addition property of equality to solve systems is called the **elimination method.**

EXAMPLE 1 Using the Elimination Method

Use the elimination method to solve the system.

$$x + y = 5 \quad (1)$$
$$x - y = 3 \quad (2)$$

Each equation in this system is a statement of equality, so the sum of the right sides equals the sum of the left sides. Adding vertically in this way gives the following.

$$x + y = 5 \quad (1)$$
$$\underline{x - y = 3} \quad (2)$$
$$2x \quad\quad = 8 \quad \text{Add left sides and add right sides.}$$
$$x = 4 \quad \text{Divide by 2.}$$

NOW TRY
EXERCISE 1

Use the elimination method to solve the system.

$$x - y = 4$$
$$3x + y = 8$$

Notice that y has been eliminated. The result, $x = 4$, gives the x-value of the solution of the given system. To find the y-value of the solution, substitute 4 for x in either of the two equations of the system. We choose equation (1).

$$x + y = 5 \quad \text{(1)}$$
$$4 + y = 5 \quad \text{Let } x = 4.$$
$$y = 1 \quad \text{Subtract 4.}$$

Check the solution, $(4, 1)$, in both equations of the given system.

CHECK	$x + y = 5$	(1)	$x - y = 3$	(2)
	$4 + 1 \overset{?}{=} 5$	Substitute.	$4 - 1 \overset{?}{=} 3$	Substitute.
	$5 = 5 \ \checkmark$ True		$3 = 3 \ \checkmark$ True	

Since both results are true, the solution set of the system is $\{(4, 1)\}$. *NOW TRY*

With the elimination method, the idea is to *eliminate* one of the variables. ***To do this, one pair of variable terms in the two equations must have coefficients that are opposites (additive inverses).***

Solving a Linear System by Elimination

Step 1 **Write both equations in standard form,** $Ax + By = C$.

Step 2 **Transform the equations as needed so that the coefficients of one pair of variable terms are opposites.** Multiply one or both equations by appropriate numbers so that the sum of the coefficients of either the x- or y-terms is 0.

Step 3 **Add** the new equations to eliminate a variable. The sum should be an equation with just one variable.

Step 4 **Solve** the equation from Step 3 for the remaining variable.

Step 5 **Substitute** the result from Step 4 into either of the original equations, and solve for the other variable.

Step 6 **Check** the solution in both of the original equations. Then write the solution set.

It does not matter which variable is eliminated first. Usually, we choose the one that is more convenient to work with.

EXAMPLE 2 Using the Elimination Method

Solve the system.

$$y + 11 = 2x \quad \text{(1)}$$
$$5x = y + 26 \quad \text{(2)}$$

Step 1 Write both equations in standard form, $Ax + By = C$.

$$-2x + y = -11 \quad \text{Subtract } 2x \text{ and } 11 \text{ in equation (1).}$$
$$5x - y = 26 \quad \text{Subtract } y \text{ in equation (2).}$$

Step 2 Because the coefficients of y are 1 and -1, adding will eliminate y. It is not necessary to multiply either equation by a number.

NOW TRY ANSWER
1. $\{(3, -1)\}$

⤷ NOW TRY
⤷ EXERCISE 2
Solve the system.

$$2x - 6 = -3y$$
$$5x - 3y = -27$$

Step 3 Add the two equations.

$$-2x + y = -11$$
$$\underline{5x - y = 26}$$
$$3x = 15 \qquad \text{Add in columns.}$$

Step 4 Solve. $\qquad\qquad x = 5 \qquad$ Divide by 3.

Step 5 Find the value of y by substituting 5 for x in either of the original equations.

$$y + 11 = 2x \qquad \text{(1)}$$
$$y + 11 = 2(5) \qquad \text{Let } x = 5.$$
$$y + 11 = 10 \qquad \text{Multiply.}$$
$$y = -1 \qquad \text{Subtract 11.}$$

Step 6 Check by substituting $x = 5$ and $y = -1$ into both of the original equations.

CHECK $\qquad y + 11 = 2x \qquad \text{(1)} \qquad\qquad 5x = y + 26 \qquad \text{(2)}$

$(-1) + 11 \overset{?}{=} 2(5) \qquad \text{Substitute.} \qquad 5(5) = -1 + 26 \qquad \text{Substitute.}$

$10 = 10 \;\checkmark\; \text{True} \qquad\qquad 25 = 25 \;\checkmark\; \text{True}$

Since $(5, -1)$ is a solution of *both* equations, the solution set is $\{(5, -1)\}$.

NOW TRY ⤸

OBJECTIVE 2 **Multiply when using the elimination method.** Sometimes we need to multiply each side of one or both equations in a system by some number before adding will eliminate a variable.

⤷ NOW TRY
⤷ EXERCISE 3
Solve the system.

$$3x - 5y = 25$$
$$2x + 8y = -6$$

EXAMPLE 3 Using the Elimination Method

Solve the system.

$$2x + 3y = -15 \qquad \text{(1)}$$
$$5x + 2y = 1 \qquad \text{(2)}$$

Adding the two equations gives $7x + 5y = -14$, which does not eliminate either variable. However, we can multiply each equation by a suitable number so that the coefficients of one of the two variables are opposites. For example, to eliminate x, we multiply each side of $2x + 3y = -15$ (equation (1)) by 5 and each side of $5x + 2y = 1$ (equation (2)) by -2.

$$10x + 15y = -75 \qquad \text{Multiply equation (1) by 5.}$$
$$\underline{-10x - 4y = -2} \qquad \text{Multiply equation (2) by } -2.$$
$$11y = -77 \qquad \text{Add.}$$
$$y = -7 \qquad \text{Divide by 11.}$$

The coefficients of x are opposites.

Find the value of x by substituting -7 for y in either equation (1) or (2).

$$5x + 2y = 1 \qquad \text{(2)}$$
$$5x + 2(-7) = 1 \qquad \text{Let } y = -7.$$
$$5x - 14 = 1 \qquad \text{Multiply.}$$
$$5x = 15 \qquad \text{Add 14.}$$
$$x = 3 \qquad \text{Divide by 5.}$$

NOW TRY ANSWERS
2. $\{(-3, 4)\}$ **3.** $\{(5, -2)\}$

Check that the solution set of the system is $\{(3, -7)\}$.

NOW TRY ⤸

NOTE In **Example 3,** we eliminated the variable x. Alternatively, we could multiply each equation of the system by a suitable number so that the variable y is eliminated.

$$2x + 3y = -15 \quad (1) \xrightarrow{\text{Multiply by 2.}} 4x + 6y = -30$$

$$5x + 2y = 1 \quad (2) \xrightarrow{\text{Multiply by } -3.} -15x - 6y = -3$$

Complete this approach and confirm that the same solution results.

⚠ **CAUTION** When using the elimination method, remember to *multiply both sides* of an equation by the same nonzero number.

OBJECTIVE 3 **Use an alternative method to find the second value in a solution.** Sometimes it is easier to find the value of the second variable in a solution by using the elimination method twice.

NOW TRY
EXERCISE 4
Solve the system.

$$4x + 9y = 3$$
$$5y = 6 - 3x$$

EXAMPLE 4 Finding the Second Value by Using an Alternative Method

Solve the system.

$$4x = 9 - 3y \quad (1)$$
$$5x - 2y = 8 \quad (2)$$

Write equation (1) in standard form by adding $3y$ to each side.

$$4x + 3y = 9 \quad (3)$$
$$5x - 2y = 8 \quad (2)$$

One way to proceed is to eliminate y by multiplying each side of equation (3) by 2 and each side of equation (2) by 3 and then adding.

$$
\begin{array}{ll}
8x + 6y = 18 & \text{Multiply equation (3) by 2.} \\
\underline{15x - 6y = 24} & \text{Multiply equation (2) by 3.} \\
23x \qquad = 42 & \text{Add.}
\end{array}
$$

The coefficients of y are opposites.

$$x = \frac{42}{23} \qquad \text{Divide by 23.}$$

Substituting $\frac{42}{23}$ for x in one of the given equations would give y, but the arithmetic would be messy. Instead, solve for y by starting again with the original equations written in standard form (equations (3) and (2)) and eliminating x.

$$
\begin{array}{ll}
20x + 15y = 45 & \text{Multiply equation (3) by 5.} \\
\underline{-20x + 8y = -32} & \text{Multiply equation (2) by } -4. \\
23y = 13 & \text{Add.}
\end{array}
$$

The coefficients of x are opposites.

$$y = \frac{13}{23} \qquad \text{Divide by 23.}$$

Check that the solution set is $\left\{\left(\frac{42}{23}, \frac{13}{23}\right)\right\}$.

NOW TRY ↻

NOW TRY ANSWER
4. $\left\{\left(\frac{39}{7}, -\frac{15}{7}\right)\right\}$

NOTE When the value of the first variable is a fraction, the method used in **Example 4** helps avoid arithmetic errors. This method could be used to solve any system.

NOW TRY
EXERCISE 5

Solve each system by the elimination method.

(a) $x - y = 2$
     $5x - 5y = 10$

(b) $4x + 3y = 0$
     $-4x - 3y = -1$

OBJECTIVE 4 **Solve special systems by elimination.**

EXAMPLE 5 **Solving Special Systems Using the Elimination Method**

Solve each system by the elimination method.

(a) $2x + 4y = 5$ (1)

                        $4x + 8y = -9$ (2)

Multiply each side of equation (1) by -2. Then add the two equations.

$$-4x - 8y = -10 \quad \text{Multiply equation (1) by } -2.$$
$$\underline{4x + 8y = -9} \quad \text{(2)}$$
$$0 = -19 \quad \text{False}$$

The false statement $0 = -19$ indicates that the given system has solution set $\emptyset$.

(b) $3x - y = 4$ (1)

                        $-9x + 3y = -12$ (2)

Multiply each side of equation (1) by 3. Then add the two equations.

$$9x - 3y = 12 \quad \text{Multiply equation (1) by 3.}$$
$$\underline{-9x + 3y = -12} \quad \text{(2)}$$
$$0 = 0 \quad \text{True}$$

A true statement occurs when the equations are equivalent. This indicates that every solution of one equation is also a solution of the other. The solution set is

$$\{(x, y) \mid 3x - y = 4\}. \qquad \text{NOW TRY}$$

NOW TRY ANSWERS
5. (a) $\{(x, y) \mid x - y = 2\}$
   (b) $\emptyset$

8.3 EXERCISES   *MyMathLab* Math XL PRACTICE   WATCH   DOWNLOAD   READ   REVIEW

🌐 *Complete solution available on the Video Resources on DVD*

Concept Check   *Answer* true *or* false *for each statement. If false, tell why.*

1. If the elimination method leads to $0 = -1$, the solution set of the system is $\{(0, -1)\}$.

2. A system that includes the equation $5x - 4y = 0$ cannot have $(4, -5)$ as a solution.

Solve each system by the elimination method. Check each solution. **See Examples 1 and 2.**

🌐 3. $x - y = -2$
     $x + y = 10$

4. $x + y = 10$
   $x - y = -6$

5. $2x + y = -5$
   $x - y = 2$

6. $2x + y = -15$
   $-x - y = 10$

🌐 7. $2y = -3x$
     $-3x - y = 3$

8. $5x = y + 5$
   $-5x + 2y = 0$

9. $6x - y = -1$
   $5y = 17 + 6x$

10. $y = 9 - 6x$
    $-6x + 3y = 15$

Solve each system by the elimination method. (Hint: In Exercises 29–34, first clear all fractions or decimals.) Check each solution. **See Examples 3–5.***

11. $2x - y = 12$
    $3x + 2y = -3$

12. $x + y = 3$
    $-3x + 2y = -19$

13. $x + 4y = 16$
    $3x + 5y = 20$

---

*The authors thank Mitchel Levy of Broward College for his suggestions for this group of exercises.

14. $2x + y = 8$
$5x - 2y = -16$

15. $2x - 8y = 0$
$4x + 5y = 0$

16. $3x - 15y = 0$
$6x + 10y = 0$

17. $3x + 3y = 33$
$5x - 2y = 27$

18. $4x - 3y = -19$
$3x + 2y = 24$

19. $5x + 4y = 12$
$3x + 5y = 15$

20. $2x + 3y = 21$
$5x - 2y = -14$

21. $5x - 4y = 15$
$-3x + 6y = -9$

22. $4x + 5y = -16$
$5x - 6y = -20$

23. $-x + 3y = 4$
$-2x + 6y = 8$

24. $6x - 2y = 24$
$-3x + y = -12$

25. $5x - 2y = 3$
$10x - 4y = 5$

26. $3x - 5y = 1$
$6x - 10y = 4$

27. $6x - 2y = -22$
$-3x + 4y = 17$

28. $5x - 4y = -1$
$x + 8y = -9$

29. $3x = 3 + 2y$
$-\dfrac{4}{3}x + y = \dfrac{1}{3}$

30. $3x = 27 + 2y$
$x - \dfrac{7}{2}y = -25$

31. $\dfrac{1}{5}x + y = \dfrac{6}{5}$
$\dfrac{1}{10}x + \dfrac{1}{3}y = \dfrac{5}{6}$

32. $\dfrac{1}{3}x + \dfrac{1}{2}y = \dfrac{13}{6}$
$\dfrac{1}{2}x - \dfrac{1}{4}y = -\dfrac{3}{4}$

33. $2.4x + 1.7y = 7.6$
$1.2x - 0.5y = 9.2$

34. $0.5x + 3.4y = 13$
$1.5x - 2.6y = -25$

35. $x + 3y = 6$
$-2x + 12 = 6y$

36. $7x + 2y = 0$
$4y = -14x$

37. $4x - 3y = 1$
$8x = 3 + 6y$

38. $5x + 8y = 10$
$24y = -15x - 10$

39. $4x = 3y - 2$
$5x + 3 = 2y$

40. $2x + 3y = 0$
$4x + 12 = 9y$

41. $24x + 12y = -7$
$16x - 18y = 17$

42. $9x + 4y = -3$
$6x + 6y = -7$

RELATING CONCEPTS EXERCISES 43–48

FOR INDIVIDUAL OR GROUP WORK

The graph shows average U.S. movie theater ticket prices from 2000 through 2008. In 2000, the average price was $5.39, as represented by the point P(2000, 5.39). In 2008, the average price was $7.18, as represented by the point Q(2008, 7.18). ***Work Exercises 43–48 in order.***

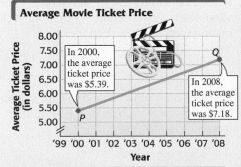

Average Movie Ticket Price

In 2000, the average ticket price was $5.39.

In 2008, the average ticket price was $7.18.

Source: Motion Picture Association of America.

(continued)

43. Line segment PQ has an equation that can be written in the form $y = ax + b$. Using the coordinates of point P with $x = 2000$ and $y = 5.39$, write an equation in the variables a and b.

44. Using the coordinates of point Q with $x = 2008$ and $y = 7.18$, write a second equation in the variables a and b.

45. Write the system of equations formed from the two equations in **Exercises 43 and 44,** and solve the system by using the elimination method.

46. (a) What is the equation of the line on which segment PQ lies?

(b) Let $x = 2007$ in the equation from part (a), and solve for y (to two decimal places). How does the result compare with the actual figure of 6.88?

PREVIEW EXERCISES

Multiply both sides of each equation by the given number. ***See Section 2.3.***

47. $2x - 3y + z = 5$ by 4

48. $-3x + 8y - z = 0$ by -3

Solve for z if $x = 1$ and $y = -2$. ***See Section 2.3.***

49. $x + 2y + 3z = 9$

50. $-3x - y + z = 1$

By what number must the first equation be multiplied so that x is eliminated when the two equations are added?

51. $x + 2y - z = 0$
   $3x - 4y + 2z = 6$

52. $x - 2y + 5z = -7$
   $-2x - 3y + 4z = -14$

SUMMARY EXERCISES on Solving Systems of Linear Equations

Guidelines for Choosing a Method to Solve a System of Linear Equations

1. If one of the equations of the system is already solved for one of the variables, as in the following systems, the substitution method is the better choice.

$$3x + 4y = 9 \qquad -5x + 3y = 9$$
$$\text{and}$$
$$y = 2x - 6 \qquad x = 3y - 7$$

2. If both equations are in standard $Ax + By = C$ form and none of the variables has coefficient -1 or 1, as in the following system, the elimination method is the better choice.

$$4x - 11y = 3$$
$$-2x + 3y = 4$$

3. If one or both of the equations are in standard form and the coefficient of one of the variables is -1 or 1, as in the following systems, either method is appropriate.

$$3x + y = -2 \qquad -x + 3y = -4$$
$$\text{and}$$
$$-5x + 2y = 4 \qquad 3x - 2y = 8$$

Concept Check   Use the preceding guidelines to solve each problem.

1. To minimize the amount of work required, tell whether you would use the substitution or elimination method to solve each system, and why. *Do not actually solve.*

   (a) $3x + 5y = 69$ **(b)** $3x + y = -7$ **(c)** $3x - 2y = 0$
   $y = 4x$ $x - y = -5$ $9x + 8y = 7$

2. Which system would be easier to solve with the substitution method? Why?

   System A: $5x - 3y = 7$ *System B:* $7x + 2y = 4$
   $2x + 8y = 3$ $y = -3x + 1$

*In Exercises 3 and 4, **(a)** solve the system by the elimination method, **(b)** solve the system by the substitution method, and **(c)** tell which method you prefer for that particular system and why.*

3. $4x - 3y = -8$ 4. $2x + 5y = 0$
   $x + 3y = 13$ $x = -3y + 1$

Solve each system by the method of your choice. (For Exercises 5–7, see your answers to **Exercise 1.***)*

5. $3x + 5y = 69$ 6. $3x + y = -7$ 7. $3x - 2y = 0$
   $y = 4x$ $x - y = -5$ $9x + 8y = 7$

8. $x + y = 7$ 9. $6x + 7y = 4$ 10. $6x - y = 5$
   $x = -3 - y$ $5x + 8y = -1$ $y = 11x$

11. $4x - 6y = 10$ 12. $3x - 5y = 7$ 13. $5x = 7 + 2y$
    $-10x + 15y = -25$ $2x + 3y = 30$ $5y = 5 - 3x$

14. $4x + 3y = 1$ 15. $2x - 3y = 7$ 16. $2x + 3y = 10$
    $3x + 2y = 2$ $-4x + 6y = 14$ $-3x + y = 18$

17. $2x + 5y = 4$ 18. $x - 3y = 7$ 19. $7x - 4y = 0$
    $x + y = -1$ $4x + y = 5$ $3x = 2y$

Solve each system by any method. First clear all fractions or decimals.

20. $\dfrac{1}{5}x + \dfrac{2}{3}y = -\dfrac{8}{5}$ 21. $\dfrac{1}{6}x + \dfrac{1}{6}y = 2$
    $3x - \phantom{\dfrac{2}{3}}y = 9$ $-\dfrac{1}{2}x - \dfrac{1}{3}y = -8$

22. $\dfrac{x}{3} - \dfrac{3y}{4} = -\dfrac{1}{2}$ 23. $\dfrac{x}{2} - \dfrac{y}{3} = 9$
    $\dfrac{x}{6} + \dfrac{y}{8} = \dfrac{3}{4}$ $\dfrac{x}{5} - \dfrac{y}{4} = 5$

24. $0.1x + y = 1.6$ 25. $0.2x - 0.3y = 0.1$
    $0.6x + 0.5y = -1.4$ $0.3x - 0.2y = 0.9$

8.4 Solving Systems of Linear Equations in Three Variables

OBJECTIVES

1 Understand the geometry of systems of three equations in three variables.

2 Solve linear systems (with three equations and three variables) by elimination.

3 Solve linear systems (with three equations and three variables) in which some of the equations have missing terms.

4 Solve special systems.

A solution of an equation in three variables, such as

$$2x + 3y - z = 4, \quad \text{Linear equation in three variables}$$

is called an **ordered triple** and is written (x, y, z). For example, the ordered triple $(0, 1, -1)$ is a solution of the preceding equation, because

$$2(0) + 3(1) - (-1) = 4$$

is a true statement. Verify that another solution of this equation is $(10, -3, 7)$.

We now extend the term *linear equation* to equations of the form

$$Ax + By + Cz + \cdots + Dw = K,$$

where not all the coefficients $A, B, C, \ldots, D$ equal 0. For example,

$$2x + 3y - 5z = 7 \quad \text{and} \quad x - 2y - z + 3w = 8$$

are linear equations, the first with three variables and the second with four.

OBJECTIVE 1 **Understand the geometry of systems of three equations in three variables.** Consider the solution of a system such as the following.

$$\begin{aligned} 4x + 8y + z &= 2 \\ x + 7y - 3z &= -14 \qquad \text{System of linear equations in three variables} \\ 2x - 3y + 2z &= 3 \end{aligned}$$

Theoretically, a system of this type can be solved by graphing. However, the graph of a linear equation with three variables is a *plane,* not a line. Since visualizing a plane requires three-dimensional graphing, the method of graphing is not practical with these systems. However, it does illustrate the number of solutions possible for such systems, as shown in **FIGURE 10**.

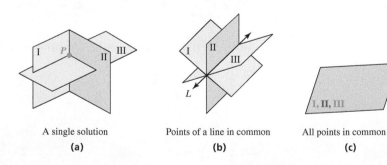

A single solution
(a)

Points of a line in common
(b)

All points in common
(c)

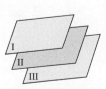

No points in common
(d)

No points in common
(e)

No points in common
(f)

No points in common
(g)

FIGURE 10

FIGURE 10 illustrates the following cases.

Graphs of Linear Systems in Three Variables

Case 1   **The three planes may meet at a single, common point** that is the solution of the system. See **FIGURE 10(a)**.

Case 2   **The three planes may have the points of a line in common,** so that the infinite set of points that satisfy the equation of the line is the solution of the system. See **FIGURE 10(b)**.

Case 3   **The three planes may coincide,** so that the solution of the system is the set of all points on a plane. See **FIGURE 10(c)**.

Case 4   **The planes may have no points common to all three,** so that there is no solution of the system. See **FIGURES 10(d)–(g)**.

OBJECTIVE 2 **Solve linear systems (with three equations and three variables) by elimination.** Since graphing to find the solution set of a system of three equations in three variables is impractical, these systems are solved with an extension of the elimination method from **Section 8.3.**

In the steps that follow, we use the term **focus variable** to identify the first variable to be eliminated in the process. The focus variable will always be present in the **working equation,** which will be used twice to eliminate this variable.

Solving a Linear System in Three Variables[*]

Step 1   **Select a variable and an equation.** A good choice for the variable, which we call the *focus variable,* is one that has coefficient 1 or −1. Then select an equation, one that contains the focus variable, as the *working equation*.

Step 2   **Eliminate the focus variable.** Use the working equation and one of the other two equations of the original system. The result is an equation in two variables.

Step 3   **Eliminate the focus variable again.** Use the working equation and the remaining equation of the original system. The result is another equation in two variables.

Step 4   **Write the equations in two variables that result from Steps 2 and 3 as a system, and solve it.** Doing this gives the values of two of the variables.

Step 5   **Find the value of the remaining variable.** Substitute the values of the two variables found in Step 4 into the working equation to obtain the value of the focus variable.

Step 6   **Check** the ordered-triple solution in *each* of the *original* equations of the system. Then write the solution set.

---

[*]The authors wish to thank Christine Heinecke Lehmann of Purdue University North Central for her suggestions here.

EXAMPLE 1 Solving a System in Three Variables

Solve the system.

$$4x + 8y + z = 2 \quad (1)$$
$$x + 7y - 3z = -14 \quad (2)$$
$$2x - 3y + 2z = 3 \quad (3)$$

Step 1 Since z in equation (1) has coefficient 1, we choose z as the focus variable and (1) as the working equation. (Another option would be to choose x as the focus variable, since it also has coefficient 1, and use (2) as the working equation.)

Focus variable
$$4x + 8y + z = 2 \quad (1) \leftarrow \text{Working equation}$$

Step 2 Multiply working equation (1) by 3 and add the result to equation (2) to eliminate focus variable z.

$$\begin{array}{ll} 12x + 24y + 3z = 6 & \text{Multiply each side of (1) by 3.} \\ \underline{x + 7y - 3z = -14} & (2) \\ 13x + 31y = -8 & \text{Add.} \quad (4) \end{array}$$

Step 3 Multiply working equation (1) by -2 and add the result to remaining equation (3) to again eliminate focus variable z.

$$\begin{array}{ll} -8x - 16y - 2z = -4 & \text{Multiply each side of (1) by } -2. \\ \underline{2x - 3y + 2z = 3} & (3) \\ -6x - 19y = -1 & \text{Add.} \quad (5) \end{array}$$

Step 4 Write the equations in two variables that result in Steps 2 and 3 as a system.

> Make sure these equations have the same variables.

$$13x + 31y = -8 \quad (4) \quad \text{The result from Step 2}$$
$$-6x - 19y = -1 \quad (5) \quad \text{The result from Step 3}$$

Now solve this system. We choose to eliminate x.

$$\begin{array}{ll} 78x + 186y = -48 & \text{Multiply each side of (4) by 6.} \\ \underline{-78x - 247y = -13} & \text{Multiply each side of (5) by 13.} \\ -61y = -61 & \text{Add.} \\ y = 1 & \text{Divide by } -61. \end{array}$$

Substitute 1 for y in either equation (4) or (5) to find x.

$$\begin{array}{ll} -6x - 19y = -1 & (5) \\ -6x - 19(1) = -1 & \text{Let } y = 1. \\ -6x - 19 = -1 & \text{Multiply.} \\ -6x = 18 & \text{Add 19.} \\ x = -3 & \text{Divide by } -6. \end{array}$$

Step 5 Now substitute the two values we found in Step 4 in working equation (1) to find the value of the remaining variable, focus variable z.

$$\begin{array}{ll} 4x + 8y + z = 2 & (1) \\ 4(-3) + 8(1) + z = 2 & \text{Let } x = -3 \text{ and } y = 1. \\ -4 + z = 2 & \text{Multiply, and then add.} \\ z = 6 & \text{Add 4.} \end{array}$$

NOW TRY
EXERCISE 1
Solve the system.

$$x - y + 2z = 1$$
$$3x + 2y + 7z = 8$$
$$-3x - 4y + 9z = -10$$

> Write the values of x, y, and z in the correct order.

Step 6 It appears that the ordered triple $(-3, 1, 6)$ is the only solution of the system. We must check that the solution satisfies all three original equations of the system. We begin with equation (1).

CHECK
$$4x + 8y + z = 2 \quad (1)$$
$$4(-3) + 8(1) + 6 \overset{?}{=} 2 \quad \text{Substitute.}$$
$$-12 + 8 + 6 \overset{?}{=} 2 \quad \text{Multiply.}$$
$$2 = 2 \ \checkmark \ \text{True}$$

In **Exercise 2** you are asked to show that $(-3, 1, 6)$ also satisfies equations (2) and (3). The solution set is $\{(-3, 1, 6)\}$.

NOW TRY

OBJECTIVE 3 **Solve linear systems (with three equations and three variables) in which some of the equations have missing terms.** If a linear system has an equation missing a term or terms, one elimination step can be omitted.

EXAMPLE 2 **Solving a System of Equations with Missing Terms**

Solve the system.

$$6x - 12y = -5 \quad (1) \quad \text{Missing } z$$
$$8y + z = 0 \quad (2) \quad \text{Missing } x$$
$$9x - z = 12 \quad (3) \quad \text{Missing } y$$

Since equation (3) is missing the variable y, one way to begin is to eliminate y again, using equations (1) and (2).

$$12x - 24y \qquad = -10 \quad \text{Multiply each side of (1) by 2.}$$

> Leave space for the missing term.

$$\underline{\qquad\ 24y + 3z = \quad 0} \quad \text{Multiply each side of (2) by 3.}$$
$$12x \qquad + 3z = -10 \quad \text{Add.} \quad (4)$$

Use the resulting equation (4) in x and z, together with equation (3), $9x - z = 12$, to eliminate z. Multiply equation (3) by 3.

$$27x - 3z = \quad 36 \qquad \text{Multiply each side of (3) by 3.}$$
$$\underline{12x + 3z = -10} \qquad (4)$$
$$39x \qquad = \quad 26 \qquad \text{Add.}$$

$$x = \frac{26}{39}, \quad \text{or} \quad \frac{2}{3} \qquad \text{Divide by 39; lowest terms}$$

We can find z by substituting this value for x in equation (3).

$$9x - z = 12 \qquad (3)$$
$$9\left(\frac{2}{3}\right) - z = 12 \qquad \text{Let } x = \tfrac{2}{3}.$$
$$6 - z = 12 \qquad \text{Multiply.}$$
$$z = -6 \qquad \text{Subtract 6. Multiply by } -1.$$

NOW TRY ANSWER
1. $\{(2, 1, 0)\}$

NOW TRY
EXERCISE 2

Solve the system.

$$3x - z = -10$$
$$4y + 5z = 24$$
$$x - 6y = -8$$

We can find y by substituting -6 for z in equation (2).

$$8y + z = 0 \qquad \text{(2)}$$
$$8y - 6 = 0 \qquad \text{Let } z = -6.$$
$$8y = 6 \qquad \text{Add 6.}$$
$$y = \frac{6}{8}, \ \text{ or } \ \frac{3}{4} \qquad \text{Divide by 8; lowest terms}$$

Check to verify that the solution set is $\left\{\left(\frac{2}{3}, \frac{3}{4}, -6\right)\right\}$. NOW TRY

OBJECTIVE 4 Solve special systems.

NOW TRY
EXERCISE 3

Solve the system.

$$x - 5y + 2z = 4$$
$$3x + y - z = 6$$
$$-2x + 10y - 4z = 7$$

EXAMPLE 3 Solving an Inconsistent System with Three Variables

Solve the system.

$$2x - 4y + 6z = 5 \qquad \text{(1)}$$
$$-x + 3y - 2z = -1 \qquad \text{(2)}$$
$$x - 2y + 3z = 1 \qquad \text{(3)}$$

> Use as the working equation, with focus variable x.

Eliminate the focus variable, x, using equations (1) and (3).

$$-2x + 4y - 6z = -2 \qquad \text{Multiply each side of (3) by } -2.$$
$$\underline{2x - 4y + 6z = \ \ 5} \qquad \text{(1)}$$
$$0 = \ \ 3 \qquad \text{Add; false}$$

The resulting false statement indicates that equations (1) and (3) have no common solution. Thus, the system is inconsistent and the solution set is $\varnothing$. The graph of this system would show the two planes parallel to one another. NOW TRY

NOTE If a false statement results when adding as in **Example 3,** it is not necessary to go any further with the solution. Since two of the three planes are parallel, it is not possible for the three planes to have any points in common.

NOW TRY
EXERCISE 4

Solve the system.

$$x - 3y + 2z = 10$$
$$-2x + 6y - 4z = -20$$
$$\frac{1}{2}x - \frac{3}{2}y + z = 5$$

EXAMPLE 4 Solving a System of Dependent Equations with Three Variables

Solve the system.

$$2x - 3y + 4z = 8 \qquad \text{(1)}$$
$$-x + \frac{3}{2}y - 2z = -4 \qquad \text{(2)}$$
$$6x - 9y + 12z = 24 \qquad \text{(3)}$$

Multiplying each side of equation (1) by 3 gives equation (3). Multiplying each side of equation (2) by -6 also gives equation (3). Because of this, the equations are dependent. All three equations have the same graph, as illustrated in **FIGURE 10(c).** The solution set is written as follows.

$$\{(x, y, z) \mid 2x - 3y + 4z = 8\} \qquad \text{Set-builder notation}$$

NOW TRY ANSWERS
2. $\{(-2, 1, 4)\}$
3. $\varnothing$
4. $\{(x, y, z) \mid x - 3y + 2z = 10\}$

Although any one of the three equations could be used to write the solution set, we use the equation in standard form with coefficients that are integers with greatest common factor 1, as we did in **Section 8.1.** NOW TRY

⌐ *NOW TRY*
  EXERCISE 5
Solve the system.

$$x - 3y + 2z = 4$$

$$\frac{1}{3}x - y + \frac{2}{3}z = 7$$

$$\frac{1}{2}x - \frac{3}{2}y + z = 2$$

EXAMPLE 5 Solving Another Special System

Solve the system.

$$2x - y + 3z = 6 \quad (1)$$

$$x - \frac{1}{2}y + \frac{3}{2}z = 3 \quad (2)$$

$$4x - 2y + 6z = 1 \quad (3)$$

Multiplying each side of equation (2) by 2 gives equation (1), so these two equations are dependent. Equations (1) and (3) are not equivalent, however. Multiplying equation (3) by $\frac{1}{2}$ does *not* give equation (1). Instead, we obtain two equations with the same coefficients, but with different constant terms.

The graphs of equations (1) and (3) have no points in common (that is, the planes are parallel). Thus, the system is inconsistent and the solution set is $\emptyset$, as illustrated in **FIGURE 10(g)**.   *NOW TRY* ⌐

NOW TRY ANSWER
5. $\emptyset$

8.4 EXERCISES

MyMathLab Math XL PRACTICE   WATCH   DOWNLOAD READ   REVIEW

1. *Concept Check* The two equations $\begin{aligned} x + y + z &= 6 \\ 2x - y + z &= 3 \end{aligned}$ have a common solution of $(1, 2, 3)$. Which equation would complete a system of three linear equations in three variables having solution set $\{(1, 2, 3)\}$?

A. $3x + 2y - z = 1$ **B.** $3x + 2y - z = 4$

C. $3x + 2y - z = 5$ **D.** $3x + 2y - z = 6$

2. Complete the work of **Example 1** and show that the ordered triple $(-3, 1, 6)$ is also a solution of equations (2) and (3).

$$x + 7y - 3z = -14 \qquad \text{Equation (2)}$$

$$2x - 3y + 2z = 3 \qquad \text{Equation (3)}$$

Solve each system of equations. ***See Example 1.***

🌐 **3.** $\begin{aligned} 2x - 5y + 3z &= -1 \\ x + 4y - 2z &= 9 \\ x - 2y - 4z &= -5 \end{aligned}$ **4.** $\begin{aligned} x + 3y - 6z &= 7 \\ 2x - y + z &= 1 \\ x + 2y + 2z &= -1 \end{aligned}$ **5.** $\begin{aligned} 3x + 2y + z &= 8 \\ 2x - 3y + 2z &= -16 \\ x + 4y - z &= 20 \end{aligned}$

6. $\begin{aligned} -3x + y - z &= -10 \\ -4x + 2y + 3z &= -1 \\ 2x + 3y - 2z &= -5 \end{aligned}$ **7.** $\begin{aligned} 2x + 5y + 2z &= 0 \\ 4x - 7y - 3z &= 1 \\ 3x - 8y - 2z &= -6 \end{aligned}$ **8.** $\begin{aligned} 5x - 2y + 3z &= -9 \\ 4x + 3y + 5z &= 4 \\ 2x + 4y - 2z &= 14 \end{aligned}$

9. $\begin{aligned} x + 2y + z &= 4 \\ 2x + y - z &= -1 \\ x - y - z &= -2 \end{aligned}$ **10.** $\begin{aligned} x - 2y + 5z &= -7 \\ -2x - 3y + 4z &= -14 \\ -3x + 5y - z &= -7 \end{aligned}$ **11.** $\begin{aligned} -x + 2y + 6z &= 2 \\ 3x + 2y + 6z &= 6 \\ x + 4y - 3z &= 1 \end{aligned}$

12. $\begin{aligned} 2x + y + 2z &= 1 \\ x + 2y + z &= 2 \\ x - y - z &= 0 \end{aligned}$ **13.** $\begin{aligned} x + y - z &= -2 \\ 2x - y + z &= -5 \\ -x + 2y - 3z &= -4 \end{aligned}$ **14.** $\begin{aligned} x + 2y + 3z &= 1 \\ -x - y + 3z &= 2 \\ -6x + y + z &= -2 \end{aligned}$

15. $\dfrac{1}{3}x + \dfrac{1}{6}y - \dfrac{2}{3}z = -1$

$-\dfrac{3}{4}x - \dfrac{1}{3}y - \dfrac{1}{4}z = 3$

$\dfrac{1}{2}x + \dfrac{3}{2}y + \dfrac{3}{4}z = 21$

16. $\dfrac{2}{3}x - \dfrac{1}{4}y + \dfrac{5}{8}z = 0$

$\dfrac{1}{5}x + \dfrac{2}{3}y - \dfrac{1}{4}z = -7$

$-\dfrac{3}{5}x + \dfrac{4}{3}y - \dfrac{7}{8}z = -5$

17. $5.5x - 2.5y + 1.6z = 11.83$
$2.2x + 5.0y - 0.1z = -5.97$
$3.3x - 7.5y + 3.2z = 21.25$

18. $6.2x - 1.4y + 2.4z = -1.80$
$3.1x + 2.8y - 0.2z = 5.68$
$9.3x - 8.4y - 4.8z = -34.20$

Solve each system of equations. ***See Example 2.***

19. $2x - 3y + 2z = -1$
$x + 2y + z = 17$
$2y - z = 7$

20. $2x - y + 3z = 6$
$x + 2y - z = 8$
$2y + z = 1$

21. $4x + 2y - 3z = 6$
$x - 4y + z = -4$
$-x + 2z = 2$

22. $2x + 3y - 4z = 4$
$x - 6y + z = -16$
$-x + 3z = 8$

23. $2x + y = 6$
$3y - 2z = -4$
$3x - 5z = -7$

24. $4x - 8y = -7$
$4y + z = 7$
$-8x + z = -4$

25. $-5x + 2y + z = 5$
$-3x - 2y - z = 3$
$-x + 6y = 1$

26. $-4x + 3y - z = 4$
$-5x - 3y + z = -4$
$-2x - 3z = 12$

27. $7x - 3z = -34$
$2y + 4z = 20$
$\dfrac{3}{4}x + \dfrac{1}{6}y = -2$

28. $5x - 2z = 8$
$4y + 3z = -9$
$\dfrac{1}{2}x + \dfrac{2}{3}y = -1$

29. $4x - z = -6$
$\dfrac{3}{5}y + \dfrac{1}{2}z = 0$
$\dfrac{1}{3}x + \dfrac{2}{3}z = -5$

30. $5x - z = 38$
$\dfrac{2}{3}y + \dfrac{1}{4}z = -17$
$\dfrac{1}{5}y + \dfrac{5}{6}z = 4$

Solve each system of equations. If the system is inconsistent or has dependent equations, say so. ***See Examples 1, 3, 4, and 5.***

31. $2x + 2y - 6z = 5$
$-3x + y - z = -2$
$-x - y + 3z = 4$

32. $-2x + 5y + z = -3$
$5x + 14y - z = -11$
$7x + 9y - 2z = -5$

33. $-5x + 5y - 20z = -40$
$x - y + 4z = 8$
$3x - 3y + 12z = 24$

34. $x + 4y - z = 3$
$-2x - 8y + 2z = -6$
$3x + 12y - 3z = 9$

35. $x + 5y - 2z = -1$
$-2x + 8y + z = -4$
$3x - y + 5z = 19$

36. $x + 3y + z = 2$
$4x + y + 2z = -4$
$5x + 2y + 3z = -2$

37. $2x + y - z = 6$
$4x + 2y - 2z = 12$
$-x - \dfrac{1}{2}y + \dfrac{1}{2}z = -3$

38. $2x - 8y + 2z = -10$
$-x + 4y - z = 5$
$\dfrac{1}{8}x - \dfrac{1}{2}y + \dfrac{1}{8}z = -\dfrac{5}{8}$

39. $x + y - 2z = 0$
$3x - y + z = 0$
$4x + 2y - z = 0$

40. $2x + 3y - z = 0$
$x - 4y + 2z = 0$
$3x - 5y - z = 0$

41. $x - 2y + \dfrac{1}{3}z = 4$

$3x - 6y + z = 12$

$-6x + 12y - 2z = -3$

42. $4x + y - 2z = 3$

$x + \dfrac{1}{4}y - \dfrac{1}{2}z = \dfrac{3}{4}$

$2x + \dfrac{1}{2}y - z = 1$

Brain Busters *Extend the method of this section to solve each system. Express the solution in the form (x, y, z, w).*

43.
$$x + y + z - w = 5$$
$$2x + y - z + w = 3$$
$$x - 2y + 3z + w = 18$$
$$-x - y + z + 2w = 8$$

44.
$$3x + y - z + 2w = 9$$
$$x + y + 2z - w = 10$$
$$x - y - z + 3w = -2$$
$$-x + y - z + w = -6$$

45.
$$3x + y - z + w = -3$$
$$2x + 4y + z - w = -7$$
$$-2x + 3y - 5z + w = 3$$
$$5x + 4y - 5z + 2w = -7$$

46.
$$x - 3y + 7z + w = 11$$
$$2x + 4y + 6z - 3w = -3$$
$$3x + 2y + z + 2w = 19$$
$$4x + y - 3z + w = 22$$

PREVIEW EXERCISES

Solve each problem. ***See Sections 2.4 and 2.7.***

47. The perimeter of a triangle is 323 in. The shortest side measures five-sixths the length of the longest side, and the medium side measures 17 in. less than the longest side. Find the lengths of the sides of the triangle.

48. The sum of the three angles of a triangle is 180°. The largest angle is twice the measure of the smallest, and the third angle measures 10° less than the largest. Find the measures of the three angles.

49. The sum of three numbers is 16. The greatest number is -3 times the least, while the middle number is four less than the greatest. Find the three numbers.

50. Witny Librun has a collection of pennies, dimes, and quarters. The number of dimes is one less than twice the number of pennies. If there are 27 coins in all worth a total of $4.20, how many of each denomination of coin is in the collection?

8.5 Applications of Systems of Linear Equations

OBJECTIVES

1 Solve geometry problems by using two variables.

2 Solve money problems by using two variables.

3 Solve mixture problems by using two variables.

4 Solve distance-rate-time problems by using two variables.

5 Solve problems with three variables by using a system of three equations.

Although some problems with two unknowns can be solved by using just one variable, it is often easier to use two variables and a system of equations. The following problem, which can be solved with a system, appeared in a Hindu work that dates back to about A.D. 850. (See **Exercise 35.**)

The mixed price of 9 citrons (a lemonlike fruit) and 7 fragrant wood apples is 107; again, the mixed price of 7 citrons and 9 fragrant wood apples is 101. O you arithmetician, tell me quickly the price of a citron and the price of a wood apple here, having distinctly separated those prices well.

PROBLEM-SOLVING HINT

When solving an applied problem using two variables, it is a good idea to pick letters that correspond to the descriptions of the unknown quantities. In the example above, we could choose c to represent the number of citrons, and w to represent the number of wood apples.

The following steps are based on the problem-solving method of **Section 2.4.**

Solving an Applied Problem by Writing a System of Equations

Step 1 **Read** the problem, several times if necessary. What information is given? What is to be found? This is often stated in the last sentence.

Step 2 **Assign variables** to represent the unknown values. Use a sketch, diagram, or table, as needed.

Step 3 **Write a system of equations** using the variable expressions.

Step 4 **Solve** the system of equations.

Step 5 **State the answer** to the problem. Label it appropriately. Does it seem reasonable?

Step 6 **Check** the answer in the words of the *original* problem.

OBJECTIVE 1 Solve geometry problems by using two variables.

EXAMPLE 1 Finding the Dimensions of a Soccer Field

A rectangular soccer field may have a width between 50 and 100 yd and a length between 100 and 130 yd. One particular soccer field has a perimeter of 320 yd. Its length measures 40 yd more than its width. What are the dimensions of this field? (*Source:* www.soccer-training-guide.com)

Step 1 **Read** the problem again. We are asked to find the dimensions of the field.

Step 2 **Assign variables.** Let L = the length and W = the width. See **FIGURE 11**.

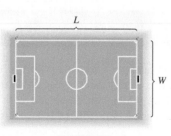

FIGURE 11

Step 3 **Write a system of equations.** Because the perimeter is 320 yd, we find one equation by using the perimeter formula.

$$2L + 2W = 320 \qquad 2L + 2W = P$$

We write a second equation using the fact that the length is 40 yd more than the width.

$$L = W + 40$$

These two equations form a system of equations.

$$2L + 2W = 320 \qquad (1)$$
$$L = W + 40 \qquad (2)$$

NOW TRY
EXERCISE 1

A rectangular parking lot has a length that is 10 ft more than twice its width. The perimeter of the parking lot is 620 ft. What are the dimensions of the parking lot?

Step 4   **Solve** the system of equations. Since equation (2), $L = W + 40$, is solved for L, we can substitute $W + 40$ for L in equation (1) and solve for W.

$$2L + 2W = 320 \qquad (1)$$
$$2(W + 40) + 2W = 320 \qquad \text{Let } L = W + 40.$$
$$2W + 80 + 2W = 320 \qquad \text{Distributive property}$$
$$4W + 80 = 320 \qquad \text{Combine like terms.}$$
$$4W = 240 \qquad \text{Subtract 80.}$$
$$W = 60 \qquad \text{Divide by 4.}$$

Be sure to use parentheses around $W + 40$.

Don't stop here.

Let $W = 60$ in the equation $L = W + 40$ to find L.

$$L = 60 + 40 = 100$$

Step 5   **State the answer.** The length is 100 yd, and the width is 60 yd. Both dimensions are within the ranges given in the problem.

Step 6   **Check.** Calculate the perimeter and the difference between the length and the width.

$$2(100) + 2(60) = 320 \qquad \text{The perimeter is 320 yd, as required.}$$
$$100 - 60 = 40 \qquad \text{Length is 40 yd more than width, as required.}$$

The answer is correct.

NOW TRY

OBJECTIVE 2   **Solve money problems by using two variables.**

EXAMPLE 2   Solving a Problem about Ticket Prices

For the 2008–2009 National Hockey League and National Basketball Association seasons, two hockey tickets and one basketball ticket purchased at their average prices would have cost $148.79. One hockey ticket and two basketball tickets would have cost $148.60. What were the average ticket prices for the two sports? (*Source:* Team Marketing Report.)

Step 1   **Read** the problem again. There are two unknowns.

Step 2   **Assign variables.**

Let h = the average price for a hockey ticket

and b = the average price for a basketball ticket.

Step 3   **Write a system of equations.** Because two hockey tickets and one basketball ticket cost a total of $148.79, one equation for the system is

$$2h + b = 148.79.$$

By similar reasoning, the second equation is

$$h + 2b = 148.60.$$

These two equations form a system of equations.

$$2h + b = 148.79 \qquad (1)$$
$$h + 2b = 148.60 \qquad (2)$$

⌐NOW TRY
↳EXERCISE 2
For the 2009–2010 season at Six Flags St. Louis, two general admission tickets and three tickets for children under 48 in. tall cost $172.98. One general admission ticket and four tickets for children under 48 in. tall cost $163.99. Determine the ticket prices for general admission and for children under 48 in. tall. (*Source:* www.sixflags.com)

Step 4   **Solve** the system. To eliminate h, multiply equation (2), $h + 2b = 148.60$, by -2 and add.

$$2h + b = 148.79 \quad (1)$$
$$\underline{-2h - 4b = -297.20} \quad \text{Multiply each side of (2) by } -2.$$
$$-3b = -148.41 \quad \text{Add.}$$
$$b = 49.47 \quad \text{Divide by } -3.$$

To find the value of h, let $b = 49.47$ in equation (2).

$$h + 2b = 148.60 \quad (2)$$
$$h + 2(49.47) = 148.60 \quad \text{Let } b = 49.47.$$
$$h + 98.94 = 148.60 \quad \text{Multiply.}$$
$$h = 49.66 \quad \text{Subtract 98.94.}$$

Step 5   **State the answer.** The average price for one basketball ticket was $49.47. For one hockey ticket, the average price was $49.66.

Step 6   **Check** that these values satisfy the conditions stated in the problem.

NOW TRY ↻

OBJECTIVE 3 **Solve mixture problems by using two variables.** We solved mixture problems in **Section 2.7** using one variable. Many mixture problems can also be solved using more than one variable and a system of equations.

EXAMPLE 3 Solving a Mixture Problem

How many ounces each of 5% hydrochloric acid and 20% hydrochloric acid must be combined to get 10 oz of solution that is 12.5% hydrochloric acid?

Step 1   **Read** the problem. Two solutions of different strengths are being mixed together to get a specific amount of a solution with an "in-between" strength.

Step 2   **Assign variables.**

Let $x =$ the number of ounces of 5% solution

and $y =$ the number of ounces of 20% solution.

Use a table to summarize the information from the problem.

Ounces of Solution	Percent (as a decimal)	Ounces of Pure Acid
x	5% = 0.05	0.05x
y	20% = 0.20	0.20y
10	12.5% = 0.125	(0.125)10

⎵ Gives equation (1)   ⎵ Gives equation (2)

Multiply the amount of each solution (given in the first column) by its concentration of acid (given in the second column) to find the amount of acid in that solution (given in the third column).

FIGURE 12 illustrates what is happening in the problem.

Ounces of solution			
x	+ y	= 10	→ Gives equation (1)
Ounces of pure acid 0.05x	0.20y	0.125(10)	→ Gives equation (2)

FIGURE 12

NOW TRY ANSWER
2. general admission: $39.99; children under 48 in. tall: $31.00

NOW TRY
EXERCISE 3
How many liters each of a 15% acid solution and a 25% acid solution should be mixed to get 30 L of an 18% acid solution?

Step 3 **Write a system of equations.** When the x ounces of 5% solution and the y ounces of 20% solution are combined, the total number of ounces is 10, giving the following equation.

$$x + y = 10 \quad (1)$$

The number of ounces of acid in the 5% solution $(0.05x)$ plus the number of ounces of acid in the 20% solution $(0.20y)$ should equal the total number of ounces of acid in the mixture, which is $(0.125)10$, or 1.25.

$$0.05x + 0.20y = 1.25 \quad (2)$$

Notice that these equations can be quickly determined by reading down the table or using the labels in FIGURE 12.

Step 4 **Solve** the system of equations (1) and (2) by eliminating x.

$$
\begin{array}{ll}
-5x - 5y = -50 & \text{Multiply each side of (1) by } -5. \\
\underline{5x + 20y = 125} & \text{Multiply each side of (2) by 100.} \\
15y = 75 & \text{Add.} \\
y = 5 & \text{Divide by 15.}
\end{array}
$$

Substitute $y = 5$ in equation (1) to find that x is also 5.

Step 5 **State the answer.** The desired mixture will require 5 oz of the 5% solution and 5 oz of the 20% solution.

Step 6 **Check.**

Total amount of solution: $\quad x + y = 5 \text{ oz} + 5 \text{ oz}$
$$= 10 \text{ oz}, \quad \text{as required.}$$

Total amount of acid: $\quad$ 5% of 5 oz + 20% of 5 oz
$$= 0.05(5) + 0.20(5)$$
$$= 1.25 \text{ oz}$$

Percent of acid in solution:

Total acid $\longrightarrow$ $\dfrac{1.25}{10} = 0.125$, or 12.5%, as required.
Total solution $\longrightarrow$

NOW TRY

OBJECTIVE 4 **Solve distance-rate-time problems by using two variables.** Motion problems require the distance formula $d = rt$, where d is distance, r is rate (or speed), and t is time.

EXAMPLE 4 Solving a Motion Problem

A car travels 250 km in the same time that a truck travels 225 km. If the rate of the car is 8 km per hr faster than the rate of the truck, find both rates.

Step 1 **Read** the problem again. Given the distances traveled, we need to find the rate of each vehicle.

Step 2 **Assign variables.**

$$\text{Let } x = \text{the rate of the car,}$$
$$\text{and } y = \text{the rate of the truck.}$$

NOW TRY ANSWER
3. 9 L of the 25% acid solution; 21 L of the 15% acid solution

NOW TRY
EXERCISE 4
Vann and Ivy Sample are planning a bicycle ride to raise money for cancer research. Vann can travel 50 mi in the same amount of time that Ivy can travel 40 mi. Determine both bicyclists' rates, if Vann's rate is 2 mph faster than Ivy's.

As in **Example 3,** a table helps organize the information. Fill in the distance for each vehicle, and the variables for the unknown rates.

	d	r	t
Car	250	x	$\frac{250}{x}$
Truck	225	y	$\frac{225}{y}$

To find the expressions for time, we solved the distance formula $d = rt$ for t. Thus, $\frac{d}{r} = t$.

Step 3 **Write a system of equations.** The car travels 8 km per hr faster than the truck. Since the two rates are x and y,
$$x = y + 8. \quad (1)$$
Both vehicles travel for the *same* time, so the times must be equal.

Time for car $\longrightarrow \dfrac{250}{x} = \dfrac{225}{y} \longleftarrow$ Time for truck

This is not a linear equation. However, multiplying each side by xy gives
$$250y = 225x, \quad (2)$$
which is linear. The system to solve consists of equations (1) and (2).
$$x = y + 8 \quad (1)$$
$$250y = 225x \quad (2)$$

Step 4 **Solve** the system by substitution. Replace x with $y + 8$ in equation (2).

$$250y = 225x \quad (2)$$
$$250y = 225(y + 8) \quad \text{Let } x = y + 8.$$

Be sure to use parentheses around $y + 8$.

$$250y = 225y + 1800 \quad \text{Distributive property}$$
$$25y = 1800 \quad \text{Subtract } 225y.$$
$$y = 72 \quad \text{Divide by 25.}$$

Because $x = y + 8$, the value of x is $72 + 8 = 80$.

Step 5 **State the answer.** The rate of the car is 80 km per hr, and the rate of the truck is 72 km per hr.

Step 6 **Check.**

$$Car: \quad t = \frac{d}{r} = \frac{250}{80} = 3.125$$
$$Truck: \quad t = \frac{d}{r} = \frac{225}{72} = 3.125$$
Times are equal.

Since 80 is 8 greater than 72, the conditions of the problem are satisfied.

NOW TRY

OBJECTIVE 5 **Solve problems with three variables by using a system of three equations.**

PROBLEM-SOLVING HINT

If an application requires finding *three* unknown quantities, we can use a system of *three* equations to solve it. We extend the method used for two unknowns.

NOW TRY ANSWER
4. Vann: 10 mph; Ivy: 8 mph

NOW TRY
EXERCISE 5

At a concession stand, a bottle of Gatorade costs $2.00, a pretzel costs $1.50, and candy items cost $1.00. Workers sold four times as many pretzels as candy items. The number of Gatorades sold exceeded the number of pretzels sold by 310. Sales for these items totaled $1520. How many of each item was sold?

EXAMPLE 5 Solving a Problem Involving Prices

At Panera Bread, a loaf of honey wheat bread costs $2.95, a loaf of sunflower bread costs $2.99, and a loaf of French bread costs $5.79. On a recent day, three times as many loaves of honey wheat bread were sold as sunflower bread. The number of loaves of French bread sold was 5 less than the number of loaves of honey wheat bread sold. Total receipts for these breads were $87.89. How many loaves of each type of bread were sold? (*Source:* Panera Bread menu.)

Step 1 **Read** the problem again. There are three unknowns in this problem.

Step 2 **Assign variables** to represent the three unknowns.

Let x = the number of loaves of honey wheat bread,

y = the number of loaves of sunflower bread,

and z = the number of loaves of French bread.

Step 3 **Write a system of three equations.** Since three times as many loaves of honey wheat bread were sold as sunflower bread,

$$x = 3y, \quad \text{or} \quad x - 3y = 0. \quad \text{Subtract } 3y. \quad (1)$$

Also, we have the information needed for another equation.

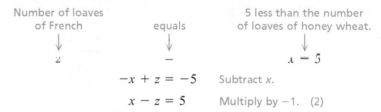

Number of loaves of French	equals	5 less than the number of loaves of honey wheat.
↓	↓	↓
z	$-$	$x - 5$

$$-x + z = -5 \qquad \text{Subtract } x.$$
$$x - z = 5 \qquad \text{Multiply by } -1. \quad (2)$$

Multiplying the cost of a loaf of each kind of bread by the number of loaves of that kind sold and adding gives the total receipts.

$$2.95x + 2.99y + 5.79z = 87.89$$

Multiply each side of this equation by 100 to clear it of decimals.

$$295x + 299y + 579z = 8789 \qquad (3)$$

Step 4 **Solve** the system of three equations.

$$x - 3y = 0 \qquad (1)$$
$$x - z = 5 \qquad (2)$$
$$295x + 299y + 579z = 8789 \qquad (3)$$

Using the method shown in **Section 8.4,** we will find that $x = 12$, $y = 4$, and $z = 7$.

Step 5 **State the answer.** The solution set is $\{(12, 4, 7)\}$, meaning that 12 loaves of honey wheat bread, 4 loaves of sunflower bread, and 7 loaves of French bread were sold.

Step 6 **Check.** Since $12 = 3 \cdot 4$, the number of loaves of honey wheat bread is three times the number of loaves of sunflower bread. Also, $12 - 7 = 5$, so the number of loaves of French bread is 5 less than the number of loaves of honey wheat bread. Multiply the appropriate cost per loaf by the number of loaves sold and add the results to check that total receipts were $87.89. *NOW TRY*

NOW TRY ANSWER
5. 60 candy items, 240 pretzels, 550 bottles of Gatorade

NOW TRY
EXERCISE 6

Katherine has a quilting shop and makes three kinds of quilts: the lone star quilt, the bandana quilt, and the log cabin quilt.

- Each lone star quilt requires 8 hr of piecework, 4 hr of machine quilting, and 2 hr of finishing.

- Each bandana quilt requires 2 hr of piecework, 2 hr of machine quilting, and 2 hr of finishing.

- Each log cabin quilt requires 10 hr of piecework, 5 hr of machine quilting, and 2 hr of finishing.

Katherine allocates 74 hr for piecework, 42 hr for machine quilting, and 24 hr for finishing quilts each month. How many of each type of quilt should be made each month if all available time must be used?

NOW TRY ANSWER

6. lone star quilts: 3;
   bandana quilts: 5;
   log cabin quilts: 4

EXAMPLE 6 Solving a Business Production Problem

A company produces three flat screen television sets: models X, Y, and Z.

- Each model X set requires 2 hr of electronics work, 2 hr of assembly time, and 1 hr of finishing time.
- Each model Y requires 1 hr of electronics work, 3 hr of assembly time, and 1 hr of finishing time.
- Each model Z requires 3 hr of electronics work, 2 hr of assembly time, and 2 hr of finishing time.

There are 100 hr available for electronics, 100 hr available for assembly, and 65 hr available for finishing per week. How many of each model should be produced each week if all available time must be used?

Step 1 **Read** the problem again. There are three unknowns.

Step 2 **Assign variables.** Then organize the information in a table.

Let x = the number of model X produced per week,

y = the number of model Y produced per week,

and z = the number of model Z produced per week.

	Each Model X	Each Model Y	Each Model Z	Totals
Hours of Electronics Work	2	1	3	100
Hours of Assembly Time	2	3	2	100
Hours of Finishing Time	1	1	2	65

Step 3 **Write a system of three equations.** The x model X sets require $2x$ hours of electronics, the y model Y sets require $1y$ (or y) hours of electronics, and the z model Z sets require $3z$ hours of electronics. Since 100 hr are available for electronics, we write the first equation.

$$2x + y + 3z = 100 \quad (1)$$

Since 100 hr are available for assembly, we can write another equation.

$$2x + 3y + 2z = 100 \quad (2)$$

The fact that 65 hr are available for finishing leads to this equation.

$$x + y + 2z = 65 \quad (3)$$

Notice that by reading across the table, we can easily determine the coefficients and constants in the equations of the system.

Step 4 **Solve** the system of equations (1), (2), and (3).

$$2x + y + 3z = 100 \quad (1)$$
$$2x + 3y + 2z = 100 \quad (2)$$
$$x + y + 2z = 65 \quad (3)$$

We find that $x = 15$, $y = 10$, and $z = 20$.

Step 5 **State the answer.** The company should produce 15 model X, 10 model Y, and 20 model Z sets per week.

Step 6 **Check** that these values satisfy the conditions of the problem. NOW TRY

8.5 EXERCISES

 MyMathLab Math XL PRACTICE WATCH DOWNLOAD READ REVIEW

⊙ *Complete solution available on the Video Resources on DVD*

Solve each problem. ***See Example 1.***

1. During the 2009 Major League Baseball season, the Los Angeles Dodgers played 162 games. They won 28 more games than they lost. What was their win-loss record that year?

2. Refer to **Exercise 1.** During the same 162-game season, the Arizona Diamondbacks lost 22 more games than they won. What was the team's win-loss record?

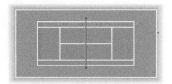

Team	W	L
L.A. Dodgers	——	——
Colorado	92	70
San Francisco	88	74
San Diego	75	87
Arizona	——	——

Source: World Almanac and Book of Facts.

⊙ 3. Venus and Serena measured a tennis court and found that it was 42 ft longer than it was wide and had a perimeter of 228 ft. What were the length and the width of the tennis court?

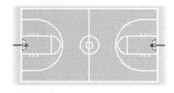

4. LeBron and Shaq measured a basketball court and found that the width of the court was 44 ft less than the length. If the perimeter was 288 ft, what were the length and the width of the basketball court?

5. In 2009, the two American telecommunication companies with the greatest revenues were AT&T and Verizon. The two companies had combined revenues of \$221.4 billion. AT&T's revenue was \$26.6 more than that of Verizon. What was the revenue for each company? (*Source: Fortune* magazine.)

6. In 2008, U.S. exports to Canada were \$110 billion more than exports to Mexico. Together, exports to these two countries totaled \$412 billion. How much were exports to each country? (*Source:* U.S. Census Bureau.)

In Exercises 7 and 8, find the measures of the angles marked x and y. Remember that **(1)** *the sum of the measures of the angles of a triangle is* 180°, **(2)** *supplementary angles have a sum of* 180°, *and* **(3)** *vertical angles have equal measures.*

7.

8.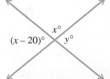

The Fan Cost Index (FCI) represents the cost of four average-price tickets, four small soft drinks, two small beers, four hot dogs, parking for one car, two game programs, and two souvenir caps to a sporting event. (*Source:* Team Marketing Report.)
 Use the concept of FCI in Exercises 9 and 10.
See Example 2.

9. For the 2008–2009 season, the FCI prices for the National Hockey League and the National Basketball Association totaled \$580.16. The hockey FCI was \$3.70 less than that of basketball. What were the FCIs for these sports?

10. In 2009, the FCI prices for Major League Baseball and the National Football League totaled $609.53. The football FCI was $215.75 more than that of baseball. What were the FCIs for these sports?

Solve each problem. **See Example 2.**

11. Andrew McGinnis works at Arby's. During one particular day he sold 15 Junior Roast Beef sandwiches and 10 Big Montana sandwiches, totaling $75.25. Another day he sold 30 Junior Roast Beef sandwiches and 5 Big Montana sandwiches, totaling $84.65. How much did each type of sandwich cost? (*Source:* Arby's menu.)

12. New York City and Washington, D.C., were the two most expensive cities for business travel in 2009. On the basis of the average total costs per day for each city (which include a hotel room, car rental, and three meals), 2 days in New York and 3 days in Washington cost $2772, while 4 days in New York and 2 days in Washington cost $3488. What was the average cost per day in each city? (*Source: Business Travel News.*)

Concept Check *The formulas $p = br$ (percentage = base × rate) and $I = prt$ (simple interest = principal × rate × time) are used in the applications in* **Exercises 17–24.** *To prepare to use these formulas, answer the questions in Exercises 13 and 14.*

13. If a container of liquid contains 60 oz of solution, what is the number of ounces of pure acid if the given solution contains the following acid concentrations?

    (a) 10%   **(b)** 25%   **(c)** 40%   **(d)** 50%

14. If $5000 is invested in an account paying simple annual interest, how much interest will be earned during the first year at the following rates?

    (a) 2%   **(b)** 3%   **(c)** 4%   **(d)** 3.5%

15. *Concept Check* If 1 pound of turkey costs $2.29, give an expression for the cost of x pounds.

16. *Concept Check* If 1 ticket to the movie *Avatar* costs $9 and y tickets are sold, give an expression for the amount collected from the sale.

Solve each problem. **See Example 3.**

🌐 17. How many gallons each of 25% alcohol and 35% alcohol should be mixed to get 20 gal of 32% alcohol?

18. How many liters each of 15% acid and 33% acid should be mixed to get 120 L of 21% acid?

Gallons of Solution	Percent (as a decimal)	Gallons of Pure Alcohol
x	25% = 0.25	
y	35% = 0.35	
20	32% =	

Liters of Solution	Percent (as a decimal)	Liters of Pure Acid
x	15% = 0.15	
y	33% =	
120	21% =	

19. Pure acid is to be added to a 10% acid solution to obtain 54 L of a 20% acid solution. What amounts of each should be used?

20. A truck radiator holds 36 L of fluid. How much pure antifreeze must be added to a mixture that is 4% antifreeze to fill the radiator with a mixture that is 20% antifreeze?

21. A party mix is made by adding nuts that sell for $2.50 per kg to a cereal mixture that sells for $1 per kg. How much of each should be added to get 30 kg of a mix that will sell for $1.70 per kg?

	Number of Kilograms	Price per Kilogram	Value
Nuts	x	2.50	
Cereal	y	1.00	
Mixture		1.70	

22. A fruit drink is made by mixing fruit juices. Such a drink with 50% juice is to be mixed with another drink that is 30% juice to get 200 L of a drink that is 45% juice. How much of each should be used?

	Liters of Drink	Percent (as a decimal)	Liters of Pure Juice
50% Juice	x	0.50	
30% Juice	y	0.30	
Mixture		0.45	

23. A total of $3000 is invested, part at 2% simple interest and part at 4%. If the total annual return from the two investments is $100, how much is invested at each rate?

Principal	Rate (as a decimal)	Interest
x	0.02	0.02x
y	0.04	0.04y
3000	✕✕✕✕✕	100

24. An investor will invest a total of $15,000 in two accounts, one paying 4% annual simple interest and the other 3%. If he wants to earn $550 annual interest, how much should he invest at each rate?

Principal	Rate (as a decimal)	Interest
x	0.04	
y	0.03	
15,000	✕✕✕✕✕	

Concept Check *The formula d = rt (distance = rate × time) is used in the applications in* **Exercises 27–30.** *To prepare to use this formula, work Exercises 25 and 26.*

25. If the rate of a boat in still water is 10 mph, and the rate of the current of a river is *x* mph, what is the rate of the boat

(a) going upstream (that is, against the current, which slows the boat down);

(b) going downstream (that is, with the current, which speeds the boat up)?

Upstream (against the current)

Downstream (with the current)

26. If the rate of a killer whale is 25 mph and the whale swims for *y* hours, give an expression for the number of miles the whale travels.

Solve each problem. ***See Example 4.***

🌐 **27.** A train travels 150 km in the same time that a plane covers 400 km. If the rate of the plane is 20 km per hr less than 3 times the rate of the train, find both rates.

	r	t	d
Train	x		150
Plane	y		400

28. A freight train and an express train leave towns 390 km apart, traveling toward one another. The freight train travels 30 km per hr slower than the express train. They pass one another 3 hr later. What are their rates?

	r	t	d
Freight Train	x	3	
Express Train	y	3	

29. In his motorboat, Bill Ruhberg travels upstream at top speed to his favorite fishing spot, a distance of 36 mi, in 2 hr. Returning, he finds that the trip downstream, still at top speed, takes only 1.5 hr. Find the rate of Bill's boat and the rate of the current. Let x = the rate of the boat and y = the rate of the current.

	r	t	d
Upstream	$x - y$	2	
Downstream	$x + y$		

30. Traveling for 3 hr into a steady head wind, a plane flies 1650 mi. The pilot determines that flying *with* the same wind for 2 hr, he could make a trip of 1300 mi. Find the rate of the plane and the wind speed.

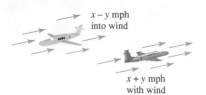

$x - y$ mph into wind

$x + y$ mph with wind

Solve each problem by using two variables. **See Examples 1–4.**

31. (See the Chapter Introduction.) How many pounds of candy that sells for $0.75 per lb must be mixed with candy that sells for $1.25 per lb to obtain 9 lb of a mixture that should sell for $0.96 per lb?

32. The top-grossing tour on the North American concert circuit for 2009 was U2, followed in second place by Bruce Springsteen and the E Street Band. Together, they took in $217.5 million from ticket sales. If Springsteen took in $28.5 million less than U2, how much did each band generate? (*Source:* Pollstar.)

33. Tickets to a production of *A Midsummer Night's Dream* at Broward College cost $5 for general admission or $4 with a student ID. If 184 people paid to see a performance and $812 was collected, how many of each type of ticket were sold?

34. At a business meeting at Panera Bread, the bill for two cappuccinos and three house lattes was $14.55. At another table, the bill for one cappuccino and two house lattes was $8.77. How much did each type of beverage cost? (*Source:* Panera Bread menu.)

35. The mixed price of 9 citrons and 7 fragrant wood apples is 107; again, the mixed price of 7 citrons and 9 fragrant wood apples is 101. O you arithmetician, tell me quickly the price of a citron and the price of a wood apple here, having distinctly separated those prices well. (*Source:* Hindu work, A.D. 850.)

36. Braving blizzard conditions on the planet Hoth, Luke Skywalker sets out in his snow speeder for a rebel base 4800 mi away. He travels into a steady head wind and makes the trip in 3 hr. Returning, he finds that the trip back, now with a tailwind, takes only 2 hr. Find the rate of Luke's snow speeder and the speed of the wind.

	r	t	d
Into Head Wind			
With Tailwind			

Solve each problem by using three variables. ***See Examples 5 and 6.*** *(In Exercises 37–40, remember that the sum of the measures of the angles of a triangle is* $180°$.)*

37. In the figure, $z = x + 10$ and $x + y = 100$. Determine a third equation involving x, y, and z, and then find the measures of the three angles.

38. In the figure, x is 10 less than y and 20 less than z. Write a system of equations and find the measures of the three angles.

39. In a certain triangle, the measure of the second angle is $10°$ greater than three times the first. The third angle measure is equal to the sum of the measures of the other two. Find the measures of the three angles.

40. The measure of the largest angle of a triangle is $12°$ less than the sum of the measures of the other two. The smallest angle measures $58°$ less than the largest. Find the measures of the angles.

41. The perimeter of a triangle is 70 cm. The longest side is 4 cm less than the sum of the other two sides. Twice the shortest side is 9 cm less than the longest side. Find the length of each side of the triangle.

42. The perimeter of a triangle is 56 in. The longest side measures 4 in. less than the sum of the other two sides. Three times the shortest side is 4 in. more than the longest side. Find the lengths of the three sides.

43. In the 2008 Summer Olympics in Beijing, China, Russia earned 5 fewer gold medals than bronze. The number of silver medals earned was 35 less than twice the number of bronze medals. Russia earned a total of 72 medals. How many of each kind of medal did Russia earn? (*Source: World Almanac and Book of Facts.*)

44. In a random sample of Americans of voting age conducted in 2010, 8% more people identified themselves as Independents than as Republicans, while 6% fewer people identified themselves as Republicans than as Democrats. Of those sampled, 2% did not identify with any of the three categories. What percent of the people in the sample identified themselves with each of the three political affiliations? (*Source:* Gallup, Inc.)

45. Tickets for the Harlem Globetrotters show at Michigan State University in 2010 cost $16, $23, or, for VIP seats, $40. If nine times as many $16 tickets were sold as VIP tickets, and the number of $16 tickets sold was 55 more than the sum of the number of $23 tickets and VIP tickets, sales of all three kinds of tickets would total $46,575. How many of each kind of ticket would have been sold? (*Source:* Breslin Student Events Center.)

46. Three kinds of tickets are available for a *Cowboy Mouth* concert: "up close," "in the middle," and "far out." "Up close" tickets cost $10 more than "in the middle" tickets, while "in the middle" tickets cost $10 more than "far out" tickets. Twice the cost of an "up close" ticket is $20 more than 3 times the cost of a "far out" ticket. Find the price of each kind of ticket.

47. A wholesaler supplies college T-shirts to three college bookstores: A, B, and C. The wholesaler recently shipped a total of 800 T-shirts to the three bookstores. In order to meet student demand at the three colleges, twice as many T-shirts were shipped to bookstore B as to bookstore A, and the number shipped to bookstore C was 40 less than the sum of the numbers shipped to the other two bookstores. How many T-shirts were shipped to each bookstore?

48. An office supply store sells three models of computer desks: A, B, and C. In January, the store sold a total of 85 computer desks. The number of model B desks was five more than the number of model C desks, and the number of model A desks was four more than twice the number of model C desks. How many of each model did the store sell in January?

49. A plant food is to be made from three chemicals. The mix must include 60% of the first and second chemicals. The second and third chemicals must be in the ratio of 4 to 3 by weight. How much of each chemical is needed to make 750 kg of the plant food?

50. How many ounces of 5% hydrochloric acid, 20% hydrochloric acid, and water must be combined to get 10 oz of solution that is 8.5% hydrochloric acid if the amount of water used must equal the total amount of the other two solutions?

Starting with the 2005–2006 season, the National Hockey League adopted a new system for awarding points used to determine team standings. A team is awarded 2 points for a win (W), 0 points for a loss in regulation play (L), and 1 point for an overtime loss (OTL). Use this information in Exercises 51 and 52.

51. During the 2008–2009 NHL regular season, the Boston Bruins played 82 games. Their wins and overtime losses resulted in a total of 116 points. They had 9 more losses in regulation play than overtime losses. How many wins, losses, and overtime losses did they have that year?

Team	GP	W	L	OTL	Points
Boston	82	——	——	——	116
Montreal	82	41	30	11	93
Buffalo	82	41	32	9	91
Ottawa	82	36	35	11	83
Toronto	82	34	35	13	81

Source: World Almanac and Book of Facts.

52. During the 2008–2009 NHL regular season, the Los Angeles Kings played 82 games. Their wins and overtime losses resulted in a total of 79 points. They had 14 more total losses (in regulation play and overtime) than wins. How many wins, losses, and overtime losses did they have that year?

Team	GP	W	L	OTL	Points
San Jose	82	53	18	11	117
Anaheim	82	42	33	7	91
Dallas	82	36	35	11	83
Phoenix	82	36	39	7	79
Los Angeles	82	——	——	——	79

Source: World Almanac and Book of Facts.

PREVIEW EXERCISES

Give **(a)** *the additive inverse and* **(b)** *the multiplicative inverse (reciprocal) of each number. See Sections 1.4 and 1.6.*

53. -6 **54.** 0.2 **55.** $\dfrac{7}{8}$ **56.** 2.25

8.6 Solving Systems of Linear Equations by Matrix Methods

OBJECTIVES

1 Define a matrix.

2 Write the augmented matrix of a system.

3 Use row operations to solve a system with two equations.

4 Use row operations to solve a system with three equations.

5 Use row operations to solve special systems.

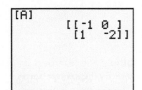

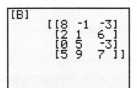

FIGURE 13

OBJECTIVE 1 Define a matrix. An ordered array of numbers such as

Columns

$$\text{Rows} \begin{bmatrix} 2 & 3 & 5 \\ 7 & 1 & 2 \end{bmatrix} \quad \text{Matrix}$$

is called a **matrix.** The numbers are called **elements** of the matrix. *Matrices* (the plural of *matrix*) are named according to the number of **rows** and **columns** they contain. The rows are read horizontally, and the columns are read vertically. This matrix is a 2×3 (read "two by three") matrix, because it has 2 rows and 3 columns. The number of rows followed by the number of columns gives the **dimensions** of the matrix.

$$\begin{bmatrix} -1 & 0 \\ 1 & -2 \end{bmatrix} \quad \begin{array}{c} 2 \times 2 \\ \text{matrix} \end{array} \qquad \begin{bmatrix} 8 & -1 & -3 \\ 2 & 1 & 6 \\ 0 & 5 & -3 \\ 5 & 9 & 7 \end{bmatrix} \quad \begin{array}{c} 4 \times 3 \\ \text{matrix} \end{array}$$

A **square matrix** is a matrix that has the same number of rows as columns. The 2×2 matrix above is a square matrix.

FIGURE 13 shows how a graphing calculator displays the preceding two matrices. Consult your owner's manual for details for using matrices.

In this section, we discuss a matrix method of solving linear systems that is a structured way of using the elimination method. The advantage of this new method is that it can be done by a graphing calculator or a computer.

OBJECTIVE 2 Write the augmented matrix of a system. To solve a linear system using matrices, we begin by writing an *augmented matrix* of the system. An **augmented matrix** has a vertical bar that separates the columns of the matrix into two groups. For example, to solve the system

$$x - 3y = 1$$
$$2x + y = -5,$$

start by writing the augmented matrix

$$\left[\begin{array}{cc|c} 1 & -3 & 1 \\ 2 & 1 & -5 \end{array}\right]. \quad \text{Augmented matrix}$$

Place the coefficients of the variables to the left of the bar, and the constants to the right. The bar separates the coefficients from the constants. *The matrix is just a shorthand way of writing the system of equations, so the rows of the augmented matrix can be treated the same as the equations of a system of equations.*

Exchanging the positions of two equations in a system does not change the system. Also, multiplying any equation in a system by a nonzero number does not change the system. Comparable changes to the augmented matrix of a system of equations produce new matrices that correspond to systems with the same solutions as the original system.

The following **row operations** produce new matrices that lead to systems having the same solutions as the original system.

> **Matrix Row Operations**
>
> **1.** Any two rows of the matrix may be interchanged.
>
> **2.** The elements of any row may be multiplied by any nonzero real number.
>
> **3.** Any row may be changed by adding to the elements of the row the product of a real number and the corresponding elements of another row.

Examples of these row operations follow.

Row operation 1

$$\begin{bmatrix} 2 & 3 & 9 \\ 4 & 8 & -3 \\ 1 & 0 & 7 \end{bmatrix} \quad \text{becomes} \quad \begin{bmatrix} 1 & 0 & 7 \\ 4 & 8 & -3 \\ 2 & 3 & 9 \end{bmatrix}$$

Interchange row 1 and row 3.

Row operation 2

$$\begin{bmatrix} 2 & 3 & 9 \\ 4 & 8 & -3 \\ 1 & 0 & 7 \end{bmatrix} \quad \text{becomes} \quad \begin{bmatrix} 6 & 9 & 27 \\ 4 & 8 & -3 \\ 1 & 0 & 7 \end{bmatrix}$$

Multiply the numbers in row 1 by 3.

Row operation 3

$$\begin{bmatrix} 2 & 3 & 9 \\ 4 & 8 & -3 \\ 1 & 0 & 7 \end{bmatrix} \quad \text{becomes} \quad \begin{bmatrix} 0 & 3 & -5 \\ 4 & 8 & -3 \\ 1 & 0 & 7 \end{bmatrix}$$

Multiply the numbers in row 3 by −2. Add them to the corresponding numbers in row 1.

The third row operation corresponds to the way we eliminated a variable from a pair of equations in previous sections.

OBJECTIVE 3 **Use row operations to solve a system with two equations.**
Row operations can be used to rewrite a matrix until it is the matrix of a system whose solution is easy to find. The goal is a matrix in the form

$$\begin{bmatrix} 1 & a & | & b \\ 0 & 1 & | & c \end{bmatrix} \quad \text{or} \quad \begin{bmatrix} 1 & a & b & | & c \\ 0 & 1 & d & | & e \\ 0 & 0 & 1 & | & f \end{bmatrix}$$

for systems with two and three equations, respectively. Notice that there are 1's down the diagonal from upper left to lower right and 0's below the 1's. A matrix written this way is said to be in **row echelon form.**

EXAMPLE 1 Using Row Operations to Solve a System with Two Variables
Use row operations to solve the system.

$$x - 3y = 1$$
$$2x + y = -5$$

We start by writing the augmented matrix of the system.

$$\begin{bmatrix} 1 & -3 & | & 1 \\ 2 & 1 & | & -5 \end{bmatrix}$$

Write the augmented matrix.

NOW TRY
EXERCISE 1
Use row operations to solve the system.

$$x + 3y = 3$$
$$2x - 3y = -12$$

Our goal is to use the various row operations to change this matrix into one that leads to a system that is easier to solve. It is best to work by columns.

We start with the first column and make sure that there is a 1 in the first row, first column, position. There already is a 1 in this position.

Next, we get 0 in every position below the first. To get a 0 in row two, column one, we add to the numbers in row two the result of multiplying each number in row one by -2. (We abbreviate this as $-2R_1 + R_2$.) Row one remains unchanged.

$$\begin{bmatrix} 1 & -3 & \Big| & 1 \\ 2 + 1(-2) & 1 + (-3)(-2) & \Big| & -5 + 1(-2) \end{bmatrix}$$

↑   ↑

Original number -2 times number
from row two   from row one

1 in the first position of column one ⟶ $\begin{bmatrix} 1 & -3 & \Big| & 1 \\ 0 & 7 & \Big| & -7 \end{bmatrix}$ $-2R_1 + R_2$
0 in every position below the first ⟶

Now we go to column two. The number 1 is needed in row two, column two. We use the second row operation, multiplying each number of row two by $\frac{1}{7}$.

Stop here—this matrix is in row echelon form. ⟶ $\begin{bmatrix} 1 & -3 & \Big| & 1 \\ 0 & 1 & \Big| & -1 \end{bmatrix}$ $\frac{1}{7}R_2$

This augmented matrix leads to the system of equations

$$\begin{array}{ll} 1x - 3y = 1 & \quad x - 3y = 1 \\ 0x + 1y = -1, & \quad\quad\quad y = -1. \end{array}$$ or

From the second equation, $y = -1$, we substitute -1 for y in the first equation to find x.

$$x - 3y = 1$$
$$x - 3(-1) = 1 \qquad \text{Let } y = -1.$$
$$x + 3 = 1 \qquad \text{Multiply.}$$
$$x = -2 \qquad \text{Subtract 3.}$$

The solution set of the system is $\{(-2, -1)\}$. Check this solution by substitution in both equations of the system.

Write the values of x and y in the correct order.

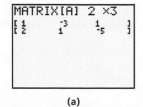
(a)

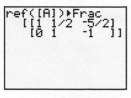
(b)
FIGURE 14

NOTE If the augmented matrix of the system in **Example 1** is entered as matrix [A] in a graphing calculator (**FIGURE 14(a)**) and the row echelon form of the matrix is found (**FIGURE 14(b)**), then the system becomes the following.

$$x + \frac{1}{2}y = -\frac{5}{2}$$
$$y = -1$$

NOW TRY

While this system looks different from the one we obtained in **Example 1**, it is equivalent, since its solution set is also $\{(-2, -1)\}$.

NOW TRY ANSWER
1. $\{(-3, 2)\}$

OBJECTIVE 4 Use row operations to solve a system with three equations.

EXAMPLE 2 Using Row Operations to Solve a System with Three Variables

Use row operations to solve the system.

$$x - y + 5z = -6$$
$$3x + 3y - z = 10$$
$$x + 3y + 2z = 5$$

Start by writing the augmented matrix of the system.

$$\begin{bmatrix} 1 & -1 & 5 & | & -6 \\ 3 & 3 & -1 & | & 10 \\ 1 & 3 & 2 & | & 5 \end{bmatrix} \quad \text{Write the augmented matrix.}$$

This matrix already has 1 in row one, column one. Next get 0's in the rest of column one. First, add to row two the results of multiplying each number of row one by -3.

$$\begin{bmatrix} 1 & -1 & 5 & | & -6 \\ 0 & 6 & -16 & | & 28 \\ 1 & 3 & 2 & | & 5 \end{bmatrix} \quad -3R_1 + R_2$$

Now add to the numbers in row three the results of multiplying each number of row one by -1.

$$\begin{bmatrix} 1 & -1 & 5 & | & -6 \\ 0 & 6 & -16 & | & 28 \\ 0 & 4 & -3 & | & 11 \end{bmatrix} \quad -1R_1 + R_3$$

Introduce 1 in row two, column two, by multiplying each number in row two by $\frac{1}{6}$.

$$\begin{bmatrix} 1 & -1 & 5 & | & -6 \\ 0 & 1 & -\frac{8}{3} & | & \frac{14}{3} \\ 0 & 4 & -3 & | & 11 \end{bmatrix} \quad \frac{1}{6}R_2$$

To obtain 0 in row three, column two, add to row three the results of multiplying each number in row two by -4.

$$\begin{bmatrix} 1 & -1 & 5 & | & -6 \\ 0 & 1 & -\frac{8}{3} & | & \frac{14}{3} \\ 0 & 0 & \frac{23}{3} & | & -\frac{23}{3} \end{bmatrix} \quad -4R_2 + R_3$$

Obtain 1 in row three, column three, by multiplying each number in row three by $\frac{3}{23}$.

This matrix is in row echelon form.

$$\begin{bmatrix} 1 & -1 & 5 & | & -6 \\ 0 & 1 & -\frac{8}{3} & | & \frac{14}{3} \\ 0 & 0 & 1 & | & -1 \end{bmatrix} \quad \frac{3}{23}R_3$$

The final matrix gives this system of equations.

$$x - y + 5z = -6$$
$$y - \frac{8}{3}z = \frac{14}{3}$$
$$z = -1$$

NOW TRY
EXERCISE 2
Use row operations to solve the system.

$$x + y - 2z = -5$$
$$-x + 2y + z = -1$$
$$2x - y + 3z = 14$$

Substitute -1 for z in the second equation, $y - \frac{8}{3}z = \frac{14}{3}$, to find that $y = 2$. Finally, substitute 2 for y and -1 for z in the first equation,

$$x - y + 5z = -6,$$

to determine that $x = 1$. The solution set of the original system is $\{(1, 2, -1)\}$. Check by substitution.

NOW TRY

OBJECTIVE 5 **Use row operations to solve special systems.**

NOW TRY
EXERCISE 3
Use row operations to solve each system.

(a) $3x - y = 8$
     $-6x + 2y = 4$

(b) $x + 2y = 7$
     $-x - 2y = -7$

EXAMPLE 3 Recognizing Inconsistent Systems or Dependent Equations

Use row operations to solve each system.

(a) $2x - 3y = 8$
     $-6x + 9y = 4$

$$\begin{bmatrix} 2 & -3 & | & 8 \\ -6 & 9 & | & 4 \end{bmatrix} \quad \text{Write the augmented matrix.}$$

$$\begin{bmatrix} 1 & -\frac{3}{2} & | & 4 \\ -6 & 9 & | & 4 \end{bmatrix} \quad \frac{1}{2}R_1$$

$$\begin{bmatrix} 1 & -\frac{3}{2} & | & 4 \\ 0 & 0 & | & 28 \end{bmatrix} \quad 6R_1 + R_2$$

The corresponding system of equations is

$$x - \frac{3}{2}y = 4$$

$$0 = 28, \quad \text{False}$$

which has no solution and is inconsistent. The solution set is $\emptyset$.

(b) $-10x + 12y = 30$
     $5x - 6y = -15$

$$\begin{bmatrix} -10 & 12 & | & 30 \\ 5 & -6 & | & -15 \end{bmatrix} \quad \text{Write the augmented matrix.}$$

$$\begin{bmatrix} 1 & -\frac{6}{5} & | & -3 \\ 5 & -6 & | & -15 \end{bmatrix} \quad -\frac{1}{10}R_1$$

$$\begin{bmatrix} 1 & -\frac{6}{5} & | & -3 \\ 0 & 0 & | & 0 \end{bmatrix} \quad -5R_1 + R_2$$

The corresponding system is

$$x - \frac{6}{5}y = -3$$

$$0 = 0, \quad \text{True}$$

NOW TRY ANSWERS
2. $\{(2, -1, 3)\}$
3. (a) $\emptyset$
   (b) $\{(x, y) \mid x + 2y = 7\}$

which has dependent equations. We use the second equation of the given system, which is in standard form, to express the solution set.

$$\{(x, y) \mid 5x - 6y = -15\}$$

NOW TRY

8.6 EXERCISES *MyMathLab* PRACTICE WATCH DOWNLOAD READ REVIEW

⊕ Complete solution available on the Video Resources on DVD

1. *Concept Check* Consider the matrix $\begin{bmatrix} -2 & 3 & 1 \\ 0 & 5 & -3 \\ 1 & 4 & 8 \end{bmatrix}$ and answer the following.

(a) What are the elements of the second row?

(b) What are the elements of the third column?

(c) Is this a square matrix? Explain why or why not.

(d) Give the matrix obtained by interchanging the first and third rows.

(e) Give the matrix obtained by multiplying the first row by $-\frac{1}{2}$.

(f) Give the matrix obtained by multiplying the third row by 3 and adding to the first row.

2. Repeat **Exercise 1** for the matrix $\begin{bmatrix} -7 & 0 & 1 \\ 3 & 2 & -2 \\ 0 & 1 & 6 \end{bmatrix}$.

Concept Check   Give the dimensions of each matrix.

3. $\begin{bmatrix} 3 & -7 \\ 4 & 5 \\ -1 & 0 \end{bmatrix}$

4. $\begin{bmatrix} 4 & 9 & 0 \\ -1 & 2 & -4 \end{bmatrix}$

5. $\begin{bmatrix} 6 & 3 \\ -2 & 5 \\ 4 & 10 \\ 1 & -1 \end{bmatrix}$

6. $\begin{bmatrix} 8 & 4 & 3 & 2 \end{bmatrix}$

*Use row operations to solve each system. **See Examples 1 and 3.***

7. $x + y = 5$
$x - y = 3$

8. $x + 2y = 7$
$x - y = -2$

9. $2x + 4y = 6$
$3x - y = 2$

10. $4x + 5y = -7$
$x - y = 5$

11. $3x + 4y = 13$
$2x - 3y = -14$

12. $5x + 2y = 8$
$3x - y = 7$

13. $-4x + 12y = 36$
$x - 3y = 9$

14. $2x - 4y = 8$
$-3x + 6y = 5$

15. $2x + y = 4$
$4x + 2y = 8$

16. $-3x - 4y = 1$
$6x + 8y = -2$

17. $-3x + 2y = 0$
$x - y = 0$

18. $-5x + 3y = 0$
$7x + 2y = 0$

*Use row operations to solve each system. **See Examples 2 and 3.***

19. $x + y - 3z = 1$
$2x - y + z = 9$
$3x + y - 4z = 8$

20. $2x + 4y - 3z = -18$
$3x + y - z = -5$
$x - 2y + 4z = 14$

21. $x + y - z = 6$
$2x - y + z = -9$
$x - 2y + 3z = 1$

22. $x + 3y - 6z = 7$
$2x - y + 2z = 0$
$x + y + 2z = -1$

23. $x - y = 1$
$y - z = 6$
$x + z = -1$

24. $x + y = 1$
$2x - z = 0$
$y + 2z = -2$

25. $x - 2y + z = 4$
$3x - 6y + 3z = 12$
$-2x + 4y - 2z = -8$

26. $x + 3y + z = 1$
$2x + 6y + 2z = 2$
$3x + 9y + 3z = 3$

27. $x + 2y + 3z = -2$
$2x + 4y + 6z = -5$
$x - y + 2z = 6$

28. $4x + 8y + 4z = 9$
$x + 3y + 4z = 10$
$5x + 10y + 5z = 12$

The augmented matrix of the system $\begin{aligned} 4x + 8y &= 44 \\ 2x - y &= -3 \end{aligned}$ *is shown in the graphing calculator screen on the left as matrix* [A]. *The screen in the middle shows the row echelon form for* [A]. *The screen on the right shows the "reduced" row echelon form, and from this it can be determined by inspection that the solution set of the system is* $\{(1, 5)\}$.

```
[A]
      [[4 8  44]
       [2 -1 -3]]
```

```
ref([A])
      [[1 2 11]
       [0 1 5 ]]
```

```
rref([A])
      [[1 0 1]
       [0 1 5]]
```

Use a graphing calculator and either matrix method illustrated to solve each system.

29. $\begin{aligned} 4x + y &= 5 \\ 2x + y &= 3 \end{aligned}$

30. $\begin{aligned} 5x + 3y &= 7 \\ 7x - 3y &= -19 \end{aligned}$

31. $\begin{aligned} 5x + y - 3z &= -6 \\ 2x + 3y + z &= 5 \\ -3x - 2y + 4z &= 3 \end{aligned}$

32. $\begin{aligned} x + y + z &= 3 \\ 3x - 3y - 4z &= -1 \\ x + y + 3z &= 11 \end{aligned}$

33. $\begin{aligned} x + z &= -3 \\ y + z &= 3 \\ x + y &= 8 \end{aligned}$

34. $\begin{aligned} x - y &= -1 \\ -y + z &= -2 \\ x + z &= -2 \end{aligned}$

PREVIEW EXERCISES

Solve each inequality. Write the solution set in interval notation and graph it. **See Section 2.8.**

35. $x - 4 \geq 12$

36. $3x + 1 > 22$

37. $-5z + 18 > -2$

38. Which one of the following inequalities is equivalent to $x < -3$?

   A. $-3x < 9$ **B.** $-3x > -9$ **C.** $-3x > 9$ **D.** $-3x < -9$

CHAPTER 8 SUMMARY

KEY TERMS

8.1

system of linear
  equations (linear system)
solution of a system
solution set of a system
set-builder notation
consistent system

inconsistent system
independent equations
dependent equations

8.4

ordered triple
focus variable
working equation

8.6

matrix
element of a matrix
row
column
square matrix

augmented matrix
row operations
row echelon form

NEW SYMBOLS

(x, y, z) ordered triple

$\begin{bmatrix} a & b & c \\ d & e & f \end{bmatrix}$ matrix with
two rows,
three columns

See how well you have learned the vocabulary in this chapter.

1. A **system of equations** consists of
   A. at least two equations with different variables
   B. two or more equations that have an infinite number of solutions
   C. two or more equations that are to be solved at the same time
   D. two or more inequalities that are to be solved.

2. The **solution set of a system of equations** is
   A. all ordered pairs that satisfy one equation of the system
   B. all ordered pairs that satisfy all the equations of the system at the same time

   C. any ordered pair that satisfies one or more equations of the system
   D. the set of values that make all the equations of the system false.

3. A **consistent system** is a system of equations
   A. with one solution
   B. with no solution
   C. with an infinite number of solutions
   D. that have the same graph.

4. An **inconsistent system** is a system of equations
   A. with one solution
   B. with no solution

   C. with an infinite number of solutions
   D. that have the same graph.

5. **Dependent equations**
   A. have different graphs
   B. have no solution
   C. have one solution
   D. are different forms of the same equation.

6. A **matrix** is
   A. an ordered pair of numbers
   B. an array of numbers with the same number of rows and columns
   C. a pair of numbers written between brackets
   D. a rectangular array of numbers.

ANSWERS

1. C; *Example:* $\begin{aligned} 3x - y &= 3 \\ 2x + y &= 7 \end{aligned}$ 2. B; *Example:* The ordered pair $(2, 3)$ satisfies both equations of the system in Answer 1, so $\{(2, 3)\}$ is the solution set of the system. 3. A; *Example:* The system in Answer 1 is consistent. The graphs of the equations intersect at exactly one point—in this case, the solution $(2, 3)$. 4. B; *Example:* The equations of two parallel lines form an inconsistent system. Their graphs never intersect, so the system has no solution. 5. D; *Example:* The equations $4x - y = 8$ and $8x - 2y = 16$ are dependent because their graphs are the same line. 6. D; *Examples:* $\begin{bmatrix} 3 & -1 & 0 \\ 4 & 2 & 1 \end{bmatrix}, \begin{bmatrix} 1 & 2 \\ 4 & 3 \end{bmatrix}$

QUICK REVIEW

CONCEPTS	EXAMPLES

8.1 Solving Systems of Linear Equations by Graphing

An ordered pair is a solution of a system if it makes all equations of the system true at the same time.

Is $(4, -1)$ a solution of the following system? $\begin{aligned} x + y &= 3 \\ 2x - y &= 9 \end{aligned}$

Yes, because $4 + (-1) = 3$ and $2(4) - (-1) = 9$ are both true, $(4, -1)$ is a solution.

To solve a linear system by graphing, follow these steps.

Step 1 Graph each equation of the system on the same axes.

Step 2 Find the coordinates of the point of intersection.

Step 3 Check. Write the solution set.

Solve the system by graphing.

$$\begin{aligned} x + y &= 5 \\ 2x - y &= 4 \end{aligned}$$

The solution $(3, 2)$ checks, so $\{(3, 2)\}$ is the solution set.

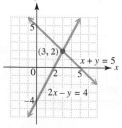

8.2 Solving Systems of Linear Equations by Substitution

Step 1 Solve one equation for either variable.

Solve by substitution.

$$\begin{aligned} x + 2y &= -5 \quad (1) \\ y &= -2x - 1 \quad (2) \end{aligned}$$

Equation (2) is already solved for y.

(continued)

CONCEPTS	EXAMPLES
Step 2 Substitute for that variable in the other equation to get an equation in one variable.	Substitute $-2x - 1$ for y in equation (1).
Step 3 Solve the equation from Step 2.	$$\begin{aligned} x + 2(-2x - 1) &= -5 &&\text{Let } y = -2x - 1 \text{ in (1).} \\ x - 4x - 2 &= -5 &&\text{Distributive property} \\ -3x - 2 &= -5 &&\text{Combine like terms.} \\ -3x &= -3 &&\text{Add 2.} \\ x &= 1 &&\text{Divide by } -3. \end{aligned}$$
Step 4 Substitute the result into the equation from Step 1 to get the value of the other variable.	To find y, let $x = 1$ in equation (2). $$y = -2(1) - 1 = -3$$
Step 5 Check. Write the solution set.	The solution, $(1, -3)$, checks, so $\{(1, -3)\}$ is the solution set.

8.3 Solving Systems of Linear Equations by Elimination

CONCEPTS	EXAMPLES
Step 1 Write both equations in standard form, $Ax + By = C$.	Solve by elimination. $$\begin{aligned} x + 3y &= 7 &&(1) \\ 3x - y &= 1 &&(2) \end{aligned}$$
Step 2 Multiply to transform the equations so that the coefficients of one pair of variable terms are opposites.	Multiply equation (1) by -3 to eliminate the x-terms.
Step 3 Add the equations to get an equation with only one variable.	$$\begin{aligned} -3x - 9y &= -21 &&\text{Multiply equation (1) by } -3. \\ \underline{3x - y} &= \underline{1} &&(2) \\ -10y &= -20 &&\text{Add.} \end{aligned}$$
Step 4 Solve the equation from Step 3.	$$y = 2 \qquad \text{Divide by } -10.$$
Step 5 Substitute the solution from Step 4 into either of the original equations to find the value of the remaining variable.	Substitute to get the value of x. $$\begin{aligned} x + 3y &= 7 &&(1) \\ x + 3(2) &= 7 &&\text{Let } y = 2. \\ x + 6 &= 7 &&\text{Multiply.} \\ x &= 1 &&\text{Subtract 6.} \end{aligned}$$
Step 6 Check. Write the solution set.	Since $1 + 3(2) = 7$ and $3(1) - 2 = 1$, the solution set is $\{(1, 2)\}$.
If the result of the addition step (Step 3) is a false statement, such as $0 = 4$, the graphs are parallel lines and *there is no solution. The solution set is* $\emptyset$.	$$\begin{aligned} x - 2y &= 6 \\ \underline{-x + 2y} &= \underline{-2} \\ 0 &= 4 \qquad \text{Solution set: } \emptyset \end{aligned}$$
If the result is a true statement, such as $0 = 0$, the graphs are the same line, and an *infinite number of ordered pairs are solutions. The solution set is written in set-builder notation as* $\{(x, y) \mid \underline{\qquad\qquad}\}$, *where a form of the equation is written in the blank.*	$$\begin{aligned} x - 2y &= 6 \\ \underline{-x + 2y} &= \underline{-6} \\ 0 &= 0 \qquad \text{Solution set: } \{(x, y) \mid x - 2y = 6\} \end{aligned}$$

8.4 Solving Systems of Linear Equations in Three Variables

Solving a Linear System in Three Variables

CONCEPTS	EXAMPLES
Step 1 Select a focus variable, preferably one with coefficient 1 or -1, and a working equation.	Solve the system. $$\begin{aligned} x + 2y - z &= 6 &&(1) \\ x + y + z &= 6 &&(2) \\ 2x + y - z &= 7 &&(3) \end{aligned}$$ We choose z as the focus variable and (2) as the working equation.

(continued)

CONCEPTS	EXAMPLES
Step 2 Eliminate the focus variable, using the working equation and one of the equations of the system.	Add equations (1) and (2). $$2x + 3y = 12 \quad (4)$$
Step 3 Eliminate the focus variable again, using the working equation and the remaining equation of the system.	Add equations (2) and (3). $$3x + 2y = 13 \quad (5)$$
Step 4 Solve the system of two equations in two variables formed by the equations from Steps 2 and 3.	Use equations (4) and (5) to eliminate x. $-6x - 9y = -36$ Multiply (4) by -3. $\underline{6x + 4y = 26}$ Multiply (5) by 2. $-5y = -10$ Add. $y = 2$ Divide by -5. To find x, substitute 2 for y in equation (4). $2x + 3(2) = 12$ Let $y = 2$ in (4). $2x + 6 = 12$ Multiply. $2x = 6$ Subtract 6. $x = 3$ Divide by 2.
Step 5 Find the value of the remaining variable.	Substitute 3 for x and 2 for y in working equation (2). $x + y + z = 6 \quad (2)$ $3 + 2 + z = 6$ $z = 1$
Step 6 Check the ordered-triple solution in each of the original equations of the system. Then write the solution set.	A check of the solution $(3, 2, 1)$ confirms that the solution set is $\{(3, 2, 1)\}$.

8.5 Applications of Systems of Linear Equations

Use the six-step problem-solving method.	The perimeter of a rectangle is 18 ft. The length is 3 ft more than twice the width. What are the dimensions of the rectangle?
Step 1 Read the problem carefully.	Let x represent the length and y represent the width. From the perimeter formula, one equation is $2x + 2y = 18$. From the problem, another equation is $x = 2y + 3$. Solve the system
Step 2 Assign variables.	
Step 3 Write a system of equations that relates the unknowns.	$$2x + 2y = 18$$
Step 4 Solve the system.	$$x = 2y + 3$$
Step 5 State the answer.	to get $x = 7$ and $y = 2$. The length is 7 ft, and the width is 2 ft. Since the perimeter is
Step 6 Check.	$$2(7) + 2(2) = 18, \quad \text{and} \quad 2(2) + 3 = 7,$$ the solution checks.

8.6 Solving Systems of Linear Equations by Matrix Methods

Matrix Row Operations
1. Any two rows of the matrix may be interchanged.

$$\begin{bmatrix} 1 & 5 & 7 \\ 3 & 9 & -2 \\ 0 & 6 & 4 \end{bmatrix} \text{ becomes } \begin{bmatrix} 3 & 9 & -2 \\ 1 & 5 & 7 \\ 0 & 6 & 4 \end{bmatrix} \quad \begin{array}{l}\text{Interchange} \\ \text{R}_1 \text{ and R}_2.\end{array}$$

(continued)

CONCEPTS	EXAMPLES

2. The elements of any row may be multiplied by any nonzero real number.

$$\begin{bmatrix} 1 & 5 & 7 \\ 3 & 9 & -2 \\ 0 & 6 & 4 \end{bmatrix} \text{ becomes } \begin{bmatrix} 1 & 5 & 7 \\ 1 & 3 & -\frac{2}{3} \\ 0 & 6 & 4 \end{bmatrix} \quad \frac{1}{3}R_2$$

3. Any row may be changed by adding to the elements of the row the product of a real number and the elements of another row.

$$\begin{bmatrix} 1 & 5 & 7 \\ 3 & 9 & -2 \\ 0 & 6 & 4 \end{bmatrix} \text{ becomes } \begin{bmatrix} 1 & 5 & 7 \\ 0 & -6 & -23 \\ 0 & 6 & 4 \end{bmatrix} \quad -3R_1 + R_2$$

A system can be solved by matrix methods. Write the augmented matrix and use row operations to obtain a matrix in row echelon form.

Solve using row operations. $\quad \begin{aligned} x + 3y &= 7 \\ 2x + y &= 4 \end{aligned}$

$$\begin{bmatrix} 1 & 3 & | & 7 \\ 2 & 1 & | & 4 \end{bmatrix} \quad \text{Write the augmented matrix.}$$

$$\begin{bmatrix} 1 & 3 & | & 7 \\ 0 & -5 & | & -10 \end{bmatrix} \quad -2R_1 + R_2$$

$$\begin{bmatrix} 1 & 3 & | & 7 \\ 0 & 1 & | & 2 \end{bmatrix} \quad -\frac{1}{5}R_2 \xrightarrow{\text{implies}} \begin{aligned} x + 3y &= 7 \\ y &= 2 \end{aligned}$$

When $y = 2$, $x + 3(2) = 7$, so $x = 1$. The solution set is $\{(1, 2)\}$.

CHAPTER 8 — REVIEW EXERCISES

8.1 *Decide whether the given ordered pair is a solution of the given system.*

1. $(3, 4)$
$$\begin{aligned} 4x - 2y &= 4 \\ 5x + y &= 19 \end{aligned}$$

2. $(-5, 2)$
$$\begin{aligned} x - 4y &= -13 \\ 2x + 3y &= 4 \end{aligned}$$

Solve each system by graphing.

3. $\begin{aligned} x + y &= 4 \\ 2x - y &= 5 \end{aligned}$

4. $\begin{aligned} x - 2y &= 4 \\ 2x + y &= -2 \end{aligned}$

5. $\begin{aligned} 2x + 4 &= 2y \\ y - x &= -3 \end{aligned}$

6. $\begin{aligned} x - 2 &= 2y \\ 2x - 4y &= 4 \end{aligned}$

8.2

7. *Concept Check* Suppose that you were asked to solve the following system by substitution. Which variable in which equation would be easiest to solve for in your first step?

$$\begin{aligned} 5x - 3y &= 7 \\ -x + 2y &= 4 \end{aligned}$$

8. *Concept Check* After solving a system of linear equations by the substitution method, a student obtained the equation "0 = 0." He gave the solution set of the system as $\{(0, 0)\}$. *WHAT WENT WRONG?*

Solve each system by the substitution method.

9. $\begin{aligned} 3x + y &= 7 \\ x &= 2y \end{aligned}$

10. $\begin{aligned} 2x - 5y &= -19 \\ y &= x + 2 \end{aligned}$

11. $\begin{aligned} 4x + 5y &= 44 \\ x + 2 &= 2y \end{aligned}$

12. $\begin{aligned} 5x + 15y &= 30 \\ x + 3y &= 6 \end{aligned}$

8.3

13. *Concept Check*   Which system does not require that we multiply one or both equations by a constant to solve the system by the elimination method?

A. $-4x + 3y = 7$
    $3x - 4y = 4$

B. $5x + 8y = 13$
   $12x + 24y = 36$

C. $2x + 3y = 5$
   $x - 3y = 12$

D. $x + 2y = 9$
   $3x - y = 6$

14. *Concept Check*   For the system

$$2x + 12y = 7 \quad (1)$$
$$3x + 4y = 1, \quad (2)$$

if we were to multiply equation (1) by -3, by what number would we have to multiply equation (2) in order to

(a) eliminate the x-terms when solving by the elimination method?

(b) eliminate the y-terms when solving by the elimination method?

Solve each system by the elimination method.

15. $2x - y = 13$
    $x + y = 8$

16. $-4x + 3y = 25$
    $6x - 5y = -39$

17. $3x - 4y = 9$
    $6x - 8y = 18$

18. $2x + y = 3$
    $-4x - 2y = 6$

8.1–8.3   *Solve each system by any method.*

19. $2x + 3y = -5$
    $3x + 4y = -8$

20. $6x - 9y = 0$
    $2x - 3y = 0$

21. $x - 2y = 5$
    $y = x - 7$

22. $\dfrac{x}{2} + \dfrac{y}{3} = 7$
    $\dfrac{x}{4} + \dfrac{2y}{3} = 8$

23. $\dfrac{3}{4}x - \dfrac{1}{3}y = \dfrac{7}{6}$
    $\dfrac{1}{2}x + \dfrac{2}{3}y = \dfrac{5}{3}$

24. $0.4x - 0.5y = -2.2$
    $0.3x + 0.2y = -0.5$

8.4   *Solve each system. If a system is inconsistent or has dependent equations, say so.*

25. $2x + 3y - z = -16$
    $x + 2y + 2z = -3$
    $-3x + y + z = -5$

26. $4x - y = 2$
    $3y + z = 9$
    $x + 2z = 7$

27. $3x - y - z = -8$
    $4x + 2y + 3z = 15$
    $-6x + 2y + 2z = 10$

8.5   *Solve each problem by using a system of equations.*

28. A regulation National Hockey League ice rink has perimeter 570 ft. The length of the rink is 30 ft longer than twice the width. What are the dimensions of an NHL ice rink? (*Source:* www.nhl.com)

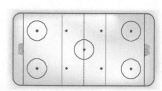

29. In 2009, the New York Yankees and the Boston Red Sox had the most expensive ticket prices in Major League Baseball. Two Yankees tickets and three Red Sox tickets purchased at their average prices cost $296.66, while three Yankees tickets and two Red Sox tickets cost $319.39. Find the average ticket price for a Yankees ticket and a Red Sox ticket. (*Source:* Team Marketing Report.)

30. A plane flies 560 mi in 1.75 hr traveling with the wind. The return trip later against the same wind takes the plane 2 hr. Find the speed of the plane and the speed of the wind. Let x = the speed of the plane and y = the speed of the wind.

	r	t	d
With Wind	$x + y$	1.75	
Against Wind		2	

31. For Valentine's Day, Ms. Sweet will mix some $2-per-lb nuts with some $1-per-lb chocolate candy to get 100 lb of mix, which she will sell at $1.30 per lb. How many pounds of each should she use?

	Number of Pounds	Price per Pound	Value
Nuts	x		
Chocolate	y		
Mixture	100		

32. The sum of the measures of the angles of a triangle is 180°. The largest angle measures 10° less than the sum of the other two. The measure of the middle-sized angle is the average of the other two. Find the measures of the three angles.

33. Noemi Alfonso-Triana sells real estate. On three recent sales, she made 10% commission, 6% commission, and 5% commission. Her total commissions on these sales were $17,000, and she sold property worth $280,000. If the 5% sale amounted to the sum of the other two, what were the three sales prices?

34. How many liters each of 8%, 10%, and 20% hydrogen peroxide should be mixed together to get 8 L of 12.5% solution if the amount of 8% solution used must be 2 L more than the amount of 20% solution used?

35. In the great baseball year of 1961, Yankee teammates Mickey Mantle, Roger Maris, and Yogi Berra combined for 137 home runs. Mantle hit 7 fewer than Maris. Maris hit 39 more than Berra. What were the home run totals for each player? (*Source:* Neft, David S., Richard M. Cohen, and Michael Lo Neft, *The Sports Encyclopedia: Baseball 2006.*)

8.6   *Solve each system of equations by using row operations.*

36. $2x + 5y = -4$
$\quad 4x - y = 14$

37. $\quad 6x + 3y = 9$
$\quad -7x + 2y = 17$

38. $\quad x + 2y - z = 1$
$\quad 3x + 4y + 2z = -2$
$\quad -2x - y + z = -1$

39. $\quad x + 3y = 7$
$\quad 3x + z = 2$
$\quad y - 2z = 4$

MIXED REVIEW EXERCISES

40. *Concept Check*   Which system, A or B, would be easier to solve using the substitution method? Why?

A. $5x - 3y = 7$
$\quad 2x + 8y = 3$

B. $7x + 2y = 4$
$\quad y = -3x + 1$

Solve by any method.

41. $\dfrac{2}{3}x + \dfrac{1}{6}y = \dfrac{19}{2}$
$\quad \dfrac{1}{3}x - \dfrac{2}{9}y = 2$

42. $\quad 2x + 5y - z = 12$
$\quad -x + y - 4z = -10$
$\quad -8x - 20y + 4z = 31$

43. $x = 7y + 10$
$\quad 2x + 3y = 3$

44. $\quad x + 4y = 17$
$\quad -3x + 2y = -9$

45. $-7x + 3y = 12$
$\quad 5x + 2y = 8$

46. $2x - 5y = 8$
$\quad 3x + 4y = 10$

47. To make a 10% acid solution, Jeffrey Guild wants to mix some 5% solution with 10 L of 20% solution. How many liters of 5% solution should he use?

48. In the 2010 Winter Olympics, Germany, the United States, and Canada won a combined total of 93 medals. Germany won seven fewer medals than the United States, while Canada won 11 fewer medals than the United States. How many medals did each country win? (*Source:* www.vancouver2010.com/olympic-medals)

CHAPTER **8**

TEST

CHAPTER
Test Prep
VIDEOS

View the complete solutions to all Chapter Test exercises on the Video Resources on DVD.

The graph shows a company's costs to produce computer parts and the revenue from the sale of computer parts.

1. At what production level does the cost equal the revenue? What is the revenue at that point?

2. Profit is revenue less cost. Estimate the profit on the sale of 1100 parts.

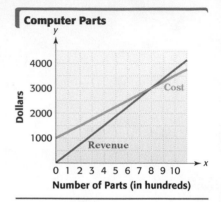

Computer Parts

3. Decide whether each ordered pair is a solution of the system.
$$2x + y = -3$$
$$x - y = -9$$

   (a) $(1, -5)$ **(b)** $(1, 10)$ **(c)** $(-4, 5)$

4. Use a graph to solve the system. $x + y = 7$
   $x - y = 5$

Solve each system by substitution or elimination. If a system is inconsistent or has dependent equations, say so.

5. $2x - 3y = 24$
   $y = -\dfrac{2}{3}x$

6. $3x - y = -8$
   $2x + 6y = 3$

7. $12x - 5y = 8$
   $3x = \dfrac{5}{4}y + 2$

8. $3x + y = 12$
   $2x - y = 3$

9. $-5x + 2y = -4$
   $6x + 3y = -6$

10. $3x + 4y = 8$
    $8y = 7 - 6x$

11. $\dfrac{6}{5}x - \dfrac{1}{3}y = -20$
    $-\dfrac{2}{3}x + \dfrac{1}{6}y = 11$

12. $3x + 5y + 3z = 2$
    $6x + 5y + z = 0$
    $3x + 10y - 2z = 6$

13. $4x + y + z = 11$
    $x - y - z = 4$
    $y + 2z = 0$

Solve each problem using a system of equations.

14. Harrison Ford is a box-office star. As of January 2010, his two top-grossing domestic films, *Star Wars Episode IV: A New Hope* and *Indiana Jones and the Kingdom of the Crystal Skull,* earned $778.0 million together. If *Indiana Jones and the Kingdom of the Crystal Skull* grossed $144.0 million less than *Star Wars Episode IV: A New Hope,* how much did each film gross? (*Source:* www.the-numbers.com)

15. Two cars start from points 420 mi apart and travel toward each other. They meet after 3.5 hr. Find the average rate of each car if one travels 30 mph slower than the other.

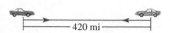

16. A chemist needs 12 L of a 40% alcohol solution. She must mix a 20% solution and a 50% solution. How many liters of each will be required to obtain what she needs?

17. A local electronics store will sell seven AC adaptors and two rechargeable flashlights for $86, or three AC adaptors and four rechargeable flashlights for $84. What is the price of a single AC adaptor and a single rechargeable flashlight?

18. The owner of a tea shop wants to mix three kinds of tea to make 100 oz of a mixture that will sell for $0.83 per oz. He uses Orange Pekoe, which sells for $0.80 per oz, Irish Breakfast, for $0.85 per oz, and Earl Grey, for $0.95 per oz. If he wants to use twice as much Orange Pekoe as Irish Breakfast, how much of each kind of tea should he use?

Solve each system using row operations.

19. $3x + 2y = 4$
$5x + 5y = 9$

20. $x + 3y + 2z = 11$
$3x + 7y + 4z = 23$
$5x + 3y - 5z = -14$

CHAPTERS (1–8)

CUMULATIVE REVIEW EXERCISES

1. List all integer factors of 40.

2. Evaluate $-2 + 6[3 - (4 - 9)]$.

3. Find the value of the expression $\dfrac{3x^2 + 2y^2}{10y + 3}$ for $x = 1$ and $y = 5$.

4. Name the property that justifies the statement: $r(s - k) = rs - rk$.

Solve each linear equation.

5. $2 - 3(6x + 2) = 4(x + 1) + 18$

6. $\dfrac{3}{2}\left(\dfrac{1}{3}x + 4\right) = 6\left(\dfrac{1}{4} + x\right)$

7. Solve the formula $P = \dfrac{kT}{V}$ for T.

Solve each linear inequality.

8. $-\dfrac{5}{6}x < 15$

9. $-8 < 2x + 3$

10. A survey measured public recognition of some classic advertising slogans. Complete the results shown in the table if 2500 people were surveyed.

Slogan (product or company)	Percent Recognition (nearest tenth of a percent)	Actual Number That Recognized Slogan (nearest whole number)
Please Don't Squeeze the . . . (Charmin®)	80.4%	
The Breakfast of Champions (Wheaties)	72.5%	
The King of Beers (Budweiser®)		1570
Like a Good Neighbor (State Farm)		1430

(Other slogans included "You're in Good Hands" (Allstate), "Snap, Crackle, Pop" (Rice Krispies®), and "The Un-Cola" (7-Up).)
Source: Department of Integrated Marketing Communications, Northwestern University.

Solve each problem.

11. On August 6, 2009, the U.S. Senate confirmed Sonia Sotomayor, as the 111th Justice of the United States Supreme Court. With 99 senators voting, 37 more voted in favor of her confirmation than voted against it. How many senators voted each way? (*Source: The New York Times.*)

12. Two angles of a triangle have the same measure. The measure of the third angle is 4° less than twice the measure of each of the equal angles. Find the measures of the three angles.

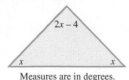
Measures are in degrees.

Graph each linear equation.

13. $x - y = 4$ **14.** $3x + y = 6$

Find the slope of each line.

15. Through $(-5, 6)$ and $(1, -2)$ **16.** Perpendicular to the line $y = 4x - 3$

Find an equation for each line. Write it in slope-intercept form.

17. Through $(-4, 1)$ with slope $\frac{1}{2}$ **18.** Through the points $(1, 3)$ and $(-2, -3)$

19. **(a)** Write an equation of the vertical line through $(9, -2)$.

   (b) Write an equation of the horizontal line through $(4, -1)$.

20. Simplify $\left(\dfrac{m^{-4}n^2}{m^2n^{-3}}\right) \cdot \left(\dfrac{m^5n^{-1}}{m^{-2}n^5}\right)$. Write the answer with only positive exponents. Assume that all variables represent nonzero real numbers.

Perform the indicated operations.

21. $(3y^2 - 2y + 6) - (-y^2 + 5y + 12)$ **22.** $(4f + 3)(3f - 1)$

23. $\left(\dfrac{1}{4}x + 5\right)^2$ **24.** $(3x^3 + 13x^2 - 17x - 7) \div (3x + 1)$

Factor each polynomial completely.

25. $2x^2 - 13x - 45$ **26.** $100t^4 - 25$ **27.** $8p^3 + 125$

28. Solve the equation $3x^2 + 4x = 7$.

29. Write $\dfrac{y^2 - 16}{y^2 - 8y + 16}$ in lowest terms.

Perform the indicated operations. Express the answer in lowest terms.

30. $\dfrac{2a^2}{a + b} \cdot \dfrac{a - b}{4a}$ **31.** $\dfrac{x + 4}{x - 2} + \dfrac{2x - 10}{x - 2}$

32. Solve the equation $\dfrac{-3x}{x + 1} + \dfrac{4x + 1}{x} = \dfrac{-3}{x^2 + x}$.

33. Suppose that $y = f(x)$ and $5x - 3y = 8$.

   (a) Find the equation that defines $f(x)$. That is, $f(x) = $ _____.

   (b) Find $f(1)$.

34. For the polynomial functions defined by

$$f(x) = x^2 + 2x - 3, \quad g(x) = 2x^3 - 3x^2 + 4x - 1, \quad \text{and} \quad h(x) = x^2,$$

   find **(a)** $(f + g)(x)$, **(b)** $(g - f)(x)$, **(c)** $(f + g)(-1)$, and **(d)** $(f \circ h)(x)$.

Solve by any method.

35. $-2x + 3y = -15$
$\quad\ \ 4x - \ \ y = 15$

36. $x - 3y = 7$
$\quad\ \ 2x - 6y = 14$

37. $x + y + z = 10$
$\quad\ \ x - y - z = 0$
$\quad\ -x + y - z = -4$

38. Ten years after the original Tickle Me Elmo became a must-have toy, a new version, called T.M.X., was released in the fall of 2006. The original Tickle Me Elmo's average cost was $12.37 less than the recommended cost of T.M.X., and one of each cost $67.63. Find the average cost of Tickle Me Elmo and the recommended cost of T.M.X. (*Source:* NPD Group, Inc.; *USA Today.*)

Inequalities and Absolute Value

9.1 Set Operations and Compound Inequalities

9.2 Absolute Value Equations and Inequalities

Summary Exercises on Solving Linear and Absolute Value Equations and Inequalities

9.3 Linear Inequalities in Two Variables

During the past 30 years, the cost of a college education in the United States has increased more rapidly than average prices of other goods and services in the economy in general. For four-year public colleges and universities, the average cost of tuition and fees, adjusted for inflation, increased 62% from the 1999–2000 school year to the 2009–2010 school year. For two-year public colleges, this increase was a more affordable 19% during the same period. Yet a college degree remains of major importance to individual long-term financial stability. (*Source:* The College Board.)

In **Exercises 63–66** of **Section 9.1,** we apply the concepts of this chapter to college student expenses.

9.1 Set Operations and Compound Inequalities

OBJECTIVES

1   Find the intersection of two sets.
2   Solve compound inequalities with the word *and*.
3   Find the union of two sets.
4   Solve compound inequalities with the word *or*.

Consider the two sets A and B defined as follows.

$$A = \{1, 2, 3\}, \qquad B = \{2, 3, 4\}$$

The set of all elements that belong to both A **and** B, called their *intersection* and symbolized $A \cap B$, is given by

$$A \cap B = \{2, 3\}. \qquad \text{Intersection}$$

The set of all elements that belong to either A **or** B, or both, called their *union* and symbolized $A \cup B$, is given by

$$A \cup B = \{1, 2, 3, 4\}. \qquad \text{Union}$$

We discuss the use of the words *and* and *or* as they relate to sets and inequalities.

OBJECTIVE 1   Find the intersection of two sets. The intersection of two sets is defined with the word *and*.

Intersection of Sets

For any two sets A and B, the **intersection** of A and B, symbolized $A \cap B$, is defined as follows.

$$A \cap B = \{x \mid x \text{ is an element of } A \text{ and } x \text{ is an element of } B\}$$

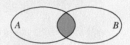

**NOW TRY
EXERCISE 1**
Let $A = \{2, 4, 6, 8\}$ and $B = \{0, 2, 6, 8\}$. Find $A \cap B$.

EXAMPLE 1   Finding the Intersection of Two Sets

Let $A = \{1, 2, 3, 4\}$ and $B = \{2, 4, 6\}$. Find $A \cap B$.

The set $A \cap B$ contains those elements that belong to both A *and* B: the numbers 2 and 4. Therefore,

$$A \cap B = \{1, 2, 3, 4\} \cap \{2, 4, 6\}$$
$$= \{2, 4\}. \qquad \text{NOW TRY}$$

A **compound inequality** consists of two inequalities linked by a connective word.

$$x + 1 \le 9 \quad \text{and} \quad x - 2 \ge 3 \qquad \text{Examples of compound inequalities}$$
$$2x > 4 \quad \text{or} \quad 3x - 6 < 5 \qquad \text{linked by } and \text{ or } or$$

OBJECTIVE 2   Solve compound inequalities with the word *and*. We use the following steps to solve a compound inequality such as "$x + 1 \le 9$ *and* $x - 2 \ge 3$."

Solving a Compound Inequality with *and*

Step 1   Solve each inequality individually.

Step 2   Since the inequalities are joined with *and,* the solution set of the compound inequality will include all numbers that satisfy both inequalities in Step 1 (the intersection of the solution sets).

NOW TRY ANSWER
1. $\{2, 6, 8\}$

NOW TRY
EXERCISE 2

Solve the compound inequality, and graph the solution set.

$x - 2 \leq 5$ and $x + 5 \geq 9$

EXAMPLE 2   Solving a Compound Inequality with *and*

Solve the compound inequality, and graph the solution set.

$$x + 1 \leq 9 \quad \text{and} \quad x - 2 \geq 3$$

Step 1 Solve each inequality individually using the addition property of inequality.

$$x + 1 \leq 9 \qquad\qquad \text{and} \qquad x - 2 \geq 3$$

$$x + 1 - 1 \leq 9 - 1 \;\; \text{Subtract 1.} \quad \text{and} \quad x - 2 + 2 \geq 3 + 2 \;\; \text{Add 2.}$$

$$x \leq 8 \qquad\qquad \text{and} \qquad x \geq 5$$

Step 2 Because of the word *and,* the solution set will include all numbers that satisfy both inequalities in Step 1 at the same time. The compound inequality is true whenever $x \leq 8$ and $x \geq 5$ are both true. See the graphs in **FIGURE 1**.

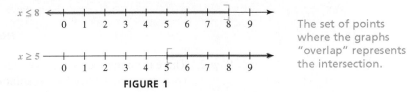

The set of points where the graphs "overlap" represents the intersection.

FIGURE 1

The intersection of the two graphs is the solution set of the compound inequality. **FIGURE 2** shows that the solution set, in interval notation, is $[5, 8]$.

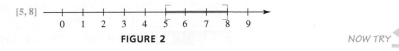

FIGURE 2

NOW TRY

NOW TRY
EXERCISE 3

Solve and graph.

$-4x - 1 < 7$ and
$\qquad\qquad 3x + 4 \geq -5$

EXAMPLE 3   Solving a Compound Inequality with *and*

Solve the compound inequality, and graph the solution set.

$$-3x - 2 > 5 \quad \text{and} \quad 5x - 1 \leq -21$$

Step 1 Solve each inequality individually.

$$-3x - 2 > 5 \qquad\qquad\qquad \text{and} \quad 5x - 1 \leq -21$$

$$-3x > 7 \quad \text{Add 2.} \qquad\quad \text{and} \qquad 5x \leq -20 \quad \text{Add 1.}$$

Reverse the inequality symbol when dividing by a negative number.

$$x < -\frac{7}{3} \quad \text{Divide by } -3. \quad \text{and} \qquad x \leq -4 \quad \text{Divide by 5.}$$

The graphs of $x < -\frac{7}{3}$ and $x \leq -4$ are shown in **FIGURE 3**.

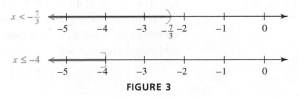

FIGURE 3

Step 2 Now find all values of x that are less than $-\frac{7}{3}$ and also less than or equal to -4. As shown in **FIGURE 4**, the solution set is $(-\infty, -4]$.

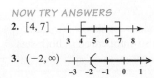
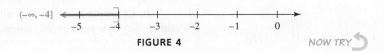

FIGURE 4

NOW TRY

NOW TRY
EXERCISE 4
Solve and graph.

$x - 7 < -12$ and
$2x + 1 > 5$

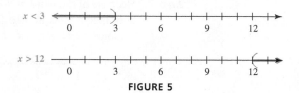

EXAMPLE 4 Solving a Compound Inequality with *and*

Solve the compound inequality, and graph the solution set.

$$x + 2 < 5 \quad \text{and} \quad x - 10 > 2$$

Step 1 Solve each inequality individually.

$$x + 2 < 5 \qquad\qquad \text{and} \quad x - 10 > 2$$
$$x < 3 \quad \text{Subtract 2.} \quad \text{and} \qquad x > 12 \quad \text{Add 10.}$$

The graphs of $x < 3$ and $x > 12$ are shown in **FIGURE 5**.

FIGURE 5

Step 2 There is no number that is both less than 3 *and* greater than 12, so the given compound inequality has no solution. The solution set is $\emptyset$. See **FIGURE 6**.

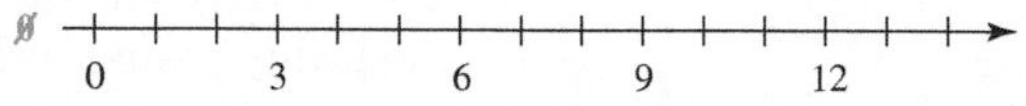

FIGURE 6

NOW TRY

OBJECTIVE 3 **Find the union of two sets.** The union of two sets is defined with the word *or*.

Union of Sets

For any two sets A and B, the **union** of A and B, symbolized $A \cup B$, is defined as follows.

$$A \cup B = \{x \mid x \text{ is an element of } A \text{ or } x \text{ is an element of } B\}$$

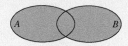

NOW TRY
EXERCISE 5
Let $A = \{5, 10, 15, 20\}$
and $B = \{5, 15, 25\}$.
Find $A \cup B$.

EXAMPLE 5 Finding the Union of Two Sets

Let $A = \{1, 2, 3, 4\}$ and $B = \{2, 4, 6\}$. Find $A \cup B$.

Begin by listing all the elements of set A: 1, 2, 3, 4. Then list any additional elements from set B. In this case the elements 2 and 4 are already listed, so the only additional element is 6.

$$A \cup B = \{1, 2, 3, 4\} \cup \{2, 4, 6\}$$
$$= \{1, 2, 3, 4, 6\}$$

The union consists of all elements in either A *or* B (or both).

NOW TRY

NOW TRY ANSWERS
4. $\emptyset$ 5. $\{5, 10, 15, 20, 25\}$

NOTE In **Example 5,** notice that although the elements 2 and 4 appeared in both sets A and B, they are written only once in $A \cup B$.

OBJECTIVE 4 **Solve compound inequalities with the word *or*.** Use the following steps to solve a compound inequality such as "$6x - 4 < 2x \ or \ -3x \leq -9$."

Solving a Compound Inequality with *or*

Step 1   Solve each inequality individually.

Step 2   Since the inequalities are joined with *or*, the solution set of the compound inequality includes all numbers that satisfy either one of the two inequalities in Step 1 (the union of the solution sets).

NOW TRY
EXERCISE 6
Solve and graph.
$-12x \leq -24 \quad or \quad x + 9 < 8$

EXAMPLE 6   Solving a Compound Inequality with *or*

Solve the compound inequality, and graph the solution set.

$$6x - 4 < 2x \quad or \quad -3x \leq -9$$

Step 1   Solve each inequality individually.

$$6x - 4 < 2x \qquad\qquad or \quad -3x \leq -9$$
$$4x < 4$$

Remember to reverse the inequality symbol.

$$x < 1 \quad \text{Divide by 4.} \quad or \qquad x \geq 3 \quad \text{Divide by } -3.$$

The graphs of these two inequalities are shown in **FIGURE 7**.

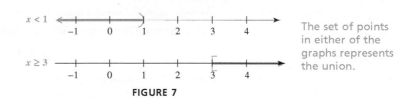

The set of points in either of the graphs represents the union.

FIGURE 7

Step 2   Since the inequalities are joined with *or*, find the union of the two solution sets. The union is shown in **FIGURE 8** and is written

$$(-\infty, 1) \cup [3, \infty).$$

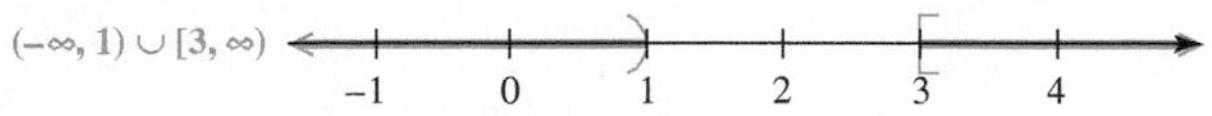

$(-\infty, 1) \cup [3, \infty)$

FIGURE 8

NOW TRY

⚠ **CAUTION**   When inequalities are used to write the solution set in **Example 6**, it *must* be written as

$$x < 1 \quad or \quad x \geq 3,$$

which keeps the numbers 1 and 3 in their order on the number line. Writing $3 \leq x < 1$, which translates using *and*, would imply that $3 \leq 1$, which is *FALSE*. There is no other way to write the solution set of such a union.

NOW TRY ANSWER
6. $(-\infty, -1) \cup [2, \infty)$

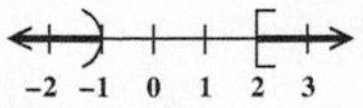

NOW TRY
EXERCISE 7
Solve and graph.

$-x + 2 < 6$ or $6x - 8 \geq 10$

EXAMPLE 7 Solving a Compound Inequality with *or*

Solve the compound inequality, and graph the solution set.

$$-4x + 1 \geq 9 \quad \text{or} \quad 5x + 3 \leq -12$$

Step 1 Solve each inequality individually.

$-4x + 1 \geq 9$		or $5x + 3 \leq -12$	
$-4x \geq 8$	Subtract 1.	or $5x \leq -15$	Subtract 3.
$x \leq -2$	Divide by −4.	or $x \leq -3$	Divide by 5.

The graphs of these two inequalities are shown in **FIGURE 9**.

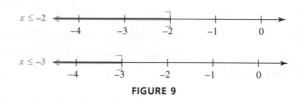

FIGURE 9

Step 2 By taking the union, we obtain the interval $(-\infty, -2]$. See **FIGURE 10**.

FIGURE 10

NOW TRY

NOW TRY
EXERCISE 8
Solve and graph.

$8x - 4 \geq 20$ or
$\qquad -2x + 1 > -9$

EXAMPLE 8 Solving a Compound Inequality with *or*

Solve the compound inequality, and graph the solution set.

$$-2x + 5 \geq 11 \quad \text{or} \quad 4x - 7 \geq -27$$

Step 1 Solve each inequality separately.

$-2x + 5 \geq 11$		or $4x - 7 \geq -27$	
$-2x \geq 6$	Subtract 5.	or $4x \geq -20$	Add 7.
$x \leq -3$	Divide by −2.	or $x \geq -5$	Divide by 4.

The graphs of these two inequalities are shown in **FIGURE 11**.

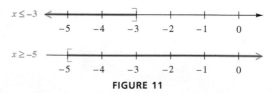

FIGURE 11

Step 2 By taking the union, we obtain every real number as a solution, since every real number satisfies at least one of the two inequalities. The set of all real numbers is written in interval notation as $(-\infty, \infty)$ and graphed as in **FIGURE 12**.

NOW TRY ANSWERS
7. $(-4, \infty)$

8. $(-\infty, \infty)$

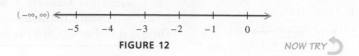

FIGURE 12

NOW TRY

*NOW TRY
EXERCISE 9*

In **Example 9,** list the elements that satisfy each set.

(a) The set of films with admissions greater than 140,000,000 and gross income less than $1,200,000,000

(b) The set of films with admissions less than 200,000,000 or gross income less than $1,200,000,000

EXAMPLE 9 Applying Intersection and Union

The five highest-grossing domestic films (adjusted for inflation) as of 2009 are listed in the table.

Five All-Time Highest-Grossing Domestic Films

Film	Admissions	Gross Income
Gone with the Wind	202,044,600	$1,450,680,400
Star Wars	178,119,600	$1,278,898,700
The Sound of Music	142,415,400	$1,022,542,400
E.T.	141,854,300	$1,018,514,100
The Ten Commandments	131,000,000	$ 940,580,000

Source: boxofficemojo.com.

List the elements of the following sets.

(a) The set of the top five films with admissions greater than 180,000,000 *and* gross income greater than $1,000,000,000

The only film that satisfies both conditions is *Gone with the Wind,* so the set is

$$\{Gone\ with\ the\ Wind\}.$$

(b) The set of the top five films with admissions less than 140,000,000 *or* gross income greater than $1,000,000,000

Here, any film that satisfies at least one of the conditions is in the set. This set includes all five films:

$$\{Gone\ with\ the\ Wind,\ Star\ Wars,\ The\ Sound\ of\ Music,\ E.T.,\ The\ Ten\ Commandments\}.$$

NOW TRY

NOW TRY ANSWERS
9. **(a)** {*The Sound of Music, E.T.*}
　(b) {*Star Wars, The Sound of Music, E.T., The Ten Commandments*}

9.1 EXERCISES

MyMathLab 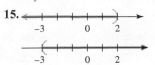   READ REVIEW

Complete solution available on the Video Resources on DVD

Concept Check   *Decide whether each statement is* true *or* false. *If it is false, explain why.*

1. The union of the solution sets of $x + 1 = 6$, $x + 1 < 6$, and $x + 1 > 6$ is $(-\infty, \infty)$.

2. The intersection of the sets $\{x \mid x \geq 9\}$ and $\{x \mid x \leq 9\}$ is $\emptyset$.

3. The union of the sets $(-\infty, 7)$ and $(7, \infty)$ is $\{7\}$.

4. The intersection of the sets $(-\infty, 7]$ and $[7, \infty)$ is $\{7\}$.

5. The intersection of the set of rational numbers and the set of irrational numbers is $\{0\}$.

6. The union of the set of rational numbers and the set of irrational numbers is the set of real numbers.

Let $A = \{1, 2, 3, 4, 5, 6\}$, $B = \{1, 3, 5\}$, $C = \{1, 6\}$ *and* $D = \{4\}$. *Specify each set.*
See Examples 1 and 5.

7. $B \cap A$ **8.** $A \cap B$ **9.** $A \cap D$ **10.** $B \cap C$

11. $B \cap \emptyset$ **12.** $A \cap \emptyset$ **13.** $A \cup B$ **14.** $B \cup D$

Concept Check   *Two sets are specified by graphs. Graph the intersection of the two sets.*

15.

16.

17.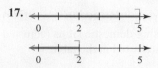

18.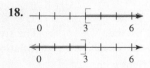

For each compound inequality, give the solution set in both interval and graph form. **See Examples 2–4.**

19. $x < 2$ and $x > -3$ **20.** $x < 5$ and $x > 0$

21. $x \le 2$ and $x \le 5$ **22.** $x \ge 3$ and $x \ge 6$

23. $x \le 3$ and $x \ge 6$ **24.** $x \le -1$ and $x \ge 3$

25. $x - 3 \le 6$ and $x + 2 \ge 7$ **26.** $x + 5 \le 11$ and $x - 3 \ge -1$

27. $-3x > 3$ and $x + 3 > 0$ **28.** $-3x < 3$ and $x + 2 < 6$

29. $3x - 4 \le 8$ and $-4x + 1 \ge -15$ **30.** $7x + 6 \le 48$ and $-4x \ge -24$

Concept Check   *Two sets are specified by graphs. Graph the union of the two sets.*

31.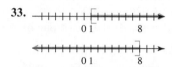

32.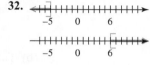

33.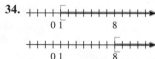

34.

For each compound inequality, give the solution set in both interval and graph form. **See Examples 6–8.**

35. $x \le 1$ or $x \le 8$ **36.** $x \ge 1$ or $x \ge 8$

37. $x \ge -2$ or $x \ge 5$ **38.** $x \le -2$ or $x \le 6$

39. $x \ge -2$ or $x \le 4$ **40.** $x \ge 5$ or $x \le 7$

41. $x + 2 > 7$ or $1 - x > 6$ **42.** $x + 1 > 3$ or $x + 4 < 2$

43. $x + 1 > 3$ or $-4x + 1 > 5$ **44.** $3x < x + 12$ or $x + 1 > 10$

45. $4x + 1 \ge -7$ or $-2x + 3 \ge 5$ **46.** $3x + 2 \le -7$ or $-2x + 1 \le 9$

Concept Check   *Express each set in the simplest interval form. (Hint: Graph each set and look for the intersection or union.)*

47. $(-\infty, -1] \cap [-4, \infty)$ **48.** $[-1, \infty) \cap (-\infty, 9]$

49. $(-\infty, -6] \cap [-9, \infty)$ **50.** $(5, 11] \cap [6, \infty)$

51. $(-\infty, 3) \cup (-\infty, -2)$ **52.** $[-9, 1] \cup (-\infty, -3)$

53. $[3, 6] \cup (4, 9)$ **54.** $[-1, 2] \cup (0, 5)$

For each compound inequality, decide whether intersection *or* union *should be used. Then give the solution set in both interval and graph form.* **See Examples 2–4 and 6–8.**

55. $x < -1$ and $x > -5$ **56.** $x > -1$ and $x < 7$

57. $x < 4$ or $x < -2$ **58.** $x < 5$ or $x < -3$

59. $-3x \le -6$ or $-3x \ge 0$ **60.** $2x - 6 \le -18$ and $2x \ge -18$

61. $x + 1 \ge 5$ and $x - 2 \le 10$ **62.** $-8x \le -24$ or $-5x \ge 15$

Average expenses for full-time resident college students at 4-year institutions during the 2007–2008 academic year are shown in the table.

College Expenses (in Dollars), 4-Year Institutions

Type of Expense	Public Schools (in-state)	Private Schools
Tuition and fees	5950	21,588
Board rates	3402	3993
Dormitory charges	4072	4812

Source: National Center for Education Statistics.

Refer to the table on college expenses. List the elements of each set. **See Example 9.**

63. The set of expenses that are less than $6500 for public schools *and* are greater than $10,000 for private schools

64. The set of expenses that are greater than $3000 for public schools *and* are less than $4000 for private schools

65. The set of expenses that are less than $6500 for public schools *or* are greater than $10,000 for private schools

66. The set of expenses that are greater than $12,000 *or* are between $5000 and $6000

RELATING CONCEPTS EXERCISES 67–72

FOR INDIVIDUAL OR GROUP WORK

The figures represent the backyards of neighbors Luigi, Maria, Than, and Joe. Find the area and the perimeter of each yard. Suppose that each resident has 150 ft of fencing and enough sod to cover 1400 ft^2 of lawn. Give the name or names of the residents whose yards satisfy each description. **Work Exercises 67–72 in order.**

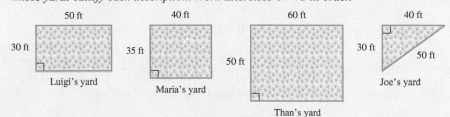

67. The yard can be fenced *and* the yard can be sodded.

68. The yard can be fenced *and* the yard cannot be sodded.

69. The yard cannot be fenced *and* the yard can be sodded.

70. The yard cannot be fenced *and* the yard cannot be sodded.

71. The yard can be fenced *or* the yard can be sodded.

72. The yard cannot be fenced *or* the yard can be sodded.

PREVIEW EXERCISES

Solve each three-part inequality. **See Section 2.8.**

73. $-5 < 2x + 1 < 5$ **74.** $-7 \leq 3x - 2 < 7$

Evaluate. **See Sections 1.4 and 1.5.**

75. $-|6| - |-11| + (-4)$ **76.** $(-5) - |-9| + |5 - 4|$

77. *True* or *false*? The absolute value of a number is always positive.

78. *True* or *false*? If $a < 0$, then $|a| = -a$.

9.2 Absolute Value Equations and Inequalities

OBJECTIVES

1. Use the distance definition of absolute value.

2. Solve equations of the form $|ax + b| = k$, for $k > 0$.

3. Solve inequalities of the form $|ax + b| < k$ and of the form $|ax + b| > k$, for $k > 0$.

4. Solve absolute value equations that involve rewriting.

5. Solve equations of the form $|ax + b| = |cx + d|$.

6. Solve special cases of absolute value equations and inequalities.

Suppose that the government of a country decides that it will comply with a certain restriction on greenhouse gas emissions *within* 3 years of 2020. This means that the *difference* between the year it will comply and 2020 is less than 3, *without regard to sign*. We state this mathematically as

$$|x - 2020| < 3, \qquad \text{Absolute value inequality}$$

where x represents the year in which it complies.

Reasoning tells us that the year must be between 2017 and 2023, and thus $2017 < x < 2023$ makes this inequality true. But what general procedure is used to solve such an inequality? We now investigate how to solve absolute value equations and inequalities.

OBJECTIVE 1 **Use the distance definition of absolute value.** In **Section 1.4**, we saw that the absolute value of a number x, written $|x|$, represents the distance from x to 0 on the number line. For example, the solutions of $|x| = 4$ are 4 and -4, as shown in **FIGURE 13**.

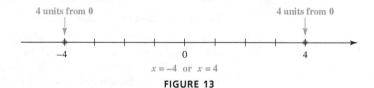

$x = -4$ or $x = 4$

FIGURE 13

Because absolute value represents distance from 0, we interpret the solutions of $|x| > 4$ to be all numbers that are *more* than four units from 0. The set $(-\infty, -4) \cup (4, \infty)$ fits this description. **FIGURE 14** shows the graph of the solution set of $|x| > 4$. Because the graph consists of two separate intervals, the solution set is described using the word *or*: $x < -4$ or $x > 4$.

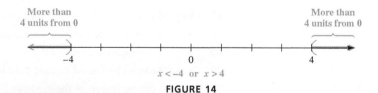

$x < -4$ or $x > 4$

FIGURE 14

The solution set of $|x| < 4$ consists of all numbers that are *less* than 4 units from 0 on the number line. This is represented by all numbers *between* -4 and 4. This set of numbers is given by $(-4, 4)$, as shown in **FIGURE 15**. Here, the graph shows that $-4 < x < 4$, which means $x > -4$ *and* $x < 4$.

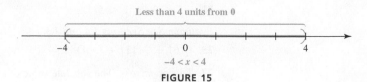

$-4 < x < 4$

FIGURE 15

The equation and inequalities just described are examples of **absolute value equations and inequalities.** They involve the absolute value of a variable expression and generally take the form

$$|ax + b| = k, \qquad |ax + b| > k, \qquad \text{or} \qquad |ax + b| < k,$$

where k is a positive number. From **FIGURES 13–15**, we see that

$$|x| = 4 \quad \text{has the same solution set as} \quad x = -4 \quad \text{or} \quad x = 4,$$
$$|x| > 4 \quad \text{has the same solution set as} \quad x < -4 \quad \text{or} \quad x > 4,$$
$$|x| < 4 \quad \text{has the same solution set as} \quad x > -4 \quad \text{and} \quad x < 4.$$

Thus, we solve an absolute value equation or inequality by solving the appropriate compound equation or inequality.

Solving Absolute Value Equations and Inequalities

Let k be a positive real number and p and q be real numbers.

Case 1   To solve $|ax + b| = k$, solve the following compound equation.

$$ax + b = k \quad \text{or} \quad ax + b = -k$$

The solution set is usually of the form $\{p, q\}$, which includes two numbers.

Case 2   To solve $|ax + b| > k$, solve the following compound inequality.

$$ax + b > k \quad \text{or} \quad ax + b < -k$$

The solution set is of the form $(-\infty, p) \cup (q, \infty)$, which is a disjoint interval.

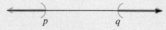

Case 3   To solve $|ax + b| < k$, solve the following three-part inequality.

$$-k < ax + b < k$$

The solution set is of the form (p, q), a single interval.

NOTE   Some people prefer to write the compound statements in Cases 1 and 2 of the preceding box as follows.

$$ax + b = k \quad \text{or} \quad -(ax + b) = k \qquad \text{Alternative for Case 1}$$
$$\text{and} \qquad ax + b > k \quad \text{or} \quad -(ax + b) > k \qquad \text{Alternative for Case 2}$$

These forms produce the same results.

OBJECTIVE 2   **Solve equations of the form** $|ax + b| = k$, **for** $k > 0$. *Remember that because absolute value refers to distance from the origin, an absolute value equation will have two parts.*

NOW TRY
EXERCISE 1
Solve $|4x - 1| = 11$.

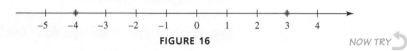

EXAMPLE 1   Solving an Absolute Value Equation

Solve $|2x + 1| = 7$. Graph the solution set.

For $|2x + 1|$ to equal 7, $2x + 1$ must be 7 units from 0 on the number line. This can happen only when $2x + 1 = 7$ or $2x + 1 = -7$. This is Case 1 in the preceding box. Solve this compound equation as follows.

$$2x + 1 = 7 \quad \text{or} \quad 2x + 1 = -7$$
$$2x = 6 \quad \text{or} \qquad 2x = -8 \qquad \text{Subtract 1.}$$
$$x = 3 \quad \text{or} \qquad x = -4 \qquad \text{Divide by 2.}$$

Check by substituting 3 and then -4 into the original absolute value equation to verify that the solution set is $\{-4, 3\}$. The graph is shown in **FIGURE 16**.

FIGURE 16   NOW TRY

OBJECTIVE 3   Solve inequalities of the form $|ax + b| < k$ and of the form $|ax + b| > k$, for $k > 0$.

NOW TRY
EXERCISE 2
Solve $|4x - 1| > 11$.

EXAMPLE 2   Solving an Absolute Value Inequality with >

Solve $|2x + 1| > 7$. Graph the solution set.

By Case 2 described in the previous box, this absolute value inequality is rewritten as

$$2x + 1 > 7 \quad \text{or} \quad 2x + 1 < -7,$$

because $2x + 1$ must represent a number that is *more* than 7 units from 0 on either side of the number line. Now, solve the compound inequality.

$$2x + 1 > 7 \quad \text{or} \quad 2x + 1 < -7$$
$$2x > 6 \quad \text{or} \qquad 2x < -8 \qquad \text{Subtract 1.}$$
$$x > 3 \quad \text{or} \qquad x < -4 \qquad \text{Divide by 2.}$$

Check these solutions. The solution set is $(-\infty, -4) \cup (3, \infty)$. See **FIGURE 17**. Notice that the graph is a disjoint interval.

FIGURE 17   NOW TRY

EXAMPLE 3   Solving an Absolute Value Inequality with <

Solve $|2x + 1| < 7$. Graph the solution set.

The expression $2x + 1$ must represent a number that is less than 7 units from 0 on either side of the number line. That is, $2x + 1$ must be between -7 and 7. As Case 3 in the previous box shows, that relationship is written as a three-part inequality.

$$-7 < 2x + 1 < 7$$
$$-8 < \quad 2x \quad < 6 \qquad \text{Subtract 1 from each part.}$$
$$-4 < \quad x \quad < 3 \qquad \text{Divide each part by 2.}$$

NOW TRY ANSWERS
1. $\left\{-\frac{5}{2}, 3\right\}$
2. $\left(-\infty, -\frac{5}{2}\right) \cup (3, \infty)$

NOW TRY
EXERCISE 3

Solve $|4x - 1| < 11$.

Check that the solution set is $(-4, 3)$. The graph consists of the single interval shown in **FIGURE 18**.

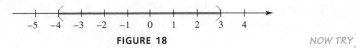

FIGURE 18   NOW TRY

Look back at **FIGURES 16, 17, AND 18**, with the graphs of

$$|2x + 1| = 7, \quad |2x + 1| > 7, \quad \text{and} \quad |2x + 1| < 7,$$

respectively. If we find the union of the three sets, we get the set of all real numbers. This is because, for any value of x, $|2x + 1|$ will satisfy one and only one of the following: It is equal to 7, greater than 7, or less than 7.

⚠ **CAUTION**   When solving absolute value equations and inequalities of the types in **Examples 1, 2, and 3,** remember the following.

1. The methods described apply when the constant is alone on one side of the equation or inequality and is *positive.*

2. Absolute value equations and absolute value inequalities of the form $|ax + b| > k$ translate into "or" compound statements.

3. Absolute value inequalities of the form $|ax + b| < k$ translate into "and" compound statements, which may be written as three-part inequalities.

4. An "or" statement *cannot* be written in three parts. It would be incorrect to write $-7 > 2x + 1 > 7$ in **Example 2,** because this would imply that $-7 > 7$, which is *false.*

OBJECTIVE 4   **Solve absolute value equations that involve rewriting.**

NOW TRY
EXERCISE 4

Solve $|10x - 2| - 2 = 12$.

EXAMPLE 4   Solving an Absolute Value Equation That Requires Rewriting

Solve $|x + 3| + 5 = 12$.

First isolate the absolute value expression on one side of the equals symbol.

$$|x + 3| + 5 = 12$$
$$|x + 3| + 5 - 5 = 12 - 5 \qquad \text{Subtract 5.}$$
$$|x + 3| = 7 \qquad \text{Combine like terms.}$$

Now use the method shown in **Example 1** to solve $|x + 3| = 7$.

$$x + 3 = 7 \quad \text{or} \quad x + 3 = -7$$
$$x = 4 \quad \text{or} \qquad x = -10 \qquad \text{Subtract 3.}$$

Check these solutions by substituting each one in the original equation.

CHECK $|x + 3| + 5 = 12$

$|4 + 3| + 5 \overset{?}{=} 12$ Let $x = 4$. $\quad$ $|-10 + 3| + 5 \overset{?}{=} 12$ Let $x = -10$.

$|7| + 5 \overset{?}{=} 12$ $\quad\quad\quad\quad\quad\quad\quad\quad\quad$ $|-7| + 5 \overset{?}{=} 12$

$12 = 12 \checkmark$ True $\quad\quad\quad\quad\quad\quad\quad$ $12 = 12 \checkmark$ True

NOW TRY ANSWERS

3. $\left(-\frac{5}{2}, 3\right)$ **4.** $\left\{-\frac{6}{5}, \frac{8}{5}\right\}$

The check confirms that the solution set is $\{-10, 4\}$.   NOW TRY

NOW TRY
EXERCISE 5

Solve each inequality.

(a) $|x - 1| - 4 \leq 2$

(b) $|x - 1| - 4 \geq 2$

EXAMPLE 5 Solving Absolute Value Inequalities That Require Rewriting

Solve each inequality.

(a)
$$|x + 3| + 5 \geq 12$$
$$|x + 3| \geq 7$$
$$x + 3 \geq 7 \quad \text{or} \quad x + 3 \leq -7$$
$$x \geq 4 \quad \text{or} \quad x \leq -10$$
Solution set: $(-\infty, -10] \cup [4, \infty)$

(b)
$$|x + 3| + 5 \leq 12$$
$$|x + 3| \leq 7$$
$$-7 \leq x + 3 \leq 7$$
$$-10 \leq \quad x \quad \leq 4$$
Solution set: $[-10, 4]$

NOW TRY

OBJECTIVE 5 **Solve equations of the form $|ax + b| = |cx + d|$.** *If two expressions have the same absolute value, they must either be equal or be negatives of each other.*

Solving $|ax + b| = |cx + d|$

To solve an absolute value equation of the form
$$|ax + b| = |cx + d|,$$
solve the following compound equation.
$$ax + b = cx + d \quad \text{or} \quad ax + b = -(cx + d)$$

NOW TRY
EXERCISE 6

Solve
$$|3x - 4| = |5x + 12|.$$

EXAMPLE 6 Solving an Equation with Two Absolute Values

Solve $|x + 6| = |2x - 3|$.

This equation is satisfied either if $x + 6$ and $2x - 3$ are equal to each other or if $x + 6$ and $2x - 3$ are negatives of each other.

$x + 6 = 2x - 3$	or $x + 6 = -(2x - 3)$	
$x + 9 = 2x$ Add 3.	or $x + 6 = -2x + 3$	Distributive property
$9 = x$ Subtract x.	or $\quad 3x = -3$	Subtract 6.
	$x = -1$	Divide by 3.

Check that the solution set is $\{-1, 9\}$.

NOW TRY

OBJECTIVE 6 **Solve special cases of absolute value equations and inequalities.** When an absolute value equation or inequality involves a *negative constant or 0* alone on one side, use the properties of absolute value to solve the equation or inequality.

Special Cases of Absolute Value

Case 1 The absolute value of an expression can never be negative. That is, $|a| \geq 0$ for all real numbers a.

Case 2 The absolute value of an expression equals 0 only when the expression is equal to 0.

NOW TRY ANSWERS
5. (a) $[-5, 7]$
   (b) $(-\infty, -5] \cup [7, \infty)$
6. $\{-8, -1\}$

NOW TRY
EXERCISE 7

Solve each equation.

(a) $|3x - 8| = -2$

(b) $|7x + 12| = 0$

EXAMPLE 7 Solving Special Cases of Absolute Value Equations

Solve each equation.

(a) $|5x - 3| = -4$

See Case 1 in the preceding box. *The absolute value of an expression can never be negative,* so there are no solutions for this equation. The solution set is $\emptyset$.

(b) $|7x - 3| = 0$

See Case 2 in the preceding box. The expression $|7x - 3|$ will equal 0 *only* if

$$7x - 3 = 0$$
$$7x = 3 \qquad \text{Add 3.}$$

Check by substituting in the original equation.

$$x = \frac{3}{7}. \qquad \text{Divide by 7.}$$

The solution of this equation is $\frac{3}{7}$. Thus, the solution set is $\left\{\frac{3}{7}\right\}$, with just one element.

NOW TRY

NOW TRY
EXERCISE 8

Solve each inequality.

(a) $|x| > -10$

(b) $|4x + 1| + 5 < 4$

(c) $|x - 2| - 3 \le -3$

EXAMPLE 8 Solving Special Cases of Absolute Value Inequalities

Solve each inequality.

(a) $|x| \ge -4$

The absolute value of a number is always greater than or equal to 0. Thus, $|x| \ge -4$ is true for *all* real numbers. The solution set is $(-\infty, \infty)$.

(b)
$$|x + 6| - 3 < -5$$
$$|x + 6| < -2 \qquad \text{Add 3 to each side.}$$

There is no number whose absolute value is less than -2, so this inequality has no solution. The solution set is $\emptyset$.

(c)
$$|x - 7| + 4 \le 4$$
$$|x - 7| \le 0 \qquad \text{Subtract 4 from each side.}$$

The value of $|x - 7|$ will never be less than 0. However, $|x - 7|$ will equal 0 when $x = 7$. Therefore, the solution set is $\{7\}$.

NOW TRY

CONNECTIONS

Absolute value is used to find the *relative error* of a measurement. If x_t represents the expected measurement and x represents the actual measurement, then the relative error in x equals the absolute value of the difference between x_t and x, divided by x_t.

$$\text{relative error in } x = \left| \frac{x_t - x}{x_t} \right|$$

In quality control situations, the relative error often must be less than some predetermined amount. For example, suppose a machine filling *quart* milk cartons is set for a relative error *no greater than* 0.05. Here $x_t = 32$ oz, the relative error $= 0.05$ oz, and we must find x, given the following condition.

$$\left| \frac{32 - x}{32} \right| \le 0.05 \qquad \text{No greater than translates as } \le.$$

For Discussion or Writing

With this tolerance level, how many *ounces* may a carton contain?

NOW TRY ANSWERS

7. (a) $\emptyset$ **(b)** $\left\{-\frac{12}{7}\right\}$

8. (a) $(-\infty, \infty)$ **(b)** $\emptyset$ **(c)** $\{2\}$

9.2 EXERCISES

🌐 *Complete solution available on the Video Resources on DVD*

Concept Check *Match each absolute value equation or inequality in Column I with the graph of its solution set in Column II.*

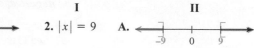

I		**II**	**I**		**II**
1. $\lvert x \rvert = 5$	**A.**		**2.** $\lvert x \rvert = 9$	**A.**	
$\lvert x \rvert < 5$	**B.**		$\lvert x \rvert > 9$	**B.**	
$\lvert x \rvert > 5$	**C.**		$\lvert x \rvert \geq 9$	**C.**	
$\lvert x \rvert \leq 5$	**D.**		$\lvert x \rvert < 9$	**D.**	
$\lvert x \rvert \geq 5$	**E.**		$\lvert x \rvert \leq 9$	**E.**	

3. *Concept Check* How many solutions will $\lvert ax + b \rvert = k$ have for each situation?

  (a) $k = 0$ **(b)** $k > 0$ **(c)** $k < 0$

📝 **4.** Explain when to use *and* and when to use *or* if you are solving an absolute value equation or inequality of the form $\lvert ax + b \rvert = k$, $\lvert ax + b \rvert < k$, or $\lvert ax + b \rvert > k$, where k is a positive number.

Solve each equation. **See Example 1.**

5. $\lvert x \rvert = 12$	**6.** $\lvert x \rvert = 14$	**7.** $\lvert 4x \rvert = 20$
8. $\lvert 5x \rvert = 30$	**9.** $\lvert x - 3 \rvert = 9$	**10.** $\lvert x - 5 \rvert = 13$
🌐 **11.** $\lvert 2x - 1 \rvert = 11$	**12.** $\lvert 2x + 3 \rvert = 19$	**13.** $\lvert 4x - 5 \rvert = 17$
14. $\lvert 5x - 1 \rvert = 21$	**15.** $\lvert 2x + 5 \rvert = 14$	**16.** $\lvert 2x - 9 \rvert = 18$
17. $\left\lvert \frac{1}{2}x + 3 \right\rvert = 2$	**18.** $\left\lvert \frac{2}{3}x - 1 \right\rvert = 5$	**19.** $\left\lvert 1 + \frac{3}{4}x \right\rvert = 7$
20. $\left\lvert 2 - \frac{5}{2}x \right\rvert = 14$	**21.** $\lvert 0.02x - 1 \rvert = 2.50$	**22.** $\lvert 0.04x - 3 \rvert = 5.96$

Solve each inequality, and graph the solution set. **See Example 2.**

23. $\lvert x \rvert > 3$	**24.** $\lvert x \rvert > 5$	**25.** $\lvert x \rvert \geq 4$
26. $\lvert x \rvert \geq 6$	🌐 **27.** $\lvert r + 5 \rvert \geq 20$	**28.** $\lvert 3r - 1 \rvert \geq 8$
29. $\lvert x + 2 \rvert > 10$	**30.** $\lvert 4x + 1 \rvert \geq 21$	**31.** $\lvert 3 - x \rvert > 5$
32. $\lvert 5 - x \rvert > 3$	**33.** $\lvert -5x + 3 \rvert \geq 12$	**34.** $\lvert -2x - 4 \rvert \geq 5$

35. *Concept Check* The graph of the solution set of $\lvert 2x + 1 \rvert = 9$ is given here.

Without actually doing the algebraic work, graph the solution set of each inequality, referring to the graph shown.

  (a) $\lvert 2x + 1 \rvert < 9$ **(b)** $\lvert 2x + 1 \rvert > 9$

36. *Concept Check* The graph of the solution set of $|3x - 4| < 5$ is given here.

Without actually doing the algebraic work, graph the solution set of the following, referring to the graph shown.

(a) $|3x - 4| = 5$ (b) $|3x - 4| > 5$

Solve each inequality, and graph the solution set. ***See Example 3.*** *(Hint: Compare your answers with those in* ***Exercises 23–34.****)*

37. $|x| \leq 3$ **38.** $|x| \leq 5$ **39.** $|x| < 4$

40. $|x| < 6$ **41.** $|r + 5| < 20$ **42.** $|3r - 1| < 8$

43. $|x + 2| \leq 10$ **44.** $|4x + 1| < 21$ **45.** $|3 - x| \leq 5$

46. $|5 - x| \leq 3$ **47.** $|-5x + 3| < 12$ **48.** $|-2x - 4| < 5$

In Exercises 49–66, decide which method of solution applies, and find the solution set. In Exercises 49–60, graph the solution set. ***See Examples 1–3.***

49. $|-4 + x| > 9$ **50.** $|-3 + x| > 8$ **51.** $|x + 5| > 20$

52. $|2x - 1| < 7$ **53.** $|7 + 2x| = 5$ **54.** $|9 - 3x| = 3$

55. $|3x - 1| \leq 11$ **56.** $|2x - 6| \leq 6$ **57.** $|-6x - 6| \leq 1$

58. $|-2x - 6| \leq 5$ **59.** $|2x - 1| \geq 7$ **60.** $|-4 + x| \leq 9$

61. $|x + 2| = 3$ **62.** $|x + 3| = 10$ **63.** $|x - 6| = 3$

64. $|x - 4| = 1$ **65.** $|2 - 0.2x| = 2$ **66.** $|5 - 0.5x| = 4$

Solve each equation or inequality. ***See Examples 4 and 5.***

67. $|x| - 1 = 4$ **68.** $|x| + 3 = 10$ 🌐 **69.** $|x + 4| + 1 = 2$

70. $|x + 5| - 2 = 12$ **71.** $|2x + 1| + 3 > 8$ **72.** $|6x - 1| - 2 > 6$

73. $|x + 5| - 6 \leq -1$ **74.** $|x - 2| - 3 \leq 4$

75. $\left|\dfrac{1}{2}x + \dfrac{1}{3}\right| + \dfrac{1}{4} - \dfrac{3}{4}$ **76.** $\left|\dfrac{2}{3}x + \dfrac{1}{6}\right| + \dfrac{1}{2} = \dfrac{5}{2}$

77. $|0.1x - 2.5| + 0.3 \geq 0.8$ **78.** $|0.5x - 3.5| + 0.2 \geq 0.6$

Solve each equation. ***See Example 6.***

🌐 **79.** $|3x + 1| = |2x + 4|$ **80.** $|7x + 12| = |x - 8|$ **81.** $\left|x - \dfrac{1}{2}\right| = \left|\dfrac{1}{2}x - 2\right|$

82. $\left|\dfrac{2}{3}x - 2\right| = \left|\dfrac{1}{3}x + 3\right|$ **83.** $|6x| = |9x + 1|$ **84.** $|13x| = |2x + 1|$

85. $|2x - 6| = |2x + 11|$ **86.** $|3x - 1| = |3x + 9|$

Solve each equation or inequality. ***See Examples 7 and 8.***

🌐 **87.** $|x| \geq -10$ **88.** $|x| \geq -15$ 🌐 **89.** $|12t - 3| = -8$

90. $|13x + 1| = -3$ **91.** $|4x + 1| = 0$ **92.** $|6x - 2| = 0$

93. $|2x - 1| = -6$ **94.** $|8x + 4| = -4$ **95.** $|x + 5| > -9$

96. $|x + 9| > -3$ **97.** $|7x + 3| \leq 0$ **98.** $|4x - 1| \leq 0$

99. $|5x - 2| = 0$ **100.** $|7x + 4| = 0$ **101.** $|x - 2| + 3 \geq 2$

102. $|x - 4| + 5 \geq 4$ **103.** $|10x + 7| + 3 < 1$ **104.** $|4x + 1| - 2 < -5$

105. The recommended daily intake (RDI) of calcium for females aged 19–50 is 1000 mg. Actual needs vary from person to person. Write this statement as an absolute value inequality, with x representing the RDI, to express the RDI plus or minus 100 mg, and solve the inequality. (*Source:* National Academy of Sciences—Institute of Medicine.)

106. The average clotting time of blood is 7.45 sec, with a variation of plus or minus 3.6 sec. Write this statement as an absolute value inequality, with x representing the time, and solve the inequality.

RELATING CONCEPTS   EXERCISES 107–110

FOR INDIVIDUAL OR GROUP WORK

The 10 tallest buildings in Houston, Texas, as of 2009 are listed, along with their heights.

Building	Height (in feet)
JPMorgan Chase Tower	1002
Wells Fargo Plaza	992
Williams Tower	901
Bank of America Center	780
Texaco Heritage Plaza	762
Enterprise Plaza	756
Centerpoint Energy Plaza	741
Continental Center I	732
Fulbright Tower	725
One Shell Plaza	714

Source: World Almanac and Book of Facts.

Use this information to **work Exercises 107–110 in order.**

107. To find the average of a group of numbers, we add the numbers and then divide by the number of numbers added. Use a calculator to find the average of the heights.

108. Let k represent the average height of these buildings. If a height x satisfies the inequality

$$|x - k| < t,$$

then the height is said to be within t feet of the average. Using your result from **Exercise 107,** list the buildings that are within 50 ft of the average.

109. Repeat **Exercise 108,** but list the buildings that are within 95 ft of the average.

110. (a) Write an absolute value inequality that describes the height of a building that is *not* within 95 ft of the average. Solve this inequality.

(b) Use the result of part (a) to list the buildings that are not within 95 ft of the average. Does your answer makes sense compared with your answer to **Exercise 109.**

PREVIEW EXERCISES

Graph each equation. **See Sections 3.2 and 7.1.**

111. $x - y = 5$

112. $x = -5y$

Decide whether each ordered pair is a solution of the equation. **See Section 3.1.**

113. $3x - 4y = 12$; $(-4, 3)$

114. $x + 2y = 0$; $(2, -1)$

SUMMARY EXERCISES on Solving Linear and Absolute Value Equations and Inequalities

Solve each equation or inequality. Give the solution set in set notation for equations and in interval notation for inequalities.

1. $4x + 1 = 49$

2. $|x - 1| = 6$

3. $6x - 9 = 12 + 3x$

4. $3x + 7 = 9 + 8x$

5. $|x + 3| = -4$

6. $2x + 1 \leq x$

7. $8x + 2 \geq 5x$

8. $4(x - 11) + 3x = 20x - 31$

9. $2x - 1 = -7$

10. $|3x - 7| - 4 = 0$

11. $6x - 5 \leq 3x + 10$

12. $|5x - 8| + 9 \geq 7$

13. $9x - 3(x + 1) = 8x - 7$

14. $|x| \geq 8$

15. $9x - 5 \geq 9x + 3$

16. $13x - 5 > 13x - 8$

17. $|x| < 5.5$

18. $4x - 1 = 12 + x$

19. $\dfrac{2}{3}x + 8 = \dfrac{1}{4}x$

20. $-\dfrac{5}{8}x \geq -20$

21. $\dfrac{1}{4}x < -6$

22. $7x - 3 + 2x = 9x - 8x$

23. $\dfrac{3}{5}x - \dfrac{1}{10} = 2$

24. $|x - 1| < 7$

25. $x + 9 + 7x = 4(3 + 2x) - 3$

26. $6 - 3(2 - x) < 2(1 + x) + 3$

27. $|2x - 3| > 11$

28. $\dfrac{x}{4} - \dfrac{2x}{3} = -10$

29. $|5x + 1| \leq 0$

30. $5x - (3 + x) \geq 2(3x + 1)$

31. $-2 \leq 3x - 1 \leq 8$

32. $-1 \leq 6 - x \leq 5$

33. $|7x - 1| = |5x + 3|$

34. $|x + 2| = |x + 4|$

35. $|1 - 3x| \geq 4$

36. $\dfrac{1}{2} \leq \dfrac{2}{3}x \leq \dfrac{5}{4}$

37. $-(x + 4) + 2 = 3x + 8$

38. $\dfrac{x}{6} - \dfrac{3x}{5} = x - 86$

39. $-6 \leq \dfrac{3}{2} - x \leq 6$

40. $|5 - x| < 4$

41. $|x - 1| \geq -6$

42. $|2x - 5| = |x + 4|$

43. $8x - (1 - x) = 3(1 + 3x) - 4$

44. $8x - (x + 3) = -(2x + 1) - 12$

45. $|x - 5| = |x + 9|$

46. $|x + 2| < -3$

47. $2x + 1 > 5$ or $3x + 4 < 1$

48. $1 - 2x \geq 5$ and $7 + 3x \geq -2$

9.3 Linear Inequalities in Two Variables

OBJECTIVES

1 Graph linear inequalities in two variables.

2 Graph an inequality with a boundary line through the origin.

3 Graph the intersection of two linear inequalities.

4 Graph the union of two linear inequalities.

OBJECTIVE 1 Graph linear inequalities in two variables. In **Chapter 2,** we graphed linear inequalities in one variable on the number line. In this section, we graph linear inequalities in two variables on a rectangular coordinate system.

Linear Inequality in Two Variables

An inequality that can be written as

$$Ax + By < C, \quad Ax + By \leq C, \quad Ax + By > C, \quad \text{or} \quad Ax + By \geq C,$$

where A, B, and C are real numbers and A and B are not both 0, is a **linear inequality in two variables.**

Consider the graph in **FIGURE 19**. The graph of the line $x + y = 5$ divides the points in the rectangular coordinate system into three sets:

1. Those points that lie on the line itself and satisfy the equation $x + y = 5$ [like $(0, 5)$, $(2, 3)$, and $(5, 0)$];

2. Those that lie in the half-plane above the line and satisfy the inequality $x + y > 5$ [like $(5, 3)$ and $(2, 4)$];

3. Those that lie in the half-plane below the line and satisfy the inequality $x + y < 5$ [like $(0, 0)$ and $(-3, -1)$].

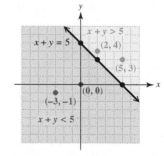

FIGURE 19

The graph of the line $x + y = 5$ is called the **boundary line** for the inequalities $x + y > 5$ and $x + y < 5$. Graphs of linear inequalities in two variables are *regions* in the real number plane that may or may not include boundary lines.

To graph a linear inequality in two variables, follow these steps.

Graphing a Linear Inequality

Step 1 **Draw the graph of the straight line that is the boundary.** Make the line solid if the inequality involves $\leq$ or $\geq$. Make the line dashed if the inequality involves $<$ or $>$.

Step 2 **Choose a test point.** Choose any point not on the line, and substitute the coordinates of that point in the inequality.

Step 3 **Shade the appropriate region.** Shade the region that includes the test point if it satisfies the original inequality. Otherwise, shade the region on the other side of the boundary line.

⚠ **CAUTION** When drawing the boundary line in Step 1, be careful to draw a solid line if the inequality includes equality ($\leq$, $\geq$) or a dashed line if equality is not included ($<$, $>$).

NOW TRY
EXERCISE 1
Graph $-x + 2y \geq 4$.

EXAMPLE 1 Graphing a Linear Inequality

Graph $3x + 2y \geq 6$.

Step 1 First graph the boundary line $3x + 2y = 6$, as shown in **FIGURE 20**.

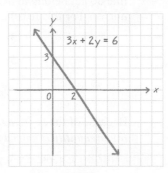

FIGURE 20

Step 2 The graph of the inequality $3x + 2y \geq 6$ includes the points of the line $3x + 2y = 6$ and either the points *above* that line or the points *below* it. To decide which, select any point not on the boundary line to use as a test point. Substitute the values from the test point, here $(0, 0)$, for x and y in the inequality.

$$3x + 2y \geq 6 \qquad \text{Original inequality}$$

(0, 0) is a convenient test point. $\qquad 3(0) + 2(0) \overset{?}{\geq} 6 \qquad \text{Let } x = 0 \text{ and } y = 0.$

$$0 \geq 6 \qquad \text{False}$$

Step 3 Because the result is false, $(0, 0)$ does *not* satisfy the inequality. The solution set includes all points on the other side of the line. See **FIGURE 21**.

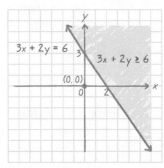

FIGURE 21 *NOW TRY*

If the inequality is written in the form $y > mx + b$ or $y < mx + b$, then the inequality symbol indicates which half-plane to shade.

If $y > mx + b$, then shade above the boundary line.

If $y < mx + b$, then shade below the boundary line.

This method works only if the inequality is solved for y.

⚠ **CAUTION** A common error in using the method just described is to use the original inequality symbol when deciding which half-plane to shade. Be sure to use the inequality symbol found in the inequality *after* it is solved for y.

⟜ NOW TRY
EXERCISE 2
Graph $3x - y < 6$.

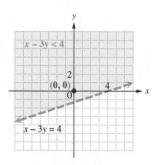

EXAMPLE 2 Graphing a Linear Inequality

Graph $x - 3y < 4$.

First graph the boundary line, shown in **FIGURE 22**. The points of the boundary line do not belong to the inequality $x - 3y < 4$ (because the inequality symbol is $<$, not $\leq$). For this reason, the line is dashed. Now solve the inequality for y.

$$x - 3y < 4$$
$$-3y < -x + 4 \qquad \text{Subtract } x.$$
$$y > \frac{1}{3}x - \frac{4}{3} \qquad \text{Multiply by } -\frac{1}{3}. \text{ Change } < \text{ to } >.$$

Because of the *is greater than* symbol that occurs **when the inequality is solved for y,** shade *above* the line.

CHECK   Choose a test point not on the line, say, $(0, 0)$.

$$x - 3y < 4$$
$$0 - 3(0) \overset{?}{<} 4 \qquad \text{Let } x = 0 \text{ and } y = 0.$$
$$0 < 4 \checkmark \text{ True}$$

This result agrees with the decision to shade above the line. The solution set, graphed in **FIGURE 22**, includes only those points in the shaded half-plane (not those on the line).

FIGURE 22

NOW TRY ⟳

⟜ NOW TRY
EXERCISE 3
Graph $x > 2$.

EXAMPLE 3 Graphing a Linear Inequality with a Vertical Boundary Line

Graph $x < 3$.

First, we graph $x = 3$, a vertical line passing through the point $(3, 0)$. We use a dashed line (why?) and choose $(0, 0)$ as a test point.

$$x < 3 \qquad \text{Original inequality}$$
$$0 \overset{?}{<} 3 \qquad \text{Let } x = 0.$$
$$0 < 3 \qquad \text{True}$$

Since $0 < 3$ is true, we shade the region containing $(0, 0)$, as in **FIGURE 23**.

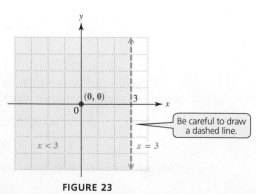

Be careful to draw a dashed line.

FIGURE 23

NOW TRY ⟳

NOW TRY ANSWERS

2. 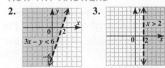 **3.**

OBJECTIVE 2 Graph an inequality with a boundary line through the origin. *If the graph of an inequality has a boundary line that goes through the origin, $(0, 0)$ cannot be used as a test point.*

NOW TRY
EXERCISE 4

Graph $y \leq -2x$.

EXAMPLE 4 Graphing a Linear Inequality with a Boundary Line through the Origin

Graph $x \leq 2y$.

Graph $x = 2y$, using a solid line. Some ordered pairs that can be used to graph this line are $(0, 0)$, $(6, 3)$, and $(4, 2)$. Since $(0, 0)$ is *on* the line $x = 2y$, it cannot be used as a test point. Instead, we choose a test point *off* the line, say $(1, 3)$.

$$x \leq 2y \qquad \text{Original inequality}$$
$$1 \overset{?}{\leq} 2(3) \qquad \text{Let } x = 1 \text{ and } y = 3.$$
$$1 \leq 6 \qquad \text{True}$$

Since $1 \leq 6$ is true, shade the region containing the test point $(1, 3)$. See **FIGURE 24**.

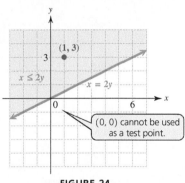

FIGURE 24

NOW TRY

OBJECTIVE 3 **Graph the intersection of two linear inequalities.** A pair of inequalities joined with the word **and** is interpreted as the intersection of the solution sets of the inequalities. ***The graph of the intersection of two or more inequalities is the region of the plane where all points satisfy all of the inequalities at the same time.***

NOW TRY
EXERCISE 5

Graph $x + y < 3$ and $y \leq 2$.

EXAMPLE 5 Graphing the Intersection of Two Inequalities

Graph $2x + 4y \geq 5$ and $x \geq 1$.

To begin, we graph each of the two inequalities $2x + 4y \geq 5$ and $x \geq 1$ separately, as shown in **FIGURES 25(a) AND (b)**. Then we use heavy shading to identify the intersection of the graphs, as shown in **FIGURE 25(c)**.

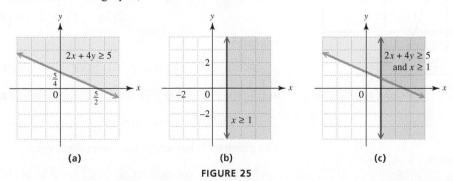

(a)   (b)   (c)

FIGURE 25

NOW TRY ANSWERS

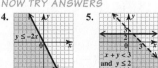

In practice, the graphs in **FIGURES 25(a) AND (b)** are graphed on the same axes.

CHECK   Using **FIGURE 25(c)**, choose a test point from each of the four regions formed by the intersection of the boundary lines. Verify that only ordered pairs in the heavily shaded region satisfy *both* inequalities.

NOW TRY

OBJECTIVE 4 **Graph the union of two linear inequalities.** When two inequalities are joined by the word *or,* we must find the union of the graphs of the inequalities. ***The graph of the union of two inequalities includes all of the points that satisfy either inequality.***

NOW TRY
EXERCISE 6

Graph

$3x - 5y < 15$ or $x > 4$.

EXAMPLE 6 Graphing the Union of Two Inequalities

Graph $2x + 4y \geq 5$ or $x \geq 1$.

The graphs of the two inequalities are shown in **FIGURES 25(a) AND (b)** in **Example 5** on the preceding page. The graph of the union is shown in **FIGURE 26**.

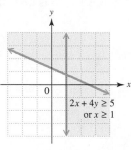

FIGURE 26

NOW TRY

CONNECTIONS

In **Section 3.2,** we saw that the x-intercept of the graph of the line $y = mx + b$ indicates the solution of the equation $mx + b = 0$. We can extend this observation to find solutions of the associated inequalities $mx + b > 0$ and $mx + b < 0$.

For example, to solve the equation

$$-2(3x + 1) = -2x + 18$$

and the associated inequalities

$$-2(3x + 1) > -2x + 18 \quad \text{and} \quad -2(3x + 1) < -2x + 18,$$

we rewrite the equation so that the right side equals 0.

$$-2(3x + 1) + 2x - 18 = 0$$

We graph

$$Y = -2(3X + 1) + 2X - 18$$

to find the x-intercept $(-5, 0)$, as shown in **FIGURE 27**.

Thus, the solution set of $-2(3x + 1) = -2x + 18$ is $\{-5\}$.

The graph of Y lies *above* the x-axis for x-values less than -5.

Thus, the solution set of $-2(3x + 1) > -2x + 18$ is $(-\infty, -5)$.

The graph of Y lies *below* the x-axis for x-values greater than -5.

Thus, the solution set of $-2(3x + 1) < -2x + 18$ is $(-5, \infty)$.

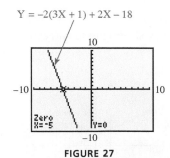

Y = −2(3X + 1) + 2X − 18

FIGURE 27

NOW TRY ANSWER

6.

For Discussion or Writing

Solve the equation in part (a) and the associated inequalities in parts (b) and (c), by graphing the left side as y in the standard viewing window of a graphing calculator. Explain your answers using the graph.

1. (a) $5x + 3 = 0$ **(b)** $5x + 3 > 0$ **(c)** $5x + 3 < 0$

2. (a) $6x + 3 = 0$ **(b)** $6x + 3 > 0$ **(c)** $6x + 3 < 0$

3. (a) $-8x - (2x + 12) = 0$ **(b)** $-8x - (2x + 12) \geq 0$

   (c) $-8x - (2x + 12) \leq 0$

4. (a) $-4x - (2x + 18) = 0$ **(b)** $-4x - (2x + 18) \geq 0$

   (c) $-4x - (2x + 18) \leq 0$

9.3 EXERCISES

MyMathLab | Math XL PRACTICE | WATCH | DOWNLOAD | READ | REVIEW

Complete solution available on the Video Resources on DVD

Concept Check   *In Exercises 1–4, fill in the first blank with either* solid *or* dashed. *Fill in the second blank with either* above *or* below.

1. The boundary of the graph of $y \leq -x + 2$ will be a _____ line, and the shading will be _____ the line.

2. The boundary of the graph of $y < -x + 2$ will be a _____ line, and the shading will be _____ the line.

3. The boundary of the graph of $y > -x + 2$ will be a _____ line, and the shading will be _____ the line.

4. The boundary of the graph of $y \geq -x + 2$ will be a _____ line, and the shading will be _____ the line.

In Exercises 5–10, the straight-line boundary has been drawn. Complete the graph by shading the correct region. ***See Examples 1–4.***

5. $x + 2y \geq 7$ **6.** $2x + y \geq 5$ **7.** $-3x + 4y > 12$

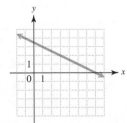   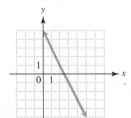 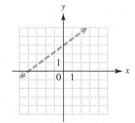

8. $x \leq 3y$ **9.** $y < -1$ **10.** $x > 4$

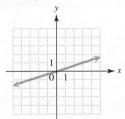   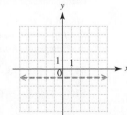 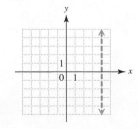

✎ **11.** Explain how to determine whether to use a dashed line or a solid line when graphing a linear inequality in two variables.

✎ **12.** Explain why the point $(0, 0)$ is not an appropriate choice for a test point when graphing an inequality whose boundary goes through the origin.

*Graph each linear inequality in two variables. **See Examples 1–4.***

🌐 **13.** $x + y \leq 2$ **14.** $x + y \leq -3$

🌐 **15.** $4x - y < 4$ **16.** $3x - y < 3$

   17. $x + 3y \geq -2$ **18.** $x + 4y \geq -3$

   19. $2x + 3y \geq 6$ **20.** $3x + 4y \geq 12$

   21. $5x - 3y > 15$ **22.** $4x - 5y > 20$

🌐 **23.** $x < -2$ **24.** $x > 1$

   25. $y \leq 5$ **26.** $y \leq -3$

   27. $x + y > 0$ **28.** $x + 2y > 0$

   29. $x - 3y \leq 0$ **30.** $x - 5y \leq 0$

   31. $y < x$ **32.** $y \leq 4x$

*Graph each compound inequality. **See Example 5.***

🌐 **33.** $x + y \leq 1$ and $x \geq 1$ **34.** $x - y \geq 2$ and $x \geq 3$

   35. $2x - y \geq 2$ and $y < 4$ **36.** $3x - y \geq 3$ and $y < 3$

   37. $x + y > -5$ and $y < -2$ **38.** $6x - 4y < 10$ and $y > 2$

*Use the method described in **Section 9.2** to write each inequality as a compound inequality, and graph its solution set in the rectangular coordinate plane.*

   39. $|x| < 3$ **40.** $|y| < 5$

   41. $|x + 1| < 2$ **42.** $|y - 3| < 2$

*Graph each compound inequality. **See Example 6.***

🌐 **43.** $x - y \geq 1$ or $y \geq 2$ **44.** $x + y \leq 2$ or $y \geq 3$

   45. $x - 2 > y$ or $x < 1$ **46.** $x + 3 < y$ or $x > 3$

   47. $3x + 2y < 6$ or $x - 2y > 2$ **48.** $x - y \geq 1$ or $x + y \leq 4$

TECHNOLOGY INSIGHTS   EXERCISES 49–56

Match each inequality in Exercises 49–52 with its calculator graph in choices A–D at the top of the next page. (Hint: Use the slope, y-intercept, and inequality symbol in making your choice.)

   49. $y \leq 3x - 6$ **50.** $y \geq 3x - 6$

   51. $y \leq -3x - 6$ **52.** $y \geq -3x - 6$

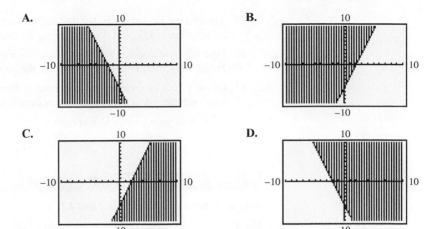

A.   **B.**

C.   **D.**

The graph of a linear equation y = mx + b is shown on a graphing calculator screen, along with the x-value of the x-intercept of the line. Use the screen to solve (a) y = 0, (b) y < 0, and (c) y > 0. See the Connections box.

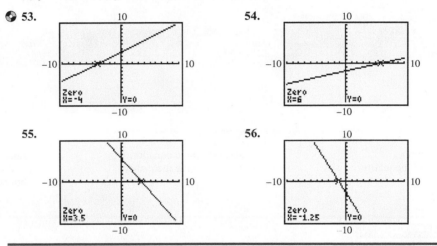

53.   **54.**

55.   **56.**

RELATING CONCEPTS   EXERCISES 57–62

FOR INDIVIDUAL OR GROUP WORK

*Suppose a factory can have no more than 200 workers on a shift, but must have at least 100 and must manufacture at least 3000 units at minimum cost. The managers need to know how many workers should be on a shift in order to produce the required units at minimal cost. **Linear programming** is a method for finding the optimal (best possible) solution that meets all the conditions for such problems.*

*Let x represent the number of workers and y represent the number of units manufactured. **Work Exercises 57–62 in order.***

57. Write three inequalities expressing the conditions given in the problem.

58. Graph the inequalities from **Exercise 57** and shade the intersection.

(continued)

59. The cost per worker is $50 per day and the cost to manufacture 1 unit is $100. Write an equation in x, y, and C representing the total daily cost C.

60. Find values of x and y for several points in or on the boundary of the shaded region. Include any "corner points." These are the points that maximize or minimize C.

61. Of the values of x and y that you chose in **Exercise 60,** which gives the least value when substituted in the cost equation from **Exercise 59?**

62. What does your answer in **Exercise 61** mean in terms of the given problem?

PREVIEW EXERCISES

*Find each power. **See Sections 1.2 and 4.1.***

63. 8^2 **64.** $(-4)^2$ **65.** -12^2 **66.** 1.5^2

CHAPTER 9 SUMMARY

KEY TERMS

9.1
intersection
compound inequality
union

9.2
absolute value equation
absolute value inequality

9.3
linear inequality in two
  variables
boundary line

NEW SYMBOLS

∩ set intersection   ∪ set union

TEST YOUR WORD POWER

See how well you have learned the vocabulary in this chapter.

1. The **intersection** of two sets A and B is the set of elements that belong
  A. to both A and B
  B. to either A or B, or both
  C. to either A or B, but not both
  D. to just A.

2. The **union** of two sets A and B is the set of elements that belong
  A. to both A and B
  B. to either A or B, or both
  C. to either A or B, but not both
  D. to just B.

3. A **linear inequality in two variables** is an inequality that can be written in the form
  A. $Ax + By < C$ or $Ax + By > C$
    ($\leq$ or $\geq$ can be used)
  B. $ax < b$
  C. $y \geq x^2$
  D. $Ax + By = C$.

ANSWERS

1. A; *Example:* If $A = \{2, 4, 6, 8\}$ and $B = \{1, 2, 3\}$, then $A \cap B = \{2\}$.   **2.** B; *Example:* Using the sets A and B from Answer 1, $A \cup B = \{1, 2, 3, 4, 6, 8\}$.   **3.** A; *Examples:* $4x + 3y < 12$, $x > 6y$, $2x \geq 4y + 5$

QUICK REVIEW

CONCEPTS

EXAMPLES

9.1 Set Operations and Compound Inequalities

Solving a Compound Inequality

Step 1 Solve each inequality in the compound inequality individually.

Step 2 If the inequalities are joined with *and,* then the solution set is the intersection of the two individual solution sets.

If the inequalities are joined with *or,* then the solution set is the union of the two individual solution sets.

Solve $x + 1 > 2$ and $2x < 6$.

$$x + 1 > 2 \quad \text{and} \quad 2x < 6$$
$$x > 1 \quad \text{and} \quad x < 3$$

The solution set is $(1, 3)$.

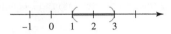

Solve $x \geq 4$ or $x \leq 0$.

The solution set is $(-\infty, 0] \cup [4, \infty)$.

9.2 Absolute Value Equations and Inequalities

Solving Absolute Value Equations and Inequalities
Let k be a positive number.

To solve $|ax + b| = k,$ solve the following compound equation.

$$ax + b = k \quad \text{or} \quad ax + b = -k$$

To solve $|ax + b| > k,$ solve the following compound inequality.

$$ax + b > k \quad \text{or} \quad ax + b < -k$$

To solve $|ax + b| < k,$ solve the following compound inequality.

$$-k < ax + b < k$$

To solve an absolute value equation of the form

$$|ax + b| = |cx + d|,$$

solve the following compound equation.

$$ax + b = cx + d \quad \text{or} \quad ax + b = -(cx + d)$$

Solve $|x - 7| = 3$.

$$x - 7 = 3 \quad \text{or} \quad x - 7 = -3$$
$$x = 10 \quad \text{or} \quad x = 4 \qquad \text{Add 7.}$$

The solution set is $\{4, 10\}$.

Solve $|x - 7| > 3$.

$$x - 7 > 3 \quad \text{or} \quad x - 7 < -3$$
$$x > 10 \quad \text{or} \quad x < 4 \qquad \text{Add 7.}$$

The solution set is $(-\infty, 4) \cup (10, \infty)$.

Solve $|x - 7| < 3$.

$$-3 < x - 7 < 3$$
$$4 < x < 10 \qquad \text{Add 7.}$$

The solution set is $(4, 10)$.

Solve $|x + 2| = |2x - 6|$.

$$x + 2 = 2x - 6 \quad \text{or} \quad x + 2 = -(2x - 6)$$
$$x = 8 \qquad\qquad\quad x + 2 = -2x + 6$$
$$3x = 4$$
$$x = \frac{4}{3}$$

The solution set is $\left\{\frac{4}{3}, 8\right\}$.

(continued)

CONCEPTS	EXAMPLES
9.3 **Linear Inequalities in Two Variables**	Graph $2x - 3y \leq 6$.
Graphing a Linear Inequality	
Step 1 Draw the graph of the line that is the boundary. Make the line solid if the inequality involves $\leq$ or $\geq$. Make the line dashed if the inequality involves $<$ or $>$.	Draw the graph of $2x - 3y = 6$. Use a solid line because of the inclusion of equality in the symbol $\leq$.
Step 2 Choose any point not on the line as a test point. Substitute the coordinates into the inequality.	Choose $(0, 0)$ as a test point. $$2(0) - 3(0) \overset{?}{\leq} 6$$ $$0 \leq 6 \quad \text{True}$$
Step 3 Shade the region that includes the test point if the test point satisfies the original inequality. Otherwise, shade the region on the other side of the boundary line.	Shade the side of the line that includes $(0, 0)$. 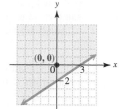

CHAPTER 9 — REVIEW EXERCISES

9.1 *Let* $A = \{a, b, c, d\}$, $B = \{a, c, e, f\}$, *and* $C = \{a, e, f, g\}$. *Find each set.*

1. $A \cap B$ **2.** $A \cap C$ **3.** $B \cup C$ **4.** $A \cup C$

Solve each compound inequality. Give the solution set in both interval and graph form.

5. $x > 6$ and $x < 9$ **6.** $x + 4 > 12$ and $x - 2 < 12$

7. $x > 5$ or $x \leq -3$ **8.** $x \geq -2$ or $x < 2$

9. $x - 4 > 6$ and $x + 3 \leq 10$ **10.** $-5x + 1 \geq 11$ or $3x + 5 \geq 26$

Express each union or intersection in simplest interval form.

11. $(-3, \infty) \cap (-\infty, 4)$ **12.** $(-\infty, 6) \cap (-\infty, 2)$

13. $(4, \infty) \cup (9, \infty)$ **14.** $(1, 2) \cup (1, \infty)$

9.2 *Solve each absolute value equation.*

15. $|x| = 7$ **16.** $|x + 2| = 9$

17. $|3x - 7| = 8$ **18.** $|x - 4| = -12$

19. $|2x - 7| + 4 = 11$ **20.** $|4x + 2| - 7 = -3$

21. $|3x + 1| = |x + 2|$ **22.** $|2x - 1| = |2x + 3|$

Solve each absolute value inequality. Give the solution set in interval form.

23. $|x| < 14$ **24.** $|-x + 6| \leq 7$ **25.** $|2x + 5| \leq 1$

26. $|x + 1| \geq -3$ **27.** $|5x - 1| > 9$ **28.** $|11x - 3| \leq -2$

29. $|11x - 3| \geq -2$ **30.** $|11x - 3| \leq 0$

9.3 *Graph the solution set of each inequality or compound inequality.*

31. $3x - 2y \leq 12$ **32.** $5x - y > 6$ **33.** $3x + 2y < 0$

34. $2x + y \leq 1$ and $x \geq 2y$ **35.** $x \geq 2$ or $y \geq 2$

36. *Concept Check*   Which one of the following has as its graph a dashed boundary line and shading below the line?

     A. $y \geq 4x + 3$ **B.** $y > 4x + 3$ **C.** $y \leq 4x + 3$ **D.** $y < 4x + 3$

MIXED REVIEW EXERCISES

Solve.

37. $x < 3$ and $x \geq -2$ **38.** $|3x + 6| \geq 0$ **39.** $|3x + 2| + 4 = 9$

40. $|x + 3| \leq 13$ **41.** $|5x - 1| > 14$ **42.** $x \geq -2$ or $x < 4$

43. $|x - 1| = |2x + 3|$ **44.** $|x + 3| \leq 1$ **45.** $|3x - 7| = 4$

46. *Concept Check*   If $k < 0$, what is the solution set of each of the following?

     (a) $|2x - 5| = k$ **(b)** $|2x - 5| < k$ **(c)** $|2x - 5| > k$

Solve. Give the solution set in both interval and graph form.

47. $x > 6$ and $x < 8$ **48.** $-5x + 1 \geq 11$ or $3x + 5 \geq 26$

Graph the solution set of each inequality.

49. $2x - 3y > -6$ **50.** $3x + 5y > 9$

51. The numbers of civilian workers (to the nearest thousand) for several states in 2008 are shown in the table.

Number of Workers

State	Female	Male
Illinois	2,918,000	3,345,000
Maine	320,000	349,000
North Carolina	2,016,000	2,242,000
Oregon	869,000	976,000
Utah	571,000	755,000
Wisconsin	1,427,000	1,526,000

Source: U.S. Bureau of Labor Statistics.

List the elements of each set.

(a) The set of states with less than 3 million female workers *and* more than 3 million male workers

(b) The set of states with less than 1 million female workers *or* more than 2 million male workers

(c) The set of states with a total of more than 7 million civilian workers

52. *Concept Check*   The solution set of $|3x + 4| = 7$ is shown on the number line.

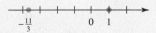

(a) What is the solution set of $|3x + 4| \geq 7$?

(b) What is the solution set of $|3x + 4| \leq 7$?

CHAPTER Test Prep VIDEOS

Step-by-step test solutions are found on the Chapter Test Prep Videos available via the Video Resources on DVD, in *MyMathLab*, or on You Tube (search "LialCombinedAlgebra").

View the complete solutions to all Chapter Test exercises on the Video Resources on DVD.

The median weekly earnings of full-time workers by occupation for a recent year were as shown in the table.

Weekly Earnings of Full-Time Workers (in dollars)

Occupation	Men	Women
Managerial/Professional	994	709
Technical/Sales/Administrative Support	655	452
Service	357	316
Operators/Fabricators/Laborers	487	351

Source: U.S. Bureau of Labor Statistics.

List the elements of each set.

1. The set of occupations with median earnings for men less than $900 and for women greater than $500

2. The set of occupations with median earnings for men greater than $600 or for women less than $400

Let $A = \{1, 2, 5, 7\}$ and $B = \{1, 5, 9, 12\}$. Write each of the following sets.

3. $A \cap B$

4. $A \cup B$

Solve each compound inequality. Give the solution set in both interval and graph form.

5. $3k \geq 6$ and $k - 4 < 5$

6. $-4x \leq -24$ or $4x - 2 < 10$

Solve each absolute value equation or inequality. Give the solution set in interval form.

7. $|4x - 3| = 7$

8. $|5 - 6x| > 12$

9. $|7 - x| \leq -1$

10. $|3 - 5x| = |2x + 8|$

11. $|-3x + 4| - 4 < -1$

12. $|12t + 7| \geq 0$

13. *Concept Check*   If $k < 0$, what is the solution set of each of the following?

   (a) $|5x + 3| < k$

   (b) $|5x + 3| > k$

   (c) $|5x + 3| = k$

Graph the solution set of each inequality or compound inequality.

14. $3x - 2y > 6$

15. $3x - y > 0$

16. $y < 2x - 1$ and $x - y < 3$

17. $x - 2 \geq y$ or $y \geq 3$

CUMULATIVE REVIEW EXERCISES

1. Match each number in Column I with the choice or choices of sets of numbers in Column II to which the number belongs.

I		II	
(a) 34	(b) 0	**A.** Natural numbers	**B.** Whole numbers
(c) 2.16	(d) $-\sqrt{36}$	**C.** Integers	**D.** Rational numbers
(e) $\sqrt{13}$	(f) $-\dfrac{4}{5}$	**E.** Irrational numbers	**F.** Real numbers

Evaluate.

2. $9 \cdot 4 - 16 \div 4$

3. $-|8 - 13| - |-4| + |-9|$

Solve.

4. $-5(8 - 2z) + 4(7 - z) = 7(8 + z) - 3$ **5.** $3(x + 2) - 5(x + 2) = -2x - 4$

6. $A = p + prt$ for t **7.** $2(m + 5) - 3m + 1 > 5$

8. A recent survey polled teens about the most important inventions of the 20th century. Complete the results shown in the table if 1500 teens were surveyed.

Most Important Invention	Percent	Actual Number
Personal computer		480
Pacemaker	26%	
Wireless communication	18%	
Television		150

Source: Lemelson–MIT Program.

9. Find the measure of each angle of the triangle.

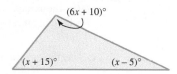

$(6x + 10)°$

$(x + 15)°$ $(x - 5)°$

Find the slope of each line described.

10. Through $(-4, 5)$ and $(2, -3)$ **11.** Horizontal, through $(4, 5)$

*Find an equation of each line. Write the equation in **(a)** slope-intercept form and in **(b)** standard form.*

12. Through $(4, -1)$, $m = -4$ **13.** Through $(0, 0)$ and $(1, 4)$

14. Graph $-3x + 4y = 12$.

Simplify. Write answers with only positive exponents. Assume that all variables represent positive real numbers.

15. $\left(\dfrac{2m^3n}{p^2}\right)^3$ **16.** $\dfrac{x^{-6}y^3z^{-1}}{x^7y^{-4}z}$

Perform the indicated operations.

17. $(3x^2 - 8x + 1) - (x^2 - 3x - 9)$ **18.** $(x + 2y)(x^2 - 2xy + 4y^2)$

19. $(3x + 2y)(5x - y)$ **20.** $\dfrac{16x^3y^5 - 8x^2y^2 + 4}{4x^2y}$

Factor each polynomial completely.

21. $m^2 + 12m + 32$ **22.** $25t^4 - 36$ **23.** $81z^2 + 72z + 16$

24. Solve the equation $(x + 4)(x - 1) = -6$.

25. For what real number(s) is the expression $\dfrac{3}{x^2 + 5x - 14}$ undefined?

Perform each indicated operation. Express answers in lowest terms.

26. $\dfrac{x^2 - 3x - 4}{x^2 + 3x} \cdot \dfrac{x^2 + 2x - 3}{x^2 - 5x + 4}$ **27.** $\dfrac{t^2 + 4t - 5}{t + 5} \div \dfrac{t - 1}{t^2 + 8t + 15}$

28. $\dfrac{2}{x + 3} - \dfrac{4}{x - 1}$ **29.** $\dfrac{\dfrac{2}{3} + \dfrac{1}{2}}{\dfrac{1}{9} - \dfrac{1}{6}}$

30. Solve the equation $\dfrac{x}{x+8} - \dfrac{3}{x-8} = \dfrac{128}{x^2-64}$.

31. The graph shows the number of pounds of shrimp caught in the United States (in thousands of pounds) in selected years.

    (a) Use the information given in the graph to find and interpret the average rate of change in the number of pounds of shrimp caught per year.

    (b) If $x = 0$ represents the year 2000, $x = 1$ represents 2001, and so on, use your answer from part (a) to write an equation of the line in slope-intercept form that models the annual amount of shrimp caught (in thousands of pounds, to the nearest whole number) for the years 2000 through 2005.

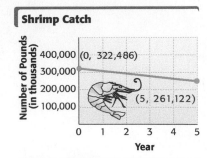

Shrimp Catch

Source: National Oceanic and Atmospheric Administration.

    (c) Use the equation from part (b) to approximate the amount of shrimp caught in 2003.

32. Give the domain and range of the relation

$$\{(-4, -2), (-1, 0), (2, 0), (5, 2)\}.$$

Does this relation define a function?

33. If $g(x) = -x^2 - 2x + 6$, find $g(3)$.

Solve each system.

34. $3x - 4y = 1$
     $2x + 3y = 12$

35. $3x - 2y = 4$
     $-6x + 4y = 7$

36. $x + 3y - 6z = 7$
     $2x - y + z = 1$
     $x + 2y + 2z = -1$

Use a system of equations to solve each problem.

37. The Star-Spangled Banner that flew over Fort McHenry during the War of 1812 had a perimeter of 144 ft. Its length measured 12 ft more than its width. Find the dimensions of this flag, which is displayed in the Smithsonian Institution's Museum of American History in Washington, DC. (*Source:* National Park Service brochure.)

38. Agbe Asiamigbe needs 9 L of a 20% solution of alcohol. Agbe has a 15% solution on hand, as well as a 30% solution. How many liters of the 15% solution and the 30% solution should Agbe mix to get the 20% solution needed?

Solve each equation or inequality.

39. $x > -4$ and $x < 4$

40. $2x + 1 > 5$ or $2 - x \geq 2$

41. $|3x - 1| = 2$

42. $|3z + 1| \geq 7$

Graph each solution set.

43. $y \leq 2x - 6$

44. $x - y \geq 3$ and $3x + 4y \leq 12$

Roots, Radicals, and Root Functions

10.1 Radical Expressions and Graphs

10.2 Rational Exponents

10.3 Simplifying Radical Expressions

10.4 Adding and Subtracting Radical Expressions

10.5 Multiplying and Dividing Radical Expressions

Summary Exercises on Operations with Radicals and Rational Exponents

10.6 Solving Equations with Radicals

10.7 Complex Numbers

The Pythagorean theorem states that in any right triangle with perpendicular sides a and b and longest side c,

$$a^2 + b^2 = c^2.$$

It is used in surveying, drafting, engineering, navigation, and many other fields. Although attributed to Pythagoras, it was known to surveyors from Egypt to China for a thousand years before Pythagoras.

In the 1939 movie *The Wizard of Oz,* the Scarecrow asks the Wizard for a brain. When the Wizard presents him with a diploma granting him a Th.D. (Doctor of Thinkology), the Scarecrow declares the following.

The sum of the square roots of any two sides of an isosceles triangle is equal to the square root of the remaining side. . . . Oh joy! Rapture! I've got a brain.

Did the Scarecrow state the Pythagorean theorem correctly? We will investigate this in **Exercises 133–134** of **Section 10.3.**

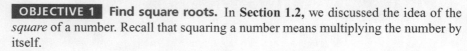

10.1 Radical Expressions and Graphs

OBJECTIVES

1 Find square roots.
2 Decide whether a given root is rational, irrational, or not a real number.
3 Find cube, fourth, and other roots.
4 Graph functions defined by radical expressions.
5 Find *n*th roots of *n*th powers.
6 Use a calculator to find roots.

OBJECTIVE 1 Find square roots. In **Section 1.2,** we discussed the idea of the *square* of a number. Recall that squaring a number means multiplying the number by itself.

$$7^2 = 7 \cdot 7 = 49 \qquad \text{The square of 7 is 49.}$$

The opposite (inverse) of squaring a number is taking its *square root.* This is equivalent to asking

"What number when multiplied by itself equals 49?"

From the example above, one answer is 7, since $7 \cdot 7 = 49$.

This discussion can be generalized.

Square Root
A number b is a **square root** of a if $b^2 = a$.

EXAMPLE 1 Finding All Square Roots of a Number

Find all square roots of 49.

We ask, "What number when multiplied by itself equals 49?" As mentioned above, one square root is 7, because $7 \cdot 7 = 49$. Another square root of 49 is −7, because

$$(-7)(-7) = 49.$$

Thus, the number 49 has *two* square roots: 7 and −7. One square root is positive, and one is negative.   NOW TRY

NOW TRY
EXERCISE 1
Find all square roots of 81.

The **positive** or **principal square root** of a number is written with the symbol $\sqrt{}$. For example, the positive square root of 121 is 11.

$$\sqrt{121} = 11$$

The symbol $-\sqrt{}$ is used for the **negative square root** of a number. For example, the negative square root of 121 is −11.

$$-\sqrt{121} = -11$$

The symbol $\sqrt{}$, called a **radical symbol,** always represents the positive square root $\left(\text{except that } \sqrt{0} = 0\right)$. The number inside the radical symbol is called the **radicand,** and the entire expression—radical symbol and radicand—is called a **radical.**

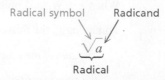

An algebraic expression containing a radical is called a **radical expression.**

The radical symbol $\sqrt{}$ has been used since 16th-century Germany and was probably derived from the letter *R.* The radical symbol in the margin comes from the Latin word *radix,* for *root.* It was first used by Leonardo of Pisa (Fibonacci) in 1220.

Early radical symbol

NOW TRY ANSWER
1. 9, −9

We summarize our discussion of square roots as follows.

Square Roots of a

If a is a positive real number, then

$$\sqrt{a} \text{ is the positive or principal square root of } a,$$

and $-\sqrt{a}$ is the negative square root of a.

For nonnegative a,

$$\sqrt{a} \cdot \sqrt{a} = \left(\sqrt{a}\right)^2 = a \quad \text{and} \quad -\sqrt{a} \cdot \left(-\sqrt{a}\right) = \left(-\sqrt{a}\right)^2 = a.$$

Also, $\sqrt{0} = 0$.

NOW TRY
EXERCISE 2
Find each square root.

(a) $\sqrt{400}$ **(b)** $-\sqrt{169}$

(c) $\sqrt{\dfrac{100}{121}}$

EXAMPLE 2   Finding Square Roots

Find each square root.

(a) $\sqrt{144}$

The radical $\sqrt{144}$ represents the positive or principal square root of 144. Think of a positive number whose square is 144.

$$12^2 = 144, \quad \text{so} \quad \sqrt{144} = 12.$$

(b) $-\sqrt{1024}$

This symbol represents the negative square root of 1024. A calculator with a square root key can be used to find $\sqrt{1024} = 32$. Therefore,

$$-\sqrt{1024} = -32.$$

(c) $\sqrt{\dfrac{4}{9}} = \dfrac{2}{3}$ **(d)** $-\sqrt{\dfrac{16}{49}} = -\dfrac{4}{7}$ **(e)** $\sqrt{0.81} = 0.9$ NOW TRY

As shown in the preceding definition, when the square root of a positive real number is squared, the result is that positive real number. $\left(\text{Also, } \left(\sqrt{0}\right)^2 = 0.\right)$

NOW TRY
EXERCISE 3
Find the square of each radical expression.

(a) $\sqrt{15}$ **(b)** $-\sqrt{23}$

(c) $\sqrt{2k^2 + 5}$

EXAMPLE 3   Squaring Radical Expressions

Find the *square* of each radical expression.

(a) $\sqrt{13}$

$$\left(\sqrt{13}\right)^2 = 13 \qquad \text{Definition of square root}$$

(b) $-\sqrt{29}$

$$\left(-\sqrt{29}\right)^2 = 29 \qquad \text{The square of a } negative \text{ number is positive.}$$

(c) $\sqrt{p^2 + 1}$

$$\left(\sqrt{p^2 + 1}\right)^2 = p^2 + 1 \qquad\qquad\qquad \text{NOW TRY}$$

NOW TRY ANSWERS
2. **(a)** 20 **(b)** -13 **(c)** $\frac{10}{11}$
3. **(a)** 15 **(b)** 23 **(c)** $2k^2 + 5$

OBJECTIVE 2 **Decide whether a given root is rational, irrational, or not a real number.** Numbers with square roots that are rational are called **perfect squares.**

Perfect squares		Rational square roots
↓		↓
25		$\sqrt{25} = 5$
144	are perfect squares since	$\sqrt{144} = 12$
$\dfrac{4}{9}$		$\sqrt{\dfrac{4}{9}} = \dfrac{2}{3}$

A number that is not a perfect square has a square root that is not a rational number. For example, $\sqrt{5}$ is not a rational number because it cannot be written as the ratio of two integers. Its decimal equivalent neither terminates nor repeats. However, $\sqrt{5}$ is a real number and corresponds to a point on the number line.

A real number that is not rational is called an **irrational number.** The number $\sqrt{5}$ is irrational. *Many square roots of integers are irrational.*

If a is a positive real number that is *not* a perfect square, then $\sqrt{a}$ is irrational.

Not every number has a real number square root. For example, there is no real number that can be squared to get -36. (The square of a real number can never be negative.) Because of this, $\sqrt{-36}$ *is not a real number.*

If a is a *negative* real number, then $\sqrt{a}$ is *not* a real number.

⚠ **CAUTION** $\sqrt{-36}$ is *not* a real number, since there is no real number that can be squared to obtain -36. However, $-\sqrt{36}$ is the negative square root of 36, or -6.

NOW TRY
EXERCISE 4
Tell whether each square root is *rational, irrational,* or *not a real number.*
(a) $\sqrt{31}$ **(b)** $\sqrt{900}$
(c) $\sqrt{-16}$

EXAMPLE 4 Identifying Types of Square Roots

Tell whether each square root is *rational, irrational,* or *not a real number.*

(a) $\sqrt{17}$ Because 17 is not a perfect square, $\sqrt{17}$ is irrational.

(b) $\sqrt{64}$ The number 64 is a perfect square, 8^2, so $\sqrt{64} = 8$, a rational number.

(c) $\sqrt{-25}$ There is no real number whose square is -25. Therefore, $\sqrt{-25}$ is not a real number.

NOW TRY

NOTE Not all irrational numbers are square roots of integers. For example, π (approximately 3.14159) is an irrational number that is not a square root of any integer.

OBJECTIVE 3 **Find cube, fourth, and other roots.** Finding the square root of a number is the opposite (inverse) of squaring a number. In a similar way, there are inverses to finding the cube of a number or to finding the fourth or greater power of a number. These inverses are, respectively, the **cube root,** written $\sqrt[3]{a}$, and the **fourth root,** written $\sqrt[4]{a}$. Similar symbols are used for other roots.

NOW TRY ANSWERS
4. (a) irrational (b) rational
(c) not a real number

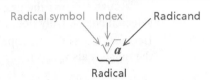

$\sqrt[n]{a}$

The *n*th root of *a*, written $\sqrt[n]{a}$, is a number whose *n*th power equals *a*. That is,

$$\sqrt[n]{a} = b \quad \text{means} \quad b^n = a.$$

In $\sqrt[n]{a}$, the number *n* is the **index** or **order** of the radical.

We could write $\sqrt[2]{a}$ instead of $\sqrt{a}$, but the simpler symbol $\sqrt{a}$ is customary, since the square root is the most commonly used root.

NOTE When working with cube roots or fourth roots, it is helpful to memorize the first few **perfect cubes** ($2^3 = 8$, $3^3 = 27$, and so on) and the first few **perfect fourth powers** ($2^4 = 16$, $3^4 = 81$, and so on). See **Exercises 63 and 64.**

NOW TRY
EXERCISE 5
Find each cube root.
(a) $\sqrt[3]{343}$ **(b)** $\sqrt[3]{-1000}$
(c) $\sqrt[3]{27}$

EXAMPLE 5 Finding Cube Roots

Find each cube root.

(a) $\sqrt[3]{8}$ What number can be cubed to give 8? Because $2^3 = 8$, $\sqrt[3]{8} = 2$.

(b) $\sqrt[3]{-8} = -2$, because $(-2)^3 = -8$.

(c) $\sqrt[3]{216} = 6$, because $6^3 = 216$.   NOW TRY

Notice in **Example 5(b)** that we can find the cube root of a negative number. (Contrast this with the square root of a negative number, which is not real.) In fact, the cube root of a positive number is positive, and the cube root of a negative number is negative. *There is only one real number cube root for each real number.*

When a radical has an *even index* (square root, fourth root, and so on), *the radicand must be nonnegative* to yield a real number root. Also, for $a > 0$,

$$\sqrt{a}, \ \sqrt[4]{a}, \ \sqrt[6]{a}, \text{ and so on are positive (principal) roots.}$$

$$-\sqrt{a}, \ -\sqrt[4]{a}, \ -\sqrt[6]{a}, \text{ and so on are negative roots.}$$

NOW TRY
EXERCISE 6
Find each root.
(a) $\sqrt[4]{625}$ **(b)** $\sqrt[4]{-625}$
(c) $\sqrt[5]{3125}$ **(d)** $\sqrt[5]{-3125}$

EXAMPLE 6 Finding Other Roots

Find each root.

(a) $\sqrt[4]{16} = 2$, because 2 is positive and $2^4 = 16$.

(b) $-\sqrt[4]{16}$ From part (a), $\sqrt[4]{16} = 2$, so the negative root is $-\sqrt[4]{16} = -2$.

(c) $\sqrt[4]{-16}$ For a fourth root to be a real number, the radicand must be nonnegative. There is no real number that equals $\sqrt[4]{-16}$.

(d) $-\sqrt[5]{32}$
First find $\sqrt[5]{32}$. Because 2 is the number whose fifth power is 32, $\sqrt[5]{32} = 2$. Since $\sqrt[5]{32} = 2$, it follows that

$$-\sqrt[5]{32} = -2.$$

(e) $\sqrt[5]{-32} = -2$, because $(-2)^5 = -32$.   NOW TRY

NOW TRY ANSWERS
5. **(a)** 7   **(b)** -10 **(c)** 3
6. **(a)** 5   **(b)** not a real number
    (c) 5   **(d)** -5

OBJECTIVE 4 **Graph functions defined by radical expressions.** A **radical expression** is an algebraic expression that contains radicals.

$$3 - \sqrt{x}, \quad \sqrt[3]{x}, \quad \text{and} \quad \sqrt{2x - 1} \qquad \text{Examples of radical expressions}$$

In earlier chapters, we graphed functions defined by polynomial and rational expressions. Now we examine the graphs of functions defined by the basic radical expressions $f(x) = \sqrt{x}$ and $f(x) = \sqrt[3]{x}$.

FIGURE 1 shows the graph of the **square root function,** together with a table of selected points. Only nonnegative values can be used for x, so the domain is $[0, \infty)$. Because $\sqrt{x}$ is the principal square root of x, it always has a nonnegative value, so the range is also $[0, \infty)$.

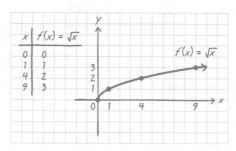

Square root function

$$f(x) = \sqrt{x}$$

Domain: $[0, \infty)$
Range: $[0, \infty)$

FIGURE 1

FIGURE 2 shows the graph of the **cube root function.** Since any real number (positive, negative, or 0) can be used for x in the cube root function, $\sqrt[3]{x}$ can be positive, negative, or 0. Thus, both the domain and the range of the cube root function are $(-\infty, \infty)$.

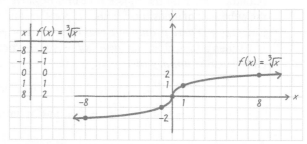

Cube root function

$$f(x) = \sqrt[3]{x}$$

Domain: $(-\infty, \infty)$
Range: $(-\infty, \infty)$

FIGURE 2

EXAMPLE 7 Graphing Functions Defined with Radicals

Graph each function by creating a table of values. Give the domain and range.

(a) $f(x) = \sqrt{x - 3}$

A table of values is given with the graph in **FIGURE 3** on the next page. The x-values were chosen in such a way that the function values are all integers. For the radicand to be nonnegative, we must have

$$x - 3 \geq 0, \quad \text{or} \quad x \geq 3.$$

Therefore, the domain of this function is $[3, \infty)$. Function values are positive or 0, so the range is $[0, \infty)$.

NOW TRY
EXERCISE 7

Graph each function. Give the domain and range.

(a) $f(x) = \sqrt{x + 1}$

(b) $f(x) = \sqrt[3]{x} - 1$

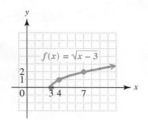

x	$f(x) = \sqrt{x-3}$
3	$\sqrt{3-3} = 0$
4	$\sqrt{4-3} = 1$
7	$\sqrt{7-3} = 2$

FIGURE 3

(b) $f(x) = \sqrt[3]{x} + 2$

See **FIGURE 4**. Both the domain and range are $(-\infty, \infty)$.

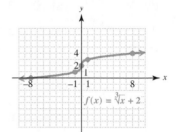

x	$f(x) = \sqrt[3]{x} + 2$
-8	$\sqrt[3]{-8} + 2 = 0$
-1	$\sqrt[3]{-1} + 2 = 1$
0	$\sqrt[3]{0} + 2 = 2$
1	$\sqrt[3]{1} + 2 = 3$
8	$\sqrt[3]{8} + 2 = 4$

FIGURE 4

NOW TRY

OBJECTIVE 5 **Find *n*th roots of *n*th powers.** Consider the expression $\sqrt{a^2}$. At first glance, you may think that it is equivalent to a. However, this is not necessarily true. For example, consider the following.

NOW TRY
EXERCISE 8

Find each square root.

(a) $\sqrt{11^2}$ (b) $\sqrt{(-11)^2}$

(c) $\sqrt{z^2}$ (d) $\sqrt{(-z)^2}$

If $a = 6$, then $\sqrt{a^2} = \sqrt{6^2} = \sqrt{36} = 6$.

If $a = -6$, then $\sqrt{a^2} = \sqrt{(-6)^2} = \sqrt{36} = 6$. ← Instead of -6, we get 6, the *absolute value* of -6.

Since the symbol $\sqrt{a^2}$ represents the *nonnegative* square root, we express $\sqrt{a^2}$ with absolute value bars, as $|a|$, because a may be a negative number.

NOW TRY ANSWERS
7. (a)

domain: $[-1, \infty)$;
range: $[0, \infty)$

(b)

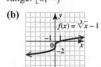

domain: $(-\infty, \infty)$;
range: $(-\infty, \infty)$

8. (a) 11 (b) 11 (c) $|z|$
   (d) $|z|$

$\sqrt{a^2}$

For any real number a, $\sqrt{a^2} = |a|$.

That is, the principal square root of a^2 is the absolute value of a.

EXAMPLE 8 Simplifying Square Roots by Using Absolute Value

Find each square root.

(a) $\sqrt{7^2} = |7| = 7$

(b) $\sqrt{(-7)^2} = |-7| = 7$

(c) $\sqrt{k^2} = |k|$

(d) $\sqrt{(-k)^2} = |-k| = |k|$

NOW TRY

We can generalize this idea to any *n*th root.

$$\sqrt[n]{a^n}$$

If *n* is an *even* positive integer, then $\sqrt[n]{a^n} = |a|.$

If *n* is an *odd* positive integer, then $\sqrt[n]{a^n} = a.$

That is, use the absolute value symbol when *n* is even. Absolute value is not used when *n* is odd.

**NOW TRY
EXERCISE 9**
Simplify each root.

(a) $\sqrt[8]{(-2)^8}$ **(b)** $\sqrt[3]{(-9)^3}$

(c) $-\sqrt[4]{(-10)^4}$ **(d)** $-\sqrt{m^8}$

(e) $\sqrt[3]{x^{18}}$ **(f)** $\sqrt[4]{t^{20}}$

EXAMPLE 9 Simplifying Higher Roots by Using Absolute Value

Simplify each root.

(a) $\sqrt[6]{(-3)^6} = |-3| = 3$ *n* is even. Use absolute value.

(b) $\sqrt[5]{(-4)^5} = -4$ *n* is odd.

(c) $-\sqrt[4]{(-9)^4} = -|-9| = -9$ *n* is even. Use absolute value.

(d) $-\sqrt{m^4} = -|m^2| = -m^2$ For all *m*, $|m^2| = m^2.$

No absolute value bars are needed here, because m^2 is nonnegative for any real number value of *m*.

(e) $\sqrt[3]{a^{12}} = a^4$, because $a^{12} = (a^4)^3.$

(f) $\sqrt[4]{x^{12}} = |x^3|$

We use absolute value to guarantee that the result is not negative (because x^3 is negative when *x* is negative). If desired $|x^3|$ can be written as $x^2 \cdot |x|.$ *NOW TRY*

OBJECTIVE 6 **Use a calculator to find roots.** While numbers such as $\sqrt{9}$ and $\sqrt[3]{-8}$ are rational, radicals are often irrational numbers. To find approximations of such radicals, we usually use a scientific or graphing calculator. For example,

$$\sqrt{15} \approx 3.872983346, \quad \sqrt[3]{10} \approx 2.15443469, \quad \text{and} \quad \sqrt[4]{2} \approx 1.189207115,$$

where the symbol $\approx$ means "is approximately equal to." In this book, we often show approximations rounded to three decimal places. Thus,

$$\sqrt{15} \approx 3.873, \quad \sqrt[3]{10} \approx 2.154, \quad \text{and} \quad \sqrt[4]{2} \approx 1.189.$$

FIGURE 5 shows how the preceding approximations are displayed on a TI-83/84 Plus graphing calculator.

There is a simple way to check that a calculator approximation is "in the ballpark." For example, because 16 is a little larger than 15, $\sqrt{16} = 4$ should be a little larger than $\sqrt{15}$. Thus, 3.873 is reasonable as an approximation for $\sqrt{15}$.

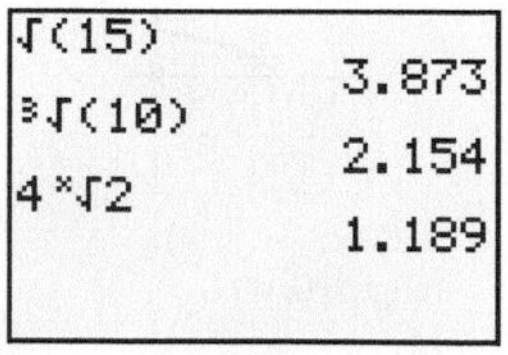

```
√(15)
            3.873
³√(10)
            2.154
4×√2
            1.189
```

FIGURE 5

NOTE The methods for finding approximations differ among makes and models of calculators. *You should always consult your owner's manual for keystroke instructions.* Be aware that graphing calculators often differ from scientific calculators in the order in which keystrokes are made.

NOW TRY ANSWERS
9. (a) 2 **(b)** -9 **(c)** -10
  (d) $-m^4$ **(e)** x^6 **(f)** $|t^5|$

NOW TRY
EXERCISE 10

Use a calculator to approximate each radical to three decimal places.

(a) $-\sqrt{92}$ **(b)** $\sqrt[4]{39}$

(c) $\sqrt[5]{33}$

EXAMPLE 10 Finding Approximations for Roots

Use a calculator to verify that each approximation is correct.

(a) $\sqrt{39} \approx 6.245$ **(b)** $-\sqrt{72} \approx -8.485$

(c) $\sqrt[3]{93} \approx 4.531$ **(d)** $\sqrt[4]{39} \approx 2.499$ NOW TRY

NOW TRY
EXERCISE 11

Use the formula in **Example 11** to approximate f to the nearest thousand if

$$L = 7 \times 10^{-5}$$

and $C = 3 \times 10^{-9}$.

EXAMPLE 11 Using Roots to Calculate Resonant Frequency

In electronics, the resonant frequency f of a circuit may be found by the formula

$$f = \frac{1}{2\pi\sqrt{LC}},$$

where f is in cycles per second, L is in henrys, and C is in farads. (Henrys and farads are units of measure in electronics.) Find the resonant frequency f if $L = 5 \times 10^{-4}$ henry and $C = 3 \times 10^{-10}$ farad. Give your answer to the nearest thousand.

Find the value of f when $L = 5 \times 10^{-4}$ and $C = 3 \times 10^{-10}$.

$$f = \frac{1}{2\pi\sqrt{LC}}$$ Given formula

$$= \frac{1}{2\pi\sqrt{(5 \times 10^{-4})(3 \times 10^{-10})}}$$ Substitute for L and C.

$$\approx 411{,}000$$ Use a calculator.

The resonant frequency f is approximately 411,000 cycles per sec.   NOW TRY

NOW TRY ANSWERS
10. (a) -9.592 **(b)** 2.499
     (c) 2.012
11. 347,000 cycles per sec

10.1 EXERCISES   *MyMathLab*   Math XL PRACTICE   WATCH   DOWNLOAD   READ   REVIEW

🌐 *Complete solution available on the Video Resources on DVD*

Concept Check   *Decide whether each statement is* true *or* false. *If false, tell why.*

1. Every positive number has two real square roots.

2. A negative number has negative real square roots.

3. Every nonnegative number has two real square roots.

4. The positive square root of a positive number is its principal square root.

5. The cube root of every nonzero real number has the same sign as the number itself.

6. Every positive number has three real cube roots.

Find all square roots of each number. **See Example 1.**

🌐 **7.** 9   **8.** 16   **9.** 64   **10.** 100   **11.** 169

12. 225   **13.** $\dfrac{25}{196}$ **14.** $\dfrac{81}{400}$ **15.** 900   **16.** 1600

Find each square root. **See Examples 2 and 4(c).**

17. $\sqrt{1}$ **18.** $\sqrt{4}$ 🌐 **19.** $\sqrt{49}$ **20.** $\sqrt{81}$ **21.** $-\sqrt{256}$

22. $-\sqrt{196}$ **23.** $-\sqrt{\dfrac{144}{121}}$ **24.** $-\sqrt{\dfrac{49}{36}}$ **25.** $\sqrt{0.64}$ **26.** $\sqrt{0.16}$

27. $\sqrt{-121}$ **28.** $\sqrt{-64}$ **29.** $-\sqrt{-49}$ **30.** $-\sqrt{-100}$

Find the square of each radical expression. **See Example 3.**

🌐 **31.** $\sqrt{19}$ **32.** $\sqrt{59}$ **33.** $-\sqrt{19}$ **34.** $-\sqrt{59}$

35. $\sqrt{\dfrac{2}{3}}$ **36.** $\sqrt{\dfrac{5}{7}}$ **37.** $\sqrt{3x^2 + 4}$ **38.** $\sqrt{9y^2 + 3}$

Concept Check *What must be true about the variable a for each statement to be true?*

39. $\sqrt{a}$ represents a positive number. **40.** $-\sqrt{a}$ represents a negative number.

41. $\sqrt{a}$ is not a real number. **42.** $-\sqrt{a}$ is not a real number.

Determine whether each number is rational, irrational, *or* not a real number. *If a number is rational, give its exact value. If a number is irrational, give a decimal approximation to the nearest thousandth. Use a calculator as necessary.* **See Examples 4 and 10.**

🌐 **43.** $\sqrt{25}$ **44.** $\sqrt{169}$ **45.** $\sqrt{29}$ **46.** $\sqrt{33}$

47. $-\sqrt{64}$ **48.** $-\sqrt{81}$ 🌐 **49.** $-\sqrt{300}$ **50.** $-\sqrt{500}$

51. $\sqrt{-29}$ **52.** $\sqrt{-47}$ **53.** $\sqrt{1200}$ **54.** $\sqrt{1500}$

Concept Check *Without using a calculator, determine between which two consecutive integers each square root lies. For example,*

$$\sqrt{75} \text{ is between 8 and 9, because } \sqrt{64} = 8, \sqrt{81} = 9, \text{ and } 64 < 75 < 81.$$

55. $\sqrt{94}$ **56.** $\sqrt{43}$ **57.** $\sqrt{51}$ **58.** $\sqrt{30}$

59. $-\sqrt{40}$ **60.** $-\sqrt{63}$ **61.** $\sqrt{23.2}$ **62.** $\sqrt{10.3}$

63. *Concept Check* To help find cube roots, complete this list of perfect cubes.

$1^3 = $ _____ $2^3 = $ _____ $3^3 = $ _____ $4^3 = $ _____ $5^3 = $ _____

$6^3 = $ _____ $7^3 = $ _____ $8^3 = $ _____ $9^3 = $ _____ $10^3 = $ _____

64. *Concept Check* To help find fourth roots, complete this list of perfect fourth powers.

$1^4 = $ _____ $2^4 = $ _____ $3^4 = $ _____ $4^4 = $ _____ $5^4 = $ _____

$6^4 = $ _____ $7^4 = $ _____ $8^4 = $ _____ $9^4 = $ _____ $10^4 = $ _____

65. Match each expression from Column I with the equivalent choice from Column II. Answers may be used more than once. **See Examples 5 and 6.**

I		II	
(a) $-\sqrt{25}$	(b) $\sqrt{-25}$	A. 3	B. -2
(c) $\sqrt[3]{-27}$	(d) $\sqrt[5]{-32}$	C. 2	D. -3
(e) $\sqrt[4]{81}$	(f) $\sqrt[3]{8}$	E. -5	F. Not a real number

66. *Concept Check*   Consider the expression $-\sqrt{-a}$. Decide whether it is *positive, negative*, 0, or *not a real number* if

(a) $a > 0$,   **(b)** $a < 0$,   **(c)** $a = 0$.

Find each root that is a real number. ***See Examples 5 and 6.***

67. $-\sqrt{81}$ **68.** $-\sqrt{121}$ **69.** $\sqrt[3]{216}$ **70.** $\sqrt[3]{343}$

71. $\sqrt[3]{-64}$ **72.** $\sqrt[3]{-125}$ **73.** $-\sqrt[3]{512}$ **74.** $-\sqrt[3]{1000}$

75. $\sqrt[4]{1296}$ **76.** $\sqrt[4]{625}$ **77.** $-\sqrt[4]{16}$ **78.** $-\sqrt[4]{256}$

79. $\sqrt[4]{-625}$ **80.** $\sqrt[4]{-256}$ **81.** $\sqrt[6]{64}$ **82.** $\sqrt[6]{729}$

83. $\sqrt[6]{-32}$ **84.** $\sqrt[8]{-1}$ **85.** $\sqrt{\dfrac{64}{81}}$ **86.** $\sqrt{\dfrac{100}{9}}$

87. $\sqrt[3]{\dfrac{64}{27}}$ **88.** $\sqrt[4]{\dfrac{81}{16}}$ **89.** $-\sqrt[6]{\dfrac{1}{64}}$ **90.** $-\sqrt[5]{\dfrac{1}{32}}$

91. $-\sqrt[3]{-27}$ **92.** $-\sqrt[3]{-64}$ **93.** $\sqrt{0.25}$ **94.** $\sqrt{0.36}$

95. $-\sqrt{0.49}$ **96.** $-\sqrt{0.81}$ **97.** $\sqrt[3]{0.001}$ **98.** $\sqrt[3]{0.125}$

Graph each function and give its domain and range. ***See Example 7.***

99. $f(x) = \sqrt{x+3}$ **100.** $f(x) = \sqrt{x-5}$

101. $f(x) = \sqrt{x-2}$ **102.** $f(x) = \sqrt{x+4}$

103. $f(x) = \sqrt[3]{x} - 3$ **104.** $f(x) = \sqrt[3]{x} + 1$

105. $f(x) = \sqrt[3]{x-3}$ **106.** $f(x) = \sqrt[3]{x+1}$

Simplify each root. ***See Examples 8 and 9.***

107. $\sqrt{12^2}$ **108.** $\sqrt{19^2}$ **109.** $\sqrt{(-10)^2}$ **110.** $\sqrt{(-13)^2}$

111. $\sqrt[6]{(-2)^6}$ **112.** $\sqrt[6]{(-4)^6}$ **113.** $\sqrt[5]{(-9)^5}$ **114.** $\sqrt[5]{(-8)^5}$

115. $-\sqrt[6]{(-5)^6}$ **116.** $-\sqrt[6]{(-7)^6}$ **117.** $\sqrt{x^2}$ **118.** $-\sqrt{x^2}$

119. $\sqrt{(-z)^2}$ **120.** $\sqrt{(-q)^2}$ **121.** $\sqrt[3]{x^3}$ **122.** $-\sqrt[3]{x^3}$

123. $\sqrt[3]{x^{15}}$ **124.** $\sqrt[3]{m^9}$ **125.** $\sqrt[6]{x^{30}}$ **126.** $\sqrt[4]{k^{20}}$

Concept Check   Choose the closest approximation of each square root.

127. $\sqrt{123.5}$ **128.** $\sqrt{67.8}$

    A. 9   **B.** 10   **C.** 11   **D.** 12   **A.** 7   **B.** 8   **C.** 9   **D.** 10

Find a decimal approximation for each radical. Round the answer to three decimal places. ***See Example 10.***

129. $\sqrt{9483}$ **130.** $\sqrt{6825}$ **131.** $\sqrt{284.361}$ **132.** $\sqrt{846.104}$

133. $-\sqrt{82}$ **134.** $-\sqrt{91}$ **135.** $\sqrt[3]{423}$ **136.** $\sqrt[3]{555}$

137. $\sqrt[4]{100}$ **138.** $\sqrt[4]{250}$ **139.** $\sqrt[5]{23.8}$ **140.** $\sqrt[5]{98.4}$

Refer to the rectangle to answer the questions in Exercises 141 and 142.

141. Which one of the following is the best estimate of its area?

    A. 50   **B.** 250   **C.** 2500   **D.** 100

142. Which one of the following is the best estimate of its perimeter?

    A. 15   **B.** 250   **C.** 100   **D.** 30

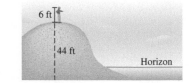

Solve each problem. See Example 11.

143. Use the formula in **Example 11** to calculate the resonant frequency of a circuit to the nearest thousand if $L = 7.237 \times 10^{-5}$ henry and $C = 2.5 \times 10^{-10}$ farad.

144. The threshold weight T for a person is the weight above which the risk of death increases greatly. The threshold weight in pounds for men aged 40–49 is related to height h in inches by the formula

$$h = 12.3 \sqrt[3]{T}.$$

What height corresponds to a threshold weight of 216 lb for a 43-year-old man? Round your answer to the nearest inch and then to the nearest tenth of a foot.

145. According to an article in *The World Scanner Report,* the distance D, in miles, to the horizon from an observer's point of view over water or "flat" earth is given by

$$D = \sqrt{2H},$$

where H is the height of the point of view, in feet. If a person whose eyes are 6 ft above ground level is standing at the top of a hill 44 ft above "flat" earth, approximately how far to the horizon will she be able to see?

146. The time t in seconds for one complete swing of a simple pendulum, where L is the length of the pendulum in feet, and g, the acceleration due to gravity, is about 32 ft per sec^2, is

$$t = 2\pi \sqrt{\frac{L}{g}}.$$

Find the time of a complete swing of a 2-ft pendulum to the nearest tenth of a second.

147. **Heron's formula** gives a method of finding the area of a triangle if the lengths of its sides are known. Suppose that a, b, and c are the lengths of the sides. Let s denote one-half of the perimeter of the triangle (called the *semiperimeter*); that is, $s = \frac{1}{2}(a + b + c)$. Then the area of the triangle is

$$\mathcal{A} = \sqrt{s(s - a)(s - b)(s - c)}.$$

Find the area of the Bermuda Triangle, to the nearest thousand square miles, if the "sides" of this triangle measure approximately 850 mi, 925 mi, and 1300 mi.

148. Use Heron's formula from **Exercise 147** to find the area of a triangle with sides of lengths $a = 11$ m, $b = 60$ m, and $c = 61$ m.

149. The coefficient of self-induction L (in henrys), the energy P stored in an electronic circuit (in joules), and the current I (in amps) are related by this formula.

$$I = \sqrt{\frac{2P}{L}}$$

(a) Find I if $P = 120$ and $L = 80$.   **(b)** Find I if $P = 100$ and $L = 40$.

150. The Vietnam Veterans Memorial in Washington, DC, is in the shape of an unenclosed isosceles triangle with equal sides of length 246.75 ft. If the triangle were enclosed, the third side would have length 438.14 ft. Use Heron's formula from **Exercise 147** to find the area of this enclosure to the nearest hundred square feet. (*Source:* Information pamphlet obtained at the Vietnam Veterans Memorial.)

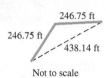

246.75 ft

246.75 ft

438.14 ft

Not to scale

PREVIEW EXERCISES

Apply the rules for exponents. Write each result with only positive exponents. Assume that all variables represent nonzero real numbers. ***See Sections 4.1 and 4.2.***

151. $x^5 \cdot x^{-1} \cdot x^{-3}$ **152.** $(4x^2y^3)(2^3x^5y)$ **153.** $\left(\dfrac{2}{3}\right)^{-3}$ **154.** $\dfrac{5}{5^{-1}}$

10.2 Rational Exponents

OBJECTIVES

1. Use exponential notation for *n*th roots.
2. Define and use expressions of the form $a^{m/n}$.
3. Convert between radicals and rational exponents.
4. Use the rules for exponents with rational exponents.

OBJECTIVE 1 Use exponential notation for *n*th roots. Consider the product $(3^{1/2})^2 = 3^{1/2} \cdot 3^{1/2}$. Using the rules of exponents from **Section 4.1,** we can simplify this product as follows.

$$(3^{1/2})^2 = 3^{1/2} \cdot 3^{1/2}$$
$$= 3^{1/2+1/2} \qquad \text{Product rule: } a^m \cdot a^n = a^{m+n}$$
$$= 3^1 \qquad \text{Add exponents.}$$
$$= 3 \qquad a^1 = a$$

Also, by definition,

$$\left(\sqrt{3}\right)^2 = \sqrt{3} \cdot \sqrt{3} = 3.$$

Since both $(3^{1/2})^2$ and $\left(\sqrt{3}\right)^2$ are equal to 3, it seems reasonable to define

$$3^{1/2} = \sqrt{3}.$$

This suggests the following generalization.

$a^{1/n}$

If $\sqrt[n]{a}$ is a real number, then $a^{1/n} = \sqrt[n]{a}.$

$$4^{1/2} = \sqrt{4}, \quad 8^{1/3} = \sqrt[3]{8}, \quad \text{and} \quad 16^{1/4} = \sqrt[4]{16} \qquad \text{Examples of } a^{1/n}$$

Notice that the denominator of the rational exponent is the index of the radical.

⌐ NOW TRY
⌐ EXERCISE 1

Evaluate each exponential.

(a) $81^{1/2}$ **(b)** $125^{1/3}$

(c) $-625^{1/4}$ **(d)** $(-625)^{1/4}$

(e) $(-125)^{1/3}$ **(f)** $\left(\dfrac{1}{16}\right)^{1/4}$

EXAMPLE 1 Evaluating Exponentials of the Form $a^{1/n}$

Evaluate each exponential.

(a) $64^{1/3} = \sqrt[3]{64} = 4$ **(b)** $100^{1/2} = \sqrt{100} = 10$

(c) $-256^{1/4} = -\sqrt[4]{256} = -4$

(d) $(-256)^{1/4} = \sqrt[4]{-256}$ is not a real number, because the radicand, -256, is negative and the index is even.

(e) $(-32)^{1/5} = \sqrt[5]{-32} = -2$ **(f)** $\left(\dfrac{1}{8}\right)^{1/3} = \sqrt[3]{\dfrac{1}{8}} = \dfrac{1}{2}$ NOW TRY ⤴

⚠ **CAUTION** Notice the difference between **Examples 1(c) and (d).** The radical in part (c) is the *negative fourth root of a positive number,* while the radical in part (d) is the *principal fourth root of a negative number, which is not a real number.*

OBJECTIVE 2 Define and use expressions of the form $a^{m/n}$. We know that $8^{1/3} = \sqrt[3]{8}$. We can define a number like $8^{2/3}$, where the numerator of the exponent is not 1. For past rules of exponents to be valid,

$$8^{2/3} = 8^{(1/3)2} = \left(8^{1/3}\right)^2.$$

Since $8^{1/3} = \sqrt[3]{8}$,

$$8^{2/3} = \left(\sqrt[3]{8}\right)^2 = 2^2 = 4.$$

Generalizing from this example, we define $a^{m/n}$ as follows.

$a^{m/n}$

If m and n are positive integers with m/n in lowest terms, then

$$a^{m/n} = \left(a^{1/n}\right)^m,$$

provided that $a^{1/n}$ is a real number. If $a^{1/n}$ is not a real number, then $a^{m/n}$ is not a real number.

EXAMPLE 2 Evaluating Exponentials of the Form $a^{m/n}$

Evaluate each exponential.

Think:
$36^{1/2} = \sqrt{36} = 6$

Think:
$125^{1/3} = \sqrt[3]{125} = 5$

(a) $36^{3/2} = (36^{1/2})^3 = 6^3 = 216$ **(b)** $125^{2/3} = (125^{1/3})^2 = 5^2 = 25$

Be careful.
The base is 4.

NOW TRY ANSWERS

1. (a) 9   **(b)** 5   **(c)** -5
    (d) It is not a real number.
    (e) -5 **(f)** $\frac{1}{2}$

(c) $-4^{5/2} = -(4^{5/2}) = -(4^{1/2})^5 = -(2)^5 = -32$

Because the base here is 4, the negative sign is *not* affected by the exponent.

NOW TRY
EXERCISE 2

Evaluate each exponential.

(a) $32^{2/5}$ **(b)** $8^{5/3}$

(c) $-100^{3/2}$ **(d)** $(-121)^{3/2}$

(e) $(-125)^{4/3}$

(d) $(-27)^{2/3} = [(-27)^{1/3}]^2 = (-3)^2 = 9$

Notice in part (c) that we first evaluate the exponential and then find its negative. In part (d), the $-$ sign is part of the base, -27.

(e) $(-100)^{3/2} = [(-100)^{1/2}]^3$, which is not a real number, since $(-100)^{1/2}$, or $\sqrt{-100}$, is not a real number.

NOW TRY

When a rational exponent is negative, the earlier interpretation of negative exponents is applied.

$a^{-m/n}$

If $a^{m/n}$ is a real number, then

$$a^{-m/n} = \frac{1}{a^{m/n}} \quad (a \neq 0).$$

NOW TRY
EXERCISE 3

Evaluate each exponential.

(a) $243^{-3/5}$ **(b)** $4^{-5/2}$

(c) $\left(\dfrac{216}{125}\right)^{-2/3}$

EXAMPLE 3 Evaluating Exponentials with Negative Rational Exponents

Evaluate each exponential.

(a) $16^{-3/4} = \dfrac{1}{16^{3/4}} = \dfrac{1}{(16^{1/4})^3} = \dfrac{1}{\left(\sqrt[4]{16}\right)^3} = \dfrac{1}{2^3} = \dfrac{1}{8}$

> The denominator of 3/4 is the index and the numerator is the exponent.

(b) $25^{-3/2} = \dfrac{1}{25^{3/2}} = \dfrac{1}{(25^{1/2})^3} = \dfrac{1}{\left(\sqrt{25}\right)^3} = \dfrac{1}{5^3} = \dfrac{1}{125}$

(c) $\left(\dfrac{8}{27}\right)^{-2/3} = \dfrac{1}{\left(\dfrac{8}{27}\right)^{2/3}} = \dfrac{1}{\left(\sqrt[3]{\dfrac{8}{27}}\right)^2} = \dfrac{1}{\left(\dfrac{2}{3}\right)^2} = \dfrac{1}{\dfrac{4}{9}} = \dfrac{9}{4}$

> $\dfrac{1}{\frac{4}{9}} = 1 \div \dfrac{4}{9} = 1 \cdot \dfrac{9}{4}$

We can also use the rule $\left(\dfrac{b}{a}\right)^{-m} = \left(\dfrac{a}{b}\right)^m$ here, as follows.

$$\left(\dfrac{8}{27}\right)^{-2/3} = \left(\dfrac{27}{8}\right)^{2/3} = \left(\sqrt[3]{\dfrac{27}{8}}\right)^2 = \left(\dfrac{3}{2}\right)^2 = \dfrac{9}{4}$$

> Take the reciprocal only of the base, *not* the exponent.

NOW TRY

⚠ CAUTION Be careful to distinguish between exponential expressions like the following.

$16^{-1/4}$, which equals $\dfrac{1}{2}$, $-16^{1/4}$, which equals -2, and $-16^{-1/4}$, which equals $-\dfrac{1}{2}$

A negative exponent does not necessarily lead to a negative result. Negative exponents lead to reciprocals, which may be positive.

NOW TRY ANSWERS

2. (a) 4 **(b)** 32 **(c)** -1000
(d) It is not a real number.
(e) 625

3. (a) $\frac{1}{27}$ **(b)** $\frac{1}{32}$ **(c)** $\frac{25}{36}$

We obtain an alternative definition of $a^{m/n}$ by using the power rule for exponents differently than in the earlier definition. If all indicated roots are real numbers,

then $\qquad a^{m/n} = a^{m(1/n)} = (a^m)^{1/n}, \quad \text{so} \quad a^{m/n} = (a^m)^{1/n}.$

$a^{m/n}$

If all indicated roots are real numbers, then

$$a^{m/n} = (a^{1/n})^m = (a^m)^{1/n}.$$

We can now evaluate an expression such as $27^{2/3}$ in two ways.

$$27^{2/3} = (27^{1/3})^2 = 3^2 = 9$$

or $\qquad 27^{2/3} = (27^2)^{1/3} = 729^{1/3} = 9 \qquad$ The result is the same.

In most cases, it is easier to use $(a^{1/n})^m$.

Radical Form of $a^{m/n}$

If all indicated roots are real numbers, then

$$a^{m/n} = \sqrt[n]{a^m} = \left(\sqrt[n]{a}\right)^m.$$

That is, raise a to the mth power and then take the nth root, or take the nth root of a and then raise to the mth power.

For example,

$$8^{2/3} = \sqrt[3]{8^2} = \sqrt[3]{64} = 4, \quad \text{and} \quad 8^{2/3} = \left(\sqrt[3]{8}\right)^2 = 2^2 = 4,$$

so $\qquad 8^{2/3} = \sqrt[3]{8^2} = \left(\sqrt[3]{8}\right)^2.$

OBJECTIVE 3 **Convert between radicals and rational exponents.** Using the definition of rational exponents, we can simplify many problems involving radicals by converting the radicals to numbers with rational exponents. After simplifying, we can convert the answer back to radical form if required.

EXAMPLE 4 Converting between Rational Exponents and Radicals

Write each exponential as a radical. Assume that all variables represent positive real numbers. Use the definition that takes the root first.

(a) $13^{1/2} = \sqrt{13}$ **(b)** $6^{3/4} = \left(\sqrt[4]{6}\right)^3$ **(c)** $9m^{5/8} = 9\left(\sqrt[8]{m}\right)^5$

(d) $6x^{2/3} - (4x)^{3/5} = 6\left(\sqrt[3]{x}\right)^2 - \left(\sqrt[5]{4x}\right)^3$

(e) $r^{-2/3} = \dfrac{1}{r^{2/3}} = \dfrac{1}{\left(\sqrt[3]{r}\right)^2}$

(f) $(a^2 + b^2)^{1/2} = \sqrt{a^2 + b^2}$ $\boxed{\sqrt{a^2 + b^2} \neq a + b}$

NOW TRY
EXERCISE 4

Write each exponential as a radical. Assume that all variables represent positive real numbers.

(a) $21^{1/2}$ **(b)** $17^{5/4}$

(c) $4t^{3/5} + (4t)^{2/3}$

(d) $w^{-2/5}$ **(e)** $(a^2 - b^2)^{1/4}$

In parts (f)–(h), write each radical as an exponential. Simplify. Assume that all variables represent positive real numbers.

(f) $\sqrt[3]{15}$ **(g)** $\sqrt[4]{4^2}$

(h) $\sqrt[4]{x^4}$

In parts (g)–(i), write each radical as an exponential. Simplify. Assume that all variables represent positive real numbers.

(g) $\sqrt{10} = 10^{1/2}$ **(h)** $\sqrt[4]{3^8} = 3^{8/4} = 3^2 = 9$

(i) $\sqrt[6]{z^6} = z$, since z is positive.

NOW TRY

NOTE In **Example 4(i)**, it is not necessary to use absolute value bars, since the directions specifically state that the variable represents a positive real number. Because the absolute value of the positive real number z is z itself, the answer is simply z.

OBJECTIVE 4 **Use the rules for exponents with rational exponents.** The definition of rational exponents allows us to apply the rules for exponents from **Sections 4.1 and 4.2.**

Rules for Rational Exponents

Let r and s be rational numbers. For all real numbers a and b for which the indicated expressions exist, the following are true.

$$a^r \cdot a^s = a^{r+s} \qquad a^{-r} = \frac{1}{a^r} \qquad \frac{a^r}{a^s} = a^{r-s} \qquad \left(\frac{a}{b}\right)^{-r} = \frac{b^r}{a^r}$$

$$(a^r)^s = a^{rs} \qquad (ab)^r = a^r b^r \qquad \left(\frac{a}{b}\right)^r = \frac{a^r}{b^r} \qquad a^{-r} = \left(\frac{1}{a}\right)^r$$

EXAMPLE 5 **Applying Rules for Rational Exponents**

Write with only positive exponents. Assume that all variables represent positive real numbers.

(a) $2^{1/2} \cdot 2^{1/4}$

$\qquad = 2^{1/2 + 1/4}$ Product rule

$\qquad = 2^{3/4}$ Add exponents.

(b) $\dfrac{5^{2/3}}{5^{7/3}}$

$\qquad = 5^{2/3 - 7/3}$ Quotient rule

$\qquad = 5^{-5/3}$ Subtract exponents.

$\qquad = \dfrac{1}{5^{5/3}}$ $a^{-r} = \frac{1}{a^r}$

(c) $\dfrac{(x^{1/2}y^{2/3})^4}{y}$

$\qquad = \dfrac{(x^{1/2})^4 (y^{2/3})^4}{y}$ Power rule

$\qquad = \dfrac{x^2 y^{8/3}}{y^1}$ Power rule

$\qquad = x^2 y^{8/3 - 1}$ Quotient rule

$\qquad = x^2 y^{5/3}$ $\frac{8}{3} - 1 = \frac{8}{3} - \frac{3}{3} = \frac{5}{3}$

NOW TRY ANSWERS

4. (a) $\sqrt{21}$ **(b)** $\left(\sqrt[4]{17}\right)^5$

    (c) $4\left(\sqrt[5]{t}\right)^3 + \left(\sqrt[3]{4t}\right)^2$

    (d) $\dfrac{1}{\left(\sqrt[5]{w}\right)^2}$ **(e)** $\sqrt[4]{a^2 - b^2}$

    (f) $15^{1/3}$ **(g)** 2 **(h)** x

NOW TRY
EXERCISE 5
Write with only positive exponents. Assume that all variables represent positive real numbers.

(a) $5^{1/4} \cdot 5^{2/3}$ **(b)** $\dfrac{9^{3/5}}{9^{7/5}}$

(c) $\dfrac{(r^{2/3}t^{1/4})^8}{t}$

(d) $\left(\dfrac{2x^{1/2}y^{-2/3}}{x^{-3/5}y^{-1/5}}\right)^{-3}$

(e) $y^{2/3}(y^{1/3} + y^{5/3})$

(d) $\left(\dfrac{x^4y^{-6}}{x^{-2}y^{1/3}}\right)^{-2/3}$

$= \dfrac{(x^4)^{-2/3}(y^{-6})^{-2/3}}{(x^{-2})^{-2/3}(y^{1/3})^{-2/3}}$ Power rule

$= \dfrac{x^{-8/3}y^4}{x^{4/3}y^{-2/9}}$ Power rule

$= x^{-8/3-4/3}y^{4-(-2/9)}$ Quotient rule

$= x^{-4}y^{38/9}$ [Use parentheses to avoid errors.] $4 - \left(-\tfrac{2}{9}\right) = \tfrac{36}{9} + \tfrac{2}{9} = \tfrac{38}{9}$

$= \dfrac{y^{38/9}}{x^4}$ Definition of negative exponent

The same result is obtained if we simplify within the parentheses first.

$$\left(\dfrac{x^4y^{-6}}{x^{-2}y^{1/3}}\right)^{-2/3}$$

$= (x^{4-(-2)}y^{-6-1/3})^{-2/3}$ Quotient rule

$= (x^6y^{-19/3})^{-2/3}$ $-6 - \tfrac{1}{3} = -\tfrac{18}{3} - \tfrac{1}{3} = -\tfrac{19}{3}$

$= (x^6)^{-2/3}(y^{-19/3})^{-2/3}$ Power rule

$= x^{-4}y^{38/9}$ Power rule

$= \dfrac{y^{38/9}}{x^4}$ Definition of negative exponent

(e) $\qquad\qquad m^{3/4}(m^{5/4} - m^{1/4})$

[Do not make the common mistake of multiplying exponents in the first step.]

$= m^{3/4}(m^{5/4}) - m^{3/4}(m^{1/4})$ Distributive property

$= m^{3/4+5/4} - m^{3/4+1/4}$ Product rule

$= m^{8/4} - m^{4/4}$ Add exponents.

$= m^2 - m$ Lowest terms in exponents

NOW TRY

⚠️ **CAUTION** Use the rules of exponents in problems like those in **Example 5.** Do not convert the expressions to radical form.

EXAMPLE 6 Applying Rules for Rational Exponents

Write all radicals as exponentials, and then apply the rules for rational exponents. Leave answers in exponential form. Assume that all variables represent positive real numbers.

(a) $\sqrt[3]{x^2} \cdot \sqrt[4]{x}$

$= x^{2/3} \cdot x^{1/4}$ Convert to rational exponents.

$= x^{2/3+1/4}$ Product rule

$= x^{8/12+3/12}$ Write exponents with a common denominator.

$= x^{11/12}$ Add exponents.

NOW TRY ANSWERS

5. (a) $5^{11/12}$ **(b)** $\dfrac{1}{9^{4/5}}$

(c) $r^{16/3}t$ **(d)** $\dfrac{y^{7/5}}{8x^{33/10}}$

(e) $y + y^{7/3}$

⌐NOW TRY
 EXERCISE 6

Write all radicals as exponentials, and then apply the rules for rational exponents. Leave answers in exponential form. Assume that all variables represent positive real numbers.

(a) $\sqrt[5]{y^3} \cdot \sqrt[3]{y}$ (b) $\dfrac{\sqrt[4]{y^3}}{\sqrt{y^5}}$

(c) $\sqrt{\sqrt[3]{y}}$

NOW TRY ANSWERS

6. (a) $y^{14/15}$ (b) $\dfrac{1}{y^{7/4}}$ (c) $y^{1/6}$

(b) $\dfrac{\sqrt{x^3}}{\sqrt[3]{x^2}}$

$= \dfrac{x^{3/2}}{x^{2/3}}$ Convert to rational exponents.

$= x^{3/2 - 2/3}$ Quotient rule

$= x^{5/6}$ $\frac{3}{2} - \frac{2}{3} = \frac{9}{6} - \frac{4}{6} = \frac{5}{6}$

(c) $\sqrt{\sqrt[4]{z}}$

$= \sqrt{z^{1/4}}$ Convert the inside radical to rational exponents.

$= (z^{1/4})^{1/2}$ Convert to rational exponents.

$= z^{1/8}$ Power rule

NOW TRY ⤸

NOTE The ability to convert between radicals and rational exponents is important in the study of exponential and logarithmic functions in **Chapter 12.**

10.2 EXERCISES

● *Complete solution available on the Video Resources on DVD*

Concept Check Match each expression from Column I with the equivalent choice from Column II.

I

1. $3^{1/2}$ 2. $(-27)^{1/3}$
3. $-16^{1/2}$ 4. $(-25)^{1/2}$
5. $(-32)^{1/5}$ 6. $(-32)^{2/5}$
7. $4^{3/2}$ 8. $6^{2/4}$
9. $-6^{2/4}$ 10. $36^{0.5}$

II

A. -4 B. 8
C. $\sqrt{3}$ D. $-\sqrt{6}$
E. -3 F. $\sqrt{6}$
G. 4 H. -2
I. 6 J. Not a real number

Evaluate each exponential. See Examples 1–3.

● 11. $169^{1/2}$ 12. $121^{1/2}$ 13. $729^{1/3}$ 14. $512^{1/3}$

15. $16^{1/4}$ 16. $625^{1/4}$ 17. $\left(\dfrac{64}{81}\right)^{1/2}$ 18. $\left(\dfrac{8}{27}\right)^{1/3}$

● 19. $(-27)^{1/3}$ 20. $(-32)^{1/5}$ ● 21. $(-144)^{1/2}$ 22. $(-36)^{1/2}$

● 23. $100^{3/2}$ 24. $64^{3/2}$ 25. $81^{3/4}$ 26. $216^{2/3}$

27. $-16^{5/2}$ 28. $-32^{3/5}$ 29. $(-8)^{4/3}$ 30. $(-243)^{2/5}$

● 31. $32^{-3/5}$ 32. $27^{-4/3}$ 33. $64^{-3/2}$ 34. $81^{-3/2}$

35. $\left(\dfrac{125}{27}\right)^{-2/3}$ 36. $\left(\dfrac{64}{125}\right)^{-2/3}$ 37. $\left(\dfrac{16}{81}\right)^{-3/4}$ 38. $\left(\dfrac{729}{64}\right)^{-5/6}$

Write with radicals. Assume that all variables represent positive real numbers. See Example 4.

● 39. $10^{1/2}$ 40. $3^{1/2}$ 41. $8^{3/4}$

42. $7^{2/3}$ ● 43. $(9q)^{5/8} - (2x)^{2/3}$ 44. $(3p)^{3/4} + (4x)^{1/3}$

45. $(2m)^{-3/2}$ 46. $(5y)^{-3/5}$ 47. $(2y + x)^{2/3}$

48. $(r + 2z)^{3/2}$ 49. $(3m^4 + 2k^2)^{-2/3}$ 50. $(5x^2 + 3z^3)^{-5/6}$

Simplify by first converting to rational exponents. Assume that all variables represent positive real numbers. See Example 4.

51. $\sqrt{2^{12}}$ 52. $\sqrt{5^{10}}$ 53. $\sqrt[3]{4^9}$ 54. $\sqrt[4]{6^8}$ ● 55. $\sqrt{x^{20}}$

56. $\sqrt{r^{50}}$ 57. $\sqrt[3]{x} \cdot \sqrt{x}$ 58. $\sqrt[4]{y} \cdot \sqrt[5]{y^2}$ 59. $\dfrac{\sqrt[3]{t^4}}{\sqrt[5]{t^4}}$ 60. $\dfrac{\sqrt[4]{w^3}}{\sqrt[6]{w}}$

Simplify each expression. Write all answers with positive exponents. Assume that all variables represent positive real numbers. **See Example 5.**

61. $3^{1/2} \cdot 3^{3/2}$

62. $6^{4/3} \cdot 6^{2/3}$

63. $\dfrac{64^{5/3}}{64^{4/3}}$

64. $\dfrac{125^{7/3}}{125^{5/3}}$

65. $y^{7/3} \cdot y^{-4/3}$

66. $r^{-8/9} \cdot r^{17/9}$

67. $x^{2/3} \cdot x^{-1/4}$

68. $x^{2/5} \cdot x^{-1/3}$

69. $\dfrac{k^{1/3}}{k^{2/3} \cdot k^{-1}}$

70. $\dfrac{z^{3/4}}{z^{5/4} \cdot z^{-2}}$

71. $\dfrac{(x^{1/4}y^{2/5})^{20}}{x^2}$

72. $\dfrac{(r^{1/5}s^{2/3})^{15}}{r^2}$

73. $\dfrac{(x^{2/3})^2}{(x^2)^{7/3}}$

74. $\dfrac{(p^3)^{1/4}}{(p^{5/4})^2}$

75. $\dfrac{m^{3/4}n^{-1/4}}{(m^2n)^{1/2}}$

76. $\dfrac{(a^2b^5)^{-1/4}}{(a^{-3}b^2)^{1/6}}$

77. $\dfrac{p^{1/5}p^{7/10}p^{1/2}}{(p^3)^{-1/5}}$

78. $\dfrac{z^{1/3}z^{-2/3}z^{1/6}}{(z^{-1/6})^3}$

79. $\left(\dfrac{b^{-3/2}}{c^{-5/3}}\right)^2 (b^{-1/4}c^{-1/3})^{-1}$

80. $\left(\dfrac{m^{-2/3}}{a^{-3/4}}\right)^4 (m^{-3/8}a^{1/4})^{-2}$

81. $\left(\dfrac{p^{-1/4}q^{-3/2}}{3^{-1}p^{-2}q^{-2/3}}\right)^{-2}$

82. $\left(\dfrac{2^{-2}w^{-3/4}x^{-5/8}}{w^{3/4}x^{-1/2}}\right)^{-3}$

83. $p^{2/3}(p^{1/3} + 2p^{4/3})$

84. $z^{5/8}(3z^{5/8} + 5z^{11/8})$

85. $k^{1/4}(k^{3/2} - k^{1/2})$

86. $r^{3/5}(r^{1/2} + r^{3/4})$

87. $6a^{7/4}(a^{-7/4} + 3a^{-3/4})$

88. $4m^{5/3}(m^{-2/3} - 4m^{-5/3})$

89. $-5x^{7/6}(x^{5/6} - x^{-1/6})$

90. $-8y^{11/7}(y^{3/7} - y^{-4/7})$

Write with rational exponents, and then apply the properties of exponents. Assume that all radicands represent positive real numbers. Give answers in exponential form. **See Example 6.**

91. $\sqrt[5]{x^3} \cdot \sqrt[4]{x}$

92. $\sqrt[6]{y^5} \cdot \sqrt[3]{y^2}$

93. $\dfrac{\sqrt{x^5}}{\sqrt{x^8}}$

94. $\dfrac{\sqrt[3]{k^5}}{\sqrt[3]{k^7}}$

95. $\sqrt{y} \cdot \sqrt[3]{yz}$

96. $\sqrt[3]{xz} \cdot \sqrt{z}$

97. $\sqrt[4]{\sqrt[3]{m}}$

98. $\sqrt[3]{\sqrt{k}}$

99. $\sqrt{\sqrt{\sqrt{x}}}$

100. $\sqrt{\sqrt{\sqrt{\sqrt{x}}}}$

101. $\sqrt{\sqrt[3]{\sqrt[4]{x}}}$

102. $\sqrt[3]{\sqrt[5]{\sqrt{y}}}$

103. Show that, in general, $\sqrt{a^2 + b^2} \neq a + b$ by replacing a with 3 and b with 4.

104. Suppose someone claims that $\sqrt[n]{a^n + b^n}$ must equal $a + b$, since, when $a = 1$ and $b = 0$, a true statement results:

$$\sqrt[n]{a^n + b^n} = \sqrt[n]{1^n + 0^n} = \sqrt[n]{1^n} = 1 = 1 + 0 = a + b.$$

Explain why this is faulty reasoning.

Solve each problem.

105. Meteorologists can determine the duration of a storm by using the function defined by

$$T(D) = 0.07D^{3/2},$$

where D is the diameter of the storm in miles and T is the time in hours. Find the duration of a storm with a diameter of 16 mi. Round your answer to the nearest tenth of an hour.

106. The threshold weight T, in pounds, for a person is the weight above which the risk of death increases greatly. The threshold weight in pounds for men aged 40–49 is related to height h in inches by the function defined by

$$h(T) = (1860.867T)^{1/3}.$$

What height corresponds to a threshold weight of 200 lb for a 46-yr-old man? Round your answer to the nearest inch and then to the nearest tenth of a foot.

The **windchill factor** is a measure of the cooling effect that the wind has on a person's skin. It calculates the equivalent cooling temperature if there were no wind. The National Weather Service uses the formula

$$\text{Windchill temperature} = 35.74 + 0.6215T - 35.75V^{4/25} + 0.4275TV^{4/25},$$

where T is the temperature in °F and V is the wind speed in miles per hour, to calculate windchill. The chart gives the windchill factor for various wind speeds and temperatures at which frostbite is a risk, and how quickly it may occur.

Temperature (°F)

Calm	40	30	20	10	0	−10	−20	−30	−40
5	36	25	13	1	−11	−22	−34	−46	−57
10	34	21	9	−4	−16	−28	−41	−53	−66
15	32	19	6	−7	−19	−32	−45	−58	−71
20	30	17	4	−9	−22	−35	−48	−61	−74
25	29	16	3	−11	−24	−37	−51	−64	−78
30	28	15	1	−12	−26	−39	−53	−67	−80
35	28	14	0	−14	−27	−41	−55	−69	−82
40	27	13	−1	−15	−29	−43	−57	−71	−84

Wind speed (mph)

Frostbites times: ☐ 30 minutes ☐ 10 minutes ☐ 5 minutes

Source: National Oceanic and Atmospheric Administration, National Weather Service.

Use the formula and a calculator to determine the windchill to the nearest tenth of a degree, given the following conditions. Compare your answers with the appropriate entries in the table.

107. 30°F, 15-mph wind

108. 10°F, 30-mph wind

109. 20°F, 20-mph wind

110. 40°F, 10-mph wind

PREVIEW EXERCISES

Simplify each pair of expressions, and then compare the results. ***See Section 10.1.***

111. $\sqrt{25} \cdot \sqrt{36}, \quad \sqrt{25 \cdot 36}$

112. $\dfrac{\sqrt[3]{27}}{\sqrt[3]{729}}, \quad \sqrt[3]{\dfrac{27}{729}}$

(10.3) Simplifying Radical Expressions

OBJECTIVES

1 Use the product rule for radicals.
2 Use the quotient rule for radicals.
3 Simplify radicals.
4 Simplify products and quotients of radicals with different indexes.
5 Use the Pythagorean theorem.
6 Use the distance formula.

OBJECTIVE 1 **Use the product rule for radicals.** Consider the expressions $\sqrt{36 \cdot 4}$ and $\sqrt{36} \cdot \sqrt{4}$. Are they equal?

$$\sqrt{36 \cdot 4} = \sqrt{144} = 12$$
$$\sqrt{36} \cdot \sqrt{4} = 6 \cdot 2 = 12$$

The result is the same.

This is an example of the **product rule for radicals.**

Product Rule for Radicals

If $\sqrt[n]{a}$ and $\sqrt[n]{b}$ are real numbers and n is a natural number, then

$$\sqrt[n]{a} \cdot \sqrt[n]{b} = \sqrt[n]{ab}.$$

That is, the product of two nth roots is the nth root of the product.

We justify the product rule by using the rules for rational exponents. Since $\sqrt[n]{a} = a^{1/n}$ and $\sqrt[n]{b} = b^{1/n}$,

$$\sqrt[n]{a} \cdot \sqrt[n]{b} = a^{1/n} \cdot b^{1/n} = (ab)^{1/n} = \sqrt[n]{ab}.$$

⚠ **CAUTION** *Use the product rule only when the radicals have the same index.*

NOW TRY EXERCISE 1

Multiply. Assume that all variables represent positive real numbers.

(a) $\sqrt{7} \cdot \sqrt{11}$

(b) $\sqrt{2mn} \cdot \sqrt{15}$

EXAMPLE 1 Using the Product Rule

Multiply. Assume that all variables represent positive real numbers.

(a) $\sqrt{5} \cdot \sqrt{7}$
$= \sqrt{5 \cdot 7}$
$= \sqrt{35}$

(b) $\sqrt{11} \cdot \sqrt{p}$
$= \sqrt{11p}$

(c) $\sqrt{7} \cdot \sqrt{11xyz}$
$= \sqrt{77xyz}$

NOW TRY

NOW TRY EXERCISE 2

Multiply. Assume that all variables represent positive real numbers.

(a) $\sqrt[3]{4} \cdot \sqrt[3]{5}$

(b) $\sqrt[4]{5t} \cdot \sqrt[4]{6r^3}$

(c) $\sqrt[7]{20x} \cdot \sqrt[7]{3xy^3}$

(d) $\sqrt[3]{5} \cdot \sqrt[4]{9}$

EXAMPLE 2 Using the Product Rule

Multiply. Assume that all variables represent positive real numbers.

(a) $\sqrt[3]{3} \cdot \sqrt[3]{12}$
$= \sqrt[3]{3 \cdot 12}$
$= \sqrt[3]{36}$ — Remember to write the index.

(b) $\sqrt[4]{8y} \cdot \sqrt[4]{3r^2}$
$= \sqrt[4]{24yr^2}$

(c) $\sqrt[6]{10m^4} \cdot \sqrt[6]{5m}$
$= \sqrt[6]{50m^5}$

(d) $\sqrt[4]{2} \cdot \sqrt[5]{2}$ cannot be simplified using the product rule for radicals, because the indexes (4 and 5) are different. NOW TRY

OBJECTIVE 2 Use the quotient rule for radicals. The **quotient rule for radicals** is similar to the product rule.

Quotient Rule for Radicals

If $\sqrt[n]{a}$ and $\sqrt[n]{b}$ are real numbers, $b \neq 0$, and n is a natural number, then

$$\sqrt[n]{\frac{a}{b}} = \frac{\sqrt[n]{a}}{\sqrt[n]{b}}.$$

That is, the nth root of a quotient is the quotient of the nth roots.

EXAMPLE 3 Using the Quotient Rule

Simplify. Assume that all variables represent positive real numbers.

(a) $\sqrt{\frac{16}{25}} = \frac{\sqrt{16}}{\sqrt{25}} = \frac{4}{5}$

(b) $\sqrt{\frac{7}{36}} = \frac{\sqrt{7}}{\sqrt{36}} = \frac{\sqrt{7}}{6}$

(c) $\sqrt[3]{-\frac{8}{125}} = \sqrt[3]{\frac{-8}{125}} = \frac{\sqrt[3]{-8}}{\sqrt[3]{125}} = \frac{-2}{5} = -\frac{2}{5}$ $\frac{-a}{b} = -\frac{a}{b}$

NOW TRY ANSWERS
1. (a) $\sqrt{77}$ (b) $\sqrt{30mn}$
2. (a) $\sqrt[3]{20}$ (b) $\sqrt[4]{30tr^3}$
   (c) $\sqrt[7]{60x^2y^3}$
   (d) This expression cannot be simplified by the product rule.

NOW TRY
EXERCISE 3

Simplify. Assume that all variables represent positive real numbers.

(a) $\sqrt{\dfrac{49}{36}}$ (b) $\sqrt{\dfrac{5}{144}}$

(c) $\sqrt[3]{-\dfrac{27}{1000}}$ (d) $\sqrt[4]{\dfrac{t}{16}}$

(e) $-\sqrt[5]{\dfrac{m^{15}}{243}}$

(d) $\sqrt[3]{\dfrac{7}{216}} = \dfrac{\sqrt[3]{7}}{\sqrt[3]{216}} = \dfrac{\sqrt[3]{7}}{6}$ (e) $\sqrt[5]{\dfrac{x}{32}} = \dfrac{\sqrt[5]{x}}{\sqrt[5]{32}} = \dfrac{\sqrt[5]{x}}{2}$

(f) $-\sqrt[3]{\dfrac{m^6}{125}} = -\dfrac{\sqrt[3]{m^6}}{\sqrt[3]{125}} = -\dfrac{m^2}{5}$ ◁ Think: $\sqrt[3]{m^6} = m^{6/3} = m^2$

NOW TRY ↻

OBJECTIVE 3 **Simplify radicals.** We use the product and quotient rules to simplify radicals. A radical is **simplified** if the following four conditions are met.

Conditions for a Simplified Radical

1. The radicand has no factor raised to a power greater than or equal to the index.

2. The radicand has no fractions.

3. No denominator contains a radical.

4. Exponents in the radicand and the index of the radical have greatest common factor 1.

EXAMPLE 4 Simplifying Roots of Numbers

Simplify.

(a) $\sqrt{24}$

Check to see whether 24 is divisible by a perfect square (the square of a natural number) such as 4, 9, 16, ... The greatest perfect square that divides into 24 is 4.

$$\sqrt{24}$$
$$= \sqrt{4 \cdot 6} \qquad \text{Factor; 4 is a perfect square.}$$
$$= \sqrt{4} \cdot \sqrt{6} \qquad \text{Product rule}$$
$$= 2\sqrt{6} \qquad \sqrt{4} = 2$$

(b) $\sqrt{108}$

As shown on the left, the number 108 is divisible by the perfect square 36. If this perfect square is not immediately clear, try factoring 108 into its prime factors, as shown on the right.

$\sqrt{108}$ | $\sqrt{108}$
$= \sqrt{36 \cdot 3}$ Factor. | $= \sqrt{2^2 \cdot 3^3}$
$= \sqrt{36} \cdot \sqrt{3}$ Product rule | $= \sqrt{2^2 \cdot 3^2 \cdot 3}$ $a^3 = a^2 \cdot a$
$= 6\sqrt{3}$ $\sqrt{36} = 6$ | $= \sqrt{2^2} \cdot \sqrt{3^2} \cdot \sqrt{3}$ Product rule
 | $= 2 \cdot 3 \cdot \sqrt{3}$ $\sqrt{2^2} = 2,\ \sqrt{3^2} = 3$
 | $= 6\sqrt{3}$ Multiply.

(c) $\sqrt{10}$

No perfect square (other than 1) divides into 10, so $\sqrt{10}$ cannot be simplified further.

NOW TRY ANSWERS

3. (a) $\dfrac{7}{6}$ (b) $\dfrac{\sqrt{5}}{12}$ (c) $-\dfrac{3}{10}$

   (d) $\dfrac{\sqrt[4]{t}}{2}$ (e) $-\dfrac{m^3}{3}$

NOW TRY
EXERCISE 4
Simplify.

(a) $\sqrt{50}$ **(b)** $\sqrt{192}$

(c) $\sqrt{42}$ **(d)** $\sqrt[3]{108}$

(e) $-\sqrt[4]{80}$

(d) $\sqrt[3]{16}$

The greatest perfect *cube* that divides into 16 is 8, so factor 16 as $8 \cdot 2$.

$\sqrt[3]{16}$ *(Remember to write the index.)*

$= \sqrt[3]{8 \cdot 2}$ 8 is a perfect cube.

$= \sqrt[3]{8} \cdot \sqrt[3]{2}$ Product rule

$= 2\sqrt[3]{2}$ $\sqrt[3]{8} = 2$

(e) $-\sqrt[4]{162}$

$= -\sqrt[4]{81 \cdot 2}$ 81 is a perfect 4th power.

(Remember the negative sign in each line.) $= -\sqrt[4]{81} \cdot \sqrt[4]{2}$ Product rule

$= -3\sqrt[4]{2}$ $\sqrt[4]{81} = 3$ NOW TRY

⚠ **CAUTION** *Be careful with which factors belong outside the radical sign and which belong inside.* Note in **Example 4(b)** how $2 \cdot 3$ is written outside because $\sqrt{2^2} = 2$ and $\sqrt{3^2} = 3$, while the remaining 3 is left inside the radical.

NOW TRY
EXERCISE 5
Simplify. Assume that all variables represent positive real numbers.

(a) $\sqrt{36x^5}$ **(b)** $\sqrt{32m^5n^4}$

(c) $\sqrt[3]{-125k^3p^7}$

(d) $-\sqrt[4]{162x^7y^8}$

EXAMPLE 5 Simplifying Radicals Involving Variables

Simplify. Assume that all variables represent positive real numbers.

(a) $\sqrt{16m^3}$

$= \sqrt{16m^2 \cdot m}$ Factor.

$= \sqrt{16m^2} \cdot \sqrt{m}$ Product rule

$= 4m\sqrt{m}$ Take the square root.

Absolute value bars are not needed around the m in color because all the variables represent *positive* real numbers.

(b) $\sqrt{200k^7q^8}$

$= \sqrt{10^2 \cdot 2 \cdot (k^3)^2 \cdot k \cdot (q^4)^2}$ Factor.

$= 10k^3q^4\sqrt{2k}$ Remove perfect square factors.

(c) $\sqrt[3]{-8x^4y^5}$

$= \sqrt[3]{(-8x^3y^3)(xy^2)}$ Choose $-8x^3y^3$ as the perfect cube that divides into $-8x^4y^5$.

$= \sqrt[3]{-8x^3y^3} \cdot \sqrt[3]{xy^2}$ Product rule

$= -2xy\sqrt[3]{xy^2}$ Take the cube root.

(d) $-\sqrt[4]{32y^9}$

$= -\sqrt[4]{(16y^8)(2y)}$ $16y^8$ is the greatest 4th power that divides $32y^9$.

$= -\sqrt[4]{16y^8} \cdot \sqrt[4]{2y}$ Product rule

$= -2y^2\sqrt[4]{2y}$ Take the fourth root.   NOW TRY

NOW TRY ANSWERS
4. (a) $5\sqrt{2}$ **(b)** $8\sqrt{3}$
  (c) $\sqrt{42}$ cannot be simplified further.
  (d) $3\sqrt[3]{4}$ **(e)** $-2\sqrt[4]{5}$
5. (a) $6x^2\sqrt{x}$ **(b)** $4m^2n^2\sqrt{2m}$
  (c) $-5kp^2\sqrt[3]{p}$ **(d)** $-3xy^2\sqrt[4]{2x^3}$

NOTE From **Example 5,** we see that if a variable is raised to a power with an exponent divisible by 2, it is a perfect square. If it is raised to a power with an exponent divisible by 3, it is a perfect cube. *In general, if it is raised to a power with an exponent divisible by n, it is a perfect nth power.*

The conditions for a simplified radical given earlier state that an exponent in the radicand and the index of the radical should have greatest common factor 1.

⌐ NOW TRY
  EXERCISE 6
Simplify. Assume that all variables represent positive real numbers.

(a) $\sqrt[6]{7^2}$ (b) $\sqrt[6]{y^4}$

EXAMPLE 6   Simplifying Radicals by Using Smaller Indexes

Simplify. Assume that all variables represent positive real numbers.

(a) $\sqrt[9]{5^6}$

We write this radical by using rational exponents and then write the exponent in lowest terms. We then express the answer as a radical.

$$\sqrt[9]{5^6} = (5^6)^{1/9} = 5^{6/9} = 5^{2/3} = \sqrt[3]{5^2}, \quad \text{or} \quad \sqrt[3]{25}$$

(b) $\sqrt[4]{p^2} = (p^2)^{1/4} = p^{2/4} = p^{1/2} = \sqrt{p}$ (Recall the assumption that $p > 0$.)

NOW TRY

These examples suggest the following rule.

$\sqrt[kn]{a^{km}}$

If m is an integer, n and k are natural numbers, and all indicated roots exist, then

$$\sqrt[kn]{a^{km}} = \sqrt[n]{a^m}.$$

OBJECTIVE 4   **Simplify products and quotients of radicals with different indexes.** We multiply and divide radicals with different indexes by using rational exponents.

⌐ NOW TRY
  EXERCISE 7
Simplify $\sqrt[3]{3} \cdot \sqrt{6}$.

EXAMPLE 7   Multiplying Radicals with Different Indexes

Simplify $\sqrt{7} \cdot \sqrt[3]{2}$.

Because the different indexes, 2 and 3, have a least common multiple of 6, use rational exponents to write each radical as a sixth root.

$$\sqrt{7} = 7^{1/2} = 7^{3/6} = \sqrt[6]{7^3} = \sqrt[6]{343}$$
$$\sqrt[3]{2} = 2^{1/3} = 2^{2/6} = \sqrt[6]{2^2} = \sqrt[6]{4}$$

Now we can multiply.

$$\sqrt{7} \cdot \sqrt[3]{2} = \sqrt[6]{343} \cdot \sqrt[6]{4} \qquad \text{Substitute; } \sqrt{7} = \sqrt[6]{343}, \sqrt[3]{2} = \sqrt[6]{4}$$
$$= \sqrt[6]{1372} \qquad \text{Product rule} \qquad \qquad \text{NOW TRY}$$

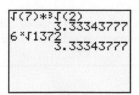

FIGURE 6

Results such as the one in **Example 7** can be supported with a calculator, as shown in **FIGURE 6**. Notice that the calculator gives the same approximation for the initial product and the final radical that we obtained.

⚠ CAUTION   The computation in **FIGURE 6** is not *proof* that the two expressions are equal. The algebra in **Example 7,** however, is valid proof of their equality.

NOW TRY ANSWERS
6. (a) $\sqrt[3]{7}$ (b) $\sqrt[3]{y^2}$
7. (a) $\sqrt[6]{1944}$

OBJECTIVE 5 **Use the Pythagorean theorem.** The **Pythagorean theorem** provides an equation that relates the lengths of the three sides of a right triangle.

Pythagorean Theorem

If a and b are the lengths of the shorter sides of a right triangle and c is the length of the longest side, then

$$a^2 + b^2 = c^2.$$

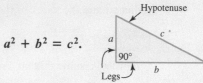

The two shorter sides are the **legs** of the triangle, and the longest side is the **hypotenuse.** The hypotenuse is the side opposite the right angle.

In **Section 11.1** we will see that an equation such as $x^2 = 7$ has two solutions: $\sqrt{7}$ (the principal, or positive, square root of 7) and $-\sqrt{7}$. Similarly, $c^2 = 52$ has two solutions, $\pm\sqrt{52} = \pm 2\sqrt{13}$. In applications we often choose only the principal square root.

NOW TRY
EXERCISE 8

Find the length of the unknown side in each triangle.

(a)

(b)

EXAMPLE 8 Using the Pythagorean Theorem

Use the Pythagorean theorem to find the length of the unknown side of the triangle in **FIGURE 7**.

$a^2 + b^2 = c^2$	Pythagorean theorem
$4^2 + 6^2 = c^2$	Let $a = 4$ and $b = 6$.
$16 + 36 = c^2$	Apply the exponents.
$c^2 = 52$	Add. Interchange sides.
$c = \sqrt{52}$	Choose the principal root.
$c = \sqrt{4 \cdot 13}$	Factor.
$c = \sqrt{4} \cdot \sqrt{13}$	Product rule
$c = 2\sqrt{13}$	Simplify.

Substitute carefully.

FIGURE 7

The length of the hypotenuse is $2\sqrt{13}$.

NOW TRY

⚠ **CAUTION** When substituting in the equation $a^2 + b^2 = c^2$, of the Pythagorean theorem, be sure that the length of the hypotenuse is substituted for c and that the lengths of the legs are substituted for a and b.

OBJECTIVE 6 **Use the distance formula.** The *distance formula* allows us to find the distance between two points in the coordinate plane, or the length of the line segment joining those two points.

FIGURE 8 on the next page shows the points $(3, -4)$ and $(-5, 3)$. The vertical line through $(-5, 3)$ and the horizontal line through $(3, -4)$ intersect at the point $(-5, -4)$. Thus, the point $(-5, -4)$ becomes the vertex of the right angle in a right triangle.

NOW TRY ANSWERS
8. (a) $\sqrt{89}$ **(b)** $6\sqrt{3}$

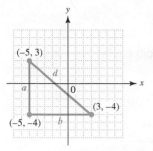

FIGURE 8

By the Pythagorean theorem, the square of the length of the hypotenuse d of the right triangle in **FIGURE 8** is equal to the sum of the squares of the lengths of the two legs a and b.

$$a^2 + b^2 = d^2$$

The length a is the difference between the y-coordinates of the endpoints. Since the x-coordinate of both points in **FIGURE 8** is -5, the side is vertical, and we can find a by finding the difference between the y-coordinates. We subtract -4 from 3 to get a positive value for a.

$$a = 3 - (-4) = 7$$

Similarly, we find b by subtracting -5 from 3.

$$b = 3 - (-5) = 8$$

Now substitute these values into the equation.

$$d^2 = a^2 + b^2$$
$$d^2 = 7^2 + 8^2 \qquad \text{Let } a = 7 \text{ and } b = 8.$$
$$d^2 = 49 + 64 \qquad \text{Apply the exponents.}$$
$$d^2 = 113 \qquad \text{Add.}$$
$$d = \sqrt{113} \qquad \text{Choose the principal root.}$$

We choose the principal root, since distance cannot be negative. Therefore, the distance between $(-5, 3)$ and $(3, -4)$ is $\sqrt{113}$.

NOTE It is customary to leave the distance in simplified radical form. Do not use a calculator to get an approximation, unless you are specifically directed to do so.

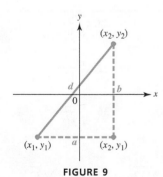

FIGURE 9

This result can be generalized. **FIGURE 9** shows the two points (x_1, y_1) and (x_2, y_2). The distance a between (x_1, y_1) and (x_2, y_1) is given by

$$a = |x_2 - x_1|,$$

and the distance b between (x_2, y_2) and (x_2, y_1) is given by

$$b = |y_2 - y_1|.$$

From the Pythagorean theorem, we obtain the following.

$$d^2 = a^2 + b^2$$
$$d^2 = (x_2 - x_1)^2 + (y_2 - y_1)^2$$

Choosing the principal square root gives the **distance formula.**

Distance Formula

The distance d between the points (x_1, y_1) and (x_2, y_2) is

$$d = \sqrt{(x_2 - x_1)^2 + (y_2 - y_1)^2}.$$

NOW TRY
EXERCISE 9

Find the distance between the points $(-4, -3)$ and $(-8, 6)$.

EXAMPLE 9 Using the Distance Formula

Find the distance between the points $(-3, 5)$ and $(6, 4)$.

Designating the points as (x_1, y_1) and (x_2, y_2) is arbitrary. We choose $(x_1, y_1) = (-3, 5)$ and $(x_2, y_2) = (6, 4)$.

$$d = \sqrt{(x_2 - x_1)^2 + (y_2 - y_1)^2}$$

$$= \sqrt{[6 - (-3)]^2 + (4 - 5)^2} \quad x_2 = 6, y_2 = 4, x_1 = -3, y_1 = 5$$

$$= \sqrt{9^2 + (-1)^2}$$

Substitute carefully.

NOW TRY ANSWER
9. $\sqrt{97}$

$$= \sqrt{82} \qquad \text{Leave in radical form.} \qquad \text{NOW TRY}$$

10.3 EXERCISES

MyMathLab   MathXL PRACTICE   WATCH   DOWNLOAD   READ   REVIEW

Complete solution available on the Video Resources on DVD

*Multiply, if possible, using the product rule. Assume that all variables represent positive real numbers. **See Examples 1 and 2.***

1. $\sqrt{3} \cdot \sqrt{3}$ **2.** $\sqrt{5} \cdot \sqrt{5}$ **3.** $\sqrt{18} \cdot \sqrt{2}$ **4.** $\sqrt{12} \cdot \sqrt{3}$

5. $\sqrt{5} \cdot \sqrt{6}$ **6.** $\sqrt{10} \cdot \sqrt{3}$ **7.** $\sqrt{14} \cdot \sqrt{x}$ **8.** $\sqrt{23} \cdot \sqrt{t}$

9. $\sqrt{14} \cdot \sqrt{3pqr}$ **10.** $\sqrt{7} \cdot \sqrt{5xt}$ **11.** $\sqrt[3]{2} \cdot \sqrt[3]{5}$ **12.** $\sqrt[3]{3} \cdot \sqrt[3]{6}$

13. $\sqrt[3]{7x} \cdot \sqrt[3]{2y}$ **14.** $\sqrt[3]{9x} \cdot \sqrt[3]{4y}$ **15.** $\sqrt[4]{11} \cdot \sqrt[4]{3}$ **16.** $\sqrt[4]{6} \cdot \sqrt[4]{9}$

17. $\sqrt[4]{2x} \cdot \sqrt[4]{3x^2}$ **18.** $\sqrt[4]{3y^2} \cdot \sqrt[4]{6y}$ **19.** $\sqrt[3]{7} \cdot \sqrt[4]{3}$ **20.** $\sqrt[5]{8} \cdot \sqrt[6]{12}$

*Simplify each radical. Assume that all variables represent positive real numbers. **See Example 3.***

21. $\sqrt{\dfrac{64}{121}}$ **22.** $\sqrt{\dfrac{16}{49}}$ **23.** $\sqrt{\dfrac{3}{25}}$ **24.** $\sqrt{\dfrac{13}{49}}$

25. $\sqrt{\dfrac{x}{25}}$ **26.** $\sqrt{\dfrac{k}{100}}$ **27.** $\sqrt{\dfrac{p^6}{81}}$ **28.** $\sqrt{\dfrac{w^{10}}{36}}$

29. $\sqrt[3]{-\dfrac{27}{64}}$ **30.** $\sqrt[3]{-\dfrac{216}{125}}$ **31.** $\sqrt[3]{\dfrac{r^2}{8}}$ **32.** $\sqrt[3]{\dfrac{t}{125}}$

33. $-\sqrt[4]{\dfrac{81}{x^4}}$ **34.** $-\sqrt[4]{\dfrac{625}{y^4}}$ **35.** $\sqrt[5]{\dfrac{1}{x^{15}}}$ **36.** $\sqrt[5]{\dfrac{32}{y^{20}}}$

*Express each radical in simplified form. **See Example 4.***

37. $\sqrt{12}$ **38.** $\sqrt{18}$ **39.** $\sqrt{288}$ **40.** $\sqrt{72}$ **41.** $-\sqrt{32}$

42. $-\sqrt{48}$ **43.** $-\sqrt{28}$ **44.** $-\sqrt{24}$ **45.** $\sqrt{30}$ **46.** $\sqrt{46}$

47. $\sqrt[3]{128}$ **48.** $\sqrt[3]{24}$ **49.** $\sqrt[3]{-16}$ **50.** $\sqrt[3]{-250}$ **51.** $\sqrt[3]{40}$

52. $\sqrt[3]{375}$ **53.** $-\sqrt[4]{512}$ **54.** $-\sqrt[4]{1250}$ **55.** $\sqrt[5]{64}$ **56.** $\sqrt[5]{128}$

57. $-\sqrt[5]{486}$ **58.** $-\sqrt[5]{2048}$ **59.** $\sqrt[6]{128}$ **60.** $\sqrt[6]{1458}$

61. A student claimed that $\sqrt[3]{14}$ is not in simplified form, since $14 = 8 + 6$, and 8 is a perfect cube. Was his reasoning correct? Why or why not?

62. Explain in your own words why $\sqrt[3]{k^4}$ is not a simplified radical.

Express each radical in simplified form. Assume that all variables represent positive real numbers. ***See Example 5.***

63. $\sqrt{72k^2}$ **64.** $\sqrt{18m^2}$ **65.** $\sqrt{144x^3y^9}$

66. $\sqrt{169s^5t^{10}}$ **67.** $\sqrt{121x^6}$ **68.** $\sqrt{256z^{12}}$

69. $-\sqrt[3]{27t^{12}}$ **70.** $-\sqrt[3]{64y^{18}}$ **71.** $-\sqrt{100m^8z^4}$

72. $-\sqrt{25t^6s^{20}}$ **73.** $-\sqrt[3]{-125a^6b^9c^{12}}$ **74.** $-\sqrt[3]{-216y^{15}x^6z^3}$

75. $\sqrt[4]{\dfrac{1}{16}r^8t^{20}}$ **76.** $\sqrt[4]{\dfrac{81}{256}t^{12}u^8}$ 🌐 **77.** $\sqrt{50x^3}$ **78.** $\sqrt{300z^3}$

79. $-\sqrt{500r^{11}}$ **80.** $-\sqrt{200p^{13}}$ **81.** $\sqrt{13x^7y^8}$ **82.** $\sqrt{23k^9p^{14}}$

83. $\sqrt[3]{8z^6w^9}$ **84.** $\sqrt[3]{64a^{15}b^{12}}$ **85.** $\sqrt[3]{-16z^5t^7}$ **86.** $\sqrt[3]{-81m^4n^{10}}$

87. $\sqrt[4]{81x^{12}y^{16}}$ **88.** $\sqrt[4]{81t^8u^{28}}$ **89.** $-\sqrt[4]{162r^{15}s^{10}}$ **90.** $-\sqrt[4]{32k^5m^{10}}$

91. $\sqrt{\dfrac{y^{11}}{36}}$ **92.** $\sqrt{\dfrac{v^{13}}{49}}$ **93.** $\sqrt[3]{\dfrac{x^{16}}{27}}$ **94.** $\sqrt[3]{\dfrac{y^{17}}{125}}$

Simplify each radical. Assume that $x \geq 0$. ***See Example 6.***

🌐 **95.** $\sqrt[4]{48^2}$ **96.** $\sqrt[4]{50^2}$ **97.** $\sqrt[4]{2^5}$

98. $\sqrt[6]{8}$ **99.** $\sqrt[10]{x^{25}}$ **100.** $\sqrt[12]{x^{44}}$

Simplify by first writing the radicals as radicals with the same index. Then multiply. Assume that all variables represent positive real numbers. ***See Example 7.***

🌐 **101.** $\sqrt[3]{4} \cdot \sqrt{3}$ **102.** $\sqrt[3]{5} \cdot \sqrt{6}$ **103.** $\sqrt[4]{3} \cdot \sqrt[3]{4}$

104. $\sqrt[5]{7} \cdot \sqrt[7]{5}$ **105.** $\sqrt{x} \cdot \sqrt[3]{x}$ **106.** $\sqrt[3]{y} \cdot \sqrt[4]{y}$

Find the unknown length in each right triangle. Simplify the answer if possible. ***See Example 8.***

🌐 **107.**

108.

109.

110.
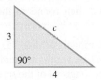

111.
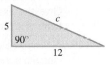

112.
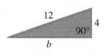

Find the distance between each pair of points. ***See Example 9.***

113. $(6, 13)$ and $(1, 1)$ **114.** $(8, 13)$ and $(2, 5)$

🌐 **115.** $(-6, 5)$ and $(3, -4)$ **116.** $(-1, 5)$ and $(-7, 7)$

117. $(-8, 2)$ and $(-4, 1)$ **118.** $(-1, 2)$ and $(5, 3)$

119. $(4.7, 2.3)$ and $(1.7, -1.7)$ **120.** $(-2.9, 18.2)$ and $(2.1, 6.2)$

121. $\left(\sqrt{2}, \sqrt{6}\right)$ and $\left(-2\sqrt{2}, 4\sqrt{6}\right)$ **122.** $\left(\sqrt{7}, 9\sqrt{3}\right)$ and $\left(-\sqrt{7}, 4\sqrt{3}\right)$

123. $(x + y, y)$ and $(x - y, x)$ **124.** $(c, c - d)$ and $(d, c + d)$

Find the perimeter of each triangle. $\left(\text{Hint: For Exercise 125, use } \sqrt{k} + \sqrt{k} = 2\sqrt{k}.\right)$

125.

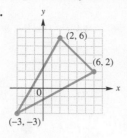

126.

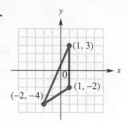

Solve each problem.

127. The following letter appeared in the column "Ask Tom Why," written by Tom Skilling of the *Chicago Tribune*:

Dear Tom,

I cannot remember the formula to calculate the distance to the horizon. I have a stunning view from my 14th-floor condo, 150 ft above the ground. How far can I see?

Ted Fleischaker; Indianapolis, Ind.

Skilling's answer was as follows:

To find the distance to the horizon in miles, take the square root of the height of your view in feet and multiply that result by 1.224. Your answer will be the number of miles to the horizon. (*Source: Chicago Tribune.*)

Assuming that Ted's eyes are 6 ft above the ground, the total height from the ground is $150 + 6 = 156$ ft. To the nearest tenth of a mile, how far can he see to the horizon?

128. The length of the diagonal of a box is given by

$$D = \sqrt{L^2 + W^2 + H^2},$$

where L, W, and H are, respectively, the length, width, and height of the box. Find the length of the diagonal D of a box that is 4 ft long, 2 ft wide, and 3 ft high. Give the exact value, and then round to the nearest tenth of a foot.

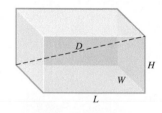

129. A Sanyo color television, model AVM-2755, has a rectangular screen with a 21.7-in. width. Its height is 16 in. What is the measure of the diagonal of the screen, to the nearest tenth of an inch? (*Source:* Actual measurements of the author's television.)

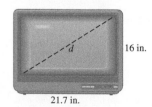

21.7 in.

130. A formula from electronics dealing with the impedance of parallel resonant circuits is

$$I = \frac{E}{\sqrt{R^2 + \omega^2 L^2}},$$

where the variables are in appropriate units. Find I if $E = 282$, $R = 100$, $L = 264$, and $\omega = 120\pi$. Give your answer to the nearest thousandth.

131. In the study of sound, one version of the law of tensions is

$$f_1 = f_2 \sqrt{\frac{F_1}{F_2}}.$$

If $F_1 = 300$, $F_2 = 60$, and $f_2 = 260$, find f_1 to the nearest unit.

132. The illumination I, in foot-candles, produced by a light source is related to the distance d, in feet, from the light source by the equation

$$d = \sqrt{\frac{k}{I}},$$

where k is a constant. If $k = 640$, how far from the light source will the illumination be 2 foot-candles? Give the exact value, and then round to the nearest tenth of a foot.

*Refer to the Chapter Opener on **page 599**. Recall that an **isosceles triangle** is a triangle that has two sides of equal length.*

133. The statement made by the Scarecrow in *The Wizard of Oz* can be proved false by providing at least one situation in which it leads to a false statement. Use the isosceles triangle shown here to prove that the statement is false.

134. Use the same style of wording as the Scarecrow to state the Pythagorean theorem correctly.

The table gives data on three different solar modules available for roofing.

Model	Watts	Volts	Amps	Size (in inches)	Cost (in dollars)
MSX-77	77	16.9	4.56	44 × 26	475
MSX-83	83	17.1	4.85	44 × 24	490
MSX-60	60	17.1	3.5	44 × 20	382

Source: Solarex table in Jade Mountain catalog.

You must determine the size of frame needed to support each panel on a roof. (Note: The sides of each frame will form a right triangle, and the hypotenuse of the triangle will be the width of the panel.) In Exercises 135–136, use the Pythagorean theorem to find the dimensions of the legs for each frame under the given conditions. Round answers to the nearest tenth.

135. The legs have equal length.

136. One leg is twice the length of the other.

PREVIEW EXERCISES

*Combine like terms. **See Section 4.4.***

137. $13x^4 - 12x^3 + 9x^4 + 2x^3$

138. $-15z^3 - z^2 + 4z^4 + 12z^8$

139. $9q^2 + 2q - 5q - q^2$

140. $7m^5 - 2m^3 + 8m^5 - m^3$

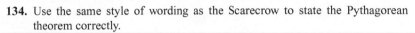

10.4 Adding and Subtracting Radical Expressions

OBJECTIVE

1 Simplify radical expressions involving addition and subtraction.

OBJECTIVE 1 **Simplify radical expressions involving addition and subtraction.** Expressions such as $4\sqrt{2} + 3\sqrt{2}$ and $2\sqrt{3} - 5\sqrt{3}$ can be simplified using the distributive property.

$$4\sqrt{2} + 3\sqrt{2}$$
$$= (4 + 3)\sqrt{2} = 7\sqrt{2}$$

This is similar to simplifying $4x + 3x$ to $7x$.

$$2\sqrt{3} - 5\sqrt{3}$$
$$= (2 - 5)\sqrt{3} = -3\sqrt{3}$$

This is similar to simplifying $2x - 5x$ to $-3x$.

Add or subtract to simplify each radical expression.

(a) $\sqrt{12} + \sqrt{75}$

(b) $-\sqrt{63t} + 3\sqrt{28t}, \quad t \geq 0$

(c) $6\sqrt{7} - 2\sqrt{3}$

⚠ **CAUTION** *Only radical expressions with the same index and the same radicand may be combined.*

EXAMPLE 1 Adding and Subtracting Radicals

Add or subtract to simplify each radical expression.

(a) $3\sqrt{24} + \sqrt{54}$

$\quad = 3\sqrt{4} \cdot \sqrt{6} + \sqrt{9} \cdot \sqrt{6}$ Product rule

$\quad = 3 \cdot 2\sqrt{6} + 3\sqrt{6}$ $\sqrt{4} = 2; \sqrt{9} = 3$

$\quad = 6\sqrt{6} + 3\sqrt{6}$ Multiply.

$\quad = 9\sqrt{6}$ $6\sqrt{6} + 3\sqrt{6} = (6 + 3)\sqrt{6}$

(b) $2\sqrt{20x} - \sqrt{45x}, \quad x \geq 0$

$\quad = 2\sqrt{4} \cdot \sqrt{5x} - \sqrt{9} \cdot \sqrt{5x}$ Product rule

$\quad = 2 \cdot 2\sqrt{5x} - 3\sqrt{5x}$ $\sqrt{4} = 2; \sqrt{9} = 3$

$\quad = 4\sqrt{5x} - 3\sqrt{5x}$ Multiply.

$\quad = \sqrt{5x}$ Combine like terms.

(c) $2\sqrt{3} - 4\sqrt{5}$ The radicands differ and are already simplified, so $2\sqrt{3} - 4\sqrt{5}$ cannot be simplified further.

NOW TRY ⟲

⚠ **CAUTION** *The root of a sum does not equal the sum of the roots.* For example,

$$\sqrt{9 + 16} \neq \sqrt{9} + \sqrt{16}$$

since $\sqrt{9 + 16} = \sqrt{25} = 5,$ but $\sqrt{9} + \sqrt{16} = 3 + 4 = 7.$

EXAMPLE 2 Adding and Subtracting Radicals with Higher Indexes

Add or subtract to simplify each radical expression. Assume that all variables represent positive real numbers.

(a) $2\sqrt[3]{16} - 5\sqrt[3]{54}$ [Remember to write the index with each radical.]

$\quad = 2\sqrt[3]{8 \cdot 2} - 5\sqrt[3]{27 \cdot 2}$ Factor.

$\quad = 2\sqrt[3]{8} \cdot \sqrt[3]{2} - 5\sqrt[3]{27} \cdot \sqrt[3]{2}$ Product rule

$\quad = 2 \cdot 2 \cdot \sqrt[3]{2} - 5 \cdot 3 \cdot \sqrt[3]{2}$ Find the cube roots.

$\quad = 4\sqrt[3]{2} - 15\sqrt[3]{2}$ Multiply.

$\quad = (4 - 15)\sqrt[3]{2}$ Distributive property

$\quad = -11\sqrt[3]{2}$ Combine like terms.

(b)

$\qquad\qquad 2\sqrt[3]{x^2y} + \sqrt[3]{8x^5y^4}$

$\quad = 2\sqrt[3]{x^2y} + \sqrt[3]{(8x^3y^3)x^2y}$ Factor.

$\quad = 2\sqrt[3]{x^2y} + \sqrt[3]{8x^3y^3} \cdot \sqrt[3]{x^2y}$ Product rule

[This result cannot be simplified further.]

$\quad = 2\sqrt[3]{x^2y} + 2xy\sqrt[3]{x^2y}$ Find the cube root.

$\quad = (2 + 2xy)\sqrt[3]{x^2y}$ Distributive property

1. (a) $7\sqrt{3}$ (b) $3\sqrt{7t}$
(c) The expression cannot be simplified further.

NOW TRY
EXERCISE 2

Add or subtract to simplify each radical expression. Assume that all variables represent positive real numbers.

(a) $3\sqrt[3]{2000} - 4\sqrt[3]{128}$

(b) $5\sqrt[4]{a^5b^3} + \sqrt[4]{81ab^7}$

(c) $\sqrt[3]{128t^4} - 2\sqrt{72t^3}$

> Be careful. The indexes are different.

(c) $5\sqrt{4x^3} + 3\sqrt[3]{64x^4}$

$= 5\sqrt{4x^2 \cdot x} + 3\sqrt[3]{64x^3 \cdot x}$ Factor.

$= 5\sqrt{4x^2} \cdot \sqrt{x} + 3\sqrt[3]{64x^3} \cdot \sqrt[3]{x}$ Product rule

$= 5 \cdot 2x\sqrt{x} + 3 \cdot 4x\sqrt[3]{x}$

> Keep track of the indexes.

$= 10x\sqrt{x} + 12x\sqrt[3]{x}$

The radicands are both x, but since the indexes are different, this expression cannot be simplified further. NOW TRY

NOW TRY
EXERCISE 3

Perform the indicated operations. Assume that all variables represent positive real numbers.

(a) $5\dfrac{\sqrt{5}}{\sqrt{45}} - 4\sqrt{\dfrac{28}{9}}$

(b) $6\sqrt[3]{\dfrac{16}{x^{12}}} + 7\sqrt[3]{\dfrac{9}{x^9}}$

EXAMPLE 3 Adding and Subtracting Radicals with Fractions

Perform the indicated operations. Assume that all variables represent positive real numbers.

(a) $2\sqrt{\dfrac{75}{16}} + 4\dfrac{\sqrt{8}}{\sqrt{32}}$

$= 2\dfrac{\sqrt{25 \cdot 3}}{\sqrt{16}} + 4\dfrac{\sqrt{4 \cdot 2}}{\sqrt{16 \cdot 2}}$ Quotient rule; factor.

$= 2\left(\dfrac{5\sqrt{3}}{4}\right) + 4\left(\dfrac{2\sqrt{2}}{4\sqrt{2}}\right)$ Product rule; find the square roots.

$= \dfrac{5\sqrt{3}}{2} + 2$ Multiply; $\dfrac{\sqrt{2}}{\sqrt{2}} = 1$.

$= \dfrac{5\sqrt{3}}{2} + \dfrac{4}{2}$ Write with a common denominator.

$= \dfrac{5\sqrt{3} + 4}{2}$ $\dfrac{a}{c} + \dfrac{b}{c} = \dfrac{a+b}{c}$

(b) $10\sqrt[3]{\dfrac{5}{x^6}} - 3\sqrt[3]{\dfrac{4}{x^9}}$

$= 10\dfrac{\sqrt[3]{5}}{\sqrt[3]{x^6}} - 3\dfrac{\sqrt[3]{4}}{\sqrt[3]{x^9}}$ Quotient rule

$= \dfrac{10\sqrt[3]{5}}{x^2} - \dfrac{3\sqrt[3]{4}}{x^3}$ Simplify denominators.

$= \dfrac{10\sqrt[3]{5} \cdot x}{x^2 \cdot x} - \dfrac{3\sqrt[3]{4}}{x^3}$ Write with a common denominator.

$= \dfrac{10x\sqrt[3]{5} - 3\sqrt[3]{4}}{x^3}$ Subtract fractions. NOW TRY

NOW TRY ANSWERS
2. (a) $14\sqrt[3]{2}$
   (b) $(5a + 3b)\sqrt[4]{ab^3}$
   (c) $4t\sqrt[3]{2t} - 12t\sqrt{2t}$
3. (a) $\dfrac{5 - 8\sqrt{7}}{3}$
   (b) $\dfrac{12\sqrt[3]{2} + 7x\sqrt[3]{9}}{x^4}$

10.4 EXERCISES

🌐 *Complete solution available on the Video Resources on DVD*

Simplify. Assume that all variables represent positive real numbers. ***See Examples 1 and 2.***

1. $\sqrt{36} - \sqrt{100}$ **2.** $\sqrt{25} - \sqrt{81}$ 🌐 **3.** $-2\sqrt{48} + 3\sqrt{75}$

4. $4\sqrt{32} - 2\sqrt{8}$ **5.** $\sqrt[3]{16} + 4\sqrt[3]{54}$ **6.** $3\sqrt[3]{24} - 2\sqrt[3]{192}$

7. $\sqrt[4]{32} + 3\sqrt[4]{2}$ **8.** $\sqrt[4]{405} - 2\sqrt[4]{5}$

9. $6\sqrt{18} - \sqrt{32} + 2\sqrt{50}$ **10.** $5\sqrt{8} + 3\sqrt{72} - 3\sqrt{50}$

11. $5\sqrt{6} + 2\sqrt{10}$ **12.** $3\sqrt{11} - 5\sqrt{13}$

13. $2\sqrt{5} + 3\sqrt{20} + 4\sqrt{45}$ **14.** $5\sqrt{54} - 2\sqrt{24} - 2\sqrt{96}$

15. $\sqrt{72x} - \sqrt{8x}$ **16.** $\sqrt{18k} - \sqrt{72k}$

17. $3\sqrt{72m^2} - 5\sqrt{32m^2} - 3\sqrt{18m^2}$ **18.** $9\sqrt{27p^2} - 14\sqrt{108p^2} + 2\sqrt{48p^2}$

19. $2\sqrt[3]{16} + \sqrt[3]{54}$ **20.** $15\sqrt[3]{81} + 4\sqrt[3]{24}$

🌐 **21.** $2\sqrt[3]{27x} - 2\sqrt[3]{8x}$ **22.** $6\sqrt[3]{128m} - 3\sqrt[3]{16m}$

23. $3\sqrt[3]{x^2y} - 5\sqrt[3]{8x^2y}$ **24.** $3\sqrt[3]{x^2y^2} - 2\sqrt[3]{64x^2y^2}$

25. $3x\sqrt[3]{xy^2} - 2\sqrt[3]{8x^4y^2}$ **26.** $6q^2\sqrt[3]{5q} - 2q\sqrt[3]{40q^4}$

27. $5\sqrt[4]{32} + 3\sqrt[4]{162}$ **28.** $2\sqrt[4]{512} + 4\sqrt[4]{32}$

29. $3\sqrt[4]{x^5y} - 2x\sqrt[4]{xy}$ **30.** $2\sqrt[4]{m^9p^6} - 3m^2p\sqrt[4]{mp^2}$

31. $2\sqrt[4]{32a^3} + 5\sqrt[4]{2a^3}$ **32.** $5\sqrt[4]{243x^3} + 2\sqrt[4]{3x^3}$

33. $\sqrt[3]{64xy^2} + \sqrt[3]{27x^4y^5}$ **34.** $\sqrt[4]{625s^3t} + \sqrt[4]{81s^7t^5}$

35. $\sqrt[3]{192st^4} - \sqrt{27s^3t}$ **36.** $\sqrt{125a^5b^5} + \sqrt[3]{125a^4b^4}$

37. $2\sqrt[3]{8x^4} + 3\sqrt[4]{16x^5}$ **38.** $3\sqrt[3]{64m^4} + 5\sqrt[4]{81m^5}$

Simplify. Assume that all variables represent positive real numbers. ***See Example 3.***

39. $\sqrt{8} - \dfrac{\sqrt{64}}{\sqrt{16}}$ **40.** $\sqrt{48} - \dfrac{\sqrt{81}}{\sqrt{9}}$ **41.** $\dfrac{2\sqrt{5}}{3} + \dfrac{\sqrt{5}}{6}$

42. $\dfrac{4\sqrt{3}}{3} + \dfrac{2\sqrt{3}}{9}$ **43.** $\sqrt{\dfrac{8}{9}} + \sqrt{\dfrac{18}{36}}$ **44.** $\sqrt{\dfrac{12}{16}} + \sqrt{\dfrac{48}{64}}$

45. $\dfrac{\sqrt{32}}{3} + \dfrac{2\sqrt{2}}{3} - \dfrac{\sqrt{2}}{\sqrt{9}}$ **46.** $\dfrac{\sqrt{27}}{2} - \dfrac{3\sqrt{3}}{2} + \dfrac{\sqrt{3}}{\sqrt{4}}$ 🌐 **47.** $3\sqrt{\dfrac{50}{9}} + 8\dfrac{\sqrt{2}}{\sqrt{8}}$

48. $5\sqrt{\dfrac{288}{25}} + 21\dfrac{\sqrt{2}}{\sqrt{18}}$ **49.** $\sqrt{\dfrac{25}{x^8}} + \sqrt{\dfrac{9}{x^6}}$ **50.** $\sqrt{\dfrac{100}{y^4}} + \sqrt{\dfrac{81}{y^{10}}}$

51. $3\sqrt[3]{\dfrac{m^5}{27}} - 2m\sqrt[3]{\dfrac{m^2}{64}}$ **52.** $2a\sqrt[4]{\dfrac{a}{16}} - 5a\sqrt[4]{\dfrac{a}{81}}$

53. $3\sqrt[3]{\dfrac{2}{x^6}} - 4\sqrt[3]{\dfrac{5}{x^9}}$ **54.** $-4\sqrt[3]{\dfrac{4}{t^9}} + 3\sqrt[3]{\dfrac{9}{t^{12}}}$

55. *Concept Check* Which sum could be simplified without first simplifying the individual radical expressions?

A. $\sqrt{50} + \sqrt{32}$ **B.** $3\sqrt{6} + 9\sqrt{6}$ **C.** $\sqrt[3]{32} + \sqrt[3]{108}$ **D.** $\sqrt[5]{6} + \sqrt[5]{192}$

56. *Concept Check* Let $a = 1$ and let $b = 64$.

(a) Evaluate $\sqrt{a} + \sqrt{b}$. Then find $\sqrt{a + b}$. Are they equal?

(b) Evaluate $\sqrt[3]{a} + \sqrt[3]{b}$. Then find $\sqrt[3]{a + b}$. Are they equal?

(c) Complete the following: In general, $\sqrt[n]{a} + \sqrt[n]{b} \neq$ _____, based on the observations in parts (a) and (b) of this exercise.

57. Even though the root indexes of the terms are not equal, the sum $\sqrt{64} + \sqrt[3]{125} + \sqrt[4]{16}$ can be simplified quite easily. What is this sum? Why can we add these terms so easily?

58. Explain why $28 - 4\sqrt{2}$ is not equal to $24\sqrt{2}$. (This is a common error among algebra students.)

Solve each problem.

59. A rectangular yard has a length of $\sqrt{192}$ m and a width of $\sqrt{48}$ m. Choose the best estimate of its dimensions. Then estimate the perimeter.

A. 14 m by 7 m   **B.** 5 m by 7 m   **C.** 14 m by 8 m   **D.** 15 m by 8 m

60. If the sides of a triangle are $\sqrt{65}$ in., $\sqrt{35}$ in., and $\sqrt{26}$ in., which one of the following is the best estimate of its perimeter?

A. 20 in.   **B.** 26 in.   **C.** 19 in.   **D.** 24 in.

Solve each problem. Give answers as simplified radical expressions.

61. Find the perimeter of the triangle.

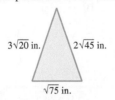

$3\sqrt{20}$ in. $2\sqrt{45}$ in.

$\sqrt{75}$ in.

62. Find the perimeter of the rectangle.

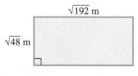

$\sqrt{192}$ m

$\sqrt{48}$ m

63. What is the perimeter of the computer graphic?

$4\sqrt{18}$ in.

$3\sqrt{12}$ in. $\sqrt{108}$ in.

$2\sqrt{72}$ in.

64. Find the area of the trapezoid.

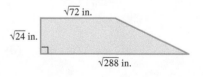

$\sqrt{72}$ in.

$\sqrt{24}$ in.

$\sqrt{288}$ in.

PREVIEW EXERCISES

Find each product. **See Sections 4.5 and 4.6.**

65. $5xy(2x^2y^3 - 4x)$ **66.** $(3x + 7)(2x - 6)$ **67.** $(a^2 + b)(a^2 - b)$

68. $(2p - 7)^2$ **69.** $(4x^3 + 3)^3$ **70.** $(2 + 3y)(2 - 3y)$

Write in lowest terms. **See Section 6.1.**

71. $\dfrac{8x^2 - 10x}{6x^2}$

72. $\dfrac{15y^3 - 9y^2}{6y}$

10.5 Multiplying and Dividing Radical Expressions

OBJECTIVES

1. Multiply radical expressions.
2. Rationalize denominators with one radical term.
3. Rationalize denominators with binomials involving radicals.
4. Write radical quotients in lowest terms.

OBJECTIVE 1 Multiply radical expressions. We multiply binomial expressions involving radicals by using the FOIL method from **Section 4.5.** Recall that the acronym **FOIL** refers to multiplying the **F**irst terms, **O**uter terms, **I**nner terms, and **L**ast terms of the binomials.

EXAMPLE 1 Multiplying Binomials Involving Radical Expressions

Multiply, using the FOIL method.

(a) $\left(\sqrt{5} + 3\right)\left(\sqrt{6} + 1\right)$

First　　Outer　　Inner　　Last
$$= \sqrt{5} \cdot \sqrt{6} + \sqrt{5} \cdot 1 + 3 \cdot \sqrt{6} + 3 \cdot 1$$
$$= \sqrt{30} + \sqrt{5} + 3\sqrt{6} + 3 \quad \longleftarrow \text{This result cannot be simplified further.}$$

(b) $\left(7 - \sqrt{3}\right)\left(\sqrt{5} + \sqrt{2}\right)$

　　　F　　O　　I　　L
$$= 7\sqrt{5} + 7\sqrt{2} - \sqrt{3} \cdot \sqrt{5} - \sqrt{3} \cdot \sqrt{2}$$
$$= 7\sqrt{5} + 7\sqrt{2} - \sqrt{15} - \sqrt{6}$$

(c) $\left(\sqrt{10} + \sqrt{3}\right)\left(\sqrt{10} - \sqrt{3}\right)$
$$= \sqrt{10} \cdot \sqrt{10} - \sqrt{10} \cdot \sqrt{3} + \sqrt{10} \cdot \sqrt{3} - \sqrt{3} \cdot \sqrt{3} \quad \text{FOIL}$$
$$= 10 - 3$$
$$= 7$$

The product $\left(\sqrt{10} + \sqrt{3}\right)\left(\sqrt{10} - \sqrt{3}\right) = \left(\sqrt{10}\right)^2 - \left(\sqrt{3}\right)^2$ is the difference of squares.

$$(x + y)(x - y) = x^2 - y^2 \quad \text{Here, } x = \sqrt{10} \text{ and } y = \sqrt{3}.$$

(d) $\left(\sqrt{7} - 3\right)^2$
$$= \left(\sqrt{7} - 3\right)\left(\sqrt{7} - 3\right)$$
$$= \sqrt{7} \cdot \sqrt{7} - 3\sqrt{7} - 3\sqrt{7} + 3 \cdot 3$$
$$= 7 - 6\sqrt{7} + 9$$
$$= 16 - 6\sqrt{7} \quad \longleftarrow \text{Be careful. These terms cannot be combined.}$$

(e) $\left(5 - \sqrt[3]{3}\right)\left(5 + \sqrt[3]{3}\right)$
$$= 5 \cdot 5 + 5\sqrt[3]{3} - 5\sqrt[3]{3} - \sqrt[3]{3} \cdot \sqrt[3]{3}$$
$$= 25 - \sqrt[3]{3^2} \quad \longleftarrow \text{Remember to write the index 3 in each radical.}$$
$$= 25 - \sqrt[3]{9}$$

**NOW TRY
EXERCISE 1**

Multiply, using the FOIL method.

(a) $\left(8 - \sqrt{5}\right)\left(9 - \sqrt{2}\right)$

(b) $\left(\sqrt{7} + \sqrt{5}\right)\left(\sqrt{7} - \sqrt{5}\right)$

(c) $\left(\sqrt{15} - 4\right)^2$

(d) $\left(8 + \sqrt[3]{5}\right)\left(8 - \sqrt[3]{5}\right)$

(e) $\left(\sqrt{m} - \sqrt{n}\right)\left(\sqrt{m} + \sqrt{n}\right),$
    $m \geq 0$ and $n \geq 0$

(f) $\left(\sqrt{k} + \sqrt{y}\right)\left(\sqrt{k} - \sqrt{y}\right)$

$\quad = \left(\sqrt{k}\right)^2 - \left(\sqrt{y}\right)^2$ *Difference of squares*

$\quad = k - y, \quad k \geq 0$ and $y \geq 0$ **NOW TRY**

NOTE In **Example 1(d)**, we could have used the formula for the square of a binomial to obtain the same result.

$$\left(\sqrt{7} - 3\right)^2$$

$$= \left(\sqrt{7}\right)^2 - 2\left(\sqrt{7}\right)(3) + 3^2 \quad (x - y)^2 = x^2 - 2xy + y^2$$

$$= 7 - 6\sqrt{7} + 9 \qquad \text{Apply the exponents. Multiply.}$$

$$= 16 - 6\sqrt{7} \qquad \text{Add.}$$

OBJECTIVE 2 **Rationalize denominators with one radical term.** As defined earlier, a simplified radical expression has no radical in the denominator. The origin of this agreement no doubt occurred before the days of high-speed calculation, when computation was a tedious process performed by hand.

For example, consider the radical expression $\dfrac{1}{\sqrt{2}}$. To find a decimal approximation by hand, it is necessary to divide 1 by a decimal approximation for $\sqrt{2}$, such as 1.414. It is much easier if the divisor is a whole number. This can be accomplished by multiplying $\dfrac{1}{\sqrt{2}}$ by 1 in the form $\dfrac{\sqrt{2}}{\sqrt{2}}$. *Multiplying by 1 in any form does not change the value of the original expression.*

$$\frac{1}{\sqrt{2}} \cdot \frac{\sqrt{2}}{\sqrt{2}} = \frac{\sqrt{2}}{2} \qquad \text{Multiply by 1; } \tfrac{\sqrt{2}}{\sqrt{2}} = 1$$

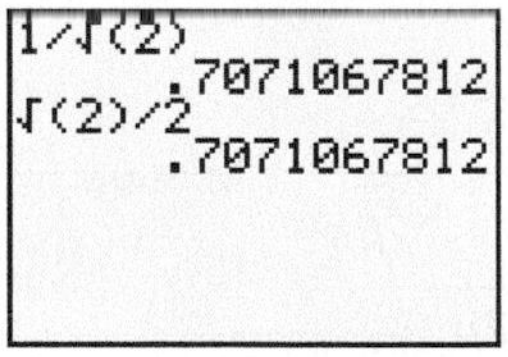

Now the computation requires dividing 1.414 by 2 to obtain 0.707, a much easier task.

With current technology, either form of this fraction can be approximated with the same number of keystrokes. See **FIGURE 10**, which shows how a calculator gives the same approximation for both forms of the expression.

FIGURE 10

> **Rationalizing the Denominator**
>
> A common way of "standardizing" the form of a radical expression is to have the denominator contain no radicals. The process of removing radicals from a denominator so that the denominator contains only rational numbers is called **rationalizing the denominator.** This is done by multiplying by a form of 1.

EXAMPLE 2 **Rationalizing Denominators with Square Roots**

Rationalize each denominator.

(a) $\dfrac{3}{\sqrt{7}}$

Multiply the numerator and denominator by $\sqrt{7}$. This is, in effect, multiplying by 1.

$$\frac{3}{\sqrt{7}} = \frac{3 \cdot \sqrt{7}}{\sqrt{7} \cdot \sqrt{7}} = \frac{3\sqrt{7}}{7} \qquad \begin{array}{l}\text{In the denominator,} \\ \sqrt{7} \cdot \sqrt{7} = \sqrt{7 \cdot 7} = \sqrt{49} = 7. \\ \text{The final denominator is now a rational number.}\end{array}$$

NOW TRY ANSWERS

1. (a) $72 - 8\sqrt{2} - 9\sqrt{5} + \sqrt{10}$
   (b) 2 (c) $31 - 8\sqrt{15}$
   (d) $64 - \sqrt[3]{25}$ (e) $m - n$

NOW TRY
EXERCISE 2
Rationalize each denominator.

(a) $\dfrac{8}{\sqrt{13}}$ **(b)** $\dfrac{9\sqrt{7}}{\sqrt{3}}$

(c) $\dfrac{-10}{\sqrt{20}}$

(b) $\dfrac{5\sqrt{2}}{\sqrt{5}} = \dfrac{5\sqrt{2}\cdot\sqrt{5}}{\sqrt{5}\cdot\sqrt{5}} = \dfrac{5\sqrt{10}}{5} = \sqrt{10}$

(c) $\dfrac{-6}{\sqrt{12}}$

Less work is involved if we simplify the radical in the denominator first.

$$\dfrac{-6}{\sqrt{12}} = \dfrac{-6}{\sqrt{4\cdot 3}} = \dfrac{-6}{2\sqrt{3}} = \dfrac{-3}{\sqrt{3}}$$

Now we rationalize the denominator.

$$\dfrac{-3}{\sqrt{3}} = \dfrac{-3\cdot\sqrt{3}}{\sqrt{3}\cdot\sqrt{3}} = \dfrac{-3\sqrt{3}}{3} = -\sqrt{3} \qquad \text{NOW TRY}$$

NOW TRY
EXERCISE 3
Simplify each radical.

(a) $-\sqrt{\dfrac{27}{80}}$

(b) $\sqrt{\dfrac{48x^8}{y^3}}$, $y > 0$

EXAMPLE 3 Rationalizing Denominators in Roots of Fractions

Simplify each radical. In part (b), $p > 0$.

(a) $-\sqrt{\dfrac{18}{125}}$

$= -\dfrac{\sqrt{18}}{\sqrt{125}}$ Quotient rule

$= -\dfrac{\sqrt{9\cdot 2}}{\sqrt{25\cdot 5}}$ Factor.

$= -\dfrac{3\sqrt{2}}{5\sqrt{5}}$ Product rule

$= -\dfrac{3\sqrt{2}\cdot\sqrt{5}}{5\sqrt{5}\cdot\sqrt{5}}$ Multiply by $\frac{\sqrt{5}}{\sqrt{5}}$.

$= -\dfrac{3\sqrt{10}}{5\cdot 5}$ Product rule

$= -\dfrac{3\sqrt{10}}{25}$ Multiply.

(b) $\sqrt{\dfrac{50m^4}{p^5}}$

$= \dfrac{\sqrt{50m^4}}{\sqrt{p^5}}$ Quotient rule

$= \dfrac{5m^2\sqrt{2}}{p^2\sqrt{p}}$ Product rule

$= \dfrac{5m^2\sqrt{2}\cdot\sqrt{p}}{p^2\sqrt{p}\cdot\sqrt{p}}$ Multiply by $\frac{\sqrt{p}}{\sqrt{p}}$.

$= \dfrac{5m^2\sqrt{2p}}{p^2\cdot p}$ Product rule

$= \dfrac{5m^2\sqrt{2p}}{p^3}$ Multiply.

NOW TRY

EXAMPLE 4 Rationalizing Denominators with Cube and Fourth Roots

Simplify.

(a) $\sqrt[3]{\dfrac{27}{16}}$

NOW TRY ANSWERS
2. (a) $\dfrac{8\sqrt{13}}{13}$ (b) $3\sqrt{21}$
   (c) $-\sqrt{5}$
3. (a) $-\dfrac{3\sqrt{15}}{20}$ (b) $\dfrac{4x^4\sqrt{3y}}{y^2}$

Use the quotient rule, and simplify the numerator and denominator.

$$\sqrt[3]{\dfrac{27}{16}} = \dfrac{\sqrt[3]{27}}{\sqrt[3]{16}} = \dfrac{3}{\sqrt[3]{8}\cdot\sqrt[3]{2}} = \dfrac{3}{2\sqrt[3]{2}}$$

Since $2\cdot 4 = 8$, a perfect cube, multiply the numerator and denominator by $\sqrt[3]{4}$.

↶ *NOW TRY*
EXERCISE 4

Simplify.

(a) $\sqrt[3]{\dfrac{8}{81}}$

(b) $\sqrt[4]{\dfrac{7x}{y}}$, $x \geq 0, y > 0$

$\dfrac{3}{2\sqrt[3]{2}}$ $\sqrt[3]{\dfrac{27}{16}} = \dfrac{3}{2\sqrt[3]{2}}$ from **page 636**

$= \dfrac{3 \cdot \sqrt[3]{4}}{2\sqrt[3]{2} \cdot \sqrt[3]{4}}$ Multiply by $\sqrt[3]{4}$ in numerator and denominator. This will give $\sqrt[3]{8} = 2$ in the denominator.

$= \dfrac{3\sqrt[3]{4}}{2\sqrt[3]{8}}$ Multiply.

$= \dfrac{3\sqrt[3]{4}}{2 \cdot 2}$ $\sqrt[3]{8} = 2$

$= \dfrac{3\sqrt[3]{4}}{4}$ Multiply.

(b) $\sqrt[4]{\dfrac{5x}{z}}$

$= \dfrac{\sqrt[4]{5x}}{\sqrt[4]{z}}$ Quotient rule

$= \dfrac{\sqrt[4]{5x}}{\sqrt[4]{z}} \cdot \dfrac{\sqrt[4]{z^3}}{\sqrt[4]{z^3}}$ Multiply by 1.

> $\sqrt[4]{z} \cdot \sqrt[4]{z^3}$
> will give $\sqrt[4]{z^4}$.

$= \dfrac{\sqrt[4]{5xz^3}}{\sqrt[4]{z^4}}$ Product rule

$= \dfrac{\sqrt[4]{5xz^3}}{z}$, $x \geq 0, z > 0$ *NOW TRY* ↷

⚠ **CAUTION** In **Example 4(a)**, a typical error is to multiply the numerator and denominator by $\sqrt[3]{2}$, forgetting that $\sqrt[3]{2} \cdot \sqrt[3]{2} = \sqrt[3]{2^2}$, which does **not** equal 2. We need *three* factors of 2 to obtain 2^3 under the radical.

$$\sqrt[3]{2} \cdot \sqrt[3]{2} \cdot \sqrt[3]{2} = \sqrt[3]{2^3} \quad \text{which does equal} \quad 2.$$

OBJECTIVE 3 **Rationalize denominators with binomials involving radicals.**
Recall the special product $(x + y)(x - y) = x^2 - y^2$. To rationalize a denominator that contains a binomial expression (one that contains exactly two terms) involving radicals, such as

$$\frac{3}{1 + \sqrt{2}},$$

we must use *conjugates*. The conjugate of $1 + \sqrt{2}$ is $1 - \sqrt{2}$. In general, $x + y$ and $x - y$ are **conjugates.**

Rationalizing a Binomial Denominator

Whenever a radical expression has a sum or difference with square root radicals in the denominator, rationalize the denominator by multiplying both the numerator and denominator by the conjugate of the denominator.

NOW TRY ANSWERS

4. (a) $\dfrac{2\sqrt[3]{9}}{9}$ **(b)** $\dfrac{\sqrt[4]{7xy^3}}{y}$

NOW TRY
EXERCISE 5

Rationalize each denominator.

(a) $\dfrac{4}{1 + \sqrt{3}}$ (b) $\dfrac{4}{5 + \sqrt{7}}$

(c) $\dfrac{\sqrt{3} + \sqrt{7}}{\sqrt{5} - \sqrt{2}}$

(d) $\dfrac{8}{\sqrt{3x} - \sqrt{y}}$,

$3x \neq y, x > 0, y > 0$

EXAMPLE 5 Rationalizing Binomial Denominators

Rationalize each denominator.

(a) $\dfrac{3}{1 + \sqrt{2}}$

Again, we are multiplying by a form of 1.

$= \dfrac{3(1 - \sqrt{2})}{(1 + \sqrt{2})(1 - \sqrt{2})}$

Multiply the numerator and denominator by $1 - \sqrt{2}$, the conjugate of the denominator.

$(1 + \sqrt{2})(1 - \sqrt{2})$
$= 1^2 - (\sqrt{2})^2$
$= 1 - 2$, or -1

The denominator is now a rational number.

$= \dfrac{3(1 - \sqrt{2})}{-1}$

$= \dfrac{3}{-1}(1 - \sqrt{2})$

$= -3(1 - \sqrt{2})$, or $-3 + 3\sqrt{2}$ Distributive property

(b) $\dfrac{5}{4 - \sqrt{3}}$

$= \dfrac{5(4 + \sqrt{3})}{(4 - \sqrt{3})(4 + \sqrt{3})}$ Multiply the numerator and denominator by $4 + \sqrt{3}$.

$= \dfrac{5(4 + \sqrt{3})}{16 - 3}$ Multiply in the denominator.

$= \dfrac{5(4 + \sqrt{3})}{13}$ Subtract in the denominator.

Notice that the numerator is left in factored form. This makes it easier to determine whether the expression is written in lowest terms.

(c) $\dfrac{\sqrt{2} - \sqrt{3}}{\sqrt{5} + \sqrt{3}}$

$= \dfrac{(\sqrt{2} - \sqrt{3})(\sqrt{5} - \sqrt{3})}{(\sqrt{5} + \sqrt{3})(\sqrt{5} - \sqrt{3})}$ Multiply the numerator and denominator by $\sqrt{5} - \sqrt{3}$.

$= \dfrac{\sqrt{10} - \sqrt{6} - \sqrt{15} + 3}{5 - 3}$ Multiply.

$= \dfrac{\sqrt{10} - \sqrt{6} - \sqrt{15} + 3}{2}$ Subtract in the denominator.

(d) $\dfrac{3}{\sqrt{5m} - \sqrt{p}}$, $5m \neq p, m > 0, p > 0$

$= \dfrac{3(\sqrt{5m} + \sqrt{p})}{(\sqrt{5m} - \sqrt{p})(\sqrt{5m} + \sqrt{p})}$ Multiply the numerator and denominator by $\sqrt{5m} + \sqrt{p}$.

$= \dfrac{3(\sqrt{5m} + \sqrt{p})}{5m - p}$ Multiply in the denominator.

NOW TRY

NOW TRY ANSWERS

5. (a) $-2(1 - \sqrt{3})$, or $-2 + 2\sqrt{3}$
(b) $\dfrac{2(5 - \sqrt{7})}{9}$
(c) $\dfrac{\sqrt{15} + \sqrt{6} + \sqrt{35} + \sqrt{14}}{3}$
(d) $\dfrac{8(\sqrt{3x} + \sqrt{y})}{3x - y}$

OBJECTIVE 4   **Write radical quotients in lowest terms.**

NOW TRY
EXERCISE 6

Write each quotient in lowest terms.

(a) $\dfrac{15 - 6\sqrt{2}}{18}$

(b) $\dfrac{15k + \sqrt{50k^2}}{20k}$, $k > 0$

EXAMPLE 6   Writing Radical Quotients in Lowest Terms

Write each quotient in lowest terms.

(a) $\dfrac{6 + 2\sqrt{5}}{4}$

This is a key step.

$= \dfrac{2\left(3 + \sqrt{5}\right)}{2 \cdot 2}$ Factor the numerator and denominator.

$= \dfrac{3 + \sqrt{5}}{2}$ Divide out the common factor.

Here is an alternative method for writing this expression in lowest terms.

$$\frac{6 + 2\sqrt{5}}{4} = \frac{6}{4} + \frac{2\sqrt{5}}{4} = \frac{3}{2} + \frac{\sqrt{5}}{2} = \frac{3 + \sqrt{5}}{2}$$

(b) $\dfrac{5y - \sqrt{8y^2}}{6y}$, $y > 0$

$= \dfrac{5y - 2y\sqrt{2}}{6y}$ $\sqrt{8y^2} = \sqrt{4y^2 \cdot 2} = 2y\sqrt{2}$

$= \dfrac{y\left(5 - 2\sqrt{2}\right)}{6y}$ Factor the numerator.

$= \dfrac{5 - 2\sqrt{2}}{6}$ Divide out the common factor.   NOW TRY

⚠ CAUTION   *Be careful to factor before writing a quotient in lowest terms.*

CONNECTIONS

In calculus, it is sometimes desirable to **rationalize the numerator.** For example, to rationalize the numerator of

$$\frac{6 - \sqrt{2}}{4},$$

we multiply the numerator and the denominator by the conjugate of the *numerator.*

$$\frac{6 - \sqrt{2}}{4} = \frac{\left(6 - \sqrt{2}\right)\left(6 + \sqrt{2}\right)}{4\left(6 + \sqrt{2}\right)} = \frac{36 - 2}{4\left(6 + \sqrt{2}\right)} = \frac{34}{4\left(6 + \sqrt{2}\right)} = \frac{17}{2\left(6 + \sqrt{2}\right)}$$

For Discussion or Writing

Rationalize the numerator of each expression. (*a* and *b* are nonnegative real numbers.)

1. $\dfrac{8\sqrt{5} - 1}{6}$ 2. $\dfrac{3\sqrt{a} + \sqrt{b}}{b}$ 3. $\dfrac{3\sqrt{a} + \sqrt{b}}{\sqrt{b} - \sqrt{a}}$ $(b \neq a)$

4. Rationalize the denominator of the expression in **Exercise 3,** and then describe the difference in the procedure you used from what you did in **Exercise 3.**

NOW TRY ANSWERS

6. (a) $\dfrac{5 - 2\sqrt{2}}{6}$ (b) $\dfrac{3 + \sqrt{2}}{4}$

10.5 EXERCISES

MyMathLab Math XL WATCH DOWNLOAD READ REVIEW

🌐 *Complete solution available on the Video Resources on DVD*

Concept Check   *Match each part of a rule for a special product in Column I with the other part in Column II. Assume that A and B represent positive real numbers.*

I

1. $\left(A + \sqrt{B}\right)\left(A - \sqrt{B}\right)$

2. $\left(\sqrt{A} + B\right)\left(\sqrt{A} - B\right)$

3. $\left(\sqrt{A} + \sqrt{B}\right)\left(\sqrt{A} - \sqrt{B}\right)$

4. $\left(\sqrt{A} + \sqrt{B}\right)^2$

5. $\left(\sqrt{A} - \sqrt{B}\right)^2$

6. $\left(\sqrt{A} + B\right)^2$

II

A. $A - B$

B. $A + 2B\sqrt{A} + B^2$

C. $A - B^2$

D. $A - 2\sqrt{AB} + B$

E. $A^2 - B$

F. $A + 2\sqrt{AB} + B$

Multiply, and then simplify each product. Assume that all variables represent positive real numbers. ***See Example 1.***

7. $\sqrt{6}\left(3 + \sqrt{2}\right)$

8. $\sqrt{2}\left(\sqrt{32} - \sqrt{9}\right)$

9. $5\left(\sqrt{72} - \sqrt{8}\right)$

10. $7\left(\sqrt{50} - \sqrt{18}\right)$

11. $\left(\sqrt{7} + 3\right)\left(\sqrt{7} - 3\right)$

12. $\left(\sqrt{3} - 5\right)\left(\sqrt{3} + 5\right)$

🌐 **13.** $\left(\sqrt{2} - \sqrt{3}\right)\left(\sqrt{2} + \sqrt{3}\right)$

14. $\left(\sqrt{7} + \sqrt{14}\right)\left(\sqrt{7} - \sqrt{14}\right)$

15. $\left(\sqrt{8} - \sqrt{2}\right)\left(\sqrt{8} + \sqrt{2}\right)$

16. $\left(\sqrt{20} - \sqrt{5}\right)\left(\sqrt{20} + \sqrt{5}\right)$

17. $\left(\sqrt{2} + 1\right)\left(\sqrt{3} - 1\right)$

18. $\left(\sqrt{3} + 3\right)\left(\sqrt{5} - 2\right)$

19. $\left(\sqrt{11} - \sqrt{7}\right)\left(\sqrt{2} + \sqrt{5}\right)$

20. $\left(\sqrt{13} - \sqrt{7}\right)\left(\sqrt{3} + \sqrt{11}\right)$

21. $\left(2\sqrt{3} + \sqrt{5}\right)\left(3\sqrt{3} - 2\sqrt{5}\right)$

22. $\left(\sqrt{7} - \sqrt{11}\right)\left(2\sqrt{7} + 3\sqrt{11}\right)$

23. $\left(\sqrt{5} + 2\right)^2$

24. $\left(\sqrt{11} - 1\right)^2$

25. $\left(\sqrt{21} - \sqrt{5}\right)^2$

26. $\left(\sqrt{6} - \sqrt{2}\right)^2$

27. $\left(2 + \sqrt[3]{6}\right)\left(2 - \sqrt[3]{6}\right)$

28. $\left(\sqrt[3]{3} + 6\right)\left(\sqrt[3]{3} - 6\right)$

29. $\left(2 + \sqrt[3]{2}\right)\left(4 - 2\sqrt[3]{2} + \sqrt[3]{4}\right)$

30. $\left(\sqrt[3]{3} - 1\right)\left(\sqrt[3]{9} + \sqrt[3]{3} + 1\right)$

31. $\left(3\sqrt{x} - \sqrt{5}\right)\left(2\sqrt{x} + 1\right)$

32. $\left(4\sqrt{p} + \sqrt{7}\right)\left(\sqrt{p} - 9\right)$

33. $\left(3\sqrt{r} - \sqrt{s}\right)\left(3\sqrt{r} + \sqrt{s}\right)$

34. $\left(\sqrt{k} + 4\sqrt{m}\right)\left(\sqrt{k} - 4\sqrt{m}\right)$

35. $\left(\sqrt[3]{2y} - 5\right)\left(4\sqrt[3]{2y} + 1\right)$

36. $\left(\sqrt[3]{9z} - 2\right)\left(5\sqrt[3]{9z} + 7\right)$

37. $\left(\sqrt{3x} + 2\right)\left(\sqrt{3x} - 2\right)$

38. $\left(\sqrt{6y} - 4\right)\left(\sqrt{6y} + 4\right)$

39. $\left(2\sqrt{x} + \sqrt{y}\right)\left(2\sqrt{x} - \sqrt{y}\right)$

40. $\left(\sqrt{p} + 5\sqrt{s}\right)\left(\sqrt{p} - 5\sqrt{s}\right)$

41. $\left[\left(\sqrt{2} + \sqrt{3}\right) - \sqrt{6}\right]\left[\left(\sqrt{2} + \sqrt{3}\right) + \sqrt{6}\right]$

42. $\left[\left(\sqrt{5} - \sqrt{2}\right) - \sqrt{3}\right]\left[\left(\sqrt{5} - \sqrt{2}\right) + \sqrt{3}\right]$

Rationalize the denominator in each expression. Assume that all variables represent positive real numbers. **See Examples 2 and 3.**

43. $\dfrac{7}{\sqrt{7}}$ **44.** $\dfrac{11}{\sqrt{11}}$ **45.** $\dfrac{15}{\sqrt{3}}$ **46.** $\dfrac{12}{\sqrt{6}}$ **47.** $\dfrac{\sqrt{3}}{\sqrt{2}}$

48. $\dfrac{\sqrt{7}}{\sqrt{6}}$ **49.** $\dfrac{9\sqrt{3}}{\sqrt{5}}$ **50.** $\dfrac{3\sqrt{2}}{\sqrt{11}}$ **51.** $\dfrac{-7}{\sqrt{48}}$ **52.** $\dfrac{-5}{\sqrt{24}}$

53. $\sqrt{\dfrac{7}{2}}$ **54.** $\sqrt{\dfrac{10}{3}}$ **55.** $-\sqrt{\dfrac{7}{50}}$ **56.** $-\sqrt{\dfrac{13}{75}}$ **57.** $\sqrt{\dfrac{24}{x}}$

58. $\sqrt{\dfrac{52}{y}}$ **59.** $\dfrac{-8\sqrt{3}}{\sqrt{k}}$ **60.** $\dfrac{-4\sqrt{13}}{\sqrt{m}}$ **61.** $-\sqrt{\dfrac{150m^5}{n^3}}$ **62.** $-\sqrt{\dfrac{98r^3}{s^5}}$

63. $\sqrt{\dfrac{288x^7}{y^9}}$ **64.** $\sqrt{\dfrac{242t^9}{u^{11}}}$ **65.** $\dfrac{5\sqrt{2m}}{\sqrt{y^3}}$

66. $\dfrac{2\sqrt{5r}}{\sqrt{m^3}}$ **67.** $-\sqrt{\dfrac{48k^2}{z}}$ **68.** $-\sqrt{\dfrac{75m^3}{p}}$

Simplify. Assume that all variables represent positive real numbers. **See Example 4.**

69. $\sqrt[3]{\dfrac{2}{3}}$ **70.** $\sqrt[3]{\dfrac{4}{5}}$ **71.** $\sqrt[3]{\dfrac{4}{9}}$ **72.** $\sqrt[3]{\dfrac{5}{16}}$ **73.** $\sqrt[3]{\dfrac{9}{32}}$

74. $\sqrt[3]{\dfrac{10}{9}}$ **75.** $-\sqrt[3]{\dfrac{2p}{r^2}}$ **76.** $-\sqrt[3]{\dfrac{6x}{y^2}}$ **77.** $\sqrt[3]{\dfrac{x^6}{y}}$ **78.** $\sqrt[3]{\dfrac{m^9}{q}}$

79. $\sqrt[4]{\dfrac{16}{x}}$ **80.** $\sqrt[4]{\dfrac{81}{y}}$ **81.** $\sqrt[4]{\dfrac{2y}{z}}$ **82.** $\sqrt[4]{\dfrac{7t}{s^2}}$

Rationalize the denominator in each expression. Assume that all variables represent positive real numbers and no denominators are 0. **See Example 5.**

83. $\dfrac{3}{4+\sqrt{5}}$ **84.** $\dfrac{4}{5+\sqrt{6}}$ **85.** $\dfrac{\sqrt{8}}{3-\sqrt{2}}$

86. $\dfrac{\sqrt{27}}{3-\sqrt{3}}$ **87.** $\dfrac{2}{3\sqrt{5}+2\sqrt{3}}$ **88.** $\dfrac{-1}{3\sqrt{2}-2\sqrt{7}}$

89. $\dfrac{\sqrt{2}-\sqrt{3}}{\sqrt{6}-\sqrt{5}}$ **90.** $\dfrac{\sqrt{5}+\sqrt{6}}{\sqrt{3}-\sqrt{2}}$ **91.** $\dfrac{m-4}{\sqrt{m}+2}$

92. $\dfrac{r-9}{\sqrt{r}-3}$ **93.** $\dfrac{4}{\sqrt{x}-2\sqrt{y}}$ **94.** $\dfrac{5}{3\sqrt{r}+\sqrt{s}}$

95. $\dfrac{\sqrt{x}-\sqrt{y}}{\sqrt{x}+\sqrt{y}}$ **96.** $\dfrac{\sqrt{a}+\sqrt{b}}{\sqrt{a}-\sqrt{b}}$ **97.** $\dfrac{5\sqrt{k}}{2\sqrt{k}+\sqrt{q}}$ **98.** $\dfrac{3\sqrt{x}}{\sqrt{x}-2\sqrt{y}}$

Write each expression in lowest terms. Assume that all variables represent positive real numbers. **See Example 6.**

99. $\dfrac{30-20\sqrt{6}}{10}$ **100.** $\dfrac{24+12\sqrt{5}}{12}$ **101.** $\dfrac{3-3\sqrt{5}}{3}$ **102.** $\dfrac{-5+5\sqrt{2}}{5}$

103. $\dfrac{16-4\sqrt{8}}{12}$ **104.** $\dfrac{12-9\sqrt{72}}{18}$ **105.** $\dfrac{6p+\sqrt{24p^3}}{3p}$ **106.** $\dfrac{11y-\sqrt{242y^5}}{22y}$

Brain Busters *Rationalize each denominator. Assume that all radicals represent real numbers and no denominators are 0.*

107. $\dfrac{3}{\sqrt{x+y}}$ **108.** $\dfrac{5}{\sqrt{m-n}}$ **109.** $\dfrac{p}{\sqrt{p+2}}$ **110.** $\dfrac{q}{\sqrt{5+q}}$

111. The following expression occurs in a certain standard problem in trigonometry.

$$\frac{1}{\sqrt{2}} \cdot \frac{\sqrt{3}}{2} - \frac{1}{\sqrt{2}} \cdot \frac{1}{2}$$

Show that it simplifies to $\dfrac{\sqrt{6}-\sqrt{2}}{4}$. Then verify, using a calculator approximation.

112. The following expression occurs in a certain standard problem in trigonometry.

$$\frac{\sqrt{3}+1}{1-\sqrt{3}}$$

Show that it simplifies to $-2 - \sqrt{3}$. Then verify, using a calculator approximation.

*Rationalize the numerator in each expression. Assume that all variables represent positive real numbers. (Hint: See the **Connections box** following **Example 6**.)*

113. $\dfrac{6-\sqrt{3}}{8}$ **114.** $\dfrac{2\sqrt{5}-3}{2}$ **115.** $\dfrac{2\sqrt{x}-\sqrt{y}}{3x}$ **116.** $\dfrac{\sqrt{p}-3\sqrt{q}}{4q}$

PREVIEW EXERCISES

*Solve each equation. **See Sections 2.3 and 5.5**.*

117. $-8x + 7 = 4$ **118.** $3x - 7 = 12$

119. $6x^2 - 7x = 3$ **120.** $x(15x - 11) = -2$

SUMMARY EXERCISES on Operations with Radicals and Rational Exponents

Conditions for a Simplified Radical

1. The radicand has no factor raised to a power greater than or equal to the index.

2. The radicand has no fractions.

3. No denominator contains a radical.

4. Exponents in the radicand and the index of the radical have greatest common factor 1.

Perform all indicated operations, and express each answer in simplest form with positive exponents. Assume that all variables represent positive real numbers.

1. $6\sqrt{10} - 12\sqrt{10}$ **2.** $\sqrt{7}(\sqrt{7}-\sqrt{2})$ **3.** $(1-\sqrt{3})(2+\sqrt{6})$

4. $\sqrt{50} - \sqrt{98} + \sqrt{72}$ **5.** $(3\sqrt{5}+2\sqrt{7})^2$ **6.** $\dfrac{-3}{\sqrt{6}}$

7. $\dfrac{8}{\sqrt{7}+\sqrt{5}}$

8. $\dfrac{1-\sqrt{2}}{1+\sqrt{2}}$

9. $\left(\sqrt{5}+7\right)\left(\sqrt{5}-7\right)$

10. $\dfrac{1}{\sqrt{x}-\sqrt{5}},\quad x\neq 5$

11. $\sqrt[3]{8a^3b^5c^9}$

12. $\dfrac{15}{\sqrt[3]{9}}$

13. $\dfrac{3}{\sqrt{5}+2}$

14. $\sqrt{\dfrac{3}{5x}}$

15. $\dfrac{16\sqrt{3}}{5\sqrt{12}}$

16. $\dfrac{2\sqrt{25}}{8\sqrt{50}}$

17. $\dfrac{-10}{\sqrt[3]{10}}$

18. $\dfrac{\sqrt{6}+\sqrt{5}}{\sqrt{6}-\sqrt{5}}$

19. $\sqrt{12x}-\sqrt{75x}$

20. $\left(5-3\sqrt{3}\right)^2$

21. $\sqrt[3]{\dfrac{13}{81}}$

22. $\dfrac{\sqrt{3}+\sqrt{7}}{\sqrt{6}-\sqrt{5}}$

23. $\dfrac{6}{\sqrt[4]{3}}$

24. $\dfrac{1}{1-\sqrt[3]{3}}$

25. $\sqrt[3]{\dfrac{x^2y}{x^{-3}y^4}}$

26. $\sqrt{12}-\sqrt{108}-\sqrt[3]{27}$

27. $\dfrac{x^{-2/3}y^{4/5}}{x^{-5/3}y^{-2/5}}$

28. $\left(\dfrac{x^{3/4}y^{2/3}}{x^{1/3}y^{5/8}}\right)^{24}$

29. $(125x^3)^{-2/3}$

30. $\dfrac{4^{1/2}+3^{1/2}}{4^{1/2}-3^{1/2}}$

31. $\sqrt[3]{16x^2}-\sqrt[3]{54x^2}+\sqrt[3]{128x^2}$

32. $\left(1-\sqrt[3]{3}\right)\left(1+\sqrt[3]{3}+\sqrt[3]{9}\right)$

Students often have trouble distinguishing between the following two types of problems:

Simplifying a Radical Involving a Square Root	**Solving an Equation Using Square Roots**
Exercise: Simplify $\sqrt{25}$.	*Exercise:* Solve $x^2=25$.
Answer: 5	*Answer:* $\{-5,5\}$
In this situation, $\sqrt{25}$ represents the positive square root of 25, namely 5.	In this situation, $x^2=25$ has two solutions, the negative square root of 25 or the positive square root of 25: $-5,5$.

In Exercises 33–40, provide the appropriate responses.

33. (a) Simplify $\sqrt{64}$.

  (b) Solve $x^2=64$.

34. (a) Simplify $\sqrt{100}$.

  (b) Solve $x^2=100$.

35. (a) Solve $x^2=16$.

  (b) Simplify $-\sqrt{16}$.

36. (a) Solve $x^2=25$.

  (b) Simplify $-\sqrt{25}$.

37. (a) Simplify $-\sqrt{\dfrac{81}{121}}$.

  (b) Solve $x^2=\dfrac{81}{121}$.

38. (a) Simplify $-\sqrt{\dfrac{49}{100}}$.

  (b) Solve $x^2=\dfrac{49}{100}$.

39. (a) Solve $x^2=0.04$.

  (b) Simplify $\sqrt{0.04}$.

40. (a) Solve $x^2=0.09$.

  (b) Simplify $\sqrt{0.09}$.

10.6 Solving Equations with Radicals

OBJECTIVES

1 Solve radical equations by using the power rule.

2 Solve radical equations that require additional steps.

3 Solve radical equations with indexes greater than 2.

4 Use the power rule to solve a formula for a specified variable.

An equation that includes one or more radical expressions with a variable is called a **radical equation**.

$$\sqrt{x-4}=8, \quad \sqrt{5x+12}=3\sqrt{2x-1}, \quad \text{and} \quad \sqrt[3]{6+x}=27 \qquad \text{Examples of radical equations}$$

OBJECTIVE 1 Solve radical equations by using the power rule. The equation $x=1$ has only one solution. Its solution set is $\{1\}$. If we square both sides of this equation, we get $x^2=1$. This new equation has *two* solutions: -1 and 1. Notice that the solution of the original equation is also a solution of the equation following squaring. However, that equation has another solution, -1, that is *not* a solution of the original equation.

When solving equations with radicals, we use this idea of raising both sides to a power. It is an application of the **power rule**.

Power Rule for Solving an Equation with Radicals

If both sides of an equation are raised to the same power, all solutions of the original equation are also solutions of the new equation.

The power rule does not say that all solutions of the new equation are solutions of the original equation. They may or may not be. Solutions that do not satisfy the original equation are called **extraneous solutions**. They must be rejected.

⚠ **CAUTION** When the power rule is used to solve an equation, *every solution of the new equation must be checked in the original equation.*

NOW TRY EXERCISE 1

Solve $\sqrt{9x+7}=5$.

EXAMPLE 1 Using the Power Rule

Solve $\sqrt{3x+4}=8$.

$$\left(\sqrt{3x+4}\right)^2=8^2 \qquad \text{Use the power rule and square each side.}$$

$(\sqrt{a})^2=\sqrt{a}\cdot\sqrt{a}=a$

$$3x+4=64 \qquad \text{Apply the exponents.}$$
$$3x=60 \qquad \text{Subtract 4.}$$
$$x=20 \qquad \text{Divide by 3.}$$

CHECK
$$\sqrt{3x+4}=8 \qquad \text{Original equation}$$
$$\sqrt{3\cdot20+4}\overset{?}{=}8 \qquad \text{Let } x=20.$$
$$\sqrt{64}\overset{?}{=}8 \qquad \text{Simplify.}$$
$$8=8 \checkmark \qquad \text{True}$$

NOW TRY ANSWER
1. $\{2\}$

Since 20 satisfies the *original* equation, the solution set is $\{20\}$. *NOW TRY*

Use the following steps to solve equations with radicals.

Solving an Equation with Radicals

Step 1 **Isolate the radical.** Make sure that one radical term is alone on one side of the equation.

Step 2 **Apply the power rule.** Raise each side of the equation to a power that is the same as the index of the radical.

Step 3 **Solve** the resulting equation. If it still contains a radical, repeat Steps 1 and 2.

Step 4 **Check** all proposed solutions in the original equation.

NOW TRY
EXERCISE 2
Solve $\sqrt{3x + 4} + 5 = 0$.

EXAMPLE 2 Using the Power Rule

Solve $\sqrt{5x - 1} + 3 = 0$.

Step 1	$\sqrt{5x - 1} = -3$	To isolate the radical on one side, subtract 3 from each side.
Step 2	$\left(\sqrt{5x - 1}\right)^2 = (-3)^2$	Square each side.
Step 3	$5x - 1 = 9$	Apply the exponents.
	$5x = 10$	Add 1.
	$x = 2$	Divide by 5.
Step 4 CHECK	$\sqrt{5x - 1} + 3 = 0$	Original equation
	$\sqrt{5 \cdot 2 - 1} + 3 \overset{?}{=} 0$	Let $x = 2$.
	$3 + 3 = 0$	False

Be sure to check the proposed solution.

This false result shows that the *proposed* solution 2 is *not* a solution of the original equation. It is extraneous. The solution set is $\emptyset$. NOW TRY

NOTE We could have determined after Step 1 that the equation in **Example 2** has no solution because the expression on the left cannot be negative. (Why?)

OBJECTIVE 2 **Solve radical equations that require additional steps.** The next examples involve finding the square of a binomial. Recall the rule from **Section 4.6.**

$$(x + y)^2 = x^2 + 2xy + y^2$$

EXAMPLE 3 Using the Power Rule (Squaring a Binomial)

Solve $\sqrt{4 - x} = x + 2$.

Step 1 The radical is alone on the left side of the equation.

Step 2 Square each side. The square of $x + 2$ is $(x + 2)^2 = x^2 + 2(x)(2) + 4$.

$$\left(\sqrt{4 - x}\right)^2 = (x + 2)^2$$ Remember the middle term.

$$4 - x = x^2 + 4x + 4$$

└ Twice the product of 2 and x

NOW TRY ANSWER
2. $\emptyset$

NOW TRY
EXERCISE 3
Solve $\sqrt{16 - x} = x + 4$.

Step 3 The new equation is quadratic, so write it in standard form.

$$4 - x = x^2 + 4x + 4 \quad \text{Equation from Step 2}$$
$$x^2 + 5x = 0 \quad \text{Subtract 4. Add } x.$$
$$x(x + 5) = 0 \quad \text{Factor.}$$

Set *each factor* equal to 0. $\rightarrow x = 0 \quad \text{or} \quad x + 5 = 0 \quad \text{Zero-factor property}$
$$x = -5 \quad \text{Solve for } x.$$

Step 4 Check each proposed solution in the original equation.

CHECK
$$\sqrt{4 - x} = x + 2 \qquad\qquad \sqrt{4 - x} = x + 2$$
$$\sqrt{4 - 0} \overset{?}{=} 0 + 2 \quad \text{Let } x = 0. \qquad \sqrt{4 - (-5)} \overset{?}{=} -5 + 2 \quad \text{Let } x = -5.$$
$$\sqrt{4} \overset{?}{=} 2 \qquad\qquad\qquad \sqrt{9} \overset{?}{=} -3$$
$$2 = 2 \checkmark \quad \text{True} \qquad\qquad 3 = -3 \quad \text{False}$$

The solution set is $\{0\}$. The other proposed solution, -5, is extraneous. *NOW TRY*

NOW TRY
EXERCISE 4
Solve
$$\sqrt{x^2 - 3x + 18} = x + 3.$$

EXAMPLE 4 Using the Power Rule (Squaring a Binomial)

Solve $\sqrt{x^2 - 4x + 9} = x - 1$.

Squaring gives $(x - 1)^2 = x^2 - 2(x)(1) + 1^2$ on the right.

$$\left(\sqrt{x^2 - 4x + 9}\right)^2 = (x - 1)^2 \quad \text{Remember the middle term.}$$
$$x^2 - 4x + 9 = x^2 - 2x + 1$$

$\uparrow$ Twice the product of x and -1

$$-2x = -8 \quad \text{Subtract } x^2 \text{ and 9. Add } 2x.$$
$$x = 4 \quad \text{Divide by } -2.$$

CHECK
$$\sqrt{x^2 - 4x + 9} = x - 1 \quad \text{Original equation}$$
$$\sqrt{4^2 - 4 \cdot 4 + 9} \overset{?}{=} 4 - 1 \quad \text{Let } x = 4.$$
$$3 = 3 \checkmark \quad \text{True}$$

The solution set is $\{4\}$. *NOW TRY*

EXAMPLE 5 Using the Power Rule (Squaring Twice)

Solve $\sqrt{5x + 6} + \sqrt{3x + 4} = 2$.

Isolate one radical on one side of the equation by subtracting $\sqrt{3x + 4}$ from each side.

$$\sqrt{5x + 6} = 2 - \sqrt{3x + 4} \quad \text{Subtract } \sqrt{3x + 4}.$$
$$\left(\sqrt{5x + 6}\right)^2 = \left(2 - \sqrt{3x + 4}\right)^2 \quad \text{Square each side.}$$
$$5x + 6 = 4 - 4\sqrt{3x + 4} + (3x + 4) \quad \text{Be careful here.}$$

Remember the middle term.

$\uparrow$ Twice the product of 2 and $-\sqrt{3x + 4}$

NOW TRY ANSWERS
3. $\{0\}$ **4.** $\{1\}$

NOW TRY
EXERCISE 5
Solve

$$\sqrt{3x + 1} - \sqrt{x + 4} = 1.$$

The equation still contains a radical, so isolate the radical term on the right and square both sides again.

$$5x + 6 = 4 - 4\sqrt{3x + 4} + 3x + 4 \qquad \text{Result after squaring}$$

$$5x + 6 = 8 - 4\sqrt{3x + 4} + 3x \qquad \text{Combine like terms.}$$

$$2x - 2 = -4\sqrt{3x + 4} \qquad \text{Subtract 8 and } 3x.$$

Divide each term by 2. ⟶ $$x - 1 = -2\sqrt{3x + 4} \qquad \text{Divide by 2.}$$

$$(x - 1)^2 = \left(-2\sqrt{3x + 4}\right)^2 \qquad \text{Square each side again.}$$

$$x^2 - 2x + 1 = (-2)^2\left(\sqrt{3x + 4}\right)^2 \qquad \text{On the right, } (ab)^2 = a^2b^2.$$

$$x^2 - 2x + 1 = 4(3x + 4) \qquad \text{Apply the exponents.}$$

$$x^2 - 2x + 1 = 12x + 16 \qquad \text{Distributive property}$$

$$x^2 - 14x - 15 = 0 \qquad \text{Standard form}$$

$$(x - 15)(x + 1) = 0 \qquad \text{Factor.}$$

$$x - 15 = 0 \quad \text{or} \quad x + 1 = 0 \qquad \text{Zero-factor property}$$

$$x = 15 \quad \text{or} \qquad x = -1 \qquad \text{Solve each equation.}$$

CHECK $$\sqrt{5x + 6} + \sqrt{3x + 4} = 2 \qquad \text{Original equation}$$

$$\sqrt{5(15) + 6} + \sqrt{3(15) + 4} \overset{?}{=} 2 \qquad \text{Let } x = 15.$$

$$\sqrt{81} + \sqrt{49} \overset{?}{=} 2 \qquad \text{Simplify.}$$

$$9 + 7 \overset{?}{=} 2 \qquad \text{Take square roots.}$$

$$16 = 2 \qquad \text{False}$$

Thus, 15 is an extraneous solution and must be rejected. Confirm that the proposed solution -1 checks, so the solution set is $\{-1\}$.   NOW TRY

OBJECTIVE 3 **Solve radical equations with indexes greater than 2.**

NOW TRY
EXERCISE 6

Solve $\sqrt[3]{4x - 5} = \sqrt[3]{3x + 2}.$

EXAMPLE 6   Using the Power Rule for a Power Greater Than 2

Solve $\sqrt[3]{z + 5} = \sqrt[3]{2z - 6}.$

$$\left(\sqrt[3]{z + 5}\right)^3 = \left(\sqrt[3]{2z - 6}\right)^3 \qquad \text{Cube each side.}$$

$$z + 5 = 2z - 6$$

$$11 = z \qquad \text{Subtract } z. \text{ Add 6.}$$

CHECK $$\sqrt[3]{z + 5} = \sqrt[3]{2z - 6} \qquad \text{Original equation}$$

$$\sqrt[3]{11 + 5} \overset{?}{=} \sqrt[3]{2 \cdot 11 - 6} \qquad \text{Let } z = 11.$$

$$\sqrt[3]{16} = \sqrt[3]{16} \ \checkmark \qquad \text{True}$$

The solution set is $\{11\}$.   NOW TRY

NOW TRY ANSWERS
5. $\{5\}$ **6.** $\{7\}$

OBJECTIVE 4 Use the power rule to solve a formula for a specified variable.

NOW TRY
EXERCISE 7
Solve the formula for a.

$$x = \sqrt{\frac{y + 2}{a}}$$

EXAMPLE 7 Solving a Formula from Electronics for a Variable

An important property of a radio-frequency transmission line is its **characteristic impedance,** represented by Z and measured in ohms. If L and C are the inductance and capacitance, respectively, per unit of length of the line, then these quantities are related by the formula $Z = \sqrt{\frac{L}{C}}$. Solve this formula for C.

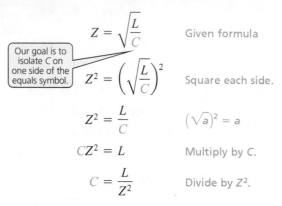

$$Z = \sqrt{\frac{L}{C}} \qquad \text{Given formula}$$

Our goal is to isolate C on one side of the equals symbol.

$$Z^2 = \left(\sqrt{\frac{L}{C}}\right)^2 \qquad \text{Square each side.}$$

$$Z^2 = \frac{L}{C} \qquad (\sqrt{a})^2 = a$$

$$CZ^2 = L \qquad \text{Multiply by } C.$$

$$C = \frac{L}{Z^2} \qquad \text{Divide by } Z^2.$$

NOW TRY

NOW TRY ANSWER

7. $a = \dfrac{y + 2}{x^2}$

10.6 EXERCISES

MyMathLab Math XL PRACTICE WATCH DOWNLOAD READ REVIEW

🌐 *Complete solution available on the Video Resources on DVD*

Concept Check *Check each equation to see if the given value for x is a solution.*

1. $\sqrt{3x + 18} - x = 0$

    (a) 6   **(b)** -3

2. $\sqrt{3x - 3} - x + 1 = 0$

    (a) 1   **(b)** 4

3. $\sqrt{x + 2} - \sqrt{9x - 2} = -2\sqrt{x - 1}$

    (a) 2   **(b)** 7

4. $\sqrt{8x - 3} - 2x = 0$

    (a) $\dfrac{3}{2}$ **(b)** $\dfrac{1}{2}$

✎ 5. Is 9 a solution of the equation $\sqrt{x} = -3$? If not, what is the solution of this equation? Explain.

✎ 6. Before even attempting to solve $\sqrt{3x + 18} = x$, how can you be sure that the equation cannot have a negative solution?

Solve each equation. ***See Examples 1–4.***

7. $\sqrt{x - 2} = 3$

8. $\sqrt{x + 1} = 7$

🌐 **9.** $\sqrt{6k - 1} = 1$

10. $\sqrt{7x - 3} = 6$

🌐 **11.** $\sqrt{4r + 3} + 1 = 0$

12. $\sqrt{5k - 3} + 2 = 0$

13. $\sqrt{3x + 1} - 4 = 0$

14. $\sqrt{5x + 1} - 11 = 0$

15. $4 - \sqrt{x - 2} = 0$

16. $9 - \sqrt{4x + 1} = 0$

17. $\sqrt{9x-4} = \sqrt{8x+1}$

18. $\sqrt{4x-2} = \sqrt{3x+5}$

19. $2\sqrt{x} = \sqrt{3x+4}$

20. $2\sqrt{x} = \sqrt{5x-16}$

21. $3\sqrt{x-1} = 2\sqrt{2x+2}$

22. $5\sqrt{4x+1} = 3\sqrt{10x+25}$

23. $x = \sqrt{x^2+4x-20}$

24. $x = \sqrt{x^2-3x+18}$

25. $x = \sqrt{x^2+3x+9}$

26. $x = \sqrt{x^2-4x-8}$

🌐 **27.** $\sqrt{9-x} = x+3$

28. $\sqrt{5-x} = x+1$

🌐 **29.** $\sqrt{k^2+2k+9} = k+3$

30. $\sqrt{x^2-3x+3} = x-1$

31. $\sqrt{x^2+12x-4} = x-4$

32. $\sqrt{x^2-15x+15} = x-5$

33. $\sqrt{r^2+9r+15} - r - 4 = 0$

34. $\sqrt{m^2+3m+12} - m - 2 = 0$

35. *Concept Check*   In solving the equation $\sqrt{3x+4} = 8 - x$, a student wrote the following for her first step. *WHAT WENT WRONG?* Solve the given equation correctly.

$$3x + 4 = 64 + x^2$$

36. *Concept Check*   In solving the equation $\sqrt{5x+6} - \sqrt{x+3} = 3$, a student wrote the following for his first step. *WHAT WENT WRONG?* Solve the given equation correctly.

$$(5x+6) + (x+3) = 9$$

Solve each equation. ***See Examples 5 and 6.***

🌐 **37.** $\sqrt[3]{2x+5} = \sqrt[3]{6x+1}$

38. $\sqrt[3]{p+5} = \sqrt[3]{2p-4}$

39. $\sqrt[3]{x^2+5x+1} = \sqrt[3]{x^2+4x}$

40. $\sqrt[3]{r^2+2r+8} = \sqrt[3]{r^2+3r+12}$

41. $\sqrt[3]{2m-1} = \sqrt[3]{m+13}$

42. $\sqrt[3]{2k-11} = \sqrt[3]{5k+1}$

43. $\sqrt[4]{x+12} = \sqrt[4]{3x-4}$

44. $\sqrt[4]{z+11} = \sqrt[4]{2z+6}$

45. $\sqrt[3]{x-8} + 2 = 0$

46. $\sqrt[3]{r+1} + 1 = 0$

47. $\sqrt[4]{2k-5} + 4 = 0$

48. $\sqrt[4]{8z-3} + 2 = 0$

49. $\sqrt{k+2} - \sqrt{k-3} = 1$

50. $\sqrt{r+6} - \sqrt{r-2} = 2$

🌐 **51.** $\sqrt{2r+11} - \sqrt{5r+1} = -1$

52. $\sqrt{3x-2} - \sqrt{x+3} = 1$

53. $\sqrt{3p+4} - \sqrt{2p-4} = 2$

54. $\sqrt{4x+5} - \sqrt{2x+2} = 1$

55. $\sqrt{3-3p} - 3 = \sqrt{3p+2}$

56. $\sqrt{4x+7} - 4 = \sqrt{4x-1}$

57. $\sqrt{2\sqrt{x+11}} = \sqrt{4x+2}$

58. $\sqrt{1+\sqrt{24-10x}} = \sqrt{3x+5}$

For each equation, write the expressions with rational exponents as radical expressions, and then solve, using the procedures explained in this section.

59. $(2x-9)^{1/2} = 2 + (x-8)^{1/2}$

60. $(3w+7)^{1/2} = 1 + (w+2)^{1/2}$

61. $(2w-1)^{2/3} - w^{1/3} = 0$

62. $(x^2-2x)^{1/3} - x^{1/3} = 0$

Solve each formula for the indicated variable. ***See Example 7.*** *(Source: Cooke, Nelson M., and Joseph B. Orleans,* Mathematics Essential to Electricity and Radio, *McGraw-Hill.)*

63. $Z = \sqrt{\dfrac{L}{C}}$ for L **64.** $r = \sqrt{\dfrac{\mathscr{A}}{\pi}}$ for $\mathscr{A}$ 🌐 **65.** $V = \sqrt{\dfrac{2K}{m}}$ for K

66. $V = \sqrt{\dfrac{2K}{m}}$ for m **67.** $r = \sqrt{\dfrac{Mm}{F}}$ for M **68.** $r = \sqrt{\dfrac{Mm}{F}}$ for F

The formula

$$N = \frac{1}{2\pi}\sqrt{\frac{a}{r}}$$

is used to find the rotational rate N of a space station. Here, a is the acceleration and r represents the radius of the space station, in meters. To find the value of r that will make N simulate the effect of gravity on Earth, the equation must be solved for r, using the required value of N. (Source: Kastner, Bernice, Space Mathematics, *NASA.)*

69. Solve the equation for r.

70. (a) Approximate the value of r so that $N = 0.063$ rotation per sec if $a = 9.8$ m per sec^2.

   (b) Approximate the value of r so that $N = 0.04$ rotation per sec if $a = 9.8$ m per sec^2.

PREVIEW EXERCISES

Perform the indicated operations. ***See Sections 4.4 and 4.5.***

71. $(5 + 9x) + (-4 - 8x)$ **72.** $(12 + 7y) - (-3 + 2y)$ **73.** $(x + 3)(2x - 5)$

Simplify each radical. ***See Section 10.5.***

74. $\dfrac{2}{4 + \sqrt{3}}$ **75.** $\dfrac{-7}{5 - \sqrt{2}}$ **76.** $\dfrac{\sqrt{2} + \sqrt{7}}{\sqrt{5} + \sqrt{3}}$

10.7 Complex Numbers

OBJECTIVES

1. Simplify numbers of the form $\sqrt{-b}$, where $b > 0$.
2. Recognize subsets of the complex numbers.
3. Add and subtract complex numbers.
4. Multiply complex numbers.
5. Divide complex numbers.
6. Find powers of i.

OBJECTIVE 1 Simplify numbers of the form $\sqrt{-b}$, where $b > 0$. The equation $x^2 + 1 = 0$ has no real number solution, since any solution must be a number whose square is -1. In the set of real numbers, all squares are nonnegative numbers because the product of two positive numbers or two negative numbers is positive and $0^2 = 0$. To provide a solution of the equation $x^2 + 1 = 0$, we introduce a new number i.

Imaginary Unit *i*

The **imaginary unit *i*** is defined as

$$i = \sqrt{-1}, \quad \text{where} \quad i^2 = -1.$$

That is, i is the principal square root of -1.

We can use this definition to define any square root of a negative real number.

$\sqrt{-b}$

For any positive real number b, $\quad \sqrt{-b} = i\sqrt{b}.$

NOW TRY
EXERCISE 1

Write each number as a product of a real number and i.

(a) $\sqrt{-49}$ (b) $-\sqrt{-121}$

(c) $\sqrt{-3}$ (d) $\sqrt{-32}$

EXAMPLE 1 Simplifying Square Roots of Negative Numbers

Write each number as a product of a real number and i.

(a) $\sqrt{-100} = i\sqrt{100} = 10i$ (b) $-\sqrt{-36} = -i\sqrt{36} = -6i$

(c) $\sqrt{-2} = i\sqrt{2}$ (d) $\sqrt{-54} = i\sqrt{54} = i\sqrt{9 \cdot 6} = 3i\sqrt{6}$

NOW TRY

⚠ **CAUTION** It is easy to mistake $\sqrt{2}i$ for $\sqrt{2i}$, with the i under the radical. For this reason, we usually write $\sqrt{2}i$ as $i\sqrt{2}$, as in the definition of $\sqrt{-b}$.

When finding a product such as $\sqrt{-4} \cdot \sqrt{-9}$, we cannot use the product rule for radicals because it applies only to *nonnegative* radicands. ***For this reason, we change $\sqrt{-b}$ to the form $i\sqrt{b}$ before performing any multiplications or divisions.***

NOW TRY
EXERCISE 2

Multiply.

(a) $\sqrt{-4} \cdot \sqrt{-16}$

(b) $\sqrt{-5} \cdot \sqrt{-11}$

(c) $\sqrt{-3} \cdot \sqrt{-12}$

(d) $\sqrt{13} \cdot \sqrt{-2}$

EXAMPLE 2 Multiplying Square Roots of Negative Numbers

Multiply.

(a) $\qquad\qquad \sqrt{-4} \cdot \sqrt{-9}$

First write all square roots in terms of i. $= i\sqrt{4} \cdot i\sqrt{9}$ $\sqrt{-b} = i\sqrt{b}$

$\qquad\qquad\qquad = i \cdot 2 \cdot i \cdot 3$ Take square roots.

$\qquad\qquad\qquad = 6i^2$ Multiply.

$\qquad\qquad\qquad = 6(-1)$ Substitute -1 for i^2.

$\qquad\qquad\qquad = -6$

(b) $\qquad\qquad \sqrt{-3} \cdot \sqrt{-7}$

First write all square roots in terms of i. $= i\sqrt{3} \cdot i\sqrt{7}$ $\sqrt{-b} = i\sqrt{b}$

$\qquad\qquad\qquad = i^2\sqrt{3 \cdot 7}$ Product rule

$\qquad\qquad\qquad = (-1)\sqrt{21}$ Substitute -1 for i^2.

$\qquad\qquad\qquad = -\sqrt{21}$

(c) $\sqrt{-2} \cdot \sqrt{-8}$ (d) $\sqrt{-5} \cdot \sqrt{6}$

$\quad = i\sqrt{2} \cdot i\sqrt{8}$ $\sqrt{-b} = i\sqrt{b}$ $= i\sqrt{5} \cdot \sqrt{6}$

$\quad = i^2\sqrt{2 \cdot 8}$ Product rule $= i\sqrt{30}$

$\quad = (-1)\sqrt{16}$ $i^2 = -1$

$\quad = -4$ Take the square root.   *NOW TRY*

NOW TRY ANSWERS
1. (a) $7i$ (b) $-11i$
   (c) $i\sqrt{3}$ (d) $4i\sqrt{2}$
2. (a) -8 (b) $-\sqrt{55}$
   (c) -6 (d) $i\sqrt{26}$

⚠ **CAUTION** Using the product rule for radicals *before* using the definition of $\sqrt{-b}$ gives a *wrong* answer. **Example 2(a)** shows that

$$\sqrt{-4} \cdot \sqrt{-9} = -6, \qquad \text{Correct}$$

but

$$\sqrt{-4(-9)} = \sqrt{36} = 6, \qquad \text{Incorrect}$$

so

$$\sqrt{-4} \cdot \sqrt{-9} \neq \sqrt{-4(-9)}.$$

NOW TRY
EXERCISE 3
Divide.

(a) $\dfrac{\sqrt{-72}}{\sqrt{-8}}$ **(b)** $\dfrac{\sqrt{-48}}{\sqrt{3}}$

EXAMPLE 3 Dividing Square Roots of Negative Numbers

Divide.

(a) $\dfrac{\sqrt{-75}}{\sqrt{-3}}$

$= \dfrac{i\sqrt{75}}{i\sqrt{3}}$ ⟵ First write all square roots in terms of i.

$= \sqrt{\dfrac{75}{3}}$ Quotient rule

$= \sqrt{25}$ Divide.

$= 5$

(b) $\dfrac{\sqrt{-32}}{\sqrt{8}}$

$= \dfrac{i\sqrt{32}}{\sqrt{8}}$ $\sqrt{-32} = i\sqrt{32}$

$= i\sqrt{\dfrac{32}{8}}$ Quotient rule

$= i\sqrt{4}$ Divide.

$= 2i$ **NOW TRY**

OBJECTIVE 2 **Recognize subsets of the complex numbers.** A new set of numbers, the *complex numbers,* are defined as follows.

Complex Number

If a and b are real numbers, then any number of the form $\boldsymbol{a + bi}$ is called a **complex number.** In the complex number $a + bi$, the number a is called the **real part** and b is called the **imaginary part.***

For a complex number $a + bi$, if $b = 0$, then $a + bi = a$, which is a real number. ***Thus, the set of real numbers is a subset of the set of complex numbers.*** If $a = 0$ and $b \neq 0$, the complex number is a **pure imaginary** number. For example, $3i$ is a pure imaginary number. A number such as $7 + 2i$ is a **nonreal complex number.** A complex number written in the form $a + bi$ is in **standard form.**

The relationships among the various sets of numbers are shown in **FIGURE 11**.

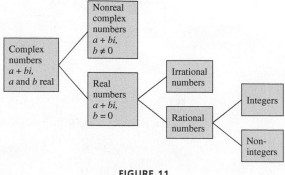

FIGURE 11

*Some texts define bi as the imaginary part of the complex number $a + bi$.

OBJECTIVE 3   **Add and subtract complex numbers.** The commutative, associative, and distributive properties for real numbers are also valid for complex numbers. *Thus, to add complex numbers, we add their real parts and add their imaginary parts.*

NOW TRY
EXERCISE 4

Add.

(a) $(-3 + 2i) + (4 + 7i)$

(b) $(5 - i) + (-3 + 3i)$
$+ (6 - 4i)$

EXAMPLE 4   Adding Complex Numbers

Add.

(a) $(2 + 3i) + (6 + 4i)$

$= (2 + 6) + (3 + 4)i$ Properties of real numbers

$= 8 + 7i$ Add real parts. Add imaginary parts.

(b) $(4 + 2i) + (3 - i) + (-6 + 3i)$

$= [4 + 3 + (-6)] + [2 + (-1) + 3]i$ Associative property

$= 1 + 4i$ Add real parts.
Add imaginary parts.   NOW TRY

To subtract complex numbers, we subtract their real parts and subtract their imaginary parts.

NOW TRY
EXERCISE 5

Subtract.

(a) $(7 + 10i) - (3 + 5i)$

(b) $(5 - 2i) - (9 - 7i)$

(c) $(-1 + 12i) - (-1 - i)$

EXAMPLE 5   Subtracting Complex Numbers

Subtract.

(a) $(6 + 5i) - (3 + 2i)$

$= (6 - 3) + (5 - 2)i$ Properties of real numbers

$= 3 + 3i$ Subtract real parts. Subtract imaginary parts.

(b) $(7 - 3i) - (8 - 6i)$

$= (7 - 8) + [-3 - (-6)]i$

$= -1 + 3i$

(c) $(-9 + 4i) - (-9 + 8i)$

$= (-9 + 9) + (4 - 8)i$

$= 0 - 4i$

$= -4i$ NOW TRY

OBJECTIVE 4   **Multiply complex numbers.**

EXAMPLE 6   Multiplying Complex Numbers

Multiply.

(a) $4i(2 + 3i)$

$= 4i(2) + 4i(3i)$ Distributive property

$= 8i + 12i^2$ Multiply.

$= 8i + 12(-1)$ Substitute -1 for i^2.

$= -12 + 8i$ Standard form

(b) $(3 + 5i)(4 - 2i)$

$= \underbrace{3(4)}_{\text{First}} + \underbrace{3(-2i)}_{\text{Outer}} + \underbrace{5i(4)}_{\text{Inner}} + \underbrace{5i(-2i)}_{\text{Last}}$ Use the FOIL method.

$= 12 - 6i + 20i - 10i^2$ Multiply.

$= 12 + 14i - 10(-1)$ Combine imaginary terms; $i^2 = -1$.

$= 12 + 14i + 10$ Multiply.

$= 22 + 14i$ Combine real terms.

NOW TRY ANSWERS

4. (a) $1 + 9i$ (b) $8 - 2i$
5. (a) $4 + 5i$ (b) $-4 + 5i$
    (c) $13i$

NOW TRY
EXERCISE 6

Multiply.

(a) $8i(3 - 5i)$

(b) $(7 - 2i)(4 + 3i)$

(c) $(2 + 3i)(1 - 5i)$

$= 2(1) + 2(-5i) + 3i(1) + 3i(-5i)$ FOIL

$= 2 - 10i + 3i - 15i^2$ Multiply.

$= 2 - 7i - 15(-1)$ | Use parentheses around -1 to avoid errors. |

$= 2 - 7i + 15$

$= 17 - 7i$

NOW TRY

The two complex numbers $a + bi$ and $a - bi$ are called **complex conjugates,** or simply *conjugates,* of each other. ***The product of a complex number and its conjugate is always a real number,*** as shown here.

$$(a + bi)(a - bi) = a^2 - abi + abi - b^2i^2$$

$$= a^2 - b^2(-1)$$

$$(a + bi)(a - bi) = a^2 + b^2$$ | The product eliminates i. |

For example, $(3 + 7i)(3 - 7i) = 3^2 + 7^2 = 9 + 49 = 58.$

OBJECTIVE 5   **Divide complex numbers.** The quotient of two complex numbers should be a complex number. To write the quotient as a complex number, we need to eliminate i in the denominator. We use conjugates and a process similar to that for rationalizing a denominator to do this.

EXAMPLE 7   Dividing Complex Numbers

Find each quotient.

(a) $\dfrac{8 + 9i}{5 + 2i}$

Multiply both the numerator and denominator by the conjugate of the denominator. The conjugate of $5 + 2i$ is $5 - 2i$.

$$\frac{8 + 9i}{5 + 2i}$$

$$= \frac{(8 + 9i)(5 - 2i)}{(5 + 2i)(5 - 2i)}$$ $\frac{5 - 2i}{5 - 2i} = 1$

$$= \frac{40 - 16i + 45i - 18i^2}{5^2 + 2^2}$$ In the denominator, $(a + bi)(a - bi) = a^2 + b^2$.

$$= \frac{58 + 29i}{29}$$ $-18i^2 = -18(-1) = 18$; Combine like terms.

$$= \frac{29(2 + i)}{29}$$ Factor the numerator.

| Factor first. Then divide out the common factor. |

$$= 2 + i$$ Lowest terms

NOW TRY ANSWERS
6. (a) $40 + 24i$ (b) $34 + 13i$

NOW TRY
EXERCISE 7

Find each quotient.

(a) $\dfrac{4 + 2i}{1 + 3i}$ (b) $\dfrac{5 - 4i}{i}$

(b) $\dfrac{1 + i}{i}$

$= \dfrac{(1 + i)(-i)}{i(-i)}$ Multiply numerator and denominator by $-i$, the conjugate of i.

$= \dfrac{-i - i^2}{-i^2}$ Distributive property; multiply.

$= \dfrac{-i - (-1)}{-(-1)}$ Substitute -1 for i^2.

Use parentheses to avoid errors.

$= \dfrac{-i + 1}{1}$

$= 1 - i$ NOW TRY

OBJECTIVE 6 **Find powers of i.** Because i^2 is defined to be -1, we can find greater powers of i as shown in the following examples.

$$i^3 = i \cdot i^2 = i(-1) = -i \qquad i^6 = i^2 \cdot i^4 = (-1) \cdot 1 = -1$$
$$i^4 = i^2 \cdot i^2 = (-1)(-1) = 1 \qquad i^7 = i^3 \cdot i^4 = (-i) \cdot 1 = -i$$
$$i^5 = i \cdot i^4 = i \cdot 1 = i \qquad i^8 = i^4 \cdot i^4 = 1 \cdot 1 = 1$$

Notice that the powers of i rotate through the four numbers i, -1, $-i$, and 1. Greater powers of i can be simplified by using the fact that $i^4 = 1$.

NOW TRY
EXERCISE 8

Find each power of i.

(a) i^{16} (b) i^{21}
(c) i^{-6} (d) i^{-13}

EXAMPLE 8 Simplifying Powers of i

Find each power of i.

(a) $i^{12} = (i^4)^3 = 1^3 = 1$

(b) $i^{39} = i^{36} \cdot i^3 = (i^4)^9 \cdot i^3 = 1^9 \cdot (-i) = -i$

(c) $i^{-2} = \dfrac{1}{i^2} = \dfrac{1}{-1} = -1$

NOW TRY ANSWERS
7. (a) $1 - i$ (b) $-4 - 5i$
8. (a) 1 (b) i (c) -1 (d) $-i$

(d) $i^{-1} = \dfrac{1}{i} = \dfrac{1(-i)}{i(-i)} = \dfrac{-i}{-i^2} = \dfrac{-i}{-(-1)} = \dfrac{-i}{1} = -i$ NOW TRY

10.7 EXERCISES *MyMathLab* Math XL PRACTICE WATCH DOWNLOAD READ REVIEW

⊙ *Complete solution available on the Video Resources on DVD*

Concept Check *Decide whether each expression is equal to* 1, -1, i, *or* $-i$.

1. $\sqrt{-1}$ **2.** $-\sqrt{-1}$ **3.** i^2 **4.** $-i^2$ **5.** $\dfrac{1}{i}$ **6.** $(-i)^2$

Write each number as a product of a real number and i. *Simplify all radical expressions.* ***See Example 1.***

⊙ **7.** $\sqrt{-169}$ **8.** $\sqrt{-225}$ **9.** $-\sqrt{-144}$ **10.** $-\sqrt{-196}$

11. $\sqrt{-5}$ **12.** $\sqrt{-21}$ **13.** $\sqrt{-48}$ **14.** $\sqrt{-96}$

Multiply or divide as indicated. ***See Examples 2 and 3.***

15. $\sqrt{-7} \cdot \sqrt{-15}$ **16.** $\sqrt{-3} \cdot \sqrt{-19}$ **17.** $\sqrt{-4} \cdot \sqrt{-25}$ **18.** $\sqrt{-9} \cdot \sqrt{-81}$

19. $\sqrt{-3} \cdot \sqrt{11}$ **20.** $\sqrt{-10} \cdot \sqrt{2}$ **21.** $\dfrac{\sqrt{-300}}{\sqrt{-100}}$ **22.** $\dfrac{\sqrt{-40}}{\sqrt{-10}}$

23. $\dfrac{\sqrt{-75}}{\sqrt{3}}$ **24.** $\dfrac{\sqrt{-160}}{\sqrt{10}}$ **25.** $\dfrac{-\sqrt{-64}}{\sqrt{-16}}$ **26.** $\dfrac{-\sqrt{-100}}{\sqrt{-25}}$

27. Every real number is a complex number. Explain why this is so.

28. Not every complex number is a real number. Give an example, and explain why this statement is true.

Add or subtract as indicated. Write your answers in the form $a + bi$. ***See Examples 4 and 5.***

29. $(3 + 2i) + (-4 + 5i)$ **30.** $(7 + 15i) + (-11 + 14i)$

31. $(5 - i) + (-5 + i)$ **32.** $(-2 + 6i) + (2 - 6i)$

33. $(4 + i) - (-3 - 2i)$ **34.** $(9 + i) - (3 + 2i)$

35. $(-3 - 4i) - (-1 - 4i)$ **36.** $(-2 - 3i) - (-5 - 3i)$

37. $(-4 + 11i) + (-2 - 4i) + (7 + 6i)$ **38.** $(-1 + i) + (2 + 5i) + (3 + 2i)$

39. $[(7 + 3i) - (4 - 2i)] + (3 + i)$ **40.** $[(7 + 2i) + (-4 - i)] - (2 + 5i)$

41. *Concept Check*   Fill in the blank with the correct response:

Because $(4 + 2i) - (3 + i) = 1 + i$, using the definition of subtraction, we can check this to find that $(1 + i) + (3 + i) =$ _____ .

42. *Concept Check*   Fill in the blank with the correct response:

Because $\dfrac{-5}{2 - i} = -2 - i$, using the definition of division, we can check this to find that $(-2 - i)(2 - i) =$ _____ .

Multiply. ***See Example 6.***

43. $(3i)(27i)$ **44.** $(5i)(125i)$ **45.** $(-8i)(-2i)$

46. $(-32i)(-2i)$ **47.** $5i(-6 + 2i)$ **48.** $3i(4 + 9i)$

49. $(4 + 3i)(1 - 2i)$ **50.** $(7 - 2i)(3 + i)$ **51.** $(4 + 5i)^2$

52. $(3 + 2i)^2$ **53.** $2i(-4 - i)^2$ **54.** $3i(-3 - i)^2$

55. $(12 + 3i)(12 - 3i)$ **56.** $(6 + 7i)(6 - 7i)$ **57.** $(4 + 9i)(4 - 9i)$

58. $(7 + 2i)(7 - 2i)$ **59.** $(1 + i)^2(1 - i)^2$ **60.** $(2 - i)^2(2 + i)^2$

61. *Concept Check*   What is the conjugate of $a + bi$?

62. *Concept Check*   If we multiply $a + bi$ by its conjugate, we get _____ , which is always a real number.

Find each quotient. ***See Example 7.***

63. $\dfrac{2}{1 - i}$ **64.** $\dfrac{2}{1 + i}$ **65.** $\dfrac{8i}{2 + 2i}$ **66.** $\dfrac{-8i}{1 + i}$

67. $\dfrac{-7 + 4i}{3 + 2i}$ **68.** $\dfrac{-38 - 8i}{7 + 3i}$ **69.** $\dfrac{2 - 3i}{2 + 3i}$ **70.** $\dfrac{-1 + 5i}{3 + 2i}$

71. $\dfrac{3 + i}{i}$ **72.** $\dfrac{5 - i}{i}$ **73.** $\dfrac{3 - i}{-i}$ **74.** $\dfrac{5 + i}{-i}$

Find each power of i. ***See Example 8.***

🌐 **75.** i^{18} **76.** i^{26} **77.** i^{89} **78.** i^{48} **79.** i^{38}

80. i^{102} **81.** i^{43} **82.** i^{83} **83.** i^{-5} **84.** i^{-17}

📝 **85.** A student simplified i^{-18} as follows:

$$i^{-18} = i^{-18} \cdot i^{20} = i^{-18+20} = i^2 = -1.$$

Explain the mathematical justification for this correct work.

📝 **86.** Explain why

$$(46 + 25i)(3 - 6i) \quad \text{and} \quad (46 + 25i)(3 - 6i)i^{12}$$

must be equal. (Do not actually perform the computation.)

Ohm's law *for the current I in a circuit with voltage E, resistance R, capacitive reactance X_c, and inductive reactance X_L is*

$$I = \frac{E}{R + (X_L - X_c)i}.$$

Use this law to work Exercises 87 and 88.

87. Find I if $E = 2 + 3i$, $R = 5$, $X_L = 4$, and $X_c = 3$.

88. Find E if $I = 1 - i$, $R = 2$, $X_L = 3$, and $X_c = 1$.

Complex numbers will appear again in this book in ***Chapter 11,*** *when we study quadratic equations. The following exercises examine how a complex number can be a solution of a quadratic equation.*

89. Show that $1 + 5i$ is a solution of

$$x^2 - 2x + 26 = 0.$$

Then show that its conjugate is also a solution.

90. Show that $3 + 2i$ is a solution of

$$x^2 - 6x + 13 = 0.$$

Then show that its conjugate is also a solution.

Brain Busters *Perform the indicated operations. Give answers in standard form.*

91. $\dfrac{3}{2 - i} + \dfrac{5}{1 + i}$ **92.** $\dfrac{2}{3 + 4i} + \dfrac{4}{1 - i}$

93. $\left(\dfrac{2 + i}{2 - i} + \dfrac{i}{1 + i}\right)i$ **94.** $\left(\dfrac{4 - i}{1 + i} - \dfrac{2i}{2 + i}\right)4i$

PREVIEW EXERCISES

Solve each equation. ***See Sections 2.3 and 5.5.***

95. $6x + 13 = 0$ **96.** $4x - 7 = 0$

97. $x(x + 3) = 40$ **98.** $2x^2 - 5x - 7 = 0$

99. $5x^2 - 3x = 2$ **100.** $-6x^2 + 7x = -10$

CHAPTER **10**

SUMMARY

KEY TERMS

10.1
square root
principal square root
negative square root
radicand
radical
perfect square
cube root

fourth root
index (order)
radical expression
square root function
cube root function

10.3
simplified radical

10.5
rationalizing the
    denominator
conjugates

10.6
radical equation
extraneous solution

10.7
complex number
real part
imaginary part
pure imaginary number
standard form
complex conjugates

NEW SYMBOLS

$\sqrt{}$ radical symbol
$\sqrt[3]{a}$ cube root of a
$\sqrt[4]{a}$ fourth root of a

$\sqrt[n]{a}$ principal nth root of a

$\approx$ is approximately equal
to

$a^{1/n}$ a to the power $\dfrac{1}{n}$

$a^{m/n}$ a to the power $\dfrac{m}{n}$

i imaginary unit

TEST YOUR WORD POWER

See how well you have learned the vocabulary in this chapter.

1. A **radicand** is
   A. the index of a radical
   B. the number or expression under
      the radical sign
   C. the positive root of a number
   D. the radical sign.

2. The **Pythagorean theorem** states
   that, in a right triangle,
   A. the sum of the measures of the
      angles is 180°
   B. the sum of the lengths of the two
      shorter sides equals the length of
      the longest side
   C. the longest side is opposite the
      right angle
   D. the square of the length of the
      longest side equals the sum of
      the squares of the lengths of the
      two shorter sides.

3. A **hypotenuse** is
   A. either of the two shorter sides of
      a triangle
   B. the shortest side of a triangle
   C. the side opposite the right angle
      in a triangle
   D. the longest side in any triangle.

4. **Rationalizing the denominator** is
   the process of
   A. eliminating fractions from a
      radical expression
   B. changing the denominator of a
      fraction from a radical to a
      rational number
   C. clearing a radical expression of
      radicals
   D. multiplying radical expressions.

5. An **extraneous solution** is a
   solution
   A. that does not satisfy the original
      equation
   B. that makes an equation true
   C. that makes an expression equal 0
   D. that checks in the original
      equation.

6. A **complex number** is
   A. a real number that includes a
      complex fraction
   B. a zero multiple of i
   C. a number of the form $a + bi$,
      where a and b are real numbers
   D. the square root of -1.

ANSWERS

1. B; *Example:* In $\sqrt{3xy}$, $3xy$ is the radicand.   **2.** D; *Example:* In a right triangle where $a = 6$, $b = 8$, and $c = 10$, $6^2 + 8^2 = 10^2$.
3. C; *Example:* In a right triangle where the sides measure 9, 12, and 15 units, the hypotenuse is the side opposite the right angle, with measure
15 units.   **4.** B; *Example:* To rationalize the denominator of $\dfrac{5}{\sqrt{3}+1}$, multiply both the numerator and denominator by $\sqrt{3} - 1$ to get $\dfrac{5(\sqrt{3}-1)}{2}$.
5. A; *Example:* The proposed solution 2 is extraneous in $\sqrt{5x-1} + 3 = 0$.   **6.** C; *Examples:* -5 (or $-5 + 0i$), $7i$ (or $0 + 7i$), $\sqrt{2} - 4i$

CONCEPTS	*EXAMPLES*

10.1 Radical Expressions and Graphs

$\sqrt[n]{a} = b$ means $b^n = a.$

$\sqrt[n]{a}$ is the principal nth root of $a.$

$\sqrt[n]{a^n} = |a|$ if n is even $\sqrt[n]{a^n} = a$ if n is odd.

Functions Defined by Radical Expressions
The square root function defined by $f(x) = \sqrt{x}$ and the cube root function defined by $f(x) = \sqrt[3]{x}$ are two important functions defined by radical expressions.

The two square roots of 64 are $\sqrt{64} = 8$ (the principal square root) and $-\sqrt{64} = -8.$

$$\sqrt[4]{(-2)^4} = |-2| = 2 \qquad \sqrt[3]{-27} = -3$$

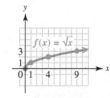

Square root function

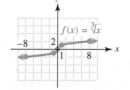

Cube root function

10.2 Rational Exponents

$a^{1/n} = \sqrt[n]{a}$ whenever $\sqrt[n]{a}$ exists.

If m and n are positive integers with $\frac{m}{n}$ in lowest terms, then $a^{m/n} = (a^{1/n})^m$, provided that $a^{1/n}$ is a real number.

All of the usual definitions and rules for exponents are valid for rational exponents.

$$81^{1/2} = \sqrt{81} = 9 \qquad -64^{1/3} = -\sqrt[3]{64} = -4$$

$$8^{5/3} = (8^{1/3})^5 = 2^5 = 32 \qquad (y^{2/5})^{10} = y^4$$

$$5^{-1/2} \cdot 5^{1/4} = 5^{-1/2+1/4} \qquad \frac{x^{-1/3}}{x^{-1/2}} = x^{-1/3-(-1/2)}$$

$$= 5^{-1/4} \qquad\qquad\qquad = x^{-1/3+1/2}$$

$$= \frac{1}{5^{1/4}} \qquad\qquad\qquad = x^{1/6}, \quad x > 0$$

10.3 Simplifying Radical Expressions

Product and Quotient Rules for Radicals

If $\sqrt[n]{a}$ and $\sqrt[n]{b}$ are real numbers and n is a natural number, then

$$\sqrt[n]{a} \cdot \sqrt[n]{b} = \sqrt[n]{ab} \quad \text{and} \quad \sqrt[n]{\frac{a}{b}} = \frac{\sqrt[n]{a}}{\sqrt[n]{b}}, \quad b \neq 0.$$

Conditions for a Simplified Radical

1. The radicand has no factor raised to a power greater than or equal to the index.

2. The radicand has no fractions.

3. No denominator contains a radical.

4. Exponents in the radicand and the index of the radical have greatest common factor 1.

$$\sqrt{3} \cdot \sqrt{7} = \sqrt{21} \qquad \sqrt[5]{x^3 y} \cdot \sqrt[5]{xy^2} = \sqrt[5]{x^4 y^3}$$

$$\frac{\sqrt{x^5}}{\sqrt{x^4}} = \sqrt{\frac{x^5}{x^4}} = \sqrt{x}, \quad x > 0$$

$$\sqrt{18} = \sqrt{9 \cdot 2} = 3\sqrt{2}$$

$$\sqrt[3]{54x^5y^3} = \sqrt[3]{27x^3y^3 \cdot 2x^2} = 3xy\sqrt[3]{2x^2}$$

$$\sqrt{\frac{7}{4}} = \frac{\sqrt{7}}{\sqrt{4}} = \frac{\sqrt{7}}{2}$$

$$\sqrt[9]{x^3} = x^{3/9} = x^{1/3}, \quad \text{or} \quad \sqrt[3]{x}$$

Pythagorean Theorem
If a and b are the lengths of the shorter sides of a right triangle and c is the length of the longest side, then

$$a^2 + b^2 = c^2.$$

Find b for the triangle in the figure.

$$10^2 + b^2 = \left(2\sqrt{61}\right)^2$$

$$b^2 = 4(61) - 100$$

$$b^2 = 144$$

$$b = 12$$

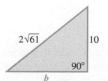

(continued)

CONCEPTS	EXAMPLES
Distance Formula The distance d between (x_1, y_1) and (x_2, y_2) is $$d = \sqrt{(x_2 - x_1)^2 + (y_2 - y_1)^2}.$$	Find the distance between $(3, -2)$ and $(-1, 1)$. $$\sqrt{(-1-3)^2 + [1-(-2)]^2}$$ $$= \sqrt{(-4)^2 + 3^2}$$ $$= \sqrt{16 + 9}$$ $$= \sqrt{25}$$ $$= 5$$
10.4 Adding and Subtracting Radical Expressions *Only radical expressions with the same index and the same radicand may be combined.*	$$2\sqrt{28} - 3\sqrt{63} + 8\sqrt{112}$$ $$= 2\sqrt{4 \cdot 7} - 3\sqrt{9 \cdot 7} + 8\sqrt{16 \cdot 7}$$ $$= 2 \cdot 2\sqrt{7} - 3 \cdot 3\sqrt{7} + 8 \cdot 4\sqrt{7}$$ $$= 4\sqrt{7} - 9\sqrt{7} + 32\sqrt{7}$$ $$= (4 - 9 + 32)\sqrt{7}$$ $$= 27\sqrt{7}$$ $$\left.\begin{array}{l}\sqrt{15} + \sqrt{30} \\ \sqrt{3} + \sqrt[3]{9}\end{array}\right\} \text{cannot be simplified further}$$
10.5 Multiplying and Dividing Radical Expressions Multiply binomial radical expressions by using the FOIL method. Special products from **Section 4.6** may apply.	$$\left(\sqrt{2} + \sqrt{7}\right)\left(\sqrt{3} - \sqrt{6}\right)$$ $$= \sqrt{6} - 2\sqrt{3} + \sqrt{21} - \sqrt{42} \qquad \sqrt{12} = 2\sqrt{3}$$ $$\left(\sqrt{5} - \sqrt{10}\right)\left(\sqrt{5} + \sqrt{10}\right)$$ $$= 5 - 10, \quad \text{or} \quad -5$$ $$\left(\sqrt{3} - \sqrt{2}\right)^2$$ $$= 3 - 2\sqrt{3} \cdot \sqrt{2} + 2$$ $$= 5 - 2\sqrt{6}$$
Rationalize the denominator by multiplying both the numerator and the denominator by the same expression, one that will yield a rational number in the final denominator.	$$\frac{\sqrt{7}}{\sqrt{5}} = \frac{\sqrt{7} \cdot \sqrt{5}}{\sqrt{5} \cdot \sqrt{5}} = \frac{\sqrt{35}}{5}$$ $$\frac{4}{\sqrt{5} - \sqrt{2}} = \frac{4\left(\sqrt{5} + \sqrt{2}\right)}{\left(\sqrt{5} - \sqrt{2}\right)\left(\sqrt{5} + \sqrt{2}\right)}$$ $$= \frac{4\left(\sqrt{5} + \sqrt{2}\right)}{5 - 2} = \frac{4\left(\sqrt{5} + \sqrt{2}\right)}{3}$$
To write a radical quotient in lowest terms, factor the numerator and denominator and then divide out any common factor(s).	$$\frac{5 + 15\sqrt{6}}{10} = \frac{5\left(1 + 3\sqrt{6}\right)}{5 \cdot 2} = \frac{1 + 3\sqrt{6}}{2}$$

(continued)

CONCEPTS	EXAMPLES
10.6 **Solving Equations with Radicals**	Solve $\sqrt{2x + 3} - x = 0$.

Solving an Equation with Radicals

Step 1   Isolate one radical on one side of the equation.

Step 2   Raise both sides of the equation to a power that is the same as the index of the radical.

Step 3   Solve the resulting equation. If it still contains a radical, repeat Steps 1 and 2.

Step 4   Check all proposed solutions in the *original* equation.

$$\sqrt{2x + 3} = x \qquad \text{Subtract } x.$$
$$\left(\sqrt{2x + 3}\right)^2 = x^2 \qquad \text{Square each side.}$$
$$2x + 3 = x^2 \qquad \text{Apply the exponents.}$$
$$x^2 - 2x - 3 = 0 \qquad \text{Standard form}$$
$$(x - 3)(x + 1) = 0 \qquad \text{Factor.}$$
$$x - 3 = 0 \quad \text{or} \quad x + 1 = 0 \qquad \text{Zero-factor property}$$
$$x = 3 \quad \text{or} \qquad x = -1 \qquad \text{Solve each equation.}$$

A check shows that 3 is a solution, but -1 is extraneous. The solution set is $\{3\}$.

10.7   **Complex Numbers**

$i = \sqrt{-1}$,   where $i^2 = -1$.

For any positive number b, $\sqrt{-b} = i\sqrt{b}$.

To multiply radicals with negative radicands, first change each factor to the form $i\sqrt{b}$ and then multiply. The same procedure applies to quotients.

$$\sqrt{-25} = i\sqrt{25} = 5i$$
$$\sqrt{-3} \cdot \sqrt{-27}$$
$$= i\sqrt{3} \cdot i\sqrt{27} \qquad \sqrt{-b} = i\sqrt{b}$$
$$= i^2\sqrt{81}$$
$$= -1 \cdot 9 \qquad i^2 = -1$$
$$= -9$$

$$\frac{\sqrt{-18}}{\sqrt{-2}} = \frac{i\sqrt{18}}{i\sqrt{2}} = \sqrt{\frac{18}{2}} = \sqrt{9} = 3$$

Adding and Subtracting Complex Numbers

Add (or subtract) the real parts and add (or subtract) the imaginary parts.

$$(5 + 3i) + (8 - 7i) \qquad\qquad (5 + 3i) - (8 - 7i)$$
$$= 13 - 4i \qquad\qquad\qquad\quad = -3 + 10i$$

Multiplying Complex Numbers

Multiply complex numbers by using the FOIL method.

$$(2 + i)(5 - 3i)$$
$$= 10 - 6i + 5i - 3i^2 \qquad \text{FOIL}$$
$$= 10 - i - 3(-1) \qquad i^2 = -1$$
$$= 10 - i + 3 \qquad \text{Multiply.}$$
$$= 13 - i \qquad \text{Combine real terms.}$$

Dividing Complex Numbers

Divide complex numbers by multiplying the numerator and the denominator by the conjugate of the denominator.

$$\frac{20}{3 + i}$$
$$= \frac{20(3 - i)}{(3 + i)(3 - i)} \qquad \text{Multiply by the conjugate.}$$
$$= \frac{20(3 - i)}{9 - i^2} \qquad (a + b)(a - b) = a^2 - b^2$$
$$= \frac{20(3 - i)}{10} \qquad i^2 = -1$$
$$= 2(3 - i), \quad \text{or} \quad 6 - 2i$$

CHAPTER (10)

REVIEW EXERCISES

10.1 *Find each root.*

1. $\sqrt{1764}$ **2.** $-\sqrt{289}$ **3.** $\sqrt[3]{216}$

4. $\sqrt[3]{-125}$ **5.** $-\sqrt[3]{27}$ **6.** $\sqrt[5]{-32}$

7. *Concept Check*   Under what conditions is $\sqrt[n]{a}$ not a real number?

8. Simplify each radical so that no radicals appear. Assume that x represents any real number.

    (a) $\sqrt{x^2}$ **(b)** $-\sqrt{x^2}$ **(c)** $\sqrt[3]{x^3}$

Use a calculator to find a decimal approximation for each number. Give the answer to the nearest thousandth.

9. $-\sqrt{47}$ **10.** $\sqrt[3]{-129}$ **11.** $\sqrt[4]{605}$

12. $\sqrt[4]{500^{-3}}$ **13.** $-\sqrt[3]{500^4}$ **14.** $-\sqrt{28^{-1}}$

Graph each function. Give the domain and range.

15. $f(x) = \sqrt{x - 1}$ **16.** $f(x) = \sqrt[3]{x} + 4$

17. What is the best estimate of the area of the triangle shown here?

    A. 3600   **B.** 30   **C.** 60   **D.** 360

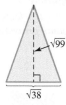

$\sqrt{99}$

$\sqrt{38}$

10.2

18. *Concept Check*   Fill in the blanks with the correct responses: One way to evaluate $8^{2/3}$ is to first find the _____ root of _____, which is _____. Then raise that result to the _____ power, to get an answer of _____. Therefore, $8^{2/3} = $ _____.

19. *Concept Check*   Which one of the following is a positive number?

    A. $(-27)^{2/3}$ **B.** $(-64)^{5/3}$ **C.** $(-100)^{1/2}$ **D.** $(-32)^{1/5}$

20. *Concept Check*   If a is a negative number and n is odd, then what must be true about m for $a^{m/n}$ to be   **(a)** positive   **(b)** negative?

21. *Concept Check*   If a is negative and n is even, is $a^{1/n}$ a real number?

Simplify. If the expression does not represent a real number, say so.

22. $49^{1/2}$ **23.** $-121^{1/2}$ **24.** $16^{5/4}$ **25.** $-8^{2/3}$

26. $-\left(\dfrac{36}{25}\right)^{3/2}$ **27.** $\left(-\dfrac{1}{8}\right)^{-5/3}$ **28.** $\left(\dfrac{81}{10,000}\right)^{-3/4}$ **29.** $(-16)^{3/4}$

30. *Concept Check*   Illustrate two different ways of writing $8^{2/3}$ as a radical expression.

31. Explain the relationship between the expressions $a^{m/n}$ and $\sqrt[n]{a^m}$. Give an example.

Write each expression as a radical.

32. $(m + 3n)^{1/2}$ **33.** $(3a + b)^{-5/3}$

Write each expression with a rational exponent.

34. $\sqrt{7^9}$ **35.** $\sqrt[5]{p^4}$

Use the rules for exponents to simplify each expression. Write the answer with only positive exponents. Assume that all variables represent positive real numbers.

36. $5^{1/4} \cdot 5^{7/4}$

37. $\dfrac{96^{2/3}}{96^{-1/3}}$

38. $\dfrac{(a^{1/3})^4}{a^{2/3}}$

39. $\dfrac{y^{-1/3} \cdot y^{5/6}}{y}$

40. $\left(\dfrac{z^{-1}x^{-3/5}}{2^{-2}z^{-1/2}x}\right)^{-1}$

41. $r^{-1/2}(r + r^{3/2})$

Simplify by first writing each radical in exponential form. Leave the answer in exponential form. Assume that all variables represent positive real numbers.

42. $\sqrt[8]{s^4}$

43. $\sqrt[6]{r^9}$

44. $\dfrac{\sqrt{p^5}}{p^2}$

45. $\sqrt[4]{k^3} \cdot \sqrt{k^3}$

46. $\sqrt[3]{m^5} \cdot \sqrt[3]{m^8}$

47. $\sqrt[4]{\sqrt[3]{z}}$

48. $\sqrt{\sqrt{\sqrt{x}}}$

49. $\sqrt[3]{\sqrt[5]{x}}$

50. $\sqrt{\sqrt[6]{\sqrt[3]{x}}}$

✎ **51.** The product rule does not apply to $3^{1/4} \cdot 2^{1/5}$. Why?

10.3 *Simplify each radical. Assume that all variables represent positive real numbers.*

52. $\sqrt{6} \cdot \sqrt{11}$

53. $\sqrt{5} \cdot \sqrt{r}$

54. $\sqrt[3]{6} \cdot \sqrt[3]{5}$

55. $\sqrt[4]{7} \cdot \sqrt[4]{3}$

56. $\sqrt{20}$

57. $\sqrt{75}$

58. $-\sqrt{125}$

59. $\sqrt[3]{-108}$

60. $\sqrt{100y^7}$

61. $\sqrt[3]{64p^4q^6}$

62. $\sqrt[3]{108a^8b^5}$

63. $\sqrt[3]{632r^8t^4}$

64. $\sqrt{\dfrac{y^3}{144}}$

65. $\sqrt[3]{\dfrac{m^{15}}{27}}$

66. $\sqrt[3]{\dfrac{r^2}{8}}$

67. $\sqrt[4]{\dfrac{a^9}{81}}$

Simplify each radical expression.

68. $\sqrt[6]{15^3}$

69. $\sqrt[4]{p^6}$

70. $\sqrt[3]{2} \cdot \sqrt[4]{5}$

71. $\sqrt{x} \cdot \sqrt[5]{x}$

72. Find the unknown length in the right triangle. Simplify the answer if applicable.

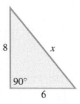

73. Find the distance between the points $(-4, 7)$ and $(10, 6)$.

10.4 *Perform the indicated operations. Assume that all variables represent positive real numbers.*

74. $2\sqrt{8} - 3\sqrt{50}$

75. $8\sqrt{80} - 3\sqrt{45}$

76. $-\sqrt{27y} + 2\sqrt{75y}$

77. $2\sqrt{54m^3} + 5\sqrt{96m^3}$

78. $3\sqrt[3]{54} + 5\sqrt[3]{16}$

79. $-6\sqrt[4]{32} + \sqrt[4]{512}$

In Exercises 80 and 81, leave answers as simplified radicals.

80. Find the perimeter of a rectangular electronic billboard having sides of lengths shown in the figure.

81. Find the perimeter of a triangular electronic highway road sign having the dimensions shown in the figure.

10.5   *Multiply.*

82. $\left(\sqrt{3} + 1\right)\left(\sqrt{3} - 2\right)$

83. $\left(\sqrt{7} + \sqrt{5}\right)\left(\sqrt{7} - \sqrt{5}\right)$

84. $\left(3\sqrt{2} + 1\right)\left(2\sqrt{2} - 3\right)$

85. $\left(\sqrt{13} - \sqrt{2}\right)^2$

86. $\left(\sqrt[3]{2} + 3\right)\left(\sqrt[3]{4} - 3\sqrt[3]{2} + 9\right)$

87. $\left(\sqrt[3]{4y} - 1\right)\left(\sqrt[3]{4y} + 3\right)$

88. Use a calculator to show that the answer to **Exercise 85**, $15 - 2\sqrt{26}$, is not equal to $13\sqrt{26}$.

89. *Concept Check*   A friend tried to rationalize the denominator of $\dfrac{5}{\sqrt[3]{6}}$, by multiplying the numerator and denominator by $\sqrt[3]{6}$. *WHAT WENT WRONG?*

Rationalize each denominator. Assume that all variables represent positive real numbers.

90. $\dfrac{\sqrt{6}}{\sqrt{5}}$

91. $\dfrac{-6\sqrt{3}}{\sqrt{2}}$

92. $\dfrac{3\sqrt{7p}}{\sqrt{y}}$

93. $\sqrt{\dfrac{11}{8}}$

94. $-\sqrt[3]{\dfrac{9}{25}}$

95. $\sqrt[3]{\dfrac{108m^3}{n^5}}$

96. $\dfrac{1}{\sqrt{2} + \sqrt{7}}$

97. $\dfrac{-5}{\sqrt{6} - 3}$

Write in lowest terms.

98. $\dfrac{2 - 2\sqrt{5}}{8}$

99. $\dfrac{4 - 8\sqrt{8}}{12}$

100. $\dfrac{-18 + \sqrt{27}}{6}$

10.6   *Solve each equation.*

101. $\sqrt{8x + 9} = 5$

102. $\sqrt{2x - 3} - 3 = 0$

103. $\sqrt{3x + 1} - 2 = -3$

104. $\sqrt{7x + 1} = x + 1$

105. $3\sqrt{x} = \sqrt{10x - 9}$

106. $\sqrt{x^2 + 3x + 7} = x + 2$

107. $\sqrt{x + 2} - \sqrt{x - 3} = 1$

108. $\sqrt[3]{5x - 1} = \sqrt[3]{3x - 2}$

109. $\sqrt[3]{2x^2 + 3x - 7} = \sqrt[3]{2x^2 + 4x + 6}$

110. $\sqrt[3]{3x^2 - 4x + 6} = \sqrt[3]{3x^2 - 2x + 8}$

111. $\sqrt[3]{1 - 2x} - \sqrt[3]{-x - 13} = 0$

112. $\sqrt[3]{11 - 2x} - \sqrt[3]{-1 - 5x} = 0$

113. $\sqrt[4]{x - 1} + 2 = 0$

114. $\sqrt[4]{2x + 3} + 1 = 0$

115. $\sqrt[4]{x + 7} = \sqrt[4]{2x}$

116. $\sqrt[4]{x + 8} = \sqrt[4]{3x}$

117. Carpenters stabilize wall frames with a diagonal brace, as shown in the figure. The length of the brace is given by $L = \sqrt{H^2 + W^2}$.

(a) Solve this formula for H.

(b) If the bottom of the brace is attached 9 ft from the corner and the brace is 12 ft long, how far up the corner post should it be nailed? Give your answer to the nearest tenth of a foot.

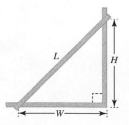

10.7   *Write each expression as a product of a real number and i.*

118. $\sqrt{-25}$

119. $\sqrt{-200}$

120. *Concept Check*   If a is a positive real number, is $-\sqrt{-a}$ a real number?

Perform the indicated operations. Give answers in standard form.

121. $(-2 + 5i) + (-8 - 7i)$ **122.** $(5 + 4i) - (-9 - 3i)$ **123.** $\sqrt{-5} \cdot \sqrt{-7}$

124. $\sqrt{-25} \cdot \sqrt{-81}$ **125.** $\dfrac{\sqrt{-72}}{\sqrt{-8}}$ **126.** $(2 + 3i)(1 - i)$

127. $(6 - 2i)^2$ **128.** $\dfrac{3 - i}{2 + i}$ **129.** $\dfrac{5 + 14i}{2 + 3i}$

Find each power of i.

130. i^{11} **131.** i^{36} **132.** i^{-10} **133.** i^{-8}

MIXED REVIEW EXERCISES

Simplify. Assume that all variables represent positive real numbers.

134. $-\sqrt[4]{256}$ **135.** $1000^{-2/3}$ **136.** $\dfrac{z^{-1/5} \cdot z^{3/10}}{z^{7/10}}$

137. $\sqrt[4]{k^{24}}$ **138.** $\sqrt[3]{54z^9t^8}$ **139.** $-5\sqrt{18} + 12\sqrt{72}$

140. $\dfrac{-1}{\sqrt{12}}$ **141.** $\sqrt[3]{\dfrac{12}{25}}$ **142.** i^{-1000}

143. $\sqrt{-49}$ **144.** $(4 - 9i) + (-1 + 2i)$ **145.** $\dfrac{\sqrt{50}}{\sqrt{-2}}$

146. $\dfrac{3 + \sqrt{54}}{6}$ **147.** $(3 + 2i)^2$ **148.** $8\sqrt[3]{x^3y^2} - 2x\sqrt[3]{y^2}$

149. $9\sqrt{5} - 4\sqrt{15}$ **150.** $\left(\sqrt{5} - \sqrt{3}\right)\left(\sqrt{7} + \sqrt{3}\right)$

Solve each equation.

151. $\sqrt{x + 4} = x - 2$ **152.** $\sqrt[3]{2x - 9} = \sqrt[3]{5x + 3}$

153. $\sqrt{6 + 2x} - 1 = \sqrt{7 - 2x}$ **154.** $\sqrt{7x + 11} - 5 = 0$

155. $\sqrt{6x + 2} - \sqrt{5x + 3} - 0$ **156.** $\sqrt{3 + 5x} - \sqrt{x + 11} - 0$

157. $3\sqrt{x} = \sqrt{8x + 9}$ **158.** $6\sqrt{x} = \sqrt{30x + 24}$

159. $\sqrt{11 + 2x} + 1 = \sqrt{5x + 1}$ **160.** $\sqrt{5x + 6} - \sqrt{x + 3} = 3$

CHAPTER 10

TEST

CHAPTER
Test Prep
VIDEOS

Step-by-step test solutions are found on the Chapter Test Prep Videos available via the Video Resources on DVD, in *MyMathLab*, or on You Tube (search "LialCombinedAlgebra").

View the complete solutions to all Chapter Test exercises on the Video Resources on DVD.

Evaluate.

1. $-\sqrt{841}$ **2.** $\sqrt[3]{-512}$ **3.** $125^{1/3}$

4. *Concept Check*   For $\sqrt{146.25}$, which choice gives the best estimate?

   A. 10   **B.** 11   **C.** 12   **D.** 13

Use a calculator to approximate each root to the nearest thousandth.

5. $\sqrt{478}$ **6.** $\sqrt[3]{-832}$

7. Graph the function defined by $f(x) = \sqrt{x + 6}$, and give the domain and range.

Simplify each expression. Assume that all variables represent positive real numbers.

8. $\left(\dfrac{16}{25}\right)^{-3/2}$

9. $(-64)^{-4/3}$

10. $\dfrac{3^{2/5}x^{-1/4}y^{2/5}}{3^{-8/5}x^{7/4}y^{1/10}}$

11. $\left(\dfrac{x^{-4}y^{-6}}{x^{-2}y^{3}}\right)^{-2/3}$

12. $7^{3/4} \cdot 7^{-1/4}$

13. $\sqrt[3]{a^4} \cdot \sqrt[3]{a^7}$

14. Use the Pythagorean theorem to find the exact length of side b in the figure.

15. Find the distance between the points $(-4, 2)$ and $(2, 10)$.

Simplify each expression. Assume that all variables represent positive real numbers.

16. $\sqrt{54x^5y^6}$

17. $\sqrt[4]{32a^7b^{13}}$

18. $\sqrt{2} \cdot \sqrt[3]{5}$ (Express as a radical.)

19. $3\sqrt{20} - 5\sqrt{80} + 4\sqrt{500}$

20. $\sqrt[3]{16t^3s^5} - \sqrt[3]{54t^6s^2}$

21. $\left(7\sqrt{5} + 4\right)\left(2\sqrt{5} - 1\right)$

22. $\left(\sqrt{3} - 2\sqrt{5}\right)^2$

23. $\dfrac{-5}{\sqrt{40}}$

24. $\dfrac{2}{\sqrt[3]{5}}$

25. $\dfrac{-4}{\sqrt{7} + \sqrt{5}}$

26. Write $\dfrac{6 + \sqrt{24}}{2}$ in lowest terms.

27. The following formula is used in physics, relating the velocity V of sound to the temperature T.

$$V = \dfrac{V_0}{\sqrt{1 - kT}}$$

(a) Find an approximation of V to the nearest tenth if $V_0 = 50$, $k = 0.01$, and $T = 30$. Use a calculator.

(b) Solve the formula for T.

Solve each equation.

28. $\sqrt[3]{5x} = \sqrt[3]{2x - 3}$

29. $x + \sqrt{x + 6} = 9 - x$

30. $\sqrt{x + 4} - \sqrt{1 - x} = -1$

In Exercises 31–33, perform the indicated operations. Give the answers in standard form.

31. $(-2 + 5i) - (3 + 6i) - 7i$

32. $(1 + 5i)(3 + i)$

33. $\dfrac{7 + i}{1 - i}$

34. Simplify i^{37}.

35. *Concept Check* Answer *true* or *false* to each of the following.

(a) $i^2 = -1$ (b) $i = \sqrt{-1}$ (c) $i = -1$ (d) $\sqrt{-3} = i\sqrt{3}$

CHAPTERS (1–10) CUMULATIVE REVIEW EXERCISES

Evaluate each expression for $a = -3$, $b = 5$, and $c = -4$.

1. $|2a^2 - 3b + c|$

2. $\dfrac{(a + b)(a + c)}{3b - 6}$

Solve each equation or inequality.

3. $3(x + 2) - 4(2x + 3) = -3x + 2$

4. $\dfrac{1}{3}x + \dfrac{1}{4}(x + 8) = x + 7$

5. $0.04x + 0.06(100 - x) = 5.88$

6. $-5 - 3(x - 2) < 11 - 2(x + 2)$

Solve each problem.

7. A piggy bank has 100 coins, all of which are nickels and quarters. The total value of the money is \$17.80. How many of each denomination are there in the bank?

8. How many liters of pure alcohol must be mixed with 40 L of 18% alcohol to obtain a 22% alcohol solution?

9. Graph the equation $4x - 3y = 12$.

10. Find the slope of the line passing through the points $(-4, 6)$ and $(2, -3)$. Then find the equation of the line and write it in the form $y = mx + b$.

Perform the indicated operations.

11. $(3k^3 - 5k^2 + 8k - 2) - (4k^3 + 11k + 7) + (2k^2 - 5k)$

12. $(8x - 7)(x + 3)$

13. $\dfrac{6y^4 - 3y^3 + 5y^2 + 6y - 9}{2y + 1}$

Factor each polynomial completely.

14. $2p^2 - 5pq + 3q^2$

15. $3k^4 + k^2 - 4$

16. $x^3 + 512$

Solve by factoring.

17. $2x^2 + 11x + 15 = 0$

18. $5x(x - 1) = 2(1 - x)$

19. For what values of the variable is the rational expression $\dfrac{4}{x^2 - 9}$ undefined?

Perform each operation and express the answer in lowest terms.

20. $\dfrac{y^2 + y - 12}{y^3 + 9y^2 + 20y} \div \dfrac{y^2 - 9}{y^3 + 3y^2}$

21. $\dfrac{1}{x + y} + \dfrac{3}{x - y}$

Simplify each complex fraction.

22. $\dfrac{\dfrac{-6}{x - 2}}{\dfrac{8}{3x - 6}}$

23. $\dfrac{x^{-1}}{y - x^{-1}}$

24. Solve the equation $\dfrac{x + 1}{x - 3} = \dfrac{4}{x - 3} + 6$.

25. Danielle can ride her bike 4 mph faster than her husband, Richard. If Danielle can ride 48 mi in the same time that Richard can ride 24 mi, what are their speeds?

26. If $f(x) = 3x - 7$, find $f(-10)$.

27. The cost of a pizza varies directly as the square of its radius. If a pizza with a 7-in. radius costs $6.00, how much should a pizza with a 9-in. radius cost, to the nearest cent?

Solve.

28. $3x - y = 23$
$2x + 3y = 8$

29. $x + y + z = 1$
$x - y - z = -3$
$x + y - z = -1$

30. In 2010, if you had sent five 2-oz letters and three 3-oz letters by first-class mail, it would have cost you $5.39. Sending three 2-oz letters and five 3-oz letters would have cost $5.73. What was the 2010 postage rate for one 2-oz letter and for one 3-oz letter? (*Source:* U.S. Postal Service.)

Solve each equation or inequality.

31. $2x + 4 < 10$ and $3x - 1 > 5$

32. $2x + 4 > 10$ or $3x - 1 < 5$

33. $|6x + 7| = 13$

34. $|2p - 5| \geq 9$

Write each expression in simplest form, using only positive exponents. Assume that all variables represent positive real numbers.

35. $\sqrt[3]{16x^2y} \cdot \sqrt[3]{3x^3y}$

36. $\sqrt{50} + \sqrt{8}$

37. $\dfrac{1}{\sqrt{10} - \sqrt{8}}$

38. Find the distance between the points $(-4, 4)$ and $(-2, 9)$.

39. Solve the equation $\sqrt{3x - 8} = x - 2$.

40. Express $\dfrac{6 - 2i}{1 - i}$ in standard form.

Quadratic Equations, Inequalities, and Functions

11.1 Solving Quadratic Equations by the Square Root Property

11.2 Solving Quadratic Equations by Completing the Square

11.3 Solving Quadratic Equations by the Quadratic Formula

11.4 Equations Quadratic in Form

Summary Exercises on Solving Quadratic Equations

11.5 Formulas and Further Applications

11.6 Graphs of Quadratic Functions

11.7 More About Parabolas and Their Applications

11.8 Polynomial and Rational Inequalities

The prices of food, gasoline, and other products have increased throughout the world. In particular, escalating oil prices in recent years have caused increases in transportation and shipping costs, which trickled down to affect prices of a variety of goods and services.

Although prices tend to go up over time, the rate at which they increase (the inflation rate) varies considerably. The Consumer Price Index (CPI) used by the U.S. government measures changes in prices for goods purchased by typical American families over time. In **Example 6** of **Section 11.5,** we use a *quadratic function* to model the CPI.

669

Solving Quadratic Equations by the Square Root Property

OBJECTIVES

1 Review the zero-factor property.

2 Solve equations of the form $x^2 = k$, where $k > 0$.

3 Solve equations of the form $(ax + b)^2 = k$, where $k > 0$.

4 Solve quadratic equations with solutions that are not real numbers.

Recall from **Section 5.5** that a *quadratic equation* is defined as follows.

Quadratic Equation

An equation that can be written in the form

$$ax^2 + bx + c = 0,$$

where a, b, and c are real numbers, with $a \neq 0$, is a **quadratic equation.** The given form is called **standard form.**

A quadratic equation is a *second-degree equation,* that is, an equation with a squared variable term and no terms of greater degree.

$$4x^2 + 4x - 5 = 0 \quad \text{and} \quad 3x^2 = 4x - 8$$

Quadratic equations (The first equation is in standard form.)

OBJECTIVE 1 **Review the zero-factor property.** In **Section 5.5** we used factoring and the zero-factor property to solve quadratic equations.

Zero-Factor Property

If two numbers have a product of 0, then at least one of the numbers must be 0. **That is, if $ab = 0$, then $a = 0$ or $b = 0$.**

NOW TRY
EXERCISE 1
Solve each equation by the zero-factor property.

(a) $x^2 - x - 20 = 0$

(b) $x^2 = 36$

EXAMPLE 1 Solving Quadratic Equations by the Zero-Factor Property

Solve each equation by the zero-factor property.

(a)
$$x^2 + 4x + 3 = 0$$
$$(x + 3)(x + 1) = 0 \qquad \text{Factor.}$$
$$x + 3 = 0 \quad \text{or} \quad x + 1 = 0 \qquad \text{Zero-factor property}$$
$$x = -3 \quad \text{or} \quad x = -1 \qquad \text{Solve each equation.}$$

The solution set is $\{-3, -1\}$.

(b)
$$x^2 = 9$$
$$x^2 - 9 = 0 \qquad \text{Subtract 9.}$$
$$(x + 3)(x - 3) = 0 \qquad \text{Factor.}$$
$$x + 3 = 0 \quad \text{or} \quad x - 3 = 0 \qquad \text{Zero-factor property}$$
$$x = -3 \quad \text{or} \quad x = 3 \qquad \text{Solve each equation.}$$

The solution set is $\{-3, 3\}$.

NOW TRY

OBJECTIVE 2 **Solve equations of the form $x^2 = k$, where $k > 0$.** In **Example 1(b),** we might also have solved $x^2 = 9$ by noticing that x must be a number whose square is 9. Thus, $x = \sqrt{9} = 3$ or $x = -\sqrt{9} = -3$. This is generalized as the **square root property.**

NOW TRY ANSWERS
1. **(a)** $\{-4, 5\}$ **(b)** $\{-6, 6\}$

Square Root Property

If k is a positive number and if $x^2 = k$, then

$$x = \sqrt{k} \quad \text{or} \quad x = -\sqrt{k}.$$

The solution set is $\left\{-\sqrt{k}, \sqrt{k}\right\}$, which can be written $\left\{\pm\sqrt{k}\right\}$. ($\pm$ is read "positive or negative" or "plus or minus.")

NOTE When we solve an equation, we must find *all* values of the variable that satisfy the equation. Therefore, we want both the positive and negative square roots of k.

NOW TRY EXERCISE 2

Solve each equation. Write radicals in simplified form.

(a) $t^2 = 25$

(b) $x^2 = 13$

(c) $3x^2 - 54 = 0$

(d) $2x^2 - 5 = 35$

EXAMPLE 2 Solving Quadratic Equations of the Form $x^2 = k$

Solve each equation. Write radicals in simplified form.

(a) $x^2 = 16$

By the square root property, if $x^2 = 16$, then

$$x = \sqrt{16} = 4 \quad \text{or} \quad x = -\sqrt{16} = -4.$$

Check each solution by substituting it for x in the original equation. The solution set is

$$\{-4, 4\}, \quad \text{or} \quad \{\pm 4\}.$$

> This notation indicates *two* solutions, one positive and one negative.

(b) $x^2 = 5$

By the square root property, if $x^2 = 5$, then

$$x = \sqrt{5} \quad \text{or} \quad x = -\sqrt{5}.$$

> Don't forget the negative solution.

The solution set is $\left\{\sqrt{5}, -\sqrt{5}\right\}$, or $\left\{\pm\sqrt{5}\right\}$.

(c)
$$4x^2 - 48 = 0$$
$$4x^2 = 48 \qquad \text{Add 48.}$$
$$x^2 = 12 \qquad \text{Divide by 4.}$$

> Don't stop here. Simplify the radicals.

$$x = \sqrt{12} \quad \text{or} \quad x = -\sqrt{12} \qquad \text{Square root property}$$
$$x = 2\sqrt{3} \quad \text{or} \quad x = -2\sqrt{3} \qquad \sqrt{12} = \sqrt{4} \cdot \sqrt{3} = 2\sqrt{3}$$

The solutions are $2\sqrt{3}$ and $-2\sqrt{3}$. Check each in the original equation.

CHECK $\qquad\qquad\qquad 4x^2 - 48 = 0 \qquad$ Original equation

$$4\left(2\sqrt{3}\right)^2 - 48 \stackrel{?}{=} 0 \quad \text{Let } x = 2\sqrt{3}. \quad\Big|\quad 4\left(-2\sqrt{3}\right)^2 - 48 \stackrel{?}{=} 0 \quad \text{Let } x = -2\sqrt{3}.$$

$$4(12) - 48 \stackrel{?}{=} 0 \qquad\qquad\qquad 4(12) - 48 \stackrel{?}{=} 0$$

$$48 - 48 \stackrel{?}{=} 0 \qquad\qquad\qquad 48 - 48 \stackrel{?}{=} 0$$

$$0 = 0 \ \checkmark \ \text{True} \qquad\qquad\qquad 0 = 0 \ \checkmark \ \text{True}$$

> $\left(2\sqrt{3}\right)^2$ $= 2^2 \cdot \left(\sqrt{3}\right)^2$

The solution set is $\left\{2\sqrt{3}, -2\sqrt{3}\right\}$, or $\left\{\pm 2\sqrt{3}\right\}$.

(d)
$$3x^2 + 5 = 11$$
$$3x^2 = 6 \qquad \text{Subtract 5.}$$
$$x^2 = 2 \qquad \text{Divide by 3.}$$
$$x = \sqrt{2} \quad \text{or} \quad x = -\sqrt{2} \qquad \text{Square root property}$$

The solution set is $\left\{\sqrt{2}, -\sqrt{2}\right\}$, or $\left\{\pm\sqrt{2}\right\}$.

NOW TRY ANSWERS

2. (a) $\{\pm 5\}$ **(b)** $\left\{\pm\sqrt{13}\right\}$
(c) $\left\{\pm 3\sqrt{2}\right\}$ **(d)** $\left\{\pm 2\sqrt{5}\right\}$

NOW TRY

⌒NOW TRY
 ✎EXERCISE 3
Tim is dropping roofing nails from the top of a roof 25 ft high into a large bucket on the ground. Use the formula in **Example 3** to determine how long it will take a nail dropped from 25 ft to hit the bottom of the bucket.

⎯⎯⎯⎯⎯⎯⎯⎯⎯

EXAMPLE 3 Using the Square Root Property in an Application

Galileo Galilei developed a formula for freely falling objects described by

$$d = 16t^2,$$

where d is the distance in feet that an object falls (disregarding air resistance) in t seconds, regardless of weight. Galileo dropped objects from the Leaning Tower of Pisa. If the Leaning Tower is about 180 ft tall, use Galileo's formula to determine how long it would take an object dropped from the top of the tower to fall to the ground. (*Source:* www.brittanica.com)

Galileo Galilei (1564–1642)

$$d = 16t^2 \qquad \text{Galileo's formula}$$
$$180 = 16t^2 \qquad \text{Let } d = 180.$$
$$11.25 = t^2 \qquad \text{Divide by 16.}$$
$$t = \sqrt{11.25} \quad \text{or} \quad t = -\sqrt{11.25} \qquad \text{Square root property}$$

Time cannot be negative, so we discard the negative solution. Since $\sqrt{11.25} \approx 3.4$, $t \approx 3.4$. The object would fall to the ground in about 3.4 sec. NOW TRY ⤸

OBJECTIVE 3 Solve equations of the form $(ax + b)^2 = k$, where $k > 0$. In each equation in **Example 2,** the exponent 2 had a single variable as its base. We can extend the square root property to solve equations in which the base is a binomial.

⌒NOW TRY
 ✎EXERCISE 4
Solve $(x - 2)^2 = 32$.

EXAMPLE 4 Solving Quadratic Equations of the Form $(x + b)^2 = k$

Solve each equation.

(a) ⌈Use $(x - 3)$⌉ $(x - 3)^2 = 16$
       ⌊as the base.⌋

$$x - 3 = \sqrt{16} \quad \text{or} \quad x - 3 = -\sqrt{16} \qquad \text{Square root property}$$
$$x - 3 = 4 \quad \text{or} \quad x - 3 = -4 \qquad \sqrt{16} = 4$$
$$x = 7 \quad \text{or} \quad x = -1 \qquad \text{Add 3.}$$

CHECK Substitute each solution in the original equation.

$(x - 3)^2 = 16$	$(x - 3)^2 = 16$
$(7 - 3)^2 \overset{?}{=} 16$ Let $x = 7$.	$(-1 - 3)^2 \overset{?}{=} 16$ Let $x = -1$.
$4^2 \overset{?}{=} 16$ Subtract.	$(-4)^2 \overset{?}{=} 16$ Subtract.
$16 = 16$ ✓ True	$16 = 16$ ✓ True

The solution set is $\{-1, 7\}$.

(b) $(x - 1)^2 = 6$

$$x - 1 = \sqrt{6} \quad \text{or} \quad x - 1 = -\sqrt{6} \qquad \text{Square root property}$$
$$x = 1 + \sqrt{6} \quad \text{or} \quad x = 1 - \sqrt{6} \qquad \text{Add 1.}$$

CHECK $\left(1 + \sqrt{6} - 1\right)^2 = \left(\sqrt{6}\right)^2 = 6$ ✓ Let $x = 1 + \sqrt{6}$.

$\left(1 - \sqrt{6} - 1\right)^2 = \left(-\sqrt{6}\right)^2 = 6$ ✓ Let $x = 1 - \sqrt{6}$.

NOW TRY ANSWERS
3. 1.25 sec **4.** $\left\{2 \pm 4\sqrt{2}\right\}$

The solution set is $\left\{1 + \sqrt{6}, 1 - \sqrt{6}\right\}$, or $\left\{1 \pm \sqrt{6}\right\}$. NOW TRY ⤸

NOW TRY
EXERCISE 5
Solve $(2t - 4)^2 = 50$.

EXAMPLE 5 Solving a Quadratic Equation of the Form $(ax + b)^2 = k$

Solve $(3r - 2)^2 = 27$.

$$(3r - 2)^2 = 27$$

$3r - 2 = \sqrt{27}$	or $\quad 3r - 2 = -\sqrt{27}$	Square root property
$3r - 2 = 3\sqrt{3}$	or $\quad 3r - 2 = -3\sqrt{3}$	$\sqrt{27} = \sqrt{9} \cdot \sqrt{3} = 3\sqrt{3}$
$3r = 2 + 3\sqrt{3}$	or $\quad 3r = 2 - 3\sqrt{3}$	Add 2.
$r = \dfrac{2 + 3\sqrt{3}}{3}$	or $\quad r = \dfrac{2 - 3\sqrt{3}}{3}$	Divide by 3.

CHECK

$$\left(3 \cdot \frac{2 + 3\sqrt{3}}{3} - 2\right)^2 \overset{?}{=} 27 \qquad \text{Let } r = \tfrac{2 + 3\sqrt{3}}{3}.$$

$$\left(2 + 3\sqrt{3} - 2\right)^2 \overset{?}{=} 27 \qquad \text{Multiply.}$$

$$\left(3\sqrt{3}\right)^2 \overset{?}{=} 27 \qquad \text{Subtract.}$$

$(ab)^2 = a^2b^2$

$$27 = 27 \quad \checkmark \qquad \text{True}$$

The check of the other solution is similar. The solution set is $\left\{\dfrac{2 \pm 3\sqrt{3}}{3}\right\}$.

NOW TRY

⚠ CAUTION The solutions in **Example 5** are fractions that cannot be simplified, since 3 is *not* a common factor in the numerator.

OBJECTIVE 4 **Solve quadratic equations with solutions that are not real numbers.** In $x^2 = k$, if $k < 0$, there will be two nonreal complex solutions.

NOW TRY
EXERCISE 6
Solve each equation.
(a) $t^2 = -24$
(b) $(x + 4)^2 = -36$

EXAMPLE 6 Solving for Nonreal Complex Solutions

Solve each equation.

(a) $$x^2 = -15$$

$x = \sqrt{-15}$	or $\quad x = -\sqrt{-15}$	Square root property
$x = i\sqrt{15}$	or $\quad x = -i\sqrt{15}$	$\sqrt{-1} = i$ (See **Section 10.7.**)

The solution set is $\left\{i\sqrt{15}, -i\sqrt{15}\right\}$, or $\left\{\pm i\sqrt{15}\right\}$.

(b) $$(x + 2)^2 = -16$$

$x + 2 = \sqrt{-16}$	or $\quad x + 2 = -\sqrt{-16}$	Square root property
$x + 2 = 4i$	or $\quad x + 2 = -4i$	$\sqrt{-16} = 4i$
$x = -2 + 4i$	or $\quad x = -2 - 4i$	Add -2.

The solution set is $\{-2 + 4i, -2 - 4i\}$, or $\{-2 \pm 4i\}$.

NOW TRY

NOW TRY ANSWERS
5. $\left\{\dfrac{4 \pm 5\sqrt{2}}{2}\right\}$
6. (a) $\left\{\pm 2i\sqrt{6}\right\}$
   (b) $\{-4 \pm 6i\}$

11.1 EXERCISES   *MyMathLab*   Math XL PRACTICE   WATCH   DOWNLOAD   READ   REVIEW

🌐 *Complete solution available on the Video Resources on DVD*

1. *Concept Check*   Which of the following are quadratic equations?

   A. $x + 2y = 0$ **B.** $x^2 - 8x + 16 = 0$ **C.** $2t^2 - 5t = 3$ **D.** $x^3 + x^2 + 4 = 0$

2. *Concept Check*   Which quadratic equation identified in **Exercise 1** is in standard form?

3. *Concept Check*   A student incorrectly solved the equation $x^2 - x - 2 = 5$ as follows. ***WHAT WENT WRONG?***

$$x^2 - x - 2 = 5$$
$$(x - 2)(x + 1) = 5 \qquad \text{Factor.}$$
$$x - 2 = 5 \quad \text{or} \quad x + 1 = 5 \qquad \text{Zero-factor property}$$
$$x = 7 \quad \text{or} \qquad x = 4 \qquad \text{Solve each equation.}$$

4. *Concept Check*   A student was asked to solve the quadratic equation $x^2 = 16$ and did not get full credit for the solution set $\{4\}$. ***WHAT WENT WRONG?***

Solve each equation by the zero-factor property. **See Example 1.**

5. $x^2 - x - 56 = 0$ **6.** $x^2 - 2x - 99 = 0$ **7.** $x^2 = 121$

8. $x^2 = 144$ **9.** $3x^2 - 13x = 30$ **10.** $5x^2 - 14x = 3$

Solve each equation by using the square root property. Simplify all radicals. **See Example 2.**

🌐 **11.** $x^2 = 81$ **12.** $z^2 = 169$ **13.** $x^2 = 14$

14. $m^2 = 22$ **15.** $t^2 = 48$ **16.** $x^2 = 54$

17. $x^2 = \dfrac{25}{4}$ **18.** $m^2 = \dfrac{36}{121}$ **19.** $x^2 = 2.25$

20. $w^2 = 56.25$ **21.** $r^2 - 3 = 0$ **22.** $x^2 - 13 = 0$

23. $x^2 - 20 = 0$ **24.** $p^2 - 50 = 0$ **25.** $7x^2 = 4$

26. $3p^2 = 10$ **27.** $3n^2 - 72 = 0$ **28.** $5z^2 - 200 = 0$

29. $5x^2 + 4 = 8$ **30.** $4p^2 - 3 = 7$ **31.** $2t^2 + 7 = 61$

32. $3x^2 + 8 = 80$ **33.** $-8x^2 = -64$ **34.** $-12x^2 = -144$

Solve each equation by using the square root property. Simplify all radicals. **See Examples 4 and 5.**

🌐 **35.** $(x - 3)^2 = 25$ **36.** $(x - 7)^2 = 16$ **37.** $(x - 4)^2 = 3$

38. $(x + 3)^2 = 11$ **39.** $(x - 8)^2 = 27$ **40.** $(p - 5)^2 = 40$

41. $(3x + 2)^2 = 49$ **42.** $(5t + 3)^2 = 36$ **43.** $(4x - 3)^2 = 9$

44. $(7z - 5)^2 = 25$ **45.** $(3x - 1)^2 = 7$ **46.** $(2x - 5)^2 = 10$

🌐 **47.** $(3k + 1)^2 = 18$ **48.** $(5z + 6)^2 = 75$ **49.** $(5 - 2x)^2 = 30$

50. $(3 - 2x)^2 = 70$ **51.** $\left(\dfrac{1}{2}x + 5\right)^2 = 12$ **52.** $\left(\dfrac{1}{3}m + 4\right)^2 = 27$

53. $(4x - 1)^2 - 48 = 0$ **54.** $(2x - 5)^2 - 180 = 0$

Use a calculator with a square root key to solve each equation. Round your answers to the nearest hundredth.

55. $(k + 2.14)^2 = 5.46$ **56.** $(r - 3.91)^2 = 9.28$

57. $(2.11p + 3.42)^2 = 9.58$ **58.** $(1.71m - 6.20)^2 = 5.41$

Find the nonreal complex solutions of each equation. ***See Example 6.***

59. $x^2 = -12$ **60.** $x^2 = -18$ **61.** $(r - 5)^2 = -4$

62. $(t + 6)^2 = -9$ **63.** $(6x - 1)^2 = -8$ **64.** $(4m - 7)^2 = -27$

In Exercises 65 and 66, round answers to the nearest tenth. ***See Example 3.***

65. The sculpture of American presidents at Mount Rushmore National Memorial is 500 ft above the valley floor. How long would it take a rock dropped from the top of the sculpture to fall to the ground? (*Source:* www.travelsd.com)

66. The Gateway Arch in St. Louis, Missouri, is 630 ft tall. How long would it take an object dropped from the top of the arch to fall to the ground? (*Source:* www.gatewayarch.com)

Solve each problem. ***See Example 3.***

67. The area $\mathcal{A}$ of a circle with radius r is given by the formula

$$\mathcal{A} = \pi r^2.$$

If a circle has area 81π in.^{2}, what is its radius?

68. The surface area S of a sphere with radius r is given by the formula

$$S = 4\pi r^2.$$

If a sphere has surface area 36π ft^2, what is its radius?

$\mathcal{A} = \pi r^2$

$S = 4\pi r^2$

The amount A that P dollars invested at an annual rate of interest r will grow to in 2 yr is

$$A = P(1 + r)^2.$$

69. At what interest rate will $100 grow to $104.04 in 2 yr?

70. At what interest rate will $500 grow to $530.45 in 2 yr?

PREVIEW EXERCISES

Simplify all radicals, and combine like terms. Express fractions in lowest terms. ***See Sections 10.3–10.5.***

71. $\dfrac{4}{5} + \sqrt{\dfrac{48}{25}}$ **72.** $\dfrac{12 - \sqrt{27}}{9}$ **73.** $\dfrac{6 + \sqrt{24}}{8}$

Factor each perfect square trinomial. ***See Section 5.4.***

74. $z^2 + 4z + 4$ **75.** $x^2 - 10x + 25$ **76.** $z^2 + z + \dfrac{1}{4}$

11.2 Solving Quadratic Equations by Completing the Square

OBJECTIVES

1. Solve quadratic equations by completing the square when the coefficient of the second-degree term is 1.

2. Solve quadratic equations by completing the square when the coefficient of the second-degree term is not 1.

3. Simplify the terms of an equation before solving.

OBJECTIVE 1 Solve quadratic equations by completing the square when the coefficient of the second-degree term is 1. The methods we have studied so far are not enough to solve an equation such as

$$x^2 + 6x + 7 = 0.$$

If we could write the equation in the form $(x + 3)^2$ equals a constant, we could solve it with the square root property discussed in **Section 11.1.** To do that, we need to have a perfect square trinomial on one side of the equation.

Recall from **Section 5.4** that the perfect square trinomial

$$x^2 + 6x + 9 \quad \text{can be factored as} \quad (x + 3)^2.$$

If we take half of 6, the coefficient of x (the first-degree term), and square it, we get the constant term, 9.

$$\left[\frac{1}{2}(6)\right]^2 = 3^2 = 9$$

Coefficient of x Constant

Similarly, in $\quad x^2 + 12x + 36, \quad \left[\frac{1}{2}(12)\right]^2 = 6^2 = 36,$

and in $\quad m^2 - 6m + 9, \quad \left[\frac{1}{2}(-6)\right]^2 = (-3)^2 = 9.$

This relationship is true in general and is the idea behind writing a quadratic equation so that the square root property can be applied.

EXAMPLE 1 Rewriting an Equation to Use the Square Root Property

Solve $x^2 + 6x + 7 = 0.$

This quadratic equation cannot be solved by factoring, and it is not in the correct form to solve using the square root property. To obtain this form, we need a perfect square trinomial on the left side of the equation.

$$x^2 + 6x + 7 = 0 \qquad \text{Original equation}$$
$$x^2 + 6x = -7 \qquad \text{Subtract 7.}$$

We must add a constant to get a perfect square trinomial on the left.

$$\underbrace{x^2 + 6x + \underline{\ ?\ }}_{\substack{\text{Needs to be a perfect} \\ \text{square trinomial}}}$$

As above, take half the coefficient of the first-degree term, $6x$, and square the result.

$$\left[\frac{1}{2}(6)\right]^2 = 3^2 = 9 \longleftarrow \text{Desired constant}$$

If we add 9 to each side of $x^2 + 6x = -7$, the equation will have a perfect square trinomial on the left side, as needed.

$$x^2 + 6x = -7$$

This is a key step. → $x^2 + 6x + 9 = -7 + 9 \qquad$ Add 9.

$$(x + 3)^2 = 2 \qquad \text{Factor. Add.}$$

NOW TRY
EXERCISE 1
Solve $x^2 + 10x + 8 = 0$.

Now use the square root property to complete the solution.

$$x + 3 = \sqrt{2} \qquad \text{or} \qquad x + 3 = -\sqrt{2}$$
$$x = -3 + \sqrt{2} \quad \text{or} \qquad x = -3 - \sqrt{2}$$

Check by substituting $-3 + \sqrt{2}$ and $-3 - \sqrt{2}$ for x in the original equation. The solution set is $\left\{-3 \pm \sqrt{2}\right\}$.   NOW TRY

The process of changing the form of the equation in **Example 1** from

$$x^2 + 6x + 7 = 0 \qquad \text{to} \qquad (x + 3)^2 = 2$$

is called **completing the square.** Completing the square changes only the form of the equation. To see this, multiply out the left side of $(x + 3)^2 = 2$ and combine like terms. Then subtract 2 from each side to see that the result is $x^2 + 6x + 7 = 0$.

NOW TRY
EXERCISE 2
Solve $x^2 - 6x = 9$.

EXAMPLE 2 Completing the Square to Solve a Quadratic Equation

Solve $x^2 - 8x = 5$.

To complete the square on $x^2 - 8x$, take half the coefficient of x and square it.

$$\frac{1}{2}(-8) = -4 \qquad \text{and} \qquad (-4)^2 = 16$$

Coefficient of x

Add the result, 16, to each side of the equation.

$$x^2 - 8x = 5 \qquad\qquad \text{Given equation}$$
$$x^2 - 8x + 16 = 5 + 16 \qquad\qquad \text{Add 16.}$$
$$(x - 4)^2 = 21 \qquad\qquad \text{Factor on the left. Add on the right.}$$
$$x - 4 = \sqrt{21} \qquad \text{or} \quad x - 4 = -\sqrt{21} \qquad \text{Square root property}$$
$$x = 4 + \sqrt{21} \quad \text{or} \qquad x = 4 - \sqrt{21} \qquad \text{Add 4.}$$

A check indicates that the solution set is $\left\{4 \pm \sqrt{21}\right\}$.   NOW TRY

Completing the Square

To solve $ax^2 + bx + c = 0$ $(a \neq 0)$ by completing the square, use these steps.

Step 1 **Be sure the second-degree (squared) term has coefficient 1.** If the coefficient of the second-degree term is 1, proceed to Step 2. If the coefficient of the second-degree term is not 1 but some other nonzero number a, divide each side of the equation by a.

Step 2 **Write the equation in correct form** so that terms with variables are on one side of the equals symbol and the constant is on the other side.

Step 3 **Square half the coefficient of the first-degree (linear) term.**

Step 4 **Add the square to each side.**

Step 5 **Factor the perfect square trinomial.** One side should now be a perfect square trinomial. Factor it as the square of a binomial. Simplify the other side.

Step 6 **Solve the equation.** Apply the square root property to complete the solution.

NOW TRY ANSWERS
1. $\left\{-5 \pm \sqrt{17}\right\}$
2. $\left\{3 \pm 3\sqrt{2}\right\}$

⤸ NOW TRY
  EXERCISE 3
Solve $x^2 + x - 3 = 0$.

EXAMPLE 3 Solving a Quadratic Equation by Completing the Square ($a = 1$)

Solve $x^2 + 5x - 1 = 0$.

Since the coefficient of the squared term is 1, begin with Step 2.

Step 2 $x^2 + 5x = 1$ Add 1 to each side.

Step 3   Take half the coefficient of the first-degree term and square the result.

$$\left[\frac{1}{2}(5)\right]^2 = \left(\frac{5}{2}\right)^2 = \frac{25}{4}$$

Step 4 $x^2 + 5x + \dfrac{25}{4} = 1 + \dfrac{25}{4}$ Add the square to each side of the equation.

Step 5 $\left(x + \dfrac{5}{2}\right)^2 = \dfrac{29}{4}$ Factor on the left. Add on the right.

Step 6 $x + \dfrac{5}{2} = \sqrt{\dfrac{29}{4}}$ or $x + \dfrac{5}{2} = -\sqrt{\dfrac{29}{4}}$ Square root property

$x + \dfrac{5}{2} = \dfrac{\sqrt{29}}{2}$ or $x + \dfrac{5}{2} = -\dfrac{\sqrt{29}}{2}$ $\sqrt{\dfrac{a}{b}} = \dfrac{\sqrt{a}}{\sqrt{b}}$

$x = -\dfrac{5}{2} + \dfrac{\sqrt{29}}{2}$ or $x = -\dfrac{5}{2} - \dfrac{\sqrt{29}}{2}$ Add $-\dfrac{5}{2}$.

$x = \dfrac{-5 + \sqrt{29}}{2}$ or $x = \dfrac{-5 - \sqrt{29}}{2}$ $\dfrac{a}{c} \pm \dfrac{b}{c} = \dfrac{a \pm b}{c}$

Check that the solution set is $\left\{\dfrac{-5 \pm \sqrt{29}}{2}\right\}$.   NOW TRY ⤸

OBJECTIVE 2 Solve quadratic equations by completing the square when the coefficient of the second-degree term is not 1. If a quadratic equation has the form

$$ax^2 + bx + c = 0, \quad \text{where} \quad a \neq 1,$$

we obtain 1 as the coefficient of x^2 by dividing each side of the equation by a.

EXAMPLE 4 Solving a Quadratic Equation by Completing the Square ($a \neq 1$)

Solve $4x^2 + 16x - 9 = 0$.

Step 1   *Before completing the square, the coefficient of x^2 must be 1,* not 4. We get 1 as the coefficient of x^2 here by dividing each side by 4.

$$4x^2 + 16x - 9 = 0 \qquad \text{Given equation}$$

The coefficient of x^2 must be 1. ⟶ $x^2 + 4x - \dfrac{9}{4} = 0$ \qquad Divide by 4.

Step 2   Write the equation so that all variable terms are on one side of the equation and all constant terms are on the other side.

$$x^2 + 4x = \dfrac{9}{4} \qquad \text{Add } \tfrac{9}{4}.$$

NOW TRY ANSWER

3. $\left\{\dfrac{-1 \pm \sqrt{13}}{2}\right\}$

**NOW TRY
EXERCISE 4**
Solve $4t^2 - 4t - 3 = 0$.

Step 3 Complete the square by taking half the coefficient of x, and squaring it.

$$\frac{1}{2}(4) = 2 \quad \text{and} \quad 2^2 = 4$$

Step 4 We add the result, 4, to each side of the equation.

$$x^2 + 4x + 4 = \frac{9}{4} + 4 \qquad \text{Add 4.}$$

Step 5 $$(x + 2)^2 = \frac{25}{4} \qquad \text{Factor; } \tfrac{9}{4} + 4 = \tfrac{9}{4} + \tfrac{16}{4} = \tfrac{25}{4}.$$

Step 6 Solve the equation by using the square root property.

$$x + 2 = \sqrt{\frac{25}{4}} \quad \text{or} \quad x + 2 = -\sqrt{\frac{25}{4}} \qquad \text{Square root property}$$

$$x + 2 = \frac{5}{2} \quad \text{or} \quad x + 2 = -\frac{5}{2} \qquad \text{Take square roots.}$$

$$x = -2 + \frac{5}{2} \quad \text{or} \quad x = -2 - \frac{5}{2} \qquad \text{Add } -2.$$

$$x = \frac{1}{2} \quad \text{or} \quad x = -\frac{9}{2} \qquad -2 = -\tfrac{4}{2}$$

CHECK

$$4x^2 + 16x - 9 = 0 \qquad\qquad\qquad 4x^2 + 16x - 9 = 0$$

$$4\left(\frac{1}{2}\right)^2 + 16\left(\frac{1}{2}\right) - 9 \overset{?}{=} 0 \quad \text{Let } x = \tfrac{1}{2}. \qquad 4\left(-\frac{9}{2}\right)^2 + 16\left(-\frac{9}{2}\right) - 9 \overset{?}{=} 0 \quad \text{Let } x = -\tfrac{9}{2}.$$

$$4\left(\frac{1}{4}\right) + 8 - 9 \overset{?}{=} 0 \qquad\qquad 4\left(\frac{81}{4}\right) - 72 - 9 \overset{?}{=} 0$$

$$1 + 8 - 9 \overset{?}{=} 0 \qquad\qquad\qquad 81 - 72 - 9 \overset{?}{=} 0$$

$$0 = 0 \ \checkmark \ \text{True} \qquad\qquad\qquad 0 - 0 \ \checkmark \ \text{True}$$

The two solutions, $\frac{1}{2}$ and $-\frac{9}{2}$, check, so the solution set is $\left\{-\frac{9}{2}, \frac{1}{2}\right\}$. NOW TRY

EXAMPLE 5 Solving a Quadratic Equation by Completing the Square ($a \neq 1$)

Solve $2x^2 - 4x - 5 = 0$.

Divide each side by 2 to get 1 as the coefficient of the second-degree term.

$$x^2 - 2x - \frac{5}{2} = 0 \qquad\qquad \text{Step 1}$$

$$x^2 - 2x = \frac{5}{2} \qquad\qquad \text{Step 2}$$

$$\left[\frac{1}{2}(-2)\right]^2 = (-1)^2 = 1 \qquad\qquad \text{Step 3}$$

NOW TRY ANSWER
4. $\left\{-\frac{1}{2}, \frac{3}{2}\right\}$

$$x^2 - 2x + 1 = \frac{5}{2} + 1 \qquad\qquad \text{Step 4}$$

NOW TRY
EXERCISE 5
Solve $3x^2 + 12x - 5 = 0$.

$$(x - 1)^2 = \frac{7}{2} \qquad \text{Step 5}$$

$$x - 1 = \sqrt{\frac{7}{2}} \qquad \text{or} \quad x - 1 = -\sqrt{\frac{7}{2}} \qquad \text{Step 6}$$

$$x = 1 + \sqrt{\frac{7}{2}} \qquad \text{or} \qquad x = 1 - \sqrt{\frac{7}{2}} \qquad \text{Add 1.}$$

$$x = 1 + \frac{\sqrt{14}}{2} \qquad \text{or} \qquad x = 1 - \frac{\sqrt{14}}{2} \qquad \sqrt{\frac{7}{2}} = \frac{\sqrt{7}}{\sqrt{2}} = \frac{\sqrt{7}}{\sqrt{2}} \cdot \frac{\sqrt{2}}{\sqrt{2}} = \frac{\sqrt{14}}{2}$$

Add the two terms in each solution as follows.

$$1 + \frac{\sqrt{14}}{2} = \frac{2}{2} + \frac{\sqrt{14}}{2} = \frac{2 + \sqrt{14}}{2} \qquad 1 = \frac{2}{2}$$

$$1 - \frac{\sqrt{14}}{2} = \frac{2}{2} - \frac{\sqrt{14}}{2} = \frac{2 - \sqrt{14}}{2}$$

Check that the solution set is $\left\{ \dfrac{2 \pm \sqrt{14}}{2} \right\}$.   NOW TRY

NOW TRY
EXERCISE 6
Solve $x^2 + 8x + 21 = 0$.

EXAMPLE 6   Solving a Quadratic Equation with Nonreal Complex Solutions

Solve $4p^2 + 8p + 5 = 0$.

$$4p^2 + 8p + 5 = 0$$

The coefficient of the second-degree term must be 1.

$$p^2 + 2p + \frac{5}{4} = 0 \qquad \text{Divide by 4.}$$

$$p^2 + 2p = -\frac{5}{4} \qquad \text{Add } -\frac{5}{4} \text{ to each side.}$$

The coefficient of p is 2. Take half of 2, square the result, and add it to each side.

$$p^2 + 2p + 1 = -\frac{5}{4} + 1 \qquad \left[\frac{1}{2}(2)\right]^2 = 1^2 = 1; \text{ Add 1.}$$

$$(p + 1)^2 = -\frac{1}{4} \qquad \begin{array}{l}\text{Factor on the left.}\\ \text{Add on the right.}\end{array}$$

$$p + 1 = \sqrt{-\frac{1}{4}} \qquad \text{or} \quad p + 1 = -\sqrt{-\frac{1}{4}} \qquad \text{Square root property}$$

$$p + 1 = \frac{1}{2}i \qquad \text{or} \quad p + 1 = -\frac{1}{2}i \qquad \sqrt{-\frac{1}{4}} = \frac{1}{2}i$$

$$p = -1 + \frac{1}{2}i \quad \text{or} \qquad p = -1 - \frac{1}{2}i \quad \text{Add } -1.$$

NOW TRY ANSWERS
5. $\left\{ \dfrac{-6 \pm \sqrt{51}}{3} \right\}$
6. $\left\{ -4 \pm i\sqrt{5} \right\}$

The solution set is $\left\{ -1 \pm \frac{1}{2}i \right\}$.   NOW TRY

OBJECTIVE 3   **Simplify the terms of an equation before solving.**

NOW TRY
EXERCISE 7
Solve $(x - 5)(x + 1) = 2$.

EXAMPLE 7   Simplifying the Terms of an Equation before Solving

Solve $(x + 3)(x - 1) = 2$.

$$(x + 3)(x - 1) = 2$$

$$x^2 + 2x - 3 = 2 \qquad \text{Multiply by using the FOIL method.}$$

$$x^2 + 2x = 5 \qquad \text{Add 3.}$$

$$x^2 + 2x + 1 = 5 + 1 \qquad \text{Complete the square. Add } \left[\frac{1}{2}(2)\right]^2 = 1^2 = 1.$$

$$(x + 1)^2 = 6 \qquad \text{Factor on the left. Add on the right.}$$

$$x + 1 = \sqrt{6} \qquad \text{or} \qquad x + 1 = -\sqrt{6} \qquad \text{Square root property}$$

$$x = -1 + \sqrt{6} \qquad \text{or} \qquad x = -1 - \sqrt{6} \qquad \text{Subtract 1.}$$

NOW TRY ANSWER
7. $\left\{ 2 \pm \sqrt{11} \right\}$

The solution set is $\left\{ -1 \pm \sqrt{6} \right\}$.

NOW TRY

11.2 EXERCISES

MyMathLab |  PRACTICE | WATCH | DOWNLOAD | READ | REVIEW

🌐 *Complete solution available on the Video Resources on DVD*

1. *Concept Check*   Which one of the two equations

$$(2x + 1)^2 = 5 \quad \text{and} \quad x^2 + 4x = 12,$$

is more suitable for solving by the square root property? Which one is more suitable for solving by completing the square?

2. Why would most students find the equation $x^2 + 4x = 20$ easier to solve by completing the square than the equation $5x^2 + 2x = 3$?

Concept Check   Decide what number must be added to make each expression a perfect square trinomial. Then factor the trinomial.

3. $x^2 + 6x +$ _____   **4.** $x^2 + 14x +$ _____   **5.** $p^2 - 12p +$ _____

6. $x^2 - 20x +$ _____   **7.** $q^2 + 9q +$ _____   **8.** $t^2 + 13t +$ _____

9. $x^2 + \dfrac{1}{4}x +$ _____   **10.** $x^2 + \dfrac{1}{2}x +$ _____   **11.** $x^2 - 0.8x +$ _____

12. *Concept Check*   What would be the first step in solving $2x^2 + 8x = 9$ by completing the square?

Determine the number that will complete the square to solve each equation, after the constant term has been written on the right side and the coefficient of the second-degree term is 1. Do not actually solve. **See Examples 1–5.**

13. $x^2 + 4x - 2 = 0$ **14.** $t^2 + 2t - 1 = 0$ **15.** $x^2 + 10x + 18 = 0$

16. $x^2 + 8x + 11 = 0$ **17.** $3w^2 - w - 24 = 0$ **18.** $4z^2 - z - 39 = 0$

Solve each equation by completing the square. Use the results of **Exercises 13–16** *to solve* **Exercises 23–26.** **See Examples 1–3.**

🌐 **19.** $x^2 - 4x = -3$ **20.** $p^2 - 2p = 8$ 🌐 **21.** $x^2 + 2x - 5 = 0$

22. $r^2 + 4r + 1 = 0$ 🌐 **23.** $x^2 + 4x - 2 = 0$ **24.** $t^2 + 2t - 1 = 0$

25. $x^2 + 10x + 18 = 0$ **26.** $x^2 + 8x + 11 = 0$ **27.** $x^2 - 8x = -4$

28. $m^2 - 4m = 14$ ⊘ **29.** $x^2 + 7x - 1 = 0$ **30.** $x^2 + 13x - 3 = 0$

*Solve each equation by completing the square. Use the results of **Exercises 17 and 18** to solve Exercises 33 and 34. **See Examples 4, 5, and 7.***

⊘ **31.** $4x^2 + 4x = 3$ **32.** $9x^2 + 3x = 2$ **33.** $3w^2 - w = 24$

34. $4z^2 - z = 39$ **35.** $2k^2 + 5k - 2 = 0$ **36.** $3r^2 + 2r - 2 = 0$

⊘ **37.** $5x^2 - 10x + 2 = 0$ **38.** $2x^2 - 16x + 25 = 0$ **39.** $9x^2 - 24x = -13$

40. $25n^2 - 20n = 1$ ⊘ **41.** $(x + 3)(x - 1) = 5$ **42.** $(x - 8)(x + 2) = 24$

43. $(r - 3)(r - 5) = 2$ **44.** $(x - 1)(x - 7) = 1$ **45.** $-x^2 + 2x = -5$

46. $-x^2 + 4x = 1$ **47.** $z^2 - \frac{4}{3}z = -\frac{1}{9}$ **48.** $p^2 - \frac{8}{3}p = -1$

49. $0.1x^2 - 0.2x - 0.1 = 0$ **50.** $0.1p^2 - 0.4p + 0.1 = 0$
    (*Hint*: First clear the decimals.)   (*Hint*: First clear the decimals.)

*Solve each equation by completing the square. Give **(a)** exact solutions and **(b)** solutions rounded to the nearest thousandth.*

51. $3r^2 - 2 = 6r + 3$ **52.** $4p + 3 = 2p^2 + 2p$

53. $(x + 1)(x + 3) = 2$ **54.** $(x - 3)(x + 1) = 1$

*Find the nonreal complex solutions of each equation. **See Example 6.***

55. $m^2 + 4m + 13 = 0$ **56.** $t^2 + 6t + 10 = 0$ **57.** $3r^2 + 4r + 4 = 0$

58. $4x^2 + 5x + 5 = 0$ **59.** $-m^2 - 6m - 12 = 0$ **60.** $-x^2 - 5x - 10 = 0$

RELATING CONCEPTS   EXERCISES 61–66

FOR INDIVIDUAL OR GROUP WORK

The Greeks had a method of completing the square geometrically in which they literally changed a figure into a square. For example, to complete the square for $x^2 + 6x$, we begin with a square of side x, as in the figure on the left. We add three rectangles of width 1 to the right side and the bottom to get a region with area $x^2 + 6x$. To fill in the corner (complete the square), we must add nine 1-by-1 squares as shown.

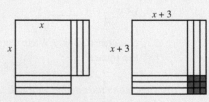

Work Exercises 61–66 in order.

61. What is the area of the original square?

62. What is the area of each strip?

63. What is the total area of the six strips?

64. What is the area of each small square in the corner of the second figure?

65. What is the total area of the small squares?

66. What is the area of the new "complete" square?

Brain Busters *Solve for x. Assume that a and b represent positive real numbers.*

67. $x^2 - b = 0$ **68.** $x^2 = 4b$ **69.** $4x^2 = b^2 + 16$

70. $9x^2 - 25a = 0$ **71.** $(5x - 2b)^2 = 3a$ **72.** $x^2 - a^2 - 36 = 0$

PREVIEW EXERCISES

Evaluate $\sqrt{b^2 - 4ac}$ *for the given values of a, b, and c.* **See Sections 1.3 and 10.1.**

73. $a = 3, b = 1, c = -1$ **74.** $a = 4, b = 11, c = -3$

75. $a = 6, b = 7, c = 2$ **76.** $a = 1, b = -6, c = 9$

11.3 Solving Quadratic Equations by the Quadratic Formula

OBJECTIVES

1. Derive the quadratic formula.
2. Solve quadratic equations by using the quadratic formula.
3. Use the discriminant to determine the number and type of solutions.

In this section, we complete the square to solve the general quadratic equation

$$ax^2 + bx + c = 0,$$

where a, b, and c are complex numbers and $a \neq 0$. The solution of this general equation gives a formula for finding the solution of *any* specific quadratic equation.

OBJECTIVE 1 **Derive the quadratic formula.** To solve $ax^2 + bx + c = 0$ by completing the square (assuming $a > 0$), we follow the steps given in **Section 11.2.**

$$ax^2 + bx + c = 0$$

$$x^2 + \frac{b}{a}x + \frac{c}{a} = 0 \qquad \text{Divide by } a. \text{ (Step 1)}$$

$$x^2 + \frac{b}{a}x = -\frac{c}{a} \qquad \text{Subtract } \tfrac{c}{a}. \text{(Step 2)}$$

$$\left[\frac{1}{2}\left(\frac{b}{a}\right)\right]^2 = \left(\frac{b}{2a}\right)^2 = \frac{b^2}{4a^2} \qquad \text{(Step 3)}$$

$$x^2 + \frac{b}{a}x + \frac{b^2}{4a^2} = -\frac{c}{a} + \frac{b^2}{4a^2} \qquad \text{Add } \tfrac{b^2}{4a^2} \text{ to each side. (Step 4)}$$

$$\left(x + \frac{b}{2a}\right)^2 = \frac{b^2}{4a^2} + \frac{-c}{a} \qquad \text{Write the left side as a perfect square. Rearrange the right side. (Step 5)}$$

$$\left(x + \frac{b}{2a}\right)^2 = \frac{b^2}{4a^2} + \frac{-4ac}{4a^2} \qquad \text{Write with a common denominator.}$$

$$\left(x + \frac{b}{2a}\right)^2 = \frac{b^2 - 4ac}{4a^2} \qquad \text{Add fractions.}$$

$$x + \frac{b}{2a} = \sqrt{\frac{b^2 - 4ac}{4a^2}} \quad \text{or} \quad x + \frac{b}{2a} = -\sqrt{\frac{b^2 - 4ac}{4a^2}} \qquad \text{Square root property (Step 6)}$$

We can simplify $\sqrt{\dfrac{b^2 - 4ac}{4a^2}}$ as $\dfrac{\sqrt{b^2 - 4ac}}{\sqrt{4a^2}}$, or $\dfrac{\sqrt{b^2 - 4ac}}{2a}$.

The right side of each equation can be expressed as follows.

$$x + \frac{b}{2a} = \frac{\sqrt{b^2 - 4ac}}{2a} \qquad \text{or} \quad x + \frac{b}{2a} = \frac{-\sqrt{b^2 - 4ac}}{2a}$$

$$x = \frac{-b}{2a} + \frac{\sqrt{b^2 - 4ac}}{2a} \qquad \text{or} \qquad x = \frac{-b}{2a} - \frac{\sqrt{b^2 - 4ac}}{2a}$$

If $a < 0$, the same two solutions are obtained.

$$x = \frac{-b + \sqrt{b^2 - 4ac}}{2a} \qquad \text{or} \qquad x = \frac{-b - \sqrt{b^2 - 4ac}}{2a}$$

The result is the **quadratic formula,** which is abbreviated as follows.

Quadratic Formula

The solutions of the equation $ax^2 + bx + c = 0$ (with $a \neq 0$) are given by

$$x = \frac{-b \pm \sqrt{b^2 - 4ac}}{2a}.$$

⚠ **CAUTION** In the quadratic formula, *the square root is added to or subtracted from the value of* $-b$ *before dividing by* $2a$.

OBJECTIVE 2 **Solve quadratic equations by using the quadratic formula.**

NOW TRY
EXERCISE 1
Solve $2x^2 + 3x - 20 = 0$.

EXAMPLE 1 Using the Quadratic Formula (Rational Solutions)

Solve $6x^2 - 5x - 4 = 0$.

This equation is in standard form, so we identify the values of a, b, and c. Here a, the coefficient of the second-degree term, is 6, and b, the coefficient of the first-degree term, is -5. The constant c is -4. Now substitute into the quadratic formula.

$$x = \frac{-b \pm \sqrt{b^2 - 4ac}}{2a} \qquad \text{Quadratic formula}$$

$$x = \frac{-(-5) \pm \sqrt{(-5)^2 - 4(6)(-4)}}{2(6)} \qquad a = 6, b = -5, c = -4$$

Use parentheses and substitute carefully to avoid errors.

$$x = \frac{5 \pm \sqrt{25 + 96}}{12}$$

$$x = \frac{5 \pm \sqrt{121}}{12} \qquad \text{Simplify the radical.}$$

$$x = \frac{5 \pm 11}{12} \qquad \text{Take the square root.}$$

There are two solutions, one from the $+$ sign and one from the $-$ sign.

$$x = \frac{5 + 11}{12} = \frac{16}{12} = \frac{4}{3} \qquad \text{or} \qquad x = \frac{5 - 11}{12} = \frac{-6}{12} = -\frac{1}{2}$$

NOW TRY ANSWER
1. $\left\{-4, \frac{5}{2}\right\}$

Check each solution in the original equation. The solution set is $\left\{-\frac{1}{2}, \frac{4}{3}\right\}$.

NOW TRY ↻

NOTE We could have used factoring to solve the equation in **Example 1.**

$$6x^2 - 5x - 4 = 0$$

$$(3x - 4)(2x + 1) = 0 \qquad \text{Factor.}$$

$$3x - 4 = 0 \quad \text{or} \quad 2x + 1 = 0 \qquad \text{Zero-factor property}$$

$$3x = 4 \quad \text{or} \qquad 2x = -1 \qquad \text{Solve each equation.}$$

$$x = \frac{4}{3} \quad \text{or} \qquad x = -\frac{1}{2} \qquad \text{Same solutions as in \textbf{Example 1}}$$

When solving quadratic equations, it is a good idea to try factoring first. If the polynomial cannot be factored or if factoring is difficult, then use the quadratic formula.

NOW TRY
EXERCISE 2
Solve $3x^2 + 1 = -5x$.

EXAMPLE 2   Using the Quadratic Formula (Irrational Solutions)

Solve $4x^2 = 8x - 1$.

Write the equation in standard form as $4x^2 - 8x + 1 = 0$. ◁ This is a key step.

$$x = \frac{-b \pm \sqrt{b^2 - 4ac}}{2a} \qquad \text{Quadratic formula}$$

$$x = \frac{-(-8) \pm \sqrt{(-8)^2 - 4(4)(1)}}{2(4)} \qquad a = 4, b = -8, c = 1$$

$$x = \frac{8 \pm \sqrt{64 - 16}}{8} \qquad \text{Simplify.}$$

$$x = \frac{8 \pm \sqrt{48}}{8}$$

$$x = \frac{8 \pm 4\sqrt{3}}{8} \qquad \sqrt{48} = \sqrt{16} \cdot \sqrt{3} = 4\sqrt{3}$$

$$x = \frac{4(2 \pm \sqrt{3})}{4(2)} \qquad \text{Factor.}$$
Factor first. Then divide out the common factor.

$$x = \frac{2 \pm \sqrt{3}}{2} \qquad \text{Lowest terms}$$

The solution set is $\left\{\dfrac{2 \pm \sqrt{3}}{2}\right\}$.

NOW TRY

⚠ **CAUTION**

1. *Every quadratic equation must be expressed in standard form $ax^2 + bx + c = 0$ before we begin to solve it,* whether we use factoring or the quadratic formula.

2. *When writing solutions in lowest terms, be sure to FACTOR FIRST. Then divide out the common factor,* as shown in the last two steps in **Example 2.**

NOW TRY ANSWER
2. $\left\{\dfrac{-5 \pm \sqrt{13}}{6}\right\}$

⌐ NOW TRY
⌐ EXERCISE 3

Solve $(x + 5)(x - 1) = -18$.

EXAMPLE 3 Using the Quadratic Formula (Nonreal Complex Solutions)

Solve $(9x + 3)(x - 1) = -8$.

$$(9x + 3)(x - 1) = -8$$

$$9x^2 - 6x - 3 = -8 \qquad \text{Multiply.}$$

Standard form ⟶ $9x^2 - 6x + 5 = 0 \qquad$ Add 8.

From the equation $9x^2 - 6x + 5 = 0$, we identify $a = 9$, $b = -6$, and $c = 5$.

$$x = \frac{-b \pm \sqrt{b^2 - 4ac}}{2a} \qquad \text{Quadratic formula}$$

$$x = \frac{-(-6) \pm \sqrt{(-6)^2 - 4(9)(5)}}{2(9)} \qquad \text{Substitute.}$$

$$x = \frac{6 \pm \sqrt{-144}}{18} \qquad \text{Simplify.}$$

$$x = \frac{6 \pm 12i}{18} \qquad \sqrt{-144} = 12i$$

$$x = \frac{6(1 \pm 2i)}{6(3)} \qquad \text{Factor.}$$

$$x = \frac{1 \pm 2i}{3} \qquad \text{Lowest terms}$$

$$x = \frac{1}{3} \pm \frac{2}{3}i \qquad \begin{array}{l}\text{Standard form } a + bi \text{ for a}\\ \text{complex number}\end{array}$$

The solution set is $\left\{\frac{1}{3} \pm \frac{2}{3}i\right\}$. NOW TRY ↻

OBJECTIVE 3 Use the discriminant to determine the number and type of solutions. The solutions of the quadratic equation $ax^2 + bx + c = 0$ are given by

$$x = \frac{-b \pm \sqrt{b^2 - 4ac}}{2a}. \quad \leftarrow \text{Discriminant}$$

If a, b, and c are integers, the type of solutions of a quadratic equation—that is, rational, irrational, or nonreal complex—is determined by the expression under the radical symbol, $b^2 - 4ac$, called the *discriminant* (because it distinguishes among the three types of solutions). By calculating the discriminant, we can predict the number and type of solutions of a quadratic equation.

Discriminant

The **discriminant** of $ax^2 + bx + c = 0$ is $b^2 - 4ac$. If a, b, and c are integers, then the number and type of solutions are determined as follows.

Discriminant	Number and Type of Solutions
Positive, and the square of an integer	Two rational solutions
Positive, but not the square of an integer	Two irrational solutions
Zero	One rational solution
Negative	Two nonreal complex solutions

NOW TRY ANSWER
3. $\{-2 \pm 3i\}$

Calculating the discriminant can also help you decide how to solve a quadratic equation. *If the discriminant is a perfect square (including 0), then the equation can be solved by factoring. Otherwise, the quadratic formula should be used.*

NOW TRY
EXERCISE 4

Find each discriminant. Use it to predict the number and type of solutions for each equation. Tell whether the equation can be solved by factoring or whether the quadratic formula should be used.

(a) $8x^2 - 6x - 5 = 0$

(b) $9x^2 = 24x - 16$

(c) $3x^2 + 2x = -1$

EXAMPLE 4 Using the Discriminant

Find the discriminant. Use it to predict the number and type of solutions for each equation. Tell whether the equation can be solved by factoring or whether the quadratic formula should be used.

(a) $6x^2 - x - 15 = 0$

We find the discriminant by evaluating $b^2 - 4ac$. Because $-x = -1x$, the value of b in this equation is -1.

$b^2 - 4ac$

> Use parentheses and substitute carefully.

$= (-1)^2 - 4(6)(-15)$ $a = 6, b = -1, c = -15$

$= 1 + 360$ Apply the exponent. Multiply.

$= 361$, or 19^2, which is a perfect square.

Since a, b, and c are integers and the discriminant 361 is a perfect square, there will be two rational solutions. The equation can be solved by factoring.

(b) $3x^2 - 4x = 5$ Write in standard form as $3x^2 - 4x - 5 = 0$.

$b^2 - 4ac$

$= (-4)^2 - 4(3)(-5)$ $a = 3, b = -4, c = -5$

$= 16 + 60$ Apply the exponent. Multiply.

$= 76$ Add.

Because 76 is positive but *not* the square of an integer and a, b, and c are integers, the equation will have two irrational solutions and is best solved using the quadratic formula.

(c) $4x^2 + x + 1 = 0$

> $x = 1x$, so $b = 1$.

$b^2 - 4ac$

$= 1^2 - 4(4)(1)$ $a = 4, b = 1, c = 1$

$= 1 - 16$ Apply the exponent. Multiply.

$= -15$ Subtract.

Because the discriminant is negative and a, b, and c are integers, this equation will have two nonreal complex solutions. The quadratic formula should be used to solve it.

(d) $4x^2 + 9 = 12x$ Write in standard form as $4x^2 - 12x + 9 = 0$.

$b^2 - 4ac$

$= (-12)^2 - 4(4)(9)$ $a = 4, b = -12, c = 9$

$= 144 - 144$ Apply the exponent. Multiply.

$= 0$ Subtract.

The discriminant is 0, so the quantity under the radical in the quadratic formula is 0, and there is only one rational solution. The equation can be solved by factoring.

NOW TRY

NOW TRY ANSWERS
4. (a) 196; two rational solutions; factoring
  (b) 0; one rational solution; factoring
  (c) −8; two nonreal complex solutions; quadratic formula

NOW TRY
EXERCISE 5

Find k so that the equation will have exactly one rational solution.

$$4x^2 + kx + 25 = 0$$

EXAMPLE 5 Using the Discriminant

Find k so that $9x^2 + kx + 4 = 0$ will have exactly one rational solution.

The equation will have only one rational solution if the discriminant is 0.

$$b^2 - 4ac$$

$$= k^2 - 4(9)(4) \qquad \text{Here, } a = 9, b = k, \text{ and } c = 4.$$

$$= k^2 - 144 \longleftarrow \text{Value of the discriminant}$$

Set the discriminant equal to 0 and solve for k.

$$k^2 - 144 = 0$$

$$k^2 = 144 \qquad \text{Add 144.}$$

$$k = 12 \quad \text{or} \quad k = -12 \qquad \text{Square root property}$$

The equation will have only one rational solution if $k = 12$ or $k = -12$.

NOW TRY

NOW TRY ANSWER
5. $20, -20$

11.3 EXERCISES

MyMathLab | Math XL PRACTICE | WATCH | DOWNLOAD | READ | REVIEW

Complete solution available on the Video Resources on DVD

Concept Check   *Answer each question in Exercises 1–4.*

1. An early version of Microsoft *Word* for Windows included the 1.0 edition of *Equation Editor*. The documentation used the following for the quadratic formula. Was this correct? If not, correct it.

$$x = -b \pm \frac{\sqrt{b^2 - 4ac}}{2a}$$

2. The Cadillac Bar in Houston, Texas, encourages patrons to write (tasteful) messages on the walls. One person wrote the quadratic formula, as shown here. Was this correct? If not, correct it.

$$x = \frac{-b\sqrt{b^2 - 4ac}}{2a}$$

3. A student incorrectly solved $5x^2 - 5x + 1 = 0$ as follows. *WHAT WENT WRONG?*

$$x = \frac{-(-5) \pm \sqrt{(-5)^2 - 4(5)(1)}}{2(5)}$$

$$x = \frac{5 \pm \sqrt{5}}{10}$$

$$x = \frac{1}{2} \pm \sqrt{5}$$

Solution set: $\left\{ \frac{1}{2} \pm \sqrt{5} \right\}$

4. A student claimed that the equation $2x^2 - 5 = 0$ cannot be solved using the quadratic formula because there is no first-degree x-term. Was the student correct? If not, give the values of a, b, and c.

Use the quadratic formula to solve each equation. (All solutions for these equations are real numbers.) ***See Examples 1 and 2.***

5. $x^2 - 8x + 15 = 0$ **6.** $x^2 + 3x - 28 = 0$ **7.** $2x^2 + 4x + 1 = 0$

8. $2x^2 + 3x - 1 = 0$ **9.** $2x^2 - 2x = 1$ **10.** $9x^2 + 6x = 1$

11. $x^2 + 18 = 10x$ **12.** $x^2 - 4 = 2x$ **13.** $4x^2 + 4x - 1 = 0$

14. $4r^2 - 4r - 19 = 0$ **15.** $2 - 2x = 3x^2$ **16.** $26r - 2 = 3r^2$

17. $\dfrac{x^2}{4} - \dfrac{x}{2} = 1$ **18.** $p^2 + \dfrac{p}{3} = \dfrac{1}{6}$ **19.** $-2t(t + 2) = -3$

20. $-3x(x + 2) = -4$ **21.** $(r - 3)(r + 5) = 2$ **22.** $(x + 1)(x - 7) = 1$

23. $(x + 2)(x - 3) = 1$ **24.** $(x - 5)(x + 2) = 6$ **25.** $p = \dfrac{5(5 - p)}{3(p + 1)}$

26. $x = \dfrac{2(x + 3)}{x + 5}$ **27.** $(2x + 1)^2 = x + 4$ **28.** $(2x - 1)^2 = x + 2$

Use the quadratic formula to solve each equation. (All solutions for these equations are non-real complex numbers.) ***See Example 3.***

29. $x^2 - 3x + 6 = 0$ **30.** $x^2 - 5x + 20 = 0$ **31.** $r^2 - 6r + 14 = 0$

32. $t^2 + 4t + 11 = 0$ **33.** $4x^2 - 4x = -7$ **34.** $9x^2 - 6x = -7$

35. $x(3x + 4) = -2$ **36.** $z(2z + 3) = -2$

37. $(2x - 1)(8x - 4) = -1$ **38.** $(x - 1)(9x - 3) = -2$

Use the discriminant to determine whether the solutions for each equation are
  A. *two rational numbers* **B.** *one rational number*
  C. *two irrational numbers* **D.** *two nonreal complex numbers.*

Tell whether the equation can be solved by factoring or whether the quadratic formula should be used. Do not actually solve. ***See Example 4.***

39. $25x^2 + 70x + 49 = 0$ **40.** $4x^2 - 28x + 49 = 0$ **41.** $x^2 + 4x + 2 = 0$

42. $9x^2 - 12x - 1 = 0$ **43.** $3x^2 = 5x + 2$ **44.** $4x^2 = 4x + 3$

45. $3m^2 - 10m + 15 = 0$ **46.** $18x^2 + 60x + 82 = 0$

Based on your answers in ***Exercises 39–46,*** *solve the equation given in each exercise.*

47. Exercise 39 **48. Exercise 40** **49. Exercise 43** **50. Exercise 44**

51. Find the discriminant for each quadratic equation. Use it to tell whether the equation can be solved by factoring or whether the quadratic formula should be used. Then solve each equation.

  (a) $3x^2 + 13x = -12$ **(b)** $2x^2 + 19 = 14x$

52. *Concept Check* Is it possible for the solution of a quadratic equation with integer coefficients to include just one irrational number? Why or why not?

Find the value of a, b, or c so that each equation will have exactly one rational solution. ***See Example 5.***

53. $p^2 + bp + 25 = 0$ **54.** $r^2 - br + 49 = 0$ **55.** $am^2 + 8m + 1 = 0$

56. $at^2 + 24t + 16 = 0$ **57.** $9x^2 - 30x + c = 0$ **58.** $4m^2 + 12m + c = 0$

59. One solution of $4x^2 + bx - 3 = 0$ is $-\frac{5}{2}$. Find b and the other solution.

60. One solution of $3x^2 - 7x + c = 0$ is $\frac{1}{3}$. Find c and the other solution.

PREVIEW EXERCISES

Solve each equation. *See Section 2.3.*

61. $\frac{3}{4}x + \frac{1}{2}x = -10$

62. $\frac{x}{5} + \frac{3x}{4} = -19$

Solve each equation. *See Section 10.6.*

63. $\sqrt{2x + 6} = x - 1$

64. $\sqrt{2x + 1} + \sqrt{x + 3} = 0$

(11.4) Equations Quadratic in Form

OBJECTIVES

1 Solve an equation with fractions by writing it in quadratic form.

2 Use quadratic equations to solve applied problems.

3 Solve an equation with radicals by writing it in quadratic form.

4 Solve an equation that is quadratic in form by substitution.

OBJECTIVE 1 **Solve an equation with fractions by writing it in quadratic form.** A variety of nonquadratic equations can be written in the form of a quadratic equation and solved by using the methods of this chapter.

EXAMPLE 1 Solving an Equation with Fractions that Leads to a Quadratic Equation

Solve $\frac{1}{x} + \frac{1}{x - 1} = \frac{7}{12}$.

Clear fractions by multiplying each term by the least common denominator, $12x(x - 1)$. (Note that the domain must be restricted to $x \neq 0, x \neq 1$.)

$$12x(x - 1)\left(\frac{1}{x} + \frac{1}{x - 1}\right) = 12x(x - 1)\left(\frac{7}{12}\right) \quad \text{Multiply by the LCD.}$$

$$12x(x - 1)\frac{1}{x} + 12x(x - 1)\frac{1}{x - 1} = 12x(x - 1)\frac{7}{12} \quad \text{Distributive property}$$

$$12(x - 1) + 12x = 7x(x - 1) \quad$$

$$12x - 12 + 12x = 7x^2 - 7x \quad \text{Distributive property}$$

$$24x - 12 = 7x^2 - 7x \quad \text{Combine like terms.}$$

$$7x^2 - 31x + 12 = 0 \quad \text{Standard form}$$

$$(7x - 3)(x - 4) = 0 \quad \text{Factor.}$$

$$7x - 3 = 0 \quad \text{or} \quad x - 4 = 0 \quad \text{Zero-factor property}$$

$$7x = 3 \quad \text{or} \quad x = 4 \quad \text{Solve for } x.$$

$$x = \frac{3}{7}$$

The solution set is $\left\{\frac{3}{7}, 4\right\}$. **NOW TRY**

NOW TRY
EXERCISE 1

Solve $\frac{2}{x} + \frac{3}{x + 2} = 1$.

NOW TRY ANSWER
1. $\{-1, 4\}$

OBJECTIVE 2 **Use quadratic equations to solve applied problems.** Some distance-rate-time (or motion) problems lead to quadratic equations. We continue to use the six-step problem-solving method from **Section 2.4.**

A small fishing boat averages 18 mph in still water. It takes the boat $\frac{9}{10}$ hr to travel 8 mi upstream and return. Find the rate of the current.

Riverboat traveling upstream—the current slows it down.

FIGURE 1

EXAMPLE 2 Solving a Motion Problem

A riverboat for tourists averages 12 mph in still water. It takes the boat 1 hr, 4 min to go 6 mi upstream and return. Find the rate of the current.

Step 1 **Read** the problem carefully.

Step 2 **Assign a variable.** Let x = the rate of the current.

The current slows down the boat when it is going upstream, so the rate of the boat going upstream is its rate in still water *less* the rate of the current, or $(12 - x)$ mph. See **FIGURE 1**.

Similarly, the current speeds up the boat as it travels downstream, so its rate downstream is $(12 + x)$ mph. Thus,

$$12 - x = \text{the rate upstream in miles per hour,}$$

and $\qquad 12 + x = \text{the rate downstream in miles per hour.}$

	d	r	t
Upstream	6	$12 - x$	$\dfrac{6}{12 - x}$
Downstream	6	$12 + x$	$\dfrac{6}{12 + x}$

Complete a table. Use the distance formula, $d = rt$, solved for time t, $t = \frac{d}{r}$, to write expressions for t.

Times in hours

Step 3 **Write an equation.** We use the total time of 1 hr, 4 min written as a fraction.

$$1 + \frac{4}{60} = 1 + \frac{1}{15} = \frac{16}{15} \text{ hr} \qquad \text{Total time}$$

The time upstream plus the time downstream equals $\frac{16}{15}$ hr.

$$\begin{array}{ccccc} \text{Time upstream} & + & \text{Time downstream} & = & \text{Total time} \\ \downarrow & & \downarrow & & \downarrow \\ \dfrac{6}{12 - x} & + & \dfrac{6}{12 + x} & = & \dfrac{16}{15} \end{array}$$

Step 4 **Solve** the equation. The LCD is $15(12 - x)(12 + x)$.

$$15(12 - x)(12 + x)\left(\frac{6}{12 - x} + \frac{6}{12 + x}\right)$$
$$= 15(12 - x)(12 + x)\left(\frac{16}{15}\right)$$

Multiply by the LCD.

$$15(12 + x) \cdot 6 + 15(12 - x) \cdot 6 = 16(12 - x)(12 + x)$$

Distributive property; multiply.

$$90(12 + x) + 90(12 - x) = 16(144 - x^2) \qquad \text{Multiply.}$$
$$1080 + 90x + 1080 - 90x = 2304 - 16x^2 \qquad \text{Distributive property}$$
$$2160 = 2304 - 16x^2 \qquad \text{Combine like terms.}$$
$$16x^2 = 144 \qquad \text{Add } 16x^2. \text{ Subtract } 2160.$$
$$x^2 = 9 \qquad \text{Divide by 16.}$$
$$x = 3 \quad \text{or} \quad x = -3 \qquad \text{Square root property}$$

Step 5 **State the answer.** The current rate cannot be -3, so the answer is 3 mph.

Step 6 **Check** that this value satisfies the original problem. NOW TRY

PROBLEM-SOLVING HINT

Recall from **Section 6.7** that a person's work rate is $\frac{1}{t}$ part of the job per hour, where t is the time in hours required to do the complete job. Thus, the part of the job the person will do in x hours is $\frac{1}{t}x$.

EXAMPLE 3 Solving a Work Problem

It takes two carpet layers 4 hr to carpet a room. If each worked alone, one of them could do the job in 1 hr less time than the other. How long would it take each carpet layer to complete the job alone?

Step 1 **Read** the problem again. There will be two answers.

Step 2 **Assign a variable.** Let x = the number of hours for the slower carpet layer to complete the job alone. Then the faster carpet layer could do the entire job in $(x - 1)$ hours. The slower person's rate is $\frac{1}{x}$, and the faster person's rate is $\frac{1}{x-1}$. Together, they do the job in 4 hr.

	Rate	Time Working Together	Fractional Part of the Job Done	
Slower Worker	$\frac{1}{x}$	4	$\frac{1}{x}(4)$	Complete a table.
Faster Worker	$\frac{1}{x-1}$	4	$\frac{1}{x-1}(4)$	

Sum is 1 whole job.

Step 3 **Write an equation.**

Part done by slower worker + Part done by faster worker = 1 whole job

$$\frac{4}{x} \qquad + \qquad \frac{4}{x-1} \qquad = \qquad 1$$

Step 4 **Solve** the equation from Step 3.

$$x(x-1)\left(\frac{4}{x} + \frac{4}{x-1}\right) = x(x-1)(1) \qquad \text{Multiply by the LCD, } x(x-1).$$

$$4(x-1) + 4x = x(x-1) \qquad \text{Distributive property}$$

$$4x - 4 + 4x = x^2 - x \qquad \text{Distributive property}$$

$$x^2 - 9x + 4 = 0 \qquad \text{Standard form}$$

This equation cannot be solved by factoring, so use the quadratic formula.

$$x = \frac{-b \pm \sqrt{b^2 - 4ac}}{2a} \qquad \text{Quadratic formula}$$

$$x = \frac{-(-9) \pm \sqrt{(-9)^2 - 4(1)(4)}}{2(1)} \qquad a = 1, b = -9, c = 4$$

$$x = \frac{9 \pm \sqrt{65}}{2} \qquad \text{Simplify.}$$

$$x = \frac{9 + \sqrt{65}}{2} \approx 8.5 \quad \text{or} \quad x = \frac{9 - \sqrt{65}}{2} \approx 0.5 \qquad \text{Use a calculator.}$$

NOW TRY
EXERCISE 3

Two electricians are running wire to finish a basement. One electrician could finish the job in 2 hr less time than the other. Together, they complete the job in 6 hr. How long (to the nearest tenth) would it take the slower electrician to complete the job alone?

NOW TRY
EXERCISE 4

Solve each equation.

(a) $x = \sqrt{9x - 20}$

(b) $x + \sqrt{x} = 20$

Step 5 **State the answer.** Only the solution 8.5 makes sense in the original problem, because if $x = 0.5$, then

$$x - 1 = 0.5 - 1 = -0.5,$$

which cannot represent the time for the faster worker. The slower worker could do the job in about 8.5 hr and the faster in about $8.5 - 1 = 7.5$ hr.

Step 6 **Check** that these results satisfy the original problem.   *NOW TRY*

OBJECTIVE 3 **Solve an equation with radicals by writing it in quadratic form.**

EXAMPLE 4 Solving Radical Equations That Lead to Quadratic Equations

Solve each equation.

(a) $x = \sqrt{6x - 8}$

This equation is not quadratic. However, squaring each side of the equation gives a quadratic equation that can be solved by factoring.

$$x^2 = \left(\sqrt{6x - 8}\right)^2 \qquad \text{Square each side.}$$
$$x^2 = 6x - 8 \qquad \left(\sqrt{a}\right)^2 = a$$
$$x^2 - 6x + 8 = 0 \qquad \text{Standard form}$$
$$(x - 4)(x - 2) = 0 \qquad \text{Factor.}$$
$$x - 4 = 0 \quad \text{or} \quad x - 2 = 0 \qquad \text{Zero-factor property}$$
$$x = 4 \quad \text{or} \qquad x = 2 \qquad \text{Proposed solutions}$$

Squaring each side of an equation can introduce extraneous solutions. *All proposed solutions must be checked in the original (not the squared) equation.*

CHECK $x = \sqrt{6x - 8}$ $x = \sqrt{6x - 8}$

$4 \overset{?}{=} \sqrt{6(4) - 8}$ Let $x = 4$. $2 \overset{?}{=} \sqrt{6(2) - 8}$ Let $x = 2$.

$4 \overset{?}{=} \sqrt{16}$ $2 \overset{?}{=} \sqrt{4}$

$4 = 4$ ✓   True $2 = 2$ ✓   True

Both solutions check, so the solution set is $\{2, 4\}$.

(b) $x + \sqrt{x} = 6$ $\boxed{(a - b)^2 = a^2 - 2ab + b^2}$

$$\sqrt{x} = 6 - x \qquad \text{Isolate the radical on one side.}$$
$$x = 36 - 12x + x^2 \qquad \text{Square each side.}$$
$$x^2 - 13x + 36 = 0 \qquad \text{Standard form}$$
$$(x - 4)(x - 9) = 0 \qquad \text{Factor.}$$
$$x - 4 = 0 \quad \text{or} \quad x - 9 = 0 \qquad \text{Zero-factor property}$$
$$x = 4 \quad \text{or} \qquad x = 9 \qquad \text{Proposed solutions}$$

CHECK $x + \sqrt{x} = 6$ $x + \sqrt{x} = 6$

$4 + \sqrt{4} \overset{?}{=} 6$ Let $x = 4$. $9 + \sqrt{9} \overset{?}{=} 6$ Let $x = 9$.

$6 = 6$ ✓ True $12 = 6$ False

Only the solution 4 checks, so the solution set is $\{4\}$.   *NOW TRY*

OBJECTIVE 4 Solve an equation that is quadratic in form by substitution.

A nonquadratic equation that can be written in the form

$$au^2 + bu + c = 0,$$

for $a \neq 0$ and an algebraic expression u, is called **quadratic in form.**

Many equations that are quadratic in form can be solved more easily by defining and substituting a "temporary" variable u for an expression involving the variable in the original equation.

⤷ *NOW TRY*
EXERCISE 5

Define a variable u, and write each equation in the form $au^2 + bu + c = 0$.

(a) $x^4 - 10x^2 + 9 = 0$

(b) $6(x + 2)^2$
$\quad - 11(x + 2) + 4 = 0$

EXAMPLE 5 Defining Substitution Variables

Define a variable u, and write each equation in the form $au^2 + bu + c = 0$.

(a) $x^4 - 13x^2 + 36 = 0$

Look at the two terms involving the variable x, ignoring their coefficients. Try to find one variable expression that is the square of the other. Since $x^4 = (x^2)^2$, we can define $u = x^2$, and rewrite the original equation as a quadratic equation.

$$u^2 - 13u + 36 = 0 \qquad \text{Here, } u = x^2.$$

(b) $2(4x - 3)^2 + 7(4x - 3) + 5 = 0$

Because this equation involves both $(4x - 3)^2$ and $(4x - 3)$, we choose $u = 4x - 3$. Substituting u for $4x - 3$ gives the quadratic equation

$$2u^2 + 7u + 5 = 0. \qquad \text{Here, } u = 4x - 3.$$

(c) $2x^{2/3} - 11x^{1/3} + 12 = 0$

We apply a power rule for exponents **(Section 4.1)**, $(a^m)^n = a^{mn}$. Because $(x^{1/3})^2 = x^{2/3}$, we define $u = x^{1/3}$. The original equation becomes

$$2u^2 - 11u + 12 = 0. \qquad \text{Here, } u = x^{1/3}. \qquad \textit{NOW TRY} \; ↻$$

EXAMPLE 6 Solving Equations That Are Quadratic in Form

Solve each equation.

(a) $x^4 - 13x^2 + 36 = 0$

We can write this equation in quadratic form by substituting u for x^2. (See **Example 5(a).**)

$$x^4 - 13x^2 + 36 = 0$$
$$(x^2)^2 - 13x^2 + 36 = 0 \qquad x^4 = (x^2)^2$$
$$u^2 - 13u + 36 = 0 \qquad \text{Let } u = x^2.$$
$$(u - 4)(u - 9) = 0 \qquad \text{Factor.}$$
$$u - 4 = 0 \quad \text{or} \quad u - 9 = 0 \qquad \text{Zero-factor property}$$

⟨Don't stop here.⟩ $\; u = 4 \quad \text{or} \quad u = 9 \qquad \text{Solve.}$

$$x^2 = 4 \quad \text{or} \quad x^2 = 9 \qquad \text{Substitute } x^2 \text{ for } u.$$
$$x = \pm 2 \quad \text{or} \quad x = \pm 3 \qquad \text{Square root property}$$

The equation $x^4 - 13x^2 + 36 = 0$, a fourth-degree equation, has four solutions, $-3, -2, 2, 3$.* The solution set is abbreviated $\{\pm 2, \pm 3\}$. Each solution can be verified by substituting it into the original equation for x.

NOW TRY ANSWERS
5. (a) $u = x^2$; $u^2 - 10u + 9 = 0$
   (b) $u = x + 2$;
   $\quad 6u^2 - 11u + 4 = 0$

*In general, an equation in which an nth-degree polynomial equals 0 has n complex solutions, although some of them may be repeated.

NOW TRY
EXERCISE 6
Solve each equation.
(a) $x^4 - 17x^2 + 16 = 0$
(b) $x^4 + 4 = 8x^2$

(b)

$$4x^4 + 1 = 5x^2$$

$$4(x^2)^2 + 1 = 5x^2 \qquad x^4 = (x^2)^2$$

$$4u^2 + 1 = 5u \qquad \text{Let } u = x^2.$$

$$4u^2 - 5u + 1 = 0 \qquad \text{Standard form}$$

$$(4u - 1)(u - 1) = 0 \qquad \text{Factor.}$$

$$4u - 1 = 0 \quad \text{or} \quad u - 1 = 0 \qquad \text{Zero-factor property}$$

$$u = \frac{1}{4} \quad \text{or} \quad u = 1 \qquad \text{Solve.}$$

This is a key step. $x^2 = \frac{1}{4} \quad \text{or} \quad x^2 = 1 \qquad \text{Substitute } x^2 \text{ for } u.$

$$x = \pm\frac{1}{2} \quad \text{or} \quad x = \pm 1 \qquad \text{Square root property}$$

Check that the solution set is $\left\{\pm\frac{1}{2}, \pm 1\right\}$.

(c)

$$x^4 = 6x^2 - 3$$

$$x^4 - 6x^2 + 3 = 0 \qquad \text{Standard form}$$

$$(x^2)^2 - 6x^2 + 3 = 0 \qquad x^4 = (x^2)^2$$

$$u^2 - 6u + 3 = 0 \qquad \text{Let } u = x^2.$$

Since this equation cannot be solved by factoring, use the quadratic formula.

$$u = \frac{-(-6) \pm \sqrt{(-6)^2 - 4(1)(3)}}{2(1)} \qquad a = 1, b = -6, c = 3$$

$$u = \frac{6 \pm \sqrt{24}}{2} \qquad \text{Simplify.}$$

$$u = \frac{6 \pm 2\sqrt{6}}{2} \qquad \sqrt{24} = \sqrt{4} \cdot \sqrt{6} = 2\sqrt{6}$$

$$u = \frac{2(3 \pm \sqrt{6})}{2} \qquad \text{Factor.}$$

$$u = 3 \pm \sqrt{6} \qquad \text{Lowest terms}$$

Find *both* square roots in each case. $x^2 = 3 + \sqrt{6} \quad \text{or} \quad x^2 = 3 - \sqrt{6} \qquad u = x^2$

$$x = \pm\sqrt{3 + \sqrt{6}} \quad \text{or} \quad x = \pm\sqrt{3 - \sqrt{6}}$$

The solution set $\left\{\pm\sqrt{3 + \sqrt{6}}, \pm\sqrt{3 - \sqrt{6}}\right\}$ contains four numbers.   **NOW TRY**

NOTE Equations like those in **Examples 6(a) and (b)** can be solved by factoring.

$$x^4 - 13x^2 + 36 = 0 \qquad \text{Example 6(a) equation}$$

$$(x^2 - 9)(x^2 - 4) = 0 \qquad \text{Factor.}$$

$$(x + 3)(x - 3)(x + 2)(x - 2) = 0 \qquad \text{Factor again.}$$

Using the zero-factor property gives the same solutions obtained in **Example 6(a).** Equations that cannot be solved by factoring (as in **Example 6(c)**) must be solved by substitution and the quadratic formula.

NOW TRY ANSWERS
6. (a) $\{\pm 1, \pm 4\}$

  (b) $\{\pm\sqrt{4 + 2\sqrt{3}},$
    $\pm\sqrt{4 - 2\sqrt{3}}\}$

Solving an Equation That Is Quadratic in Form by Substitution

Step 1 **Define a temporary variable *u*,** based on the relationship between the variable expressions in the given equation. Substitute *u* in the original equation and rewrite the equation in the form $au^2 + bu + c = 0$.

Step 2 **Solve the quadratic equation obtained in Step 1** by factoring or the quadratic formula.

Step 3 **Replace *u* with the expression it defined in Step 1.**

Step 4 **Solve the resulting equations for the original variable.**

Step 5 **Check** all solutions by substituting them in the original equation.

NOW TRY
EXERCISE 7

Solve each equation.

(a) $6(x-4)^2 + 11(x-4) - 10 = 0$

(b) $2x^{2/3} - 7x^{1/3} + 3 = 0$

EXAMPLE 7 Solving Equations That Are Quadratic in Form

Solve each equation.

(a) $2(4x-3)^2 + 7(4x-3) + 5 = 0$

Step 1 Because of the repeated quantity $4x - 3$, substitute *u* for $4x - 3$. (See **Example 5(b).**)

$$2(4x-3)^2 + 7(4x-3) + 5 = 0$$
$$2u^2 + 7u + 5 = 0 \qquad \text{Let } u = 4x - 3.$$

Step 2 $\qquad (2u+5)(u+1) = 0 \qquad$ Factor.

$\qquad 2u + 5 = 0 \quad$ or $\quad u + 1 = 0 \qquad$ Zero-factor property

Don't stop here. $\quad u = -\dfrac{5}{2} \quad$ or $\qquad u = -1 \qquad$ Solve for *u*.

Step 3 $\quad 4x - 3 = -\dfrac{5}{2} \quad$ or $\quad 4x - 3 = -1 \qquad$ Substitute $4x - 3$ for *u*.

Step 4 $\qquad 4x = \dfrac{1}{2} \quad$ or $\qquad 4x = 2 \qquad$ Solve for *x*.

$\qquad x = \dfrac{1}{8} \quad$ or $\qquad x = \dfrac{1}{2}$

Step 5 Check that the solution set of the original equation is $\left\{\frac{1}{8}, \frac{1}{2}\right\}$.

(b) $2x^{2/3} - 11x^{1/3} + 12 = 0$

Substitute *u* for $x^{1/3}$. (See **Example 5(c).**)

$$2u^2 - 11u + 12 = 0 \qquad \text{Let } x^{1/3} = u; x^{2/3} = u^2.$$
$$(2u-3)(u-4) = 0 \qquad \text{Factor.}$$

$2u - 3 = 0 \quad$ or $\quad u - 4 = 0 \qquad$ Zero-factor property

$u = \dfrac{3}{2} \quad$ or $\qquad u = 4 \qquad$ Solve for *u*.

$x^{1/3} = \dfrac{3}{2} \quad$ or $\quad x^{1/3} = 4 \qquad u = x^{1/3}$

$(x^{1/3})^3 = \left(\dfrac{3}{2}\right)^3 \quad$ or $\quad (x^{1/3})^3 = 4^3 \qquad$ Cube each side.

$x = \dfrac{27}{8} \quad$ or $\qquad x = 64$

NOW TRY ANSWERS

7. (a) $\left\{\frac{3}{2}, \frac{14}{3}\right\}$ (b) $\left\{\frac{1}{8}, 27\right\}$

Check that the solution set is $\left\{\frac{27}{8}, 64\right\}$.

NOW TRY

⚠ **CAUTION**   A common error when solving problems like those in **Examples 6 and 7** is to stop too soon. ***Once you have solved for u, remember to substitute and solve for the values of the original variable.***

11.4 EXERCISES   *MyMathLab*

🌐 *Complete solution available on the Video Resources on DVD*

Concept Check   Write a sentence describing the first step you would take to solve each equation. Do not actually solve.

1. $\dfrac{14}{x} = x - 5$

2. $\sqrt{1 + x} + x = 5$

3. $(x^2 + x)^2 - 8(x^2 + x) + 12 = 0$

4. $3x = \sqrt{16 - 10x}$

5. *Concept Check*   Study this incorrect "solution." *WHAT WENT WRONG?*

$$x = \sqrt{3x + 4}$$
$$x^2 = 3x + 4$$

   Square each side.

$$x^2 - 3x - 4 = 0$$
$$(x - 4)(x + 1) = 0$$
$$x - 4 = 0 \quad \text{or} \quad x + 1 = 0$$
$$x = 4 \quad \text{or} \qquad x = -1$$

Solution set: $\{4, -1\}$

6. *Concept Check*   Study this incorrect "solution." *WHAT WENT WRONG?*

$$2(x - 1)^2 - 3(x - 1) + 1 = 0$$
$$2u^2 - 3u + 1 = 0$$

   Let $u = x - 1$.

$$(2u - 1)(u - 1) = 0$$
$$2u - 1 = 0 \quad \text{or} \quad u - 1 = 0$$
$$u = \frac{1}{2} \quad \text{or} \qquad u = 1$$

Solution set: $\left\{\frac{1}{2}, 1\right\}$

*Solve each equation. Check your solutions. **See Example 1.***

7. $\dfrac{14}{x} = x - 5$

8. $\dfrac{-12}{x} = x + 8$

9. $1 - \dfrac{3}{x} - \dfrac{28}{x^2} = 0$

10. $4 - \dfrac{7}{r} - \dfrac{2}{r^2} = 0$

11. $3 - \dfrac{1}{t} = \dfrac{2}{t^2}$

12. $1 + \dfrac{2}{x} = \dfrac{3}{x^2}$

🌐 **13.** $\dfrac{1}{x} + \dfrac{2}{x + 2} = \dfrac{17}{35}$

14. $\dfrac{2}{m} + \dfrac{3}{m + 9} = \dfrac{11}{4}$

15. $\dfrac{2}{x + 1} + \dfrac{3}{x + 2} = \dfrac{7}{2}$

16. $\dfrac{4}{3 - p} + \dfrac{2}{5 - p} = \dfrac{26}{15}$

17. $\dfrac{3}{2x} - \dfrac{1}{2(x + 2)} = 1$

18. $\dfrac{4}{3x} - \dfrac{1}{2(x + 1)} = 1$

19. $3 = \dfrac{1}{t + 2} + \dfrac{2}{(t + 2)^2}$

20. $1 + \dfrac{2}{3z + 2} = \dfrac{15}{(3z + 2)^2}$

21. $\dfrac{6}{p} = 2 + \dfrac{p}{p + 1}$

22. $\dfrac{x}{2 - x} + \dfrac{2}{x} = 5$

23. $1 - \dfrac{1}{2x + 1} - \dfrac{1}{(2x + 1)^2} = 0$

24. $1 - \dfrac{1}{3x - 2} - \dfrac{1}{(3x - 2)^2} = 0$

Concept Check *Answer each question.*

25. A boat goes 20 mph in still water, and the rate of the current is t mph.

(a) What is the rate of the boat when it travels upstream?

(b) What is the rate of the boat when it travels downstream?

26. (a) If it takes m hours to grade a set of papers, what is the grader's rate (in job per hour)?

(b) How much of the job will the grader do in 2 hr?

Solve each problem. ***See Examples 2 and 3.***

27. On a windy day William Kunz found that he could go 16 mi downstream and then 4 mi back upstream at top speed in a total of 48 min. What was the top speed of William's boat if the rate of the current was 15 mph?

	d	r	t
Upstream	4	$x - 15$	
Downstream	16		

28. Vera Koutsoyannis flew her plane for 6 hr at a constant rate. She traveled 810 mi with the wind, then turned around and traveled 720 mi against the wind. The wind speed was a constant 15 mph. Find the rate of the plane.

	d	r	t
With Wind	810		
Against Wind	720		

29. The distance from Jackson to Lodi is about 40 mi, as is the distance from Lodi to Manteca. Adrian Iorgoni drove from Jackson to Lodi, stopped in Lodi for a high-energy drink, and then drove on to Manteca at 10 mph faster. Driving time for the entire trip was 88 min. Find the rate from Jackson to Lodi. (*Source: State Farm Road Atlas.*)

30. Medicine Hat and Cranbrook are 300 km apart. Steve Roig-Watnik rides his Harley 20 km per hr faster than Mohammad Shakil rides his Yamaha. Find Steve's average rate if he travels from Cranbrook to Medicine Hat in $1\frac{1}{4}$ hr less time than Mohammad. (*Source: State Farm Road Atlas.*)

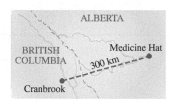

31. Working together, two people can cut a large lawn in 2 hr. One person can do the job alone in 1 hr less time than the other. How long (to the nearest tenth) would it take the faster worker to do the job? (*Hint: x* is the time of the faster worker.)

	Rate	Time Working Together	Fractional Part of the Job Done
Faster Worker	$\frac{1}{x}$	2	
Slower Worker		2	

32. Working together, two people can clean an office building in 5 hr. One person is new to the job and would take 2 hr longer than the other person to clean the building alone. How long (to the nearest tenth) would it take the new worker to clean the building alone?

	Rate	Time Working Together	Fractional Part of the Job Done
Faster Worker			
Slower Worker			

33. Rusty and Nancy Brauner are planting flats of spring flowers. Working alone, Rusty would take 2 hr longer than Nancy to plant the flowers. Working together, they do the job in 12 hr. How long (to the nearest tenth) would it have taken each person working alone?

34. Joel Spring can work through a stack of invoices in 1 hr less time than Noel White can. Working together they take $1\frac{1}{2}$ hr. How long (to the nearest tenth) would it take each person working alone?

35. Two pipes together can fill a tank in 2 hr. One of the pipes, used alone, takes 3 hr longer than the other to fill the tank. How long would each pipe take to fill the tank alone?

36. A washing machine can be filled in 6 min if both the hot and cold water taps are fully opened. Filling the washer with hot water alone takes 9 min longer than filling it with cold water alone. How long does it take to fill the washer with cold water?

*Solve each equation. Check your solutions. **See Example 4.***

37. $x = \sqrt{7x - 10}$ **38.** $z = \sqrt{5z - 4}$ **39.** $2x = \sqrt{11x + 3}$

40. $4x = \sqrt{6x + 1}$ **41.** $3x = \sqrt{16 - 10x}$ **42.** $4t = \sqrt{8t + 3}$

43. $t + \sqrt{t} = 12$ **44.** $p - 2\sqrt{p} = 8$ **45.** $x = \sqrt{\dfrac{6 - 13x}{5}}$

46. $r = \sqrt{\dfrac{20 - 19r}{6}}$ **47.** $-x = \sqrt{\dfrac{8 - 2x}{3}}$ **48.** $-x = \sqrt{\dfrac{3x + 7}{4}}$

*Solve each equation. Check your solutions. **See Examples 5–7.***

49. $x^4 - 29x^2 + 100 = 0$ **50.** $x^4 - 37x^2 + 36 = 0$

51. $4q^4 - 13q^2 + 9 = 0$ **52.** $9x^4 - 25x^2 + 16 = 0$

53. $x^4 + 48 = 16x^2$ **54.** $z^4 + 72 = 17z^2$

55. $(x + 3)^2 + 5(x + 3) + 6 = 0$ **56.** $(x - 4)^2 + (x - 4) - 20 = 0$

57. $3(m + 4)^2 - 8 = 2(m + 4)$ **58.** $(t + 5)^2 + 6 = 7(t + 5)$

59. $x^{2/3} + x^{1/3} - 2 = 0$ **60.** $x^{2/3} - 2x^{1/3} - 3 = 0$

61. $r^{2/3} + r^{1/3} - 12 = 0$ **62.** $3x^{2/3} - x^{1/3} - 24 = 0$

63. $4x^{4/3} - 13x^{2/3} + 9 = 0$ **64.** $9t^{4/3} - 25t^{2/3} + 16 = 0$

65. $2 + \dfrac{5}{3x - 1} = \dfrac{-2}{(3x - 1)^2}$ **66.** $3 - \dfrac{7}{2p + 2} = \dfrac{6}{(2p + 2)^2}$

67. $2 - 6(z - 1)^{-2} = (z - 1)^{-1}$ **68.** $3 - 2(x - 1)^{-1} = (x - 1)^{-2}$

*The equations in Exercises 69–82 are not grouped by type. Solve each equation. Exercises 81 and 82 require knowledge of complex numbers. **See Examples 1 and 4–7.***

69. $12x^4 - 11x^2 + 2 = 0$ **70.** $\left(x - \dfrac{1}{2}\right)^2 + 5\left(x - \dfrac{1}{2}\right) - 4 = 0$

71. $\sqrt{2x + 3} = 2 + \sqrt{x - 2}$ **72.** $\sqrt{m + 1} = -1 + \sqrt{2m}$

73. $2\left(1 + \sqrt{r}\right)^2 = 13\left(1 + \sqrt{r}\right) - 6$ **74.** $(x^2 + x)^2 + 12 = 8(x^2 + x)$

75. $2m^6 + 11m^3 + 5 = 0$ **76.** $8x^6 + 513x^3 + 64 = 0$

77. $6 = 7(2w - 3)^{-1} + 3(2w - 3)^{-2}$ **78.** $x^6 - 10x^3 = -9$

79. $2x^4 - 9x^2 = -2$ **80.** $8x^4 + 1 = 11x^2$

81. $2x^4 + x^2 - 3 = 0$ **82.** $4x^4 + 5x^2 + 1 = 0$

Solve each equation for the specified variable. ***See Section 2.5.***

83. $P = 2L + 2W$ for W **84.** $A = \dfrac{1}{2}bh$ for h **85.** $F = \dfrac{9}{5}C + 32$ for C

SUMMARY EXERCISES on Solving Quadratic Equations

We have introduced four methods for solving quadratic equations written in standard form $ax^2 + bx + c = 0.$

Method	Advantages	Disadvantages
Factoring	This is usually the fastest method.	Not all polynomials are factorable. Some factorable polynomials are difficult to factor.
Square root property	This is the simplest method for solving equations of the form $(ax + b)^2 = c$.	Few equations are given in this form.
Completing the square	This method can always be used, although most people prefer the quadratic formula.	It requires more steps than other methods.
Quadratic formula	This method can always be used.	Sign errors are common when evaluating $\sqrt{b^2 - 4ac}$.

Concept Check *Decide whether* factoring, *the* square root property, *or the* quadratic formula *is most appropriate for solving each quadratic equation. Do not actually solve.*

1. $(2x + 3)^2 = 4$ **2.** $4x^2 - 3x = 1$ **3.** $x^2 + 5x - 8 = 0$

4. $2x^2 + 3x = 1$ **5.** $3x^2 = 2 - 5x$ **6.** $x^2 = 5$

Solve each quadratic equation by the method of your choice.

7. $p^2 = 7$ **8.** $6x^2 - x - 15 = 0$ **9.** $n^2 + 6n + 4 = 0$

10. $(x - 3)^2 = 25$ **11.** $\dfrac{5}{x} + \dfrac{12}{x^2} = 2$ **12.** $3x^2 = 3 - 8x$

13. $2r^2 - 4r + 1 = 0$ ***14.** $x^2 = -12$ **15.** $x\sqrt{2} = \sqrt{5x - 2}$

16. $x^4 - 10x^2 + 9 = 0$ **17.** $(2x + 3)^2 = 8$ **18.** $\dfrac{2}{x} + \dfrac{1}{x - 2} = \dfrac{5}{3}$

19. $t^4 + 14 = 9t^2$ **20.** $8x^2 - 4x = 2$ ***21.** $z^2 + z + 1 = 0$

22. $5x^6 + 2x^3 - 7 = 0$ **23.** $4t^2 - 12t + 9 = 0$ **24.** $x\sqrt{3} = \sqrt{2 - x}$

25. $r^2 - 72 = 0$ **26.** $-3x^2 + 4x = -4$ **27.** $x^2 - 5x - 36 = 0$

28. $w^2 = 169$ ***29.** $3p^2 = 6p - 4$ **30.** $z = \sqrt{\dfrac{5z + 3}{2}}$

*31. $\dfrac{4}{r^2} + 3 = \dfrac{1}{r}$ **32.** $2(3x - 1)^2 + 5(3x - 1) = -2$

---

*This exercise requires knowledge of complex numbers.

(11.5)

Formulas and Further Applications

OBJECTIVES

1 Solve formulas for variables involving squares and square roots.

2 Solve applied problems using the Pythagorean theorem.

3 Solve applied problems using area formulas.

4 Solve applied problems using quadratic functions as models.

OBJECTIVE 1 Solve formulas for variables involving squares and square roots.

EXAMPLE 1 Solving for Variables Involving Squares or Square Roots

Solve each formula for the given variable. Keep $\pm$ in the answer in part (a).

(a) $w = \dfrac{kFr}{v^2}$ for v

$$w = \frac{kFr}{v^2} \qquad \text{The goal is to isolate } v \text{ on one side.}$$

$$v^2 w = kFr \qquad \text{Multiply by } v^2.$$

$$v^2 = \frac{kFr}{w} \qquad \text{Divide by } w.$$

$$v = \pm\sqrt{\frac{kFr}{w}} \qquad \text{Square root property}$$

$$v = \frac{\pm\sqrt{kFr}}{\sqrt{w}} \cdot \frac{\sqrt{w}}{\sqrt{w}} \qquad \text{Rationalize the denominator.}$$

$$v = \frac{\pm\sqrt{kFrw}}{w} \qquad \begin{array}{l}\sqrt{a} \cdot \sqrt{b} = \sqrt{ab}; \\ \sqrt{a} \cdot \sqrt{a} = a\end{array}$$

(b) $d = \sqrt{\dfrac{4\mathcal{A}}{\pi}}$ for $\mathcal{A}$

$$d = \sqrt{\frac{4\mathcal{A}}{\pi}} \qquad \text{The goal is to isolate } \mathcal{A} \text{ on one side.}$$

$$d^2 - \frac{4\mathcal{A}}{\pi} \qquad \text{Square both sides.}$$

$$\pi d^2 = 4\mathcal{A} \qquad \text{Multiply by } \pi.$$

$$\frac{\pi d^2}{4} = \mathcal{A}, \quad \text{or} \quad \mathcal{A} = \frac{\pi d^2}{4} \qquad \text{Divide by 4.} \qquad \text{NOW TRY}$$

NOTE In formulas like $v = \dfrac{\pm\sqrt{kFrw}}{w}$ in **Example 1(a),** we include both positive and negative values.

EXAMPLE 2 Solving for a Variable That Appears in First- and Second-Degree Terms

Solve $s = 2t^2 + kt$ for t.

Since the given equation has terms with t^2 and t, write it in standard form $ax^2 + bx + c = 0$, with t as the variable instead of x.

$$s = 2t^2 + kt$$

$$0 = 2t^2 + kt - s \qquad \text{Subtract } s.$$

$$2t^2 + kt - s = 0 \qquad \text{Standard form}$$

NOW TRY EXERCISE 1

Solve each formula for the given variable. Keep $\pm$ in the answer in part (a).

(a) $n = \dfrac{ab}{E^2}$ for E

(b) $S = \sqrt{\dfrac{pq}{n}}$ for p

NOW TRY ANSWERS

1. (a) $E = \dfrac{\pm\sqrt{abn}}{n}$

(b) $p = \dfrac{nS^2}{q}$

NOW TRY
EXERCISE 2
Solve for r.

$$r^2 + 9r = -c$$

To solve $2t^2 + kt - s = 0$, use the quadratic formula with $a = 2$, $b = k$, and $c = -s$.

$$t = \frac{-k \pm \sqrt{k^2 - 4(2)(-s)}}{2(2)} \qquad \text{Substitute.}$$

$$t = \frac{-k \pm \sqrt{k^2 + 8s}}{4} \qquad \text{Solve for } t.$$

The solutions are $t = \dfrac{-k + \sqrt{k^2 + 8s}}{4}$ and $t = \dfrac{-k - \sqrt{k^2 + 8s}}{4}$.   NOW TRY

OBJECTIVE 2 Solve applied problems using the Pythagorean theorem. The Pythagorean theorem, represented by the equation

$$a^2 + b^2 = c^2,$$

is illustrated in **FIGURE 2** and was introduced in **Sections 5.6 and 10.3**. It is used to solve applications involving right triangles.

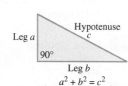

$a^2 + b^2 = c^2$
Pythagorean theorem

FIGURE 2

NOW TRY
EXERCISE 3
Matt Porter is building a new barn, with length 10 ft more than width. While determining the footprint of the barn, he measured the diagonal as 50 ft. What will be the dimensions of the barn?

EXAMPLE 3   Using the Pythagorean Theorem

Two cars left an intersection at the same time, one heading due north, the other due west. Some time later, they were exactly 100 mi apart. The car headed north had gone 20 mi farther than the car headed west. How far had each car traveled?

Step 1   **Read** the problem carefully.

Step 2   **Assign a variable.**

Let x = the distance traveled by the car headed west.

Then $x + 20$ = the distance traveled by the car headed north.

See **FIGURE 3**. The cars are 100 mi apart, so the hypotenuse of the right triangle equals 100.

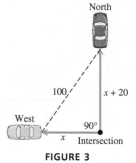

FIGURE 3

Step 3   **Write an equation.** Use the Pythagorean theorem.

$$a^2 + b^2 = c^2$$

$$x^2 + (x + 20)^2 = 100^2$$

$(x + y)^2 = x^2 + 2xy + y^2$

Step 4   **Solve.** $x^2 + x^2 + 40x + 400 = 10{,}000$ Square the binomial.

$$2x^2 + 40x - 9600 = 0 \qquad \text{Standard form}$$

$$x^2 + 20x - 4800 = 0 \qquad \text{Divide by 2.}$$

$$(x + 80)(x - 60) = 0 \qquad \text{Factor.}$$

$x + 80 = 0$ or $x - 60 = 0$ Zero-factor property

$x = -80$ or $x = 60$ Solve for x.

NOW TRY ANSWERS

2. $r = \dfrac{-9 \pm \sqrt{81 - 4c}}{2}$

3. 30 ft by 40 ft

Step 5   **State the answer.** Since distance cannot be negative, discard the negative solution. The required distances are 60 mi and 60 + 20 = 80 mi.

Step 6   **Check.** Since $60^2 + 80^2 = 100^2$, the answer is correct.   NOW TRY

OBJECTIVE 3 Solve applied problems using area formulas.

NOW TRY
EXERCISE 4
A football practice field is 30 yd wide and 40 yd long. A strip of grass sod of uniform width is to be placed around the perimeter of the practice field. There is enough money budgeted for 296 sq yd of sod. How wide will the strip be?

EXAMPLE 4 Solving an Area Problem

A rectangular reflecting pool in a park is 20 ft wide and 30 ft long. The gardener wants to plant a strip of grass of uniform width around the edge of the pool. She has enough seed to cover 336 ft². How wide will the strip be?

FIGURE 4

Step 1 **Read** the problem carefully.

Step 2 **Assign a variable.** The pool is shown in **FIGURE 4**.

Let x = the unknown width of the grass strip.

Then $20 + 2x$ = the width of the large rectangle (the width of the pool plus two grass strips),

and $30 + 2x$ = the length of the large rectangle.

Step 3 **Write an equation.** Refer to **FIGURE 4**.

$(30 + 2x)(20 + 2x)$ Area of large rectangle (length · width)

$30 \cdot 20,$ or 600 Area of pool (in square feet)

The area of the large rectangle minus the area of the pool should equal 336 ft², the area of the grass strip.

$$\underset{\downarrow}{\begin{matrix}\text{Area}\\\text{of large}\\\text{rectangle}\end{matrix}} - \underset{\downarrow}{\begin{matrix}\text{Area}\\\text{of}\\\text{pool}\end{matrix}} = \underset{\downarrow}{\begin{matrix}\text{Area}\\\text{of}\\\text{grass}\end{matrix}}$$

$$(30 + 2x)(20 + 2x) - 600 = 336$$

Step 4 **Solve.**

$$600 + 100x + 4x^2 - 600 = 336 \qquad \text{Multiply.}$$
$$4x^2 + 100x - 336 = 0 \qquad \text{Standard form}$$
$$x^2 + 25x - 84 = 0 \qquad \text{Divide by 4.}$$
$$(x + 28)(x - 3) = 0 \qquad \text{Factor.}$$
$$x + 28 = 0 \quad \text{or} \quad x - 3 = 0 \qquad \text{Zero-factor property}$$
$$x = -28 \quad \text{or} \quad x = 3 \qquad \text{Solve for } x.$$

Step 5 **State the answer.** The width cannot be -28 ft, so the grass strip should be 3 ft wide.

Step 6 **Check.** If $x = 3$, we can find the area of the large rectangle (which includes the grass strip).

$$(30 + 2 \cdot 3)(20 + 2 \cdot 3) = 36 \cdot 26 = 936 \text{ ft}^2 \qquad \text{Area of pool and strip}$$

The area of the pool is $30 \cdot 20 = 600$ ft². So, the area of the grass strip is $936 - 600 = 336$ ft², as required. The answer is correct.   *NOW TRY*

OBJECTIVE 4 Solve applied problems using quadratic functions as models.

Some applied problems can be modeled by *quadratic functions,* which for real numbers a, b, and c, can be written in the form

$$f(x) = ax^2 + bx + c, \quad \text{with } a \neq 0.$$

NOW TRY ANSWER
4. 2 yd

NOW TRY
EXERCISE 5

If an object is projected upward from the top of a 120-ft building at 60 ft per sec, its position (in feet above the ground) is given by

$$s(t) = -16t^2 + 60t + 120,$$

where t is time in seconds after it was projected. When does it hit the ground (to the nearest tenth)?

EXAMPLE 5 Solving an Applied Problem Using a Quadratic Function

If an object is projected upward from the top of a 144-ft building at 112 ft per sec, its position (in feet above the ground) is given by

$$s(t) = -16t^2 + 112t + 144,$$

where t is time in seconds after it was projected. When does it hit the ground?

When the object hits the ground, its distance above the ground is 0. We must find the value of t that makes $s(t) = 0$.

$$0 = -16t^2 + 112t + 144 \qquad \text{Let } s(t) = 0.$$
$$0 = t^2 - 7t - 9 \qquad \text{Divide by } -16.$$
$$t = \frac{-(-7) \pm \sqrt{(-7)^2 - 4(1)(-9)}}{2(1)} \qquad \text{Substitute into the quadratic formula.}$$
$$t = \frac{7 \pm \sqrt{85}}{2} \approx \frac{7 \pm 9.2}{2} \qquad \text{Use a calculator.}$$

The solutions are $t \approx 8.1$ or $t \approx -1.1$. Time cannot be negative, so we discard the negative solution. The object hits the ground about 8.1 sec after it is projected. NOW TRY

NOW TRY
EXERCISE 6

Refer to **Example 6.**

(a) Use the model to approximate the CPI for 2005, to the nearest whole number.

(b) In what year did the CPI reach 500? (Round down for the year.)

EXAMPLE 6 Using a Quadratic Function to Model the CPI

The Consumer Price Index (CPI) is used to measure trends in prices for a "basket" of goods purchased by typical American families. This index uses a base year of 1967, which means that the index number for 1967 is 100. The quadratic function defined by

$$f(x) = -0.065x^2 + 14.8x + 249$$

approximates the CPI for the years 1980–2005, where x is the number of years that have elapsed since 1980. (*Source:* Bureau of Labor Statistics.)

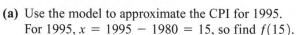

(a) Use the model to approximate the CPI for 1995.
For 1995, $x = 1995 - 1980 = 15$, so find $f(15)$.

$$f(x) = -0.065x^2 + 14.8x + 249 \qquad \text{Given model}$$
$$f(15) = -0.065(15)^2 + 14.8(15) + 249 \qquad \text{Let } x = 15.$$
$$f(15) \approx 456 \qquad \text{Nearest whole number}$$

The CPI for 1995 was about 456.

(b) In what year did the CPI reach 550?
Find the value of x that makes $f(x) = 550$.

$$f(x) = -0.065x^2 + 14.8x + 249 \qquad \text{Given model}$$
$$550 = -0.065x^2 + 14.8x + 249 \qquad \text{Let } f(x) = 550.$$
$$0 = -0.065x^2 + 14.8x - 301 \qquad \text{Standard form}$$
$$x = \frac{-14.8 \pm \sqrt{14.8^2 - 4(-0.065)(-301)}}{2(-0.065)} \qquad \begin{array}{l} \text{Use } a = -0.065, b = 14.8, \\ \text{and } c = -301 \text{ in the} \\ \text{quadratic formula.} \end{array}$$
$$x \approx 22.6 \quad \text{or} \quad x \approx 205.1$$

NOW TRY ANSWERS
5. 5.2 sec after it is projected
6. (a) 578 **(b)** 1998

Rounding the first solution 22.6 down, the CPI first reached 550 in $1980 + 22 = 2002$. (Reject the solution $x \approx 205.1$, as this corresponds to a year far beyond the period covered by the model.) NOW TRY

11.5 EXERCISES

🌐 *Complete solution available on the Video Resources on DVD*

Concept Check   *Answer each question in Exercises 1–4.*

1. In solving a formula that has the specified variable in the denominator, what is the first step?

2. What is the first step in solving a formula like $gw^2 = 2r$ for w?

3. What is the first step in solving a formula like $gw^2 = kw + 24$ for w?

4. Why is it particularly important to check all proposed solutions to an applied problem against the information in the original problem?

In Exercises 5 and 6, solve for m in terms of the other variables ($m > 0$).

5.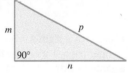

6.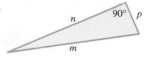

Solve each equation for the indicated variable. (Leave ± in your answers.) ***See Examples 1 and 2.***

7. $d = kt^2$ for t

8. $S = 6e^2$ for e

🌀 9. $I = \dfrac{ks}{d^2}$ for d

10. $R = \dfrac{k}{d^2}$ for d

11. $F = \dfrac{kA}{v^2}$ for v

12. $L = \dfrac{kd^4}{h^2}$ for h

13. $V = \dfrac{1}{3}\pi r^2 h$ for r

14. $V = \pi(r^2 + R^2)h$ for r

🌐 15. $At^2 + Bt = -C$ for t

16. $S = 2\pi rh + \pi r^2$ for r

17. $D = \sqrt{kh}$ for h

18. $F = \dfrac{k}{\sqrt{d}}$ for d

19. $p = \sqrt{\dfrac{k\ell}{g}}$ for ℓ

20. $p = \sqrt{\dfrac{k\ell}{g}}$ for g

21. $S = 4\pi r^2$ for r

22. $s = kwd^2$ for d

Brain Busters   *Solve each equation for the indicated variable. (Leave ± in your answers.)*

23. $p = \dfrac{E^2 R}{(r + R)^2}$ for R $(E > 0)$

24. $S(6S - t) = t^2$ for S

25. $10p^2c^2 + 7pcr = 12r^2$ for r

26. $S = vt + \dfrac{1}{2}gt^2$ for t

27. $LI^2 + RI + \dfrac{1}{c} = 0$ for I

28. $P = EI - RI^2$ for I

Solve each problem. When appropriate, round answers to the nearest tenth. ***See Example 3.***

29. Find the lengths of the sides of the triangle.

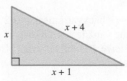

30. Find the lengths of the sides of the triangle.

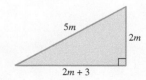

31. Two ships leave port at the same time, one heading due south and the other heading due east. Several hours later, they are 170 mi apart. If the ship traveling south traveled 70 mi farther than the other ship, how many miles did they each travel?

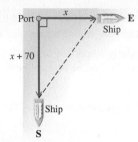

32. Deborah Israel is flying a kite that is 30 ft farther above her hand than its horizontal distance from her. The string from her hand to the kite is 150 ft long. How high is the kite?

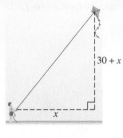

33. A game board is in the shape of a right triangle. The hypotenuse is 2 inches longer than the longer leg, and the longer leg is 1 inch less than twice as long as the shorter leg. How long is each side of the game board?

34. Manuel Bovi is planting a vegetable garden in the shape of a right triangle. The longer leg is 3 ft longer than the shorter leg, and the hypotenuse is 3 ft longer than the longer leg. Find the lengths of the three sides of the garden.

35. The diagonal of a rectangular rug measures 26 ft, and the length is 4 ft more than twice the width. Find the length and width of the rug.

36. A 13-ft ladder is leaning against a house. The distance from the bottom of the ladder to the house is 7 ft less than the distance from the top of the ladder to the ground. How far is the bottom of the ladder from the house?

Solve each problem. ***See Example 4.***

37. A club swimming pool is 30 ft wide and 40 ft long. The club members want an exposed aggregate border in a strip of uniform width around the pool. They have enough material for 296 ft². How wide can the strip be?

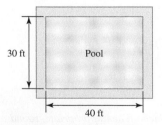

38. Lyudmila Slavina wants to buy a rug for a room that is 20 ft long and 15 ft wide. She wants to leave an even strip of flooring uncovered around the edges of the room. How wide a strip will she have if she buys a rug with an area of 234 ft²?

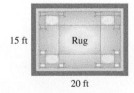

39. A rectangle has a length 2 m less than twice its width. When 5 m are added to the width, the resulting figure is a square with an area of 144 m². Find the dimensions of the original rectangle.

40. Mariana Coanda's backyard measures 20 m by 30 m. She wants to put a flower garden in the middle of the yard, leaving a strip of grass of uniform width around the flower garden. Mariana must have 184 m² of grass. Under these conditions, what will the length and width of the garden be?

41. A rectangular piece of sheet metal has a length that is 4 in. less than twice the width. A square piece 2 in. on a side is cut from each corner. The sides are then turned up to form an uncovered box of volume 256 in.^{3}. Find the length and width of the original piece of metal.

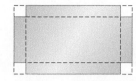

42. Another rectangular piece of sheet metal is 2 in. longer than it is wide. A square piece 3 in. on a side is cut from each corner. The sides are then turned up to form an uncovered box of volume 765 in.^{3}. Find the dimensions of the original piece of metal.

Solve each problem. When appropriate, round answers to the nearest tenth. ***See Example 5.***

43. An object is projected directly upward from the ground. After t seconds its distance in feet above the ground is

$$s(t) = 144t - 16t^2.$$

After how many seconds will the object be 128 ft above the ground? (*Hint:* Look for a common factor before solving the equation.)

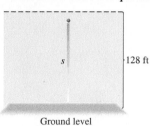

Ground level

44. When does the object in **Exercise 43** strike the ground?

45. A ball is projected upward from the ground. Its distance in feet from the ground in t seconds is given by

$$s(t) = -16t^2 + 128t.$$

At what times will the ball be 213 ft from the ground?

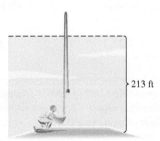

213 ft

46. A toy rocket is launched from ground level. Its distance in feet from the ground in t seconds is given by

$$s(t) = -16t^2 + 208t.$$

At what times will the rocket be 550 ft from the ground?

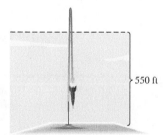

550 ft

47. The function defined by

$$D(t) = 13t^2 - 100t$$

gives the distance in feet a car going approximately 68 mph will skid in t seconds. Find the time it would take for the car to skid 180 ft.

48. The function given in **Exercise 47** becomes $D(t) = 13t^2 - 73t$ for a car going 50 mph. Find the time it takes for this car to skid 218 ft.

A ball is projected upward from ground level, and its distance in feet from the ground in t seconds is given by $s(t) = -16t^2 + 160t$.

49. After how many seconds does the ball reach a height of 400 ft? How would you describe in words its position at this height?

50. After how many seconds does the ball reach a height of 425 ft? How would you interpret the mathematical result here?

Solve each problem using a quadratic equation.

51. A certain bakery has found that the daily demand for blueberry muffins is $\frac{3200}{p}$, where p is the price of a muffin in cents. The daily supply is $3p - 200$. Find the price at which supply and demand are equal.

52. In one area the demand for compact discs is $\frac{700}{P}$ per day, where P is the price in dollars per disc. The supply is $5P - 1$ per day. At what price, to the nearest cent, does supply equal demand?

53. The formula

$$A = P(1 + r)^2$$

gives the amount A in dollars that P dollars will grow to in 2 yr at interest rate r (where r is given as a decimal), using compound interest. What interest rate will cause $2000 to grow to $2142.45 in 2 yr?

54. Use the formula $A = P(1 + r)^2$ to find the interest rate r at which a principal P of $10,000 will increase to $10,920.25 in 2 yr.

William Froude was a 19th century naval architect who used the expression

$$\frac{v^2}{g\ell}$$

in shipbuilding. This expression, known as the **Froude number,** *was also used by R. McNeill Alexander in his research on dinosaurs. (Source: "How Dinosaurs Ran,"* Scientific American, *April 1991.) In Exercises 55 and 56, find the value of v (in meters per second), given* $g = 9.8$ m per sec^2. (Round to the nearest tenth.)

55. Rhinoceros: $\ell = 1.2$; Froude number $= 2.57$

56. Triceratops: $\ell = 2.8$; Froude number $= 0.16$

Recall that corresponding sides of similar triangles are proportional. Use this fact to find the lengths of the indicated sides of each pair of similar triangles. Check all possible solutions in both triangles. Sides of a triangle cannot be negative (and are not drawn to scale here).

57. Side AC

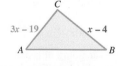

58. Side RQ

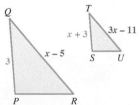

Total spending (in billions of dollars) in the United States from all sources on physician and clinical services for the years 2000–2007 are shown in the bar graph on the next page and can be modeled by the quadratic function defined by

$$f(x) = 0.3214x^2 + 25.06x + 288.2.$$

Here, $x = 0$ represents 2000, $x = 1$ represents 2001, and so on. Use the graph and the model to work Exercises 59–62. **See Example 6.**

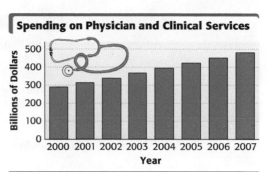

Spending on Physician and Clinical Services

Source: U.S. Centers for Medicare and Medicaid Services.

59. (a) Use the graph to estimate spending on physician and clinical services in 2005 to the nearest $10 billion.

(b) Use the model to approximate spending to the nearest $10 billion. How does this result compare to your estimate in part (a)?

60. Based on the model, in what year did spending on physician and clinical services first exceed $350 billion? (Round down for the year.) How does this result compare to the amount of spending shown in the graph?

61. Based on the model, in what year did spending on physician and clinical services first exceed $400 billion? (Round down for the year.) How does this result compare to the amount of spending shown in the graph?

📝 **62.** If these data were modeled by a *linear* function defined by $f(x) = ax + b$, would the value of a be positive or negative? Explain.

PREVIEW EXERCISES

*Find each function value. **See Section 7.4.***

63. $f(x) = x^2 + 4x - 3$. Find $f(2)$.   **64.** $f(x) = 2(x - 3)^2 + 5$. Find $f(3)$.

65. Graph $f(x) = 2x^2$. Give the domain and range. **See Sections 4.4 and 7.3.**

11.6 Graphs of Quadratic Functions

OBJECTIVES

1 Graph a quadratic function.

2 Graph parabolas with horizontal and vertical shifts.

3 Use the coefficient of x^2 to predict the shape and direction in which a parabola opens.

4 Find a quadratic function to model data.

OBJECTIVE 1 **Graph a quadratic function. FIGURE 5** gives a graph of the simplest *quadratic function*, defined by $y = x^2$. This graph is called a **parabola.** (See **Section 4.4.**) The point $(0, 0)$, the lowest point on the curve, is the **vertex** of this parabola. The vertical line through the vertex is the **axis** of the parabola, here $x = 0$. A parabola is **symmetric about its axis**—if the graph were folded along the axis, the two portions of the curve would coincide.

As **FIGURE 5** suggests, x can be any real number, so the domain of the function defined by $y = x^2$ is $(-\infty, \infty)$. Since y is always non-negative, the range is $[0, \infty)$.

x	y
−2	4
−1	1
0	0
1	1
2	4

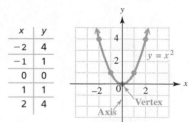

FIGURE 5

> ### Quadratic Function
>
> A function that can be written in the form
>
> $$f(x) = ax^2 + bx + c$$
>
> for real numbers a, b, and c, with $a \neq 0$, is a **quadratic function.**

The graph of any quadratic function is a parabola with a vertical axis.

NOTE We use the variable y and function notation $f(x)$ interchangeably. Although we use the letter f most often to name quadratic functions, other letters can be used. We use the capital letter F to distinguish between different parabolas graphed on the same coordinate axes.

Parabolas have a special reflecting property that makes them useful in the design of telescopes, radar equipment, solar furnaces, and automobile headlights. (See the figure.)

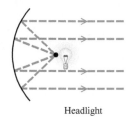

Headlight

OBJECTIVE 2 **Graph parabolas with horizontal and vertical shifts.** Parabolas need not have their vertices at the origin, as does the graph of $f(x) = x^2$.

NOW TRY
EXERCISE 1

Graph $f(x) = x^2 - 3$. Give the vertex, axis, domain, and range.

EXAMPLE 1 Graphing a Parabola (Vertical Shift)

Graph $F(x) = x^2 - 2$.

The graph of $F(x) = x^2 - 2$ has the same shape as that of $f(x) = x^2$ but is *shifted*, or *translated*, 2 units down, with vertex $(0, -2)$. Every function value is 2 less than the corresponding function value of $f(x) = x^2$. Plotting points on both sides of the vertex gives the graph in **FIGURE 6**.

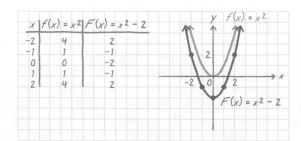

x	$f(x) = x^2$	$F(x) = x^2 - 2$
-2	4	2
-1	1	-1
0	0	-2
1	1	-1
2	4	2

$F(x) = x^2 - 2$
Vertex: $(0, -2)$
Axis: $x = 0$
Domain: $(-\infty, \infty)$
Range: $[-2, \infty)$
The graph of $f(x) = x^2$ is shown for comparison.

FIGURE 6

This parabola is symmetric about its axis $x = 0$, so the plotted points are "mirror images" of each other. Since x can be any real number, the domain is still $(-\infty, \infty)$. The value of y (or $F(x)$) is always greater than or equal to -2, so the range is $[-2, \infty)$.

NOW TRY

NOW TRY ANSWER

1.

$f(x) = x^2 - 3$

vertex: $(0, -3)$; axis: $x = 0$;
domain: $(-\infty, \infty)$; range: $[-3, \infty)$

Vertical Shift

The graph of $F(x) = x^2 + k$ is a parabola.

- The graph has the same shape as the graph of $f(x) = x^2$.
- The parabola is shifted k units up if $k > 0$, and $|k|$ units down if $k < 0$.
- The vertex of the parabola is $(0, k)$.

**NOW TRY
EXERCISE 2**

Graph $f(x) = (x + 1)^2$. Give the vertex, axis, domain, and range.

EXAMPLE 2 Graphing a Parabola (Horizontal Shift)

Graph $F(x) = (x - 2)^2$.

If $x = 2$, then $F(x) = 0$, giving the vertex $(2, 0)$. The graph of $F(x) = (x - 2)^2$ has the same shape as that of $f(x) = x^2$ but is shifted 2 units to the right. Plotting points on one side of the vertex, and using symmetry about the axis $x = 2$ to find corresponding points on the other side, gives the graph in **FIGURE 7**.

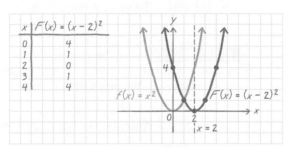

$F(x) = (x - 2)^2$
Vertex: $(2, 0)$
Axis: $x = 2$
Domain: $(-\infty, \infty)$
Range: $[0, \infty)$

FIGURE 7

NOW TRY

Horizontal Shift

The graph of $F(x) = (x - h)^2$ is a parabola.

- The graph has the same shape as the graph of $f(x) = x^2$.
- The parabola is shifted h units to the right if $h > 0$, and $|h|$ units to the left if $h < 0$.
- The vertex of the parabola is $(h, 0)$.

⚠ **CAUTION** *Errors frequently occur when horizontal shifts are involved.* To determine the direction and magnitude of a horizontal shift, find the value that causes the expression $x - h$ to equal 0, as shown below.

$$F(x) = (x - 5)^2 \qquad\qquad F(x) = (x + 5)^2$$

Shift the graph of $F(x)$ **5 units to the right,** because $+5$ causes $x - 5$ to equal 0.

Shift the graph of $F(x)$ **5 units to the left,** because -5 causes $x + 5$ to equal 0.

NOW TRY ANSWER

2.

vertex: $(-1, 0)$; axis: $x = -1$; domain: $(-\infty, \infty)$; range: $[0, \infty)$

EXAMPLE 3 Graphing a Parabola (Horizontal and Vertical Shifts)

Graph $F(x) = (x + 3)^2 - 2$.

This graph has the same shape as that of $f(x) = x^2$, but is shifted 3 units to the left (since $x + 3 = 0$ if $x = -3$) and 2 units down (because of the -2). See **FIGURE 8** on the next page.

NOW TRY
EXERCISE 3
Graph $f(x) = (x + 1)^2 - 2$.
Give the vertex, axis, domain,
and range.

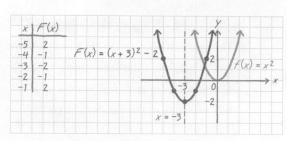

FIGURE 8

$F(x) = (x + 3)^2 - 2$
Vertex: $(-3, -2)$
Axis: $x = -3$
Domain: $(-\infty, \infty)$
Range: $[-2, \infty)$

NOW TRY

Vertex and Axis of a Parabola

The graph of $F(x) = (x - h)^2 + k$ is a parabola.

- The graph has the same shape as the graph of $f(x) = x^2$.
- The vertex of the parabola is (h, k).
- The axis is the vertical line $x = h$.

OBJECTIVE 3 **Use the coefficient of x^2 to predict the shape and direction in which a parabola opens.** Not all parabolas open up, and not all parabolas have the same shape as the graph of $f(x) = x^2$.

NOW TRY
EXERCISE 4
Graph $f(x) = -3x^2$. Give
the vertex, axis, domain,
and range.

EXAMPLE 4 **Graphing a Parabola That Opens Down**

Graph $f(x) = -\frac{1}{2}x^2$.

This parabola is shown in **FIGURE 9**. The coefficient $-\frac{1}{2}$ affects the shape of the graph—the $\frac{1}{2}$ makes the parabola wider $\left(\text{since the values of } \frac{1}{2}x^2 \text{ increase more slowly than those of } x^2\right)$, and the negative sign makes the parabola open down. The graph is not shifted in any direction. Unlike the parabolas graphed in **Examples 1–3,** the vertex here has the *greatest* function value of any point on the graph.

x	f(x)
-2	-2
-1	$-\frac{1}{2}$
0	0
1	$-\frac{1}{2}$
2	-2

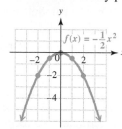

$f(x) = -\frac{1}{2}x^2$
Vertex: $(0, 0)$
Axis: $x = 0$
Domain: $(-\infty, \infty)$
Range: $(-\infty, 0]$

FIGURE 9

NOW TRY

NOW TRY ANSWERS

3.
$f(x) = (x+1)^2 - 2$
vertex: $(-1, -2)$; axis: $x = -1$;
domain: $(-\infty, \infty)$; range: $[-2, \infty)$

4.
$f(x) = -3x^2$
vertex: $(0, 0)$; axis: $x = 0$;
domain: $(-\infty, \infty)$; range: $(-\infty, 0]$

General Characteristics of $F(x) = a(x - h)^2 + k$ $(a \neq 0)$

1. The graph of the quadratic function defined by
$$F(x) = a(x - h)^2 + k, \quad \text{with } a \neq 0,$$
is a parabola with vertex (h, k) and the vertical line $x = h$ as axis.

2. The graph opens up if a is positive and down if a is negative.

3. The graph is wider than that of $f(x) = x^2$ if $0 < |a| < 1$.
The graph is narrower than that of $f(x) = x^2$ if $|a| > 1$.

NOW TRY
EXERCISE 5

Graph $f(x) = 2(x - 1)^2 + 2$.

EXAMPLE 5 Using the General Characteristics to Graph a Parabola

Graph $F(x) = -2(x + 3)^2 + 4$.

The parabola opens down (because $a < 0$) and is narrower than the graph of $f(x) = x^2$, since $|-2| = 2$ and $2 > 1$. This causes values of $F(x)$ to decrease more quickly than those of $f(x) = -x^2$. This parabola has vertex $(-3, 4)$, as shown in **FIGURE 10**. To complete the graph, we plotted the ordered pairs $(-4, 2)$ and, by symmetry, $(-2, 2)$. Symmetry can be used to find additional ordered pairs that satisfy the equation.

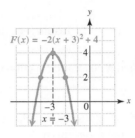

$F(x) = -2(x + 3)^2 + 4$
Vertex: $(-3, 4)$
Axis: $x = -3$
Domain: $(-\infty, \infty)$
Range: $(-\infty, 4]$

FIGURE 10

NOW TRY

OBJECTIVE 4 Find a quadratic function to model data.

EXAMPLE 6 Modeling the Number of Multiple Births

The number of higher-order multiple births (triplets or more) in the United States has declined in recent years, as shown by the data in the table. Here, x represents the number of years since 1995 and y represents the number of higher-order multiple births.

Year	x	y
1995	0	4973
1996	1	5939
1997	2	6737
1999	4	7321
2001	6	7471
2003	8	7663
2004	9	7275
2005	10	6694

Source: National Center for Health Statistics.

Find a quadratic function that models the data.

A scatter diagram of the ordered pairs (x, y) is shown in **FIGURE 11** on the next page. The general shape suggested by the scatter diagram indicates that a parabola should approximate these points, as shown by the dashed curve in **FIGURE 12**. The equation for such a parabola would have a negative coefficient for x^2 since the graph opens down.

NOW TRY ANSWER

5.

$f(x) = 2(x - 1)^2 + 2$

NOW TRY
EXERCISE 6

Using the points $(0, 4973)$, $(4, 7321)$, and $(8, 7663)$, find another quadratic model for the data on higher-order multiple births in **Example 6.**

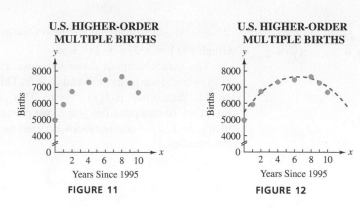

FIGURE 11

FIGURE 12

To find a quadratic function of the form

$$y = ax^2 + bx + c$$

that models, or *fits*, these data, we choose three representative ordered pairs and use them to write a system of three equations. Using

$$(0, 4973), \quad (4, 7321), \quad \text{and} \quad (10, 6694),$$

we substitute the x- and y-values from the ordered pairs into the quadratic form $y = ax^2 + bx + c$ to get three equations.

$$a(0)^2 + b(0) + c = 4973 \qquad \text{or} \qquad c = 4973 \qquad (1)$$
$$a(4)^2 + b(4) + c = 7321 \qquad \text{or} \qquad 16a + 4b + c = 7321 \qquad (2)$$
$$a(10)^2 + b(10) + c = 6694 \qquad \text{or} \qquad 100a + 10b + c = 6694 \qquad (3)$$

We can find the values of a, b, and c by solving this system of three equations in three variables using the methods of **Section 8.4.** From equation (1), $c = 4973$. Substitute 4973 for c in equations (2) and (3) to obtain two equations.

$$16a + 4b + 4973 = 7321, \qquad \text{or} \qquad 16a + 4b = 2348 \qquad (4)$$
$$100a + 10b + 4973 = 6694, \qquad \text{or} \qquad 100a + 10b = 1721 \qquad (5)$$

We can eliminate b from this system of equations in two variables by multiplying equation (4) by -5 and equation (5) by 2, and adding the results.

$$120a = -8298$$
$$a = -69.15 \qquad \text{Divide by 120. Use a calculator.}$$

We substitute -69.15 for a in equation (4) or (5) to find that $b = 863.6$. Using the values we have found for a, b, and c, our model is defined by

$$y = -69.15x^2 + 863.6x + 4973. \qquad \text{NOW TRY}$$

NOTE In **Example 6,** if we had chosen three different ordered pairs of data, a slightly different model would result. The *quadratic regression* feature on a graphing calculator can also be used to generate the quadratic model that best fits given data. See your owner's manual for details.

NOW TRY ANSWER
6. $y = -62.69x^2 + 837.75x + 4973$

11.6 EXERCISES

● *Complete solution available
on the Video Resources on DVD*

1. *Concept Check* Match each quadratic function with its graph from choices A–D.

(a) $f(x) = (x + 2)^2 - 1$

(b) $f(x) = (x + 2)^2 + 1$

(c) $f(x) = (x - 2)^2 - 1$

(d) $f(x) = (x - 2)^2 + 1$

A.

B.

C.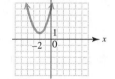

D.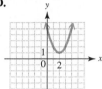

2. *Concept Check* Match each quadratic function with its graph from choices A–D.

(a) $f(x) = -x^2 + 2$

(b) $f(x) = -x^2 - 2$

(c) $f(x) = -(x + 2)^2$

(d) $f(x) = -(x - 2)^2$

A.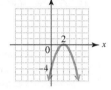

B.

C.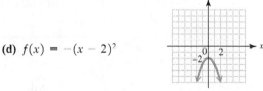

D.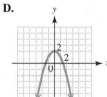

Identify the vertex of each parabola. ***See Examples 1–4.***

3. $f(x) = -3x^2$ **4.** $f(x) = \dfrac{1}{2}x^2$ **5.** $f(x) = x^2 + 4$ **6.** $f(x) = x^2 - 4$

7. $f(x) = (x - 1)^2$ **8.** $f(x) = (x + 3)^2$ **9.** $f(x) = (x + 3)^2 - 4$

10. $f(x) = (x + 5)^2 - 8$ **11.** $f(x) = -(x - 5)^2 + 6$ **12.** $f(x) = -(x - 2)^2 + 1$

*For each quadratic function, tell whether the graph opens up or down and whether the graph
is wider, narrower, or the same shape as the graph of $f(x) = x^2$.* ***See Examples 4 and 5.***

13. $f(x) = -\dfrac{2}{5}x^2$

14. $f(x) = -2x^2$

15. $f(x) = 3x^2 + 1$

16. $f(x) = \dfrac{2}{3}x^2 - 4$

17. $f(x) = -4(x + 2)^2 + 5$

18. $f(x) = -\dfrac{1}{3}(x + 6)^2 + 3$

19. *Concept Check* Match each quadratic function with the description of the parabola that is its graph.

(a) $f(x) = (x - 4)^2 - 2$ **A.** Vertex $(2, -4)$, opens down

(b) $f(x) = (x - 2)^2 - 4$ **B.** Vertex $(2, -4)$, opens up

(c) $f(x) = -(x - 4)^2 - 2$ **C.** Vertex $(4, -2)$, opens down

(d) $f(x) = -(x - 2)^2 - 4$ **D.** Vertex $(4, -2)$, opens up

20. *Concept Check* For $f(x) = a(x - h)^2 + k$, in what quadrant is the vertex if

(a) $h > 0, k > 0$ (b) $h > 0, k < 0$ (c) $h < 0, k > 0$ (d) $h < 0, k < 0$?

Graph each parabola. Plot at least two points as well as the vertex. Give the vertex, axis, domain, and range in Exercises 27–36. **See Examples 1–5.**

21. $f(x) = -2x^2$ **22.** $f(x) = -\dfrac{1}{3}x^2$ **23.** $f(x) = x^2 - 1$

24. $f(x) = x^2 + 3$ **25.** $f(x) = -x^2 + 2$ **26.** $f(x) = -x^2 - 2$

27. $f(x) = (x - 4)^2$ **28.** $f(x) = (x + 1)^2$

29. $f(x) = (x + 2)^2 - 1$ **30.** $f(x) = (x - 1)^2 + 2$

31. $f(x) = 2(x - 2)^2 - 4$ **32.** $f(x) = 3(x - 2)^2 + 1$

33. $f(x) = -\dfrac{1}{2}(x + 1)^2 + 2$ **34.** $f(x) = -\dfrac{2}{3}(x + 2)^2 + 1$

35. $f(x) = 2(x - 2)^2 - 3$ **36.** $f(x) = \dfrac{4}{3}(x - 3)^2 - 2$

Concept Check In Exercises 37–42, tell whether a linear or quadratic function would be a more appropriate model for each set of graphed data. If linear, tell whether the slope should be positive or negative. If quadratic, tell whether the coefficient a of x^2 should be positive or negative. **See Example 6.**

37. TIME SPENT PLAYING VIDEO GAMES

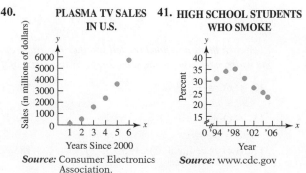

Source: Veronis Suhler Stevenson.

38. AVERAGE DAILY VOLUME OF FIRST-CLASS MAIL

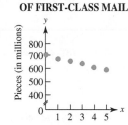

Source: General Accounting Office.

39. FOOD ASSISTANCE SPENDING IN IOWA

Source: Iowa Department of Human Services.

40. PLASMA TV SALES IN U.S.

Source: Consumer Electronics Association.

41. HIGH SCHOOL STUDENTS WHO SMOKE

Source: www.cdc.gov

42. SOCIAL SECURITY ASSETS*

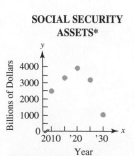

*Projected
Source: Social Security Administration.

Solve each problem. ***See Example 6.***

43. Sales of digital cameras in the United States (in millions of dollars) between 2000 and 2006 are shown in the table. In the year column, 0 represents 2000, 1 represents 2001, and so on.

Year	Sales
0	1825
1	1972
2	2794
3	3921
4	4739
5	5611
6	7805

Source: Consumer Electronics Association.

(a) Use the ordered pairs (year, sales) to make a scatter diagram of the data.

(b) Use the scatter diagram to decide whether a linear or quadratic function would better model the data. If quadratic, should the coefficient a of x^2 be positive or negative?

(c) Use the ordered pairs $(0, 1825)$, $(3, 3921)$, and $(6, 7805)$ to find a quadratic function that models the data. Round the values of a, b, and c in your model to the nearest tenth, as necessary.

(d) Use your model from part (c) to approximate the sales of digital cameras in the United States in 2007. Round your answer to the nearest whole number (of millions).

(e) Sales of digital cameras were $6517 million in 2007. Based on this, is the model valid for 2007? Explain.

44. The number (in thousands) of new, privately owned housing units started in the United States is shown in the table for the years 2002–2008. In the year column, 2 represents 2002, 3 represents 2003, and so on.

Year	Housing Starts (thousands)
2	1700
3	1850
4	1960
5	2070
6	1800
7	1360
8	910

Source: U.S. Census Bureau.

(a) Use the ordered pairs (year, housing starts) to make a scatter diagram of the data.

(b) Would a linear or quadratic function better model the data?

(c) Should the coefficient a of x^2 in a quadratic model be positive or negative?

(d) Use the ordered pairs $(2, 1700)$, $(4, 1960)$, and $(7, 1360)$ to find a quadratic function that models the data. Round the values of a, b, and c in your model to the nearest whole number, as necessary.

(e) Use your model from part (d) to approximate the number of housing starts during 2003 and 2008 to the nearest thousand. How well does the model approximate the actual data from the table?

45. In **Example 6,** we determined that the quadratic function defined by

$$y = -69.15x^2 + 863.6x + 4973$$

modeled the number of higher-order multiple births, where x represents the number of years since 1995.

   (a) Use this model to approximate the number of higher-order births in 2006 to the nearest whole number.

   (b) The actual number of higher-order births in 2006 was 6540. (*Source:* National Center for Health Statistics.) How does the approximation using the model compare to the actual number for 2006?

46. Should the model from **Exercise 45** be used to approximate the rate of higher-order multiple births in years after 2006? Explain.

TECHNOLOGY INSIGHTS   EXERCISES 47–48

*Recall from **Sections 3.2 and 7.1** that the x-value of the x-intercept of the graph of the line $y = mx + b$ is the solution of the linear equation $mx + b = 0$. In the same way, the x-values of the x-intercepts of the graph of the parabola $y = ax^2 + bx + c$ are the real solutions of the quadratic equation $ax^2 + bx + c = 0$.*

   In Exercises 47–48, the calculator graphs show the x-values of the x-intercepts of the graph of the polynomial in the equation. Use the graphs to solve each equation.

47. $x^2 - x - 20 = 0$

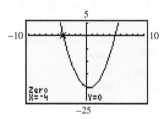 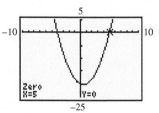

48. $x^2 + 9x + 14 = 0$

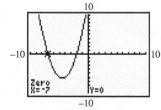 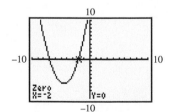

PREVIEW EXERCISES

Complete each factoring. See Section 5.1.

49. $-2x^2 + 6x =$ _____ $(x^2 - 3x)$ **50.** $-3x^2 - 15x =$ _____ $(x^2 + 5x)$

Solve each quadratic equation by factoring or by completing the square. See Sections 11.1 and 11.2.

51. $x^2 + 3x - 4 = 0$ **52.** $x^2 - x - 6 = 0$

53. $x^2 + 6x - 3 = 0$ **54.** $x^2 + 8x - 4 = 0$

More About Parabolas and Their Applications

OBJECTIVES

1 Find the vertex of a vertical parabola.

2 Graph a quadratic function.

3 Use the discriminant to find the number of x-intercepts of a parabola with a vertical axis.

4 Use quadratic functions to solve problems involving maximum or minimum value.

5 Graph parabolas with horizontal axes.

OBJECTIVE 1 Find the vertex of a vertical parabola. When the equation of a parabola is given in the form $f(x) = ax^2 + bx + c$, there are two ways to locate the vertex.

1. Complete the square, as shown in **Examples 1 and 2,** or

2. Use a formula derived by completing the square, as shown in **Example 3.**

EXAMPLE 1 Completing the Square to Find the Vertex ($a = 1$)

Find the vertex of the graph of $f(x) = x^2 - 4x + 5$.

We can express $x^2 - 4x + 5$ in the form $(x - h)^2 + k$ by completing the square on $x^2 - 4x$, as in **Section 11.2.** The process is slightly different here because we want to keep $f(x)$ alone on one side of the equation. Instead of adding the appropriate number to each side, we *add and subtract* it on the right.

$$f(x) = x^2 - 4x + 5$$
$$= (x^2 - 4x \quad) + 5 \qquad \text{Group the variable terms.}$$

This is equivalent to adding 0. $\qquad \left[\frac{1}{2}(-4)\right]^2 = (-2)^2 = 4$

$$= (x^2 - 4x + 4 - 4) + 5 \qquad \text{Add and subtract 4.}$$
$$= (x^2 - 4x + 4) - 4 + 5 \qquad \text{Bring } -4 \text{ outside the parentheses.}$$
$$f(x) = (x - 2)^2 + 1 \qquad \text{Factor. Combine like terms.}$$

The vertex of this parabola is $(2, 1)$.

NOW TRY

NOW TRY
EXERCISE 1
Find the vertex of the graph of
$f(x) = x^2 + 2x - 8$.

NOW TRY
EXERCISE 2
Find the vertex of the graph of
$f(x) = -4x^2 + 16x - 10$.

EXAMPLE 2 Completing the Square to Find the Vertex ($a \neq 1$)

Find the vertex of the graph of $f(x) = -3x^2 + 6x - 1$.

Because the x^2-term has a coefficient other than 1, we factor that coefficient out of the first two terms before completing the square.

$$f(x) = -3x^2 + 6x - 1$$
$$= -3(x^2 - 2x) - 1 \qquad \text{Factor out } -3.$$

$$\left[\frac{1}{2}(-2)\right]^2 = (-1)^2 = 1$$

$$= -3(x^2 - 2x + 1 - 1) - 1 \qquad \text{Add and subtract 1 within the parentheses.}$$

Now bring -1 *outside the parentheses. Be sure to multiply it by* -3.

$$= -3(x^2 - 2x + 1) + (-3)(-1) - 1 \qquad \text{Distributive property}$$
$$= -3(x^2 - 2x + 1) + 3 - 1 \qquad \text{This is a key step.}$$
$$f(x) = -3(x - 1)^2 + 2 \qquad \text{Factor. Combine like terms.}$$

The vertex is $(1, 2)$.

NOW TRY

NOW TRY ANSWERS
1. $(-1, -9)$ **2.** $(2, 6)$

To derive a formula for the vertex of the graph of the quadratic function defined by $f(x) = ax^2 + bx + c$ (with $a \neq 0$), complete the square.

$$f(x) = ax^2 + bx + c \qquad \text{Standard form}$$

$$= a\left(x^2 + \frac{b}{a}x\right) + c \qquad \begin{array}{l}\text{Factor } a \text{ from the}\\ \text{first two terms.}\end{array}$$

$$\left[\tfrac{1}{2}\left(\tfrac{b}{a}\right)\right]^2 = \left(\tfrac{b}{2a}\right)^2 = \tfrac{b^2}{4a^2}$$

$$= a\left(x^2 + \frac{b}{a}x + \frac{b^2}{4a^2} - \frac{b^2}{4a^2}\right) + c \qquad \text{Add and subtract } \tfrac{b^2}{4a^2}.$$

$$= a\left(x^2 + \frac{b}{a}x + \frac{b^2}{4a^2}\right) + a\left(-\frac{b^2}{4a^2}\right) + c \qquad \text{Distributive property}$$

$$= a\left(x^2 + \frac{b}{a}x + \frac{b^2}{4a^2}\right) - \frac{b^2}{4a} + c \qquad -\tfrac{ab^2}{4a^2} = -\tfrac{b^2}{4a}$$

$$= a\left(x + \frac{b}{2a}\right)^2 + \frac{4ac - b^2}{4a} \qquad \begin{array}{l}\text{Factor. Rewrite terms with}\\ \text{a common denominator.}\end{array}$$

$$f(x) = a\left[x - \underbrace{\left(\frac{-b}{2a}\right)}_{h}\right]^2 + \underbrace{\frac{4ac - b^2}{4a}}_{k} \qquad \begin{array}{l}f(x) = a(x - h)^2 + k\\ \text{The vertex } (h, k) \text{ can be ex-}\\ \text{pressed in terms of } a, b, \text{ and } c.\end{array}$$

The expression for k can be found by replacing x with $\frac{-b}{2a}$. Using function notation, if $y = f(x)$, then the y-value of the vertex is $f\left(\frac{-b}{2a}\right)$.

Vertex Formula

The graph of the quadratic function defined by $f(x) = ax^2 + bx + c$ (with $a \neq 0$) has vertex

$$\left(\frac{-b}{2a}, f\left(\frac{-b}{2a}\right)\right),$$

and the axis of the parabola is the line

$$x = \frac{-b}{2a}.$$

NOW TRY
EXERCISE 3

Use the vertex formula to find the vertex of the graph of

$$f(x) = 3x^2 - 2x + 8.$$

EXAMPLE 3 Using the Formula to Find the Vertex

Use the vertex formula to find the vertex of the graph of $f(x) = x^2 - x - 6$.

The x-coordinate of the vertex of the parabola is given by $\frac{-b}{2a}$.

$$\frac{-b}{2a} = \frac{-(-1)}{2(1)} = \frac{1}{2} \quad \begin{array}{l}a = 1, b = -1, \text{and } c = -6.\\ \leftarrow x\text{-coordinate of vertex}\end{array}$$

The y-coordinate is $f\left(\frac{-b}{2a}\right) = f\left(\frac{1}{2}\right)$.

$$f\left(\frac{1}{2}\right) = \left(\frac{1}{2}\right)^2 - \frac{1}{2} - 6 = \frac{1}{4} - \frac{1}{2} - 6 = -\frac{25}{4} \leftarrow y\text{-coordinate of vertex}$$

NOW TRY ANSWER
3. $\left(\frac{1}{3}, \frac{23}{3}\right)$

The vertex is $\left(\frac{1}{2}, -\frac{25}{4}\right)$.

NOW TRY

OBJECTIVE 2 **Graph a quadratic function.** We give a general approach.

Graphing a Quadratic Function $y = f(x)$

Step 1 **Determine whether the graph opens up or down.** If $a > 0$, the parabola opens up. If $a < 0$, it opens down.

Step 2 **Find the vertex.** Use the vertex formula or completing the square.

Step 3 **Find any intercepts.** To find the x-intercepts (if any), solve $f(x) = 0$. To find the y-intercept, evaluate $f(0)$.

Step 4 **Complete the graph.** Plot the points found so far. Find and plot additional points as needed, using symmetry about the axis.

NOW TRY
EXERCISE 4

Graph the quadratic function defined by
$$f(x) = x^2 + 2x - 3.$$
Give the vertex, axis, domain, and range.

EXAMPLE 4 Graphing a Quadratic Function

Graph the quadratic function defined by $f(x) = x^2 - x - 6$.

Step 1 From the equation, $a = 1$, so the graph of the function opens up.

Step 2 The vertex, $\left(\frac{1}{2}, -\frac{25}{4}\right)$, was found in **Example 3** by using the vertex formula.

Step 3 Find any intercepts. Since the vertex, $\left(\frac{1}{2}, -\frac{25}{4}\right)$, is in quadrant IV and the graph opens up, there will be two x-intercepts. Let $f(x) = 0$ and solve.

$$f(x) = x^2 - x - 6$$
$$0 = x^2 - x - 6 \qquad \text{Let } f(x) = 0.$$
$$0 = (x - 3)(x + 2) \qquad \text{Factor.}$$
$$x - 3 = 0 \quad \text{or} \quad x + 2 = 0 \qquad \text{Zero-factor property}$$
$$x = 3 \quad \text{or} \qquad x = -2 \qquad \text{Solve each equation.}$$

The x-intercepts are $(3, 0)$ and $(-2, 0)$. Find the y-intercept by evaluating $f(0)$.

$$f(x) = x^2 - x - 6$$
$$f(0) = 0^2 - 0 - 6 \qquad \text{Let } x = 0.$$
$$f(0) = -6$$

The y-intercept is $(0, -6)$.

Step 4 Plot the points found so far and additional points as needed using symmetry about the axis, $x = \frac{1}{2}$. The graph is shown in **FIGURE 13**.

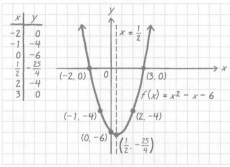

$f(x) = x^2 - x - 6$
Vertex: $\left(\frac{1}{2}, -\frac{25}{4}\right)$
Axis: $x = \frac{1}{2}$
Domain: $(-\infty, \infty)$
Range: $\left[-\frac{25}{4}, \infty\right)$

FIGURE 13

NOW TRY ANSWER

4.

$x = -1$

$(-3, 0)$ $(1, 0)$
$(-1, -4)$ $(0, -3)$
$f(x) = x^2 + 2x - 3$

vertex: $(-1, -4)$; axis: $x = -1$;
domain: $(-\infty, \infty)$; range: $[-4, \infty)$

NOW TRY

OBJECTIVE 3 **Use the discriminant to find the number of x-intercepts of a parabola with a vertical axis.** Recall from **Section 11.3** that

$$b^2 - 4ac \quad \text{Discriminant}$$

is called the *discriminant* of the quadratic equation $ax^2 + bx + c = 0$ and that we can use it to determine the number of real solutions of a quadratic equation.

In a similar way, we can use the discriminant of a quadratic *function* to determine the number of x-intercepts of its graph. The three possibilities are shown in **FIGURE 14**.

1. If the discriminant is positive, the parabola will have two x-intercepts.

2. If the discriminant is 0, there will be only one x-intercept, and it will be the vertex of the parabola.

3. If the discriminant is negative, the graph will have no x-intercepts.

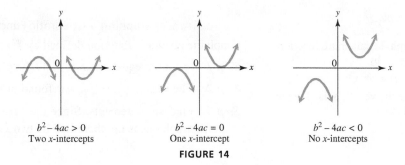

| $b^2 - 4ac > 0$ | $b^2 - 4ac = 0$ | $b^2 - 4ac < 0$ |
| Two x-intercepts | One x-intercept | No x-intercepts |

FIGURE 14

NOW TRY
EXERCISE 5

Find the discriminant and use it to determine the number of x-intercepts of the graph of each quadratic function.

(a) $f(x) = -2x^2 + 3x - 2$

(b) $f(x) = 3x^2 + 2x - 1$

(c) $f(x) = 4x^2 - 12x + 9$

EXAMPLE 5 Using the Discriminant to Determine the Number of x-Intercepts

Find the discriminant and use it to determine the number of x-intercepts of the graph of each quadratic function.

(a) $f(x) = 2x^2 + 3x - 5$

$$b^2 - 4ac \qquad \text{Discriminant}$$
$$= 3^2 - 4(2)(-5) \qquad a = 2, b = 3, c = -5$$
$$= 9 - (-40) \qquad \text{Apply the exponent. Multiply.}$$
$$= 49 \qquad \text{Subtract.}$$

Since the discriminant is positive, the parabola has two x-intercepts.

(b) $f(x) = -3x^2 - 1$

$$b^2 - 4ac$$
$$= 0^2 - 4(-3)(-1) \qquad a = -3, b = 0, c = -1$$
$$= -12$$

The discriminant is negative, so the graph has no x-intercepts.

(c) $f(x) = 9x^2 + 6x + 1$

$$b^2 - 4ac$$
$$= 6^2 - 4(9)(1) \qquad a = 9, b = 6, c = 1$$
$$= 0$$

NOW TRY ANSWERS
5. (a) -7; none **(b)** 16; two
(c) 0; one

The parabola has only one x-intercept (its vertex).

NOW TRY

OBJECTIVE 4 **Use quadratic functions to solve problems involving maximum or minimum value.** The vertex of the graph of a quadratic function is either the highest or the lowest point on the parabola. It provides the following information.

1. The y-value of the vertex gives the maximum or minimum value of y.

2. The x-value tells where the maximum or minimum occurs.

> **PROBLEM-SOLVING HINT**
>
> In many applied problems we must find the greatest or least value of some quantity. When we can express that quantity in terms of a quadratic function, the value of k in the vertex (h, k) gives that optimum value.

⌐ *NOW TRY*
ↄ *EXERCISE 6*

Solve the problem in **Example 6** if the farmer has only 80 ft of fencing.

EXAMPLE 6 Finding the Maximum Area of a Rectangular Region

A farmer has 120 ft of fencing to enclose a rectangular area next to a building. (See **FIGURE 15**.) Find the maximum area he can enclose and the dimensions of the field when the area is maximized.

FIGURE 15

Let $x =$ the width of the field.

$$x + x + \text{length} = 120 \qquad \text{Sum of the sides is 120 ft.}$$
$$2x + \text{length} = 120 \qquad \text{Combine like terms.}$$
$$\text{length} = 120 - 2x \qquad \text{Subtract } 2x.$$

The area $\mathcal{A}(x)$ is given by the product of the length and width.

$$\mathcal{A}(x) = (120 - 2x)x \qquad \text{Area = length · width}$$
$$\mathcal{A}(x) = 120x - 2x^2 \qquad \text{Distributive property}$$

To determine the maximum area, use the vertex formula to find the vertex of the parabola given by $\mathcal{A}(x) = 120x - 2x^2$. Write the equation in standard form.

$$\mathcal{A}(x) = -2x^2 + 120x \qquad a = -2, b = 120, c = 0$$

Then
$$x = \frac{-b}{2a} = \frac{-120}{2(-2)} = \frac{-120}{-4} = 30,$$

and
$$\mathcal{A}(30) = -2(30)^2 + 120(30) = -2(900) + 3600 = 1800.$$

The graph is a parabola that opens down, and its vertex is $(30, 1800)$. Thus, the maximum area will be 1800 ft². This area will occur if x, the width of the field, is 30 ft and the length is

$$120 - 2(30) = 60 \text{ ft.} \qquad \text{NOW TRY} ↄ$$

NOW TRY ANSWER
6. The field should be 20 ft by 40 ft with maximum area 800 ft².

⚠️ **CAUTION** *Be careful when interpreting the meanings of the coordinates of the vertex.* The first coordinate, x, gives the value for which the *function value, y or $f(x)$,* is a maximum or a minimum. Be sure to read the problem carefully to determine whether you are asked to find the value of the independent variable, the function value, or both.

NOW TRY
EXERCISE 7

A stomp rocket is launched from the ground with an initial velocity of 48 ft per sec so that its distance in feet above the ground after t seconds is

$$s(t) = -16t^2 + 48t.$$

Find the maximum height attained by the rocket and the number of seconds it takes to reach that height.

EXAMPLE 7 Finding the Maximum Height Attained by a Projectile

If air resistance is neglected, a projectile on Earth shot straight upward with an initial velocity of 40 m per sec will be at a height s in meters given by

$$s(t) = -4.9t^2 + 40t,$$

where t is the number of seconds elapsed after projection. After how many seconds will it reach its maximum height, and what is this maximum height?

For this function, $a = -4.9$, $b = 40$, and $c = 0$. Use the vertex formula.

$$t = \frac{-b}{2a} = \frac{-40}{2(-4.9)} \approx 4.1 \qquad \text{Use a calculator.}$$

This indicates that the maximum height is attained at 4.1 sec. To find this maximum height, calculate $s(4.1)$.

$$s(t) = -4.9t^2 + 40t$$

$$s(4.1) = -4.9(4.1)^2 + 40(4.1) \qquad \text{Let } t = 4.1.$$

$$s(4.1) \approx 81.6 \qquad \text{Use a calculator.}$$

The projectile will attain a maximum height of approximately 81.6 m at 4.1 sec.

NOW TRY

OBJECTIVE 5 **Graph parabolas with horizontal axes.** If x and y are interchanged in the equation

$$y = ax^2 + bx + c,$$

the equation becomes

$$x = ay^2 + by + c.$$

Because of the interchange of the roles of x and y, these parabolas are horizontal (with horizontal lines as axes).

Graph of a Horizontal Parabola

The graph of $x = ay^2 + by + c$ or $x = a(y - k)^2 + h$ is a parabola.

- The vertex of the parabola is (h, k).
- The axis is the horizontal line $y = k$.
- The graph opens to the right if $a > 0$ and to the left if $a < 0$.

NOW TRY ANSWER
7. 36 ft; 1.5 sec

NOW TRY
EXERCISE 8

Graph $x = (y + 2)^2 - 1$. Give the vertex, axis, domain, and range.

EXAMPLE 8 Graphing a Horizontal Parabola ($a = 1$)

Graph $x = (y - 2)^2 - 3$. Give the vertex, axis, domain, and range.

This graph has its vertex at $(-3, 2)$, since the roles of x and y are interchanged. It opens to the right (the positive x-direction) because $a = 1$ and $1 > 0$, and has the same shape as $y = x^2$. Plotting a few additional points gives the graph shown in **FIGURE 16**.

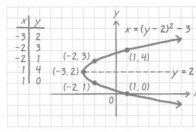

$x = (y - 2)^2 - 3$
Vertex: $(-3, 2)$
Axis: $y = 2$
Domain: $[-3, \infty)$
Range: $(-\infty, \infty)$

FIGURE 16

NOW TRY

NOW TRY
EXERCISE 9

Graph $x = -3y^2 - 6y - 5$. Give the vertex, axis, domain, and range.

EXAMPLE 9 Completing the Square to Graph a Horizontal Parabola ($a \neq 1$)

Graph $x = -2y^2 + 4y - 3$. Give the vertex, axis, domain, and range of the relation.

$$x = -2y^2 + 4y - 3$$
$$= -2(y^2 - 2y) - 3 \qquad \text{Factor out } -2.$$
$$= -2(y^2 - 2y + 1 - 1) - 3 \qquad \text{Complete the square within the parentheses. Add and subtract 1.}$$
$$= -2(y^2 - 2y + 1) + (-2)(-1) - 3 \qquad \text{Distributive property}$$
$$\boxed{\text{Be careful here.}}$$
$$x = -2(y - 1)^2 - 1 \qquad \text{Factor. Simplify.}$$

Because of the negative coefficient -2 in $x = -2(y - 1)^2 - 1$, the graph opens to the left (the negative x-direction). The graph is narrower than the graph of $y = x^2$ because $|-2| > 1$. See **FIGURE 17**.

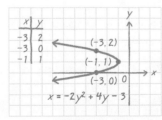

$x = -2y^2 + 4y - 3$
Vertex: $(-1, 1)$
Axis: $y = 1$
Domain: $(-\infty, -1]$
Range: $(-\infty, \infty)$

FIGURE 17

NOW TRY

NOW TRY ANSWERS
8.

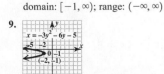

vertex: $(-1, -2)$; axis: $y = -2$;
domain: $[-1, \infty)$; range: $(-\infty, \infty)$

9.

vertex: $(-2, -1)$; axis: $y = -1$;
domain: $(-\infty, -2]$; range: $(-\infty, \infty)$

⚠ **CAUTION** *Only quadratic equations solved for y (whose graphs are vertical parabolas) are examples of functions.* The horizontal parabolas in **Examples 8 and 9** are *not* graphs of functions, because they do not satisfy the conditions of the vertical line test.

In summary, the graphs of parabolas fall into the following categories.

Graphs of Parabolas

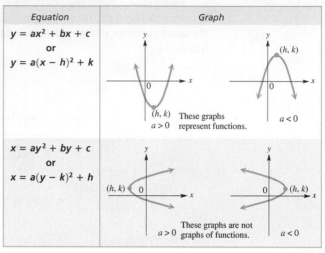

Equation	Graph
$y = ax^2 + bx + c$ or $y = a(x - h)^2 + k$	These graphs represent functions. $a > 0$, $a < 0$
$x = ay^2 + by + c$ or $x = a(y - k)^2 + h$	These graphs are not graphs of functions. $a > 0$, $a < 0$

11.7 EXERCISES MyMathLab Math XL PRACTICE WATCH DOWNLOAD READ REVIEW

 Complete solution available on the Video Resources on DVD

Concept Check *In Exercises 1–4, answer each question.*

1. How can you determine just by looking at the equation of a parabola whether it has a vertical or a horizontal axis?

2. Why can't the graph of a quadratic function be a parabola with a horizontal axis?

3. How can you determine the number of x-intercepts of the graph of a quadratic function without graphing the function?

4. If the vertex of the graph of a quadratic function is $(1, -3)$, and the graph opens down, how many x-intercepts does the graph have?

Find the vertex of each parabola. ***See Examples 1–3.***

5. $f(x) = x^2 + 8x + 10$

6. $f(x) = x^2 + 10x + 23$

7. $f(x) = -2x^2 + 4x - 5$

8. $f(x) = -3x^2 + 12x - 8$

9. $f(x) = x^2 + x - 7$

10. $f(x) = x^2 - x + 5$

Find the vertex of each parabola. For each equation, decide whether the graph opens up, down, to the left, or to the right, and whether it is wider, narrower, or the same shape as the graph of $y = x^2$. If it is a parabola with vertical axis, find the discriminant and use it to determine the number of x-intercepts. ***See Examples 1–3, 5, 8, and 9.***

11. $f(x) = 2x^2 + 4x + 5$

12. $f(x) = 3x^2 - 6x + 4$

13. $f(x) = -x^2 + 5x + 3$

14. $f(x) = -x^2 + 7x + 2$

15. $x = \frac{1}{3}y^2 + 6y + 24$

16. $x = \frac{1}{2}y^2 + 10y - 5$

Concept Check Match each equation in Exercises 17–22 with its graph in choices A–F.

17. $y = 2x^2 + 4x - 3$

18. $y = -x^2 + 3x + 5$

19. $y = -\dfrac{1}{2}x^2 - x + 1$

20. $x = y^2 + 6y + 3$

21. $x = -y^2 - 2y + 4$

22. $x = 3y^2 + 6y + 5$

A.

B.

C.

D.

E.

F.
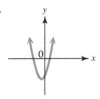

*Graph each parabola. (Use the results of **Exercises 5–8** to help graph the parabolas in Exercises 23–26.) Give the vertex, axis, domain, and range. **See Examples 4, 8, and 9.***

23. $f(x) = x^2 + 8x + 10$

24. $f(x) = x^2 + 10x + 23$

25. $f(x) = -2x^2 + 4x - 5$

26. $f(x) = -3x^2 + 12x - 8$

27. $x = (y + 2)^2 + 1$

28. $x = (y + 3)^2 - 2$

29. $x = -\dfrac{1}{5}y^2 + 2y - 4$

30. $x = -\dfrac{1}{2}y^2 - 4y - 6$

31. $x = 3y^2 + 12y + 5$

32. $x = 4y^2 + 16y + 11$

*Solve each problem. **See Examples 6 and 7.***

33. Find the pair of numbers whose sum is 40 and whose product is a maximum. (*Hint:* Let x and $40 - x$ represent the two numbers.)

34. Find the pair of numbers whose sum is 60 and whose product is a maximum.

35. Polk Community College wants to construct a rectangular parking lot on land bordered on one side by a highway. It has 280 ft of fencing that is to be used to fence off the other three sides. What should be the dimensions of the lot if the enclosed area is to be a maximum? What is the maximum area?

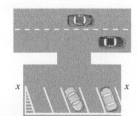

36. Bonnie Wolansky has 100 ft of fencing material to enclose a rectangular exercise run for her dog. One side of the run will border her house, so she will only need to fence three sides. What dimensions will give the enclosure the maximum area? What is the maximum area?

37. If an object on Earth is projected upward with an initial velocity of 32 ft per sec, then its height after t seconds is given by

$$s(t) = -16t^2 + 32t.$$

Find the maximum height attained by the object and the number of seconds it takes to hit the ground.

38. A projectile on Earth is fired straight upward so that its distance (in feet) above the ground t seconds after firing is given by

$$s(t) = -16t^2 + 400t.$$

Find the maximum height it reaches and the number of seconds it takes to reach that height.

39. After experimentation, two physics students from American River College find that when a bottle of California wine is shaken several times, held upright, and uncorked, its cork travels according to the function defined by

$$s(t) = -16t^2 + 64t + 1,$$

where s is its height in feet above the ground t seconds after being released. After how many seconds will it reach its maximum height? What is the maximum height?

40. Professor Barbu has found that the number of students attending his intermediate algebra class is approximated by

$$S(x) = -x^2 + 20x + 80,$$

where x is the number of hours that the Campus Center is open daily. Find the number of hours that the center should be open so that the number of students attending class is a maximum. What is this maximum number of students?

41. Klaus Loewy has a taco stand. He has found that his daily costs are approximated by

$$C(x) = x^2 - 40x + 610,$$

where $C(x)$ is the cost, in dollars, to sell x units of tacos. Find the number of units of tacos he should sell to minimize his costs. What is the minimum cost?

42. Mohammad Asghar has a frozen yogurt cart. His daily costs are approximated by

$$C(x) = x^2 - 70x + 1500,$$

where $C(x)$ is the cost, in dollars, to sell x units of frozen yogurt. Find the number of units of frozen yogurt he must sell to minimize his costs. What is the minimum cost?

43. The total receipts from individual income taxes by the U.S. Treasury in the years 2000–2007 can be modeled by the quadratic function defined by

$$f(x) = 22.88x^2 - 141.3x + 1044,$$

where $x = 0$ represents 2000, $x = 1$ represents 2001, and so on, and $f(x)$ is in billions of dollars. (*Source: World Almanac and Book of Facts.*)

(a) Since the coefficient of x^2 given in the model is positive, the graph of this quadratic function is a parabola that opens up. Will the y-value of the vertex of this graph be a maximum or minimum?

(b) In what year during this period were total receipts from individual taxes a minimum? (Round down for the year.) Use the actual x-value of the vertex, to the nearest tenth, to find this amount.

44. The percent of births in the United States to teenage mothers in the years 1990–2005 can be modeled by the quadratic function defined by

$$f(x) = -0.0198x^2 + 0.1054x + 12.87,$$

where $x = 0$ represents 1990, $x = 1$ represents 1991, and so on. (*Source:* U.S. National Center for Health Statistics.)

(a) Since the coefficient of x^2 in the model is negative, the graph of this quadratic function is a parabola that opens down. Will the y-value of the vertex of this graph be a maximum or a minimum?

(b) In what year during this period was the percent of births in the U.S. to teenage mothers a maximum? (Round down for the year.) Use the actual x-value of the vertex, to the nearest tenth, to find this percent.

45. The graph on the next page shows how Social Security trust fund assets are expected to change, and suggests that a quadratic function would be a good fit to the data. The data are approximated by the function defined by

$$f(x) = -20.57x^2 + 758.9x - 3140.$$

In the model, $x = 10$ represents 2010, $x = 15$ represents 2015, and so on, and $f(x)$ is in billions of dollars.

(a) *Concept Check*   How could you have predicted this quadratic model would have a negative coefficient for x^2, based only on the graph shown?

(b) Algebraically determine the vertex of the graph, with coordinates to four significant digits.

(c) Interpret the answer to part (b) as it applies to this application.

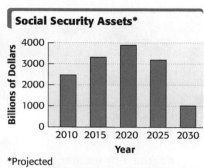

Social Security Assets*

*Projected

Source: Social Security Administration.

46. The graph shows the performance of investment portfolios with different mixtures of U.S. and foreign investments over a 25-yr period.

(a) Is this the graph of a function? Explain.

(b) What investment mixture shown on the graph appears to represent the vertex? What relative amount of risk does this point represent? What return on investment does it provide?

(c) Which point on the graph represents the riskiest investment mixture? What return on investment does it provide?

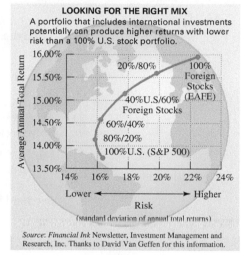

LOOKING FOR THE RIGHT MIX
A portfolio that includes international investments potentially can produce higher returns with lower risk than a 100% U.S. stock portfolio.

Source: Financial Ink Newsletter, Investment Management and Research, Inc. Thanks to David Van Geffen for this information.

47. A charter flight charges a fare of $200 per person, plus $4 per person for each unsold seat on the plane. If the plane holds 100 passengers and if x represents the number of unsold seats, find the following.

(a) A function defined by $R(x)$ that describes the total revenue received for the flight (*Hint:* Multiply the number of people flying, $100 - x$, by the price per ticket, $200 + 4x$.)

(b) The graph of the function from part (a)

(c) The number of unsold seats that will produce the maximum revenue

(d) The maximum revenue

48. For a trip to a resort, a charter bus company charges a fare of $48 per person, plus $2 per person for each unsold seat on the bus. If the bus has 42 seats and x represents the number of unsold seats, find the following.

(a) A function defined by $R(x)$ that describes the total revenue from the trip (*Hint:* Multiply the total number riding, $42 - x$, by the price per ticket, $48 + 2x$.)

(b) The graph of the function from part (a)

(c) The number of unsold seats that produces the maximum revenue

(d) The maximum revenue

PREVIEW EXERCISES

Graph each interval on a number line. See Section 2.8.

49. $[1, 5]$ **50.** $(-6, 1]$ **51.** $(-\infty, 1] \cup [5, \infty)$

Solve each inequality. See Section 2.8.

52. $3 - x \le 5$ **53.** $-2x + 1 < 4$ **54.** $-\dfrac{1}{2}x - 3 > 5$

(11.8) Polynomial and Rational Inequalities

OBJECTIVES

1. Solve quadratic inequalities.
2. Solve polynomial inequalities of degree 3 or greater.
3. Solve rational inequalities.

OBJECTIVE 1 **Solve quadratic inequalities.** Now we combine the methods of solving linear inequalities with the methods of solving quadratic equations to solve *quadratic inequalities*.

Quadratic Inequality

A **quadratic inequality** can be written in the form

$$ax^2 + bx + c < 0, \qquad ax^2 + bx + c > 0,$$

$$ax^2 + bx + c \le 0, \qquad \text{or} \qquad ax^2 + bx + c \ge 0,$$

where a, b, and c are real numbers, with $a \ne 0$.

One way to solve a quadratic inequality is by graphing the related quadratic function.

EXAMPLE 1 Solving Quadratic Inequalities by Graphing

Solve each inequality.

(a) $x^2 - x - 12 > 0$

To solve the inequality, we graph the related quadratic function defined by $f(x) = x^2 - x - 12$. We are particularly interested in the x-intercepts, which are found as in **Section 11.7** by letting $f(x) = 0$ and solving the following quadratic equation.

$$x^2 - x - 12 = 0$$

$$(x - 4)(x + 3) = 0 \qquad \text{Factor.}$$

$$x - 4 = 0 \quad \text{or} \quad x + 3 = 0 \qquad \text{Zero-factor property}$$

$$x = 4 \quad \text{or} \qquad x = -3 \leftarrow \text{The } x\text{-intercepts are } (4,0) \text{ and } (-3,0).$$

The graph, which opens up since the coefficient of x^2 is positive, is shown in **FIGURE 18(a)**. Notice from this graph that x-values less than -3 or greater than 4 result in y-values *greater than* 0. Thus, the solution set of $x^2 - x - 12 > 0$, written in interval notation, is $(-\infty, -3) \cup (4, \infty)$.

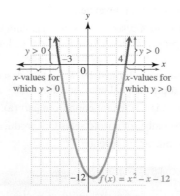

The graph is *above* the x-axis for $(-\infty, -3) \cup (4, \infty)$.

(a)

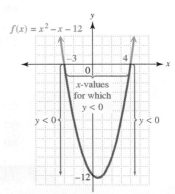

The graph is *below* the x-axis for $(-3, 4)$.

(b)

FIGURE 18

↶ *NOW TRY*
EXERCISE 1

Use the graph to solve each quadratic inequality.

$f(x) = x^2 - 3x - 4$

(a) $x^2 - 3x - 4 > 0$

(b) $x^2 - 3x - 4 < 0$

(b) $x^2 - x - 12 < 0$

We want values of y that are *less than* 0. Referring to **FIGURE 18(b)**, we notice from the graph that x-values between -3 and 4 result in y-values less than 0. Thus, the solution set of $x^2 - x - 12 < 0$, written in interval notation, is $(-3, 4)$. *NOW TRY* ↶

NOTE If the inequalities in **Example 1** had used $\geq$ and $\leq$, the solution sets would have included the x-values of the intercepts, which make the quadratic expression equal to 0. They would have been written in interval notation as

$$(-\infty, -3] \cup [4, \infty) \quad \text{and} \quad [-3, 4].$$

Square brackets would indicate that the endpoints -3 and 4 are *included* in the solution sets.

Another method for solving a quadratic inequality uses the basic ideas of **Example 1** without actually graphing the related quadratic function.

EXAMPLE 2 **Solving a Quadratic Inequality Using Test Numbers**

Solve and graph the solution set of $x^2 - x - 12 > 0$.

Solve the quadratic equation $x^2 - x - 12 = 0$ by factoring, as in **Example 1(a)**.

$$(x - 4)(x + 3) = 0$$

$$x - 4 = 0 \quad \text{or} \quad x + 3 = 0$$

$$x = 4 \quad \text{or} \quad x = -3$$

The numbers 4 and -3 divide a number line into Intervals A, B, and C, as shown in **FIGURE 19**. *Be careful to put the lesser number on the left.*

Interval A	Interval B	Interval C
T −3	F 4	T

FIGURE 19

Notice the similarity between **FIGURE 19** and the *x*-axis with intercepts $(-3, 0)$ and $(4, 0)$ in **FIGURE 18(a)**.

The numbers 4 and -3 are the only numbers that make the quadratic expression $x^2 - x - 12$ equal to 0. All other numbers make the expression either positive or negative. The sign of the expression can change from positive to negative or from negative to positive only at a number that makes it 0. Therefore, if one number in an interval satisfies the inequality, then all the numbers in that interval will satisfy the inequality.

To see if the numbers in Interval A satisfy the inequality, choose any number from Interval A in **FIGURE 19** (that is, any number less than -3). We choose -5. Substitute this test number for x in the original inequality $x^2 - x - 12 > 0$.

$$x^2 - x - 12 > 0 \quad \text{Original inequality}$$

$$(-5)^2 - (-5) - 12 \overset{?}{>} 0 \quad \text{Let } x = -5.$$

Use parentheses to avoid sign errors.

$$25 + 5 - 12 \overset{?}{>} 0 \quad \text{Simplify.}$$

$$18 > 0 \checkmark \text{ True}$$

Because -5 satisfies the inequality, *all* numbers from Interval A are solutions.

NOW TRY ANSWERS
1. **(a)** $(-\infty, -1) \cup (4, \infty)$
(b) $(-1, 4)$

⌐NOW TRY
↳ EXERCISE 2
Solve and graph the solution set.

$$x^2 + 2x - 8 > 0$$

Now try 0 from Interval B.

$$x^2 - x - 12 > 0 \qquad \text{Original inequality}$$
$$0^2 - 0 - 12 \overset{?}{>} 0 \qquad \text{Let } x = 0.$$
$$-12 > 0 \qquad \text{False}$$

The numbers in Interval B are *not* solutions. Verify that the test number 5 from Interval C satisfies the inequality, so all numbers there are also solutions.

Based on these results (shown by the colored letters in **FIGURE 19**), the solution set includes the numbers in Intervals A and C, as shown on the graph in **FIGURE 20**. The solution set is written in interval notation as

$$(-\infty, -3) \cup (4, \infty).$$

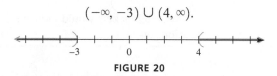

FIGURE 20

This agrees with the solution set found in **Example 1(a).**   NOW TRY ⤴

In summary, follow these steps to solve a quadratic inequality.

Solving a Quadratic Inequality

Step 1   **Write the inequality as an equation and solve it.**

Step 2   **Use the solutions from Step 1 to determine intervals.** Graph the numbers found in Step 1 on a number line. These numbers divide the number line into intervals.

Step 3   **Find the intervals that satisfy the inequality.** Substitute a test number from each interval into the original inequality to determine the intervals that satisfy the inequality. All numbers in those intervals are in the solution set. A graph of the solution set will usually look like one of these. (Square brackets might be used instead of parentheses.)

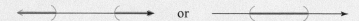

Step 4   **Consider the endpoints separately.** The numbers from Step 1 are included in the solution set if the inequality symbol is ≤ or ≥. They are not included if it is < or >.

⌐NOW TRY
↳ EXERCISE 3
Solve each inequality.

(a) $(4x - 1)^2 > -3$

(b) $(4x - 1)^2 < -3$

NOW TRY ANSWERS
2. $(-\infty, -4) \cup (2, \infty)$

⟵+⟩++++++⟨+⟶
  −4   0   2

3. (a) $(-\infty, \infty)$ (b) ∅

EXAMPLE 3   Solving Special Cases

Solve each inequality.

(a) $(2x - 3)^2 > -1$

Because $(2x - 3)^2$ is never negative, it is always greater than -1. Thus, the solution set for $(2x - 3)^2 > -1$ is the set of all real numbers, $(-\infty, \infty)$.

(b) $(2x - 3)^2 < -1$

Using the same reasoning as in part (a), there is no solution for this inequality. The solution set is ∅.   NOW TRY ⤴

OBJECTIVE 2 Solve polynomial inequalities of degree 3 or greater.

NOW TRY
EXERCISE 4
Solve and graph the solution set.

$(x + 4)(x - 3)(2x + 1) \le 0$

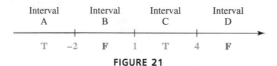 **EXAMPLE 4** Solving a Third-Degree Polynomial Inequality

Solve and graph the solution set of $(x - 1)(x + 2)(x - 4) \le 0$.

This is a *cubic* (third-degree) inequality rather than a quadratic inequality, but it can be solved using the preceding method by extending the zero-factor property to more than two factors. (Step 1)

$$(x - 1)(x + 2)(x - 4) = 0 \qquad \text{Set the factored polynomial \textit{equal} to 0.}$$

$$x - 1 = 0 \quad \text{or} \quad x + 2 = 0 \quad \text{or} \quad x - 4 = 0 \qquad \text{Zero-factor property}$$

$$x = 1 \quad \text{or} \qquad x = -2 \quad \text{or} \qquad x = 4 \qquad \text{Solve each equation.}$$

Locate the numbers -2, 1, and 4 on a number line, as in **FIGURE 21**, to determine the Intervals A, B, C, and D. (Step 2)

Interval A		Interval B		Interval C		Interval D
T	-2	F	1	T	4	F

FIGURE 21

Substitute a test number from each interval in the *original* inequality to determine which intervals satisfy the inequality. (Step 3)

Interval	Test Number	Test of Inequality	True or False?
A	-3	$-28 \le 0$	T
B	0	$8 \le 0$	F
C	2	$-8 \le 0$	T
D	5	$28 \le 0$	F

We use a table to organize this information. (Verify it.)

The numbers in Intervals A and C are in the solution set, which is written in interval notation as $(-\infty, -2] \cup [1, 4]$, and graphed in **FIGURE 22**. The three endpoints are included since the inequality symbol, $\le$, includes equality. (Step 4)

FIGURE 22

NOW TRY

OBJECTIVE 3 Solve rational inequalities. Inequalities that involve rational expressions, called **rational inequalities,** are solved similarly using the following steps.

Solving a Rational Inequality

Step 1 **Write the inequality so that 0 is on one side** and there is a single fraction on the other side.

Step 2 **Determine the numbers that make the numerator or denominator equal to 0.**

Step 3 **Divide a number line into intervals.** Use the numbers from Step 2.

Step 4 **Find the intervals that satisfy the inequality.** Test a number from each interval by substituting it into the *original* inequality.

Step 5 **Consider the endpoints separately.** Exclude any values that make the denominator 0.

NOW TRY ANSWER
4. $(-\infty, -4] \cup \left[-\frac{1}{2}, 3\right]$

> ⚠ **CAUTION** *When solving a rational inequality, any number that makes the denominator 0 must be excluded from the solution set.*

↰ *NOW TRY*
EXERCISE 5

Solve and graph the solution set.

$$\frac{3}{x+1} > 4$$

EXAMPLE 5 Solving a Rational Inequality

Solve and graph the solution set of $\dfrac{-1}{x-3} > 1$.

Write the inequality so that 0 is on one side. (Step 1)

$$\frac{-1}{x-3} - 1 > 0 \qquad \text{Subtract 1.}$$

$$\frac{-1}{x-3} - \frac{x-3}{x-3} > 0 \qquad \text{Use } x-3 \text{ as the common denominator.}$$

> Be careful with signs. $\dfrac{-1-x+3}{x-3} > 0 \qquad$ Write the left side as a single fraction.

$$\frac{-x+2}{x-3} > 0 \qquad \text{Combine like terms in the numerator.}$$

The sign of $\frac{-x+2}{x-3}$ will change from positive to negative or negative to positive only at those numbers that make the numerator or denominator 0. The number 2 makes the numerator 0, and 3 makes the denominator 0. (Step 2) These two numbers, 2 and 3, divide a number line into three intervals. See **FIGURE 23**. (Step 3)

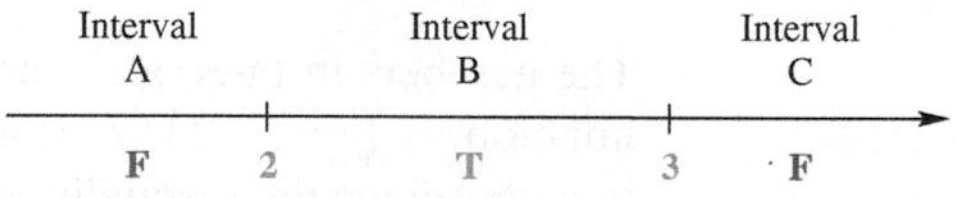

Interval A   Interval B   Interval C

F   2   T   3 ·F

FIGURE 23

Testing a number from each interval in the *original* inequality, $\frac{-1}{x-3} > 1$, gives the results shown in the table. (Step 4)

Interval	Test Number	Test of Inequality	True or False?
A	0	$\frac{1}{3} > 1$	F
B	2.5	$2 > 1$	T
C	4	$-1 > 1$	F

The solution set is the interval $(2, 3)$. This interval does not include 3 since it would make the denominator of the original equality 0. The number 2 is not included either since the inequality symbol, $>$, does not include equality. (Step 5) See **FIGURE 24**.

NOW TRY ANSWER
5. $\left(-1, -\frac{1}{4}\right)$

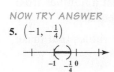

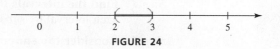

FIGURE 24

NOW TRY ↻

Solve and graph the solution set.

$$\frac{x - 3}{x + 3} \le 2$$

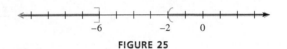 **EXAMPLE 6** Solving a Rational Inequality

Solve and graph the solution set of $\dfrac{x - 2}{x + 2} \le 2$.

Write the inequality so that 0 is on one side. (Step 1)

$$\frac{x - 2}{x + 2} - 2 \le 0 \qquad \text{Subtract 2.}$$

$$\frac{x - 2}{x + 2} - \frac{2(x + 2)}{x + 2} \le 0 \qquad \text{Use } x + 2 \text{ as the common denominator.}$$

Be careful with signs. $$\frac{x - 2 - 2x - 4}{x + 2} \le 0 \qquad \text{Write as a single fraction.}$$

$$\frac{-x - 6}{x + 2} \le 0 \qquad \text{Combine like terms in the numerator.}$$

The number -6 makes the numerator 0, and -2 makes the denominator 0. (Step 2) These two numbers determine three intervals. (Step 3) Test one number from each interval (Step 4) to see that the solution set is

$$(-\infty, -6] \cup (-2, \infty).$$

The number -6 satisfies the original inequality, but -2 does not since it makes the denominator 0. (Step 5) **FIGURE 25** shows a graph of the solution set.

NOW TRY ANSWER
6. $(-\infty, -9] \cup (-3, \infty)$

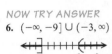

FIGURE 25

NOW TRY

11.8 EXERCISES

Complete solution available on the Video Resources on DVD

In Exercises 1–3, the graph of a quadratic function f is given. Use the graph to find the solution set of each equation or inequality. **See Example 1.**

1. (a) $x^2 - 4x + 3 = 0$
   (b) $x^2 - 4x + 3 > 0$
   (c) $x^2 - 4x + 3 < 0$

2. (a) $3x^2 + 10x - 8 = 0$
   (b) $3x^2 + 10x - 8 \ge 0$
   (c) $3x^2 + 10x - 8 < 0$

3. (a) $-x^2 + 3x + 10 = 0$
   (b) $-x^2 + 3x + 10 \ge 0$
   (c) $-x^2 + 3x + 10 \le 0$

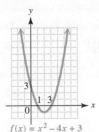

$f(x) = x^2 - 4x + 3$

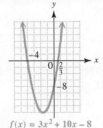

$f(x) = 3x^2 + 10x - 8$

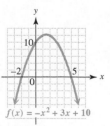

$f(x) = -x^2 + 3x + 10$

4. *Concept Check* The solution set of the inequality $x^2 + x - 12 < 0$ is the interval $(-4, 3)$. Without actually performing any work, give the solution set of the inequality $x^2 + x - 12 \ge 0$.

Solve each inequality, and graph the solution set. ***See Example 2.*** *(Hint: In Exercises 21 and 22, use the quadratic formula.)*

5. $(x + 1)(x - 5) > 0$

6. $(x + 6)(x - 2) > 0$

7. $(x + 4)(x - 6) < 0$

8. $(x + 4)(x - 8) < 0$

9. $x^2 - 4x + 3 \geq 0$

10. $x^2 - 3x - 10 \geq 0$

11. $10x^2 + 9x \geq 9$

12. $3x^2 + 10x \geq 8$

13. $4x^2 - 9 \leq 0$

14. $9x^2 - 25 \leq 0$

15. $6x^2 + x \geq 1$

16. $4x^2 + 7x \geq -3$

17. $z^2 - 4z \geq 0$

18. $x^2 + 2x < 0$

19. $3x^2 - 5x \leq 0$

20. $2z^2 + 3z > 0$

21. $x^2 - 6x + 6 \geq 0$

22. $3x^2 - 6x + 2 \leq 0$

Solve each inequality. ***See Example 3.***

23. $(4 - 3x)^2 \geq -2$

24. $(7 - 6x)^2 \geq -1$

25. $(3x + 5)^2 \leq -4$

26. $(8x + 5)^2 \leq -5$

Solve each inequality, and graph the solution set. ***See Example 4.***

27. $(x - 1)(x - 2)(x - 4) < 0$

28. $(2x + 1)(3x - 2)(4x + 7) < 0$

29. $(x - 4)(2x + 3)(3x - 1) \geq 0$

30. $(x + 2)(4x - 3)(2x + 7) \geq 0$

Solve each inequality, and graph the solution set. ***See Examples 5 and 6.***

31. $\dfrac{x - 1}{x - 4} > 0$

32. $\dfrac{x + 1}{x - 5} > 0$

33. $\dfrac{2x + 3}{x - 5} \leq 0$

34. $\dfrac{3x + 7}{x - 3} \leq 0$

35. $\dfrac{8}{x - 2} \geq 2$

36. $\dfrac{20}{x - 1} \geq 1$

37. $\dfrac{3}{2x - 1} < 2$

38. $\dfrac{6}{x - 1} < 1$

39. $\dfrac{x - 3}{x + 2} \geq 2$

40. $\dfrac{m + 4}{m + 5} \geq 2$

41. $\dfrac{x - 8}{x - 4} < 3$

42. $\dfrac{2t - 3}{t + 1} > 4$

43. $\dfrac{4k}{2k - 1} < k$

44. $\dfrac{r}{r + 2} < 2r$

45. $\dfrac{2x - 3}{x^2 + 1} \geq 0$

46. $\dfrac{9x - 8}{4x^2 + 25} < 0$

47. $\dfrac{(3x - 5)^2}{x + 2} > 0$

48. $\dfrac{(5x - 3)^2}{2x + 1} \leq 0$

PREVIEW EXERCISES

Give the domain and the range of each function. ***See Section 7.3.***

49. $\{(0, 1), (1, 2), (2, 4), (3, 8)\}$

50. $f(x) = x^2$

Decide whether each graph is that of a function. ***See Section 7.3.***

51.

52.

CHAPTER (**11**)

SUMMARY

KEY TERMS

11.1

quadratic equation

11.3

quadratic formula
discriminant

11.4

quadratic in form

11.6

parabola
vertex

axis
quadratic function

11.8

quadratic inequality
rational inequality

TEST YOUR WORD POWER

See how well you have learned the vocabulary in this chapter.

1. The **quadratic formula** is
   A. a formula to find the number of solutions of a quadratic equation
   B. a formula to find the type of solutions of a quadratic equation
   C. the standard form of a quadratic equation
   D. a general formula for solving any quadratic equation.

2. A **quadratic function** is a function that can be written in the form
   A. $f(x) = mx + b$ for real numbers m and b
   B. $f(x) = \frac{P(x)}{Q(x)}$, where $Q(x) \neq 0$
   C. $f(x) = ax^2 + bx + c$ for real numbers $a, b,$ and c $(a \neq 0)$
   D. $f(x) = \sqrt{x}$ for $x \geq 0$.

3. A **parabola** is the graph of
   A. any equation in two variables
   B. a linear equation
   C. an equation of degree 3
   D. a quadratic equation in two variables, where one is first-degree.

4. The **vertex** of a parabola is
   A. the point where the graph intersects the y-axis
   B. the point where the graph intersects the x-axis
   C. the lowest point on a parabola that opens up or the highest point on a parabola that opens down
   D. the origin.

5. The **axis** of a parabola is
   A. either the x-axis or the y-axis
   B. the vertical line (of a vertical parabola) or the horizontal line (of a horizontal parabola) through the vertex
   C. the lowest or highest point on the graph of a parabola
   D. a line through the origin.

6. A parabola is **symmetric about its axis** since
   A. its graph is near the axis
   B. its graph is identical on each side of the axis
   C. its graph looks different on each side of the axis
   D. its graph intersects the axis.

ANSWERS

1. D; *Example:* The solutions of $ax^2 + bx + c = 0$ $(a \neq 0)$ are given by $x = \dfrac{-b \pm \sqrt{b^2 - 4ac}}{2a}$.   **2.** C; *Examples:* $f(x) = x^2 - 2$, $f(x) = (x + 4)^2 + 1, f(x) = x^2 - 4x + 5$ **3.** D; *Examples:* See the figures in the Quick Review for **Sections 11.6 and 11.7.**   **4.** C; *Example:* The graph of $y = (x + 3)^2$ has vertex $(-3, 0)$, which is the lowest point on the graph.   **5.** B; *Example:* The axis of $y = (x + 3)^2$ is the vertical line $x = -3$.   **6.** B; *Example:* Since the graph of $y = (x + 3)^2$ is symmetric about its axis $x = -3$, the points $(-2, 1)$ and $(-4, 1)$ are on the graph.

QUICK REVIEW

CONCEPTS	EXAMPLES
11.1 Solving Quadratic Equations by the Square Root Property	Solve $(x - 1)^2 = 8$.
Square Root Property	
If x and k are complex numbers and $x^2 = k$, then $$x = \sqrt{k} \quad \text{or} \quad x = -\sqrt{k}.$$	$x - 1 = \sqrt{8}$ or $x - 1 = -\sqrt{8}$ $x = 1 + 2\sqrt{2}$ or $x = 1 - 2\sqrt{2}$ The solution set is $\{1 + 2\sqrt{2}, 1 - 2\sqrt{2}\}$, or $\{1 \pm 2\sqrt{2}\}$.

(continued)

CONCEPTS	EXAMPLES

11.2 Solving Quadratic Equations by Completing the Square

Completing the Square

To solve $ax^2 + bx + c = 0$ (with $a \neq 0$):

Step 1 If $a \neq 1$, divide each side by a.

Step 2 Write the equation with the variable terms on one side and the constant on the other.

Step 3 Take half the coefficient of x and square it.

Step 4 Add the square to each side.

Step 5 Factor the perfect square trinomial, and write it as the square of a binomial. Simplify the other side.

Step 6 Use the square root property to complete the solution.

Solve $2x^2 - 4x - 18 = 0$.

$$x^2 - 2x - 9 = 0 \qquad \text{Divide by 2.}$$
$$x^2 - 2x = 9 \qquad \text{Add 9.}$$
$$\left[\tfrac{1}{2}(-2)\right]^2 = (-1)^2 = 1$$
$$x^2 - 2x + 1 = 9 + 1 \qquad \text{Add 1.}$$
$$(x - 1)^2 = 10 \qquad \text{Factor. Add.}$$
$$x - 1 = \sqrt{10} \quad \text{or} \quad x - 1 = -\sqrt{10} \qquad \text{Square root property}$$
$$x = 1 + \sqrt{10} \quad \text{or} \quad x = 1 - \sqrt{10}$$

The solution set is $\left\{1 + \sqrt{10}, 1 - \sqrt{10}\right\}$, or $\left\{1 \pm \sqrt{10}\right\}$

11.3 Solving Quadratic Equations by the Quadratic Formula

Quadratic Formula

The solutions of $ax^2 + bx + c = 0$ (with $a \neq 0$) are given by
$$x = \frac{-b \pm \sqrt{b^2 - 4ac}}{2a}.$$

The Discriminant

If a, b, and c are integers, then the discriminant, $b^2 - 4ac$, of $ax^2 + bx + c = 0$ determines the number and type of solutions as follows.

Discriminant	Number and Type of Solutions
Positive, the square of an integer	Two rational solutions
Positive, not the square of an integer	Two irrational solutions
Zero	One rational solution
Negative	Two nonreal complex solutions

Solve $3x^2 + 5x + 2 = 0$.
$$x = \frac{-5 \pm \sqrt{5^2 - 4(3)(2)}}{2(3)} = \frac{-5 \pm 1}{6}$$
$$x = \frac{-5 + 1}{6} = -\frac{2}{3} \quad \text{or} \quad x = \frac{-5 - 1}{6} = -1$$

The solution set is $\left\{-1, -\frac{2}{3}\right\}$.

For $x^2 + 3x - 10 = 0$, the discriminant is
$$3^2 - 4(1)(-10) = 49. \qquad \text{Two rational solutions}$$
For $4x^2 + x + 1 = 0$, the discriminant is
$$1^2 - 4(4)(1) = -15. \qquad \text{Two nonreal complex solutions}$$

11.4 Equations Quadratic in Form

A nonquadratic equation that can be written in the form
$$au^2 + bu + c = 0,$$
for $a \neq 0$ and an algebraic expression u, is called quadratic in form. Substitute u for the expression, solve for u, and then solve for the variable in the expression.

Solve $3(x + 5)^2 + 7(x + 5) + 2 = 0$.
$$3u^2 + 7u + 2 = 0 \qquad \text{Let } u = x + 5.$$
$$(3u + 1)(u + 2) = 0 \qquad \text{Factor.}$$
$$u = -\frac{1}{3} \quad \text{or} \quad u = -2$$
$$x + 5 = -\frac{1}{3} \quad \text{or} \quad x + 5 = -2 \qquad x + 5 = u$$
$$x = -\frac{16}{3} \quad \text{or} \quad x = -7 \qquad \text{Subtract 5.}$$

The solution set is $\left\{-7, -\frac{16}{3}\right\}$.

(continued)

CONCEPTS	EXAMPLES

11.5 Formulas and Further Applications

To solve a formula for a squared variable, proceed as follows.

(a) If the variable appears only to the second power: Isolate the squared variable on one side of the equation, and then use the square root property.

(b) If the variable appears to the first and second powers: Write the equation in standard form, and then use the quadratic formula.

Solve $A = \dfrac{2mp}{r^2}$ for r.

$r^2 A = 2mp$ Multiply by r^2.

$r^2 = \dfrac{2mp}{A}$ Divide by A.

$r = \pm\sqrt{\dfrac{2mp}{A}}$ Square root property

$r = \dfrac{\pm\sqrt{2mpA}}{A}$ Rationalize denominator.

Solve $x^2 + rx = t$ for x.

$x^2 + rx - t = 0$ Standard form

$x = \dfrac{-r \pm \sqrt{r^2 - 4(1)(-t)}}{2(1)}$

$a = 1, b = r, c = -t$

$x = \dfrac{-r \pm \sqrt{r^2 + 4t}}{2}$

11.6 Graphs of Quadratic Functions

1. The graph of the quadratic function defined by $F(x) = a(x - h)^2 + k$, $a \neq 0$, is a parabola with vertex at (h, k) and the vertical line $x = h$ as axis.

2. The graph opens up if a is positive and down if a is negative.

3. The graph is wider than the graph of $f(x) = x^2$ if $0 < |a| < 1$ and narrower if $|a| > 1$.

Graph $f(x) = -(x + 3)^2 + 1$.

The graph opens down since $a < 0$.
Vertex: $(-3, 1)$
Axis: $x = -3$
Domain: $(-\infty, \infty)$
Range: $(-\infty, 1]$

11.7 More about Parabolas and Their Applications

The vertex of the graph of $f(x) = ax^2 + bx + c$, $a \neq 0$, may be found by completing the square.

The vertex has coordinates $\left(\dfrac{-b}{2a}, f\left(\dfrac{-b}{2a}\right)\right)$.

Graphing a Quadratic Function

Step 1 Determine whether the graph opens up or down.

Step 2 Find the vertex.

Step 3 Find the x-intercepts (if any). Find the y-intercept.

Step 4 Find and plot additional points as needed.

Horizontal Parabolas

The graph of

$$x = ay^2 + by + c \quad \text{or} \quad x = a(y - k)^2 + h$$

is a horizontal parabola with vertex (h, k) and the horizontal line $y = k$ as axis. The graph opens to the right if $a > 0$ and to the left if $a < 0$.

Horizontal parabolas do not represent functions.

Graph $f(x) = x^2 + 4x + 3$.

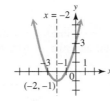

The graph opens up since $a > 0$.
Vertex: $(-2, -1)$
The solutions of $x^2 + 4x + 3 = 0$ are -1 and -3, so the x-intercepts are $(-1, 0)$ and $(-3, 0)$.
$f(0) = 3$, so the y-intercept is $(0, 3)$.
Domain: $(-\infty, \infty)$
Range: $[-1, \infty)$

Graph $x = 2y^2 + 6y + 5$.

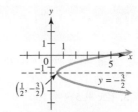

The graph opens to the right since $a > 0$.
Vertex: $\left(\dfrac{1}{2}, -\dfrac{3}{2}\right)$
Axis: $y = -\dfrac{3}{2}$
Domain: $\left[\dfrac{1}{2}, \infty\right)$
Range: $(-\infty, \infty)$

(continued)

CONCEPTS	EXAMPLES
11.8 **Polynomial and Rational Inequalities**	
Solving a Quadratic (or Higher-Degree Polynomial) Inequality	Solve $2x^2 + 5x + 2 < 0$.
Step 1 Write the inequality as an equation and solve.	$$2x^2 + 5x + 2 = 0$$ $$(2x + 1)(x + 2) = 0$$ $$x = -\tfrac{1}{2} \quad \text{or} \quad x = -2$$
Step 2 Use the numbers found in Step 1 to divide a number line into intervals.	Intervals: $(-\infty, -2)$, $\left(-2, -\tfrac{1}{2}\right), \left(-\tfrac{1}{2}, \infty\right)$
Step 3 Substitute a test number from each interval into the original inequality to determine the intervals that belong to the solution set.	Test values: $-3, -1, 0$ $x = -3$ makes the original inequality false, $x = -1$ makes it true, and $x = 0$ makes it false. Choose the interval(s) which yield(s) a true
Step 4 Consider the endpoints separately.	statement. The solution set is the interval $\left(-2, -\tfrac{1}{2}\right)$.
Solving a Rational Inequality	Solve $\dfrac{x}{x + 2} \geq 4$.
Step 1 Write the inequality so that 0 is on one side and there is a single fraction on the other side.	$$\dfrac{x}{x + 2} - 4 \geq 0 \qquad \text{Subtract 4.}$$ $$\dfrac{x}{x + 2} - \dfrac{4(x + 2)}{x + 2} \geq 0 \qquad \text{Write with a common denominator.}$$ $$\dfrac{-3x - 8}{x + 2} \geq 0 \qquad \text{Subtract fractions.}$$
Step 2 Determine the numbers that make the numerator or denominator 0.	$-\tfrac{8}{3}$ makes the numerator 0, and -2 makes the denominator 0.
Step 3 Use the numbers from Step 2 to divide a number line into intervals.	
Step 4 Substitute a test number from each interval into the original inequality to determine the intervals that belong to the solution set.	-4 from A makes the original inequality false, $-\tfrac{7}{3}$ from B makes it true, and 0 from C makes it false.
Step 5 Consider the endpoints separately.	The solution set is the interval $\left[-\tfrac{8}{3}, -2\right)$. The endpoint -2 is not included since it makes the denominator 0.

CHAPTER **11**

REVIEW EXERCISES

11.1 *Solve each equation by using the square root property.*

1. $t^2 = 121$

2. $p^2 = 3$

3. $(2x + 5)^2 = 100$

*4. $(3x - 2)^2 = -25$

*This exercise requires knowledge of complex numbers.

5. *Concept Check*   A student gave the following "solution." *WHAT WENT WRONG?*

$$x^2 = 12$$
$$x = \sqrt{12} \quad \text{Square root property}$$
$$x = 2\sqrt{3} \quad \text{Simplify.}$$

Solution set: $\left\{2\sqrt{3}\right\}$

6. The Singapore Flyer, the world's largest Ferris wheel as of 2008, has a height of 165 m. To find how long it would take a wallet dropped from the top of the Singapore Flyer to reach the ground, use the metric version of Galileo's formula,

$$d = 4.9t^2 \quad \text{(where } d \text{ is in meters).}$$

Round your answer to the nearest tenth of a second. (*Source:* www.singaporeflyer.com)

11.2   *Solve each equation by completing the square.*

7. $x^2 + 4x = 15$ **8.** $2x^2 - 3x = -1$

9. $2z^2 + 8z - 3 = 0$ ***10.** $4x^2 - 3x + 6 = 0$

11.3   *Solve each equation by using the quadratic formula.*

11. $2x^2 + x - 21 = 0$ **12.** $x^2 + 5x = 7$ **13.** $(t + 3)(t - 4) = -2$

*14. $2x^2 + 3x + 4 = 0$ ***15.** $3p^2 = 2(2p - 1)$ **16.** $x(2x - 7) = 3x^2 + 3$

Use the discriminant to predict whether the solutions to each equation are

A. *two rational numbers*   **B.** *one rational number*

C. *two irrational numbers*   **D.** *two nonreal complex numbers.*

17. (a) $x^2 + 5x + 2 = 0$ **(b)** $4t^2 = 3 - 4t$

18. (a) $4x^2 = 6x - 8$ **(b)** $9z^2 + 30z + 25 = 0$

11.4   *Solve each equation. Check your solutions.*

19. $\dfrac{15}{x} = 2x - 1$ **20.** $\dfrac{1}{n} + \dfrac{2}{n + 1} = 2$

21. $-2r - \sqrt{\dfrac{48 - 20r}{2}}$ **22.** $8(3x + 5)^2 + 2(3x + 5) - 1 = 0$

23. $2x^{2/3} - x^{1/3} - 28 = 0$ **24.** $p^4 - 10p^2 + 9 = 0$

Solve each problem. Round answers to the nearest tenth, as necessary.

25. Bahaa Mourad paddled a canoe 20 mi upstream, then paddled back. If the rate of the current was 3 mph and the total trip took 7 hr, what was Bahaa's rate?

26. Carol-Ann Vassell drove 8 mi to pick up a friend, and then drove 11 mi to a mall at a rate 15 mph faster. If Carol-Ann's total travel time was 24 min, what was her rate on the trip to pick up her friend?

27. An old machine processes a batch of checks in 1 hr more time than a new one. How long would it take the old machine to process a batch of checks that the two machines together process in 2 hr?

28. Zoran Pantic can process a stack of invoices 1 hr faster than Claude Sassine can. Working together, they take 1.5 hr. How long would it take each person working alone?

11.5   *Solve each formula for the indicated variable. (Give answers with ±.)*

29. $k = \dfrac{rF}{wv^2}$ for v **30.** $p = \sqrt{\dfrac{yz}{6}}$ for y **31.** $mt^2 = 3mt + 6$ for t

---

*This exercise requires knowledge of complex numbers.

Solve each problem. Round answers to the nearest tenth, as necessary.

32. A large machine requires a part in the shape of a right triangle with a hypotenuse 9 ft less than twice the length of the longer leg. The shorter leg must be $\frac{3}{4}$ the length of the longer leg. Find the lengths of the three sides of the part.

33. A square has an area of 256 cm². If the same amount is removed from one dimension and added to the other, the resulting rectangle has an area 16 cm² less. Find the dimensions of the rectangle.

34. Allen Moser wants to buy a mat for a photograph that measures 14 in. by 20 in. He wants to have an even border around the picture when it is mounted on the mat. If the area of the mat he chooses is 352 in.², how wide will the border be?

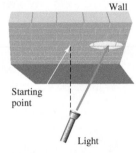

35. If a square piece of cardboard has 3-in. squares cut from its corners and then has the flaps folded up to form an open-top box, the volume of the box is given by the formula $V = 3(x - 6)^2$, where x is the length of each side of the original piece of cardboard in inches. What original length would yield a box with volume 432 in.³?

36. Wachovia Center Tower in Raleigh, North Carolina, is 400 ft high. Suppose that a ball is projected upward from the top of the tower, and its position in feet above the ground is given by the quadratic function defined by

$$f(t) = -16t^2 + 45t + 400,$$

where t is the number of seconds elapsed. How long will it take for the ball to reach a height of 200 ft above the ground? (*Source: World Almanac and Book of Facts.*)

37. A searchlight moves horizontally back and forth along a wall with the distance of the light from a starting point at t minutes given by the quadratic function defined by

$$f(t) = 100t^2 - 300t.$$

How long will it take before the light returns to the starting point?

38. Internet publishing and broadcasting revenue in the United States (in millions of dollars) for the years 2004–2007 is shown in the graph and can be modeled by the quadratic function defined by

$$f(x) = 230.5x^2 - 252.9x + 5987.$$

In the model, $x = 4$ represents 2004, $x = 5$ represents 2005, and so on.

(a) Use the model to approximate revenue from Internet publishing and broadcasting in 2007 to the nearest million dollars. How does this result compare to the number suggested by the graph?

(b) Based on the model, in what year did the revenue from Internet publishing and broadcasting reach $14,000 million ($14 billion)? (Round down for the year.) How does this result compare to the number shown in the graph?

`11.6–11.7` *Identify the vertex of each parabola.*

39. $f(x) = -(x - 1)^2$

40. $f(x) = (x - 3)^2 + 7$

41. $x = (y - 3)^2 - 4$

42. $y = -3x^2 + 4x - 2$

Graph each parabola. Give the vertex, axis, domain, and range.

43. $y = 2(x - 2)^2 - 3$

44. $f(x) = -2x^2 + 8x - 5$

45. $x = 2(y + 3)^2 - 4$

46. $x = -\dfrac{1}{2}y^2 + 6y - 14$

Solve each problem.

47. Total consumer spending on computers, peripherals, and software in the United States for selected years is given in the table. Let $x = 0$ represent 1985, $x = 5$ represent 1990, and so on.

(a) Use the data for 1985, 1995, and 2005 in the quadratic form $ax^2 + bx + c = y$ to write a system of three equations.

(b) Solve the system from part (a) to get a quadratic function f that models the data.

(c) Use the model found in part (b) to approximate consumer spending for computers, peripherals, and software games in 2006 to the nearest tenth. How does your answer compare to the actual data from the table?

CONSUMER SPENDING ON COMPUTERS, PERIPHERALS, AND SOFTWARE

Year	Spending (billions of dollars)
1985	2.9
1990	8.9
1995	24.3
2000	43.8
2004	51.6
2005	56.5
2006	61.4

Source: Bureau of Economic Analysis.

48. The height (in feet) of a projectile t seconds after being fired from Earth into the air is given by

$$f(t) = -16t^2 + 160t.$$

Find the number of seconds required for the projectile to reach maximum height. What is the maximum height?

49. Find the length and width of a rectangle having a perimeter of 200 m if the area is to be a maximum. What is the maximum area?

`11.8` *Solve each inequality, and graph the solution set.*

50. $(x - 4)(2x + 3) > 0$

51. $x^2 + x \leq 12$

52. $(x + 2)(x - 3)(x + 5) \leq 0$

53. $(4x + 3)^2 \leq -4$

54. $\dfrac{6}{2z - 1} < 2$

55. $\dfrac{3t + 4}{t - 2} \leq 1$

MIXED REVIEW EXERCISES

Solve.

56. $V = r^2 + R^2h$ for R

*57. $3t^2 - 6t = -4$

58. $(3x + 11)^2 = 7$

59. $S = \dfrac{Id^2}{k}$ for d

60. $(8x - 7)^2 \geq -1$

61. $2x - \sqrt{x} = 6$

---

*This exercise requires knowledge of complex numbers.

(continued)

62. $x^4 - 8x^2 = -1$ **63.** $\dfrac{-2}{x + 5} \leq -5$ **64.** $6 + \dfrac{15}{s^2} = -\dfrac{19}{s}$

65. $(x^2 - 2x)^2 = 11(x^2 - 2x) - 24$ **66.** $(r - 1)(2r + 3)(r + 6) < 0$

67. *Concept Check*   Match each equation in parts (a)–(f) with the figure that most closely resembles its graph in choices A–F.

(a) $g(x) = x^2 - 5$ **(b)** $h(x) = -x^2 + 4$ **(c)** $F(x) = (x - 1)^2$

(d) $G(x) = (x + 1)^2$ **(e)** $H(x) = (x - 1)^2 + 1$ **(f)** $K(x) = (x + 1)^2 + 1$

A.

B.

C.

D.

E.

F.

68. Graph $f(x) = 4x^2 + 4x - 2$. Give the vertex, axis, domain, and range.

69. In 4 hr, Rajeed Carriman can go 15 mi upriver and come back. The rate of the current is 5 mph. Find the rate of the boat in still water.

70. Two pieces of a large wooden puzzle fit together to form a rectangle with length 1 cm less than twice the width. The diagonal, where the two pieces meet, is 2.5 cm in length. Find the length and width of the rectangle.

CHAPTER (11)

TEST

 CHAPTER Test Prep VIDEOS

Step-by-step test solutions are found on the Chapter Test Prep Videos available via the Video Resources on DVD, in *MyMathLab* , or on YouTube (search "LialCombinedAlgebra").

View the complete solutions to all Chapter Test exercises on the Video Resources on DVD.

Solve each equation by using the square root property.

1. $t^2 = 54$ **2.** $(7x + 3)^2 = 25$

3. Solve $x^2 + 2x = 4$ by completing the square.

Solve each equation by using the quadratic formula.

4. $2x^2 - 3x - 1 = 0$ ***5.** $3t^2 - 4t = -5$

*6. *Concept Check*   If k is a negative number, then which one of the following equations will have two nonreal complex solutions?

A. $x^2 = 4k$ **B.** $x^2 = -4k$ **C.** $(x + 2)^2 = -k$ **D.** $x^2 + k = 0$

7. What is the discriminant for $2x^2 - 8x - 3 = 0$? How many and what type of solutions does this equation have? (Do not actually solve.)

---

*This exercise requires knowledge of complex numbers.

Solve by any method.

8. $3x = \sqrt{\dfrac{9x + 2}{2}}$

9. $3 - \dfrac{16}{x} - \dfrac{12}{x^2} = 0$

10. $4x^2 + 7x - 3 = 0$

11. $9x^4 + 4 = 37x^2$

12. $12 = (2n + 1)^2 + (2n + 1)$

13. Solve $S = 4\pi r^2$ for r. (Leave $\pm$ in your answer.)

Solve each problem.

14. Terry and Callie do word processing. For a certain prospectus, Callie can prepare it 2 hr faster than Terry can. If they work together, they can do the entire prospectus in 5 hr. How long will it take each of them working alone to prepare the prospectus? Round your answers to the nearest tenth of an hour.

15. Qihong Shen paddled a canoe 10 mi upstream and then paddled back to the starting point. If the rate of the current was 3 mph and the entire trip took $3\frac{1}{2}$ hr, what was Qihong's rate?

16. Endre Borsos has a pool 24 ft long and 10 ft wide. He wants to construct a concrete walk around the pool. If he plans for the walk to be of uniform width and cover 152 ft², what will the width of the walk be?

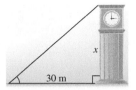

17. At a point 30 m from the base of a tower, the distance to the top of the tower is 2 m more than twice the height of the tower. Find the height of the tower.

18. *Concept Check*   Which one of the following figures most closely resembles the graph of $f(x) = a(x - h)^2 + k$ if $a < 0, h > 0$, and $k < 0$?

A.

B.

C.

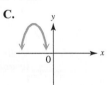

D.

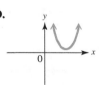

Graph each parabola. Identify the vertex, axis, domain, and range.

19. $f(x) = \dfrac{1}{2}x^2 - 2$

20. $f(x) = -x^2 + 4x - 1$

21. $x = -(y - 2)^2 + 2$

Solve each problem.

22. The total number (in millions) of civilians employed in the United States during the years 2004–2008 can be modeled by the quadratic function defined by

$$f(x) = -0.529x^2 + 8.00x + 115$$

where $x = 4$ represents 2004, $x = 5$ represents 2005, and so on. (*Source:* U.S. Bureau of Labor Statistics.)

(a) Based on this model, how many civilians, to the nearest million, were employed in the United States in 2004?

(b) In what year during this period was the maximum civilian employment? (Round down for the year.) To the nearest million, what was the total civilian employment in that year? Use the actual x-value, to the nearest tenth, to find this number.

23. Houston Community College is planning to construct a rectangular parking lot on land bordered on one side by a highway. The plan is to use 640 ft of fencing to fence off the other three sides. What should the dimensions of the lot be if the enclosed area is to be a maximum?

Solve each inequality, and graph the solution set.

24. $2x^2 + 7x > 15$

25. $\dfrac{5}{t - 4} \leq 1$

CHAPTERS (1–11) CUMULATIVE REVIEW EXERCISES

1. Let $S = \left\{ -\frac{7}{3}, -2, -\sqrt{3}, 0, 0.7, \sqrt{12}, \sqrt{-8}, 7, \frac{32}{3} \right\}$. List the elements of S that are elements of each set.

   (a) Integers   **(b)** Rational numbers   **(c)** Real numbers   **(d)** Complex numbers

Solve each equation or inequality.

2. $7 - (4 + 3t) + 2t = -6(t - 2) - 5$

3. $|6x - 9| = |-4x + 2|$

4. $2x = \sqrt{\dfrac{5x + 2}{3}}$

5. $\dfrac{3}{x - 3} - \dfrac{2}{x - 2} = \dfrac{3}{x^2 - 5x + 6}$

6. $(r - 5)(2r + 3) = 1$

7. $x^4 - 5x^2 + 4 = 0$

8. $-2x + 4 \leq -x + 3$

9. $|3x - 7| \leq 1$

10. $x^2 - 4x + 3 < 0$

11. $\dfrac{3}{p + 2} > 1$

Graph each relation. Tell whether or not y can be expressed as a function f of x, and if so, give its domain and range, and write using function notation.

12. $4x - 5y = 15$

13. $4x - 5y < 15$

14. $y = -2(x - 1)^2 + 3$

15. Find the slope and intercepts of the line with equation
$$-2x + 7y = 16.$$

16. Write an equation for the specified line. Express each equation in slope-intercept form.

   (a) Through $(2, -3)$ and parallel to the line with equation $5x + 2y = 6$

   (b) Through $(-4, 1)$ and perpendicular to the line with equation $5x + 2y = 6$

Write with positive exponents only. Assume that variables represent positive real numbers.

17. $\left(\dfrac{x^{-3}y^2}{x^5 y^{-2}} \right)^{-1}$

18. $\dfrac{(4x^{-2})^2(2y^3)}{8x^{-3}y^5}$

Perform the indicated operations.

19. $\left(\dfrac{2}{3}t + 9 \right)^2$

20. Divide $4x^3 + 2x^2 - x + 26$ by $x + 2$.

Factor completely.

21. $24m^2 + 2m - 15$

22. $8x^3 + 27y^3$

23. $9x^2 - 30xy + 25y^2$

Perform the indicated operations or simplify the complex fraction, and express each answer in lowest terms. Assume denominators are nonzero.

24. $\dfrac{5x + 2}{-6} \div \dfrac{15x + 6}{5}$ **25.** $\dfrac{3}{2 - x} - \dfrac{5}{x} + \dfrac{6}{x^2 - 2x}$ **26.** $\dfrac{\dfrac{r}{s} - \dfrac{s}{r}}{\dfrac{r}{s} + 1}$

Solve each system of equations.

27. $2x - 4y = 10$
$\quad\ \ 9x + 3y = 3$

28. $\ \ x + \ y + 2z = 3$
$\quad\ \ -x + \ y + \ z = -5$
$\quad\ \ 2x + 3y - \ z = -8$

29. In 2009, the two American computer software companies with the greatest revenues were Microsoft and Oracle. The two companies had combined revenues of \$82.8 billion. Revenues for Microsoft were \$6.8 billion less than three times those of Oracle. What were the 2009 revenues for each company? (*Source: Fortune.*)

Simplify each radical expression.

30. $\sqrt[3]{\dfrac{27}{16}}$ **31.** $\dfrac{2}{\sqrt{7} - \sqrt{5}}$

32. Two cars left an intersection at the same time, one heading due south and the other due east. Later they were exactly 95 mi apart. The car heading east had gone 38 mi less than twice as far as the car heading south. How far had each car traveled?

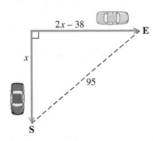

CHAPTER 12

Inverse, Exponential, and Logarithmic Functions

12.1 Inverse Functions

12.2 Exponential Functions

12.3 Logarithmic Functions

12.4 Properties of Logarithms

12.5 Common and Natural Logarithms

12.6 Exponential and Logarithmic Equations; Further Applications

In 2001, Apple Computer Inc., introduced the iPod. By mid-2009, the company had sold over 220 million of the popular music players, in spite of warnings by experts that listening to the devices at high volumes may put people at increased risk of hearing loss.

In **Example 4** of **Section 12.5,** we use a *logarithmic function* to calculate the volume level, in *decibels,* of an iPod.

12.1 Inverse Functions

In this chapter we study two important types of functions, *exponential* and *logarithmic*. These functions are related: They are *inverses* of one another.

OBJECTIVE 1 Decide whether a function is one-to-one and, if it is, find its inverse. Suppose we define the function

$$G = \{(-2, 2), (-1, 1), (0, 0), (1, 3), (2, 5)\}.$$

We can form another set of ordered pairs from G by interchanging the x- and y-values of each pair in G. We can call this set F, so

$$F = \{(2, -2), (1, -1), (0, 0), (3, 1), (5, 2)\}.$$

To show that these two sets are related as just described, F is called the *inverse* of G. For a function f to have an inverse, f must be a *one-to-one function*.

One-to-One Function

In a **one-to-one function,** each x-value corresponds to only one y-value, and each y-value corresponds to only one x-value.

The function shown in **FIGURE 1(a)** is not one-to-one because the y-value 7 corresponds to *two* x-values, 2 and 3. That is, the ordered pairs $(2, 7)$ and $(3, 7)$ both belong to the function. The function in **FIGURE 1(b)** is one-to-one.

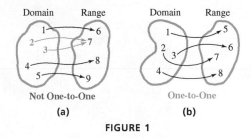

FIGURE 1

The *inverse* of any one-to-one function f is found by interchanging the components of the ordered pairs of f. The inverse of f is written f^{-1}. Read f^{-1} as **"the inverse of f"** or **"f-inverse."**

⚠ **CAUTION** The symbol $f^{-1}(x)$ does **not** represent $\dfrac{1}{f(x)}$.

The definition of the inverse of a function follows.

Inverse of a Function

The **inverse** of a one-to-one function f, written f^{-1}, is the set of all ordered pairs of the form (y, x), where (x, y) belongs to f. Since the inverse is formed by interchanging x and y, the domain of f becomes the range of f^{-1} and the range of f becomes the domain of f^{-1}.

For inverses f and f^{-1}, it follows that for all x in their domains,

$$(f \circ f^{-1})(x) = x \quad \text{and} \quad (f^{-1} \circ f)(x) = x.$$

NOW TRY
EXERCISE 1

Decide whether each function is one-to-one. If it is, find the inverse.

(a) $F = \{(-1, -2), (0, 0)$
$\quad (1, -2), (2, -8)\}$

(b) $G = \{(0, 0), (1, 1),$
$\quad (4, 2), (9, 3)\}$

(c) The number of stories and height of several tall buildings are given in the table.

Stories	Height
31	639
35	582
40	620
41	639
64	810

EXAMPLE 1 Finding Inverses of One-to-One Functions

Decide whether each function is one-to-one. If it is, find the inverse.

(a) $F = \{(-2, 1), (-1, 0), (0, 1), (1, 2), (2, 2)\}$

Each x-value in F corresponds to just one y-value. However, the y-value 1 corresponds to two x-values, -2 and 0. Also, the y-value 2 corresponds to both 1 and 2. Because some y-values correspond to more than one x-value, F is not one-to-one and does not have an inverse.

(b) $G = \{(3, 1), (0, 2), (2, 3), (4, 0)\}$

Every x-value in G corresponds to only one y-value, and every y-value corresponds to only one x-value, so G is a one-to-one function. The inverse function is found by interchanging the x- and y-values in each ordered pair.

$$G^{-1} = \{(1, 3), (2, 0), (3, 2), (0, 4)\}$$

The domain and range of G become the range and domain, respectively, of G^{-1}.

(c) The table shows the number of days in which the air in Connecticut exceeded the 8-hour average ground-level ozone standard for the years 1997–2006.

Year	Number of Days Exceeding Standard	Year	Number of Days Exceeding Standard
1997	27	2002	36
1998	25	2003	14
1999	33	2004	6
2000	13	2005	20
2001	26	2006	13

Source: U.S. Environmental Protection Agency.

Let f be the function defined in the table, with the years forming the domain and the numbers of days exceeding the ozone standard forming the range. Then f is not one-to-one, because in two different years (2000 and 2006), the number of days with unacceptable ozone levels was the same, 13.   NOW TRY

OBJECTIVE 2 **Use the horizontal line test to determine whether a function is one-to-one.** By graphing a function and observing the graph, we can use the *horizontal line test* to tell whether the function is one-to-one.

Horizontal Line Test

A function is one-to-one if every horizontal line intersects the graph of the function at most once.

NOW TRY ANSWERS
1. (a) not one-to-one
(b) one-to-one;
$\quad G^{-1} = \{(0, 0), (1, 1),$
$\quad\quad (2, 4), (3, 9)\}$
(c) not one-to-one

The horizontal line test follows from the definition of a one-to-one function. Any two points that lie on the same horizontal line have the same y-coordinate. No two ordered pairs that belong to a one-to-one function may have the same y-coordinate. Therefore, no horizontal line will intersect the graph of a one-to-one function more than once.

NOW TRY
EXERCISE 2

Use the horizontal line test to determine whether each graph is the graph of a one-to-one function.

(a)

(b)

EXAMPLE 2 Using the Horizontal Line Test

Use the horizontal line test to determine whether each graph is the graph of a one-to-one function.

(a)

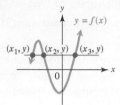

(b)

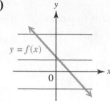

Because a horizontal line intersects the graph in more than one point (actually three points), the function is not one-to-one.

Every horizontal line will intersect the graph in exactly one point. This function is one-to-one.

NOW TRY

OBJECTIVE 3 **Find the equation of the inverse of a function.** The inverse of a one-to-one function is found by interchanging the x- and y-values of each of its ordered pairs. The equation of the inverse of a function defined by $y = f(x)$ is found in the same way.

Finding the Equation of the Inverse of $y = f(x)$

For a one-to-one function f defined by an equation $y = f(x)$, find the defining equation of the inverse as follows.

Step 1 Interchange x and y.

Step 2 Solve for y.

Step 3 Replace y with $f^{-1}(x)$.

EXAMPLE 3 Finding Equations of Inverses

Decide whether each equation defines a one-to-one function. If so, find the equation that defines the inverse.

(a) $f(x) = 2x + 5$

The graph of $y = 2x + 5$ is a nonvertical line, so by the horizontal line test, f is a one-to-one function. To find the inverse, let $y = f(x)$ and follow the steps.

$$y = 2x + 5$$
$$x = 2y + 5 \qquad \text{Interchange } x \text{ and } y. \text{ (Step 1)}$$
$$2y = x - 5 \qquad \text{Solve for } y. \text{ (Step 2)}$$
$$y = \frac{x - 5}{2}$$
$$f^{-1}(x) = \frac{x - 5}{2} \qquad \text{Replace } y \text{ with } f^{-1}(x). \text{ (Step 3)}$$

This equation can be written as follows.

NOW TRY ANSWERS
2. (a) one-to-one
(b) not one-to-one

$$f^{-1}(x) = \frac{x}{2} - \frac{5}{2}, \quad \text{or} \quad f^{-1}(x) = \frac{1}{2}x - \frac{5}{2} \qquad \tfrac{a-b}{c} = \tfrac{a}{c} - \tfrac{b}{c}$$

Decide whether each equation defines a one-to-one function. If so, find the equation that defines the inverse.

(a) $f(x) = 5x - 7$

(b) $f(x) = (x + 1)^2$

(c) $f(x) = x^3 - 4$

Thus, f^{-1} is a linear function. In the function defined by

$$y = 2x + 5,$$

the value of y is found by starting with a value of x, multiplying by 2, and adding 5. The equation

$$f^{-1}(x) = \frac{x - 5}{2}$$

for the inverse has us *subtract* 5, and then *divide* by 2. This shows how an inverse is used to "undo" what a function does to the variable x.

(b) $y = x^2 + 2$

This equation has a vertical parabola as its graph, so some horizontal lines will intersect the graph at two points. For example, both $x = 3$ and $x = -3$ correspond to $y = 11$. Because of the x^2-term, there are many pairs of x-values that correspond to the same y-value. This means that the function defined by $y = x^2 + 2$ is not one-to-one and does not have an inverse.

Alternatively, applying the steps for finding the equation of an inverse leads to the following.

$$y = x^2 + 2$$

$$x = y^2 + 2 \qquad \text{Interchange } x \text{ and } y.$$

$$y^2 = x - 2 \qquad \text{Solve for } y.$$

$$y = \pm\sqrt{x - 2} \qquad \text{Square root property}$$

The last step shows that there are two y-values for each choice of $x > 2$, so we again see that the given function is not one-to-one. It does not have an inverse.

(c) $f(x) = (x - 2)^3$

Because of the cube, each value of x produces a different value of y, so this is a one-to-one function.

$$f(x) = (x - 2)^3$$

$$y = (x - 2)^3 \qquad \text{Replace } f(x) \text{ with } y.$$

$$x = (y - 2)^3 \qquad \text{Interchange } x \text{ and } y.$$

$$\sqrt[3]{x} = \sqrt[3]{(y - 2)^3} \qquad \text{Take the cube root on each side.}$$

$$\sqrt[3]{x} = y - 2 \qquad \sqrt[3]{a^3} = a$$

$$y = \sqrt[3]{x} + 2 \qquad \text{Solve for } y.$$

$$f^{-1}(x) = \sqrt[3]{x} + 2 \qquad \text{Replace } y \text{ with } f^{-1}(x). \qquad \text{NOW TRY}$$

3. **(a)** one-to-one function;
$f^{-1}(x) = \frac{x + 7}{5}$, or
$f^{-1}(x) = \frac{1}{5}x + \frac{7}{5}$
(b) not a one-to-one function
(c) one-to-one function;
$f^{-1}(x) = \sqrt[3]{x + 4}$

OBJECTIVE 4 **Graph f^{-1}, given the graph of f.** One way to graph the inverse of a function f whose equation is given is as follows.

1. Find several ordered pairs that belong to f.

2. Interchange x and y to obtain ordered pairs that belong to f^{-1}.

3. Plot those points, and sketch the graph of f^{-1} through them.

A simpler way is to select points on the graph of f and use symmetry to find corresponding points on the graph of f^{-1}.

For example, suppose the point (a, b) shown in FIGURE 2 belongs to a one-to-one function f. Then the point (b, a) belongs to f^{-1}. The line segment connecting (a, b) and (b, a) is perpendicular to, and cut in half by, the line $y = x$. The points (a, b) and (b, a) are "mirror images" of each other with respect to $y = x$.

We can find the graph of f^{-1} from the graph of f by locating the mirror image of each point in f with respect to the line $y = x$.

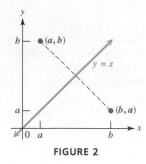

FIGURE 2

NOW TRY
EXERCISE 4

Use the given graph to graph the inverse of f.

EXAMPLE 4 Graphing the Inverse

Graph the inverses of the functions f (shown in blue) in FIGURE 3.

In FIGURE 3 the graphs of two functions f are shown in blue. Their inverses are shown in red. In each case, the graph of f^{-1} is a reflection of the graph of f with respect to the line $y = x$.

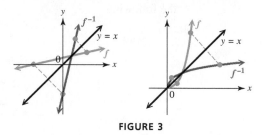

FIGURE 3

NOW TRY

CONNECTIONS

In **Example 3** we showed that the inverse of the one-to-one function defined by $f(x) = 2x + 5$ is given by $f^{-1}(x) = \frac{x-5}{2}$. If we use a square viewing window of a graphing calculator and graph

$$y_1 = f(x) = 2x + 5, \quad y_2 = f^{-1}(x) = \frac{x-5}{2}, \quad \text{and} \quad y_3 = x,$$

we can see how this reflection appears on the screen. See FIGURE 4.

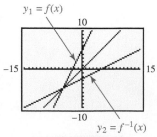

FIGURE 4

NOW TRY ANSWER

4.

For Discussion or Writing

Some graphing calculators have the capability to "draw" the inverse of a function. Use a graphing calculator to draw the graphs of $f(x) = x^3 + 2$ and its inverse in a square viewing window.

12.1 EXERCISES

MyMathLab *Math XL* PRACTICE   WATCH   DOWNLOAD   READ   REVIEW

🌐 *Complete solution available on the Video Resources on DVD*

In Exercises 1–4, write a few sentences of explanation. ***See Example 1.***

🌐 **1.** A study found that the trans fat content in fast-food products varied widely around the world, based on the type of frying oil used, as shown in the table. If the set of countries is the domain and the set of trans fat percentages is the range of the function consisting of the six pairs listed, is it a one-to-one function? Why or why not?

Country	Percentage of Trans Fat in McDonald's Chicken
Scotland	14
France	11
United States	11
Peru	9
Russia	5
Denmark	1

Source: New England Journal of Medicine.

2. The table shows the number of uncontrolled hazardous waste sites in 2008 that require further investigation to determine whether remedies are needed under the Superfund program. The eight states listed are ranked in the top ten on the EPA's National Priority List.

If this correspondence is considered to be a function that pairs each state with its number of uncontrolled waste sites, is it one-to-one? If not, explain why.

State	Number of Sites
New Jersey	116
California	97
Pennsylvania	96
New York	86
Michigan	67
Florida	52
Illinois	49
Texas	49

Source: U.S. Environmental Protection Agency.

3. The road mileage between Denver, Colorado, and several selected U.S. cities is shown in the table. If we consider this as a function that pairs each city with a distance, is it a one-to-one function? How could we change the answer to this question by adding 1 mile to one of the distances shown?

City	Distance to Denver (in miles)
Atlanta	1398
Dallas	781
Indianapolis	1058
Kansas City, MO	600
Los Angeles	1059
San Francisco	1235

4. Suppose you consider the set of ordered pairs (x, y) such that x represents a person in your mathematics class and y represents that person's father. Explain how this function might not be a one-to-one function.

In Exercises 5–8, choose the correct response from the given list.

5. *Concept Check*   If a function is made up of ordered pairs in such a way that the same y-value appears in a correspondence with two different x-values, then

A. the function is one-to-one   **B.** the function is not one-to-one

C. its graph does not pass the vertical line test

D. it has an inverse function associated with it.

6. Which equation defines a one-to-one function? Explain why the others are not, using specific examples.

    A. $f(x) = x$ **B.** $f(x) = x^2$ **C.** $f(x) = |x|$ **D.** $f(x) = -x^2 + 2x - 1$

7. Only one of the graphs illustrates a one-to-one function. Which one is it? **(See Example 2.)**

    A.   **B.** 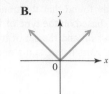   **C.**   **D.**

8. *Concept Check*   If a function f is one-to-one and the point (p, q) lies on the graph of f, then which point *must* lie on the graph of f^{-1}?

    A. $(-p, q)$ **B.** $(-q, -p)$ **C.** $(p, -q)$ **D.** (q, p)

*If the function is one-to-one, find its inverse. **See Examples 1–3.***

9. $\{(3, 6), (2, 10), (5, 12)\}$ **10.** $\left\{(-1, 3), (0, 5), (5, 0), \left(7, -\dfrac{1}{2}\right)\right\}$

11. $\{(-1, 3), (2, 7), (4, 3), (5, 8)\}$ **12.** $\{(-8, 6), (-4, 3), (0, 6), (5, 10)\}$

13. $f(x) = 2x + 4$ **14.** $f(x) = 3x + 1$

15. $g(x) = \sqrt{x - 3}, \quad x \geq 3$ **16.** $g(x) = \sqrt{x + 2}, \quad x \geq -2$

17. $f(x) = 3x^2 + 2$ **18.** $f(x) = 4x^2 - 1$

19. $f(x) = x^3 - 4$ **20.** $f(x) = x^3 + 5$

Concept Check   Let $f(x) = 2^x$. We will see in the next section that this function is one-to-one. Find each value, always working part (a) before part (b).

21. **(a)** $f(3)$ **22.** **(a)** $f(4)$ **23.** **(a)** $f(0)$ **24.** **(a)** $f(-2)$

    (b) $f^{-1}(8)$ **(b)** $f^{-1}(16)$ **(b)** $f^{-1}(1)$ **(b)** $f^{-1}\left(\dfrac{1}{4}\right)$

*The graphs of some functions are given in Exercises 25–30. **(a)** Use the horizontal line test to determine whether the function is one-to-one. **(b)** If the function is one-to-one, then graph the inverse of the function. (Remember that if f is one-to-one and (a, b) is on the graph of f, then (b, a) is on the graph of f^{-1}.) **See Example 4.***

25. 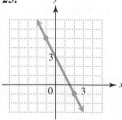   **26.** 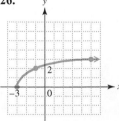   **27.**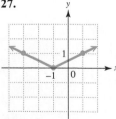

28. 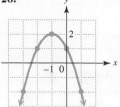   **29.** 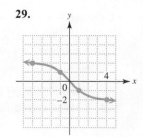   **30.**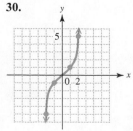

Each function defined in Exercises 31–38 is a one-to-one function. Graph the function as a solid line (or curve) and then graph its inverse on the same set of axes as a dashed line (or curve). In Exercises 35–38 complete the table so that graphing the function will be easier. **See Example 4.**

31. $f(x) = 2x - 1$ **32.** $f(x) = 2x + 3$ **33.** $g(x) = -4x$ **34.** $g(x) = -2x$

35. $f(x) = \sqrt{x}$,   **36.** $f(x) = -\sqrt{x}$,   **37.** $f(x) = x^3 - 2$ **38.** $f(x) = x^3 + 3$
    $x \geq 0$ $x \geq 0$

x	$f(x)$
0	
1	
4	

x	$f(x)$
0	
1	
4	

x	$f(x)$
-1	
0	
1	
2	

x	$f(x)$
-2	
-1	
0	
1	

RELATING CONCEPTS   EXERCISES 39–42

FOR INDIVIDUAL OR GROUP WORK

Inverse functions can be used to send and receive coded information. A simple example might use the function defined by $f(x) = 2x + 5$. *(Note that it is one-to-one.) Suppose that each letter of the alphabet is assigned a numerical value according to its position, as follows.*

This is an Enigma machine, used by the Germans in World War II to send coded messages.

A	1	G	7	L	12	Q	17	V	22
B	2	H	8	M	13	R	18	W	23
C	3	I	9	N	14	S	19	X	24
D	4	J	10	O	15	T	20	Y	25
E	5	K	11	P	16	U	21	Z	26
F	6								

Using the function, the word ALGEBRA *would be encoded as*

$$7 \quad 29 \quad 19 \quad 15 \quad 9 \quad 41 \quad 7,$$

because

$$f(A) = f(1) = 2(1) + 5 = 7, \quad f(L) = f(12) = 2(12) + 5 = 29, \quad \text{and so on.}$$

The message would then be decoded by using the inverse of f, *defined by* $f^{-1}(x) = \frac{x - 5}{2}$ $\left(\text{or } f^{-1}(x) = \frac{1}{2}x - \frac{5}{2} \right)$. *For example,*

$$f^{-1}(7) = \frac{7 - 5}{2} = 1 = A, \quad f^{-1}(29) = \frac{29 - 5}{2} = 12 = L, \quad \text{and so on.}$$

Work Exercises 39–42 in order.

39. Suppose that you are an agent for a detective agency. Today's function for your code is defined by $f(x) = 4x - 5$. Find the rule for f^{-1} algebraically.

40. You receive the following coded message today. (Read across from left to right.)

47 95 23 67 -1 59 27 31 51 23 7 -1 43 7 79 43 -1 75 55 67
31 71 75 27 15 23 67 15 -1 75 15 71 75 75 27 31 51
23 71 31 51 7 15 71 43 31 7 15 11 3 67 15 -1 11

Use the letter/number assignment described earlier to decode the message.

 41. Why is a one-to-one function essential in this encoding/decoding process?

42. Use $f(x) = x^3 + 4$ to encode your name, using the letter/number assignment described earlier.

Each function defined is one-to-one. Find the inverse algebraically, and then graph both the function and its inverse on the same graphing calculator screen. Use a square viewing window. **See the Connections box.**

43. $f(x) = 2x - 7$ **44.** $f(x) = -3x + 2$

45. $f(x) = x^3 + 5$ **46.** $f(x) = \sqrt[3]{x + 2}$

PREVIEW EXERCISES

If $f(x) = 4^x$, find each value indicated. In Exercise 50, use a calculator, and give the answer to the nearest hundredth. **See Sections 7.4 and 10.2.**

47. $f(3)$ **48.** $f\left(\dfrac{1}{2}\right)$ **49.** $f\left(-\dfrac{1}{2}\right)$ **50.** $f(2.73)$

(12.2) Exponential Functions

OBJECTIVES

1. Define an exponential function.
2. Graph an exponential function.
3. Solve exponential equations of the form $a^x = a^k$ for x.
4. Use exponential functions in applications involving growth or decay.

OBJECTIVE 1 **Define an exponential function.** In **Section 10.2** we showed how to evaluate 2^x for rational values of x.

$$2^3 = 8, \quad 2^{-1} = \frac{1}{2}, \quad 2^{1/2} = \sqrt{2}, \quad \text{and} \quad 2^{3/4} = \sqrt[4]{2^3} = \sqrt[4]{8}$$

Examples of 2^x for rational x

In more advanced courses it is shown that 2^x exists for all real number values of x, both rational and irrational. The following definition of an exponential function assumes that a^x exists for all real numbers x.

Exponential Function

For $a > 0$, $a \neq 1$, and all real numbers x,

$$f(x) = a^x$$

defines the **exponential function with base a.**

NOTE *The two restrictions on the value of a in the definition of an exponential function $f(x) = a^x$ are important.*

1. The restriction $a > 0$ is necessary so that the function can be defined for all real numbers x. Letting a be negative ($a = -2$, for instance) and letting $x = \frac{1}{2}$ would give the expression $(-2)^{1/2}$, which is not real.
2. The restriction $a \neq 1$ is necessary because 1 raised to any power is equal to 1, resulting in the linear function defined by $f(x) = 1$.

OBJECTIVE 2 **Graph an exponential function.** When graphing an exponential function of the form $f(x) = a^x$, pay particular attention to whether $a > 1$ or $0 < a < 1$.

NOW TRY
EXERCISE 1
Graph $y = 4^x$.

EXAMPLE 1 Graphing an Exponential Function $(a > 1)$

Graph $f(x) = 2^x$. Then compare it to the graph of $F(x) = 5^x$.

Choose some values of x, and find the corresponding values of $f(x)$. Plotting these points and drawing a smooth curve through them gives the darker graph shown in **FIGURE 5**. This graph is typical of the graphs of exponential functions of the form $F(x) = a^x$, where $a > 1$. *The larger the value of a, the faster the graph rises.* To see this, compare the graph of $F(x) = 5^x$ with the graph of $f(x) = 2^x$ in **FIGURE 5**.

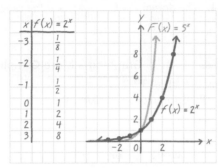

Exponential function with base $a > 1$

Domain: $(-\infty, \infty)$
Range: $(0, \infty)$

The function is one-to-one, and its graph rises from left to right.

FIGURE 5

The vertical line test assures us that the graphs in **FIGURE 5** represent functions. **FIGURE 5** also shows an important characteristic of exponential functions with $a > 1$: *As x gets larger, y increases at a faster and faster rate.*   NOW TRY

⚠ **CAUTION** The graph of an exponential function *approaches* the x-axis, but does **not** touch it.

NOW TRY
EXERCISE 2
Graph $g(x) = \left(\frac{1}{10}\right)^x$.

EXAMPLE 2 Graphing an Exponential Function $(0 < a < 1)$

Graph $g(x) = \left(\frac{1}{2}\right)^x$.

Again, find some points on the graph. The graph, shown in **FIGURE 6**, is very similar to that of $f(x) = 2^x$ (**FIGURE 5**) except that here *as x gets larger, y decreases.* This graph is typical of the graph of a function of the form $f(x) = a^x$, where $0 < a < 1$.

NOW TRY ANSWERS
1.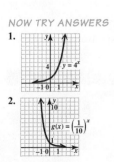
2.

Exponential function with base $0 < a < 1$

Domain: $(-\infty, \infty)$
Range: $(0, \infty)$

The function is one-to-one, and its graph falls from left to right.

FIGURE 6   NOW TRY

> **Characteristics of the Graph of $f(x) = a^x$**
>
> 1. The graph contains the point $(0, 1)$.
>
> 2. The function is one-to-one. When $a > 1$, the graph will *rise* from left to right. (See **FIGURE 5**.) When $0 < a < 1$, the graph will *fall* from left to right. (See **FIGURE 6**.) In both cases, the graph goes from the second quadrant to the first.
>
> 3. The graph will approach the x-axis, but never touch it. (Such a line is called an **asymptote.**)
>
> 4. The domain is $(-\infty, \infty)$, and the range is $(0, \infty)$.

NOW TRY
EXERCISE 3
Graph $f(x) = 4^{2x-1}$.

EXAMPLE 3 Graphing a More Complicated Exponential Function

Graph $f(x) = 3^{2x-4}$.

Find some ordered pairs. We let $x = 0$ and $x = 2$ and find values of $f(x)$, or y.

$$y = 3^{2(0)-4} \qquad \text{Let } x = 0.$$

$$y = 3^{-4}, \quad \text{or} \quad \frac{1}{81}$$

$$y = 3^{2(2)-4} \qquad \text{Let } x = 2.$$

$$y = 3^0, \quad \text{or} \quad 1$$

These ordered pairs, $\left(0, \frac{1}{81}\right)$ and $(2, 1)$, along with the other ordered pairs shown in the table, lead to the graph in **FIGURE 7**. The graph is similar to the graph of $f(x) = 3^x$ except that it is shifted to the right and rises more rapidly.

x	y
0	$\frac{1}{81}$
1	$\frac{1}{9}$
2	1
3	9

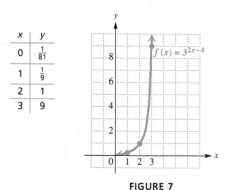

FIGURE 7

NOW TRY

OBJECTIVE 3 Solve exponential equations of the form $a^x = a^k$ for x.
Until this chapter, we have solved only equations that had the variable as a base, like $x^2 = 8$. In these equations, all exponents have been constants. An **exponential equation** is an equation that has a variable in an exponent, such as

$$9^x = 27.$$

We can use the following property to solve certain exponential equations.

> **Property for Solving an Exponential Equation**
>
> For $a > 0$ and $a \neq 1$, if $a^x = a^y$ then $x = y$.

NOW TRY ANSWER
3.
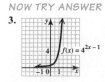

This property would not necessarily be true if $a = 1$.

Solving an Exponential Equation

Step 1   **Each side must have the same base.** If the two sides of the equation do not have the same base, express each as a power of the same base if possible.

Step 2   **Simplify exponents** if necessary, using the rules of exponents.

Step 3   **Set exponents equal** using the property given in this section.

Step 4   **Solve** the equation obtained in Step 3.

NOW TRY
EXERCISE 4
Solve the equation.

$$8^x = 16$$

EXAMPLE 4   Solving an Exponential Equation

Solve the equation $9^x = 27$.

$$9^x = 27$$

$$(3^2)^x = 3^3 \qquad \text{Write with the same base;}$$
$$\qquad\qquad\qquad 9 = 3^2 \text{ and } 27 = 3^3. \text{ (Step 1)}$$

$$3^{2x} = 3^3 \qquad \text{Power rule for exponents (Step 2)}$$

$$2x = 3 \qquad \text{If } a^x = a^y, \text{ then } x = y. \text{ (Step 3)}$$

$$x = \frac{3}{2} \qquad \text{Solve for } x. \text{ (Step 4)}$$

CHECK   Substitute $\frac{3}{2}$ for x.

$$9^x = 9^{3/2} = (9^{1/2})^3 = 3^3 = 27 \quad \checkmark \quad \text{True}$$

The solution set is $\left\{\frac{3}{2}\right\}$.   NOW TRY

EXAMPLE 5   Solving Exponential Equations

Solve each equation.

(a) $4^{3x-1} = 16^{x+2}$ Be careful multiplying the exponents.

$$4^{3x-1} = (4^2)^{x+2} \qquad \text{Write with the same base; } 16 = 4^2.$$

$$4^{3x-1} = 4^{2x+4} \qquad \text{Power rule for exponents}$$

$$3x - 1 = 2x + 4 \qquad \text{Set exponents equal.}$$

$$x = 5 \qquad \text{Subtract } 2x. \text{ Add 1.}$$

Verify that the solution set is $\{5\}$.

(b) $6^x = \dfrac{1}{216}$

$$6^x = \frac{1}{6^3} \qquad 216 = 6^3$$

$$6^x = 6^{-3} \qquad \text{Write with the same base; } \frac{1}{6^3} = 6^{-3}.$$

$$x = -3 \qquad \text{Set exponents equal.}$$

CHECK $6^x = 6^{-3} = \dfrac{1}{6^3} = \dfrac{1}{216}$ $\checkmark$ Substitute -3 for x; true

NOW TRY ANSWER
4. $\left\{\frac{4}{3}\right\}$

The solution set is $\{-3\}$.

NOW TRY
EXERCISE 5
Solve each equation.

(a) $3^{2x-1} = 27^{x+4}$

(b) $5^x = \dfrac{1}{625}$

(c) $\left(\dfrac{2}{7}\right)^x = \dfrac{343}{8}$

(c) $\left(\dfrac{2}{3}\right)^x = \dfrac{9}{4}$

$\left(\dfrac{2}{3}\right)^x = \left(\dfrac{4}{9}\right)^{-1}$ $\dfrac{9}{4} = \left(\dfrac{4}{9}\right)^{-1}$

$\left(\dfrac{2}{3}\right)^x = \left[\left(\dfrac{2}{3}\right)^2\right]^{-1}$ Write with the same base.

$\left(\dfrac{2}{3}\right)^x = \left(\dfrac{2}{3}\right)^{-2}$ Power rule for exponents

$x = -2$ Set exponents equal.

Check that the solution set is $\{-2\}$.   NOW TRY

NOTE The steps used in **Examples 4 and 5** cannot be applied to an equation like

$$3^x = 12$$

because Step 1 cannot easily be done. A method for solving such exponential equations is given in **Section 12.6.**

OBJECTIVE 4 **Use exponential functions in applications involving growth or decay.**

EXAMPLE 6 Solving an Application Involving Exponential Growth

The graph in **FIGURE 8** shows the concentration of carbon dioxide (in parts per million) in the air. This concentration is increasing exponentially.

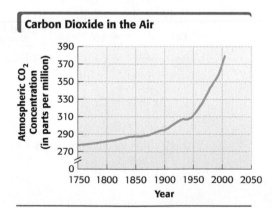

Carbon Dioxide in the Air

Source: Sacramento Bee; National Oceanic and Atmospheric Administration.

FIGURE 8

The data are approximated by the function defined by

$$f(x) = 266(1.001)^x,$$

where x is the number of years since 1750. Use this function and a calculator to approximate the concentration of carbon dioxide in parts per million, to the nearest unit, for each year.

NOW TRY
EXERCISE 6
Use the function in **Example 6** to approximate, to the nearest unit, the carbon dioxide concentration in 2000.

(a) 1900

Because x represents the number of years since 1750, $x = 1900 - 1750 = 150$.

$$f(x) = 266(1.001)^x \qquad \text{Given function}$$
$$f(150) = 266(1.001)^{150} \qquad \text{Let } x = 150.$$
$$f(150) \approx 309 \text{ parts per million} \qquad \text{Use a calculator.}$$

The concentration in 1900 was about 309 parts per million.

(b) 1950

$$f(200) = 266(1.001)^{200} \qquad x = 1950 - 1750 = 200$$
$$f(200) \approx 325 \text{ parts per million} \qquad \text{Use a calculator.}$$

The concentration in 1950 was about 325 parts per million.   *NOW TRY*

NOW TRY
EXERCISE 7
Use the function in **Example 7** to approximate the pressure at 6000 m. Round to the nearest unit.

EXAMPLE 7   Applying an Exponential Decay Function

The atmospheric pressure (in millibars) at a given altitude x, in meters, can be approximated by the function defined by

$$f(x) = 1038(1.000134)^{-x}, \quad \text{for values of } x \text{ between 0 and 10,000.}$$

Because the base is greater than 1 and the coefficient of x in the exponent is negative, function values decrease as x increases. This means that as altitude increases, atmospheric pressure decreases. (*Source:* Miller, A. and J. Thompson, *Elements of Meteorology,* Fourth Edition, Charles E. Merrill Publishing Company.)

(a) According to this function, what is the pressure at ground level?

$$f(0) = 1038(1.000134)^{-0} \qquad \text{Let } x = 0.$$

At ground level, $x = 0$.

$$= 1038(1) \qquad a^0 = 1$$
$$= 1038$$

The pressure is 1038 millibars.

(b) Approximate the pressure at 5000 m. Round to the nearest unit.

$$f(5000) = 1038(1.000134)^{-5000} \qquad \text{Let } x = 5000.$$
$$f(5000) \approx 531 \qquad \text{Use a calculator.}$$

The pressure is approximately 531 millibars.   *NOW TRY*

NOW TRY ANSWERS
6. 342 parts per million
7. approximately 465 millibars

12.2 EXERCISES   *MyMathLab*   Math XL
PRACTICE   WATCH   DOWNLOAD   READ   REVIEW

 Complete solution available on the Video Resources on DVD

Concept Check   Choose the correct response in Exercises 1–3.

1. Which point lies on the graph of $f(x) = 3^x$?

   A. $(1, 0)$ **B.** $(3, 1)$ **C.** $(0, 1)$ **D.** $\left(\sqrt{3}, \dfrac{1}{3} \right)$

2. Which statement is true?

   A. The point $\left(\frac{1}{2}, \sqrt{5} \right)$ lies on the graph of $f(x) = 5^x$.

   B. For any $a > 1$, the graph of $f(x) = a^x$ falls from left to right.

   C. The y-intercept of the graph of $f(x) = 10^x$ is $(0, 10)$.

   D. The graph of $y = 4^x$ rises at a faster rate than the graph of $y = 10^x$.

3. The asymptote of the graph of $f(x) = a^x$

 A. is the x-axis   **B.** is the y-axis

 C. has equation $x = 1$ **D.** has equation $y = 1$.

4. In your own words, describe the characteristics of the graph of an exponential function. Use the exponential function defined by $f(x) = 3^x$ (**Exercise 5**) and the words *asymptote*, *domain*, and *range* in your explanation.

Graph each exponential function. See Examples 1–3.

5. $f(x) = 3^x$

6. $f(x) = 5^x$

7. $g(x) = \left(\dfrac{1}{3}\right)^x$

8. $g(x) = \left(\dfrac{1}{5}\right)^x$

9. $y = 4^{-x}$

10. $y = 6^{-x}$

11. $y = 2^{2x-2}$

12. $y = 2^{2x+1}$

13. *Concept Check* For an exponential function defined by $f(x) = a^x$, if $a > 1$, the graph _____ from left to right. If $0 < a < 1$, the graph _____ from
 (rises/falls)   (rises/falls)
 left to right.

14. *Concept Check* Based on your answers in **Exercise 13,** make a conjecture (an educated guess) concerning whether an exponential function defined by $f(x) = a^x$ is one-to-one. Then decide whether it has an inverse based on the concepts of **Section 12.1.**

Solve each equation. See Examples 4 and 5.

15. $6^x = 36$

16. $8^x = 64$

17. $100^x = 1000$

18. $8^x = 4$

19. $16^{2x+1} = 64^{x+3}$

20. $9^{2x-8} = 27^{x-4}$

21. $5^x = \dfrac{1}{125}$

22. $3^x = \dfrac{1}{81}$

23. $5^x = 0.2$

24. $10^x = 0.1$

25. $\left(\dfrac{3}{2}\right)^x = \dfrac{8}{27}$

26. $\left(\dfrac{4}{3}\right)^x = \dfrac{27}{64}$

Use the exponential key of a calculator to find an approximation to the nearest thousandth.

27. $12^{2.6}$

28. $13^{1.8}$

29. $0.5^{3.921}$

30. $0.6^{4.917}$

31. $2.718^{2.5}$

32. $2.718^{-3.1}$

A major scientific periodical published an article in 1990 dealing with the problem of global warming. The article was accompanied by a graph that illustrated two possible scenarios.

(a) The warming might be modeled by an exponential function of the form

$$y = (1.046 \times 10^{-38})(1.0444^x).$$

(b) The warming might be modeled by a linear function of the form

$$y = 0.009x - 17.67.$$

 In both cases, x represents the year, and y represents the increase in degrees Celsius due to the warming. Use these functions to approximate the increase in temperature for each of the following years.

33. 2000   **34.** 2010   **35.** 2020   **36.** 2040

Solve each problem. ***See Examples 6 and 7.***

37. Based on figures from 1970 through 2005, the worldwide carbon dioxide emissions in millions of metric tons are approximated by the exponential function defined by

$$f(x) = 4231(1.0174)^x,$$

where $x = 0$ corresponds to 1970, $x = 5$ corresponds to 1975, and so on. (*Source:* Carbon Dioxide Information Analysis Center.) Give answers to the nearest unit.

(a) Use this model to approximate the emissions in 1980.

(b) Use this model to approximate the emissions in 1995.

(c) In 2000, the actual amount of emissions was 6735 million tons. How does this compare to the number that the model provides?

38. Based on figures from 1980 through 2007, the municipal solid waste generated in millions of tons can be approximated by the exponential function defined by

$$f(x) = 159.51(1.0186)^x,$$

where $x = 0$ corresponds to 1980, $x = 5$ corresponds to 1985, and so on. (*Source:* U.S. Environmental Protection Agency.) Give answers to the nearest hundredth.

(a) Use the model to approximate the number of tons of this waste in 1980.

(b) Use the model to approximate the number of tons of this waste in 1995.

(c) In 2007, the actual number of millions of tons of this waste was 254.1. How does this compare to the number that the model provides?

39. A small business estimates that the value $V(t)$ of a copy machine is decreasing according to the function defined by

$$V(t) = 5000(2)^{-0.15t},$$

where t is the number of years that have elapsed since the machine was purchased, and $V(t)$ is in dollars.

(a) What was the original value of the machine?

(b) What is the value of the machine 5 yr after purchase, to the nearest dollar?

(c) What is the value of the machine 10 yr after purchase, to the nearest dollar?

(d) Graph the function.

40. The amount of radioactive material in an ore sample is given by the function defined by

$$A(t) = 100(3.2)^{-0.5t},$$

where $A(t)$ is the amount present, in grams, of the sample t months after the initial measurement.

(a) How much was present at the initial measurement? (*Hint:* $t = 0$.)

(b) How much was present 2 months later?

(c) How much was present 10 months later?

(d) Graph the function.

41. Refer to the function in **Exercise 39.** When will the value of the machine be $2500? (*Hint:* Let $V(t) = 2500$, divide both sides by 5000, and use the method of **Example 4.**)

42. Refer to the function in **Exercise 39.** When will the value of the machine be $1250?

PREVIEW EXERCISES

Determine what number would have to be placed in each box for the statement to be true. See ***Sections 4.1, 4.2, and 10.2.***

43. $2^\square = 16$ **44.** $2^\square = \dfrac{1}{16}$ **45.** $2^\square = 1$ **46.** $2^\square = \sqrt{2}$

12.3 Logarithmic Functions

OBJECTIVES

1 Define a logarithm.

2 Convert between exponential and logarithmic forms.

3 Solve logarithmic equations of the form $\log_a b = k$ for a, b, or k.

4 Define and graph logarithmic functions.

5 Use logarithmic functions in applications involving growth or decay.

The graph of $y = 2^x$ is the curve shown in blue in **FIGURE 9**. Because $y = 2^x$ defines a one-to-one function, it has an inverse. Interchanging x and y gives

$$x = 2^y, \quad \text{the inverse of} \quad y = 2^x. \quad \text{Roles of } x \text{ and } y \text{ are interchanged.}$$

As we saw in **Section 12.1,** the graph of the inverse is found by reflecting the graph of $y = 2^x$ about the line $y = x$. The graph of $x = 2^y$ is shown as a red curve in **FIGURE 9**.

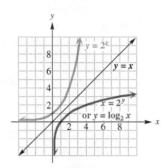

FIGURE 9

OBJECTIVE 1 **Define a logarithm.** We cannot solve the equation $x = 2^y$ for the dependent variable y with the methods presented up to now. The following definition is used to solve $x = 2^y$ for y.

Logarithm

For all positive numbers a, with $a \neq 1$, and all positive numbers x,

$$y = \log_a x \quad \text{means the same as} \quad x = a^y.$$

This key statement should be memorized. The abbreviation **log** is used for the word **logarithm**. Read $\log_a x$ as "**the logarithm of x with base a**" or "**the base a logarithm of x.**" To remember the location of the base and the exponent in each form, refer to the following diagrams.

Exponent
↓
Logarithmic form: $y = \log_a x$
↑
Base

Exponent
↓
Exponential form: $x = a^y$
↑
Base

In work with logarithmic form and exponential form, remember the following.

Meaning of $\log_a x$

A logarithm is an exponent. ***The expression $\log_a x$ represents the exponent to which the base a must be raised to obtain x.***

OBJECTIVE 2 **Convert between exponential and logarithmic forms.** We can use the definition of logarithm to convert between exponential and logarithmic forms.

EXERCISE 1

(a) Write $6^3 = 216$ in logarithmic form.

(b) Write $\log_{64} 4 = \frac{1}{3}$ in exponential form.

EXAMPLE 1 **Converting Between Exponential and Logarithmic Forms**

The table shows several pairs of equivalent forms.

Exponential Form	Logarithmic Form
$3^2 = 9$	$\log_3 9 = 2$
$\left(\frac{1}{5}\right)^{-2} = 25$	$\log_{1/5} 25 = -2$
$10^5 = 100{,}000$	$\log_{10} 100{,}000 = 5$
$4^{-3} = \frac{1}{64}$	$\log_4 \frac{1}{64} = -3$

$y = \log_a x$
means
$x = a^y.$

OBJECTIVE 3 **Solve logarithmic equations of the form $\log_a b = k$ for a, b, or k.** A **logarithmic equation** is an equation with a logarithm in at least one term.

EXAMPLE 2 **Solving Logarithmic Equations**

Solve each equation.

(a) $\log_4 x = -2$

By the definition of logarithm, $\log_4 x = -2$ is equivalent to $x = 4^{-2}$.

$$x = 4^{-2} = \frac{1}{16}$$

The solution set is $\left\{\frac{1}{16}\right\}$.

(b) $\qquad\qquad \log_{1/2}(3x + 1) = 2$

$\qquad\qquad\qquad 3x + 1 = \left(\frac{1}{2}\right)^2$ *This is a key step* Write in exponential form.

$\qquad\qquad\qquad 3x + 1 = \frac{1}{4}$ Apply the exponent.

$\qquad\qquad\qquad 12x + 4 = 1$ Multiply each term by 4.

$\qquad\qquad\qquad 12x = -3$ Subtract 4.

$\qquad\qquad\qquad x = -\frac{1}{4}$ Divide by 12. Write in lowest terms.

CHECK $\quad \log_{1/2}\left(3\left(-\frac{1}{4}\right) + 1\right) \overset{?}{=} 2$ Let $x = -\frac{1}{4}$.

$\qquad\qquad\qquad \log_{1/2} \frac{1}{4} \overset{?}{=} 2$ Simplify within parentheses.

$\qquad\qquad\qquad \left(\frac{1}{2}\right)^2 = \frac{1}{4}$ ✓ Exponential form; true

The solution set is $\left\{-\frac{1}{4}\right\}$.

(c) $\qquad\qquad\qquad \log_x 3 = 2$

$\qquad\qquad\qquad x^2 = 3$ Write in exponential form.

Be careful here.
$-\sqrt{3}$ is extraneous. $\qquad x = \pm\sqrt{3}$ Take square roots.

Only the *principal* square root satisfies the equation since the base must be a positive number. The solution set is $\left\{\sqrt{3}\right\}$.

NOW TRY ANSWERS
1. **(a)** $\log_6 216 = 3$
  (b) $64^{1/3} = 4$

NOW TRY
EXERCISE 2

Solve each equation.

(a) $\log_2 x = -5$

(b) $\log_{3/2} (2x - 1) = 3$

(c) $\log_x 10 = 2$

(d) $\log_{125} \sqrt[3]{5} = x$

(d)

$$\log_{49} \sqrt[3]{7} = x$$

$$49^x = \sqrt[3]{7} \qquad \text{Write in exponential form.}$$

$$(7^2)^x = 7^{1/3} \qquad \text{Write with the same base.}$$

$$7^{2x} = 7^{1/3} \qquad \text{Power rule for exponents}$$

$$2x = \frac{1}{3} \qquad \text{Set exponents equal.}$$

$$x = \frac{1}{6} \qquad \begin{array}{l}\text{Divide by 2 (which is the same}\\ \text{as multiplying by } \frac{1}{2}).\end{array}$$

The solution set is $\left\{\frac{1}{6}\right\}$. NOW TRY

For any real number b, we know that $b^1 = b$ and for $b \neq 0$, $b^0 = 1$. Writing these statements in logarithmic form gives the following properties of logarithms.

Properties of Logarithms

For any positive real number b, with $b \neq 1$, the following are true.

$$\log_b b = 1 \qquad \text{and} \qquad \log_b 1 = 0$$

NOW TRY
EXERCISE 3

Evaluate each logarithm.

(a) $\log_{10} 10$

(b) $\log_8 1$

(c) $\log_{0.1} 1$

EXAMPLE 3 Using Properties of Logarithms

Evaluate each logarithm.

(a) $\log_7 7 = 1 \qquad \log_b b = 1$

(b) $\log_{\sqrt{2}} \sqrt{2} = 1$

(c) $\log_9 1 = 0 \qquad \log_b 1 = 0$

(d) $\log_{0.2} 1 = 0$ NOW TRY

OBJECTIVE 4 **Define and graph logarithmic functions.** Now we define the logarithmic function with base a.

Logarithmic Function

If a and x are positive numbers, with $a \neq 1$, then

$$g(x) = \log_a x$$

defines the **logarithmic function with base a.**

EXAMPLE 4 Graphing a Logarithmic Function ($a > 1$)

Graph $f(x) = \log_2 x$.

NOW TRY ANSWERS

2. (a) $\left\{\frac{1}{32}\right\}$ (b) $\left\{\frac{35}{16}\right\}$
   (c) $\left\{\sqrt{10}\right\}$ (d) $\left\{\frac{1}{9}\right\}$

3. (a) 1 (b) 0 (c) 0

By writing $y = f(x) = \log_2 x$ in exponential form as $x = 2^y$, we can identify ordered pairs that satisfy the equation. It is easier to choose values for y and find the corresponding values of x. Plotting the points in the table of ordered pairs and connecting them with a smooth curve gives the graph in **FIGURE 10** on the next page. This graph is typical of logarithmic functions with base $a > 1$.

NOW TRY
EXERCISE 4
Graph $f(x) = \log_6 x$.

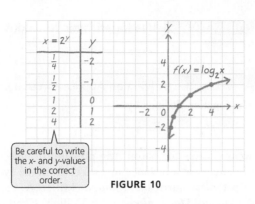

**Logarithmic function
with base $a > 1$**

Domain: $(0, \infty)$

Range: $(-\infty, \infty)$

The function is one-to-one, and its graph rises from left to right.

Be careful to write the x- and y-values in the correct order.

FIGURE 10

NOW TRY

NOW TRY
EXERCISE 5
Graph $g(x) = \log_{1/4} x$.

EXAMPLE 5 Graphing a Logarithmic Function $(0 < a < 1)$

Graph $g(x) = \log_{1/2} x$.

We write $y = g(x) = \log_{1/2} x$ in exponential form as $x = \left(\frac{1}{2}\right)^y$, then choose values for y and find the corresponding values of x. Plotting these points and connecting them with a smooth curve gives the graph in **FIGURE 11**. This graph is typical of logarithmic functions with base $0 < a < 1$.

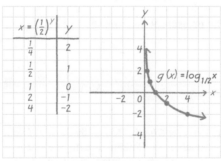

**Logarithmic function
with base $0 < a < 1$**

Domain: $(0, \infty)$

Range: $(-\infty, \infty)$

The function is one-to-one, and its graph falls from left to right.

FIGURE 11

NOW TRY

NOTE See the box titled "Characteristics of the Graph of $f(x) = a^x$" on **page 760.** Below we give a similar set of characteristics for the graph of $g(x) = \log_a x$. Compare the four characteristics one by one to see how the concepts of inverse functions, introduced in **Section 12.1,** are illustrated by these two classes of functions.

NOW TRY ANSWERS
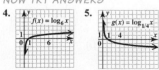

Characteristics of the Graph of $g(x) = \log_a x$

1. The graph contains the point $(1, 0)$.

2. The function is one-to-one. When $a > 1$, the graph will *rise* from left to right, from the fourth quadrant to the first. (See **FIGURE 10.**) When $0 < a < 1$, the graph will *fall* from left to right, from the first quadrant to the fourth. (See **FIGURE 11.**)

3. The graph will approach the y-axis, but never touch it. (The y-axis is an asymptote.)

4. The domain is $(0, \infty)$, and the range is $(-\infty, \infty)$.

OBJECTIVE 5 **Use logarithmic functions in applications involving growth or decay.**

NOW TRY
EXERCISE 6

Suppose the gross national product (GNP) of a small country (in millions of dollars) is approximated by

$$G(t) = 15.0 + 2.00 \log_{10} t,$$

where t is time in years since 2003. Approximate to the nearest tenth the GNP for each value of t.

(a) $t = 1$ **(b)** $t = 10$

NOW TRY ANSWERS
6. (a) $15.0 million
  (b) $17.0 million

EXAMPLE 6 **Solving an Application of a Logarithmic Function**

The function defined by

$$f(x) = 27 + 1.105 \log_{10} (x + 1)$$

approximates the barometric pressure in inches of mercury at a distance of x miles from the eye of a typical hurricane. (*Source:* Miller, A. and R. Anthes, *Meteorology,* Fifth Edition, Charles E. Merrill Publishing Company.) Approximate the pressure 9 mi from the eye of the hurricane. Let $x = 9$, and find $f(9)$.

$f(9) = 27 + 1.105 \log_{10} (9 + 1)$	Let $x = 9$.
$f(9) = 27 + 1.105 \log_{10} 10$	Add inside parentheses.
$f(9) = 27 + 1.105(1)$	$\log_{10} 10 = 1$
$f(9) = 28.105$	Add.

The pressure 9 mi from the eye of the hurricane is 28.105 in.   NOW TRY

12.3 EXERCISES

 MyMathLab Math XL PRACTICE WATCH DOWNLOAD READ REVIEW

 *Complete solution available on the Video Resources on DVD*

1. *Concept Check* Match the logarithmic equation in Column I with the corresponding exponential equation from Column II. **See Example 1.**

I	II
(a) $\log_{1/3} 3 = -1$	**A.** $8^{1/3} = \sqrt[3]{8}$
(b) $\log_5 1 = 0$	**B.** $\left(\frac{1}{3}\right)^{-1} = 3$
(c) $\log_2 \sqrt{2} = \frac{1}{2}$	**C.** $4^1 = 4$
(d) $\log_{10} 1000 = 3$	**D.** $2^{1/2} = \sqrt{2}$
(e) $\log_8 \sqrt[3]{8} = \frac{1}{3}$	**E.** $5^0 = 1$
(f) $\log_4 4 = 1$	**F.** $10^3 = 1000$

2. *Concept Check* Match the logarithm in Column I with its value in Column II. (*Example:* $\log_3 9 = 2$ because 2 is the exponent to which 3 must be raised in order to obtain 9.)

I	II
(a) $\log_4 16$	**A.** -2
(b) $\log_3 81$	**B.** -1
(c) $\log_3 \left(\frac{1}{3}\right)$	**C.** 2
(d) $\log_{10} 0.01$	**D.** 0
(e) $\log_5 \sqrt{5}$	**E.** $\frac{1}{2}$
(f) $\log_{13} 1$	**F.** 4

Write in logarithmic form. ***See Example 1.***

 3. $4^5 = 1024$ **4.** $3^6 = 729$ **5.** $\left(\frac{1}{2}\right)^{-3} = 8$ **6.** $\left(\frac{1}{6}\right)^{-3} = 216$

7. $10^{-3} = 0.001$ **8.** $36^{1/2} = 6$ **9.** $\sqrt[4]{625} = 5$ **10.** $\sqrt[3]{343} = 7$

11. $8^{-2/3} = \frac{1}{4}$ **12.** $16^{-3/4} = \frac{1}{8}$ **13.** $5^0 = 1$ **14.** $7^0 = 1$

Write in exponential form. **See Example 1.**

15. $\log_4 64 = 3$

16. $\log_2 512 = 9$

17. $\log_{10} \dfrac{1}{10,000} = -4$

18. $\log_{100} 100 = 1$

19. $\log_6 1 = 0$

20. $\log_\pi 1 = 0$

21. $\log_9 3 = \dfrac{1}{2}$

22. $\log_{64} 2 = \dfrac{1}{6}$

23. $\log_{1/4} \dfrac{1}{2} = \dfrac{1}{2}$

24. $\log_{1/8} \dfrac{1}{2} = \dfrac{1}{3}$

25. $\log_5 5^{-1} = -1$

26. $\log_{10} 10^{-2} = -2$

27. Match each logarithm in Column I with its value in Column II. **See Example 3.**

	I		II
(a)	$\log_8 8$	**A.**	-1
(b)	$\log_{16} 1$	**B.**	0
(c)	$\log_{0.3} 1$	**C.**	1
(d)	$\log_{\sqrt 7} \sqrt 7$	**D.**	0.1

28. When a student asked his teacher to explain how to evaluate

$$\log_9 3$$

without showing any work, his teacher told him, "Think radically." Explain what the teacher meant by this hint.

Solve each equation. **See Examples 2 and 3.**

29. $x = \log_{27} 3$

30. $x = \log_{125} 5$

31. $\log_x 9 = \dfrac{1}{2}$

32. $\log_x 5 = \dfrac{1}{2}$

33. $\log_x 125 = -3$

34. $\log_x 64 = -6$

35. $\log_{12} x = 0$

36. $\log_4 x = 0$

37. $\log_x x = 1$

38. $\log_x 1 = 0$

39. $\log_x \dfrac{1}{25} = -2$

40. $\log_x \dfrac{1}{10} = -1$

41. $\log_8 32 = x$

42. $\log_{81} 27 = x$

43. $\log_\pi \pi^4 = x$

44. $\log_{\sqrt 2} \left(\sqrt 2 \right)^9 = x$

45. $\log_6 \sqrt{216} = x$

46. $\log_4 \sqrt{64} = x$

47. $\log_4 (2x + 4) = 3$

48. $\log_3 (2x + 7) = 4$

If (p, q) is on the graph of $f(x) = a^x$ (for $a > 0$ and $a \neq 1$), then (q, p) is on the graph of $f^{-1}(x) = \log_a x$. Use this fact, and refer to the graphs required in **Exercises 5–8 in Section 12.2** *to graph each logarithmic function.* **See Examples 4 and 5.**

49. $y = \log_3 x$

50. $y = \log_5 x$

51. $y = \log_{1/3} x$

52. $y = \log_{1/5} x$

53. Explain why 1 is not allowed as a base for a logarithmic function.

54. Compare the summary of facts about the graph of $f(x) = a^x$ in **Section 12.2** with the similar summary of facts about the graph of $g(x) = \log_a x$ in this section. Make a list of the facts that reinforce the concept that f and g are inverse functions.

55. *Concept Check* The domain of $f(x) = a^x$ is $(-\infty, \infty)$, while the range is $(0, \infty)$. Therefore, since $g(x) = \log_a x$ defines the inverse of f, the domain of g is _____, while the range of g is _____.

56. *Concept Check* The graphs of both $f(x) = 3^x$ and $g(x) = \log_3 x$ rise from left to right. Which one rises at a faster rate?

Concept Check Use the graph at the right to predict the value of $f(t)$ for the given value of t.

57. $t = 0$

58. $t = 10$

59. $t = 60$

60. Show that the points determined in **Exercises 57–59** lie on the graph of $f(t) = 8 \log_5 (2t + 5)$.

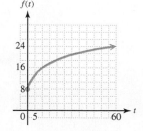

Solve each problem. ***See Example 6.***

🌐 **61.** For 1981–2003, the number of billion cubic feet of natural gas gross withdrawals from crude oil wells in the United States can be approximated by the function defined by

$$f(x) = 3800 + 585 \log_2 x,$$

where $x = 1$ corresponds to 1981, $x = 2$ to 1982, and so on. (*Source:* Energy Information Administration.) Use this function to approximate, to the nearest unit, the number of cubic feet withdrawn in each of the following years.

(a) 1982   **(b)** 1988   **(c)** 1996

62. According to selected figures from the last two decades of the 20th century, the number of trillion cubic feet of dry natural gas consumed worldwide can be approximated by the function defined by

$$f(x) = 51.47 + 6.044 \log_2 x,$$

where $x = 1$ corresponds to 1980, $x = 2$ to 1981, and so on. (*Source:* Energy Information Administration.) Use the function to approximate, to the nearest hundredth, consumption in each year.

(a) 1980   **(b)** 1987   **(c)** 1995

63. Sales (in thousands of units) of a new product are approximated by the function defined by

$$S(t) = 100 + 30 \log_3 (2t + 1),$$

where t is the number of years after the product is introduced.

(a) What were the sales, to the nearest unit, after 1 yr?

(b) What were the sales, to the nearest unit, after 13 yr?

(c) Graph $y = S(t)$.

64. A study showed that the number of mice in an old abandoned house was approximated by the function defined by

$$M(t) = 6 \log_4 (2t + 4),$$

where t is measured in months and $t = 0$ corresponds to January 2008. Find the number of mice in the house in

(a) January 2008   **(b)** July 2008   **(c)** July 2010.

(d) Graph the function.

The ***Richter scale*** *is used to measure the intensity of earthquakes. The Richter scale rating of an earthquake of intensity x is given by*

$$R = \log_{10} \frac{x}{x_0},$$

where x_0 *is the intensity of an earthquake of a certain (small) size. The figure here shows Richter scale ratings for Southern California earthquakes from 1930 to 2000 with magnitudes greater than 4.7.*

65. The 1994 Northridge earthquake had a Richter scale rating of 6.7. The 1992 Landers earthquake had a rating of 7.3. How much more powerful was the Landers earthquake than the Northridge earthquake?

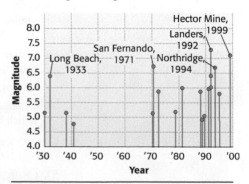

Southern California Earthquakes
(with magnitudes greater than 4.7)

Source: Caltech; U.S. Geological Survey.

66. Compare the smallest rated earthquake in the figure (at 4.8) with the Landers quake. How much more powerful was the Landers quake?

Some graphing calculators have the capability of drawing the inverse of a function. For example, the two screens that follow show the graphs of $f(x) = 2^x$ and $g(x) = \log_2 x$. The graph of g was obtained by drawing the graph of f^{-1}, since $g(x) = f^{-1}(x)$. (Compare to **FIGURE 9** *in this section.)*

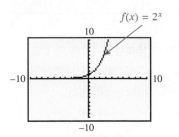

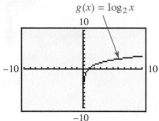

Use a graphing calculator with the capability of drawing the inverse of a function to draw the graph of each logarithmic function. Use the standard viewing window.

67. $g(x) = \log_3 x$
(Compare to **Exercise 49.**)

68. $g(x) = \log_5 x$
(Compare to **Exercise 50.**)

69. $g(x) = \log_{1/3} x$
(Compare to **Exercise 51.**)

70. $g(x) = \log_{1/5} x$
(Compare to **Exercise 52.**)

PREVIEW EXERCISES

*Simplify each expression. Write answers using only positive exponents. **See Sections 4.1 and 4.2.***

71. $4^7 \cdot 4^2$

72. $\dfrac{5^{-3}}{5^8}$

73. $\dfrac{7^8}{7^{-4}}$

74. $(9^3)^{-2}$

12.4 Properties of Logarithms

OBJECTIVES

1 Use the product rule for logarithms.

2 Use the quotient rule for logarithms.

3 Use the power rule for logarithms.

4 Use properties to write alternative forms of logarithmic expressions.

Logarithms were used as an aid to numerical calculation for several hundred years. Today the widespread use of calculators has made the use of logarithms for calculation obsolete. However, logarithms are still very important in applications and in further work in mathematics.

OBJECTIVE 1 **Use the product rule for logarithms.** One way in which logarithms simplify problems is by changing a problem of multiplication into one of addition. We know that $\log_2 4 = 2$, $\log_2 8 = 3$, and $\log_2 32 = 5$.

$$\log_2 32 = \log_2 4 + \log_2 8 \qquad 5 = 2 + 3$$
$$\log_2 (4 \cdot 8) = \log_2 4 + \log_2 8 \qquad 32 = 4 \cdot 8$$

This is an example of the following rule.

Product Rule for Logarithms

If x, y, and b are positive real numbers, where $b \neq 1$, then the following is true.

$$\log_b xy = \log_b x + \log_b y$$

That is, the logarithm of a product is the sum of the logarithms of the factors.

NOTE The word statement of the product rule can be restated by replacing "logarithm" with "exponent." The rule then becomes the familiar rule for multiplying exponential expressions: The *exponent* of a product is the sum of the *exponents* of the factors.

To prove this rule, let $m = \log_b x$ and $n = \log_b y$, and recall that

$$\log_b x = m \quad \text{means} \quad b^m = x \quad \text{and} \quad \log_b y = n \quad \text{means} \quad b^n = y.$$

Now consider the product xy.

$$xy = b^m \cdot b^n \qquad \text{Substitute.}$$
$$xy = b^{m+n} \qquad \text{Product rule for exponents}$$
$$\log_b xy = m + n \qquad \text{Convert to logarithmic form.}$$
$$\log_b xy = \log_b x + \log_b y \qquad \text{Substitute.}$$

The last statement is the result we wished to prove.

NOW TRY
EXERCISE 1

Use the product rule to rewrite each logarithm.

(a) $\log_{10} (7 \cdot 9)$

(b) $\log_5 11 + \log_5 8$

(c) $\log_5 (5x), \quad x > 0$

(d) $\log_2 t^3, \quad t > 0$

EXAMPLE 1 Using the Product Rule

Use the product rule to rewrite each logarithm. Assume $x > 0$.

(a) $\log_5 (6 \cdot 9)$

$\quad = \log_5 6 + \log_5 9 \qquad$ Product rule

(b) $\log_7 8 + \log_7 12$

$\quad = \log_7 (8 \cdot 12) \qquad$ Product rule

$\quad = \log_7 96 \qquad$ Multiply.

(c) $\log_3 (3x)$

$\quad = \log_3 3 + \log_3 x \qquad$ Product rule

$\quad = 1 + \log_3 x \qquad \log_3 3 = 1$

(d) $\log_4 x^3$

$\quad = \log_4 (x \cdot x \cdot x) \qquad x^3 = x \cdot x \cdot x$

$\quad = \log_4 x + \log_4 x + \log_4 x \qquad$ Product rule

$\quad = 3 \log_4 x \qquad$ Combine like terms. NOW TRY

OBJECTIVE 2 **Use the quotient rule for logarithms.** The rule for division is similar to the rule for multiplication.

Quotient Rule for Logarithms

If x, y, and b are positive real numbers, where $b \neq 1$, then the following is true.

$$\log_b \frac{x}{y} = \log_b x - \log_b y$$

That is, the logarithm of a quotient is the difference between the logarithm of the numerator and the logarithm of the denominator.

NOW TRY ANSWERS
1. **(a)** $\log_{10} 7 + \log_{10} 9$
 (b) $\log_5 88$
 (c) $1 + \log_5 x$
 (d) $3 \log_2 t$

The proof of this rule is similar to the proof of the product rule.

NOW TRY
EXERCISE 2

Use the quotient rule to rewrite each logarithm.

(a) $\log_{10} \dfrac{7}{9}$

(b) $\log_4 x - \log_4 12, \quad x > 0$

(c) $\log_5 \dfrac{25}{27}$

EXAMPLE 2 Using the Quotient Rule

Use the quotient rule to rewrite each logarithm. Assume $x > 0$.

(a) $\log_4 \dfrac{7}{9}$

$= \log_4 7 - \log_4 9$ Quotient rule

(b) $\log_5 6 - \log_5 x$

$= \log_5 \dfrac{6}{x}$ Quotient rule

(c) $\log_3 \dfrac{27}{5}$

$= \log_3 27 - \log_3 5$ Quotient rule

$= 3 - \log_3 5$ $\log_3 27 = 3$ NOW TRY

⚠ **CAUTION** *There is no property of logarithms to rewrite the logarithm of a sum or difference.* For example, we *cannot* write $\log_b (x + y)$ in terms of $\log_b x$ and $\log_b y$. Also,

$$\log_b \frac{x}{y} \neq \frac{\log_b x}{\log_b y}.$$

OBJECTIVE 3 **Use the power rule for logarithms.** An exponential expression such as 2^3 means $2 \cdot 2 \cdot 2$. The base is used as a factor 3 times. Similarly, the product rule can be extended to rewrite the logarithm of a power as the product of the exponent and the logarithm of the base.

$\log_5 2^3$	$\log_2 7^4$
$= \log_5 (2 \cdot 2 \cdot 2)$	$= \log_2 (7 \cdot 7 \cdot 7 \cdot 7)$
$= \log_5 2 + \log_5 2 + \log_5 2$	$= \log_2 7 + \log_2 7 + \log_2 7 + \log_2 7$
$= 3 \log_5 2$	$= 4 \log_2 7$

Furthermore, we saw in **Example 1(d)** that $\log_4 x^3 = 3 \log_4 x$. These examples suggest the following rule.

Power Rule for Logarithms

If x and b are positive real numbers, where $b \neq 1$, and if r is any real number, then the following is true.

$$\log_b x^r = r \log_b x$$

That is, the logarithm of a number to a power equals the exponent times the logarithm of the number.

NOW TRY ANSWERS
2. **(a)** $\log_{10} 7 - \log_{10} 9$

  (b) $\log_4 \frac{x}{12}$

  (c) $2 - \log_5 27$

As further examples of this rule,

$$\log_b m^5 = 5 \log_b m \quad \text{and} \quad \log_3 5^4 = 4 \log_3 5.$$

To prove the power rule, let $\log_b x = m$.

$$b^m = x \qquad \text{Convert to exponential form.}$$
$$(b^m)^r = x^r \qquad \text{Raise to the power } r.$$
$$b^{mr} = x^r \qquad \text{Power rule for exponents}$$
$$\log_b x^r = rm \qquad \text{Convert to logarithmic form; commutative property}$$
$$\log_b x^r = r \log_b x \qquad m = \log_b x \text{ from above}$$

This is the statement to be proved.

As a special case of the power rule, let $r = \frac{1}{p}$, so

$$\log_b \sqrt[p]{x} = \log_b x^{1/p} = \frac{1}{p} \log_b x.$$

For example, using this result, with $x > 0$,

$$\log_b \sqrt[5]{x} = \log_b x^{1/5} = \frac{1}{5} \log_b x \qquad \text{and} \qquad \log_b \sqrt[3]{x^4} = \log_b x^{4/3} = \frac{4}{3} \log_b x.$$

Another special case is

$$\log_b \frac{1}{x} = \log_b x^{-1} = -\log_b x.$$

NOW TRY
EXERCISE 3

Use the power rule to rewrite each logarithm. Assume $a > 0, x > 0$, and $a \neq 1$.

(a) $\log_7 5^3$ **(b)** $\log_a \sqrt{10}$
(c) $\log_3 \sqrt[4]{x^3}$

EXAMPLE 3 Using the Power Rule

Use the power rule to rewrite each logarithm. Assume $b > 0, x > 0$, and $b \neq 1$.

(a) $\log_5 4^2$
$= 2 \log_5 4$ Power rule

(b) $\log_b x^5$
$= 5 \log_b x$ Power rule

(c) $\log_b \sqrt{7}$
$= \log_b 7^{1/2}$ $\sqrt{x} = x^{1/2}$
$= \frac{1}{2} \log_b 7$ Power rule

(d) $\log_2 \sqrt[5]{x^2}$
$= \log_2 x^{2/5}$ $\sqrt[5]{x^2} = x^{2/5}$
$= \frac{2}{5} \log_2 x$ Power rule

NOW TRY

Two special properties involving both exponential and logarithmic expressions come directly from the fact that logarithmic and exponential functions are inverses of each other.

Special Properties

If $b > 0$ and $b \neq 1$, then the following are true.
$$b^{\log_b x} = x, \quad x > 0 \qquad \text{and} \qquad \log_b b^x = x$$

To prove the first statement, let $y = \log_b x$.

$$y = \log_b x$$
$$b^y = x \qquad \text{Convert to exponential form.}$$
$$b^{\log_b x} = x \qquad \text{Replace } y \text{ with } \log_b x.$$

The proof of the second statement is similar.

NOW TRY ANSWERS
3. (a) $3 \log_7 5$ **(b)** $\frac{1}{2} \log_a 10$
(c) $\frac{3}{4} \log_3 x$

NOW TRY
EXERCISE 4
Find each value.

(a) $\log_4 4^7$

(b) $\log_{10} 10{,}000$

(c) $8^{\log_8 5}$

EXAMPLE 4 Using the Special Properties

Find each value.

(a) $\log_5 5^4 = 4$, since $\log_b b^x = x$.

(b) $\log_3 9 = \log_3 3^2 = 2$

(c) $4^{\log_4 10} = 10$

NOW TRY

We summarize the properties of logarithms.

Properties of Logarithms

If x, y, and b are positive real numbers, where $b \neq 1$, and r is any real number, then the following are true.

Product Rule $\log_b xy = \log_b x + \log_b y$

Quotient Rule $\log_b \dfrac{x}{y} = \log_b x - \log_b y$

Power Rule $\log_b x^r = r \log_b x$

Special Properties $b^{\log_b x} = x$ and $\log_b b^x = x$

OBJECTIVE 4 Use properties to write alternative forms of logarithmic expressions.

EXAMPLE 5 Writing Logarithms in Alternative Forms

Use the properties of logarithms to rewrite each expression if possible. Assume that all variables represent positive real numbers.

(a) $\log_4 4x^3$

$= \log_4 4 + \log_4 x^3$ Product rule

$= 1 + 3 \log_4 x$ $\log_4 4 = 1$; power rule

(b) $\log_7 \sqrt{\dfrac{m}{n}}$

$= \log_7 \left(\dfrac{m}{n}\right)^{1/2}$ Write the radical expression with a rational exponent.

$= \dfrac{1}{2} \log_7 \dfrac{m}{n}$ Power rule

$= \dfrac{1}{2}(\log_7 m - \log_7 n)$ Quotient rule

(c) $\log_5 \dfrac{a^2}{bc}$

$= \log_5 a^2 - \log_5 bc$ Quotient rule

$= 2 \log_5 a - \log_5 bc$ Power rule

$= 2 \log_5 a - (\log_5 b + \log_5 c)$ Product rule

$= 2 \log_5 a - \log_5 b - \log_5 c$ Parentheses are necessary here.

NOW TRY ANSWERS
4. **(a)** 7 **(b)** 4 **(c)** 5

NOW TRY
EXERCISE 5

Use properties of logarithms to rewrite each expression if possible. Assume that all variables represent positive real numbers.

(a) $\log_3 9z^4$

(b) $\log_6 \sqrt{\dfrac{n}{3m}}$

(c) $\log_2 x + 3 \log_2 y - \log_2 z$

(d) $\log_5 (x + 10)$
$+ \log_5 (x - 10)$
$- \dfrac{3}{5} \log_5 x, \quad x > 10$

(e) $\log_7 (49 + 2x)$

(d) $4 \log_b m - \log_b n, \quad b \neq 1$

$= \log_b m^4 - \log_b n \qquad$ Power rule

$= \log_b \dfrac{m^4}{n} \qquad\qquad$ Quotient rule

(e) $\log_b (x + 1) + \log_b (2x + 1) - \dfrac{2}{3} \log_b x, \quad b \neq 1$

$= \log_b (x + 1) + \log_b (2x + 1) - \log_b x^{2/3} \qquad$ Power rule

$= \log_b \dfrac{(x + 1)(2x + 1)}{x^{2/3}} \qquad$ Product and quotient rules

$= \log_b \dfrac{2x^2 + 3x + 1}{x^{2/3}} \qquad$ Multiply in the numerator.

(f) $\log_8 (2p + 3r)$ cannot be rewritten using the properties of logarithms. There is no property of logarithms to rewrite the logarithm of a sum. NOW TRY

In the next example, we use numerical values for $\log_2 5$ and $\log_2 3$. While we use the equals symbol to give these values, they are actually just approximations since most logarithms of this type are irrational numbers. *We use $=$ with the understanding that the values are correct to four decimal places.*

NOW TRY
EXERCISE 6

Given that $\log_2 7 = 2.8074$ and $\log_2 10 = 3.3219$, evaluate the following.

(a) $\log_2 70$ (b) $\log_2 0.7$

(c) $\log_2 49$

EXAMPLE 6 Using the Properties of Logarithms with Numerical Values

Given that $\log_2 5 = 2.3219$ and $\log_2 3 = 1.5850$, evaluate the following.

(a) $\log_2 15$

$= \log_2(3 \cdot 5) \qquad$ Factor 15.

$= \log_2 3 + \log_2 5 \qquad$ Product rule

$= 1.5850 + 2.3219 \qquad$ Substitute the given values.

$= 3.9069 \qquad$ Add.

(b) $\log_2 0.6$

$= \log_2 \dfrac{3}{5} \qquad 0.6 = \frac{6}{10} = \frac{3}{5}$

$= \log_2 3 - \log_2 5 \qquad$ Quotient rule

$= 1.5850 - 2.3219 \qquad$ Substitute the given values.

$= -0.7369 \qquad$ Subtract.

(c) $\log_2 27$

$= \log_2 3^3 \qquad$ Write 27 as a power of 3.

$= 3 \log_2 3 \qquad$ Power rule

$= 3(1.5850) \qquad$ Substitute the given value.

$= 4.7550 \qquad$ Multiply. NOW TRY

NOW TRY ANSWERS
5. (a) $2 + 4 \log_3 z$
(b) $\frac{1}{2}(\log_6 n - \log_6 3 - \log_6 m)$
(c) $\log_2 \dfrac{xy^3}{z}$ (d) $\log_5 \dfrac{x^2 - 100}{x^{3/5}}$
(e) cannot be rewritten
6. (a) 6.1293 (b) -0.5145
(c) 5.6148

NOW TRY
EXERCISE 7
Decide whether each statement
is *true* or *false*.
(a) $\log_2 16 + \log_2 16 = \log_2 32$
(b) $(\log_2 4)(\log_3 9) = \log_6 36$

EXAMPLE 7 Deciding Whether Statements about Logarithms Are True

Decide whether each statement is *true* or *false*.

(a) $\log_2 8 - \log_2 4 = \log_2 4$

Evaluate each side.

$\log_2 8 - \log_2 4$	Left side	$\log_2 4$	Right side
$= \log_2 2^3 - \log_2 2^2$	Write 8 and 4 as powers of 2.	$= \log_2 2^2$	Write 4 as a power of 2.
$= 3 - 2$	$\log_a a^x = x$	$= 2$	$\log_a a^x = x$
$= 1$	Subtract.		

The statement is false because $1 \neq 2$.

(b) $\log_3 (\log_2 8) = \dfrac{\log_7 49}{\log_8 64}$

Evaluate each side.

$\log_3 (\log_2 8)$	Left side	$\dfrac{\log_7 49}{\log_8 64}$	Right side
$= \log_3 (\log_2 2^3)$	Write 8 as a power of 2.	$= \dfrac{\log_7 7^2}{\log_8 8^2}$	Write 49 and 64 using exponents.
$= \log_3 3$	$\log_a a^x = x$	$= \dfrac{2}{2}$	$\log_a a^x = x$
$= 1$	$3 = 3^1$	$= 1$	Simplify.

The statement is true because $1 = 1$.

NOW TRY

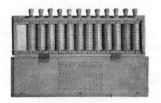
Napier's Rods
Source: IBM Corporate Archives.

CONNECTIONS

Long before the days of calculators and computers, the search for making calculations easier was an ongoing process. Machines built by Charles Babbage and Blaise Pascal, a system of "rods" used by John Napier, and slide rules were the forerunners of today's electronic marvels. The invention of logarithms by John Napier in the sixteenth century was a great breakthrough in the search for easier methods of calculation.

Since logarithms are exponents, their properties allowed users of tables of common logarithms to multiply by adding, divide by subtracting, raise to powers by multiplying, and take roots by dividing. Although logarithms are no longer used for computations, they play an important part in higher mathematics.

For Discussion or Writing

1. To multiply 458.3 by 294.6 using logarithms, we add $\log_{10} 458.3$ and $\log_{10} 294.6$, and then find 10 to this power. Perform this multiplication using the ⟨ log x ⟩ key* and the ⟨ 10^x ⟩ key on your calculator. Check your answer by multiplying directly with your calculator.

2. Try division, raising to a power, and taking a root by this method.

*In this text, the notation log x is used to mean $\log_{10} x$. This is also the meaning of the log key on calculators.

12.4 EXERCISES MyMathLab Math XL PRACTICE WATCH DOWNLOAD READ REVIEW

⊕ *Complete solution available on the Video Resources on DVD*

Use the indicated rule of logarithms to complete each equation. ***See Examples 1–4.***

1. $\log_{10}(7 \cdot 8) = $ _____ (product rule)

2. $\log_{10}\dfrac{7}{8} = $ _____ (quotient rule)

3. $3^{\log_3 4} = $ _____ (special property)

4. $\log_{10} 3^6 = $ _____ (power rule)

5. $\log_3 3^9 = $ _____ (special property)

6. Evaluate $\log_2(8 + 8)$. Then evaluate $\log_2 8 + \log_2 8$. Are the results the same? How could you change the operation in the first expression to make the two expressions equal?

Use the properties of logarithms to express each logarithm as a sum or difference of logarithms, or as a single number if possible. Assume that all variables represent positive real numbers. ***See Examples 1–5.***

7. $\log_7(4 \cdot 5)$ **8.** $\log_8(9 \cdot 11)$ **9.** $\log_5 \dfrac{8}{3}$

10. $\log_3 \dfrac{7}{5}$ **11.** $\log_4 6^2$ **12.** $\log_5 7^4$

13. $\log_3 \dfrac{\sqrt[3]{4}}{x^2 y}$ **14.** $\log_7 \dfrac{\sqrt[3]{13}}{pq^2}$ **15.** $\log_3 \sqrt{\dfrac{xy}{5}}$

16. $\log_6 \sqrt{\dfrac{pq}{7}}$ **17.** $\log_2 \dfrac{\sqrt[3]{x} \cdot \sqrt[5]{y}}{r^2}$ **18.** $\log_4 \dfrac{\sqrt[4]{z} \cdot \sqrt[5]{w}}{s^2}$

19. *Concept Check* A student erroneously wrote $\log_a(x + y) = \log_a x + \log_a y$. When his teacher explained that this was indeed wrong, the student claimed that he had used the distributive property. *WHAT WENT WRONG?*

20. Write a few sentences explaining how the rules for multiplying and dividing powers of the same base are similar to the rules for finding logarithms of products and quotients.

Use the properties of logarithms to write each expression as a single logarithm. Assume that all variables are defined in such a way that the variable expressions are positive, and bases are positive numbers not equal to 1. ***See Examples 1–5.***

21. $\log_b x + \log_b y$ **22.** $\log_b w + \log_b z$

23. $\log_a m - \log_a n$ **24.** $\log_b x - \log_b y$

25. $(\log_a r - \log_a s) + 3 \log_a t$ **26.** $(\log_a p - \log_a q) + 2 \log_a r$

27. $3 \log_a 5 - 4 \log_a 3$ **28.** $3 \log_a 5 - \dfrac{1}{2} \log_a 9$

29. $\log_{10}(x + 3) + \log_{10}(x - 3)$ **30.** $\log_{10}(x + 4) + \log_{10}(x - 4)$

31. $3 \log_p x + \dfrac{1}{2} \log_p y - \dfrac{3}{2} \log_p z - 3 \log_p a$

32. $\dfrac{1}{3} \log_b x + \dfrac{2}{3} \log_b y - \dfrac{3}{4} \log_b s - \dfrac{2}{3} \log_b t$

To four decimal places, the values of $\log_{10} 2$ *and* $\log_{10} 9$ *are*

$$\log_{10} 2 = 0.3010 \quad \text{and} \quad \log_{10} 9 = 0.9542.$$

Evaluate each logarithm by applying the appropriate rule or rules from this section. DO NOT USE A CALCULATOR. **See Example 6.**

🌐 **33.** $\log_{10} 18$ **34.** $\log_{10} 4$ **35.** $\log_{10} \dfrac{2}{9}$

36. $\log_{10} \dfrac{9}{2}$ **37.** $\log_{10} 36$ **38.** $\log_{10} 162$

39. $\log_{10} \sqrt[4]{9}$ **40.** $\log_{10} \sqrt[5]{2}$ **41.** $\log_{10} 3$

42. $\log_{10} \dfrac{1}{9}$ **43.** $\log_{10} 9^5$ **44.** $\log_{10} 2^{19}$

Decide whether each statement is true *or* false. **See Example 7.**

🌐 **45.** $\log_2 (8 + 32) = \log_2 8 + \log_2 32$ **46.** $\log_2 (64 - 16) = \log_2 64 - \log_2 16$

47. $\log_3 7 + \log_3 7^{-1} = 0$ **48.** $\log_3 49 + \log_3 49^{-1} = 0$

49. $\log_6 60 - \log_6 10 = 1$ **50.** $\log_3 8 + \log_3 \dfrac{1}{8} = 0$

51. $\dfrac{\log_{10} 7}{\log_{10} 14} = \dfrac{1}{2}$ **52.** $\dfrac{\log_{10} 10}{\log_{10} 100} = \dfrac{1}{10}$

53. *Concept Check*   Refer to the Note following the word statement of the product rule for logarithms in this section. Now, state the quotient rule in words, replacing "logarithm" with "exponent."

📝 **54.** Explain why the statement for the power rule for logarithms requires that x be a positive real number.

55. *Concept Check*   Why can't we determine a logarithm of 0? (*Hint*: Think of the definition of logarithm.)

56. *Concept Check*   Consider the following "proof" that $\log_2 16$ does not exist.

$$\log_2 16$$
$$= \log_2 (-4)(-4)$$
$$= \log_2 (-4) + \log_2 (-4)$$

Since the logarithm of a negative number is not defined, the final step cannot be evaluated, and so $\log_2 16$ does not exist. *WHAT WENT WRONG?*

PREVIEW EXERCISES

Write each exponential statement in logarithmic form. **See Section 12.3.**

57. $10^4 = 10{,}000$ **58.** $10^{1/2} = \sqrt{10}$ **59.** $10^{-2} = 0.01$

Write each logarithmic statement in exponential form. **See Section 12.3.**

60. $\log_{10} 0.001 = -3$ **61.** $\log_{10} 1 = 0$ **62.** $\log_{10} \sqrt[3]{10} = \dfrac{1}{3}$

12.5 Common and Natural Logarithms

OBJECTIVES

1 Evaluate common logarithms using a calculator.

2 Use common logarithms in applications.

3 Evaluate natural logarithms using a calculator.

4 Use natural logarithms in applications.

5 Use the change-of-base rule.

Logarithms are important in many applications in biology, engineering, economics, and social science. In this section we find numerical approximations for logarithms. Traditionally, base 10 logarithms were used most often because our number system is base 10. Logarithms to base 10 are called **common logarithms,** and

$$\log_{10} x \text{ is abbreviated as } \log x,$$

where the base is understood to be 10.

OBJECTIVE 1 **Evaluate common logarithms using a calculator.** In the first example, we give the results of evaluating some common logarithms using a calculator with a (LOG) key. Consult your calculator manual to see how to use this key.

EXAMPLE 1 Evaluating Common Logarithms

Using a calculator, evaluate each logarithm to four decimal places.

(a) $\log 327.1 \approx 2.5147$ (b) $\log 437{,}000 \approx 5.6405$

(c) $\log 0.0615 \approx -1.2111$

FIGURE 12 shows how a graphing calculator displays these common logarithms to four decimal places.

```
log(327.1)
             2.5147
log(437000)
             5.6405
log(.0615)
            -1.2111
```

FIGURE 12

NOW TRY

NOW TRY EXERCISE 1

Using a calculator, evaluate each logarithm to four decimal places.

(a) log 115   (b) log 0.25

In **Example 1(c),** $\log 0.0615 \approx -1.2111$, a negative result. *The common logarithm of a number between 0 and 1 is always negative* because the logarithm is the exponent on 10 that produces the number. In this case, we have

$$10^{-1.2111} \approx 0.0615.$$

If the exponent (the logarithm) were positive, the result would be greater than 1 because $10^0 = 1$. The graph in **FIGURE 13** illustrates these concepts.

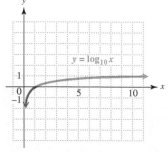

FIGURE 13

OBJECTIVE 2 **Use common logarithms in applications.** In chemistry, pH is a measure of the acidity or alkalinity of a solution. Pure water, for example, has pH 7. In general, acids have pH numbers less than 7, and alkaline solutions have pH values greater than 7, as shown in **FIGURE 14** on the next page.

NOW TRY ANSWERS
1. (a) 2.0607   (b) −0.6021

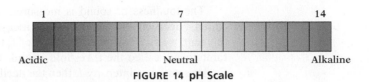

1	7	14

Acidic   Neutral   Alkaline

FIGURE 14 pH Scale

The **pH** of a solution is defined as

$$pH = -\log [H_3O^+],$$

where $[H_3O^+]$ is the hydronium ion concentration in moles per liter. *It is customary to round pH values to the nearest tenth.*

NOW TRY
EXERCISE 2

Water taken from a wetland has a hydronium ion concentration of

$$3.4 \times 10^{-5}.$$

Find the pH value for the water and classify the wetland as a rich fen, a poor fen, or a bog.

EXAMPLE 2   Using pH in an Application

Wetlands are classified as *bogs, fens, marshes,* and *swamps,* on the basis of pH values. A pH value between 6.0 and 7.5, such as that of Summerby Swamp in Michigan's Hiawatha National Forest, indicates that the wetland is a "rich fen." When the pH is between 3.0 and 6.0, the wetland is a "poor fen," and if the pH falls to 3.0 or less, it is a "bog." (*Source:* Mohlenbrock, R., "Summerby Swamp, Michigan," *Natural History.*)

Suppose that the hydronium ion concentration of a sample of water from a wetland is 6.3×10^{-3}. How would this wetland be classified?

$pH = -\log (6.3 \times 10^{-3})$	Definition of pH
$pH = -(\log 6.3 + \log 10^{-3})$	Product rule
$pH = -[0.7993 - 3(1)]$	Use a calculator to find log 6.3.
$pH = -0.7993 + 3$	Distributive property
$pH \approx 2.2$	Add.

Since the pH is less than 3.0, the wetland is a bog.   NOW TRY

NOW TRY
EXERCISE 3

Find the hydronium ion concentration of a solution with pH 2.6.

EXAMPLE 3   Finding Hydronium Ion Concentration

Find the hydronium ion concentration of drinking water with pH 6.5.

$pH = -\log [H_3O^+]$	
$6.5 = -\log [H_3O^+]$	Let pH = 6.5.
$\log [H_3O^+] = -6.5$	Multiply by −1.

Solve for $[H_3O^+]$ by writing the equation in exponential form using base 10.

$[H_3O^+] = 10^{-6.5}$	
$[H_3O^+] \approx 3.2 \times 10^{-7}$	Use a calculator.

NOW TRY

NOW TRY ANSWERS
2. 4.5; poor fen
3. 2.5×10^{-3}

The loudness of sound is measured in a unit called a **decibel,** abbreviated **dB.** To measure with this unit, we first assign an intensity of I_0 to a very faint sound, called the **threshold sound.** If a particular sound has intensity I, then the decibel level of this louder sound is

$$D = 10 \log \left(\frac{I}{I_0} \right).$$

The table gives average decibel levels for some common sounds. Any sound over 85 dB exceeds what hearing experts consider safe. Permanent hearing damage can be suffered at levels above 150 dB.

Decibel Level	Example
60	Normal conversation
90	Rush hour traffic, lawn mower
100	Garbage truck, chain saw, pneumatic drill
120	Rock concert, thunderclap
140	Gunshot blast, jet engine
180	Rocket launching pad

Source: Deafness Research Foundation.

**NOW TRY
EXERCISE 4**

Find the decibel level to the nearest whole number of the sound from a jet engine with intensity I of

$$6.312 \times 10^{13} I_0.$$

EXAMPLE 4 Measuring the Loudness of Sound

If music delivered through the earphones of an iPod has intensity I of $3.162 \times 10^9 I_0$, find the average decibel level.

$D = 10 \log \left(\dfrac{I}{I_0} \right)$

$D = 10 \log \left(\dfrac{3.162 \times 10^9 I_0}{I_0} \right)$ Substitute the given value for *I*.

$D = 10 \log (3.162 \times 10^9)$

$D \approx 95$ Use a calculator. Round to the nearest unit.

> Substitute the given value for *I.*

NOW TRY

OBJECTIVE 3 **Evaluate natural logarithms using a calculator.** Logarithms used in applications are often **natural logarithms,** which have as base the number **e.** The number *e*, like π, is a **universal constant.** The letter *e* was chosen to honor Leonhard Euler, who published extensive results on the number in 1748. Since it is an irrational number, its decimal expansion never terminates and never repeats.

e

$$e \approx 2.718281828$$

A calculator with an $\boxed{e^x}$ key can approximate powers of *e*.

$e^2 \approx 7.389056099, \quad e^3 \approx 20.08553692, \quad e^{0.6} \approx 1.8221188$ Powers of *e*

Logarithms with base *e* are called natural logarithms because they occur in natural situations that involve growth or decay. The base *e* logarithm of *x* is written **ln *x*** (read "el en *x*"). The graph of $y = \ln x$ is given in **FIGURE 15** on the next page.

NOW TRY ANSWER
4. 138 dB

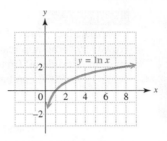

FIGURE 15

A calculator key labeled $\boxed{\text{ln } x}$ is used to evaluate natural logarithms. Consult your calculator manual to see how to use this key.

NOW TRY
EXERCISE 5

Using a calculator, evaluate each logarithm to four decimal places.

(a) ln 0.26   **(b)** ln 12

(c) ln 150

EXAMPLE 5 Evaluating Natural Logarithms

Using a calculator, evaluate each logarithm to four decimal places.

(a) ln 0.5841 ≈ −0.5377

As with common logarithms, *a number between 0 and 1 has a negative natural logarithm.*

(b) ln 192.7 ≈ 5.2611   **(c)** ln 10.84 ≈ 2.3832

See **FIGURE 16**.

FIGURE 16

NOW TRY

OBJECTIVE 4 **Use natural logarithms in applications.**

NOW TRY
EXERCISE 6

Use the logarithmic function in **Example 6** to approximate the altitude when atmospheric pressure is 600 millibars. Round to the nearest hundred.

EXAMPLE 6 Applying a Natural Logarithmic Function

The altitude in meters that corresponds to an atmospheric pressure of x millibars is given by the logarithmic function defined by

$$f(x) = 51{,}600 - 7457 \ln x.$$

(*Source:* Miller, A. and J. Thompson, *Elements of Meteorology,* Fourth Edition, Charles E. Merrill Publishing Company.) Use this function to find the altitude when atmospheric pressure is 400 millibars. Round to the nearest hundred.

Let $x = 400$ and substitute in the expression for $f(x)$.

$$f(400) = 51{,}600 - 7457 \ln 400 \qquad \text{Let } x = 400.$$
$$f(400) \approx 6900 \qquad \text{Use a calculator.}$$

Atmospheric pressure is 400 millibars at approximately 6900 m.   NOW TRY

NOTE In **Example 6,** the final answer was obtained using a calculator *without* rounding the intermediate values. In general, it is best to wait until the final step to round the answer. Round-offs in intermediate steps can lead to a buildup of round-off error, which may cause the final answer to have an incorrect final decimal place digit or digits.

NOW TRY ANSWERS
5. (a) −1.3471   **(b)** 2.4849
   (c) 5.0106
6. approximately 3900 m

Leonhard Euler (1707–1783)
The number *e* is named after Euler.

OBJECTIVE 5 **Use the change-of-base rule.** We have used a calculator to approximate the values of common logarithms (base 10) and natural logarithms (base *e*). However, some applications involve logarithms with other bases. For example, the amount of crude oil (in millions of barrels) imported into the United States during the years 1990–2008 can be approximated by the function

$$f(x) = 2014 + 384.7 \log_2 x,$$

where $x = 1$ represents 1990, $x = 2$ represents 1991, and so on. (*Source:* U.S. Energy Information Administration.) To use this function, we need to find a base 2 logarithm. The following rule is used to convert logarithms from one base to another.

Change-of-Base Rule

If $a > 0$, $a \neq 1$, $b > 0$, $b \neq 1$, and $x > 0$, then the following is true.

$$\log_a x = \frac{\log_b x}{\log_b a}$$

NOTE Any positive number other than 1 can be used for base *b* in the change-of-base rule. Usually the only practical bases are *e* and 10 because calculators generally give logarithms only for these two bases.

To derive the change-of-base rule, let $\log_a x = m$.

$$\log_a x = m$$

$$a^m = x \qquad \text{Change to exponential form.}$$

Since logarithmic functions are one-to-one, if all variables are positive and if $x = y$, then $\log_b x = \log_b y$.

$$\log_b (a^m) = \log_b x \qquad \text{Take the logarithm on each side.}$$

$$m \log_b a = \log_b x \qquad \text{Power rule}$$

$$(\log_a x)(\log_b a) = \log_b x \qquad \text{Substitute for } m.$$

$$\log_a x = \frac{\log_b x}{\log_b a} \qquad \text{Divide by } \log_b a.$$

NOW TRY
EXERCISE 7

Evaluate $\log_8 60$ to four decimal places.

EXAMPLE 7 Using the Change-of-Base Rule

Evaluate $\log_5 12$ to four decimal places.
Use common logarithms and the change-of-base rule.

$$\log_5 12 = \frac{\log 12}{\log 5} \approx 1.5440 \quad \text{Use a calculator.}$$

NOW TRY

NOTE Either common or natural logarithms can be used when applying the change-of-base rule. Verify that the same value is found in **Example 7** if natural logarithms are used.

NOW TRY ANSWER
7. 1.9690

NOW TRY
EXERCISE 8

Use the model in **Example 8** to estimate total crude oil imports into the United States in 2002. Compare this to the actual amount of 3336 million barrels.

EXAMPLE 8 Using the Change-of-Base Rule in an Application

Use natural logarithms in the change-of-base rule and the function defined by

$$f(x) = 2014 + 384.7 \log_2 x$$

(given earlier) to estimate total crude oil imports (in millions of barrels) into the United States in 2006. Compare this to the actual amount of 3685 million barrels. In the equation, $x = 1$ represents 1990.

$$f(x) = 2014 + 384.7 \log_2 x$$

$$f(17) = 2014 + 384.7 \log_2 17 \qquad \text{For 2006, } x = 17.$$

$$= 2014 + 384.7 \left(\frac{\ln 17}{\ln 2} \right) \qquad \text{Change-of-base rule}$$

$$\approx 3586 \qquad \text{Use a calculator.}$$

NOW TRY ANSWER
8. 3438 million barrels; This is greater than the actual amount.

The model gives about 3586 million barrels for 2006, which is less than the actual amount.

NOW TRY

12.5 EXERCISES

MyMathLab

🌐 *Complete solution available on the Video Resources on DVD*

Concept Check   Choose the correct response in Exercises 1–4.

1. What is the base in the expression log x?

    A. e **B.** 1   **C.** 10   **D.** x

2. What is the base in the expression ln x?

    A. e **B.** 1   **C.** 10   **D.** x

3. Since $10^0 = 1$ and $10^1 = 10$, between what two consecutive integers is the value of log 6.3?

    A. 6 and 7   **B.** 10 and 11   **C.** 0 and 1   **D.** −1 and 0

4. Since $e^1 \approx 2.718$ and $e^2 \approx 7.389$, between what two consecutive integers is the value of ln 6.3?

    A. 6 and 7   **B.** 2 and 3   **C.** 1 and 2   **D.** 0 and 1

5. *Concept Check*   Without using a calculator, give the value of log $10^{31.6}$.

6. *Concept Check*   Without using a calculator, give the value of ln $e^{\sqrt{3}}$.

You will need a calculator for the remaining exercises in this set.

*Find each logarithm. Give approximations to four decimal places. **See Examples 1 and 5.***

🌐 **7.** log 43	**8.** log 98	**9.** log 328.4
10. log 457.2	**11.** log 0.0326	**12.** log 0.1741
13. log (4.76×10^9)	**14.** log (2.13×10^4)	🌐 **15.** ln 7.84
16. ln 8.32	**17.** ln 0.0556	**18.** ln 0.0217
19. ln 388.1	**20.** ln 942.6	**21.** ln $(8.59 \times e^2)$
22. ln $(7.46 \times e^3)$	**23.** ln 10	**24.** log e

25. Use your calculator to find approximations of the following logarithms.

    (a) log 356.8   (b) log 35.68   (c) log 3.568

    ✎ (d) Observe your answers and make a conjecture concerning the decimal values of the common logarithms of numbers greater than 1 that have the same digits.

26. Let k represent the number of letters in your last name.

    (a) Use your calculator to find log k.

    (b) Raise 10 to the power indicated by the number in part (a). What is your result?

    ✎ (c) Use the concepts of **Section 12.1** to explain why you obtained the answer you found in part (b). Would it matter what number you used for k to observe the same result?

*Suppose that water from a wetland area is sampled and found to have the given hydronium ion concentration. Is the wetland a rich fen, a poor fen, or a bog? **See Example 2.***

27. 3.1×10^{-5} 28. 2.5×10^{-5} 🌐 29. 2.5×10^{-2}

30. 3.6×10^{-2} 31. 2.7×10^{-7} 32. 2.5×10^{-7}

*Find the pH of the substance with the given hydronium ion concentration. **See Example 2.***

33. Ammonia, 2.5×10^{-12} 34. Sodium bicarbonate, 4.0×10^{-9}

35. Grapes, 5.0×10^{-5} 36. Tuna, 1.3×10^{-6}

*Find the hydronium ion concentration of the substance with the given pH. **See Example 3.***

🌐 37. Human blood plasma, 7.4   38. Human gastric contents, 2.0

39. Spinach, 5.4   40. Bananas, 4.6

*Solve each problem. **See Examples 4 and 6.***

🌐 41. Consumers can now enjoy movies at home in elaborate home-theater systems. Find the average decibel level

$$D = 10 \log \left(\frac{I}{I_0} \right)$$

for each movie with the given intensity I.

(a) *Avatar;* $5.012 \times 10^{10} I_0$

(b) *Iron Man 2;* $10^{10} I_0$

(c) *Clash of the Titans;* $6,310,000,000 \, I_0$

42. The time t in years for an amount increasing at a rate of r (in decimal form) to double is given by

$$t(r) = \frac{\ln 2}{\ln (1 + r)}.$$

This is called **doubling time.** Find the doubling time to the nearest tenth for an investment at each interest rate.

(a) 2% (or 0.02)   (b) 5% (or 0.05)   (c) 8% (or 0.08)

🌐 43. The number of years, $N(r)$, since two independently evolving languages split off from a common ancestral language is approximated by

$$N(r) = -5000 \ln r,$$

where r is the percent of words (in decimal form) from the ancestral language common to both languages now. Find the number of years (to the nearest hundred years) since the split for each percent of common words.

(a) 85% (or 0.85)   (b) 35% (or 0.35)   (c) 10% (or 0.10)

44. The concentration of a drug injected into the bloodstream decreases with time. The intervals of time T when the drug should be administered are given by

$$T = \frac{1}{k} \ln \frac{C_2}{C_1},$$

where k is a constant determined by the drug in use, C_2 is the concentration at which the drug is harmful, and C_1 is the concentration below which the drug is ineffective. (*Source:* Horelick, Brindell and Sinan Koont, "Applications of Calculus to Medicine: Prescribing Safe and Effective Dosage," *UMAP Module 202.*) Thus, if $T = 4$, the drug should be administered every 4 hr. For a certain drug, $k = \frac{1}{3}$, $C_2 = 5$, and $C_1 = 2$. How often should the drug be administered? (*Hint:* Round down.)

45. The growth of outpatient surgeries as a percent of total surgeries at hospitals is approximated by

$$f(x) = -1317 + 304 \ln x,$$

where x is the number of years since 1900. (*Source:* American Hospital Association.)

(a) What does this function predict for the percent of outpatient surgeries in 1998?

(b) When did outpatient surgeries reach 50%? (*Hint:* Substitute for y, then write the equation in exponential form to solve it.)

46. In the central Sierra Nevada of California, the percent of moisture that falls as snow rather than rain is approximated reasonably well by

$$f(x) = 86.3 \ln x - 680,$$

where x is the altitude in feet.

(a) What percent of the moisture at 5000 ft falls as snow?

(b) What percent at 7500 ft falls as snow?

47. The **cost-benefit equation**

$$T = -0.642 - 189 \ln (1 - p)$$

describes the approximate tax T, in dollars per ton, that would result in a $p\%$ (in decimal form) reduction in carbon dioxide emissions.

(a) What tax will reduce emissions 25%?

(b) Explain why the equation is not valid for $p = 0$ or $p = 1$.

48. The age in years of a female blue whale of length L in feet is approximated by

$$t = -2.57 \ln \left(\frac{87 - L}{63} \right).$$

(a) How old is a female blue whale that measures 80 ft?

(b) The equation that defines t has domain $24 < L < 87$. Explain why.

Use the change-of-base rule (with either common or natural logarithms) to find each logarithm to four decimal places. ***See Example 7.***

49. $\log_3 12$

50. $\log_4 18$

51. $\log_5 3$

52. $\log_7 4$

53. $\log_3 \sqrt{2}$

54. $\log_6 \sqrt[3]{5}$

55. $\log_\pi e$

56. $\log_\pi 10$

57. $\log_e 12$

58. To solve the equation $5^x = 7$, we must find the exponent to which 5 must be raised in order to obtain 7. This is $\log_5 7$.

(a) Use the change-of-base rule and your calculator to find $\log_5 7$.

(b) Raise 5 to the number you found in part (a). What is your result?

(c) Using as many decimal places as your calculator gives, write the solution set of $5^x = 7$. (Equations of this type will be studied in more detail in **Section 12.6**.)

59. Let m be the number of letters in your first name, and let n be the number of letters in your last name.

(a) In your own words, explain what $\log_m n$ means.

(b) Use your calculator to find $\log_m n$.

(c) Raise m to the power indicated by the number found in part (b). What is your result?

60. The value of e can be expressed as

$$e = 1 + \frac{1}{1} + \frac{1}{1 \cdot 2} + \frac{1}{1 \cdot 2 \cdot 3} + \frac{1}{1 \cdot 2 \cdot 3 \cdot 4} + \cdots.$$

Approximate e using two terms of this expression, then three terms, four terms, five terms, and six terms. How close is the approximation to the value of $e \approx 2.718281828$ with six terms? Does this infinite sum approach the value of e very quickly?

*Solve each application of a logarithmic function (from **Exercises 61 and 62** of **Section 12.3**).*

61. For 1981–2003, the number of billion cubic feet of natural gas gross withdrawals from crude oil wells in the United States can be approximated by the function defined by

$$f(x) = 3800 + 585 \log_2 x,$$

where $x = 1$ represents 1981, $x = 2$ represents 1982, and so on. (*Source:* Energy Information Administration.) Use this function to approximate the number of cubic feet withdrawn in 2003, to the nearest unit.

62. According to selected figures from the last two decades of the 20th century, the number of trillion cubic feet of dry natural gas consumed worldwide can be approximated by the function defined by

$$f(x) = 51.47 + 6.044 \log_2 x,$$

where $x = 1$ represents 1980, $x = 2$ represents 1981, and so on. (*Source:* Energy Information Administration.) Use this function to approximate consumption in 2003, to the nearest hundredth.

PREVIEW EXERCISES

*Solve each equation. **See Sections 12.2 and 12.3**.*

63. $4^{2x} = 8^{3x+1}$

64. $2^{5x} = \left(\dfrac{1}{16}\right)^{x+3}$

65. $\log_3 (x + 4) = 2$

66. $\log_x 64 = 2$

67. $\log_{1/2} 8 = x$

68. $\log_a 1 = 0$

*Write as a single logarithm. Assume $x > 0$. **See Section 12.4**.*

69. $\log (x + 2) + \log (x + 3)$

70. $\log_4 (x + 4) - 2 \log_4 (3x + 1)$

12.6 Exponential and Logarithmic Equations; Further Applications

OBJECTIVES

1 Solve equations involving variables in the exponents.

2 Solve equations involving logarithms.

3 Solve applications of compound interest.

4 Solve applications involving base e exponential growth and decay.

We solved exponential and logarithmic equations in **Sections 12.2 and 12.3.** General methods for solving these equations depend on the following properties.

Properties for Solving Exponential and Logarithmic Equations

For all real numbers $b > 0$, $b \neq 1$, and any real numbers x and y, the following are true.

1. If $x = y$, then $b^x = b^y$.
2. If $b^x = b^y$, then $x = y$.
3. If $x = y$, and $x > 0$, $y > 0$, then $\log_b x = \log_b y$.
4. If $x > 0$, $y > 0$, and $\log_b x = \log_b y$, then $x = y$.

We used Property 2 to solve exponential equations in **Section 12.2.**

OBJECTIVE 1 Solve equations involving variables in the exponents. In **Examples 1 and 2,** we use Property 3.

⌐ *NOW TRY*
↳ *EXERCISE 1*
Solve the equation. Approximate the solution to three decimal places.
$$5^x = 20$$

EXAMPLE 1 Solving an Exponential Equation

Solve $3^x = 12$. Approximate the solution to three decimal places.

$$3^x = 12$$

$$\log 3^x = \log 12 \qquad \text{Property 3 (common logs)}$$

$$x \log 3 = \log 12 \qquad \text{Power rule}$$

$$\text{Exact solution} \longrightarrow x = \frac{\log 12}{\log 3} \qquad \text{Divide by log 3.}$$

$$\text{Decimal approximation} \longrightarrow x \approx 2.262 \qquad \text{Use a calculator.}$$

CHECK $\quad 3^x = 3^{2.262} \approx 12 \;\checkmark \qquad$ Use a calculator; true

The solution set is $\{2.262\}$. *NOW TRY* ↻

⚠ **CAUTION** Be careful: $\frac{\log 12}{\log 3}$ is *not* equal to log 4. Check to see that

$$\log 4 \approx 0.6021, \quad \text{but} \quad \frac{\log 12}{\log 3} \approx 2.262.$$

When an exponential equation has e as the base, as in the next example, it is easiest to use base e logarithms.

NOW TRY ANSWER
1. $\{1.861\}$

NOW TRY
EXERCISE 2

Solve $e^{0.12x} = 10$. Approximate the solution to three decimal places.

EXAMPLE 2 Solving an Exponential Equation with Base *e*

Solve $e^{0.003x} = 40$. Approximate the solution to three decimal places.

$$\ln e^{0.003x} = \ln 40 \qquad \text{Property 3 (natural logs)}$$

$$0.003x \ln e = \ln 40 \qquad \text{Power rule}$$

$$0.003x = \ln 40 \qquad \ln e = \ln e^1 = 1$$

$$x = \frac{\ln 40}{0.003} \qquad \text{Divide by 0.003.}$$

$$x \approx 1229.626 \qquad \text{Use a calculator.}$$

The solution set is $\{1229.626\}$. Check that $e^{0.003(1229.626)} \approx 40$.

NOW TRY

General Method for Solving an Exponential Equation

Take logarithms to the same base on both sides and then use the power rule of logarithms or the special property $\log_b b^x = x$. (See **Examples 1 and 2.**)

As a special case, if both sides can be written as exponentials with the same base, do so, and set the exponents equal. (See **Section 12.2.**)

OBJECTIVE 2 Solve equations involving logarithms. We use the definition of logarithm and the properties of logarithms to change equations to exponential form.

NOW TRY
EXERCISE 3

NOW TRY
EXERCISE 3

Solve $\log_5 (x - 1)^3 = 2$. Give the exact solution.

EXAMPLE 3 Solving a Logarithmic Equation

Solve $\log_2 (x + 5)^3 = 4$. Give the exact solution.

$$\log_2 (x + 5)^3 = 4$$

$$(x + 5)^3 = 2^4 \qquad \text{Convert to exponential form.}$$

$$(x + 5)^3 = 16 \qquad 2^4 = 16$$

$$x + 5 = \sqrt[3]{16} \qquad \text{Take the cube root on each side.}$$

$$x = -5 + \sqrt[3]{16} \qquad \text{Add } -5.$$

$$x = -5 + 2\sqrt[3]{2} \qquad \sqrt[3]{16} = \sqrt[3]{8 \cdot 2} = \sqrt[3]{8} \cdot \sqrt[3]{2} = 2\sqrt[3]{2}$$

CHECK $\qquad \log_2 (x + 5)^3 = 4 \qquad$ Original equation

$$\log_2 (-5 + 2\sqrt[3]{2} + 5)^3 \overset{?}{=} 4 \qquad \text{Let } x = -5 + 2\sqrt[3]{2}.$$

$$\log_2 \left(2\sqrt[3]{2}\right)^3 \overset{?}{=} 4 \qquad \text{Work inside the parentheses.}$$

$$\log_2 16 \overset{?}{=} 4 \qquad \left(2\sqrt[3]{2}\right)^3 = 2^3(\sqrt[3]{2})^3 = 8 \cdot 2 = 16$$

$$2^4 \overset{?}{=} 16 \qquad \text{Write in exponential form.}$$

$$16 = 16 \checkmark \qquad \text{True}$$

A true statement results, so the solution set is $\left\{-5 + 2\sqrt[3]{2}\right\}$.

NOW TRY

⚠ **CAUTION** Recall that the domain of $y = \log_b x$ is $(0, \infty)$. *For this reason, always check that each proposed solution of an equation with logarithms yields only logarithms of positive numbers in the original equation.*

NOW TRY ANSWERS
2. $\{19.188\}$ **3.** $\left\{1 + \sqrt[3]{25}\right\}$

NOW TRY
EXERCISE 4
Solve.
$\log_4 (2x + 13) - \log_4 (x + 1)$
$= \log_4 10$

EXAMPLE 4 Solving a Logarithmic Equation

Solve $\log_2 (x + 1) - \log_2 x = \log_2 7$.

$$\log_2 (x + 1) - \log_2 x = \log_2 7$$

Transform the left side to an expression with only *one* logarithm.

$$\log_2 \frac{x + 1}{x} = \log_2 7 \qquad \text{Quotient rule}$$

$$\frac{x + 1}{x} = 7 \qquad \text{Property 4}$$

$$x + 1 = 7x \qquad \text{Multiply by } x.$$

$$1 = 6x \qquad \text{Subtract } x.$$

This proposed solution must be checked.

$$\frac{1}{6} = x \qquad \text{Divide by 6.}$$

Since we cannot take the logarithm of a *nonpositive* number, both $x + 1$ and x must be positive here. If $x = \frac{1}{6}$, then this condition is satisfied.

CHECK
$$\log_2 (x + 1) - \log_2 x = \log_2 7 \qquad \text{Original equation}$$

$$\log_2 \left(\frac{1}{6} + 1\right) - \log_2 \frac{1}{6} \overset{?}{=} \log_2 7 \qquad \text{Let } x = \frac{1}{6}.$$

$$\log_2 \frac{7}{6} - \log_2 \frac{1}{6} \overset{?}{=} \log_2 7 \qquad \text{Add.}$$

$$\log_2 \frac{\frac{7}{6}}{\frac{1}{6}} \overset{?}{=} \log_2 7 \qquad \text{Quotient rule}$$

$$\boxed{\frac{\frac{7}{6}}{\frac{1}{6}} = \frac{7}{6} \div \frac{1}{6} = \frac{7}{6} \cdot \frac{6}{1} = 7}$$

$$\log_2 7 = \log_2 7 \quad \checkmark \text{ True}$$

A true statement results, so the solution set is $\left\{\frac{1}{6}\right\}$.   NOW TRY

NOW TRY
EXERCISE 5
Solve.
$\log_4 (x + 2) + \log_4 2x = 2$

EXAMPLE 5 Solving a Logarithmic Equation

Solve $\log x + \log (x - 21) = 2$.

$$\log x + \log (x - 21) = 2$$

$$\log x(x - 21) = 2 \qquad \text{Product rule}$$

The base is 10.

$$x(x - 21) = 10^2 \qquad \text{Write in exponential form.}$$

$$x^2 - 21x = 100 \qquad \text{Distributive property; multiply.}$$

$$x^2 - 21x - 100 = 0 \qquad \text{Standard form}$$

$$(x - 25)(x + 4) = 0 \qquad \text{Factor.}$$

$$x - 25 = 0 \quad \text{or} \quad x + 4 = 0 \qquad \text{Zero-factor property}$$

$$x = 25 \quad \text{or} \quad x = -4 \qquad \text{Proposed solutions}$$

The value -4 must be rejected as a solution since it leads to the logarithm of a negative number in the original equation.

$$\log (-4) + \log (-4 - 21) = 2 \qquad \text{The left side is undefined.}$$

NOW TRY ANSWERS
4. $\left\{\frac{3}{8}\right\}$ 5. $\{2\}$

Check that the only solution is 25, so the solution set is $\{25\}$.   NOW TRY

⚠ **CAUTION** *Do not reject a potential solution just because it is nonpositive. Reject any value that leads to the logarithm of a nonpositive number.*

Solving a Logarithmic Equation

Step 1 **Transform the equation so that a single logarithm appears on one side.** Use the product rule or quotient rule of logarithms to do this.

Step 2 **(a) Use Property 4.** If $\log_b x = \log_b y$, then $x = y$. (See **Example 4.**)

(b) Write the equation in exponential form. If $\log_b x = k$, then $x = b^k$. (See **Examples 3 and 5.**)

OBJECTIVE 3 **Solve applications of compound interest.** We have solved simple interest problems using the formula

$$I = prt. \qquad \text{Simple interest formula}$$

In most cases, interest paid or charged is **compound interest** (interest paid on both principal and interest). The formula for compound interest is an application of exponential functions. In this book, monetary amounts are given to the nearest cent.

Compound Interest Formula (for a Finite Number of Periods)

If a principal of P dollars is deposited at an annual rate of interest r compounded (paid) n times per year, then the account will contain

$$A = P\left(1 + \frac{r}{n}\right)^{nt}$$

dollars after t years. (In this formula, r is expressed as a decimal.)

NOW TRY
EXERCISE 6
How much money will there be in an account at the end of 10 yr if $10,000 is deposited at 2.5% compounded monthly?

EXAMPLE 6 Solving a Compound Interest Problem for A

How much money will there be in an account at the end of 5 yr if $1000 is deposited at 3% compounded quarterly? (Assume no withdrawals are made.)

Because interest is compounded quarterly, $n = 4$. The other given values are $P = 1000$, $r = 0.03$ (because 3% = 0.03), and $t = 5$.

$$A = P\left(1 + \frac{r}{n}\right)^{nt} \qquad \text{Compound interest formula}$$

$$A = 1000\left(1 + \frac{0.03}{4}\right)^{4 \cdot 5} \qquad \text{Substitute the given values.}$$

$$A = 1000(1.0075)^{20} \qquad \text{Simplify.}$$

$$A = 1161.18 \qquad \begin{array}{l}\text{Use a calculator.}\\ \text{Round to the nearest cent.}\end{array}$$

The account will contain $1161.18. (The actual amount of interest earned is $1161.18 − $1000 = $161.18. Why?)   NOW TRY

NOW TRY ANSWER
6. $12,836.92

⌐ *NOW TRY*
⤷ *EXERCISE 7*

Approximate the time it would take for money deposited in an account paying 4% interest compounded quarterly to double. Round to the nearest hundredth.

EXAMPLE 7 Solving a Compound Interest Problem for t

Suppose inflation is averaging 3% per year. Approximate the time it will take for prices to double. Round to the nearest hundredth.

We want the number of years t for P dollars to grow to $2P$ dollars at a rate of 3% per year. In the compound interest formula, we substitute $2P$ for A, and let $r = 0.03$ and $n = 1$.

$$2P = P\left(1 + \frac{0.03}{1}\right)^{1t} \qquad \text{Substitute in the compound interest formula.}$$

$$2 = (1.03)^t \qquad \text{Divide by } P. \text{ Simplify.}$$

$$\log 2 = \log (1.03)^t \qquad \text{Property 3}$$

$$\log 2 = t \log (1.03) \qquad \text{Power rule}$$

$$t = \frac{\log 2}{\log 1.03} \qquad \text{Interchange sides. Divide by log 1.03.}$$

$$t \approx 23.45 \qquad \text{Use a calculator.}$$

Prices will double in about 23.45 yr. (This is called the **doubling time** of the money.) To check, verify that $1.03^{23.45} \approx 2$.   *NOW TRY*⤸

Interest can be compounded annually, semiannually, quarterly, daily, and so on. The number of compounding periods can get larger and larger. If the value of n is allowed to approach infinity, we have an example of **continuous compounding.** The formula for continuous compounding is derived in advanced courses, and is an example of exponential growth involving the number e.

Continuous Compound Interest Formula

If a principal of P dollars is deposited at an annual rate of interest r compounded continuously for t years, the final amount A on deposit is given by

$$A = Pe^{rt}.$$

EXAMPLE 8 Solving a Continuous Compound Interest Problem

In **Example 6** we found that $1000 invested for 5 yr at 3% interest compounded quarterly would grow to $1161.18.

(a) How much would this same investment grow to if interest were compounded continuously?

$$A = Pe^{rt} \qquad \text{Continuous compounding formula}$$

$$A = 1000e^{0.03(5)} \qquad \text{Let } P = 1000, r = 0.03, \text{ and } t = 5.$$

$$A = 1000e^{0.15} \qquad \text{Multiply in the exponent.}$$

$$A = 1161.83 \qquad \text{Use a calculator. Round to the nearest cent.}$$

Continuous compounding would cause the investment to grow to $1161.83. This is $0.65 more than the amount the investment grew to in **Example 6,** when interest was compounded quarterly.

NOW TRY ANSWER
7. 17.42 yr

NOW TRY
EXERCISE 8

Suppose that $4000 is invested at 3% interest for 2 yr.

(a) How much will the investment grow to if it is compounded continuously?

(b) Approximate the time it would take for the amount to double. Round to the nearest tenth.

(b) Approximate the time it would take for the initial investment to triple its original amount. Round to the nearest tenth.

We must find the value of t that will cause A to be $3(\$1000) = \$3000$.

$$A = Pe^{rt} \qquad \text{Continuous compounding formula}$$

$$3000 = 1000e^{0.03t} \qquad \text{Let } A = 3P = 3000, P = 1000, r = 0.03.$$

$$3 = e^{0.03t} \qquad \text{Divide by 1000.}$$

$$\ln 3 = \ln e^{0.03t} \qquad \text{Take natural logarithms.}$$

$$\ln 3 = 0.03t \qquad \ln e^k = k$$

$$t = \frac{\ln 3}{0.03} \qquad \text{Divide by 0.03.}$$

$$t \approx 36.6 \qquad \text{Use a calculator.}$$

It would take about 36.6 yr for the original investment to triple.   NOW TRY

OBJECTIVE 4 **Solve applications involving base e exponential growth and decay.** When situations involve growth or decay of a population, the amount or number of some quantity present at time t can be approximated by

$$y = y_0 e^{kt}.$$

In this equation, y_0 is the amount or number present at time $t = 0$ and k is a constant.

The continuous compounding of money is an example of exponential growth. In **Example 9,** we investigate exponential decay.

EXAMPLE 9 Solving an Application Involving Exponential Decay

Carbon 14 is a radioactive form of carbon that is found in all living plants and animals. After a plant or animal dies, the radioactive carbon 14 disintegrates according to the function defined by

$$y = y_0 e^{-0.000121t},$$

where t is time in years, y is the amount of the sample at time t, and y_0 is the initial amount present at $t = 0$.

NOW TRY
EXERCISE 9

Radium 226 decays according to the function defined by

$$y = y_0 e^{-0.00043t},$$

where t is time in years.

(a) If an initial sample contains $y_0 = 4.5$ g of radium 226, how many grams, to the nearest tenth, will be present after 150 yr?

(b) Approximate the half-life of radium 226. Round to the nearest unit.

(a) If an initial sample contains $y_0 = 10$ g of carbon 14, how many grams, to the nearest tenth, will be present after 3000 yr?

Let $y_0 = 10$ and $t = 3000$ in the formula, and use a calculator.

$$y = 10e^{-0.000121(3000)} \approx 6.96 \text{ g}$$

(b) About how long would it take for the initial sample to decay to half of its original amount? (This is called the **half-life.**) Round to the nearest unit.

Let $y = \frac{1}{2}(10) = 5$, and solve for t.

$$5 = 10e^{-0.000121t} \qquad \text{Substitute in } y = y_0 e^{kt}.$$

$$\frac{1}{2} = e^{-0.000121t} \qquad \text{Divide by 10.}$$

$$\ln \frac{1}{2} = -0.000121t \qquad \text{Take natural logarithms; } \ln e^k = k.$$

$$t = \frac{\ln \frac{1}{2}}{-0.000121} \qquad \text{Interchange sides. Divide by } -0.000121.$$

$$t \approx 5728 \qquad \text{Use a calculator.}$$

The half-life is about 5728 yr.   NOW TRY

NOW TRY ANSWERS
8. (a) $4247.35 (b) 23.1 yr
9. (a) 4.2 g (b) 1612 yr

> **CONNECTIONS**
>
> Recall that the x-intercepts of the graph of a function f correspond to the real solutions of the equation $f(x) = 0$. In **Example 1,** we solved the equation $3^x = 12$ algebraically using rules for logarithms and found the solution set to be $\{2.262\}$. This can be supported graphically by showing that the x-intercept of the graph of the function defined by $y = 3^x - 12$ corresponds to this solution. See **FIGURE 17.**

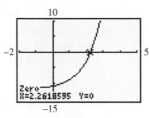

FIGURE 17

For Discussion or Writing

In **Example 5,** we solved $\log x + \log (x - 21) = 2$ to find the solution set $\{25\}$. (We rejected the proposed solution -4 since it led to the logarithm of a negative number.) Show that the x-intercept of the graph of the function defined by $y = \log x + \log (x - 21) - 2$ supports this result.

12.6 EXERCISES

MyMathLab   Math XL PRACTICE   WATCH   DOWNLOAD   READ   REVIEW

○ *Complete solution available on the Video Resources on DVD*

Many of the problems in these exercises require a scientific calculator.

Solve each equation. Give solutions to three decimal places. See **Example 1.**

1. $7^x = 5$

2. $4^x = 3$

3. $9^{-x+2} = 13$

4. $6^{-x+1} = 22$

5. $3^{2x} = 14$

6. $5^{0.3x} = 11$

7. $2^{x+3} = 5^x$

8. $6^{x+3} = 4^x$

9. $2^{x+3} = 3^{x-4}$

10. $4^{x-2} = 5^{3x+2}$

11. $4^{2x+3} = 6^{x-1}$

12. $3^{2x+1} = 5^{x-1}$

*Solve each equation. Use natural logarithms. When appropriate, give solutions to three decimal places. See **Example 2.***

13. $e^{0.012x} = 23$

14. $e^{0.006x} = 30$

15. $e^{-0.205x} = 9$

16. $e^{-0.103x} = 7$

17. $\ln e^{3x} = 9$

18. $\ln e^{2x} = 4$

19. $\ln e^{0.45x} = \sqrt{7}$

20. $\ln e^{0.04x} = \sqrt{3}$

21. $\ln e^{-x} = \pi$

22. $\ln e^{2x} = \pi$

23. $e^{\ln 2x} = e^{\ln(x+1)}$

24. $e^{\ln(6-x)} = e^{\ln(4+2x)}$

25. Solve one of the equations in **Exercises 13–16** using common logarithms rather than natural logarithms. (You should get the same solution.) Explain why using natural logarithms is a better choice.

26. *Concept Check*   If you were asked to solve

$$10^{0.0025x} = 75,$$

would natural or common logarithms be a better choice? Why?

Solve each equation. Give the exact solution. ***See Example 3.***

27. $\log_3 (6x + 5) = 2$

28. $\log_5 (12x - 8) = 3$

29. $\log_2 (2x - 1) = 5$

30. $\log_6 (4x + 2) = 2$

31. $\log_7 (x + 1)^3 = 2$

32. $\log_4 (x - 3)^3 = 4$

33. *Concept Check* Suppose that in solving a logarithmic equation having the term $\log (x - 3)$, you obtain a proposed solution of 2. All algebraic work is correct. Why must you reject 2 as a solution of the equation?

34. *Concept Check* Suppose that in solving a logarithmic equation having the term $\log (3 - x)$, you obtain a proposed solution of -4. All algebraic work is correct. Should you reject -4 as a solution of the equation? Why or why not?

Solve each equation. Give exact solutions. ***See Examples 4 and 5.***

35. $\log (6x + 1) = \log 3$

36. $\log (7 - 2x) = \log 4$

37. $\log_5 (3t + 2) - \log_5 t = \log_5 4$

38. $\log_2 (x + 5) - \log_2 (x - 1) = \log_2 3$

39. $\log 4x - \log (x - 3) = \log 2$

40. $\log (-x) + \log 3 = \log (2x - 15)$

41. $\log_2 x + \log_2 (x - 7) = 3$

42. $\log (2x - 1) + \log 10x = \log 10$

43. $\log 5x - \log (2x - 1) = \log 4$

44. $\log_3 x + \log_3 (2x + 5) = 1$

45. $\log_2 x + \log_2 (x - 6) = 4$

46. $\log_2 x + \log_2 (x + 4) = 5$

Solve each problem. ***See Examples 6–8.***

47. **(a)** How much money will there be in an account at the end of 6 yr if $2000 is deposited at 4% compounded quarterly? (Assume no withdrawals are made.)

(b) To one decimal place, how long will it take for the account to grow to $3000?

48. **(a)** How much money will there be in an account at the end of 7 yr if $3000 is deposited at 3.5% compounded quarterly? (Assume no withdrawals are made.)

(b) To one decimal place, when will the account grow to $5000?

49. **(a)** What will be the amount A in an account with initial principal $4000 if interest is compounded continuously at an annual rate of 3.5% for 6 yr?

(b) To one decimal place, how long will it take for the initial amount to double?

50. Refer to **Exercise 48(a).** Does the money grow to a greater value under those conditions, or when invested for 7 yr at 3% compounded continuously?

51. Find the amount of money in an account after 12 yr if $5000 is deposited at 7% annual interest compounded as follows.

(a) Annually   **(b)** Semiannually   **(c)** Quarterly

(d) Daily (Use $n = 365$.)   **(e)** Continuously

52. How much money will be in an account at the end of 8 yr if $4500 is deposited at 6% annual interest compounded as follows?

(a) Annually   **(b)** Semiannually   **(c)** Quarterly

(d) Daily (Use $n = 365$.)   **(e)** Continuously

53. How much money must be deposited today to amount to $1850 in 40 yr at 6.5% compounded continuously?

54. How much money must be deposited today to amount to $1000 in 10 yr at 5% compounded continuously?

Solve each problem. **See Example 9.**

55. The total volume in millions of tons of materials recovered from municipal solid waste collections in the United States during the period 1980–2007 can be approximated by the function defined by

$$f(x) = 15.94e^{0.0656x},$$

where $x = 0$ corresponds to 1980, $x = 1$ to 1981, and so on. Approximate, to the nearest tenth, the volume recovered each year. (*Source:* U.S. Environmental Protection Agency.)

(a) 1980 (b) 1990 (c) 2000 (d) 2007

56. Worldwide emissions in millions of metric tons of the greenhouse gas carbon dioxide from fossil fuel consumption during the period 1990–2006 can be modeled by the function defined by

$$f(x) = 20,761e^{0.01882x},$$

where $x = 0$ corresponds to 1990, $x = 1$ to 1991, and so on. Approximate, to the nearest unit, the emissions for each year. (*Source:* U.S. Department of Energy.)

(a) 1990 (b) 1995 (c) 2000 (d) 2006

57. Revenues of software publishers in the United States for the years 2004–2007 can be modeled by the function defined by

$$S(x) = 112,047e^{0.0827x},$$

where $x = 0$ represents 2004, $x = 1$ represents 2005, and so on, and $S(x)$ is in millions of dollars. Approximate, to the nearest unit, consumer expenditures for 2007. (*Source:* U.S. Census Bureau.)

58. Based on selected figures obtained during the years 1980–2007, the total number of bachelor's degrees earned in the United States can be modeled by the function defined by

$$D(x) = 900,584e^{0.0185x},$$

where $x = 0$ corresponds to 1980, $x = 10$ corresponds to 1990, and so on. Approximate, to the nearest unit, the number of bachelor's degrees earned in 2005. (*Source:* U.S. National Center for Education Statistics.)

59. Suppose that the amount, in grams, of plutonium 241 present in a given sample is determined by the function defined by

$$A(t) = 2.00e^{-0.053t},$$

where t is measured in years. Approximate the amount present, to the nearest hundredth, in the sample after the given number of years.

(a) 4 (b) 10 (c) 20 (d) What was the initial amount present?

60. Suppose that the amount, in grams, of radium 226 present in a given sample is determined by the function defined by

$$A(t) = 3.25e^{-0.00043t},$$

where t is measured in years. Approximate the amount present, to the nearest hundredth, in the sample after the given number of years.

(a) 20 (b) 100 (c) 500 (d) What was the initial amount present?

61. A sample of 400 g of lead 210 decays to polonium 210 according to the function defined by

$$A(t) = 400e^{-0.032t},$$

where t is time in years. Approximate answers to the nearest hundredth.

(a) How much lead will be left in the sample after 25 yr?

(b) How long will it take the initial sample to decay to half of its original amount?

62. The concentration of a drug in a person's system decreases according to the function defined by

$$C(t) = 2e^{-0.125t},$$

where $C(t)$ is in appropriate units, and t is in hours. Approximate answers to the nearest hundredth.

(a) How much of the drug will be in the system after 1 hr?

(b) Approximate the time it will take for the concentration to be half of its original amount.

63. Refer to **Exercise 55.** Assuming that the function continued to apply past 2007, in what year can we expect the volume of materials recovered to reach 130 million tons? (*Source:* Environmental Protection Agency.)

64. Refer to **Exercise 56.** Assuming that the function continued to apply past 2006, in what year can we expect worldwide carbon dioxide emissions from fossil fuel consumption to reach 34,000 million metric tons? (*Source:* U.S. Department of Energy.)

TECHNOLOGY INSIGHTS EXERCISES 65–66

65. The function defined by

$$A(x) = 3.25e^{-0.00043x},$$

with $x = t$, described in **Exercise 60,** is graphed on the screen at the right. Interpret the meanings of X and Y in the display at the bottom of the screen in the context of **Exercise 60.**

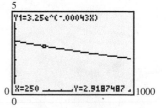

66. The screen shows a table of selected values for the function defined by $Y_1 = \left(1 + \frac{1}{X}\right)^X$.

(a) Why is there an error message for X = 0?

(b) What number does the function value seem to approach as X takes on larger and larger values?

(c) Use a calculator to evaluate this function for X = 1,000,000. What value do you get? Now evaluate $e = e^1$. How close are these two values?

(d) Make a conjecture: As the values of x approach infinity, the value of $\left(1 + \frac{1}{x}\right)^x$ approaches _____.

PREVIEW EXERCISES

Graph each function. **See Section 11.6.**

67. $f(x) = 2x^2$

68. $f(x) = x^2 - 1$

69. $f(x) = (x + 1)^2$

70. $f(x) = (x - 1)^2 + 2$

CHAPTER 12 SUMMARY

KEY TERMS

12.1

one-to-one function
inverse of a function

12.2

exponential function
asymptote
exponential equation

12.3

logarithm
logarithmic equation
logarithmic function
    with base a

12.5

common logarithm
natural logarithm
universal constant

12.6

compound interest
continuous compounding

NEW SYMBOLS

$f^{-1}(x)$ the inverse of $f(x)$
$\log_a x$ the logarithm of x
    with base a

$\log x$ common (base 10)
    logarithm of x

$\ln x$ natural (base e)
    logarithm of x

e a constant,
    approximately
    2.718281828

TEST YOUR WORD POWER

See how well you have learned the vocabulary in this chapter:

1. In a **one-to-one function**
   A. each x-value corresponds to only one y-value
   B. each x-value corresponds to one or more y-values
   C. each x-value is the same as each y-value
   D. each x-value corresponds to only one y-value and each y-value corresponds to only one x-value.

2. If f is a one-to-one function, then the **inverse** of f is
   A. the set of all solutions of f
   B. the set of all ordered pairs formed by interchanging the coordinates of the ordered pairs of f
   C. the set of all ordered pairs that are the opposite (negative) of the coordinates of the ordered pairs of f

   D. an equation involving an exponential expression.

3. An **exponential function** is a function defined by an expression of the form
   A. $f(x) = ax^2 + bx + c$ for real numbers a, b, c $(a \neq 0)$
   B. $f(x) = \log_a x$ for positive numbers a and x $(a \neq 1)$
   C. $f(x) = a^x$ for all real numbers x $(a > 0, a \neq 1)$
   D. $f(x) = \sqrt{x}$ for $x \geq 0$.

4. An **asymptote** is
   A. a line that a graph intersects just once
   B. a line that the graph of a function more and more closely approaches as the x-values increase or decrease

   C. the x-axis or y-axis
   D. a line about which a graph is symmetric.

5. A **logarithm** is
   A. an exponent
   B. a base
   C. an equation
   D. a polynomial.

6. A **logarithmic function** is a function that is defined by an expression of the form
   A. $f(x) = ax^2 + bx + c$ for real numbers a, b, c $(a \neq 0)$
   B. $f(x) = \log_a x$ for positive numbers a and x $(a \neq 1)$
   C. $f(x) = a^x$ for all real numbers x $(a > 0, a \neq 1)$
   D. $f(x) = \sqrt{x}$ for $x \geq 0$.

ANSWERS

1. D; *Example:* The function $f = \{(0, 2), (1, -1), (3, 5), (-2, 3)\}$ is one-to-one.   **2.** B; *Example:* The inverse of the one-to-one function f defined in Answer 1 is $f^{-1} = \{(2, 0), (-1, 1), (5, 3), (3, -2)\}$.   **3.** C; *Examples:* $f(x) = 4^x, g(x) = \left(\frac{1}{2}\right)^x, h(x) = 2^{-x+3}$ **4.** B; *Example:* The graph of $f(x) = 2^x$ has the x-axis $(y = 0)$ as an asymptote.   **5.** A; *Example:* $\log_a x$ is the exponent to which a must be raised to obtain x; $\log_3 9 = 2$ since $3^2 = 9$.   **6.** B; *Examples:* $y = \log_3 x, y = \log_{1/3} x$

CONCEPTS	EXAMPLES

12.1 Inverse Functions

Horizontal Line Test

A function is one-to-one if every horizontal line intersects the graph of the function at most once.

Find f^{-1} if $f(x) = 2x - 3$.

The graph of f is a non-horizontal straight line, so f is one-to-one by the horizontal line test.

Inverse Functions

For a one-to-one function f defined by an equation $y = f(x)$, the equation that defines the inverse function f^{-1} is found by interchanging x and y, solving for y, and replacing y with $f^{-1}(x)$.

To find $f^{-1}(x)$, interchange x and y in the equation $y = 2x - 3$.
$$x = 2y - 3$$

Solve for y to get $\quad y = \dfrac{x + 3}{2}.$

Therefore, $\quad f^{-1}(x) = \dfrac{x + 3}{2}$, or $f^{-1}(x) = \dfrac{1}{2}x + \dfrac{3}{2}.$

In general, the graph of f^{-1} is the mirror image of the graph of f with respect to the line $y = x$.

The graphs of a function f and its inverse f^{-1} are shown here.

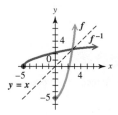

12.2 Exponential Functions

For $a > 0$, $a \neq 1$, $f(x) = a^x$ defines the exponential function with base a.

Graph of $f(x) = a^x$

1. The graph contains the point $(0, 1)$.
2. When $a > 1$, the graph rises from left to right. When $0 < a < 1$, the graph falls from left to right.
3. The x-axis is an asymptote.
4. The domain is $(-\infty, \infty)$, and the range is $(0, \infty)$.

$f(x) = 3^x$ defines the exponential function with base 3.

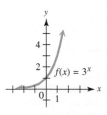

12.3 Logarithmic Functions

$y = \log_a x$ means $x = a^y$.

For $b > 0, b \neq 1$, $\quad \log_b b = 1 \quad$ and $\quad \log_b 1 = 0.$

$y = \log_2 x$ means $x = 2^y.$

$$\log_3 3 = 1 \qquad \log_5 1 = 0$$

(continued)

CONCEPTS	EXAMPLES

For $a > 0, a \neq 1, x > 0, g(x) = \log_a x$ defines the logarithmic function with base a.

Graph of $g(x) = \log_a x$

1. The graph contains the point $(1, 0)$.
2. When $a > 1$, the graph rises from left to right. When $0 < a < 1$, the graph falls from left to right.
3. The y-axis is an asymptote.
4. The domain is $(0, \infty)$, and the range is $(-\infty, \infty)$.

$g(x) = \log_3 x$ defines the logarithmic function with base 3.

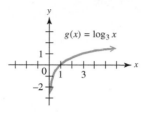

12.4   Properties of Logarithms

Product Rule $\log_a xy = \log_a x + \log_a y$

Quotient Rule $\log_a \dfrac{x}{y} = \log_a x - \log_a y$

Power Rule $\log_a x^r = r \log_a x$

Special Properties
$$b^{\log_b x} = x \quad \text{and} \quad \log_b b^x = x$$

$\log_2 3m = \log_2 3 + \log_2 m$ Product rule

$\log_5 \dfrac{9}{4} = \log_5 9 - \log_5 4$ Quotient rule

$\log_{10} 2^3 = 3 \log_{10} 2$ Power rule

$6^{\log_6 10} = 10 \qquad \log_3 3^4 = 4$ Special properties

---

12.5   Common and Natural Logarithms

Common logarithms (base 10) are used in applications such as pH, sound level, and intensity of an earthquake.

Use the formula $\text{pH} = -\log\left[H_3O^+\right]$ to find the pH (to one decimal place) of grapes with hydronium ion concentration 5.0×10^{-5}.

$$\begin{aligned} \text{pH} &= -\log\left(5.0 \times 10^{-5}\right) &&\text{Substitute.} \\ &= -(\log 5.0 + \log 10^{-5}) &&\text{Property of logarithms} \\ &\approx 4.3 &&\text{Evaluate with a calculator.} \end{aligned}$$

Natural logarithms (base e) are often found in formulas for applications of growth and decay, such as time for money invested to double, decay of chemical compounds, and biological growth.

Use the formula for doubling time (in years) $t(r) = \dfrac{\ln 2}{\ln(1 + r)}$ to find the doubling time to the nearest tenth at an interest rate of 4%.

$$\begin{aligned} t(0.04) &= \dfrac{\ln 2}{\ln (1 + 0.04)} &&\text{Substitute.} \\ &\approx 17.7 &&\text{Evaluate with a calculator.} \end{aligned}$$

The doubling time is about 17.7 yr.

Change-of-Base Rule

If $a > 0, a \neq 1, b > 0, b \neq 1, x > 0$, then

$$\log_a x = \dfrac{\log_b x}{\log_b a}.$$

$$\log_3 17 = \dfrac{\ln 17}{\ln 3} = \dfrac{\log 17}{\log 3} \approx 2.5789$$

12.6   Exponential and Logarithmic Equations; Further Applications

To solve exponential equations, use these properties $(b > 0, b \neq 1)$.

1. If $b^x = b^y$, then $x = y$.

Solve.
$$\begin{aligned} 2^{3x} &= 2^5 \\ 3x &= 5 &&\text{Set exponents equal.} \\ x &= \dfrac{5}{3} &&\text{Divide by 3.} \end{aligned}$$

The solution set is $\left\{\dfrac{5}{3}\right\}$.

(continued)

CONCEPTS	EXAMPLES
2. If $x = y, x > 0, y > 0$, then $\log_b x = \log_b y$.	Solve. $\quad 5^m = 8$
	$\quad\quad\log 5^m = \log 8 \quad\quad$ Take common logarithms.
	$\quad\quad m \log 5 = \log 8 \quad\quad$ Power rule
	$\quad\quad m = \dfrac{\log 8}{\log 5} \approx 1.2920 \quad$ Divide by log 5.
	The solution set is $\{1.2920\}$.
To solve logarithmic equations, use these properties, where $b > 0, b \neq 1, x > 0, y > 0$. First use the properties of **Section 12.4,** if necessary, to write the equation in the proper form.	
1. If $\log_b x = \log_b y$, then $x = y$.	Solve. $\quad\quad \log_3 2x = \log_3 (x + 1)$
	$\quad\quad\quad 2x = x + 1$
	$\quad\quad\quad\quad x = 1 \quad\quad$ Subtract x.
	This value checks, so the solution set is $\{1\}$.
2. If $\log_b x = y$, then $b^y = x$.	Solve. $\quad \log_2 (3x - 1) = 4$
	$\quad\quad 3x - 1 = 2^4 \quad\quad$ Exponential form
	$\quad\quad 3x - 1 = 16 \quad\quad$ Apply the exponent.
	$\quad\quad 3x = 17 \quad\quad$ Add 1.
	$\quad\quad x = \dfrac{17}{3} \quad\quad$ Divide by 3.
Always check proposed solutions in logarithmic equations.	This value checks, so the solution set is $\left\{\frac{17}{3}\right\}$.

CHAPTER (12)

REVIEW EXERCISES

12.1 *Determine whether each graph is the graph of a one-to-one function.*

1.

2.

Determine whether each function is one-to-one. If it is, find its inverse.

3. $f(x) = -3x + 7$ **4.** $f(x) = \sqrt[3]{6x - 4}$ **5.** $f(x) = -x^2 + 3$

6. The table lists caffeine amounts in several popular 12-oz sodas. If the set of sodas is the domain and the set of caffeine amounts is the range of the function consisting of the six pairs listed, is it a one-to-one function? Why or why not?

Soda	Caffeine (mg)
Mountain Dew	55
Diet Coke	45
Dr. Pepper	41
Sunkist Orange Soda	41
Diet Pepsi-Cola	36
Coca-Cola Classic	34

Source: National Soft Drink Association.

Each function graphed is one-to-one. Graph its inverse.

7.

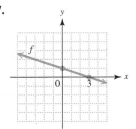

8.

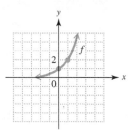

12.2 *Graph each function.*

9. $f(x) = 3^x$

10. $f(x) = \left(\dfrac{1}{3}\right)^x$

11. $y = 2^{2x+3}$

Solve each equation.

12. $5^{2x+1} = 25$

13. $4^{3x} = 8^{x+4}$

14. $\left(\dfrac{1}{27}\right)^{x-1} = 9^{2x}$

15. Sulfur dioxide emissions in the United States, in millions of tons, from 1970 through 2007 can be approximated by the exponential function defined by

$$S(x) = 33.07(1.0241)^{-x},$$

where $x = 0$ corresponds to 1970, $x = 5$ to 1975, and so on. Use this function to approximate, to the nearest tenth, the amounts for each year. (*Source:* U.S. Environmental Protection Agency.)

(a) 1975   **(b)** 1995   **(c)** 2005

12.3 *Graph each function.*

16. $g(x) = \log_3 x$ (*Hint:* See **Exercise 9.**)   **17.** $g(x) = \log_{1/3} x$ (*Hint:* See **Exercise 10.**)

Solve each equation.

18. $\log_8 64 = x$

19. $\log_2 \sqrt{8} = x$

20. $\log_x\left(\dfrac{1}{49}\right) = -2$

21. $\log_4 x = \dfrac{3}{2}$

22. $\log_k 4 = 1$

23. $\log_b b^2 = 2$

✐ **24.** In your own words, explain the meaning of $\log_b a$.

25. *Concept Check*   Based on the meaning of $\log_b a$, what is the simplest form of $b^{\log_b a}$?

26. A company has found that total sales, in thousands of dollars, are given by the function defined by

$$S(x) = 100 \log_2 (x + 2),$$

where x is the number of weeks after a major advertising campaign was introduced.

(a) What were the total sales 6 weeks after the campaign was introduced?

(b) Graph the function.

12.4   *Apply the properties of logarithms to express each logarithm as a sum or difference of logarithms. Assume that all variables represent positive real numbers.*

27. $\log_2 3xy^2$

28. $\log_4 \dfrac{\sqrt{x} \cdot w^2}{z}$

Apply the properties of logarithms to write each expression as a single logarithm. Assume that all variables represent positive real numbers, $b \neq 1$.

29. $\log_b 3 + \log_b x - 2 \log_b y$

30. $\log_3 (x + 7) - \log_3 (4x + 6)$

12.5   *Evaluate each logarithm. Give approximations to four decimal places.*

31. $\log 28.9$

32. $\log 0.257$

33. $\ln 28.9$

34. $\ln 0.257$

Use the change-of-base rule (with either common or natural logarithms) to find each logarithm. Give approximations to four decimal places.

35. $\log_{16} 13$

36. $\log_4 12$

Use the formula $\mathrm{pH} = -\log\left[H_3O^+\right]$ *to find the* pH *of each substance with the given hydronium ion concentration.*

37. Milk, 4.0×10^{-7}

38. Crackers, 3.8×10^{-9}

39. If orange juice has pH 4.6, what is its hydronium ion concentration?

40. The magnitude of a star is defined by the equation

$$M = 6 - 2.5 \log \frac{I}{I_0},$$

where I_0 is the measure of the faintest star and I is the actual intensity of the star being measured. The dimmest stars are of magnitude 6, and the brightest are of magnitude 1. Determine the ratio of intensities between stars of magnitude 1 and 3.

41. **Section 12.5, Exercise 42** introduced the doubling function defined by

$$t(r) = \frac{\ln 2}{\ln (1 + r)},$$

that gives the number of years required to double your money when it is invested at interest rate r (in decimal form) compounded annually. How long does it take to double your money at each rate? Round answers to the nearest year.

(a) 4%   **(b)** 6%   **(c)** 10%   **(d)** 12%

✐ **(e)** Compare each answer in parts (a)–(d) with the following numbers. What do you find?

$$\frac{72}{4}, \frac{72}{6}, \frac{72}{10}, \frac{72}{12}$$

12.6 *Solve each equation. Give solutions to three decimal places.*

42. $3^x = 9.42$　　　　　　**43.** $2^{x-1} = 15$　　　　　　**44.** $e^{0.06x} = 3$

Solve each equation. Give exact solutions.

45. $\log_3 (9x + 8) = 2$　　　　　　**46.** $\log_5 (x + 6)^3 = 2$

47. $\log_3 (x + 2) - \log_3 x = \log_3 2$　　　　**48.** $\log (2x + 3) = 1 + \log x$

49. $\log_4 x + \log_4 (8 - x) = 2$　　　　**50.** $\log_2 x + \log_2 (x + 15) = \log_2 16$

51. *Concept Check*　Consider the following "solution" of the equation $\log x^2 = 2$. *WHAT WENT WRONG?* Give the correct solution set.

$$\log x^2 = 2 \qquad \text{Original equation}$$
$$2 \log x = 2 \qquad \text{Power rule for logarithms}$$
$$\log x = 1 \qquad \text{Divide each side by 2.}$$
$$x = 10^1 \qquad \text{Write in exponential form.}$$
$$x = 10 \qquad 10^1 = 10$$

Solution set: $\{10\}$

Solve each problem. Use a calculator as necessary.

52. If \$20,000 is deposited at 4% annual interest compounded quarterly, how much will be in the account after 5 yr, assuming no withdrawals are made?

53. How much will \$10,000 compounded continuously at 3.75% annual interest amount to in 3 yr?

54. Which is a better plan?

　　　　Plan A:　Invest \$1000 at 4% compounded quarterly for 3 yr
　　　　Plan B:　Invest \$1000 at 3.9% compounded monthly for 3 yr

55. What is the half-life of a radioactive substance that decays according to the function

$$Q(t) = A_0 e^{-0.05t}, \quad \text{where } t \text{ is in days?}$$

56. A machine purchased for business use **depreciates,** or loses value, over a period of years. The value of the machine at the end of its useful life is called its **scrap value.** By one method of depreciation (where it is assumed a constant percentage of the value depreciates annually), the scrap value, S, is given by

$$S = C(1 - r)^n,$$

where C is the original cost, n is the useful life in years, and r is the constant percent of depreciation.

(a) Find the scrap value of a machine costing \$30,000, having a useful life of 12 yr and a constant annual rate of depreciation of 15%.

(b) A machine has a "half-life" of 6 yr. Find the constant annual rate of depreciation.

57. Recall from **Exercise 43** in **Section 12.5** that the number of years, $N(r)$, since two independently evolving languages split off from a common ancestral language is approximated by

$$N(r) = -5000 \ln r,$$

where r is the percent of words from the ancestral language common to both languages now. Find r if the split occurred 2000 yr ago.

58. *Concept Check*　Which one is *not* a representation of the solution of $7^x = 23$?

A. $\dfrac{\log 23}{\log 7}$　　　**B.** $\dfrac{\ln 23}{\ln 7}$　　　**C.** $\log_7 23$　　　**D.** $\log_{23} 7$

MIXED REVIEW EXERCISES

Evaluate.

59. $\log_2 128$ **60.** $5^{\log_5 36}$ **61.** $e^{\ln 4}$

62. $10^{\log e}$ **63.** $\log_3 3^{-5}$ **64.** $\ln e^{5.4}$

Solve.

65. $\log_3 (x + 9) = 4$ **66.** $\ln e^x = 3$ **67.** $\log_x \dfrac{1}{81} = 2$

68. $27^x = 81$ **69.** $2^{2x-3} = 8$

70. $5^{x+2} = 25^{2x+1}$ **71.** $\log_3 (x + 1) - \log_3 x = 2$

72. $\log (3x - 1) = \log 10$ **73.** $\ln (x^2 + 3x + 4) = \ln 2$

74. Consider the logarithmic equation

$$\log (2x + 3) = \log x + 1.$$

    (a) Solve the equation using properties of logarithms.

    (b) If $Y_1 = \log (2X + 3)$ and $Y_2 = \log X + 1$, then the graph of $Y_1 - Y_2$ looks like that shown. Explain how the display at the bottom of the screen confirms the solution set found in part (a).

75. Based on selected figures from 1980 through 2007, the fractional part (as a decimal) of the generation of municipal solid waste recovered can be approximated by the function defined by

$$R(x) = 0.0997(e^{0.0470x}),$$

where $x = 0$ corresponds to 1980, $x = 10$ to 1990, and so on. Based on this model, approximate the percent, to the nearest hundredth, of municipal solid waste recovered in 2005. (*Source:* U.S. Environmental Protection Agency.)

76. One measure of the diversity of the species in an ecological community is the **index of diversity,** the logarithmic expression

$$-(p_1 \ln p_1 + p_2 \ln p_2 + \cdots + p_n \ln p_n),$$

where $p_1, p_2, \ldots, p_n$ are the proportions of a sample belonging to each of n species in the sample. (*Source:* Ludwig, John and James Reynolds, *Statistical Ecology: A Primer on Methods and Computing,* New York, John Wiley and Sons.) Approximate the index of diversity to the nearest thousandth if a sample of 100 from a community produces the following numbers.

    (a) 90 of one species, 10 of another   **(b)** 60 of one species, 40 of another

---

CHAPTER (**12**)   **TEST**   Step-by-step test solutions are found on the Chapter Test Prep Videos available via the Video Resources on DVD, in *MyMathLab*, or on YouTube (search "LialCombinedAlgebra").

View the complete solutions to all Chapter Test exercises on the Video Resources on DVD.

1. Decide whether each function is one-to-one.

    (a) $f(x) = x^2 + 9$ **(b)**

2. Find $f^{-1}(x)$ for the one-to-one function defined by $f(x) = \sqrt[3]{x + 7}$.

3. Graph the inverse of f, given the graph of f.

Graph each function.

4. $f(x) = 6^x$

5. $g(x) = \log_6 x$

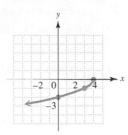 **6.** Explain how the graph of the function in **Exercise 5** can be obtained from the graph of the function in **Exercise 4**.

Solve each equation. Give the exact solution.

7. $5^x = \dfrac{1}{625}$

8. $2^{3x-7} = 8^{2x+2}$

9. A 2008 report predicted that the U.S. Hispanic population will increase from 46.9 million in 2008 to 132.8 million in 2050. (*Source:* U.S. Census Bureau.) Assuming an exponential growth pattern, the population is approximated by

$$f(x) = 46.9e^{0.0247x},$$

where x represents the number of years since 2008. Use this function to approximate, to the nearest tenth, the Hispanic population in each year.

(a) 2015   **(b)** 2030

10. Write in logarithmic form: $4^{-2} = 0.0625$.

11. Write in exponential form: $\log_7 49 = 2$.

Solve each equation.

12. $\log_{1/2} x = -5$

13. $x = \log_9 3$

14. $\log_x 16 = 4$

15. *Concept Check*   Fill in the blanks with the correct responses: The value of $\log_2 32$ is _____. This means that if we raise _____ to the _____ power, the result is _____.

Use properties of logarithms to write each expression as a sum or difference of logarithms. Assume that variables represent positive real numbers.

16. $\log_3 x^2 y$

17. $\log_5 \left(\dfrac{\sqrt{x}}{yz} \right)$

Use properties of logarithms to write each expression as a single logarithm. Assume that variables represent positive real numbers, $b \neq 1$.

18. $3 \log_b s - \log_b t$

19. $\dfrac{1}{4} \log_b r + 2 \log_b s - \dfrac{2}{3} \log_b t$

20. Use a calculator to approximate each logarithm to four decimal places.

(a) $\log 23.1$ **(b)** $\ln 0.82$

21. Use the change-of-base rule to express $\log_3 19$

    (a) in terms of common logarithms   **(b)** in terms of natural logarithms

    (c) correct to four decimal places.

22. Solve $3^x = 78$, giving the solution to three decimal places.

23. Solve $\log_8 (x + 5) + \log_8 (x - 2) = 1$.

24. Suppose that \$10,000 is invested at 4.5% annual interest, compounded quarterly. How much will be in the account in 5 yr if no money is withdrawn?

25. Suppose that \$15,000 is invested at 5% annual interest, compounded continuously.

    (a) How much will be in the account in 5 yr if no money is withdrawn?

    (b) How long will it take for the initial principal to double?

CHAPTERS (1–12) CUMULATIVE REVIEW EXERCISES

Let $S = \left\{ -\frac{9}{4}, -2, -\sqrt{2}, 0, 0.6, \sqrt{11}, \sqrt{-8}, 6, \frac{30}{3} \right\}$. List the elements of S that are members of each set.

    1. Integers   **2.** Rational numbers   **3.** Irrational numbers

Simplify each expression.

    4. $|-8| + 6 - |-2| - (-6 + 2)$ **5.** $2(-5) + (-8)(4) - (-3)$

Solve each equation or inequality.

    6. $7 - (3 + 4x) + 2x = -5(x - 1) - 3$ **7.** $2x + 2 \le 5x - 1$

    8. $|2x - 5| = 9$ **9.** $|4x + 2| > 10$

   10. $\sqrt{2x + 1} - \sqrt{x} = 1$ **11.** $3x^2 - x - 1 = 0$

   12. $x^2 + 2x - 8 > 0$ **13.** $x^4 - 5x^2 + 4 = 0$ **14.** $5^{x+3} = \left(\dfrac{1}{25}\right)^{3x+2}$

Graph.

   15. $5x + 2y = 10$ **16.** $-4x + y \le 5$

   17. $f(x) = \dfrac{1}{3}(x - 1)^2 + 2$ **18.** $f(x) = 2^x$ **19.** $f(x) = \log_3 x$

20. The graph indicates that the number of international travelers to the United States increased from 41,218 thousand in 2003 to 57,949 thousand in 2008.

    (a) Is this the graph of a function?

    (b) What is the slope, to the nearest tenth, of the line in the graph? Interpret the slope in the context of U.S. travelers to foreign countries.

21. Find an equation of the line through $(5, -1)$ and parallel to the line with equation $3x - 4y = 12$. Write the equation in slope-intercept form.

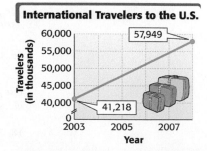

International Travelers to the U.S.

Source: U.S. Department of Commerce.

Perform the indicated operations.

22. $(2p + 3)(3p - 1)$ **23.** $(4k - 3)^2$

24. $(3m^3 + 2m^2 - 5m) - (8m^3 + 2m - 4)$

25. Divide $6t^4 + 17t^3 - 4t^2 + 9t + 4$ by $3t + 1$.

Factor.

26. $8x + x^3$ **27.** $24y^2 - 7y - 6$ **28.** $5z^3 - 19z^2 - 4z$

29. $16a^2 - 25b^4$ **30.** $8c^3 + d^3$ **31.** $16r^2 + 56rq + 49q^2$

Perform the indicated operations.

32. $\dfrac{(5p^3)^4(-3p^7)}{2p^2(4p^4)}$ **33.** $\dfrac{x^2 - 9}{x^2 + 7x + 12} \div \dfrac{x - 3}{x + 5}$ **34.** $\dfrac{2}{k + 3} - \dfrac{5}{k - 2}$

Solve each system.

35. $5x - 3y = 14$ **36.** $x + 2y + 3z = 11$
$\quad\;\; 2x + 5y = 18$ $3x - \;\; y + \;\; z = 8$
                                                  $2x + 2y - 3z = -12$

37. Candy worth $1.00 per lb is to be mixed with 10 lb of candy worth $1.96 per lb to get a mixture that will be sold for $1.60 per lb. How many pounds of the $1.00 candy should be used?

Number of Pounds	Price per Pound	Value
x	$1.00	$1x$
	$1.60	

Simplify.

38. $\sqrt{288}$ **39.** $2\sqrt{32} - 5\sqrt{98}$ **40.** $(5 + 4i)(5 - 4i)$

41. Rewrite the following using the product, quotient, and power properties of logarithms.

$$\log \frac{x^3\sqrt{y}}{z}$$

42. Let the number of bacteria present in a certain culture be given by

$$B(t) = 25{,}000e^{0.2t},$$

where t is time measured in hours, and $t = 0$ corresponds to noon. Approximate, to the nearest hundred, the number of bacteria present at each time.

(a) noon   **(b)** 1 P.M.   **(c)** 2 P.M.

(d) When will the population double?

Nonlinear Functions, Conic Sections, and Nonlinear Systems

13.1 Additional Graphs of Functions

13.2 The Circle and the Ellipse

13.3 The Hyperbola and Functions Defined by Radicals

13.4 Nonlinear Systems of Equations

13.5 Second-Degree Inequalities and Systems of Inequalities

In this chapter, we study a group of curves known as *conic sections*. One conic section, the *ellipse*, has a special reflecting property responsible for "whispering galleries." In a whispering gallery, a person whispering at a certain point in the room can be heard clearly at another point across the room.

The Old House Chamber of the U.S. Capitol, now called Statuary Hall, is a whispering gallery. History has it that John Quincy Adams, whose desk was positioned at exactly the right point beneath the ellipsoidal ceiling, often pretended to sleep there as he listened to political opponents whispering strategies across the room. (*Source:* Aikman, Lonnelle, *We, the People, The Story of the United States Capitol.*)

In **Section 13.2,** we investigate ellipses.

813

(13.1) Additional Graphs of Functions

OBJECTIVES

1 Recognize the graphs of the elementary functions defined by $|x|, \frac{1}{x}$, and $\sqrt{x}$, and graph their translations.

2 Recognize and graph step functions.

OBJECTIVE 1 **Recognize the graphs of the elementary functions defined by $|x|, \frac{1}{x}$, and $\sqrt{x}$, and graph their translations.** Earlier, we introduced the function defined by $f(x) = x^2$, sometimes called the **squaring function.** Another elementary function is the **absolute value function,** defined by $f(x) = |x|$. This function pairs each real number with its absolute value. Its graph is shown in **FIGURE 1**.

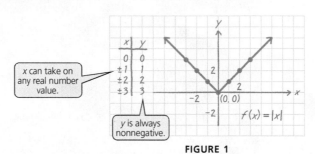

Absolute value function
$$f(x) = |x|$$
Domain: $(-\infty, \infty)$
Range: $[0, \infty)$

FIGURE 1

The **reciprocal function,** defined by $f(x) = \frac{1}{x}$, is a *rational function.* Its graph is shown in **FIGURE 2**. Since x can never equal 0, as x gets closer and closer to 0, $\frac{1}{x}$ approaches either ∞ or $-\infty$. Also, $\frac{1}{x}$ can never equal 0, and as x approaches ∞ or $-\infty$, $\frac{1}{x}$ approaches 0. The axes are called **asymptotes** for the function.

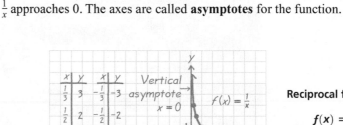

Reciprocal function
$$f(x) = \frac{1}{x}$$
Domain: $(-\infty, 0) \cup (0, \infty)$
Range: $(-\infty, 0) \cup (0, \infty)$

FIGURE 2

The **square root function,** defined by $f(x) = \sqrt{x}$ and introduced in **Section 10.1,** is shown in **FIGURE 3**.

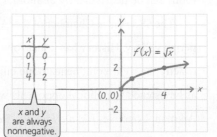

Square root function
$$f(x) = \sqrt{x}$$
Domain: $[0, \infty)$
Range: $[0, \infty)$

FIGURE 3

The graphs of these elementary functions can be shifted, or translated, just as we did with the graph of $f(x) = x^2$ in **Section 11.6**.

NOW TRY
EXERCISE 1

Graph $f(x) = \frac{1}{x+3}$. Give the domain and range.

EXAMPLE 1 Applying a Horizontal Shift

Graph $f(x) = |x - 2|$. Give the domain and range.

The graph of $y = (x - 2)^2$ is obtained by shifting the graph of $y = x^2$ two units to the right. In a similar manner, the graph of $f(x) = |x - 2|$ is found by shifting the graph of $y = |x|$ two units to the right, as shown in **FIGURE 4**.

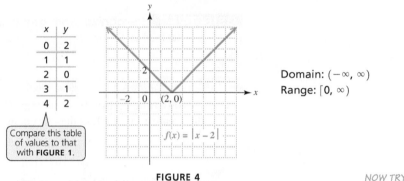

x	y
0	2
1	1
2	0
3	1
4	2

Compare this table of values to that with **FIGURE 1**.

Domain: $(-\infty, \infty)$
Range: $[0, \infty)$

$f(x) = |x - 2|$

FIGURE 4   NOW TRY

NOW TRY
EXERCISE 2

Graph $f(x) = \sqrt{x} + 2$. Give the domain and range.

EXAMPLE 2 Applying a Vertical Shift

Graph $f(x) = \frac{1}{x} + 3$. Give the domain and range.

The graph is found by shifting the graph of $y = \frac{1}{x}$ three units up. See **FIGURE 5**.

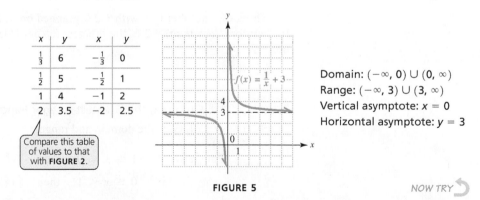

x	y	x	y
$\frac{1}{3}$	6	$-\frac{1}{3}$	0
$\frac{1}{2}$	5	$-\frac{1}{2}$	1
1	4	-1	2
2	3.5	-2	2.5

Compare this table of values to that with **FIGURE 2**.

$f(x) = \frac{1}{x} + 3$

Domain: $(-\infty, 0) \cup (0, \infty)$
Range: $(-\infty, 3) \cup (3, \infty)$
Vertical asymptote: $x = 0$
Horizontal asymptote: $y = 3$

FIGURE 5   NOW TRY

 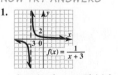

EXAMPLE 3 Applying Both Horizontal and Vertical Shifts

Graph $f(x) = \sqrt{x + 1} - 4$. Give the domain and range.

The graph of $y = (x + 1)^2 - 4$ is obtained by shifting the graph of $y = x^2$ one unit to the left and four units down. Following this pattern, we shift the graph of $y = \sqrt{x}$ one unit to the left and four units down to get the graph of $f(x) = \sqrt{x + 1} - 4$. See **FIGURE 6** on the next page.

NOW TRY
EXERCISE 3

Graph $f(x) = |x + 1| - 3$.
Give the domain and range.

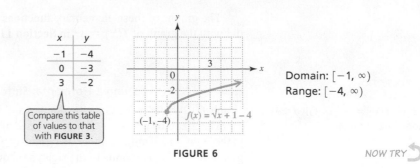

x	y
−1	−4
0	−3
3	−2

Compare this table of values to that with **FIGURE 3**.

$f(x) = \sqrt{x + 1} - 4$

$(−1, −4)$

Domain: $[-1, \infty)$
Range: $[-4, \infty)$

FIGURE 6

NOW TRY

OBJECTIVE 2 **Recognize and graph step functions.** The greatest integer function is defined as follows.

$f(x) = [\![x]\!]$

The **greatest integer function,** written $f(x) = [\![x]\!]$, pairs every real number x with the greatest integer less than or equal to x.

NOW TRY
EXERCISE 4

Evaluate each expression.

(a) $[\![5]\!]$ (b) $[\![-6]\!]$

(c) $[\![3.5]\!]$ (d) $[\![-4.1]\!]$

EXAMPLE 4 Finding the Greatest Integer

Evaluate each expression.

(a) $[\![8]\!] = 8$ (b) $[\![-1]\!] = -1$ (c) $[\![0]\!] = 0$

(d) $[\![7.45]\!] = 7$ The greatest integer *less than or equal to* 7.45 is 7.

(e) $[\![-2.6]\!] = -3$

Think of a number line with -2.6 graphed on it. Since -3 is to the *left of* (and is, therefore, *less than*) -2.6, the greatest integer less than or equal to -2.6 is -3, **not** -2.

NOW TRY

EXAMPLE 5 Graphing the Greatest Integer Function

Graph $f(x) = [\![x]\!]$. Give the domain and range.

For $[\![x]\!]$, if $-1 \leq x < 0$, then $[\![x]\!] = -1$;

if $0 \leq x < 1$, then $[\![x]\!] = 0$;

if $1 \leq x < 2$, then $[\![x]\!] = 1$;

if $2 \leq x < 3$, then $[\![x]\!] = 2$;

if $3 \leq x < 4$, then $[\![x]\!] = 3$, and so on.

NOW TRY ANSWERS

3.

$f(x) = |x + 1| - 3$

domain: $(-\infty, \infty)$; range: $[-3, \infty)$

4. (a) 5 (b) −6 (c) 3 (d) −5

Thus, the graph, as shown in **FIGURE 7** on the next page, consists of a series of horizontal line segments. In each one, the left endpoint is included and the right endpoint is excluded. These segments continue infinitely following this pattern to the left and right. The appearance of the graph is the reason that this function is called a **step function.**

NOW TRY
EXERCISE 5

Graph $f(x) = [\![x - 1]\!]$. Give the domain and range.

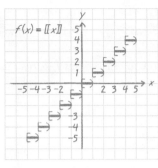

FIGURE 7

Greatest integer function

$$f(x) = [\![x]\!]$$

Domain: $(-\infty, \infty)$
Range: $\{\ldots, -3, -2, -1, 0, 1, 2, 3, \ldots\}$
(the set of integers)

The graph of a step function also may be shifted. For example, the graph of

$$h(x) = [\![x - 2]\!]$$

is the same as the graph of $f(x) = [\![x]\!]$ shifted two units to the right. Similarly, the graph of

$$g(x) = [\![x]\!] + 2$$

is the graph of $f(x)$ shifted two units up.   NOW TRY

NOW TRY
EXERCISE 6

The cost of parking a car at an airport hourly parking lot is $4 for the first hour and $2 for each additional hour or fraction thereof. Let $f(x) =$ the cost of parking a car for x hours. Graph $f(x)$ for x in the interval $(0, 5]$.

EXAMPLE 6 Applying a Greatest Integer Function

An overnight delivery service charges $25 for a package weighing up to 2 lb. For each additional pound or fraction of a pound there is an additional charge of $3. Let $D(x)$, or y, represent the cost to send a package weighing x pounds. Graph $D(x)$ for x in the interval $(0, 6]$.

For x in the interval $(0, 2]$, $y = 25$.

For x in the interval $(2, 3]$, $y = 25 + 3 = 28$.

For x in the interval $(3, 4]$, $y = 28 + 3 = 31$.

For x in the interval $(4, 5]$, $y = 31 + 3 = 34$.

For x in the interval $(5, 6]$, $y = 34 + 3 = 37$.

The graph, which is that of a step function, is shown in **FIGURE 8**.

NOW TRY ANSWERS

5.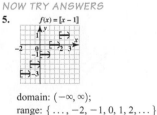

domain: $(-\infty, \infty)$;
range: $\{\ldots, -2, -1, 0, 1, 2, \ldots\}$

6.

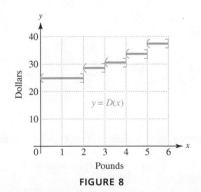

FIGURE 8

NOW TRY

13.1 EXERCISES

MyMathLab   Math XP PRACTICE   WATCH   DOWNLOAD   READ   REVIEW

⊙ *Complete solution available on the Video Resources on DVD*

Concept Check   *For Exercises 1–6, refer to the basic graphs in A–F.*

A.   **B.**   **C.**

D.   **E.** 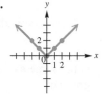   **F.**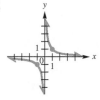

1. Which is the graph of $f(x) = |x|$? The lowest point on its graph has coordinates (——, ——).

2. Which is the graph of $f(x) = x^2$? Give the domain and range.

3. Which is the graph of $f(x) = [\![x]\!]$? Give the domain and range.

4. Which is the graph of $f(x) = \sqrt{x}$? Give the domain and range.

5. Which is not the graph of a function? Why?

6. Which is the graph of $f(x) = \frac{1}{x}$? The lines with equations $x = 0$ and $y = 0$ are called its _____.

Concept Check   *Without actually plotting points, match each function defined by the absolute value expression with its graph.*

7. $f(x) = |x - 2| + 2$ **A.**   **B.**

8. $f(x) = |x + 2| + 2$

9. $f(x) = |x - 2| - 2$ **C.** 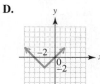   **D.**

10. $f(x) = |x + 2| - 2$

*Graph each function. Give the domain and range. **See Examples 1–3.***

⊙ 11. $f(x) = |x + 1|$ 12. $f(x) = |x - 1|$ ⊙ 13. $f(x) = \frac{1}{x} + 1$

14. $f(x) = \frac{1}{x} - 1$ 15. $f(x) = \sqrt{x - 2}$ 16. $f(x) = \sqrt{x + 5}$

17. $f(x) = \dfrac{1}{x - 2}$ **18.** $f(x) = \dfrac{1}{x + 2}$ 🌐 **19.** $f(x) = \sqrt{x + 3} - 3$

20. $f(x) = \sqrt{x - 2} + 2$ **21.** $f(x) = |x - 3| + 1$ **22.** $f(x) = |x + 1| - 4$

23. *Concept Check* How is the graph of $f(x) = \frac{1}{x - 3} + 2$ obtained from the graph of $g(x) = \frac{1}{x}$?

24. *Concept Check* How is the graph of $f(x) = \frac{1}{x + 5} - 3$ obtained from the graph of $g(x) = \frac{1}{x}$?

*Evaulate each expression. See **Example 4.***

25. $[\![3]\!]$ **26.** $[\![18]\!]$ **27.** $[\![4.5]\!]$ **28.** $[\![8.7]\!]$ 🌐 **29.** $\left[\!\!\left[\dfrac{1}{2}\right]\!\!\right]$

30. $\left[\!\!\left[\dfrac{3}{4}\right]\!\!\right]$ **31.** $[\![-14]\!]$ **32.** $[\![-5]\!]$ 🌐 **33.** $[\![-10.1]\!]$ **34.** $[\![-6.9]\!]$

*Graph each step function. See **Examples 5 and 6.***

35. $f(x) = [\![x]\!] - 1$ **36.** $f(x) = [\![x]\!] + 1$

🌐 **37.** $f(x) = [\![x - 3]\!]$ **38.** $f(x) = [\![x + 2]\!]$

39. Assume that postage rates are 44¢ for the first ounce, plus 17¢ for each additional ounce, and that each letter carries one 44¢ stamp and as many 17¢ stamps as necessary. Graph the function defined by

$$y = p(x) = \text{the number of stamps}$$

on a letter weighing x ounces. Use the interval $(0, 5]$.

40. The cost of parking a car at an airport hourly parking lot is \$3 for the first half-hour and \$2 for each additional half-hour or fraction thereof. Graph the function defined by $y = f(x) =$ the cost of parking a car for x hours. Use the interval $(0, 2]$.

41. A certain long-distance carrier provides service between Podunk and Nowhereville. If x represents the number of minutes for the call, where $x > 0$, then the function f defined by

$$f(x) = 0.40[\![x]\!] + 0.75$$

gives the total cost of the call in dollars. Find the cost of a 5.5-minute call.

42. See Exercise 41. Find the cost of a 20.75-minute call.

PREVIEW EXERCISES

*Find the distance between each pair of points. **See Section 10.3.***

43. $(2, -1)$ and $(4, 3)$ **44.** (x, y) and $(-2, 5)$ **45.** (x, y) and (h, k)

13.2 The Circle and the Ellipse

OBJECTIVES

1 Find an equation of a circle given the center and radius.

2 Determine the center and radius of a circle given its equation.

3 Recognize an equation of an ellipse.

4 Graph ellipses.

When an infinite cone is intersected by a plane, the resulting figure is called a **conic section.** The parabola is one example of a conic section. Circles, ellipses, and hyperbolas may also result. See **FIGURE 9.**

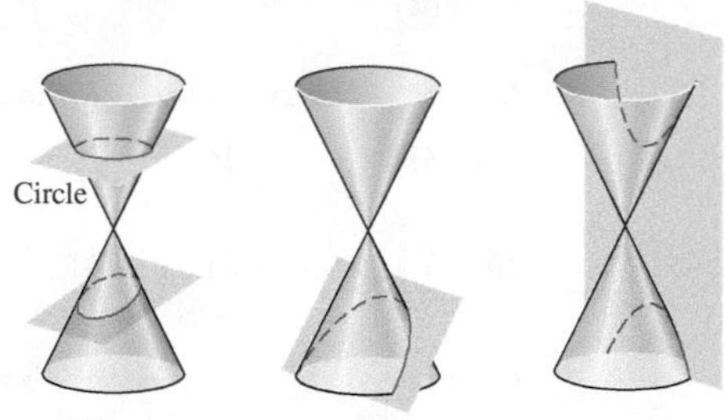

Circle

Ellipse   Parabola   Hyperbola

FIGURE 9

OBJECTIVE 1 **Find an equation of a circle given the center and radius.** A **circle** is the set of all points in a plane that lie a fixed distance from a fixed point. The fixed point is called the **center,** and the fixed distance is called the **radius.** We use the distance formula from **Section 10.3** to find an equation of a circle.

NOW TRY EXERCISE 1

Find an equation of the circle with radius 6 and center at $(0, 0)$, and graph it.

EXAMPLE 1 Finding an Equation of a Circle and Graphing It

Find an equation of the circle with radius 3 and center at $(0, 0)$, and graph it.

If the point (x, y) is on the circle, then the distance from (x, y) to the center $(0, 0)$ is 3.

$$\sqrt{(x_2 - x_1)^2 + (y_2 - y_1)^2} = d \quad \text{Distance formula}$$

$$\sqrt{(x - 0)^2 + (y - 0)^2} = 3 \quad \begin{array}{l}\text{Let } x_1 = 0, y_1 = 0,\\ \text{and } d = 3.\end{array}$$

$$x^2 + y^2 = 9 \quad \text{Square each side.}$$

An equation of this circle is $x^2 + y^2 = 9$. The graph is shown in **FIGURE 10.**

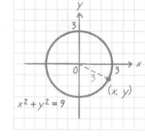

FIGURE 10

NOW TRY

A circle may not be centered at the origin, as seen in the next example.

EXAMPLE 2 Finding an Equation of a Circle and Graphing It

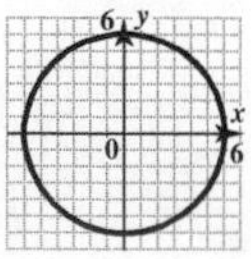

Find an equation of the circle with center at $(4, -3)$ and radius 5, and graph it.

$$\sqrt{(x - 4)^2 + [y - (-3)]^2} = 5 \quad \begin{array}{l}\text{Let } x_1 = 4, y_1 = -3, \text{ and } d = 5\\ \text{in the distance formula.}\end{array}$$

$$(x - 4)^2 + (y + 3)^2 = 25 \quad \text{Square each side.}$$

NOW TRY
EXERCISE 2

Find an equation of the circle with center at $(-2, 2)$ and radius 3, and graph it.

To graph the circle, plot the center $(4, -3)$, then move 5 units right, left, up, and down from the center, plotting the points

$$(9, -3), \quad (-1, -3), \quad (4, 2), \quad \text{and} \quad (4, -8).$$

Draw a smooth curve through these four points, sketching one quarter of the circle at a time. See **FIGURE 11**.

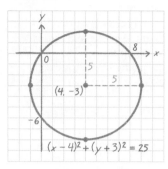

FIGURE 11

NOW TRY

Examples 1 and 2 suggest the form of an equation of a circle with radius r and center at (h, k). If (x, y) is a point on the circle, then the distance from the center (h, k) to the point (x, y) is r. By the distance formula,

$$\sqrt{(x - h)^2 + (y - k)^2} = r.$$

Squaring both sides gives the **center-radius form** of the equation of a circle.

Equation of a Circle (Center-Radius Form)

An equation of a circle with radius r and center (h, k) is

$$(x - h)^2 + (y - k)^2 = r^2.$$

NOW TRY
EXERCISE 3
Find an equation of the circle with center at $(-5, 4)$ and radius $\sqrt{6}$.

EXAMPLE 3 Using the Center-Radius Form of the Equation of a Circle

Find an equation of the circle with center at $(-1, 2)$ and radius $\sqrt{7}$.

$$(x - h)^2 + (y - k)^2 = r^2 \qquad \text{Center-radius form}$$

$$[x - (-1)]^2 + (y - 2)^2 = (\sqrt{7})^2 \qquad \text{Let } h = -1, k = 2, \text{ and } r = \sqrt{7}.$$

(Pay attention to signs here.) $(x + 1)^2 + (y - 2)^2 = 7 \qquad \text{Simplify; } (\sqrt{a})^2 = a$

NOW TRY

NOTE If a circle has its center at the origin $(0, 0)$, then its equation becomes

$$(x - 0)^2 + (y - 0)^2 = r^2 \qquad \text{Let } h = 0, k = 0 \text{ in the center-radius form.}$$

$$x^2 + y^2 = r^2. \qquad \text{See Example 1.}$$

OBJECTIVE 2 **Determine the center and radius of a circle given its equation.**
In the equation found in **Example 2**, multiplying out $(x - 4)^2$ and $(y + 3)^2$ gives

$$(x - 4)^2 + (y + 3)^2 = 25$$

$$x^2 - 8x + 16 + y^2 + 6y + 9 = 25 \qquad \text{Square each binomial.}$$

$$x^2 + y^2 - 8x + 6y = 0. \qquad \text{Subtract 25.}$$

This general form suggests that an equation with both x^2- and y^2-terms with equal coefficients may represent a circle.

NOW TRY ANSWERS
2. $(x + 2)^2 + (y - 2)^2 = 9$

3. $(x + 5)^2 + (y - 4)^2 = 6$

NOW TRY
EXERCISE 4

Find the center and radius of the circle.

$$x^2 + y^2 - 8x + 10y - 8 = 0$$

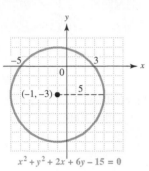

$$x^2 + y^2 + 2x + 6y - 15 = 0$$

FIGURE 12

EXAMPLE 4   Completing the Square to Find the Center and Radius

Find the center and radius of the circle $x^2 + y^2 + 2x + 6y - 15 = 0$, and graph it.

Since the equation has x^2- and y^2-terms with equal coefficients, its graph might be that of a circle. To find the center and radius, complete the squares on x and y.

$x^2 + y^2 + 2x + 6y = 15$	Transform so that the constant is on the right.
$(x^2 + 2x \qquad) + (y^2 + 6y \qquad) = 15$	Write in anticipation of completing the square.
$\left[\dfrac{1}{2}(2)\right]^2 = 1 \qquad \left[\dfrac{1}{2}(6)\right]^2 = 9$	Square half the coefficient of each middle term.
$(x^2 + 2x + 1) + (y^2 + 6y + 9) = 15 + 1 + 9$	Complete the squares on both x and y.
$(x + 1)^2 + (y + 3)^2 = 25$	Factor on the left. Add on the right.
$[x - (-1)]^2 + [y - (-3)]^2 = 5^2$	Center-radius form

Add 1 and 9 on *both* sides of the equation.

The final equation shows that the graph is a circle with center at $(-1, -3)$ and radius 5, as shown in **FIGURE 12**.

NOW TRY

NOTE Consider the following.

1. If the procedure of **Example 4** leads to an equation of the form

$$(x - h)^2 + (y - k)^2 = 0,$$

then the graph is the single point (h, k).

2. If the constant on the right side is *negative,* then the equation has *no graph*.

OBJECTIVE 3   **Recognize an equation of an ellipse.** An **ellipse** is the set of all points in a plane the *sum* of whose distances from two fixed points is constant. These fixed points are called **foci** (singular: *focus*). The ellipse in **FIGURE 13** has foci $(c, 0)$ and $(-c, 0)$, with x-intercepts $(a, 0)$ and $(-a, 0)$ and y-intercepts $(0, b)$ and $(0, -b)$. It is shown in more advanced courses that $c^2 = a^2 - b^2$ for an ellipse of this type. The origin is the **center** of the ellipse.

An ellipse has the following equation.

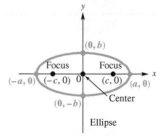

FIGURE 13

Equation of an Ellipse

The ellipse whose x-intercepts are $(a, 0)$ and $(-a, 0)$ and whose y-intercepts are $(0, b)$ and $(0, -b)$ has an equation of the form

$$\frac{x^2}{a^2} + \frac{y^2}{b^2} = 1.$$

NOW TRY ANSWER
4. center: $(4, -5)$; radius: 7

NOTE A circle is a special case of an ellipse, where $a^2 = b^2$.

When a ray of light or sound emanating from one focus of an ellipse bounces off the ellipse, it passes through the other focus. See **FIGURE 14**. As mentioned in the chapter introduction, this reflecting property is responsible for whispering galleries. John Quincy Adams was able to listen in on his opponents' conversations because his desk was positioned at one of the foci beneath the ellipsoidal ceiling and his opponents were located across the room at the other focus.

Elliptical bicycle gears are designed to respond to the legs' natural strengths and weaknesses. At the top and bottom of the powerstroke, where the legs have the least leverage, the gear offers little resistance, but as the gear rotates, the resistance increases. This allows the legs to apply more power where it is most naturally available. See **FIGURE 15**.

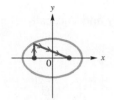

Reflecting property of an ellipse

FIGURE 14

FIGURE 15

OBJECTIVE 4 **Graph ellipses.**

EXAMPLE 5 Graphing Ellipses

Graph each ellipse.

(a) $\dfrac{x^2}{49} + \dfrac{y^2}{36} = 1$

Here, $a^2 = 49$, so $a = 7$, and the x-intercepts are $(7, 0)$ and $(-7, 0)$. Similarly, $b^2 = 36$, so $b = 6$, and the y-intercepts are $(0, 6)$ and $(0, -6)$. Plotting the intercepts and sketching the ellipse through them gives the graph in **FIGURE 16**.

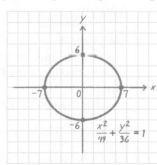

FIGURE 16

(b) $\dfrac{x^2}{36} + \dfrac{y^2}{121} = 1$

The x-intercepts are $(6, 0)$ and $(-6, 0)$, and the y-intercepts are $(0, 11)$ and $(0, -11)$. Join these with the smooth curve of an ellipse. See **FIGURE 17**.

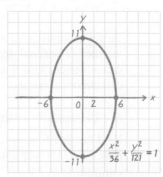

FIGURE 17

NOW TRY
EXERCISE 5

Graph $\dfrac{x^2}{16} + \dfrac{y^2}{25} = 1.$

NOW TRY ANSWER

5.

$\dfrac{x^2}{16} + \dfrac{y^2}{25} = 1$

NOW TRY

NOW TRY
EXERCISE 6
Graph
$$\frac{(x-3)^2}{36} + \frac{(y-4)^2}{4} = 1.$$

EXAMPLE 6 Graphing an Ellipse Shifted Horizontally and Vertically

Graph $\dfrac{(x-2)^2}{25} + \dfrac{(y+3)^2}{49} = 1.$

Just as $(x-2)^2$ and $(y+3)^2$ would indicate that the center of a circle would be $(2,-3)$, so it is with this ellipse. **FIGURE 18** shows that the graph goes through the four points

$$(2,4), \quad (7,-3), \quad (2,-10),$$
$$\text{and} \quad (-3,-3).$$

The x-values of these points are found by adding $\pm a = \pm 5$ to 2, and the y-values come from adding $\pm b = \pm 7$ to -3.

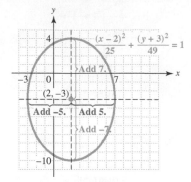

FIGURE 18

NOW TRY

NOTE *Graphs of circles and ellipses are not graphs of functions.* The only conic section whose graph represents a function is the vertical parabola with equation $f(x) = ax^2 + bx + c.$

CONNECTIONS

A graphing calculator in function mode cannot directly graph a circle or an ellipse, since they do not represent functions. We must first solve the equation for y, getting two functions y_1 and y_2. The union of these two graphs is the graph of the entire figure.

For example, to graph $(x+3)^2 + (y+2)^2 = 25$, begin by solving for y.

$$(x+3)^2 + (y+2)^2 = 25$$

$$(y+2)^2 = 25 - (x+3)^2 \qquad \text{Subtract } (x+3)^2.$$

$$y + 2 = \pm\sqrt{25 - (x+3)^2} \qquad \text{Take square roots.}$$

$$\boxed{\text{Remember both roots.}} \quad y = -2 \pm \sqrt{25 - (x+3)^2} \qquad \text{Add } -2.$$

The two functions to be graphed are

$$y_1 = -2 + \sqrt{25 - (x+3)^2} \qquad \text{and} \qquad y_2 = -2 - \sqrt{25 - (x+3)^2}.$$

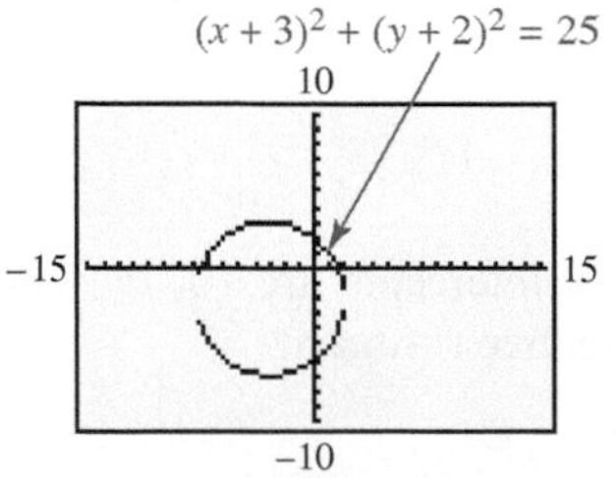

To get an undistorted screen, a **square viewing window** must be used. (Refer to your instruction manual for details.) See **FIGURE 19.** The two semicircles seem to be disconnected. This is because the graphs are nearly vertical at those points, and the calculator cannot show a true picture of the behavior there.

$(x+3)^2 + (y+2)^2 = 25$

Square Viewing Window

FIGURE 19

For Discussion or Writing

Find the two functions y_1 and y_2 to use to obtain the graph of the circle with equation $(x-3)^2 + (y+1)^2 = 36$. Then graph the circle using a square viewing window.

NOW TRY ANSWER
6.
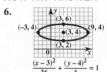
$\frac{(x-3)^2}{36} + \frac{(y-4)^2}{4} = 1$

13.2 EXERCISES

 MyMathLab Math XL PRACTICE WATCH DOWNLOAD READ REVIEW

● *Complete solution available on the Video Resources on DVD*

● **1. See Example 1.** Consider the circle whose equation is $x^2 + y^2 = 25$.

(a) What are the coordinates of its center?   (b) What is its radius?

(c) Sketch its graph.

📝 **2.** Why does a set of points defined by a circle *not* satisfy the definition of a function?

Concept Check   Match each equation with the correct graph.

3. $(x - 3)^2 + (y - 2)^2 = 25$ **A.**

4. $(x - 3)^2 + (y + 2)^2 = 25$

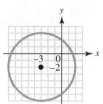

B.

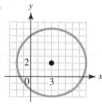

5. $(x + 3)^2 + (y - 2)^2 = 25$ **C.**

6. $(x + 3)^2 + (y + 2)^2 = 25$

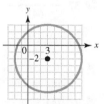

D.

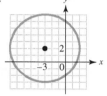

*Find the equation of a circle satisfying the given conditions. **See Examples 2 and 3.***

● **7.** Center: $(-4, 3)$; radius: 2

8. Center: $(5, -2)$; radius: 4

● **9.** Center: $(-8, -5)$; radius: $\sqrt{5}$

10. Center: $(-12, 13)$; radius: $\sqrt{7}$

*Find the center and radius of each circle. (Hint: In Exercises 15 and 16, divide each side by a common factor.) **See Example 4.***

● **11.** $x^2 + y^2 + 4x + 6y + 9 = 0$

12. $x^2 + y^2 - 8x - 12y + 3 = 0$

13. $x^2 + y^2 + 10x - 14y - 7 = 0$

14. $x^2 + y^2 - 2x + 4y - 4 = 0$

15. $3x^2 + 3y^2 - 12x - 24y + 12 = 0$

16. $2x^2 + 2y^2 + 20x + 16y + 10 = 0$

*Graph each circle. Identify the center if it is not at the origin. **See Examples 1, 2, and 4.***

17. $x^2 + y^2 = 9$

18. $x^2 + y^2 = 4$

19. $2y^2 = 10 - 2x^2$

20. $3x^2 = 48 - 3y^2$

21. $(x + 3)^2 + (y - 2)^2 = 9$

22. $(x - 1)^2 + (y + 3)^2 = 16$

23. $x^2 + y^2 - 4x - 6y + 9 = 0$

24. $x^2 + y^2 + 8x + 2y - 8 = 0$

25. $x^2 + y^2 + 6x - 6y + 9 = 0$

26. $x^2 + y^2 - 4x + 10y + 20 = 0$

📝 **27.** A circle can be drawn on a piece of posterboard by fastening one end of a string with a thumbtack, pulling the string taut with a pencil, and tracing a curve, as shown in the figure. Explain why this method works.

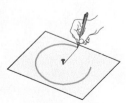

28. An ellipse can be drawn on a piece of posterboard by fastening two ends of a length of string with thumbtacks, pulling the string taut with a pencil, and tracing a curve, as shown in the figure. Explain why this method works.

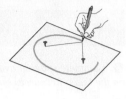

Graph each ellipse. See Examples 5 and 6.

29. $\dfrac{x^2}{9} + \dfrac{y^2}{25} = 1$

30. $\dfrac{x^2}{9} + \dfrac{y^2}{16} = 1$

31. $\dfrac{x^2}{36} + \dfrac{y^2}{16} = 1$

32. $\dfrac{x^2}{9} + \dfrac{y^2}{4} = 1$

33. $\dfrac{x^2}{16} + \dfrac{y^2}{4} = 1$

34. $\dfrac{x^2}{49} + \dfrac{y^2}{81} = 1$

35. $\dfrac{y^2}{25} = 1 - \dfrac{x^2}{49}$

36. $\dfrac{y^2}{9} = 1 - \dfrac{x^2}{16}$

37. $\dfrac{(x + 1)^2}{64} + \dfrac{(y - 2)^2}{49} = 1$

38. $\dfrac{(x - 4)^2}{9} + \dfrac{(y + 2)^2}{4} = 1$

39. $\dfrac{(x - 2)^2}{16} + \dfrac{(y - 1)^2}{9} = 1$

40. $\dfrac{(x + 3)^2}{25} + \dfrac{(y + 2)^2}{36} = 1$

41. Explain why a set of ordered pairs whose graph forms an ellipse does not satisfy the definition of a function.

42. (a) How many points are there on the graph of $(x - 4)^2 + (y - 1)^2 = 0$? Explain.

(b) How many points are there on the graph of $(x - 4)^2 + (y - 1)^2 = -1$? Explain.

TECHNOLOGY INSIGHTS EXERCISES 43 AND 44

43. The circle shown in the calculator graph was created using function mode, with a square viewing window. It is the graph of

$$(x + 2)^2 + (y - 4)^2 = 16.$$

What are the two functions y_1 and y_2 that were used to obtain this graph?

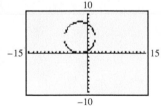

44. The ellipse shown in the calculator graph was graphed using function mode, with a square viewing window. It is the graph of

$$\dfrac{x^2}{4} + \dfrac{y^2}{9} = 1.$$

What are the two functions y_1 and y_2 that were used to obtain this graph?

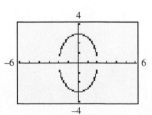

 Use a graphing calculator in function mode to graph each circle or ellipse. Use a square viewing window. See the Connections box.

45. $x^2 + y^2 = 36$

46. $(x - 2)^2 + y^2 = 49$

47. $\dfrac{x^2}{16} + \dfrac{y^2}{4} = 1$

48. $\dfrac{(x - 3)^2}{25} + \dfrac{y^2}{9} = 1$

*A **lithotripter** is a machine used to crush kidney stones using shock waves. The patient is placed in an elliptical tub with the kidney stone at one focus of the ellipse. A beam is projected from the other focus to the tub, so that it reflects to hit the kidney stone. See the figure.*

49. Suppose a lithotripter is based on the ellipse with equation

$$\frac{x^2}{36} + \frac{y^2}{9} = 1.$$

How far from the center of the ellipse must the kidney stone and the source of the beam be placed? (*Hint:* Use the fact that $c^2 = a^2 - b^2$, since $a > b$ here.)

50. Rework **Exercise 49** if the equation of the ellipse is

$$9x^2 + 4y^2 = 36.$$

(*Hint:* Write the equation in fractional form by dividing each term by 36, and use $c^2 = b^2 - a^2$, since $b > a$ here.)

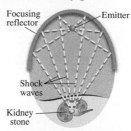

The top of an ellipse is illustrated in this depiction of how a lithotripter crushes a kidney stone.

Solve each problem.

51. An arch has the shape of half an ellipse. The equation of the ellipse is

$$100x^2 + 324y^2 = 32,400,$$

where x and y are in meters.

(a) How high is the center of the arch?

(b) How wide is the arch across the bottom?

NOT TO SCALE

52. A one-way street passes under an overpass, which is in the form of the top half of an ellipse, as shown in the figure. Suppose that a truck 12 ft wide passes directly under the overpass. What is the maximum possible height of this truck?

NOT TO SCALE

In Exercises 53 and 54, see **FIGURE 13** *and use the fact that* $c^2 = a^2 - b^2$, *where* $a^2 > b^2$.

53. The orbit of Mars is an ellipse with the sun at one focus. For x and y in millions of miles, the equation of the orbit is

$$\frac{x^2}{141.7^2} + \frac{y^2}{141.1^2} = 1.$$

(*Source:* Kaler, James B., *Astronomy!*, Addison-Wesley.)

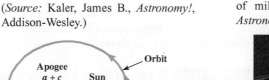

$c^2 = a^2 - b^2$ **NOT TO SCALE**

(a) Find the greatest distance (the **apogee**) from Mars to the sun.

(b) Find the least distance (the **perigee**) from Mars to the sun.

54. The orbit of Venus around the sun (one of the foci) is an ellipse with equation

$$\frac{x^2}{5013} + \frac{y^2}{4970} = 1,$$

where x and y are measured in millions of miles. (*Source:* Kaler, James B., *Astronomy!*, Addison-Wesley.)

(a) Find the greatest distance between Venus and the sun.

(b) Find the least distance between Venus and the sun.

For Exercises 55–57, **see Sections 3.1 and 7.1.**

55. Plot the points $(3, 4)$, $(-3, 4)$, $(3, -4)$, and $(-3, -4)$.

56. Sketch the graphs of $y = \frac{4}{3}x$ and $y = -\frac{4}{3}x$ on the same axes.

57. Find the x- and y-intercepts of the graph of $4x + 3y = 12$.

58. Solve the equation $x^2 = 121$. **See Section 11.1.**

13.3 The Hyperbola and Functions Defined by Radicals

OBJECTIVES

1. Recognize the equation of a hyperbola.
2. Graph hyperbolas by using asymptotes.
3. Identify conic sections by their equations.
4. Graph certain square root functions.

OBJECTIVE 1 **Recognize the equation of a hyperbola.** A **hyperbola** is the set of all points in a plane such that the absolute value of the *difference* of the distances from two fixed points (the *foci*) is constant. The graph of a hyperbola has two parts, called *branches,* and two intercepts (or *vertices*) that lie on its axis, called the **transverse axis.** The hyperbola in **FIGURE 20** has a horizontal transverse axis, with foci $(c, 0)$ and $(-c, 0)$ and x-intercepts $(a, 0)$ and $(-a, 0)$. (A hyperbola with vertical transverse axis would have its intercepts on the y-axis.)

A hyperbola centered at the origin has one of the following equations. It is shown in more advanced courses that for a hyperbola, $c^2 = a^2 + b^2$.

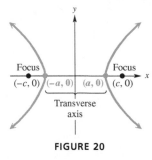

FIGURE 20

Equations of Hyperbolas

A hyperbola with x-intercepts $(a, 0)$ and $(-a, 0)$ has an equation of the form

$$\frac{x^2}{a^2} - \frac{y^2}{b^2} = 1. \quad \text{Transverse axis on } x\text{-axis}$$

A hyperbola with y-intercepts $(0, b)$ and $(0, -b)$ has an equation of the form

$$\frac{y^2}{b^2} - \frac{x^2}{a^2} = 1. \quad \text{Transverse axis on } y\text{-axis}$$

If we were to throw two stones into a pond, the ensuing concentric ripples would be shaped like a hyperbola. A cross-section of the cooling towers for a nuclear power plant is hyperbolic, as shown in the photo.

OBJECTIVE 2 **Graph hyperbolas by using asymptotes.** The two branches of the graph of a hyperbola approach a pair of intersecting straight lines, which are its asymptotes. See **FIGURE 21** on the next page. The asymptotes are useful for sketching the graph of the hyperbola.

Asymptotes of Hyperbolas

The extended diagonals of the rectangle with vertices (corners) at the points (a, b), $(-a, b)$, $(-a, -b)$, and $(a, -b)$ are the **asymptotes** of the hyperbolas

$$\frac{x^2}{a^2} - \frac{y^2}{b^2} = 1 \quad \text{and} \quad \frac{y^2}{b^2} - \frac{x^2}{a^2} = 1.$$

This rectangle is called the **fundamental rectangle.** Using the methods of **Chapter 3 or Chapter 7,** we could show that the equations of these asymptotes are

$$y = \frac{b}{a}x \quad \text{and} \quad y = -\frac{b}{a}x.$$ Equations of the asymptotes of a hyperbola

To graph hyperbolas, follow these steps.

Graphing a Hyperbola

Step 1 **Find the intercepts.** Locate the intercepts at $(a, 0)$ and $(-a, 0)$ if the x^2-term has a positive coefficient, or at $(0, b)$ and $(0, -b)$ if the y^2-term has a positive coefficient.

Step 2 **Find the fundamental rectangle.** Locate the vertices of the fundamental rectangle at (a, b), $(-a, b)$, $(-a, -b)$, and $(a, -b)$.

Step 3 **Sketch the asymptotes.** The extended diagonals of the rectangle are the asymptotes of the hyperbola, and they have equations $y = \pm\frac{b}{a}x$.

Step 4 **Draw the graph.** Sketch each branch of the hyperbola through an intercept and approaching (but not touching) the asymptotes.

NOW TRY
EXERCISE 1

Graph $\dfrac{x^2}{25} - \dfrac{y^2}{9} = 1.$

EXAMPLE 1 Graphing a Horizontal Hyperbola

Graph $\dfrac{x^2}{16} - \dfrac{y^2}{25} = 1.$

Step 1 Here $a = 4$ and $b = 5$. The x-intercepts are $(4, 0)$ and $(-4, 0)$.

Step 2 The four points $(4, 5)$, $(-4, 5)$, $(-4, -5)$, and $(4, -5)$ are the vertices of the fundamental rectangle, as shown in **FIGURE 21** below.

Steps 3 and 4 The equations of the asymptotes are $y = \pm\frac{5}{4}x$, and the hyperbola approaches these lines as x and y get larger and larger in absolute value. *NOW TRY*

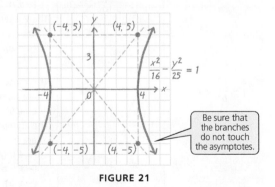

Be sure that the branches do not touch the asymptotes.

FIGURE 21

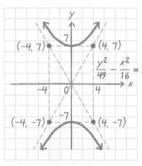

FIGURE 22

NOW TRY
EXERCISE 2

Graph $\dfrac{y^2}{9} - \dfrac{x^2}{16} = 1.$

NOW TRY ANSWERS

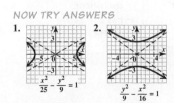

EXAMPLE 2 Graphing a Vertical Hyperbola

Graph $\dfrac{y^2}{49} - \dfrac{x^2}{16} = 1.$

This hyperbola has y-intercepts $(0, 7)$ and $(0, -7)$. The asymptotes are the extended diagonals of the rectangle with vertices at $(4, 7)$, $(-4, 7)$, $(-4, -7)$, and $(4, -7)$. Their equations are $y = \pm\frac{7}{4}x$. See **FIGURE 22** above. *NOW TRY*

NOTE As with circles and ellipses, hyperbolas are graphed with a graphing calculator by first writing the equations of two functions whose union is equivalent to the equation of the hyperbola. A square window gives a truer shape for hyperbolas, too.

SUMMARY OF CONIC SECTIONS

Equation	Graph	Description	Identification
$y = ax^2 + bx + c$ or $y = a(x - h)^2 + k$	Parabola	It opens up if $a > 0$, down if $a < 0$. The vertex is (h, k).	It has an x^2-term. y is not squared.
$x = ay^2 + by + c$ or $x = a(y - k)^2 + h$	Parabola	It opens to the right if $a > 0$, to the left if $a < 0$. The vertex is (h, k).	It has a y^2-term. x is not squared.
$(x - h)^2 + (y - k)^2 = r^2$	Circle	The center is (h, k), and the radius is r.	x^2- and y^2-terms have the same positive coefficient.
$\dfrac{x^2}{a^2} + \dfrac{y^2}{b^2} = 1$	Ellipse	The x-intercepts are $(a, 0)$ and $(-a, 0)$. The y-intercepts are $(0, b)$ and $(0, -b)$.	x^2- and y^2-terms have different positive coefficients.
$\dfrac{x^2}{a^2} - \dfrac{y^2}{b^2} = 1$	Hyperbola	The x-intercepts are $(a, 0)$ and $(-a, 0)$. The asymptotes are found from (a, b), $(a, -b)$, $(-a, -b)$, and $(-a, b)$.	x^2 has a positive coefficient. y^2 has a negative coefficient.
$\dfrac{y^2}{b^2} - \dfrac{x^2}{a^2} = 1$	Hyperbola	The y-intercepts are $(0, b)$ and $(0, -b)$. The asymptotes are found from (a, b), $(a, -b)$, $(-a, -b)$, and $(-a, b)$.	y^2 has a positive coefficient. x^2 has a negative coefficient.

OBJECTIVE 3 **Identify conic sections by their equations.** Rewriting a second-degree equation in one of the forms given for ellipses, hyperbolas, circles, or parabolas makes it possible to identify the graph of the equation.

NOW TRY
EXERCISE 3

Identify the graph of each equation.

(a) $y^2 - 10 = -x^2$

(b) $y - 2x^2 = 8$

(c) $3x^2 + y^2 = 4$

EXAMPLE 3 Identifying the Graphs of Equations

Identify the graph of each equation.

(a) $9x^2 = 108 + 12y^2$

Both variables are squared, so the graph is either an ellipse or a hyperbola. (This situation also occurs for a circle, which is a special case of an ellipse.) Rewrite the equation so that the x^2- and y^2-terms are on one side of the equation and 1 is on the other.

$$9x^2 - 12y^2 = 108 \qquad \text{Subtract } 12y^2.$$

$$\frac{x^2}{12} - \frac{y^2}{9} = 1 \qquad \text{Divide by 108.}$$

The graph of this equation is a hyperbola.

(b) $x^2 = y - 3$

Only one of the two variables, x, is squared, so this is the vertical parabola $y = x^2 + 3$.

(c) $x^2 = 9 - y^2$

Write the variable terms on the same side of the equation.

$$x^2 + y^2 = 9 \qquad \text{Add } y^2.$$

The graph of this equation is a circle with center at the origin and radius 3.

NOW TRY

OBJECTIVE 4 **Graph certain square root functions.** Recall from the vertical line test that no vertical line will intersect the graph of a function in more than one point. Thus, the graphs of horizontal parabolas, all circles and ellipses, and most hyperbolas discussed in this chapter do not satisfy the conditions of a function. However, by considering only a part of each graph, we have the graph of a function, as seen in **FIGURE 23**.

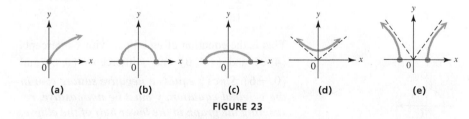

(a)   (b)   (c)   (d)   (e)

FIGURE 23

In parts (a)–(d) of **FIGURE 23**, the top portion of a conic section is shown (parabola, circle, ellipse, and hyperbola, respectively). In part (e), the top two portions of a hyperbola are shown. In each case, the graph is that of a function since the graph satisfies the conditions of the vertical line test.

In **Sections 10.1 and 13.1,** we observed the square root function defined by $f(x) = \sqrt{x}$. To find equations for the types of graphs shown in **FIGURE 23**, we extend its definition.

NOW TRY ANSWERS
3. **(a)** circle **(b)** parabola
    (c) ellipse

> **Generalized Square Root Function**
>
> For an algebraic expression in x defined by u, with $u \geq 0$, a function of the form
>
> $$f(x) = \sqrt{u}$$
>
> is a **generalized square root function.**

NOW TRY
EXERCISE 4

Graph $f(x) = \sqrt{64 - x^2}$.
Give the domain and range.

EXAMPLE 4 Graphing a Semicircle

Graph $f(x) = \sqrt{25 - x^2}$. Give the domain and range.

$$f(x) = \sqrt{25 - x^2} \qquad \text{Given function}$$

$$\boxed{(\sqrt{a})^2 = a} \qquad y = \sqrt{25 - x^2} \qquad \text{Replace } f(x) \text{ with } y.$$

$$y^2 = 25 - x^2 \qquad \text{Square each side.}$$

$$x^2 + y^2 = 25 \qquad \text{Add } x^2.$$

This is the graph of a circle with center at $(0, 0)$ and radius 5. Since $f(x)$, or y, represents a principal square root in the original equation, $f(x)$ must be nonnegative. This restricts the graph to the upper half of the circle, as shown in **FIGURE 24**. The domain is $[-5, 5]$, and the range is $[0, 5]$.

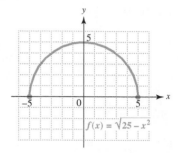

FIGURE 24

NOW TRY

NOW TRY
EXERCISE 5

Graph $\dfrac{y}{4} = -\sqrt{1 - \dfrac{x^2}{9}}$.
Give the domain and range.

EXAMPLE 5 Graphing a Portion of an Ellipse

Graph $\dfrac{y}{6} = -\sqrt{1 - \dfrac{x^2}{16}}$. Give the domain and range.

Square each side to get an equation whose form is known.

$$\left(\frac{y}{6}\right)^2 = \left(-\sqrt{1 - \frac{x^2}{16}}\right)^2 \qquad \text{Square each side.}$$

$$\frac{y^2}{36} = 1 - \frac{x^2}{16} \qquad \text{Apply the exponents.}$$

$$\frac{x^2}{16} + \frac{y^2}{36} = 1 \qquad \text{Add } \tfrac{x^2}{16}.$$

This is the equation of an ellipse with x-intercepts $(4, 0)$ and $(-4, 0)$ and y-intercepts $(0, 6)$ and $(0, -6)$. *Since $\frac{y}{6}$ equals a negative square root in the original equation, y must be nonpositive, restricting the graph to the lower half of the ellipse,* as shown in **FIGURE 25**. The domain is $[-4, 4]$, and the range is $[-6, 0]$.

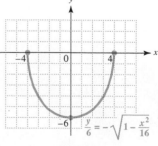

FIGURE 25

NOW TRY

NOW TRY ANSWERS

4.

domain: $[-8, 8]$; range: $[0, 8]$

5.

domain: $[-3, 3]$; range: $[-4, 0]$

NOTE Root functions like those graphed in **FIGURES 24 and 25**, can be entered and graphed directly with a graphing calculator.

13.3 EXERCISES   *MyMathLab*

Math XL PRACTICE	WATCH	DOWNLOAD	READ	REVIEW

⊙ *Complete solution available on the Video Resources on DVD*

Concept Check   *Based on the discussions of ellipses in the previous section and of hyperbolas in this section, match each equation with its graph.*

1. $\dfrac{x^2}{25} + \dfrac{y^2}{9} = 1$

A.

B.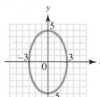

2. $\dfrac{x^2}{9} + \dfrac{y^2}{25} = 1$

3. $\dfrac{x^2}{9} - \dfrac{y^2}{25} = 1$

C.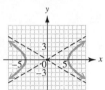

D.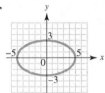

4. $\dfrac{x^2}{25} - \dfrac{y^2}{9} = 1$

*Graph each hyperbola. **See Examples 1 and 2.***

⊙ **5.** $\dfrac{x^2}{16} - \dfrac{y^2}{9} = 1$ **6.** $\dfrac{x^2}{25} - \dfrac{y^2}{9} = 1$ ⊙ **7.** $\dfrac{y^2}{4} - \dfrac{x^2}{25} = 1$

8. $\dfrac{y^2}{9} - \dfrac{x^2}{4} = 1$ **9.** $\dfrac{x^2}{25} - \dfrac{y^2}{36} = 1$ **10.** $\dfrac{x^2}{49} - \dfrac{y^2}{16} = 1$

11. $\dfrac{y^2}{16} - \dfrac{x^2}{16} = 1$ **12.** $\dfrac{y^2}{9} - \dfrac{x^2}{9} = 1$

Identify the graph of each equation as a parabola, circle, ellipse, *or* hyperbola, *and then sketch the graph. **See Example 3.***

13. $x^2 - y^2 = 16$ **14.** $x^2 + y^2 = 16$ ⊙ **15.** $4x^2 + y^2 = 16$

16. $9x^2 = 144 + 16y^2$ **17.** $y^2 = 36 - x^2$ **18.** $9x^2 + 25y^2 = 225$

19. $x^2 - 2y = 0$ **20.** $x^2 + 9y^2 = 9$ **21.** $y^2 = 4 + x^2$

✎ **22.** State in your own words the major difference between the definitions of *ellipse* and *hyperbola*.

*Graph each generalized square root function. Give the domain and range. **See Examples 4 and 5.***

⊙ **23.** $f(x) = \sqrt{16 - x^2}$ **24.** $f(x) = \sqrt{9 - x^2}$ ⊙ **25.** $f(x) = -\sqrt{36 - x^2}$

26. $f(x) = -\sqrt{25 - x^2}$ **27.** $y = -2\sqrt{1 - \dfrac{x^2}{9}}$ **28.** $y = -3\sqrt{1 - \dfrac{x^2}{25}}$

29. $\dfrac{y}{3} = \sqrt{1 + \dfrac{x^2}{9}}$ **30.** $\dfrac{y}{2} = \sqrt{1 + \dfrac{x^2}{4}}$

*In **Section 13.2, Example 6,** we saw that the center of an ellipse may be shifted away from the origin. The same process applies to hyperbolas. For example, the hyperbola shown at the right,*

$$\frac{(x+5)^2}{4} - \frac{(y-2)^2}{9} = 1,$$

has the same graph as

$$\frac{x^2}{4} - \frac{y^2}{9} = 1,$$

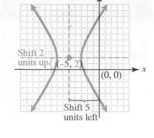

but it is centered at $(-5, 2)$. Graph each hyperbola with center shifted away from the origin.

31. $\dfrac{(x-2)^2}{4} - \dfrac{(y+1)^2}{9} = 1$

32. $\dfrac{(x+3)^2}{16} - \dfrac{(y-2)^2}{25} = 1$

33. $\dfrac{y^2}{36} - \dfrac{(x-2)^2}{49} = 1$

34. $\dfrac{(y-5)^2}{9} - \dfrac{x^2}{25} = 1$

Solve each problem.

35. Two buildings in a sports complex are shaped and positioned like a portion of the branches of the hyperbola with equation

$$400x^2 - 625y^2 = 250,000,$$

where x and y are in meters.

(a) How far apart are the buildings at their closest point?

(b) Find the distance d in the figure.

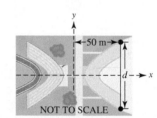

NOT TO SCALE

36. In rugby, after a *try* (similar to a touchdown in American football) the scoring team attempts a kick for extra points. The ball must be kicked from directly behind the point where the try was scored. The kicker can choose the distance but cannot move the ball sideways. It can be shown that the kicker's best choice is on the hyperbola with equation

$$\frac{x^2}{g^2} - \frac{y^2}{g^2} = 1,$$

where $2g$ is the distance between the goal posts. Since the hyperbola approaches its asymptotes, it is easier for the kicker to estimate points on the asymptotes instead

of on the hyperbola. What are the asymptotes of this hyperbola? Why is it relatively easy to estimate them? (*Source:* Isaksen, Daniel C., "How to Kick a Field Goal," *The College Mathematics Journal.*)

EXERCISES 37 AND 38

37. The hyperbola shown in the figure was graphed in function mode, with a square viewing window. It is the graph of $\dfrac{x^2}{9} - y^2 = 1$. What are the two functions y_1 and y_2 that were used to obtain this graph?

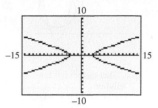

38. Repeat **Exercise 37** for the graph of $\dfrac{y^2}{9} - x^2 = 1$, shown in the figure.

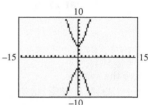

 Use a graphing calculator in function mode to graph each hyperbola. Use a square viewing window.

39. $\dfrac{x^2}{25} - \dfrac{y^2}{49} = 1$ **40.** $\dfrac{x^2}{4} - \dfrac{y^2}{16} = 1$ **41.** $y^2 - 9x^2 = 9$ **42.** $y^2 - 9x^2 = 36$

PREVIEW EXERCISES

Solve each system. See Sections 8.1–8.3.

43. $2x + y = 13$ **44.** $9x + 2y = 10$ **45.** $4x - 3y = -10$ **46.** $5x + 7y = 6$
    $y - 3x + 3$ $x - y - -5$ $4x + 6y - 8$ $10x - 3y - 46$

Solve each equation. See Section 11.4.

47. $2x^4 - 5x^2 - 3 = 0$ **48.** $x^4 - 7x^2 + 12 = 0$

(13.4) Nonlinear Systems of Equations

OBJECTIVES

1 Solve a nonlinear system by substitution.

2 Solve a nonlinear system by elimination.

3 Solve a nonlinear system that requires a combination of methods.

An equation in which some terms have more than one variable or a variable of degree 2 or greater is called a **nonlinear equation.** A **nonlinear system of equations** includes at least one nonlinear equation.

When solving a nonlinear system, it helps to visualize the types of graphs of the equations of the system to determine the possible number of points of intersection. For example, if a system includes two equations where the graph of one is a circle and the graph of the other is a line, then there may be zero, one, or two points of intersection, as illustrated in **FIGURE 26.**

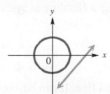
No points of intersection

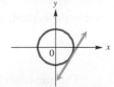
One point of intersection

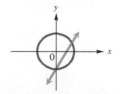
Two points of intersection

FIGURE 26

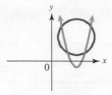

This system has four solutions, since there are four points of intersection.

FIGURE 27

⌐ NOW TRY
⌐ EXERCISE 1

Solve the system.

$$4x^2 + y^2 = 36$$
$$x - y = 3$$

If a system consists of two second-degree equations, then there may be zero, one, two, three, or four solutions. **FIGURE 27** shows a case where a system consisting of a circle and a parabola has four solutions, all made up of ordered pairs of real numbers.

OBJECTIVE 1 Solve a nonlinear system by substitution. We can usually solve a nonlinear system by the substitution method (**Section 8.2**) when one equation is linear.

EXAMPLE 1 Solving a Nonlinear System by Substitution

Solve the system.

$$x^2 + y^2 = 9 \qquad (1)$$
$$2x - y = 3 \qquad (2)$$

The graph of (1) is a circle and the graph of (2) is a line, so the graphs could intersect in zero, one, or two points, as in **FIGURE 26** on the preceding page. We solve the linear equation (2) for one of the two variables and then substitute the resulting expression into the nonlinear equation.

$$2x - y = 3 \qquad (2)$$
$$y = 2x - 3 \qquad \text{Solve for } y. \quad (3)$$

Substitute $2x - 3$ for y in equation (1).

$$x^2 + y^2 = 9 \qquad (1)$$
$$x^2 + (2x - 3)^2 = 9 \qquad \text{Let } y = 2x - 3.$$
$$x^2 + 4x^2 - 12x + 9 = 9 \qquad \text{Square } 2x - 3.$$
$$5x^2 - 12x = 0 \qquad \text{Combine like terms. Subtract 9.}$$
$$x(5x - 12) = 0 \qquad \text{Factor. The GCF is } x.$$

Set *both* factors equal to 0. → $x = 0 \quad \text{or} \quad 5x - 12 = 0 \qquad \text{Zero-factor property}$

$$x = \frac{12}{5}$$

Let $x = 0$ in equation (3) to get $y = -3$. If $x = \frac{12}{5}$, then $y = \frac{9}{5}$. The solution set of the system is

$$\left\{ (0, -3), \left(\frac{12}{5}, \frac{9}{5} \right) \right\}.$$

See the graph in **FIGURE 28**.

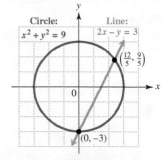

FIGURE 28

NOW TRY

EXAMPLE 2 Solving a Nonlinear System by Substitution

Solve the system.

$$6x - y = 5 \qquad (1)$$
$$xy = 4 \qquad (2)$$

The graph of (1) is a line. It can be shown by plotting points that the graph of (2) is a hyperbola. Visualizing a line and a hyperbola indicates that there may be zero, one, or two points of intersection.

NOW TRY ANSWER
1. $\left\{ (3, 0), \left(-\frac{9}{5}, -\frac{24}{5} \right) \right\}$

NOW TRY
EXERCISE 2
Solve the system.

$$xy = 2$$
$$x - 3y = 1$$

Since neither equation has a squared term, we can solve either equation for one of the variables and then substitute the result into the other equation. Solving $xy = 4$ for x gives $x = \frac{4}{y}$. We substitute $\frac{4}{y}$ for x in equation (1).

$$6x - y = 5 \qquad (1)$$

$$6\left(\frac{4}{y}\right) - y = 5 \qquad \text{Let } x = \frac{4}{y}.$$

$$\frac{24}{y} - y = 5 \qquad \text{Multiply.}$$

$$24 - y^2 = 5y \qquad \text{Multiply by } y, \; y \neq 0.$$

$$y^2 + 5y - 24 = 0 \qquad \text{Standard form}$$

$$(y - 3)(y + 8) = 0 \qquad \text{Factor.}$$

$$y = 3 \quad \text{or} \quad y = -8 \qquad \text{Zero-factor property}$$

We substitute these results into $x = \frac{4}{y}$ to obtain the corresponding values of x.

$$\text{If } y = 3, \qquad \text{then } x = \frac{4}{3}.$$

$$\text{If } y = -8, \quad \text{then } x = -\frac{1}{2}.$$

The solution set of the system is

$$\left\{ \left(\frac{4}{3}, 3\right), \left(-\frac{1}{2}, -8\right) \right\}.$$

See the graph in **FIGURE 29**.

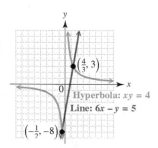

FIGURE 29

NOW TRY

OBJECTIVE 2 **Solve a nonlinear system by elimination.** We can often use the elimination method **(Section 8.3)** when both equations of a nonlinear system are second degree.

EXAMPLE 3   Solving a Nonlinear System by Elimination

Solve the system.

$$x^2 + y^2 = 9 \qquad (1)$$

$$2x^2 - y^2 = -6 \qquad (2)$$

The graph of (1) is a circle, while the graph of (2) is a hyperbola. By analyzing the possibilities, we conclude that there may be zero, one, two, three, or four points of intersection. Adding the two equations will eliminate y.

$$\begin{array}{ll} x^2 + y^2 = 9 & (1) \\ \underline{2x^2 - y^2 = -6} & (2) \\ 3x^2 = 3 & \text{Add.} \\ x^2 = 1 & \text{Divide by 3.} \\ x = 1 \quad \text{or} \quad x = -1 & \text{Square root property} \end{array}$$

NOW TRY ANSWER
2. $\left\{(-2, -1), \left(3, \frac{2}{3}\right)\right\}$

NOW TRY
EXERCISE 3

Solve the system.

$$x^2 + y^2 = 16$$
$$4x^2 + 13y^2 = 100$$

Each value of x gives corresponding values for y when substituted into one of the original equations. Using equation (1) gives the following.

$x^2 + y^2 = 9$ (1)	$x^2 + y^2 = 9$ (1)
$1^2 + y^2 = 9$ Let $x = 1$.	$(-1)^2 + y^2 = 9$ Let $x = -1$.
$y^2 = 8$	$y^2 = 8$
$y = \sqrt{8}$ or $y = -\sqrt{8}$	$y = 2\sqrt{2}$ or $y = -2\sqrt{2}$
$y = 2\sqrt{2}$ or $y = -2\sqrt{2}$	

The solution set is

$$\left\{ \left(1, 2\sqrt{2}\right), \left(1, -2\sqrt{2}\right), \right.$$
$$\left. \left(-1, 2\sqrt{2}\right), \left(-1, -2\sqrt{2}\right) \right\}.$$

FIGURE 30 shows the four points of intersection.

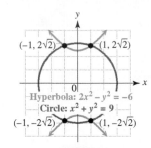

FIGURE 30

NOW TRY

OBJECTIVE 3 Solve a nonlinear system that requires a combination of methods.

EXAMPLE 4 Solving a Nonlinear System by a Combination of Methods

Solve the system.

$$x^2 + 2xy - y^2 = 7 \quad (1)$$
$$x^2 - y^2 = 3 \quad (2)$$

While we have not graphed equations like (1), its graph is a hyperbola. The graph of (2) is also a hyperbola. Two hyperbolas may have zero, one, two, three, or four points of intersection. We use the elimination method here in combination with the substitution method.

$$x^2 + 2xy - y^2 = 7 \quad (1)$$
$$-x^2 + y^2 = -3 \quad \text{Multiply (2) by } -1.$$

The x^2- and y^2-terms were eliminated.

$$2xy = 4 \quad \text{Add.}$$

Next, we solve $2xy = 4$ for one of the variables. We choose y.

$$2xy = 4$$
$$y = \frac{2}{x} \quad \text{Divide by } 2x. \quad (3)$$

Now, we substitute $y = \frac{2}{x}$ into one of the original equations.

$$x^2 - y^2 = 3 \quad \text{The substitution is easier in (2).}$$
$$x^2 - \left(\frac{2}{x}\right)^2 = 3 \quad \text{Let } y = \frac{2}{x}.$$
$$x^2 - \frac{4}{x^2} = 3 \quad \text{Square } \frac{2}{x}.$$
$$x^4 - 4 = 3x^2 \quad \text{Multiply by } x^2, x \neq 0.$$

NOW TRY ANSWER

3. $\left\{ \left(2\sqrt{3}, 2\right), \left(2\sqrt{3}, -2\right), \right.$
$\left. \left(-2\sqrt{3}, 2\right), \left(-2\sqrt{3}, -2\right) \right\}$

NOW TRY EXERCISE 4

Solve the system.

$$x^2 + 3xy - y^2 = 23$$
$$x^2 - y^2 = 5$$

$x^4 - 3x^2 - 4 = 0$	Subtract $3x^2$.
$(x^2 - 4)(x^2 + 1) = 0$	Factor.
$x^2 - 4 = 0$ or $x^2 + 1 = 0$	Zero-factor property
$x^2 = 4$ or $x^2 = -1$	Solve each equation.
$x = 2$ or $x = -2$ or $x = i$ or $x = -i$	

Substituting these four values into $y = \frac{2}{x}$ (equation (3)) gives the corresponding values for y.

If $x = 2$, then $y = \frac{2}{2} = 1$.

If $x = -2$, then $y = \frac{2}{-2} = -1$.

If $x = i$, then $y = \frac{2}{i} = \frac{2}{i} \cdot \frac{-i}{-i} = -2i$.

If $x = -i$, then $y = \frac{2}{-i} = \frac{2}{-i} \cdot \frac{i}{i} = 2i$.

Multiply by the complex conjugate of the denominator. $i(-i) = 1$

If we substitute the x-values we found into equation (1) or (2) instead of into equation (3), we get extraneous solutions. ***It is always wise to check all solutions in both of the given equations.*** There are four ordered pairs in the solution set, two with real values and two with pure imaginary values. The solution set is

$$\{(2, 1), (-2, -1), (i, -2i), (-i, 2i)\}.$$

The graph of the system, shown in **FIGURE 31**, shows only the two real intersection points because the graph is in the real number plane. In general, if solutions contain nonreal complex numbers as components, they do not appear on the graph

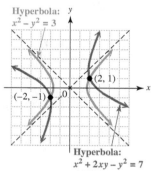

Hyperbola:
$x^2 - y^2 = 3$
y
(2, 1)
(−2, −1)
0
x
Hyperbola:
$x^2 + 2xy - y^2 = 7$

FIGURE 31

NOW TRY

NOTE It is not essential to visualize the number of points of intersection of the graphs in order to solve a nonlinear system. Sometimes we are unfamiliar with the graphs or, as in **Example 4,** there are nonreal complex solutions that do not appear as points of intersection in the real plane. Visualizing the geometry of the graphs is only an aid to solving these systems.

CONNECTIONS

If the equations in a nonlinear system can be solved for y, then we can graph the equations of the system with a graphing calculator and use the capabilities of the calculator to identify all intersection points.

For instance, the two equations in **Example 3** would require graphing four separate functions.

$$Y_1 = \sqrt{9 - X^2},\ Y_2 = -\sqrt{9 - X^2},\ Y_3 = \sqrt{2X^2 + 6},\ \text{and } Y_4 = -\sqrt{2X^2 + 6}$$

FIGURE 32 indicates the coordinates of one of the points of intersection.

6.2
−9.4
9.4
Intersection
X=1
Y=2.8284271
−6.2

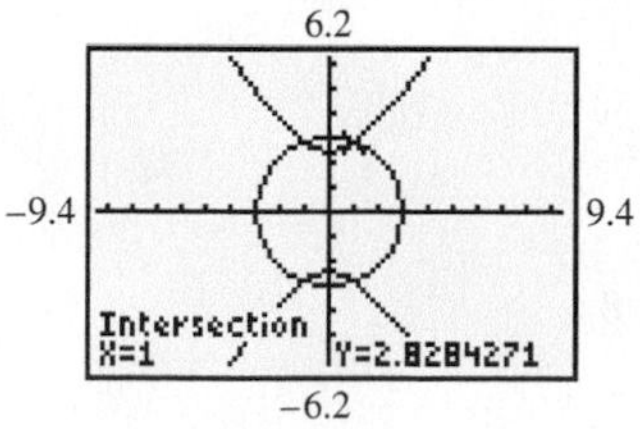

FIGURE 32

NOW TRY ANSWER

4. $\{(3, 2), (-3, -2), (2i, -3i), (-2i, 3i)\}$

13.4 EXERCISES **MyMathLab** Math XL PRACTICE · WATCH · DOWNLOAD · READ · REVIEW

🌀 *Complete solution available on the Video Resources on DVD*

Concept Check Each sketch represents the graphs of a pair of equations in a system. How many points are in each solution set?

1.

2.

3.

4.

Concept Check Suppose that a nonlinear system is composed of equations whose graphs are those described, and the number of points of intersection of the two graphs is as given. Make a sketch satisfying these conditions. (There may be more than one way to do this.)

5. A line and a circle; no points

6. A line and a circle; one point

7. A line and a hyperbola; one point

8. A line and an ellipse; no points

9. A circle and an ellipse; four points

10. A parabola and an ellipse; one point

11. A parabola and an ellipse; four points

12. A parabola and a hyperbola; two points

Solve each system by the substitution method. ***See Examples 1 and 2.***

13. $y = 4x^2 - x$
    $y = x$

14. $y = x^2 + 6x$
    $3y = 12x$

15. $y = x^2 + 6x + 9$
    $x + y = 3$

16. $y = x^2 + 8x + 16$
    $x - y = -4$

🌀 **17.** $x^2 + y^2 = 2$
    $2x + y = 1$

18. $2x^2 + 4y^2 = 4$
    $x = 4y$

🌀 **19.** $xy = 4$
    $3x + 2y = -10$

20. $xy = -5$
    $2x + y = 3$

21. $xy = -3$
    $x + y = -2$

22. $xy = 12$
    $x + y = 8$

23. $y = 3x^2 + 6x$
    $y = x^2 - x - 6$

24. $y = 2x^2 + 1$
    $y = 5x^2 + 2x - 7$

25. $2x^2 - y^2 = 6$
    $y = x^2 - 3$

26. $x^2 + y^2 = 4$
    $y = x^2 - 2$

27. $x^2 - xy + y^2 = 0$
    $x - 2y = 1$

28. $x^2 - 3x + y^2 = 4$
    $2x - y = 3$

Solve each system by the elimination method or a combination of the elimination and substi-tution methods. ***See Examples 3 and 4.***

29. $3x^2 + 2y^2 = 12$
$x^2 + 2y^2 = 4$

30. $5x^2 - 2y^2 = -13$
$3x^2 + 4y^2 = 39$

31. $2x^2 + 3y^2 = 6$
$x^2 + 3y^2 = 3$

32. $6x^2 + y^2 = 9$
$3x^2 + 4y^2 = 36$

🌐 **33.** $2x^2 + y^2 = 28$
$4x^2 - 5y^2 = 28$

34. $x^2 + 6y^2 = 9$
$4x^2 + 3y^2 = 36$

35. $2x^2 = 8 - 2y^2$
$3x^2 = 24 - 4y^2$

36. $5x^2 = 20 - 5y^2$
$2y^2 = 2 - x^2$

37. $x^2 + xy + y^2 = 15$
$x^2 + y^2 = 10$

38. $2x^2 + 3xy + 2y^2 = 21$
$x^2 + y^2 = 6$

🌐 **39.** $3x^2 + 2xy - 3y^2 = 5$
$-x^2 - 3xy + y^2 = 3$

40. $-2x^2 + 7xy - 3y^2 = 4$
$2x^2 - 3xy + 3y^2 = 4$

Use a graphing calculator to solve each system. Then confirm your answer algebraically.

41. $xy = -6$
$x + y = -1$

42. $y = 2x^2 + 4x$
$y = -x^2 - 1$

Solve each problem by using a nonlinear system.

43. The area of a rectangular rug is 84 ft^2 and its perimeter is 38 ft. Find the length and width of the rug.

44. Find the length and width of a rectangular room whose perimeter is 50 m and whose area is 100 m^2.

45. A company has found that the price p (in dollars) of its scientific calculator is related to the supply x (in thousands) by the equation

$$px = 16.$$

The price is related to the demand x (in thousands) for the calculator by the equation

$$p = 10x + 12.$$

The **equilibrium price** is the value of p where demand equals supply. Find the equilibrium price and the supply/demand at that price. (*Hint:* Demand, price, and supply must all be positive.)

46. The calculator company in **Exercise 45** has determined that the cost y to make x (thousand) calculators is

$$y = 4x^2 + 36x + 20,$$

while the revenue y from the sale of x (thousand) calculators is

$$36x^2 - 3y = 0.$$

Find the **break-even point,** where cost equals revenue.

PREVIEW EXERCISES

Graph each inequality. ***See Section 9.3.***

47. $2x - y \le 4$

48. $-x + 3y > 9$

(13.5) Second-Degree Inequalities and Systems of Inequalities

OBJECTIVES

1 Graph second-degree inequalities.
2 Graph the solution set of a system of inequalities.

OBJECTIVE 1 **Graph second-degree inequalities.** A **second-degree inequality** is an inequality with at least one variable of degree 2 and no variable with degree greater than 2.

EXAMPLE 1 Graphing a Second-Degree Inequality

Graph $x^2 + y^2 \leq 36$.

NOW TRY
EXERCISE 1
Graph $x^2 + y^2 \geq 9$.

The boundary of the inequality $x^2 + y^2 \leq 36$ is the graph of the equation $x^2 + y^2 = 36$, a circle with radius 6 and center at the origin, as shown in **FIGURE 33**.

The inequality $x^2 + y^2 \leq 36$ will include either the points outside the circle or the points inside the circle, as well as the boundary. To decide which region to shade, we substitute any test point not on the circle into the original inequality.

$$x^2 + y^2 \leq 36 \qquad \text{Original inequality}$$
$$0^2 + 0^2 \overset{?}{\leq} 36 \qquad \text{Use } (0, 0) \text{ as a test point.}$$
$$0 \leq 36 \ \checkmark \quad \text{True}$$

Since a true statement results, the original inequality includes the points *inside* the circle, the shaded region in **FIGURE 33**, and the boundary.

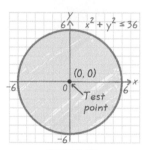

FIGURE 33

NOW TRY

NOTE Since the substitution is easy, the origin is the test point of choice unless the graph actually passes through $(0, 0)$.

NOW TRY
EXERCISE 2
Graph $y \geq -(x + 2)^2 + 1$.

EXAMPLE 2 Graphing a Second-Degree Inequality

Graph $y < -2(x - 4)^2 - 3$.

The boundary, $y = -2(x - 4)^2 - 3$, is a parabola that opens down with vertex at $(4, -3)$.

$$y < -2(x - 4)^2 - 3 \qquad \text{Original inequality}$$
$$0 \overset{?}{<} -2(0 - 4)^2 - 3 \qquad \text{Use } (0, 0) \text{ as a test point.}$$
$$0 \overset{?}{<} -32 - 3 \qquad \text{Simplify.}$$
$$0 < -35 \qquad \text{False}$$

Because the final inequality is a false statement, the points in the region containing $(0, 0)$ do not satisfy the inequality. In **FIGURE 34** the parabola is drawn as a dashed curve since the points of the parabola itself do not satisfy the inequality, and the region inside (or below) the parabola is shaded.

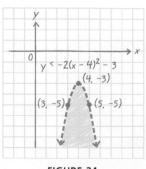

FIGURE 34

NOW TRY

NOW TRY ANSWERS
1.   2.

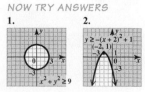

NOW TRY
EXERCISE 3

Graph $25x^2 - 16y^2 > 400$.

EXAMPLE 3 Graphing a Second-Degree Inequality

Graph $16y^2 \le 144 + 9x^2$.

$$16y^2 - 9x^2 \le 144 \qquad \text{Subtract } 9x^2.$$

$$\frac{y^2}{9} - \frac{x^2}{16} \le 1 \qquad \text{Divide by 144.}$$

This form shows that the boundary is the hyperbola given by

$$\frac{y^2}{9} - \frac{x^2}{16} = 1.$$

Since the graph is a vertical hyperbola, the desired region will be either the region between the branches or the regions above the top branch and below the bottom branch. Choose $(0, 0)$ as a test point. Substituting into the original inequality leads to $0 \le 144$, a true statement, so the region between the branches containing $(0, 0)$ is shaded, as shown in **FIGURE 35**.

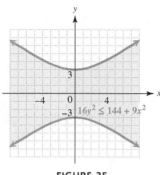

FIGURE 35

NOW TRY

OBJECTIVE 2 **Graph the solution set of a system of inequalities.** If two or more inequalities are considered at the same time, we have a **system of inequalities.** To find the solution set of the system, we find the intersection of the graphs (solution sets) of the inequalities in the system.

NOW TRY
EXERCISE 4

Graph the solution set of the system.

$$x^2 + y^2 > 9$$
$$y > x^2 - 1$$

EXAMPLE 4 Graphing a System of Two Inequalities

Graph the solution set of the system.

$$2x + 3y > 6$$
$$x^2 + y^2 < 16$$

Begin by graphing the solution set of $2x + 3y > 6$. The boundary line is the graph of $2x + 3y = 6$ and is a dashed line because of the symbol $>$. The test point $(0, 0)$ leads to a false statement in the inequality $2x + 3y > 6$, so shade the region above the line, as shown in **FIGURE 36**.

The graph of $x^2 + y^2 < 16$ is the interior of a dashed circle centered at the origin with radius 4. This is shown in **FIGURE 37**.

NOW TRY ANSWERS

3.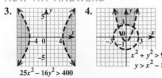

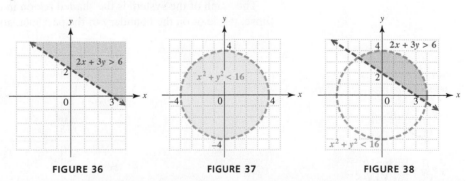

FIGURE 36   **FIGURE 37**   **FIGURE 38**

The graph of the solution set of the system is the intersection of the graphs of the two inequalities. The overlapping region in **FIGURE 38** is the solution set.   NOW TRY

NOW TRY
EXERCISE 5

Graph the solution set of the system.

$$3x + 2y > 6$$
$$y \geq \frac{1}{2}x - 2$$
$$x \geq 0$$

EXAMPLE 5 Graphing a Linear System of Three Inequalities

Graph the solution set of the system.

$$x + y < 1$$
$$y \leq 2x + 3$$
$$y \geq -2$$

Graph each inequality separately, on the same axes. The graph of $x + y < 1$ consists of all points that lie below the dashed line $x + y = 1$. The graph of $y \leq 2x + 3$ is the region that lies below the solid line $y = 2x + 3$. Finally, the graph of $y \geq -2$ is the region above the solid horizontal line $y = -2$.

The graph of the system, the intersection of these three graphs, is the triangular region enclosed by the three boundary lines in **FIGURE 39**, including two of its boundaries.

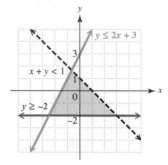

FIGURE 39

NOW TRY

NOW TRY
EXERCISE 6

Graph the solution set of the system.

$$\frac{x^2}{4} + \frac{y^2}{16} \leq 1$$
$$y \leq x^2 - 2$$
$$y + 3 > 0$$

EXAMPLE 6 Graphing a System of Three Inequalities

Graph the solution set of the system.

$$y \geq x^2 - 2x + 1$$
$$2x^2 + y^2 > 4$$
$$y < 4$$

The graph of $y = x^2 - 2x + 1$ is a parabola with vertex at $(1, 0)$. Those points above (or in the interior of) the parabola satisfy the condition $y > x^2 - 2x + 1$. Thus, the solution set of $y \geq x^2 - 2x + 1$ includes points on the parabola or in the interior.

The graph of the equation $2x^2 + y^2 = 4$ is an ellipse. We draw it as a dashed curve. To satisfy the inequality $2x^2 + y^2 > 4$, a point must lie outside the ellipse. The graph of $y < 4$ includes all points below the dashed line $y = 4$.

The graph of the system is the shaded region in **FIGURE 40**, which lies outside the ellipse, inside or on the boundary of the parabola, and below the line $y = 4$.

NOW TRY ANSWERS

5.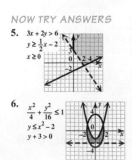

6.

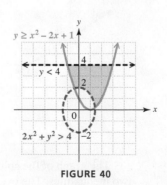

FIGURE 40

NOW TRY

13.5 EXERCISES

MyMathLab

Complete solution available on the Video Resources on DVD

1. *Concept Check*   Which one of the following is a description of the graph of the solution set of the following system?

$$x^2 + y^2 < 25$$
$$y > -2$$

A. All points outside the circle $x^2 + y^2 = 25$ and above the line $y = -2$

B. All points outside the circle $x^2 + y^2 = 25$ and below the line $y = -2$

C. All points inside the circle $x^2 + y^2 = 25$ and above the line $y = -2$

D. All points inside the circle $x^2 + y^2 = 25$ and below the line $y = -2$

2. *Concept Check*   Fill in each blank with the appropriate response. The graph of the system

$$y > x^2 + 1$$
$$\frac{x^2}{9} + \frac{y^2}{4} > 1$$
$$y < 5$$

consists of all points _____ the parabola $y = x^2 + 1$, _____ the
(above/below)   (inside/outside)

ellipse $\frac{x^2}{9} + \frac{y^2}{4} = 1$, and _____ the line $y = 5$.
(above/below)

Concept Check   *Match each nonlinear inequality with its graph.*

3. $y \geq x^2 + 4$ **4.** $y \leq x^2 + 4$ **5.** $y < x^2 + 4$ **6.** $y > x^2 + 4$

A. 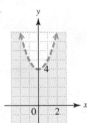   **B.** 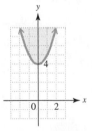   **C.** 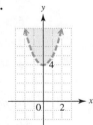   **D.**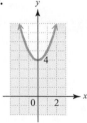

Graph each nonlinear inequality. See Examples 1–3.

7. $y^2 > 4 + x^2$

8. $y^2 \leq 4 - 2x^2$

 9. $y \geq x^2 - 2$

10. $x^2 \leq 16 - y^2$

11. $2y^2 \geq 8 - x^2$

12. $x^2 \leq 16 + 4y^2$

13. $y \leq x^2 + 4x + 2$

14. $9x^2 < 16y^2 - 144$

15. $9x^2 > 16y^2 + 144$

16. $4y^2 \leq 36 - 9x^2$

17. $x^2 - 4 \geq -4y^2$

18. $x \geq y^2 - 8y + 14$

19. $x \leq -y^2 + 6y - 7$

20. $y^2 - 16x^2 \leq 16$

Graph each system of inequalities. ***See Examples 4–6.***

21. $2x + 5y < 10$
$x - 2y < 4$

22. $3x - y > -6$
$4x + 3y > 12$

23. $5x - 3y \leq 15$
$4x + y \geq 4$

24. $4x - 3y \leq 0$
$x + y \leq 5$

25. $x \leq 5$
$y \leq 4$

26. $x \geq -2$
$y \leq 4$

27. $y > x^2 - 4$
$y < -x^2 + 3$

28. $x^2 - y^2 \geq 9$
$\dfrac{x^2}{16} + \dfrac{y^2}{9} \leq 1$

29. $x^2 + y^2 \geq 4$
$x + y \leq 5$
$x \geq 0$
$y \geq 0$

30. $y^2 - x^2 \geq 4$
$-5 \leq y \leq 5$

31. $y \leq -x^2$
$y \geq x - 3$
$y \leq -1$
$x < 1$

32. $y < x^2$
$y > -2$
$x + y < 3$
$3x - 2y > -6$

For each nonlinear inequality in Exercises 33–40, a restriction is placed on one or both variables. For example, the inequality

$$x^2 + y^2 \leq 4, \quad x \geq 0$$

is graphed in the figure. Only the right half of the interior of the circle and its boundary is shaded, because of the restriction that x must be nonnegative. Graph each nonlinear inequality with the given restrictions.

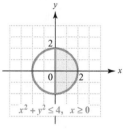
$x^2 + y^2 \leq 4, \quad x \geq 0$

33. $x^2 + y^2 > 36, \quad x \geq 0$

34. $4x^2 + 25y^2 < 100, \quad y < 0$

35. $x < y^2 - 3, \quad x < 0$

36. $x^2 - y^2 < 4, \quad x < 0$

37. $4x^2 - y^2 > 16, \quad x < 0$

38. $x^2 + y^2 > 4, \quad y < 0$

39. $x^2 + 4y^2 \geq 1, \quad x \geq 0, y \geq 0$

40. $2x^2 - 32y^2 \leq 8, \quad x \leq 0, y \geq 0$

Use the shading feature of a graphing calculator to graph each system.

41. $y \geq x - 3$
$y \leq -x + 4$

42. $y \geq -x^2 + 5$
$y \leq x^2 - 3$

43. $y < x^2 + 4x + 4$
$y > -3$

44. $y > (x - 4)^2 - 3$
$y < 5$

PREVIEW EXERCISES

Evaluate each expression for ***(a)*** $n = 1$, ***(b)*** $n = 2$, ***(c)*** $n = 3$, *and* ***(d)*** $n = 4$. ***See Sections 1.3 and 1.6.***

45. $\dfrac{n + 5}{n}$

46. $\dfrac{n - 1}{n + 1}$

47. $n^2 - n$

48. $n(n - 3)$

CHAPTER 13 SUMMARY

13.1
squaring function
absolute value function
reciprocal function
asymptotes
square root function
greatest integer function
step function

13.2
conic section
circle
center (of circle)
radius
center-radius form
ellipse
foci (singular: focus)
center (of ellipse)

13.3
hyperbola
transverse axis
asymptotes of a
    hyperbola
fundamental rectangle
generalized square root
    function

13.4
nonlinear equation
nonlinear system of
    equations

13.5
second-degree inequality
system of inequalities

NEW SYMBOLS

$[\![x]\!]$ greatest integer less than or equal to x

TEST YOUR WORD POWER

See how well you have learned the vocabulary in this chapter.

1. **Conic sections** are
   A. graphs of first-degree equations
   B. the result of two or more intersecting planes
   C. graphs of first-degree inequalities
   D. figures that result from the intersection of an infinite cone with a plane.

2. A **circle** is the set of all points in a plane
   A. such that the absolute value of the difference of the distances from two fixed points is constant
   B. that lie a fixed distance from a fixed point
   C. the sum of whose distances from two fixed points is constant
   D. that make up the graph of any second-degree equation.

3. An **ellipse** is the set of all points in a plane
   A. such that the absolute value of the difference of the distances from two fixed points is constant
   B. that lie a fixed distance from a fixed point
   C. the sum of whose distances from two fixed points is constant
   D. that make up the graph of any second-degree equation.

4. A **hyperbola** is the set of all points in a plane
   A. such that the absolute value of the difference of the distances from two fixed points is constant
   B. that lie a fixed distance from a fixed point
   C. the sum of whose distances from two fixed points is constant
   D. that make up the graph of any second-degree equation.

5. A **nonlinear equation** is an equation
   A. in which some terms have more than one variable or a variable of degree 2 or greater
   B. in which the terms have only one variable
   C. of degree 1
   D. of a linear function.

6. A **nonlinear system of equations** is a system
   A. with at least one linear equation
   B. with two or more inequalities
   C. with at least one nonlinear equation
   D. with at least two linear equations.

ANSWERS

1. D; *Example:* Parabolas, circles, ellipses, and hyperbolas are conic sections. 2. B; *Example:* See the graph of $x^2 + y^2 = 9$ in **FIGURE 10** of **Section 13.2**. 3. C; *Example:* See the graph of $\frac{x^2}{49} + \frac{y^2}{36} = 1$ in **FIGURE 16** of **Section 13.2**. 4. A; *Example:* See the graph of $\frac{x^2}{16} - \frac{y^2}{25} = 1$ in **FIGURE 21** of **Section 13.3**. 5. A; *Examples:* $y = x^2 + 8x + 16$, $xy = 5$, $2x^2 - y^2 = 6$ 6. C; *Example:* $x^2 + y^2 = 2$ $2x + y = 1$

QUICK REVIEW

CONCEPTS	EXAMPLES

13.1 Additional Graphs of Functions

Other Functions

In addition to the squaring function, some other elementary functions include the following:

- Absolute value function, defined by $f(x) = |x|$
- Reciprocal function, defined by $f(x) = \frac{1}{x}$
- Square root function, defined by $f(x) = \sqrt{x}$
- Greatest integer function, defined by $f(x) = [\![x]\!]$, which is a step function.

Their graphs can be translated, as shown in the first three examples at the right.

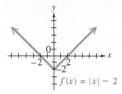

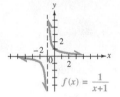

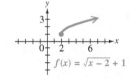

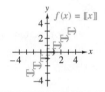

13.2 The Circle and the Ellipse

Circle

The circle with radius r and center at (h, k) has an equation of the form

$$(x - h)^2 + (y - k)^2 = r^2.$$

The circle with equation $(x + 2)^2 + (y - 3)^2 = 25$, which can be written $[x - (-2)]^2 + (y - 3)^2 = 5^2$, has center $(-2, 3)$ and radius 5.

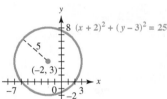

Ellipse

The ellipse whose x-intercepts are $(a, 0)$ and $(-a, 0)$ and whose y-intercepts are $(0, b)$ and $(0, -b)$ has an equation of the form

$$\frac{x^2}{a^2} + \frac{y^2}{b^2} = 1.$$

Graph $\dfrac{x^2}{9} + \dfrac{y^2}{4} = 1.$

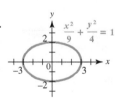

13.3 The Hyperbola and Functions Defined by Radicals

Hyperbola

A hyperbola with x-intercepts $(a, 0)$ and $(-a, 0)$ has an equation of the form

$$\frac{x^2}{a^2} - \frac{y^2}{b^2} = 1,$$

and a hyperbola with y-intercepts $(0, b)$ and $(0, -b)$ has an equation of the form

$$\frac{y^2}{b^2} - \frac{x^2}{a^2} = 1.$$

The extended diagonals of the fundamental rectangle with vertices at the points (a, b), $(-a, b)$, $(-a, -b)$, and $(a, -b)$ are the asymptotes of these hyperbolas.

Graph $\dfrac{x^2}{4} - \dfrac{y^2}{4} = 1.$

The graph has x-intercepts $(2, 0)$ and $(-2, 0)$.

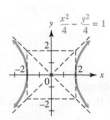

The fundamental rectangle has vertices at $(2, 2)$, $(-2, 2)$, $(-2, -2)$, and $(2, -2)$.

(continued)

CONCEPTS	EXAMPLES
Graphing a Generalized Square Root Function To graph a generalized square root function defined by $$f(x) = \sqrt{u}$$ for an algebraic expression u, with $u \geq 0$, square each side so that the equation can be easily recognized. Then graph only the part indicated by the original equation.	Graph $y = -\sqrt{4 - x^2}$. Square each side and rearrange terms to get $$x^2 + y^2 = 4.$$ This equation has a circle as its graph. However, graph only the lower half of the circle, since the original equation indicates that y cannot be positive. 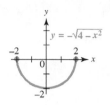

13.4 Nonlinear Systems of Equations

Solving a Nonlinear System A nonlinear system can be solved by the substitution method, the elimination method, or a combination of the two.	Solve the system. $$x^2 + 2xy - y^2 = 14 \quad (1)$$ $$x^2 - y^2 = -16 \quad (2)$$ Multiply equation (2) by -1 and use elimination. $\qquad x^2 + 2xy - y^2 - 14$ $\qquad \underline{-x^2 \qquad\quad + y^2 = 16}$ $\qquad\qquad\qquad 2xy \qquad = 30$ $\qquad\qquad\qquad\quad xy = 15$ Solve $xy = 15$ for y to obtain $y = \frac{15}{x}$, and substitute into equation (2). $$x^2 - y^2 = -16 \quad (2)$$ $$x^2 - \left(\frac{15}{x}\right)^2 = -16 \quad \text{Let } y = \frac{15}{x}.$$ $$x^2 - \frac{225}{x^2} = -16 \quad \text{Apply the exponent.}$$ $$x^4 + 16x^2 - 225 = 0 \quad \text{Multiply by } x^2. \text{ Add } 16x^2.$$ $$(x^2 - 9)(x^2 + 25) = 0 \quad \text{Factor.}$$ $$x = \pm 3 \quad \text{or} \quad x = \pm 5i \quad \text{Zero-factor property}$$ Find corresponding y-values to get the solution set $$\{(3, 5), (-3, -5), (5i, -3i), (-5i, 3i)\}.$$

13.5 Second-Degree Inequalities and Systems of Inequalities

Graphing a Second-Degree Inequality To graph a second-degree inequality, graph the corresponding equation as a boundary and use test points to determine which region(s) form the solution set. Shade the appropriate region(s). **Graphing a System of Inequalities** The solution set of a system of inequalities is the intersection of the solution sets of the individual inequalities.	Graph $$y \geq x^2 - 2x + 3.$$ 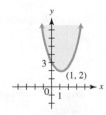	Graph the solution set of the system $$3x - 5y > -15$$ $$x^2 + y^2 \leq 25.$$ 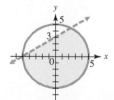

CHAPTER (13)

REVIEW EXERCISES

13.1 *Graph each function.*

1. $f(x) = |x + 4|$

2. $f(x) = \dfrac{1}{x - 4}$

3. $f(x) = \sqrt{x} + 3$

4. $f(x) = [\![x]\!] - 2$

13.2 *Write an equation for each circle.*

5. Center $(-2, 4)$, $r = 3$

6. Center $(-1, -3)$, $r = 5$

7. Center $(4, 2)$, $r = 6$

Find the center and radius of each circle.

8. $x^2 + y^2 + 6x - 4y - 3 = 0$

9. $x^2 + y^2 - 8x - 2y + 13 = 0$

10. $2x^2 + 2y^2 + 4x + 20y = -34$

11. $4x^2 + 4y^2 - 24x + 16y = 48$

Graph each equation.

12. $x^2 + y^2 = 16$

13. $\dfrac{x^2}{16} + \dfrac{y^2}{9} = 1$

14. $\dfrac{x^2}{49} + \dfrac{y^2}{25} = 1$

15. A satellite is in an elliptical orbit around Earth with perigee altitude of 160 km and apogee altitude of 16,000 km. See the figure. (*Source:* Kastner, Bernice, *Space Mathematics,* NASA.) Find the equation of the ellipse. (*Hint:* Use the fact that $c^2 = a^2 - b^2$ here.)

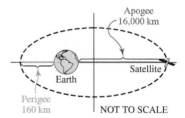

Apogee
16,000 km

Satellite

Earth

Perigee
160 km

NOT TO SCALE

16. (a) The Roman Colosseum is an ellipse with $a = 310$ ft and $b = \frac{513}{2}$ ft. Find the distance, to the nearest tenth, between the foci of this ellipse.

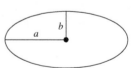

(b) The approximate perimeter of an ellipse is given by

$$P \approx 2\pi \sqrt{\dfrac{a^2 + b^2}{2}},$$

where a and b are the lengths given in part (a). Use this formula to find the approximate perimeter, to the nearest tenth, of the Roman Colosseum.

13.3 *Graph each equation.*

17. $\dfrac{x^2}{16} - \dfrac{y^2}{25} = 1$

18. $\dfrac{y^2}{25} - \dfrac{x^2}{4} = 1$

19. $f(x) = -\sqrt{16 - x^2}$

Identify the graph of each equation as a parabola, circle, ellipse, *or* hyperbola.

20. $x^2 + y^2 = 64$

21. $y = 2x^2 - 3$

22. $y^2 = 2x^2 - 8$

23. $y^2 = 8 - 2x^2$

24. $x = y^2 + 4$

25. $x^2 - y^2 = 64$

26. Ships and planes often use a location-finding system called LORAN. With this system, a radio transmitter at M sends out a series of pulses. When each pulse is received at transmitter S, it then sends out a pulse. A ship at P receives pulses from both M and S. A receiver on the ship measures the difference in the arrival times of the pulses. A special map gives hyperbolas that correspond to the differences in arrival times (which give the distances d_1 and d_2 in the figure.) The ship can then be located as lying on a branch of a particular hyperbola.

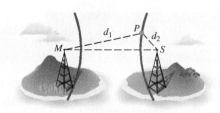

Suppose $d_1 = 80$ mi and $d_2 = 30$ mi, and the distance between transmitters M and S is 100 mi. Use the definition to find an equation of the hyperbola on which the ship is located.

13.4   *Solve each system.*

27. $2y = 3x - x^2$
$x + 2y = -12$

28. $y + 1 = x^2 + 2x$
$y + 2x = 4$

29. $x^2 + 3y^2 = 28$
$y - x = -2$

30. $xy = 8$
$x - 2y = 6$

31. $x^2 + y^2 = 6$
$x^2 - 2y^2 = -6$

32. $3x^2 - 2y^2 = 12$
$x^2 + 4y^2 = 18$

33. *Concept Check*   How many solutions are possible for a system of two equations whose graphs are a circle and a line?

34. *Concept Check*   How many solutions are possible for a system of two equations whose graphs are a parabola and a hyperbola?

13.5   *Graph each inequality.*

35. $9x^2 \geq 16y^2 + 144$

36. $4x^2 + y^2 \geq 16$

37. $y < -(x + 2)^2 + 1$

Graph each system of inequalities.

38. $2x + 5y \leq 10$
$3x - y \leq 6$

39. $|x| \leq 2$
$|y| > 1$
$4x^2 + 9y^2 \leq 36$

40. $9x^2 \leq 4y^2 + 36$
$x^2 + y^2 \leq 16$

MIXED REVIEW EXERCISES

Graph.

41. $\dfrac{y^2}{4} - 1 = \dfrac{x^2}{9}$

42. $x^2 + y^2 = 25$

43. $x^2 + 9y^2 = 9$

44. $x^2 - 9y^2 = 9$

45. $f(x) = \sqrt{4 - x}$

46. $4y > 3x - 12$
$x^2 < 16 - y^2$

CHAPTER **13**

TEST

 CHAPTER
Test Prep
VIDEOS

Step-by-step test solutions are found on the Chapter Test Prep Videos available via the Video Resources on DVD, in *MyMathLab*, or on YouTube (search "LialCombinedAlgebra").

View the complete solutions to all Chapter Test exercises on the Video Resources on DVD.

Concept Check *Fill in each blank with the correct response.*

1. For the reciprocal function defined by $f(x) = \frac{1}{x}$, _____ is the only real number not in the domain.

2. The range of the square root function, given by $f(x) = \sqrt{x}$, is _____.

3. The range of $f(x) = [\![x]\!]$, the greatest integer function, is _____.

4. *Concept Check* Match each function with its graph from choices A–D.

(a) $f(x) = \sqrt{x-2}$ **A.** 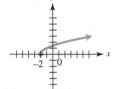 **B.**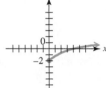

(b) $f(x) = \sqrt{x+2}$

(c) $f(x) = \sqrt{x} + 2$ **C.** 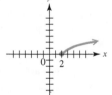 **D.**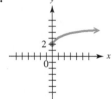

(d) $f(x) = \sqrt{x} - 2$

5. Sketch the graph of $f(x) = |x - 3| + 4$. Give the domain and range.

6. Find the center and radius of the circle whose equation is $(x-2)^2 + (y+3)^2 = 16$. Sketch the graph.

7. Find the center and radius of the circle whose equation is $x^2 + y^2 + 8x - 2y = 8$.

Graph.

8. $f(x) = \sqrt{9 - x^2}$

9. $4x^2 + 9y^2 = 36$

10. $16y^2 - 4x^2 = 64$

11. $\frac{y}{2} = -\sqrt{1 - \frac{x^2}{9}}$

Identify the graph of each equation as a parabola, hyperbola, ellipse, *or* circle.

12. $6x^2 + 4y^2 = 12$

13. $16x^2 = 144 + 9y^2$

14. $y^2 = 20 - x^2$

15. $4y^2 + 4x = 9$

Solve each system.

16. $2x - y = 9$
$xy = 5$

17. $x - 4 = 3y$
$x^2 + y^2 = 8$

18. $x^2 + y^2 = 25$
$x^2 - 2y^2 = 16$

19. Graph the inequality $y < x^2 - 2$.

20. Graph the system $\begin{array}{l} x^2 + 25y^2 \le 25 \\ x^2 + y^2 \le 9. \end{array}$

1. Find the slope of the line through $(2, 5)$ and $(-4, 1)$.

2. Find the equation of the line through the point $(-3, -2)$ and perpendicular to the graph of $2x - 3y = 7$.

Perform the indicated operations.

3. $(5y - 3)^2$

4. $\dfrac{8x^4 - 4x^3 + 2x^2 + 13x + 8}{2x + 1}$

Factor.

5. $12x^2 - 7x - 10$ **6.** $z^4 - 1$ **7.** $a^3 - 27b^3$

Perform the indicated operations.

8. $\dfrac{y^2 - 4}{y^2 - y - 6} \div \dfrac{y^2 - 2y}{y - 1}$ **9.** $\dfrac{5}{c + 5} - \dfrac{2}{c + 3}$ **10.** $\dfrac{p}{p^2 + p} + \dfrac{1}{p^2 + p}$

11. Henry Harris and Lawrence Hawkins want to clean their office. Henry can do the job alone in 3 hr, while Lawrence can do it alone in 2 hr. How long will it take them if they work together?

Solve each system.

12. $3x - y = 12$
$2x + 3y = -3$

13. $x + y - 2z = 9$
$2x + y + z = 7$
$3x - y - z = 13$

14. $xy = -5$
$2x + y - 3$

15. Al and Bev traveled from their apartment to a picnic 20 mi away. Al traveled on his bike while Bev, who left later, took her car. Al's average rate was half of Bev's average rate. The trip took Al $\frac{1}{2}$ hr longer than Bev. What was Bev's average rate?

Simplify. Assume all variables represent positive real numbers.

16. $\dfrac{(2a)^{-2}a^4}{a^{-3}}$

17. $4\sqrt[3]{16} - 2\sqrt[3]{54}$

18. $\dfrac{3\sqrt{5x}}{\sqrt{2x}}$

19. $\dfrac{5 + 3i}{2 - i}$

Solve for real solutions.

20. $4 - (2x + 3) + x = 5x - 3$ **21.** $-4x + 7 \geq 6x + 1$

22. $|5x| - 6 = 14$ **23.** $|2p - 5| > 15$

24. $2\sqrt{x} = \sqrt{5x + 3}$ **25.** $10q^2 + 13q = 3$ **26.** $3x^2 - 3x - 2 = 0$

27. $2(x^2 - 3)^2 - 5(x^2 - 3) = 12$ **28.** $\log(x + 2) + \log(x - 1) = 1$

29. Solve $F = \dfrac{kwv^2}{r}$ for v.   **30.** If $f(x) = x^3 + 4$, find $f^{-1}(x)$.

31. Evaluate.   **(a)** $3^{\log_3 4}$ **(b)** $e^{\ln 7}$

32. Use properties of logarithms to write $2\log(3x + 7) - \log 4$ as a single logarithm.

33. The bar graph shows online U.S. retail sales (in billions of dollars).

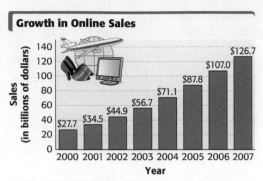

Growth in Online Sales

Source: U.S. Census Bureau.

A reasonable model for sales *y* in billions of dollars is the exponential function defined by

$$y = 28.43(1.25)^x,$$

where *x* is the number of years since 2000.

(a) Use the model to estimate sales in 2005. (*Hint:* Let $x = 5$.)

(b) Use the model to estimate sales in 2008.

34. Give the domain and range of the function defined by $f(x) = |x - 3|$.

Graph.

35. $f(x) = -3x + 5$

36. $f(x) = -2(x - 1)^2 + 3$

37. $\dfrac{x^2}{25} + \dfrac{y^2}{16} \leq 1$

38. $f(x) = \sqrt{x - 2}$

39. $\dfrac{x^2}{4} - \dfrac{y^2}{16} = 1$

40. $f(x) = 3^x$

Sequences and Series

14.1 Sequences and Series

14.2 Arithmetic Sequences

14.3 Geometric Sequences

14.4 The Binomial Theorem

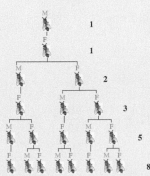

The male honeybee hatches from an unfertilized egg, while the female hatches from a fertilized one. The "family tree" of a male honeybee is shown at the left, where M represents male and F represents female. Starting with the male honeybee at the top, and counting the number of bees in each generation, we obtain the following numbers in the order shown.

$$1, 1, 2, 3, 5, 8$$

Notice the pattern. After the first two terms (1 and 1), each successive term is obtained by adding the two previous terms. This sequence of numbers is called the *Fibonacci sequence*.

In this chapter, we study *sequences* and sums of terms of sequences, known as *series*.

855

14.1 Sequences and Series

OBJECTIVES

1 Find the terms of a sequence, given the general term.

2 Find the general term of a sequence.

3 Use sequences to solve applied problems.

4 Use summation notation to evaluate a series.

5 Write a series with summation notation.

6 Find the arithmetic mean (average) of a group of numbers.

In the Palace of the Alhambra, residence of the Moorish rulers of Granada, Spain, the Sultana's quarters feature an interesting architectural pattern:

There are 2 matched marble slabs inlaid in the floor, 4 walls, an octagon (8-sided) ceiling, 16 windows, 32 arches, and so on.

If this pattern is continued indefinitely, the set of numbers forms an *infinite sequence* whose *terms* are powers of 2.

Sequence

An **infinite sequence** is a function with the set of all positive integers as the domain. A **finite sequence** is a function with domain of the form $\{1, 2, 3, \ldots, n\}$, where n is a positive integer.

OBJECTIVE 1 Find the terms of a sequence, given the general term. For any positive integer n, the function value of a sequence is written as a_n (read "*a* sub-*n*"). The function values $a_1, a_2, a_3, \ldots$, written in order, are the **terms** of the sequence, with a_1 the first term, a_2 the second term, and so on. The expression a_n, which defines the sequence, is called the **general term** of the sequence.

In the Palace of the Alhambra example, the first five terms of the sequence are

$$a_1 = 2, \quad a_2 = 4, \quad a_3 = 8, \quad a_4 = 16, \quad \text{and} \quad a_5 = 32.$$

The general term for this sequence is $a_n = 2^n$.

NOW TRY EXERCISE 1

Given an infinite sequence with $a_n = 5 - 3n$, find a_3.

EXAMPLE 1 Writing the Terms of Sequences from the General Term

Given an infinite sequence with $a_n = n + \frac{1}{n}$, find the following.

(a) The second term of the sequence

$$a_2 = 2 + \frac{1}{2} = \frac{5}{2} \qquad \text{Replace } n \text{ with 2.}$$

(b) $a_{10} = 10 + \frac{1}{10} = \frac{101}{10} \qquad 10 = \frac{100}{10}$ **(c)** $a_{12} = 12 + \frac{1}{12} = \frac{145}{12} \qquad 12 = \frac{144}{12}$

NOW TRY

Graphing calculators can be used to generate and graph sequences, as shown in **FIGURE 1** on the next page. The calculator must be in dot mode, so that the discrete points on the graph are not connected. *Remember that the domain of a sequence consists only of positive integers.*

NOW TRY ANSWER
1. $a_3 = -4$

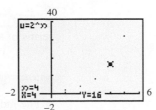

The first five terms of
the sequence $a_n = 2^n$

(a)

The first five terms of $a_n = 2^n$ are graphed
here. The display indicates that the fourth
term is 16; that is, $a_4 = 2^4 = 16$.

(b)

FIGURE 1

OBJECTIVE 2 Find the general term of a sequence. Sometimes we need to
find a general term to fit the first few terms of a given sequence.

  Finding the General Term of a Sequence

Determine an expression for the general term a_n of the sequence.

$$5, 10, 15, 20, 25, \ldots$$

Notice that the terms are all multiples of 5. The first term is $5(1)$, the second is
$5(2)$, and so on. The general term

$$a_n = 5n$$

will produce the given first five terms.

NOW TRY

⚠ **CAUTION** Remember that when determining a general term, as in **Example 2,**
there may be more than one way to express it.

OBJECTIVE 3 Use sequences to solve applied problems. Practical problems
may involve *finite sequences.*

  Using a Sequence in an Application

Saad Alarachi borrows $5000 and agrees to pay $500 monthly, plus interest of 1% on
the unpaid balance from the beginning of the first month. Find the payments for the
first four months and the remaining debt at the end of that period.

The payments and remaining balances are calculated as follows.

First month	Payment:	$500 + 0.01($5000) = $550
	Balance:	$5000 − $500 = $4500
Second month	Payment:	$500 + 0.01($4500) = $545
	Balance:	$5000 − 2 · $500 = $4000
Third month	Payment:	$500 + 0.01($4000) = $540
	Balance:	$5000 − 3 · $500 = $3500
Fourth month	Payment:	$500 + 0.01($3500) = $535
	Balance:	$5000 − 4 · $500 = $3000

The payments for the first four months are

$$\$550, \$545, \$540, \$535$$

and the remaining debt at the end of the period is $3000.

NOW TRY

---

*NOW TRY
EXERCISE 2*

Find an expression for the general term a_n of the sequence.

$$-3, 9, -27, 81, \ldots$$

*NOW TRY
EXERCISE 3*

Chase borrows $8000 and
agrees to pay $400 monthly,
plus interest of 2% on the unpaid balance from the beginning of the first month. Find
the payments for the first four
months and the remaining
debt at the end of that period.

NOW TRY ANSWERS
2. $a_n = (-3)^n$
3. payments: $560, $552, $544,
$536; balance: $6400

OBJECTIVE 4 **Use summation notation to evaluate a series.** By adding the terms of a sequence, we obtain a *series*.

Series

The indicated sum of the terms of a sequence is called a **series.**

For example, if we consider the sum of the payments listed in **Example 3,** namely,

$$550 + 545 + 540 + 535,$$

we have a series that represents the total payments for the first four months. Since a sequence can be finite or infinite, there are both finite and infinite series.

We use a compact notation, called **summation notation,** to write a series from the general term of the corresponding sequence. In mathematics, the Greek letter **Σ (sigma)** is used to denote summation. For example, the sum of the first six terms of the sequence with general term $a_n = 3n + 2$ is written as

$$\sum_{i=1}^{6} (3i + 2).$$

The letter i is called the **index of summation.** We read this as "the sum from $i = 1$ to 6 of $3i + 2$." To find this sum, we replace the letter i in $3i + 2$ with 1, 2, 3, 4, 5, and 6, and add the resulting terms.

⚠ CAUTION This use of i as the index of summation has no connection with the complex number i.

EXAMPLE 4 Evaluating Series Written in Summation Notation

Write out the terms and evaluate each series.

(a) $\sum_{i=1}^{6} (3i + 2)$ Multiply and then add.

$$= (3 \cdot 1 + 2) + (3 \cdot 2 + 2) + (3 \cdot 3 + 2)$$
$$+ (3 \cdot 4 + 2) + (3 \cdot 5 + 2) + (3 \cdot 6 + 2)$$ Replace i with 1, 2, 3, 4, 5, 6.

$$= 5 + 8 + 11 + 14 + 17 + 20$$ Work inside the parentheses.

$$= 75$$ Add.

(b) $\sum_{i=1}^{5} (i - 4)$

$$= (1 - 4) + (2 - 4) + (3 - 4) + (4 - 4) + (5 - 4)$$ $i = 1, 2, 3, 4, 5$

$$= -3 - 2 - 1 + 0 + 1$$ Subtract.

$$= -5$$ Simplify.

NOW TRY
EXERCISE 4

Write out the terms and evaluate the series.

$$\sum_{i=1}^{5}(i^2 - 4)$$

(c) $\displaystyle\sum_{i=3}^{7} 3i^2$

$$= 3(3)^2 + 3(4)^2 + 3(5)^2 + 3(6)^2 + 3(7)^2 \qquad i = 3, 4, 5, 6, 7$$
$$= 27 + 48 + 75 + 108 + 147 \qquad\qquad \text{Square, and then multiply.}$$
$$= 405 \qquad\qquad \text{Add.} \qquad\qquad \textit{NOW TRY}$$

OBJECTIVE 5 **Write a series with summation notation.** In **Example 4,** we started with summation notation and wrote each series using + signs. Given a series, we can write it with summation notation by observing a pattern in the terms and writing the general term accordingly.

NOW TRY
EXERCISE 5

Write each sum with summation notation.

(a) $3 + 5 + 7 + 9 + 11$

(b) $-1 - 4 - 9 - 16 - 25$

EXAMPLE 5 Writing Series with Summation Notation

Write each sum with summation notation.

(a) $2 + 5 + 8 + 11$

First, find a general term a_n that will give these four terms for $a_1, a_2, a_3,$ and $a_4,$ respectively. Each term is one less than a multiple of 3, so try $3i - 1$ as the general term.

$$3(1) - 1 = 2 \qquad i = 1$$
$$3(2) - 1 = 5 \qquad i = 2$$
$$3(3) - 1 = 8 \qquad i = 3$$
$$3(4) - 1 = 11 \qquad i = 4$$

(Remember, there may be other expressions that also work.) Since i ranges from 1 to 4,

$$2 + 5 + 8 + 11 = \sum_{i=1}^{4}(3i - 1).$$

(b) $8 + 27 + 64 + 125 + 216$

These numbers are the cubes of 2, 3, 4, 5, and 6, so the general term is i^3.

$$8 + 27 + 64 + 125 + 216 = \sum_{i=2}^{6} i^3 \qquad\qquad \textit{NOW TRY}$$

OBJECTIVE 6 **Find the arithmetic mean (average) of a group of numbers.**

Arithmetic Mean or Average

The **arithmetic mean,** or **average,** of a group of numbers is symbolized $\bar{x}$ and is found by dividing their sum by the number of numbers. That is,

$$\bar{x} = \frac{\displaystyle\sum_{i=1}^{n} x_i}{n}.$$

NOW TRY ANSWERS

4. $-3 + 0 + 5 + 12 + 21 = 35$

5. (a) $\displaystyle\sum_{i=1}^{5}(2i + 1)$ **(b)** $\displaystyle\sum_{i=1}^{5} -i^2$

The values of x_i represent the individual numbers in the group, and n represents the number of numbers.

NOW TRY
EXERCISE 6

The following table shows the top 5 American Quarter Horse States in 2009 based on the total number of registered Quarter Horses. To the nearest whole number, what is the average number of Quarter Horses registered per state in these top five states?

State	Number of Registered Quarter Horses
Texas	461,054
Oklahoma	188,381
California	136,583
Missouri	107,630
Colorado	93,958

Source: American Quarter Horse Association.

NOW TRY ANSWER
6. 197,521

EXAMPLE 6 Finding the Arithmetic Mean, or Average

The following table shows the number of FDIC-insured financial institutions for each year during the period from 2002 through 2008. What was the average number of institutions per year for this 7-yr period?

Year	Number of Institutions
2002	9369
2003	9194
2004	8988
2005	8845
2006	8691
2007	8544
2008	8314

Source: U.S. Federal Deposit Insurance Corporation.

$$\bar{x} = \frac{\sum\limits_{i=1}^{7} x_i}{7}$$ Let $x_1 = 9369$, $x_2 = 9194$, and so on. There are 7 numbers in the group, so $n = 7$.

$$= \frac{9369 + 9194 + 8988 + 8845 + 8691 + 8544 + 8314}{7}$$

$$= 8849 \quad \text{(rounded to the nearest unit)}$$

The average number of institutions per year for this 7-yr period was 8849.

NOW TRY

14.1 EXERCISES   *MyMathLab*   Math XP PRACTICE   WATCH   DOWNLOAD   READ   REVIEW

🌐 *Complete solution available on the Video Resources on DVD*

Write out the first five terms of each sequence. **See Example 1.**

1. $a_n = n + 1$

2. $a_n = n + 4$

3. $a_n = \dfrac{n + 3}{n}$

4. $a_n = \dfrac{n + 2}{n}$

5. $a_n = 3^n$

6. $a_n = 2^n$

7. $a_n = \dfrac{1}{n^2}$

8. $a_n = \dfrac{-2}{n^2}$

9. $a_n = 5(-1)^{n-1}$

10. $a_n = 6(-1)^{n+1}$

11. $a_n = n - \dfrac{1}{n}$

12. $a_n = n + \dfrac{4}{n}$

Find the indicated term for each sequence. **See Example 1.**

13. $a_n = -9n + 2$; a_8

14. $a_n = 3n - 7$; a_{12}

15. $a_n = \dfrac{3n + 7}{2n - 5}$; a_{14}

16. $a_n = \dfrac{5n - 9}{3n + 8}$; a_{16}

17. $a_n = (n + 1)(2n + 3)$; a_8

18. $a_n = (5n - 2)(3n + 1)$; a_{10}

Find a general term a_n for the given terms of each sequence. **See Example 2.**

🌐 **19.** 4, 8, 12, 16, …

20. 7, 14, 21, 28, …

21. −8, −16, −24, −32, …

22. −10, −20, −30, −40, …

23. $\dfrac{1}{3}, \dfrac{1}{9}, \dfrac{1}{27}, \dfrac{1}{81}, \ldots$

24. $\dfrac{2}{5}, \dfrac{2}{25}, \dfrac{2}{125}, \dfrac{2}{625}, \ldots$

25. $\dfrac{2}{5}, \dfrac{3}{6}, \dfrac{4}{7}, \dfrac{5}{8}, \ldots$

26. $\dfrac{1}{2}, \dfrac{2}{3}, \dfrac{3}{4}, \dfrac{4}{5}, \ldots$

Solve each applied problem by writing the first few terms of a sequence. **See Example 3.**

🌐 **27.** Horacio Loschak borrows $1000 and agrees to pay $100 plus interest of 1% on the unpaid balance each month. Find the payments for the first six months and the remaining debt at the end of that period.

28. Leslie Maruri is offered a new modeling job with a salary of $20{,}000 + 2500n$ dollars per year at the end of the nth year. Write a sequence showing her salary at the end of each of the first 5 yr. If she continues in this way, what will her salary be at the end of the tenth year?

29. Suppose that an automobile loses $\frac{1}{5}$ of its value each year; that is, at the end of any given year, the value is $\frac{4}{5}$ of the value at the beginning of that year. If a car costs $20,000 new, what is its value at the end of 5 yr, to the nearest dollar?

30. A certain car loses $\frac{1}{2}$ of its value each year. If this car cost $40,000 new, what is its value at the end of 6 yr?

Write out each series and evaluate it. **See Example 4.**

🌐 **31.** $\displaystyle\sum_{i=1}^{5} (i + 3)$

32. $\displaystyle\sum_{i=1}^{6} (i + 9)$

33. $\displaystyle\sum_{i=1}^{3} (i^2 + 2)$

34. $\displaystyle\sum_{i=1}^{4} (i^3 + 3)$

35. $\displaystyle\sum_{i=1}^{6} (-1)^i$

36. $\displaystyle\sum_{i=1}^{5} (-1)^i \cdot i$

37. $\displaystyle\sum_{i=3}^{7} (i - 3)(i + 2)$

38. $\displaystyle\sum_{i=2}^{6} (i + 3)(i - 4)$

Write each series with summation notation. **See Example 5.**

🌐 **39.** $3 + 4 + 5 + 6 + 7$

40. $7 + 8 + 9 + 10 + 11$

41. $-2 + 4 - 8 + 16 - 32$

42. $-1 + 2 - 3 + 4 - 5 + 6$

43. $1 + 4 + 9 + 16$

44. $1 + 16 + 81 + 256$

📝 **45.** Explain the basic difference between a sequence and a series.

46. *Concept Check* Consider the following statement. *WHAT WENT WRONG?*

For the sequence defined by $a_n = 2n + 4$, find $a_{1/2}$.

Find the arithmetic mean for each collection of numbers. **See Example 6.**

47. 8, 11, 14, 9, 7, 6, 8

48. 10, 12, 8, 19, 23, 12

49. 5, 9, 8, 2, 4, 7, 3, 2, 0

50. 2, 1, 4, 8, 3, 7, 10, 8, 0

Solve each problem. ***See Example 6.***

51. The number of mutual funds operating in the United States available to investors each year during the period 2004 through 2008 is given in the table.

Year	Number of Funds Available
2004	8041
2005	7975
2006	8117
2007	8024
2008	8022

Source: Investment Company Institute.

To the nearest whole number, what was the average number of funds available per year during the given period?

52. The total assets of mutual funds operating in the United States, in billions of dollars, for each year during the period 2004 through 2008 are shown in the table. What were the average assets per year during this period?

Year	Assets (in billions of dollars)
2004	8107
2005	8905
2006	10,397
2007	12,000
2008	9601

Source: Investment Company Institute.

PREVIEW EXERCISES

Find the values of a and d by solving each system. ***See Sections 8.2 and 8.3.***

53. $a + 3d = 12$
$a + 8d = 22$

54. $a + 7d = 12$
$a + 2d = 7$

55. Evaluate $a + (n - 1)d$ for $a = -2, n = 5,$ and $d = 3$. **See Sections 1.3–1.5.**

(14.2) Arithmetic Sequences

OBJECTIVES

1 Find the common difference of an arithmetic sequence.

2 Find the general term of an arithmetic sequence.

3 Use an arithmetic sequence in an application.

4 Find any specified term or the number of terms of an arithmetic sequence.

5 Find the sum of a specified number of terms of an arithmetic sequence.

OBJECTIVE 1 **Find the common difference of an arithmetic sequence.** In this section, we introduce a special type of sequence that has many applications.

Arithmetic Sequence

An **arithmetic sequence,** or **arithmetic progression,** is a sequence in which each term after the first is found by adding a constant number to the preceding term.

For example, the sequence

$$6, 11, 16, 21, 26, \ldots \quad \text{Arithmetic sequence}$$

is an arithmetic sequence, since the difference between any two adjacent terms is always 5. The number 5 is called the **common difference** of the arithmetic sequence. The common difference, d, is found by subtracting a_n from a_{n+1} in any such pair of terms.

$$d = a_{n+1} - a_n \quad \text{Common difference}$$

NOW TRY
EXERCISE 1

Determine the common difference d for the arithmetic sequence.

$-4, -13, -22, -31, -40, \ldots$

 NOW TRY
EXERCISE 2

Write the first five terms of the arithmetic sequence with first term 10 and common difference -8.

EXAMPLE 1 Finding the Common Difference

Determine the common difference d for the arithmetic sequence.

$$-11, -4, 3, 10, 17, 24, \ldots$$

Since the sequence is arithmetic, d is the difference between any two adjacent terms: $a_{n+1} - a_n$. We arbitrarily choose the terms 10 and 17.

$$d = 17 - 10, \quad \text{or} \quad 7$$

Verify that *any* two adjacent terms would give the same result.   *NOW TRY*

EXAMPLE 2 Writing the Terms of a Sequence from the First Term and the Common Difference

Write the first five terms of the arithmetic sequence with first term 3 and common difference -2.

The second term is found by adding -2 to the first term 3, getting 1. For the next term, add -2 to 1, and so on. The first five terms are

$$3, 1, -1, -3, -5.$$ *NOW TRY*

OBJECTIVE 2 **Find the general term of an arithmetic sequence.** Generalizing from **Example 2,** if we know the first term a_1 and the common difference d of an arithmetic sequence, then the sequence is completely defined as

$$a_1, \quad a_2 = a_1 + d, \quad a_3 = a_1 + 2d, \quad a_4 = a_1 + 3d, \ldots.$$

Writing the terms of the sequence in this way suggests the following formula for a_n.

General Term of an Arithmetic Sequence

The general term of an arithmetic sequence with first term a_1 and common difference d is

$$a_n = a_1 + (n - 1)d.$$

Since $a_n = a_1 + (n - 1)d = dn + (a_1 - d)$ is a linear function in n, any linear expression of the form $kn + c$, where k and c are real numbers, defines an arithmetic sequence.

EXAMPLE 3 Finding the General Term of an Arithmetic Sequence

Determine the general term of the arithmetic sequence.

$$-9, -6, -3, 0, 3, 6, \ldots$$

Then use the general term to find a_{20}.

The first term is $a_1 = -9$.

$$d = -3 - (-6), \quad \text{or} \quad 3. \qquad \text{Let } d = a_3 - a_2.$$

Now find a_n.

$$a_n = a_1 + (n - 1)d \qquad \text{Formula for } a_n$$
$$a_n = -9 + (n - 1)(3) \qquad \text{Let } a_1 = -9, d = 3.$$
$$a_n = -9 + 3n - 3 \qquad \text{Distributive property}$$
$$a_n = 3n - 12 \qquad \text{Combine like terms.}$$

NOW TRY ANSWERS
1. $d = -9$
2. $10, 2, -6, -14, -22$

NOW TRY
EXERCISE 3

Determine the general term of the arithmetic sequence.

$$-5, 0, 5, 10, 15, \dots$$

Then use the general term to find a_{20}.

The general term is $a_n = 3n - 12$. Now find a_{20}.

$$
\begin{aligned}
a_{20} &= 3(20) - 12 && \text{Let } n = 20. \\
&= 60 - 12 && \text{Multiply.} \\
&= 48 && \text{Subtract.}
\end{aligned}
$$

NOW TRY ↻

OBJECTIVE 3 **Use an arithmetic sequence in an application.**

NOW TRY
EXERCISE 4

Ginny Tiller is saving money for her son's college education. She makes an initial contribution of $1000 and deposits an additional $120 each month for the next 96 months. Disregarding interest, how much money will be in the account after 96 months?

EXAMPLE 4 Applying an Arithmetic Sequence

Leonid Bekker's uncle decides to start a fund for Leonid's education. He makes an initial contribution of $3000 and deposits an additional $500 each month. Thus, after one month the fund will have $3000 + $500 = $3500. How much will it have after 24 months? (Disregard any interest.)

After n months, the fund will contain

$$a_n = 3000 + 500n \text{ dollars.} \qquad \text{Use an arithmetic sequence.}$$

To find the amount in the fund after 24 months, find a_{24}.

$$
\begin{aligned}
a_{24} &= 3000 + 500(24) && \text{Let } n = 24. \\
&= 3000 + 12{,}000 && \text{Multiply.} \\
&= 15{,}000 && \text{Add.}
\end{aligned}
$$

The account will contain $15,000 (disregarding interest) after 24 months.

NOW TRY ↻

OBJECTIVE 4 **Find any specified term or the number of terms of an arithmetic sequence.** The formula for the general term of an arithmetic sequence has four variables: $a_n, a_1, n,$ and d. If we know any three of these, the formula can be used to find the value of the fourth variable.

EXAMPLE 5 Finding Specified Terms in Sequences

Evaluate the indicated term for each arithmetic sequence.

(a) $a_1 = -6, d = 12; \quad a_{15}$

$$
\begin{aligned}
a_n &= a_1 + (n - 1)d && \text{Formula for } a_n \\
a_{15} &= a_1 + (15 - 1)d && \text{Let } n = 15. \\
&= -6 + 14(12) && \text{Let } a_1 = -6, d = 12. \\
&= 162 && \text{Multiply, and then add.}
\end{aligned}
$$

(b) $a_5 = 2$ and $a_{11} = -10; \quad a_{17}$

Any term can be found if a_1 and d are known. Use the formula for a_n.

$$
\begin{array}{ll}
a_5 = a_1 + (5 - 1)d & \qquad a_{11} = a_1 + (11 - 1)d \\
a_5 = a_1 + 4d & \qquad a_{11} = a_1 + 10d \\
2 = a_1 + 4d \quad {\scriptstyle a_5 = 2} & \qquad -10 = a_1 + 10d \quad {\scriptstyle a_{11} = -10}
\end{array}
$$

This gives a system of two equations in two variables, a_1 and d.

$$
\begin{aligned}
a_1 + 4d &= 2 && (1) \\
a_1 + 10d &= -10 && (2)
\end{aligned}
$$

NOW TRY ANSWERS
3. $a_n = 5n - 10; a_{20} = 90$
4. $12,520

NOW TRY
EXERCISE 5

Evaluate the indicated term for each arithmetic sequence.

(a) $a_1 = 21$ and $d = -3$; a_{22}

(b) $a_7 = 25$ and $a_{12} = 40$; a_{19}

Multiply equation (2) by -1 and add to equation (1) to eliminate a_1.

$$
\begin{array}{ll}
a_1 + 4d = 2 & \text{(1)} \\
\underline{-a_1 - 10d = 10} & \text{-1 times (2)} \\
-6d = 12 & \text{Add.} \\
d = -2 & \text{Divide by -6.}
\end{array}
$$

Now find a_1 by substituting -2 for d into either equation.

$$
\begin{array}{ll}
a_1 + 10(-2) = -10 & \text{Let $d = -2$ in (2).} \\
a_1 - 20 = -10 & \text{Multiply.} \\
a_1 = 10 & \text{Add 20.}
\end{array}
$$

Use the formula for a_n to find a_{17}.

$$
\begin{array}{ll}
a_{17} = a_1 + (17 - 1)d & \text{Let $n = 17$.} \\
= a_1 + 16d & \text{Subtract.} \\
= 10 + 16(-2) & \text{Let $a_1 = 10$, $d = -2$.} \\
= -22 & \text{Simplify.}
\end{array}
$$

Multiply and then add.

NOW TRY

NOW TRY
EXERCISE 6

Evaluate the number of terms in the arithmetic sequence.

$$1, \frac{4}{3}, \frac{5}{3}, 2, \ldots, 11$$

EXAMPLE 6 Finding the Number of Terms in a Sequence

Evaluate the number of terms in the arithmetic sequence.

$$-8, -2, 4, 10, \ldots, 52$$

Let n represent the number of terms in the sequence. Since $a_n = 52$, $a_1 = -8$, and $d = -2 - (-8) = 6$, use the formula for a_n to find n.

$$
\begin{array}{ll}
a_n = a_1 + (n - 1)d & \text{Formula for a_n} \\
52 = -8 + (n - 1)(6) & \text{Let $a_n = 52$, $a_1 = -8$, $d = 6$.} \\
52 = -8 + 6n - 6 & \text{Distributive property} \\
66 = 6n & \text{Simplify.} \\
n = 11 & \text{Divide by 6.}
\end{array}
$$

The sequence has 11 terms.

NOW TRY

OBJECTIVE 5 **Find the sum of a specified number of terms of an arithmetic sequence.** To find a formula for the sum S_n of the first n terms of a given arithmetic sequence, we can write out the terms in two ways. We start with the first term, and then with the last term. Then we add the terms in columns.

$$
\begin{array}{l}
S_n = a_1 + (a_1 + d) + (a_1 + 2d) + \cdots + [a_1 + (n - 1)d] \\
\underline{S_n = a_n + (a_n - d) + (a_n - 2d) + \cdots + [a_n - (n - 1)d]} \\
2S_n = (a_1 + a_n) + (a_1 + a_n) + (a_1 + a_n) + \cdots + (a_1 + a_n)
\end{array}
$$

The right-hand side of this expression contains n terms, each equal to $a_1 + a_n$.

$$2S_n = n(a_1 + a_n)$$

Formula for S_n

$$S_n = \frac{n}{2}(a_1 + a_n) \qquad \text{Divide by 2.}$$

NOW TRY ANSWERS
5. (a) -42 **(b)** 61
6. 31

⟲ *NOW TRY*
EXERCISE 7
Evaluate the sum of the first seven terms of the arithmetic sequence in which $a_n = 5n - 7$.

EXAMPLE 7 **Finding the Sum of the First *n* Terms of an Arithmetic Sequence**

Evaluate the sum of the first five terms of the arithmetic sequence in which $a_n = 2n - 5$.

Begin by evaluating a_1 and a_5.

$$a_1 = 2(1) - 5 \qquad\qquad a_5 = 2(5) - 5$$
$$= -3 \qquad\qquad\qquad = 5$$

Now evaluate the sum using $a_1 = -3$, $a_5 = 5$, and $n = 5$.

$$S_n = \frac{n}{2}(a_1 + a_n) \qquad \text{Formula for } S_n$$

$$S_5 = \frac{5}{2}(-3 + 5) \qquad \text{Substitute.}$$

$$= \frac{5}{2}(2) \qquad\qquad \text{Add.}$$

$$= 5 \qquad\qquad\qquad \text{Multiply.} \qquad\qquad \textit{NOW TRY} ⟳$$

It is possible to express the sum S_n of an arithmetic sequence in terms of a_1 and d, the quantities that define the sequence. Since

$$S_n = \frac{n}{2}(a_1 + a_n) \qquad \text{and} \qquad a_n = a_1 + (n - 1)d,$$

by substituting the expression for a_n into the expression for S_n we obtain

$$S_n = \frac{n}{2}(a_1 + [a_1 + (n - 1)d]) \qquad \text{Substitute for } a_n.$$

$$S_n = \frac{n}{2}[2a_1 + (n - 1)d]. \qquad \text{Combine like terms.}$$

The summary box gives both of the alternative forms that may be used to find the sum of the first *n* terms of an arithmetic sequence.

Sum of the First *n* Terms of an Arithmetic Sequence

The sum of the first *n* terms of the arithmetic sequence with first term a_1, *n*th term a_n, and common difference *d* is given by either formula.

$$S_n = \frac{n}{2}(a_1 + a_n) \qquad \text{or} \qquad S_n = \frac{n}{2}[2a_1 + (n - 1)d]$$

EXAMPLE 8 **Finding the Sum of the First *n* Terms of an Arithmetic Sequence**

Evaluate the sum of the first eight terms of the arithmetic sequence having first term 3 and common difference -2.

Since the known values, $a_1 = 3$, $d = -2$, and $n = 8$, appear in the second formula for S_n, we use it.

NOW TRY ANSWER
7. 91

NOW TRY
EXERCISE 8

Evaluate the sum of the first nine terms of the arithmetic sequence having first term -8 and common difference -5.

$$S_n = \frac{n}{2}[2a_1 + (n-1)d] \qquad \text{Second formula for } S_n$$

$$S_8 = \frac{8}{2}[2(3) + (8-1)(-2)] \qquad \text{Let } a_1 = 3, d = -2, n = 8.$$

$$= 4[6 - 14] \qquad \text{Work inside the brackets.}$$

$$= -32 \qquad \text{Subtract and then multiply.}$$

NOW TRY

As mentioned earlier, linear expressions of the form $kn + c$, where k and c are real numbers, define an arithmetic sequence. For example, the sequences defined by $a_n = 2n + 5$ and $a_n = n - 3$ are arithmetic sequences. For this reason,

$$\sum_{i=1}^{n} (ki + c)$$

represents the sum of the first n terms of an arithmetic sequence having first term $a_1 = k(1) + c = k + c$ and general term $a_n = k(n) + c = kn + c$. We can find this sum with the first formula for S_n, as shown in the next example.

NOW TRY
EXERCISE 9

Evaluate $\displaystyle\sum_{i=1}^{11} (5i - 7)$.

EXAMPLE 9 Using S_n to Evaluate a Summation

Evaluate $\displaystyle\sum_{i=1}^{12} (2i - 1)$.

This is the sum of the first 12 terms of the arithmetic sequence having $a_n = 2n - 1$. This sum, S_{12}, is found with the first formula for S_n.

$$S_n = \frac{n}{2}(a_1 + a_n) \qquad \text{First formula for } S_n$$

$$S_{12} = \frac{12}{2}[(2(1) - 1) + (2(12) - 1)] \qquad \text{Let } n = 12.$$

 a_1 a_{12}

$$= 6(1 + 23) \qquad \text{Evaluate } a_1 \text{ and } a_{12}.$$

$$= 6(24) \qquad \text{Add.}$$

$$= 144 \qquad \text{Multiply.}$$

NOW TRY ANSWERS
8. -252 **9.** 253

NOW TRY

14.2 EXERCISES   *MyMathLab* Math XL PRACTICE   WATCH   DOWNLOAD   READ   REVIEW

⊙ *Complete solution available on the Video Resources on DVD*

If the given sequence is arithmetic, find the common difference d. If the sequence is not arithmetic, say so. **See Example 1.**

1. $1, 2, 3, 4, 5, \ldots$

2. $2, 5, 8, 11, \ldots$

3. $2, -4, 6, -8, 10, -12, \ldots$

4. $1, 2, 4, 7, 11, 16, \ldots$

5. $10, 5, 0, -5, -10, \ldots$

6. $-6, -10, -14, -18, \ldots$

Write the first five terms of each arithmetic sequence. See Example 2.

🌐 **7.** $a_1 = 5, d = 4$ **8.** $a_1 = 6, d = 7$

9. $a_1 = -2, d = -4$ **10.** $a_1 = -3, d = -5$

Use the formula for a_n to find the general term of each arithmetic sequence. See Example 3.

🌐 **11.** $a_1 = 2, d = 5$ **12.** $a_1 = 5, d = 3$ **13.** $3, \dfrac{15}{4}, \dfrac{9}{2}, \dfrac{21}{4}, \ldots$

14. $1, \dfrac{5}{3}, \dfrac{7}{3}, 3, \ldots$ **15.** $-3, 0, 3, \ldots$ **16.** $-10, -5, 0, \ldots$

Evaluate the indicated term for each arithmetic sequence. See Examples 3 and 5.

🌐 **17.** $a_1 = 4, d = 3;\quad a_{25}$ **18.** $a_1 = 1, d = -3;\quad a_{12}$

19. $2, 4, 6, \ldots;\quad a_{24}$ **20.** $1, 5, 9, \ldots;\quad a_{50}$

21. $a_{12} = -45, a_{10} = -37;\quad a_1$ **22.** $a_{10} = -2, a_{15} = -8;\quad a_3$

Evaluate the number of terms in each arithmetic sequence. See Example 6.

🌐 **23.** $3, 5, 7, \ldots, 33$ **24.** $4, 1, -2, \ldots, -32$

25. $\dfrac{3}{4}, 3, \dfrac{21}{4}, \ldots, 12$ **26.** $2, \dfrac{3}{2}, 1, \dfrac{1}{2}, \ldots, -5$

27. *Concept Check*   In the formula for S_n, what does n represent?

📝 **28.** Explain when you would use each of the two formulas for S_n.

Evaluate S_6 for each arithmetic sequence. See Examples 7 and 8.

🌐 **29.** $a_1 = 6, d = 3$ **30.** $a_1 = 5, d = 4$ **31.** $a_1 = 7, d = -3$

32. $a_1 = -5, d = -4$ 🌐 **33.** $a_n = 4 + 3n$ **34.** $a_n = 9 + 5n$

Use a formula for S_n to evaluate each series. See Example 9.

🌐 **35.** $\displaystyle\sum_{i=1}^{10} (8i - 5)$ **36.** $\displaystyle\sum_{i=1}^{17} (3i - 1)$ **37.** $\displaystyle\sum_{i=1}^{20} \left(\dfrac{3}{2}i + 4\right)$

38. $\displaystyle\sum_{i=1}^{11} \left(\dfrac{1}{2}i - 1\right)$ **39.** $\displaystyle\sum_{i=1}^{250} i$ **40.** $\displaystyle\sum_{i=1}^{2000} i$

Solve each problem. (Hint: Immediately after reading the problem, determine whether you need to find a specific term of a sequence or the sum of the terms of a sequence.) See Examples 4, 7, 8, and 9.

🌐 **41.** Nancy Bondy's aunt has promised to deposit $1 in her account on the first day of her birthday month, $2 on the second day, $3 on the third day, and so on for 30 days. How much will this amount to over the entire month?

42. Repeat **Exercise 41,** but assume that the deposits are $2, $4, $6, and so on, and that the month is February of a leap year.

43. Suppose that Cherian Mathew is offered a job at $1600 per month with a guaranteed increase of $50 every six months for 5 yr. What will Cherian's salary be at the end of that time?

44. Repeat **Exercise 43,** but assume that the starting salary is $2000 per month and the guaranteed increase is $100 every four months for 3 yr.

45. A seating section in a theater-in-the-round has 20 seats in the first row, 22 in the second row, 24 in the third row, and so on for 25 rows. How many seats are there in the last row? How many seats are there in the section?

46. Constantin Arne has started on a fitness program. He plans to jog 10 min per day for the first week and then add 10 min per day each week until he is jogging an hour each day. In which week will this occur? What is the total number of minutes he will run during the first four weeks?

47. A child builds with blocks, placing 35 blocks in the first row, 31 in the second row, 27 in the third row, and so on. Continuing this pattern, can she end with a row containing exactly 1 block? If not, how many blocks will the last row contain? How many rows can she build this way?

48. A stack of firewood has 28 pieces on the bottom, 24 on top of those, then 20, and so on. If there are 108 pieces of wood, how many rows are there? (*Hint:* $n \leq 7$.)

PREVIEW EXERCISES

Evaluate ar^n for the given values of a, r, and n. **See Section 4.1.**

49. $a = 2, r = 3, n = 2$ **50.** $a = 3, r = 2, n = 4$

51. $a = 4, r = \dfrac{1}{2}, n = 3$ **52.** $a = 5, r = \dfrac{1}{4}, n = 2$

(14.3) Geometric Sequences

OBJECTIVES

1 Find the common ratio of a geometric sequence.

2 Find the general term of a geometric sequence.

3 Find any specified term of a geometric sequence.

4 Find the sum of a specified number of terms of a geometric sequence.

5 Apply the formula for the future value of an ordinary annuity.

6 Find the sum of an infinite number of terms of certain geometric sequences.

In an arithmetic sequence, each term after the first is found by *adding* a fixed number to the previous term. A *geometric sequence* is defined as follows.

Geometric Sequence

A **geometric sequence,** or **geometric progression,** is a sequence in which each term after the first is found by multiplying the preceding term by a nonzero constant.

OBJECTIVE 1 **Find the common ratio of a geometric sequence.** We find the constant multiplier, called the **common ratio,** by dividing any term a_{n+1} by the preceding term, a_n.

$$r = \frac{a_{n+1}}{a_n} \quad \text{Common ratio}$$

For example,

$$2, 6, 18, 54, 162, \ldots \quad \text{Geometric sequence}$$

is a geometric sequence in which the first term, a_1, is 2 and the common ratio is

$$r = \frac{6}{2} = \frac{18}{6} = \frac{54}{18} = \frac{162}{54} = 3. \leftarrow \frac{a_{n+1}}{a_n} = 3 \text{ for all } n.$$

⌐ *NOW TRY*
⌐ *EXERCISE 1*
Determine r for the geometric sequence.

$$\frac{1}{4}, -1, 4, -16, 64, \ldots$$

EXAMPLE 1 Finding the Common Ratio

Determine the common ratio r for the geometric sequence.

$$15, \frac{15}{2}, \frac{15}{4}, \frac{15}{8}, \ldots$$

To find r, choose any two successive terms and divide the second one by the first. We choose the second and third terms of the sequence.

$$r = \frac{a_3}{a_2}$$

$$= \frac{\frac{15}{4}}{\frac{15}{2}} \qquad \text{Substitute.}$$

$$= \frac{15}{4} \div \frac{15}{2} \qquad \text{Write as division.}$$

$$= \frac{15}{4} \cdot \frac{2}{15} \qquad \text{Definition of division}$$

$$= \frac{1}{2} \qquad \text{Multiply. Write in lowest terms.}$$

Any other two successive terms could have been used to find r. Additional terms of the sequence can be found by multiplying each successive term by $\frac{1}{2}$. *NOW TRY* ⌐

OBJECTIVE 2 **Find the general term of a geometric sequence.** The general term a_n of a geometric sequence $a_1, a_2, a_3, \ldots$ is expressed in terms of a_1 and r by writing the first few terms as

$$a_1, \quad a_2 = a_1 r, \quad a_3 = a_1 r^2, \quad a_4 = a_1 r^3, \ldots,$$

which suggests the next rule.

General Term of a Geometric Sequence

The general term of the geometric sequence with first term a_1 and common ratio r is

$$a_n = a_1 r^{n-1}.$$

⚠ **CAUTION** In finding $a_1 r^{n-1}$, be careful to use the correct order of operations. The value of r^{n-1} must be found first. Then multiply the result by a_1.

⌐ *NOW TRY*
⌐ *EXERCISE 2*
Determine the general term of the sequence.

$$\frac{1}{4}, -1, 4, -16, 64, \ldots$$

NOW TRY ANSWERS
1. -4 **2.** $a_n = \frac{1}{4}(-4)^{n-1}$

EXAMPLE 2 Finding the General Term of a Geometric Sequence

Determine the general term of the sequence in **Example 1.**
The first term is $a_1 = 15$ and the common ratio is $r = \frac{1}{2}$.

$$a_n = a_1 r^{n-1} = 15\left(\frac{1}{2}\right)^{n-1} \qquad \text{Substitute into the formula for } a_n.$$

It is not possible to simplify further, because the exponent must be applied before the multiplication can be done. *NOW TRY* ⌐

OBJECTIVE 3 **Find any specified term of a geometric sequence.** We can use the formula for the general term to find any particular term.

NOW TRY
EXERCISE 3

Evaluate the indicated term for each geometric sequence.

(a) $a_1 = 3, r = 2;$ a_8

(b) $10, 2, \frac{2}{5}, \frac{2}{25}, \ldots;$ a_7

EXAMPLE 3 Finding Specified Terms in Sequences

Evaluate the indicated term for each geometric sequence.

(a) $a_1 = 4, r = -3;$ a_6
Use the formula for the general term.

$$a_n = a_1 r^{n-1} \qquad \text{Formula for } a_n$$
$$a_6 = a_1 \cdot r^{6-1} \qquad \text{Let } n = 6.$$

Evaluate $(-3)^5$ and then multiply.

$$= 4 \cdot (-3)^5 \qquad \text{Let } a_1 = 4, r = -3.$$
$$= -972 \qquad \text{Simplify.}$$

(b) $\dfrac{3}{4}, \dfrac{3}{8}, \dfrac{3}{16}, \ldots;$ a_7

$$a_7 = \frac{3}{4} \cdot \left(\frac{1}{2}\right)^{7-1} \qquad \text{Let } a_1 = \tfrac{3}{4}, r = \tfrac{1}{2}, n = 7.$$

$$= \frac{3}{4} \cdot \frac{1}{64} \qquad \text{Apply the exponent.}$$

$$= \frac{3}{256} \qquad \text{Multiply.} \qquad \qquad \text{NOW TRY}$$

NOW TRY
EXERCISE 4

Write the first five terms of the geometric sequence whose first term is 25 and whose common ratio is $-\frac{1}{5}$.

EXAMPLE 4 Writing the Terms of a Sequence

Write the first five terms of the geometric sequence whose first term is 5 and whose common ratio is $\frac{1}{2}$.

$$a_1 = 5, \quad a_2 = 5\left(\frac{1}{2}\right) = \frac{5}{2}, \quad a_3 = 5\left(\frac{1}{2}\right)^2 = \frac{5}{4}, \qquad \text{Use } a_n = a_1 r^{n-1}, \text{ with}$$
$$a_4 = 5\left(\frac{1}{2}\right)^3 = \frac{5}{8}, \quad a_5 = 5\left(\frac{1}{2}\right)^4 = \frac{5}{16} \qquad \begin{array}{l} a_1 = 5, r = \tfrac{1}{2}, \text{ and} \\ n = 1, 2, 3, 4, 5. \end{array}$$

NOW TRY

OBJECTIVE 4 **Find the sum of a specified number of terms of a geometric sequence.** It is convenient to have a formula for the sum S_n of the first n terms of a geometric sequence. We can develop a formula by first writing out S_n.

$$S_n = a_1 + a_1 r + a_1 r^2 + a_1 r^3 + \cdots + a_1 r^{n-1}$$

Next, we multiply both sides by $-r$.

$$-rS_n = -a_1 r - a_1 r^2 - a_1 r^3 - a_1 r^4 - \cdots - a_1 r^n$$

Now add.

$$S_n = a_1 + a_1 r + a_1 r^2 + a_1 r^3 + \cdots + a_1 r^{n-1}$$
$$\underline{-rS_n = \qquad -a_1 r - a_1 r^2 - a_1 r^3 - \cdots - a_1 r^{n-1} - a_1 r^n}$$
$$S_n - rS_n = a_1 \qquad \qquad \qquad \qquad \qquad - a_1 r^n$$

$$S_n(1 - r) = a_1 - a_1 r^n \qquad \text{Factor on the left.}$$

$$S_n = \frac{a_1(1 - r^n)}{1 - r} \qquad \begin{array}{l} \text{Factor on the right.} \\ \text{Divide each side by } 1 - r. \end{array}$$

NOW TRY ANSWERS

3. (a) $3(2)^7 = 384$

   (b) $10\left(\frac{1}{5}\right)^6 = \frac{2}{3125}$

4. $a_1 = 25, a_2 = -5, a_3 = 1,$
   $a_4 = -\frac{1}{5}, a_5 = \frac{1}{25}$

Sum of the First n Terms of a Geometric Sequence

The sum of the first n terms of the geometric sequence with first term a_1 and common ratio r is

$$S_n = \frac{a_1(1 - r^n)}{1 - r} \quad (r \neq 1).$$

If $r = 1$, then $S_n = a_1 + a_1 + a_1 + \cdots + a_1 = na_1$.

Multiplying the formula for S_n by $\frac{-1}{-1}$ gives an alternative form.

$$S_n = \frac{a_1(1 - r^n)}{1 - r} \cdot \frac{-1}{-1} = \frac{a_1(r^n - 1)}{r - 1} \qquad \text{Alternative form}$$

NOW TRY
EXERCISE 5
Evaluate the sum of the first six terms of the geometric sequence with first term 4 and common ratio 2.

EXAMPLE 5 Finding the Sum of the First n Terms of a Geometric Sequence

Evaluate the sum of the first six terms of the geometric sequence with first term -2 and common ratio 3.

$$S_n = \frac{a_1(1 - r^n)}{1 - r} \qquad \text{Formula for } S_n$$

$$S_6 = \frac{-2(1 - 3^6)}{1 - 3} \qquad \text{Let } n = 6, a_1 = -2, r = 3.$$

$$= \frac{-2(1 - 729)}{-2} \qquad \text{Evaluate } 3^6. \text{ Subtract in the denominator.}$$

$$= -728 \qquad \text{Simplify.} \qquad \text{NOW TRY}$$

A series of the form

$$\sum_{i=1}^{n} a \cdot b^i$$

represents the sum of the first n terms of a geometric sequence having first term $a_1 = a \cdot b^1 = ab$ and common ratio b. The next example illustrates this form.

NOW TRY
EXERCISE 6
Evaluate $\displaystyle\sum_{i=1}^{5} 8\left(\frac{1}{2}\right)^i$.

EXAMPLE 6 Using the Formula for S_n to Find a Summation

Evaluate $\displaystyle\sum_{i=1}^{4} 3 \cdot 2^i$.

Since the series is in the form $\displaystyle\sum_{i=1}^{n} a \cdot b^i$, it represents the sum of the first n terms of the geometric sequence with $a_1 = a \cdot b^1$ and $r = b$.

$$S_n = \frac{a_1(1 - r^n)}{1 - r} \qquad \text{Formula for } S_n$$

$$S_4 = \frac{6(1 - 2^4)}{1 - 2} \qquad \text{Let } n = 4, a_1 = 6, r = 2.$$

$$= \frac{6(1 - 16)}{-1} \qquad \text{Evaluate } 2^4. \text{ Subtract in the denominator.}$$

$$= 90 \qquad \text{Simplify.} \qquad \text{NOW TRY}$$

NOW TRY ANSWERS
5. 252 **6.** 7.75, or $\frac{31}{4}$

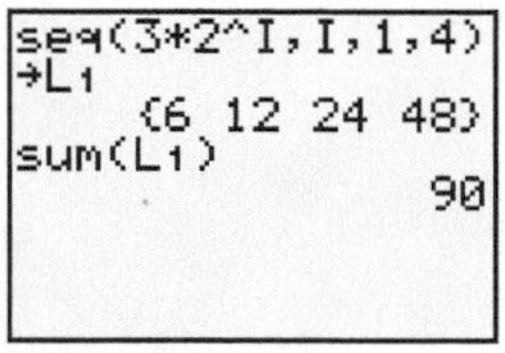

```
seq(3*2^I,I,1,4)
→L₁
      {6 12 24 48}
sum(L₁)
              90
```

FIGURE 2

FIGURE 2 shows how a graphing calculator can store the terms in a list and then find the sum of these terms. The figure supports the result of **Example 6.**

OBJECTIVE 5 **Apply the formula for the future value of an ordinary annuity.** A sequence of equal payments made over equal periods is called an **annuity.** If the payments are made at the end of the period, and if the frequency of payments is the same as the frequency of compounding, the annuity is called an **ordinary annuity.** The time between payments is the **payment period,** and the time from the beginning of the first payment period to the end of the last is called the **term of the annuity.** The **future value of the annuity,** the final sum on deposit, is defined as the sum of the compound amounts of all the payments, compounded to the end of the term.

We state the following formula without proof.

Future Value of an Ordinary Annuity

The future value of an ordinary annuity is

$$S = R\left[\frac{(1+i)^n - 1}{i}\right],$$

where
S is the future value,
R is the payment at the end of each period,
i is the interest rate per period, and
n is the number of periods.

NOW TRY
EXERCISE 7

(a) Billy Harmon deposits $600 at the end of each year into an account paying 2.5% per yr, compounded annually. Find the total amount on deposit after 18 yr.

(b) How much will be in Billy Harmon's account after 18 yr if he deposits $100 at the end of each month at 3% interest compounded monthly?

EXAMPLE 7 Applying the Formula for the Future Value of an Annuity

(a) Igor Kalugin is an athlete who believes that his playing career will last 7 yr. He deposits $22,000 at the end of each year for 7 yr in an account paying 6% compounded annually. How much will he have on deposit after 7 yr?

Igor's payments form an ordinary annuity with $R = 22,000$, $n = 7$, and $i = 0.06$. The future value of this annuity (from the formula) is

$$S = 22,000\left[\frac{(1.06)^7 - 1}{0.06}\right]$$

$$= 184,664.43, \quad \text{or} \quad \$184,664.43. \qquad \text{Use a calculator.}$$

(b) Amy Loschak has decided to deposit $200 at the end of each month in an account that pays interest of 4.8% compounded monthly for retirement in 20 yr. How much will be in the account at that time?

Because the interest is compounded monthly, $i = \frac{0.048}{12}$. Also, $R = 200$ and $n = 12(20)$. The future value is

$$S = 200\left[\frac{\left(1 + \dfrac{0.048}{12}\right)^{12(20)} - 1}{\dfrac{0.048}{12}}\right] = 80,335.01, \quad \text{or} \quad \$80,335.01.$$

NOW TRY

OBJECTIVE 6 **Find the sum of an infinite number of terms of certain geometric sequences.** Consider an infinite geometric sequence such as

$$\frac{1}{3}, \frac{1}{6}, \frac{1}{12}, \frac{1}{24}, \frac{1}{48}, \ldots$$

The sum of the first two terms is

$$S_2 = \frac{1}{3} + \frac{1}{6} = \frac{1}{2} = 0.5.$$

In a similar manner, we can find additional "partial sums."

$$S_3 = S_2 + \frac{1}{12} = \frac{1}{2} + \frac{1}{12} = \frac{7}{12} \approx 0.583, \quad S_4 = S_3 + \frac{1}{24} = \frac{7}{12} + \frac{1}{24} = \frac{15}{24} = 0.625,$$

$$S_5 = \frac{31}{48} \approx 0.64583, \quad S_6 = \frac{21}{32} = 0.65625, \quad S_7 = \frac{127}{192} \approx 0.6614583.$$

Each term of the geometric sequence is less than the preceding one, so each additional term is contributing less and less to the partial sum. In decimal form (to the nearest thousandth), the first 7 terms and the 10th term are given in the table.

Term	a_1	a_2	a_3	a_4	a_5	a_6	a_7	a_{10}
Value	0.333	0.167	0.083	0.042	0.021	0.010	0.005	0.001

As the table suggests, the value of a term gets closer and closer to 0 as the number of the term increases. To express this idea, we say that as n increases without bound (written $n \to \infty$), the limit of the term a_n is 0, written

$$\lim_{n \to \infty} a_n = 0.$$

A number that can be defined as the sum of an infinite number of terms of a geometric sequence is found by starting with the expression for the sum of a finite number of terms.

$$S_n = \frac{a_1(1 - r^n)}{1 - r}$$

If $|r| < 1$, then as n increases without bound, the value of r^n gets closer and closer to 0. As r^n approaches 0, $1 - r^n$ approaches $1 - 0 = 1$, and S_n approaches the quotient $\frac{a_1}{1 - r}$.

$$\lim_{r^n \to 0} S_n = \lim_{r^n \to 0} \frac{a_1(1 - r^n)}{1 - r} = \frac{a_1(1 - 0)}{1 - r} = \frac{a_1}{1 - r}$$

This limit is defined to be the sum of the infinite geometric sequence.

$$a_1 + a_1 r + a_1 r^2 + a_1 r^3 + \cdots = \frac{a_1}{1 - r}, \quad \text{if } |r| < 1$$

Sum of the Terms of an Infinite Geometric Sequence

The sum S of the terms of an infinite geometric sequence with first term a_1 and common ratio r, where $|r| < 1$, is

$$S = \frac{a_1}{1 - r}.$$

If $|r| \geq 1$, then the sum does not exist.

Now consider $|r| > 1$. For example, suppose the sequence is

$$6, 12, 24, \ldots, 3(2)^n, \ldots.$$

In this kind of sequence, as n increases, the value of r^n also increases and so does the sum S_n. Since each new term adds a greater and greater amount to the sum, there is no limit to the value of S_n. The sum S does not exist. A similar situation exists if $r = 1$.

NOW TRY
EXERCISE 8

Evaluate the sum of the terms of the infinite geometric sequence with $a_1 = -4$ and $r = \frac{2}{3}$.

EXAMPLE 8   Finding the Sum of the Terms of an Infinite Geometric Sequence

Evaluate the sum of the terms of the infinite geometric sequence with $a_1 = 3$ and $r = -\frac{1}{3}$.

Substitute into the formula.

$$S = \frac{a_1}{1 - r} \qquad \text{Infinite sum formula}$$

$$= \frac{3}{1 - \left(-\frac{1}{3}\right)} \qquad \text{Let } a_1 = 3, r = -\frac{1}{3}.$$

$$= \frac{3}{\frac{4}{3}} \qquad \text{Simplify the denominator.}$$

$$= 3 \div \frac{4}{3} \qquad \text{Write as division.}$$

$$= 3 \cdot \frac{3}{4} \qquad \text{Definition of division}$$

$$= \frac{9}{4} \qquad \text{Multiply.} \qquad \text{NOW TRY}$$

In summation notation, the sum of an infinite geometric sequence is written as

$$\sum_{i=1}^{\infty} a_i.$$

For instance, the sum in **Example 8** would be written

$$\sum_{i=1}^{\infty} 3\left(-\frac{1}{3}\right)^{i-1}.$$

NOW TRY
EXERCISE 9

Evaluate $\displaystyle\sum_{i=1}^{\infty} \left(\frac{5}{8}\right)\left(\frac{3}{4}\right)^{i}$.

EXAMPLE 9   Finding the Sum of the Terms of an Infinite Geometric Series

Evaluate $\displaystyle\sum_{i=1}^{\infty} \left(\frac{1}{2}\right)^{i}$.

This is the infinite geometric series

$$\frac{1}{2} + \frac{1}{4} + \frac{1}{8} + \cdots,$$

with $a_1 = \frac{1}{2}$ and $r = \frac{1}{2}$. Since $|r| < 1$, we find the sum as follows.

$$S = \frac{a_1}{1 - r}$$

$$= \frac{\frac{1}{2}}{1 - \frac{1}{2}} \qquad \text{Let } a_1 = \frac{1}{2}, r = \frac{1}{2}.$$

$$= \frac{\frac{1}{2}}{\frac{1}{2}} \qquad \text{Simplify the denominator.}$$

$$= 1 \qquad \text{Divide.} \qquad \text{NOW TRY}$$

NOW TRY ANSWERS
8. -12 **9.** $\frac{15}{8}$

14.3 EXERCISES

MyMathLab Math XL PRACTICE WATCH DOWNLOAD READ REVIEW

Complete solution available on the Video Resources on DVD

If the given sequence is geometric, find the common ratio r. If the sequence is not geometric, say so. See Example 1.

1. $4, 8, 16, 32, \ldots$

2. $5, 15, 45, 135, \ldots$

3. $\frac{1}{3}, \frac{2}{3}, \frac{3}{3}, \frac{4}{3}, \ldots$

4. $\frac{5}{7}, \frac{8}{7}, \frac{11}{7}, 2, \ldots$

5. $1, -3, 9, -27, 81, \ldots$

6. $2, -8, 32, -128, \ldots$

7. $1, -\frac{1}{2}, \frac{1}{4}, -\frac{1}{8}, \ldots$

8. $\frac{2}{3}, -\frac{2}{15}, \frac{2}{75}, -\frac{2}{375}, \ldots$

Find a general term for each geometric sequence. See Example 2.

9. $-5, -10, -20, \ldots$

10. $-2, -6, -18, \ldots$

11. $-2, \frac{2}{3}, -\frac{2}{9}, \ldots$

12. $-3, \frac{3}{2}, -\frac{3}{4}, \ldots$

13. $10, -2, \frac{2}{5}, \ldots$

14. $8, -2, \frac{1}{2}, \ldots$

Evaluate the indicated term for each geometric sequence. See Example 3.

15. $a_1 = 2, r = 5; \quad a_{10}$

16. $a_1 = 1, r = 3; \quad a_{15}$

17. $\frac{1}{2}, \frac{1}{6}, \frac{1}{18}, \ldots; \quad a_{12}$

18. $\frac{2}{3}, \frac{1}{3}, \frac{1}{6}, \ldots; \quad a_{18}$

19. $a_3 = \frac{1}{2}, a_7 = \frac{1}{32}; \quad a_{25}$

20. $a_5 = 48, a_8 = -384; \quad a_{10}$

Write the first five terms of each geometric sequence. See Example 4.

21. $a_1 = 2, r = 3$

22. $a_1 = 4, r = 2$

23. $a_1 = 5, r = -\frac{1}{5}$

24. $a_1 = 6, r = -\frac{1}{3}$

Use the formula for S_n to determine the sum of the terms of each geometric sequence. See Examples 5 and 6. In Exercises 27–32, give the answer to the nearest thousandth.

25. $\frac{1}{3}, \frac{1}{9}, \frac{1}{27}, \frac{1}{81}, \frac{1}{243}$

26. $\frac{4}{3}, \frac{8}{3}, \frac{16}{3}, \frac{32}{3}, \frac{64}{3}, \frac{128}{3}$

27. $-\frac{4}{3}, -\frac{4}{9}, -\frac{4}{27}, -\frac{4}{81}, -\frac{4}{243}, -\frac{4}{729}$

28. $\frac{5}{16}, -\frac{5}{32}, \frac{5}{64}, -\frac{5}{128}, \frac{5}{256}$

29. $\sum_{i=1}^{7} 4\left(\frac{2}{5}\right)^i$

30. $\sum_{i=1}^{8} 5\left(\frac{2}{3}\right)^i$

31. $\sum_{i=1}^{10} (-2)\left(\frac{3}{5}\right)^i$

32. $\sum_{i=1}^{6} (-2)\left(-\frac{1}{2}\right)^i$

Solve each problem involving an ordinary annuity. See Example 7.

33. A father opened a savings account for his daughter on her first birthday, depositing $1000. Each year on her birthday he deposits another $1000, making the last deposit on her 21st birthday. If the account pays 4.4% interest compounded annually, how much is in the account at the end of the day on the daughter's 21st birthday?

34. B. G. Thompson puts \$1000 in a retirement account at the end of each quarter $\left(\frac{1}{4} \text{ of a year}\right)$ for 15 yr. If the account pays 4% annual interest compounded quarterly, how much will be in the account at that time?

35. At the end of each quarter, a 50-year-old woman puts \$1200 in a retirement account that pays 5% interest compounded quarterly. When she reaches age 60, she withdraws the entire amount and places it in a mutual fund that pays 6% interest compounded monthly. From then on, she deposits \$300 in the mutual fund at the end of each month. How much is in the account when she reaches age 65?

36. Derrick Ruffin deposits \$10,000 at the end of each year for 12 yr in an account paying 5% compounded annually. He then puts the total amount on deposit in another account paying 6% compounded semiannually for another 9 yr. Find the final amount on deposit after the entire 21-yr period.

*Find the sum, if it exists, of the terms of each infinite geometric sequence. **See Examples 8 and 9.***

37. $a_1 = 6, r = \dfrac{1}{3}$

38. $a_1 = 10, r = \dfrac{1}{5}$

39. $a_1 = 1000, r = -\dfrac{1}{10}$

40. $a_1 = 8800, r = -\dfrac{3}{5}$

41. $\displaystyle\sum_{i=1}^{\infty} \dfrac{9}{8}\left(-\dfrac{2}{3}\right)^i$

42. $\displaystyle\sum_{i=1}^{\infty} \dfrac{3}{5}\left(\dfrac{5}{6}\right)^i$

43. $\displaystyle\sum_{i=1}^{\infty} \dfrac{12}{5}\left(\dfrac{5}{4}\right)^i$

44. $\displaystyle\sum_{i=1}^{\infty} \left(-\dfrac{16}{3}\right)\left(-\dfrac{9}{8}\right)^i$

Solve each application. (Hint: Immediately after reading the problem, determine whether you need to find a specific term of a sequence or the sum of the terms of a sequence.)

45. When dropped from a certain height, a ball rebounds $\frac{3}{5}$ of the original height. How high will the ball rebound after the fourth bounce if it was dropped from a height of 10 ft?

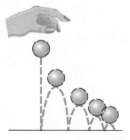

46. A fully wound yo-yo has a string 40 in. long. It is allowed to drop, and on its first rebound it returns to a height 15 in. lower than its original height. Assuming that this "rebound ratio" remains constant until the yo-yo comes to rest, how far does it travel on its third trip up the string?

47. A particular substance decays in such a way that it loses half its weight each day. In how many days will 256 g of the substance be reduced to 32 g? How much of the substance is left after 10 days?

48. A tracer dye is injected into a system with an ingestion and an excretion. After 1 hr, $\frac{2}{3}$ of the dye is left. At the end of the second hour, $\frac{2}{3}$ of the remaining dye is left, and so on. If one unit of the dye is injected, how much is left after 6 hr?

49. In a certain community, the consumption of electricity has increased about 6% per yr.

    (a) If a community uses 1.1 billion units of electricity now, how much will it use 5 yr from now?

    (b) Find the number of years it will take for the consumption to double.

50. Suppose the community in **Exercise 49** reduces its increase in consumption to 2% per yr.

    (a) How much will it use 5 yr from now?

    (b) Find the number of years it will take for the consumption to double.

51. A machine depreciates by $\frac{1}{4}$ of its value each year. If it cost \$50,000 new, what is its value after 8 yr?

52. Refer to **Exercise 46.** Theoretically, how far does the yo-yo travel before coming to rest?

RELATING CONCEPTS EXERCISES 53–58

FOR INDIVIDUAL OR GROUP WORK

*In **Chapter 1,** we learned that any repeating decimal is a rational number; that is, it can be expressed as a quotient of integers. Thus, the repeating decimal*

$$0.99999\ldots,$$

*with an endless string of 9s, must be a rational number. **Work Exercises 53–58 in order,** to discover the surprising simplest form of this rational number.*

53. Use long division to write a repeating decimal representation for $\frac{1}{3}$.

54. Use long division to write a repeating decimal representation for $\frac{2}{3}$.

55. Because $\frac{1}{3} + \frac{2}{3} = 1$, the sum of the decimal representations in **Exercises 53 and 54** must also equal 1. Line up the decimals in the usual vertical method for addition, and obtain the repeating decimal result. The value of this decimal is exactly 1.

56. The repeating decimal $0.99999\ldots$ can be written as the sum of the terms of a geometric sequence with $a_1 = 0.9$ and $r = 0.1$.

$$0.99999\ldots = 0.9 + 0.9(0.1) + 0.9(0.1)^2 + 0.9(0.1)^3 + 0.9(0.1)^4 + 0.9(0.1)^5 + \cdots$$

    Since $|0.1| < 1$, this sum can be found from the formula $S = \dfrac{a_1}{1 - r}$. Use this formula to support the result you found another way in **Exercises 53–55.**

57. Which one of the following is true, based on your results in **Exercises 55 and 56?**

    A. $0.99999\ldots < 1$ **B.** $0.99999\ldots = 1$ **C.** $0.99999\ldots \approx 1$

58. Show that $0.49999\ldots = \frac{1}{2}$.

PREVIEW EXERCISES

*Multiply. **See Section 4.6.***

59. $(3x + 2y)^2$ **60.** $(4x - 3y)^2$

61. $(a - b)^3$ **62.** $(x + y)^4$

14.4 The Binomial Theorem

OBJECTIVES

1 Expand a binomial raised to a power.

2 Find any specified term of the expansion of a binomial.

OBJECTIVE 1 **Expand a binomial raised to a power.** Observe the expansion of the expression $(x + y)^n$ for the first six nonnegative integer values of n.

$$(x + y)^0 = 1,$$
$$(x + y)^1 = x + y,$$
$$(x + y)^2 = x^2 + 2xy + y^2,$$
$$(x + y)^3 = x^3 + 3x^2y + 3xy^2 + y^3,$$
$$(x + y)^4 = x^4 + 4x^3y + 6x^2y^2 + 4xy^3 + y^4,$$
$$(x + y)^5 = x^5 + 5x^4y + 10x^3y^2 + 10x^2y^3 + 5xy^4 + y^5$$

Expansions of $(x + y)^n$

By identifying patterns, we can write a general expansion for $(x + y)^n$.

First, if n is a positive integer, each expansion after $(x + y)^0$ begins with x raised to the same power to which the binomial is raised. That is, the expansion of $(x + y)^1$ has a first term of x^1, the expansion of $(x + y)^2$ has a first term of x^2, and so on. Also, the last term in each expansion is y to this same power, so the expansion of $(x + y)^n$ should begin with the term x^n and end with the term y^n.

The exponents on x decrease by 1 in each term after the first, while the exponents on y, beginning with y in the second term, increase by 1 in each succeeding term. Thus, the *variables* in the expansion of $(x + y)^n$ have the following pattern.

$$x^n, \quad x^{n-1}y, \quad x^{n-2}y^2, \quad x^{n-3}y^3, \quad \ldots, \quad xy^{n-1}, \quad y^n$$

This pattern suggests that the sum of the exponents on x and y in each term is n. For example, in the third term shown, the variable part is $x^{n-2}y^2$ and the sum of the exponents, $n - 2$ and 2, is n.

Now examine the pattern for the *coefficients* of the terms of the preceding expansions. Writing the coefficients alone in a triangular pattern gives **Pascal's triangle,** named in honor of the 17th-century mathematician Blaise Pascal.

Blaise Pascal (1623–1662)

Pascal's Triangle

```
              1
            1   1
          1   2   1
        1   3   3   1
      1   4   6   4   1
    1   5  10  10   5   1      and so on
```

The first and last terms of each row are 1. Each number in the interior of the triangle is the sum of the two numbers just above it (one to the right and one to the left). For example, in the fifth row from the top, 4 is the sum of 1 and 3, 6 is the sum of 3 and 3, and so on.

To obtain the coefficients for $(x + y)^6$, we attach the seventh row to the table by starting and ending with 1, and adding pairs of numbers from the sixth row.

$$1 \quad 6 \quad 15 \quad 20 \quad 15 \quad 6 \quad 1 \quad \text{Seventh row}$$

We then use these coefficients to expand $(x + y)^6$ as

$$(x + y)^6 = x^6 + 6x^5y + 15x^4y^2 + 20x^3y^3 + 15x^2y^4 + 6xy^5 + y^6.$$

Although it is possible to use Pascal's triangle to find the coefficients in $(x + y)^n$ for any positive integer value of n, it is impractical for large values of n. A more efficient way to determine these coefficients uses the symbol **n!** (read **"n factorial"**), defined as follows.

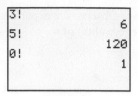

FIGURE 3

> **n Factorial (n!)**
>
> For any positive integer n,
> $$n! = n(n - 1)(n - 2)(n - 3) \cdots (2)(1).$$
> By definition, $0! = 1$.

NOW TRY
EXERCISE 1
Evaluate.

$$7!$$

EXAMPLE 1 Evaluating Factorials

Evaluate each factorial.

(a) $3! = 3 \cdot 2 \cdot 1 = 6$ **(b)** $5! = 5 \cdot 4 \cdot 3 \cdot 2 \cdot 1 = 120$

(c) $0! = 1$ 0! is defined to be 1.

FIGURE 3 shows how a graphing calculator computes factorials.   NOW TRY

NOW TRY
EXERCISE 2
Find the value of each expression.

(a) $\dfrac{8!}{6!2!}$ **(b)** $\dfrac{8!}{5!3!}$

(c) $\dfrac{6!}{6!0!}$ **(d)** $\dfrac{6!}{5!1!}$

EXAMPLE 2 Evaluating Expressions Involving Factorials

Find the value of each expression.

(a) $\dfrac{5!}{4!1!} = \dfrac{5 \cdot 4 \cdot 3 \cdot 2 \cdot 1}{(4 \cdot 3 \cdot 2 \cdot 1)(1)} = 5$

(b) $\dfrac{5!}{3!2!} = \dfrac{5 \cdot 4 \cdot 3 \cdot 2 \cdot 1}{(3 \cdot 2 \cdot 1)(2 \cdot 1)} = \dfrac{5 \cdot 4}{2 \cdot 1} = 10$

(c) $\dfrac{6!}{3!3!} = \dfrac{6 \cdot 5 \cdot 4 \cdot 3 \cdot 2 \cdot 1}{(3 \cdot 2 \cdot 1)(3 \cdot 2 \cdot 1)} = \dfrac{6 \cdot 5 \cdot 4}{3 \cdot 2 \cdot 1} = 20$

(d) $\dfrac{4!}{4!0!} = \dfrac{4 \cdot 3 \cdot 2 \cdot 1}{(4 \cdot 3 \cdot 2 \cdot 1)(1)} = 1$ NOW TRY

Now look again at the coefficients of the expansion

$$\bullet \quad (x + y)^5 = x^5 + 5x^4y + 10x^3y^2 + 10x^2y^3 + 5xy^4 + y^5.$$

The coefficient of the second term is 5, and the exponents on the variables in that term are 4 and 1. From **Example 2(a)**, $\frac{5!}{4!1!} = 5$. The coefficient of the third term is 10, and the exponents are 3 and 2. From **Example 2(b)**, $\frac{5!}{3!2!} = 10$. Similar results are true for the remaining terms. The first term can be written as $1x^5y^0$, and the last term can be written as $1x^0y^5$. Then the coefficient of the first term should be $\frac{5!}{5!0!} = 1$, and the coefficient of the last term would be $\frac{5!}{0!5!} = 1$.

The coefficient of a term in $(x + y)^n$ in which the variable part is $x^r y^{n-r}$ is

$$\frac{n!}{r!(n - r)!}. \quad \text{This is called a \textbf{binomial coefficient.}}$$

The binomial coefficient $\frac{n!}{r!(n - r)!}$ is often represented by the symbol $_nC_r$. This notation comes from the fact that if we choose *combinations* of n things taken r at a time, the result is given by that expression. We read $_nC_r$ as **"combinations of n things taken r at a time."** Another common representation is $\binom{n}{r}$.

NOW TRY ANSWERS
1. 5040
2. (a) 28   (b) 56   (c) 1   (d) 6

Formula for the Binomial Coefficient $_nC_r$

For nonnegative integers n and r, where $r \leq n$,

$$_nC_r = \frac{n!}{r!(n-r)!}.$$

NOW TRY
EXERCISE 3

Evaluate $_7C_2$.

EXAMPLE 3 Evaluating Binomial Coefficients

Evaluate each binomial coefficient.

(a) $_5C_4 = \dfrac{5!}{4!(5-4)!}$ Let $n = 5$, $r = 4$.

$ = \dfrac{5!}{4!1!}$ Subtract.

$ = \dfrac{5 \cdot 4 \cdot 3 \cdot 2 \cdot 1}{4 \cdot 3 \cdot 2 \cdot 1 \cdot 1}$ Definition of n factorial

$ = 5$ Lowest terms

Binomial coefficients will always be whole numbers.

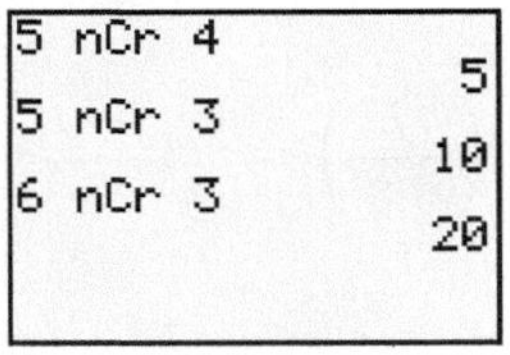

```
5 nCr 4
              5
5 nCr 3
             10
6 nCr 3
             20
```

FIGURE 4

(b) $_5C_3 = \dfrac{5!}{3!(5-3)!} = \dfrac{5!}{3!2!} = \dfrac{5 \cdot 4 \cdot 3 \cdot 2 \cdot 1}{3 \cdot 2 \cdot 1 \cdot 2 \cdot 1} = 10$

(c) $_6C_3 = \dfrac{6!}{3!(6-3)!} = \dfrac{6!}{3!3!} = \dfrac{6 \cdot 5 \cdot 4 \cdot 3 \cdot 2 \cdot 1}{3 \cdot 2 \cdot 1 \cdot 3 \cdot 2 \cdot 1} = 20$

FIGURE 4 shows how a graphing calculator displays the binomial coefficients computed here.

NOW TRY

We now state the **binomial theorem,** or the **general binomial expansion.**

Binomial Theorem

For any positive integer n,

$$(x + y)^n = x^n + \frac{n!}{1!(n-1)!}x^{n-1}y + \frac{n!}{2!(n-2)!}x^{n-2}y^2$$

$$+ \frac{n!}{3!(n-3)!}x^{n-3}y^3 + \cdots + \frac{n!}{(n-1)!1!}xy^{n-1} + y^n.$$

The binomial theorem can be written in summation notation as

$$(x + y)^n = \sum_{k=0}^{n} \frac{n!}{k!(n-k)!}x^{n-k}y^k.$$

NOTE We used the letter k as the summation index letter in the statement just given. This is customary notation in mathematics.

NOW TRY ANSWER
3. 21

NOW TRY
EXERCISE 4

Expand $(a + 3b)^5$.

EXAMPLE 4 Using the Binomial Theorem

Expand $(2m + 3)^4$.

$$(2m + 3)^4$$

$$= (2m)^4 + \frac{4!}{1!3!}(2m)^3(3) + \frac{4!}{2!2!}(2m)^2(3)^2 + \frac{4!}{3!1!}(2m)(3)^3 + 3^4$$

Remember:
$(ab)^m = a^m b^m$

$$= 16m^4 + 4(8m^3)(3) + 6(4m^2)(9) + 4(2m)(27) + 81$$

$$= 16m^4 + 96m^3 + 216m^2 + 216m + 81 \qquad \text{NOW TRY}$$

NOW TRY
EXERCISE 5

Expand $\left(\dfrac{x}{3} - 2y\right)^4$.

EXAMPLE 5 Using the Binomial Theorem

Expand $\left(a - \dfrac{b}{2}\right)^5$.

$$\left(a - \frac{b}{2}\right)^5$$

$$= a^5 + \frac{5!}{1!4!}a^4\left(-\frac{b}{2}\right) + \frac{5!}{2!3!}a^3\left(-\frac{b}{2}\right)^2 + \frac{5!}{3!2!}a^2\left(-\frac{b}{2}\right)^3$$

$$+ \frac{5!}{4!1!}a\left(-\frac{b}{2}\right)^4 + \left(-\frac{b}{2}\right)^5$$

$$= a^5 + 5a^4\left(-\frac{b}{2}\right) + 10a^3\left(\frac{b^2}{4}\right) + 10a^2\left(-\frac{b^3}{8}\right)$$

$$+ 5a\left(\frac{b^4}{16}\right) + \left(-\frac{b^5}{32}\right)$$

Notice that signs alternate positive and negative.

$$= a^5 - \frac{5}{2}a^4b + \frac{5}{2}a^3b^2 - \frac{5}{4}a^2b^3 + \frac{5}{16}ab^4 - \frac{1}{32}b^5 \quad \text{NOW TRY}$$

⚠ **CAUTION** When the binomial is the *difference* of two terms, as in **Example 5,** the signs of the terms in the expansion will alternate. Those terms with odd exponents on the second variable expression $\left(-\frac{b}{2} \text{ in } \textbf{Example 5}\right)$ will be negative, while those with even exponents on the second variable expression will be positive.

OBJECTIVE 2 Find any specified term of the expansion of a binomial. Any single term of a binomial expansion can be determined without writing out the whole expansion. For example, if $n \geq 10$, then the 10th term of $(x + y)^n$ has y raised to the ninth power (since y has the power of 1 in the second term, the power of 2 in the third term, and so on). Since the exponents on x and y in any term must have a sum of n, the exponent on x in the 10th term is $n - 9$. The quantities 9 and $n - 9$ determine the factorials in the denominator of the coefficient. Thus, the 10th term of $(x + y)^n$ is

$$\frac{n!}{9!(n - 9)!}x^{n-9}y^9.$$

NOW TRY ANSWERS
4. $a^5 + 15a^4b + 90a^3b^2 + 270a^2b^3 + 405ab^4 + 243b^5$
5. $\dfrac{x^4}{81} - \dfrac{8x^3y}{27} + \dfrac{8x^2y^2}{3} - \dfrac{32xy^3}{3} + 16y^4$

rth Term of the Binomial Expansion

If $n \geq r - 1$, then the rth term of the expansion of $(x + y)^n$ is

$$\frac{n!}{(r - 1)![n - (r - 1)]!}x^{n-(r-1)}y^{r-1}.$$

In this general expression, remember to start with the exponent on y, which is 1 less than the term number r. Then subtract that exponent from n to get the exponent on x: $n - (r - 1)$. The two exponents are then used as the factorials in the denominator of the coefficient.

NOW TRY
EXERCISE 6
Find the sixth term of the expansion of $(2m - n^2)^8$.

EXAMPLE 6 Finding a Single Term of a Binomial Expansion

Find the fourth term of the expansion of $(a + 2b)^{10}$.

In the fourth term, $2b$ has an exponent of $4 - 1 = 3$ and a has an exponent of $10 - 3 = 7$. The fourth term is determined as follows.

$$\frac{10!}{3!7!}(a^7)(2b)^3 \quad \boxed{\text{Parentheses MUST be used for } 2b.}$$

$$= \frac{10 \cdot 9 \cdot 8}{3 \cdot 2 \cdot 1}(a^7)(8b^3) \qquad \text{Let } n = 10, x = a, y = 2b, r = 4.$$

$$= 120a^7(8b^3) \qquad \text{Simplify the factorials.}$$

$$= 960a^7b^3 \qquad \text{Multiply.} \qquad \text{NOW TRY}$$

NOW TRY ANSWER
6. $-448m^3n^{10}$

14.4 EXERCISES

MyMathLab | Math XL PRACTICE | WATCH | DOWNLOAD | READ | REVIEW

🌐 *Complete solution available on the Video Resources on DVD*

Evaluate each expression. See Examples 1–3.

🌐 **1.** $6!$ **2.** $4!$ **3.** $8!$ **4.** $9!$ 🌐 **5.** $\dfrac{6!}{4!2!}$

6. $\dfrac{7!}{3!4!}$ **7.** $\dfrac{4!}{0!4!}$ **8.** $\dfrac{5!}{5!0!}$ **9.** $4! \cdot 5$ **10.** $6! \cdot 7$

🌐 **11.** $_6C_2$ **12.** $_7C_4$ **13.** $_{13}C_{11}$ **14.** $_{13}C_2$

Use the binomial theorem to expand each expression. See Examples 4 and 5.

15. $(m + n)^4$ **16.** $(x + r)^5$ **17.** $(a - b)^5$ **18.** $(p - q)^4$

🌐 **19.** $(2x + 3)^3$ **20.** $(4x + 2)^3$ 🌐 **21.** $\left(\dfrac{x}{2} - y\right)^4$ **22.** $\left(\dfrac{x}{3} - 2y\right)^5$

23. $(x^2 + 1)^4$ **24.** $(y^3 + 2)^4$ **25.** $(3x^2 - y^2)^3$ **26.** $(2p^2 - q^2)^3$

Write the first four terms of each binomial expansion. See Examples 4 and 5.

27. $(r + 2s)^{12}$ **28.** $(m + 3n)^{20}$ **29.** $(3x - y)^{14}$

30. $(2p - 3q)^{11}$ **31.** $(t^2 + u^2)^{10}$ **32.** $(x^2 + y^2)^{15}$

Find the indicated term of each binomial expansion. See Example 6.

🌐 **33.** $(2m + n)^{10}$; fourth term   **34.** $(a + 3b)^{12}$; fifth term

35. $\left(x + \dfrac{y}{2}\right)^8$; seventh term   **36.** $\left(a + \dfrac{b}{3}\right)^{15}$; eighth term

37. $(k - 1)^9$; third term   **38.** $(r - 4)^{11}$; fourth term

39. The middle term of $(x^2 + 2y)^6$ **40.** The middle term of $(m^3 + 2y)^8$

41. The term with x^9y^4 in $(3x^3 - 4y^2)^5$ **42.** The term with x^8y^2 in $(2x^2 + 3y)^6$

CHAPTER **14** SUMMARY

KEY TERMS

14.1
infinite sequence
finite sequence
terms of a sequence
general term
series
summation notation

index of summation
arithmetic mean (average)

14.2
arithmetic sequence
  (arithmetic progression)
common difference

14.3
geometric sequence
  (geometric progression)
common ratio
annuity
ordinary annuity
payment period

future value of an annuity
term of an annuity

14.4
Pascal's triangle
binomial theorem (general
  binomial expansion)

NEW SYMBOLS

a_n nth term of a
     sequence

$\sum\limits_{i=1}^{n} a_i$ summation notation

S_n sum of first n terms
     of a sequence

$\lim\limits_{n \to \infty} a_n$ limit of a_n as n gets
     larger and larger

$\sum\limits_{i=1}^{\infty} a_i$ sum of an infinite
     number of terms

$n!$ n factorial

$_nC_r$ binomial coefficient
     (combinations of n
     things taken r at a time)

TEST YOUR WORD POWER

See how well you have learned the vocabulary in this chapter.

1. An **infinite sequence** is
   A. the values of a function
   B. a function whose domain is the
      set of positive integers
   C. the sum of the terms of a function
   D. the average of a group of
      numbers.

2. A **series** is
   A. the sum of the terms of a
      sequence
   B. the product of the terms of a
      sequence
   C. the average of the terms of a
      sequence
   D. the function values of a sequence.

3. An **arithmetic sequence** is a
   sequence in which
   A. each term after the first is a
      constant multiple of the
      preceding term

   B. the numbers are written in a
      triangular array
   C. the terms are added
   D. each term after the first differs
      from the preceding term by a
      common amount.

4. A **geometric sequence** is a sequence
   in which
   A. each term after the first is a
      constant multiple of the
      preceding term
   B. the numbers are written in a
      triangular array
   C. the terms are multiplied
   D. each term after the first differs
      from the preceding term by a
      common amount.

5. The **common difference** is
   A. the average of the terms in a
      sequence

   B. the constant multiplier in a
      geometric sequence
   C. the difference between any two
      adjacent terms in an arithmetic
      sequence
   D. the sum of the terms of an
      arithmetic sequence.

6. The **common ratio** is
   A. the average of the terms in a
      sequence
   B. the constant multiplier in a
      geometric sequence
   C. the difference between any two
      adjacent terms in an arithmetic
      sequence
   D. the product of the terms of a
      geometric sequence.

ANSWERS

1. B; *Example:* The ordered list of numbers 3, 6, 9, 12, 15, . . . is an infinite sequence.

2. A; *Example:* $3 + 6 + 9 + 12 + 15$, written in summation notation as $\sum\limits_{i=1}^{5} 3i$, is a series.

3. D; *Example:* The sequence $-3, 2, 7, 12, 17, \ldots$ is arithmetic.

4. A; *Example:* The sequence 1, 4, 16, 64, 256, . . . is geometric.

5. C; *Example:* The common difference of the arithmetic sequence in Answer 3 is 5, since $2 - (-3) = 5$, $7 - 2 = 5$, and so on.

6. B; *Example:* The common ratio of the geometric sequence in Answer 4 is 4, since $\frac{4}{1} = \frac{16}{4} = \frac{64}{16} = \frac{256}{64} = 4$.

QUICK REVIEW

CONCEPTS	EXAMPLES

14.1 Sequences and Series

A finite sequence is a function with domain

$$\{1, 2, 3, \ldots n\},$$

while an infinite sequence has domain

$$\{1, 2, 3, \ldots \}.$$

The nth term of a sequence is symbolized a_n. A series is an indicated sum of the terms of a sequence.

$1, \dfrac{1}{2}, \dfrac{1}{3}, \dfrac{1}{4}, \ldots, \dfrac{1}{n}$ has general term $a_n = \dfrac{1}{n}$.

The corresponding series is the *sum*

$$1 + \frac{1}{2} + \frac{1}{3} + \frac{1}{4} + \cdots + \frac{1}{n} = \sum_{i=1}^{n} \frac{1}{i}.$$

14.2 Arithmetic Sequences

Assume that a_1 is the first term, a_n is the nth term, and d is the common difference.

Common Difference

$$d = a_{n+1} - a_n$$

Consider the arithmetic sequence

$$2, 5, 8, 11, \ldots.$$

$a_1 = 2$ a_1 is the first term.

$d = 5 - 2 = 3$ Use $a_2 - a_1$.

(Any two successive terms could have been used.)

nth Term

$$a_n = a_1 + (n - 1)d$$

The tenth term is

$$a_{10} = 2 + (10 - 1)(3) \quad \text{Let } n = 10.$$
$$= 2 + 9 \cdot 3, \quad \text{or} \quad 29.$$

Sum of the First n Terms

$$S_n = \frac{n}{2}(a_1 + a_n)$$

or

$$S_n = \frac{n}{2}[2a_1 + (n - 1)d]$$

The sum of the first ten terms can be found in either way.

$$S_{10} = \frac{10}{2}(2 + a_{10}) \qquad \qquad S_{10} = \frac{10}{2}[2(2) + (10 - 1)(3)]$$
$$= 5(2 + 29) \qquad \qquad \qquad = 5(4 + 9 \cdot 3)$$
$$= 5(31) \qquad \qquad \qquad \qquad = 5(4 + 27)$$
$$= 155 \qquad \qquad \qquad \qquad = 5(31)$$
$$\qquad \qquad \qquad \qquad \qquad = 155$$

14.3 Geometric Sequences

Assume that a_1 is the first term, a_n is the nth term, and r is the common ratio.

Common Ratio

$$r = \frac{a_{n+1}}{a_n}$$

Consider the geometric sequence

$$1, 2, 4, 8, \ldots.$$

$a_1 = 1$ a_1 is the first term.

$r = \dfrac{8}{4} = 2$ Use $\dfrac{a_4}{a_3}$.

(Any two successive terms could have been used.)

nth Term

$$a_n = a_1 r^{n-1}$$

The sixth term is

$$a_6 = (1)(2)^{6-1} = 1(2)^5 = 32. \quad \text{Let } n = 6.$$

Sum of the First n Terms

$$S_n = \frac{a_1(1 - r^n)}{1 - r} \quad (r \neq 1)$$

The sum of the first six terms is

$$S_6 = \frac{1(1 - 2^6)}{1 - 2} = \frac{1 - 64}{-1} = 63.$$

(continued)

CONCEPTS	EXAMPLES
Future Value of an Ordinary Annuity $$S = R\left[\frac{(1 + i)^n - 1}{i}\right],$$ where S is the future value, R is the payment at the end of each period, i is the interest rate per period, and n is the number of periods.	If \$5800 is deposited into an ordinary annuity at the end of each quarter for 4 yr and interest is earned at 2.4% compounded quarterly, then $$R = \$5800, \quad i = \frac{0.024}{4} = 0.006, \quad n = 4(4) = 16,$$ and $$S = 5800\left[\frac{(1 + 0.006)^{16} - 1}{0.006}\right] = \$97,095.24.$$
Sum of the Terms of an Infinite Geometric Sequence with $|r| < 1$ $$S = \frac{a_1}{1 - r}$$	The sum S of the terms of an infinite geometric sequence with $a_1 = 1$ and $r = \frac{1}{2}$ is $$S = \frac{1}{1 - \frac{1}{2}} = \frac{1}{\frac{1}{2}} = 1 \cdot \frac{2}{1} = 2.$$

14.4 The Binomial Theorem

Factorials For any positive integer n, $$n! = n(n - 1)(n - 2) \cdots (2)(1).$$ By definition, $\qquad$ $0! = 1.$	$$4! = 4 \cdot 3 \cdot 2 \cdot 1 = 24$$
Binomial Coefficient $${}_nC_r = \frac{n!}{r!(n - r)!}, \quad r \le n$$	$${}_5C_3 = \frac{5!}{3!(5 - 3)!} = \frac{5!}{3!2!} = \frac{5 \cdot 4 \cdot 3 \cdot 2 \cdot 1}{3 \cdot 2 \cdot 1 \cdot 2 \cdot 1} = 10$$
General Binomial Expansion For any positive integer n, $(x + y)^n$ $$= x^n + \frac{n!}{1!(n - 1)!}x^{n-1}y + \frac{n!}{2!(n - 2)!}x^{n-2}y^2$$ $$+ \frac{n!}{3!(n - 3)!}x^{n-3}y^3 + \cdots + \frac{n!}{(n - 1)!1!}xy^{n-1}$$ $$+ y^n.$$	$(2x - 3)^4$ $$= (2x)^4 + \frac{4!}{1!3!}(2x)^3(-3) + \frac{4!}{2!2!}(2x)^2(-3)^2 +$$ $$\frac{4!}{3!1!}(2x)(-3)^3 + (-3)^4$$ $$= 2^4x^4 - 4(2)^3x^3(3) + 6(2)^2x^2(9) - 4(2x)(27) + 81$$ $$= 16x^4 - 12(8)x^3 + 54(4)x^2 - 216x + 81$$ $$= 16x^4 - 96x^3 + 216x^2 - 216x + 81$$
rth Term of the Binomial Expansion of $(x + y)^n$ $$\frac{n!}{(r - 1)![n - (r - 1)]!}x^{n-(r-1)}y^{r-1}$$	The eighth term of $(a - 2b)^{10}$ is $$\frac{10!}{7!3!}a^3(-2b)^7$$ $$= \frac{10 \cdot 9 \cdot 8}{3 \cdot 2 \cdot 1}a^3(-2)^7b^7 \qquad \begin{array}{l} n = 10, \ x = a, \\ y = -2b, \ r = 8 \end{array}$$ $$= 120(-128)a^3b^7 \qquad \text{Simplify.}$$ $$= -15,360a^3b^7. \qquad \text{Multiply.}$$

CHAPTER (14)

REVIEW EXERCISES

14.1 *Write out the first four terms of each sequence.*

1. $a_n = 2n - 3$

2. $a_n = \dfrac{n-1}{n}$

3. $a_n = n^2$

4. $a_n = \left(\dfrac{1}{2}\right)^n$

5. $a_n = (n + 1)(n - 1)$

6. $a_n = n(-1)^{n-1}$

Write each series as a sum of terms.

7. $\displaystyle\sum_{i=1}^{5} i^2$

8. $\displaystyle\sum_{i=1}^{6} (i + 1)$

9. $\displaystyle\sum_{i=3}^{6} (5i - 4)$

Evaluate each series.

10. $\displaystyle\sum_{i=1}^{4} (i + 2)$

11. $\displaystyle\sum_{i=1}^{6} 2^i$

12. $\displaystyle\sum_{i=4}^{7} \dfrac{i}{i + 1}$

13. Find the arithmetic mean, or average, of the total retirement assets of Americans for the years 2004 through 2008 shown in the table. Round to the nearest unit (in billions).

Year	Assets (in billions of dollars)
2004	13,778
2005	14,862
2006	16,680
2007	17,916
2008	13,985

Source: Investment Company Institute.

14.2–14.3 *Decide whether each sequence is* arithmetic, geometric, *or* neither. *If the sequence is arithmetic, find the common difference d. If it is geometric, find the common ratio r.*

14. 2, 5, 8, 11, . . .

15. −6, −2, 2, 6, 10, . . .

16. $\dfrac{2}{3}, -\dfrac{1}{3}, \dfrac{1}{6}, -\dfrac{1}{12}, \ldots$

17. −1, 1, −1, 1, −1, . . .

18. 64, 32, 8, $\dfrac{1}{2}$, . . .

19. 64, 32, 16, 8, . . .

20. *Concept Check*   Refer to the Chapter Opener on **page 855**. What is the eleventh term of the Fibonacci sequence?

14.2 *Determine the indicated term of each arithmetic sequence.*

21. $a_1 = -2, d = 5;\quad a_{16}$

22. $a_6 = 12, a_8 = 18;\quad a_{25}$

Determine the general term of each arithmetic sequence.

23. $a_1 = -4, d = -5$

24. 6, 3, 0, −3, . . .

Determine the number of terms in each arithmetic sequence.

25. 7, 10, 13, . . . , 49

26. 5, 1, −3, . . . , −79

Evaluate S_8 for each arithmetic sequence.

27. $a_1 = -2, d = 6$

28. $a_n = -2 + 5n$

14.3 *Determine the general term for each geometric sequence.*

29. −1, −4, −16, . . .

30. $\dfrac{2}{3}, \dfrac{2}{15}, \dfrac{2}{75}, \ldots$

Determine the indicated term for each geometric sequence.

31. $2, -6, 18, \ldots;$ a_{11}

32. $a_3 = 20, a_5 = 80;$ a_{10}

Evaluate each sum if it exists.

33. $\displaystyle\sum_{i=1}^{5} \left(\frac{1}{4}\right)^i$

34. $\displaystyle\sum_{i=1}^{8} \frac{3}{4}(-1)^i$

35. $\displaystyle\sum_{i=1}^{\infty} 4\left(\frac{1}{5}\right)^i$

36. $\displaystyle\sum_{i=1}^{\infty} 2(3)^i$

14.4 *Use the binomial theorem to expand each binomial.*

37. $(2p - q)^5$

38. $(x^2 + 3y)^4$

39. $(3t^3 - s^2)^4$

40. Write the fourth term of the expansion of $(3a + 2b)^{19}$.

MIXED REVIEW EXERCISES

Determine the indicated term and evaluate S_{10} for each sequence.

41. a_{10}: geometric; $-3, 6, -12, \ldots$

42. a_{40}: arithmetic; $1, 7, 13, \ldots$

43. a_{15}: arithmetic; $a_1 = -4,$ $d = 3$

44. a_9: geometric; $a_1 = 1,$ $r = -3$

Determine the general term for each arithmetic or geometric sequence.

45. $2, 8, 32, \ldots$

46. $2, 7, 12, \ldots$

47. $12, 9, 6, \ldots$

48. $27, 9, 3, \ldots$

Solve each problem.

49. When Faith's sled goes down the hill near her home, she covers 3 ft in the first second. Then, for each second after that, she goes 4 ft more than in the preceding second. If the distance she covers going down is 210 ft, how long does it take her to reach the bottom?

50. An ordinary annuity is set up so that $672 is deposited at the end of each quarter for 7 yr. The money earns 4.5% annual interest compounded quarterly. What is the future value of the annuity?

51. The school population in Middleton has been dropping 3% per yr. The current population is 50,000. If this trend continues, what will the population be in 6 yr?

52. A pump removes $\frac{1}{2}$ of the liquid in a container with each stroke. What fraction of the liquid is left in the container after seven strokes?

53. Consider the repeating decimal number $0.55555\ldots$.

   (a) Write it as the sum of the terms of an infinite geometric sequence.

   (b) What is r for this sequence?

   (c) Find this infinite sum if it exists, and write it as a common fraction in lowest terms.

54. Can the sum of the terms of the infinite geometric sequence defined by $a_n = 5(2)^n$ be found? Explain.

CHAPTER 14

Test

View the complete solutions to all Chapter Test exercises on the Video Resources on DVD.

Write the first five terms of each sequence described.

1. $a_n = (-1)^n + 1$

2. arithmetic, with $a_1 = 4$ and $d = 2$

3. geometric, with $a_4 = 6$ and $r = \frac{1}{2}$

Determine a_4 for each sequence described.

4. arithmetic, with $a_1 = 6$ and $d = -2$

5. geometric, with $a_5 = 16$ and $a_7 = 9$

Evaluate S_5 for each sequence described.

6. arithmetic, with $a_2 = 12$ and $a_3 = 15$

7. geometric, with $a_5 = 4$ and $a_7 = 1$

8. The numbers of commercial bank offices (main offices and branches) in the United States for the years 2004 through 2008 are given in the table. What was the average number of banks per year for that period? Round to the nearest unit.

Year	Number
2004	78,473
2005	80,967
2006	83,860
2007	86,150
2008	97,103

Source: U.S. Federal Deposit Insurance Corporation.

9. If $4000 is deposited in an ordinary annuity at the end of each quarter for 7 yr and earns 6% interest compounded quarterly, how much will be in the account at the end of this term?

10. *Concept Check*   Under what conditions does an infinite geometric series have a sum?

Determine each sum that exists.

11. $\displaystyle\sum_{i=1}^{5} (2i + 8)$

12. $\displaystyle\sum_{i=1}^{6} (3i - 5)$

13. $\displaystyle\sum_{i=1}^{500} i$

14. $\displaystyle\sum_{i=1}^{3} \frac{1}{2}(4^i)$

15. $\displaystyle\sum_{i=1}^{\infty} \left(\frac{1}{4}\right)^i$

16. $\displaystyle\sum_{i=1}^{\infty} 6\left(\frac{3}{2}\right)^i$

Evaluate.

17. $8!$

18. $0!$

19. $\dfrac{6!}{4!2!}$

20. $_{12}C_{10}$

21. Expand $(3k - 5)^4$.

22. Write the fifth term of the expansion of $\left(2x - \dfrac{y}{3}\right)^{12}$.

Solve each problem.

23. Christian Sabau bought a new dishwasher for $300. He agreed to pay $20 per month for 15 months, plus interest of 1% each month, on the unpaid balance. Find the total cost of the machine.

24. During the summer months, the population of a certain insect colony triples each week. If there are 20 insects in the colony at the end of the first week in July, how many are present by the end of September? (Assume exactly four weeks in a month.)

CHAPTERS (1–14)

CUMULATIVE REVIEW EXERCISES

Simplify each expression.

1. $|-7| + 6 - |-10| - (-8 + 3)$ **2.** $4(-6) + (-8)(5) - (-9)$

Let $P = \left\{-\frac{8}{3}, 10, 0, \sqrt{13}, -\sqrt{3}, \frac{45}{15}, \sqrt{-7}, 0.82, -3\right\}$. *List the elements of P that are members of each set.*

3. Rational numbers   **4.** Irrational numbers

Solve each equation or inequality.

5. $9 - (5 + 3x) + 5x = -4(x - 3) - 7$ **6.** $7x + 18 \le 9x - 2$

7. $|4x - 3| = 21$ **8.** $\dfrac{x + 3}{12} - \dfrac{x - 3}{6} = 0$

9. $2x > 8$ or $-3x > 9$ **10.** $|2x - 5| \ge 11$

11. $2x^2 + x = 10$ **12.** $x^2 - x - 6 \le 0$

13. $\dfrac{4}{x - 3} - \dfrac{6}{x + 3} = \dfrac{24}{x^2 - 9}$ **14.** $6x^2 + 5x = 8$

15. $3^{2x-1} = 81$ **16.** $\log_8 x + \log_8 (x + 2) = 1$

Perform the indicated operations.

17. $(4p + 2)(5p - 3)$ **18.** $(3k - 7)^2$

19. $(2m^3 - 3m^2 + 8m) - (7m^3 + 5m - 8)$

20. Divide $6t^4 + 5t^3 - 18t^2 + 14t - 1$ by $3t - 2$.

Factor.

21. $6z^3 + 5z^2 - 4z$ **22.** $49a^4 - 9b^2$ **23.** $c^3 + 27d^3$

Simplify.

24. $\left(\dfrac{2}{3}\right)^{-2}$ **25.** $\dfrac{(3p^2)^3(-2p^6)}{4p^3(5p^7)}$

26. $\dfrac{x^2 - 16}{x^2 + 2x - 8} \div \dfrac{x - 4}{x + 7}$ **27.** $\dfrac{5}{p^2 + 3p} - \dfrac{2}{p^2 - 4p}$

28. $5\sqrt{72} - 4\sqrt{50}$ **29.** $(8 + 3i)(8 - 3i)$

30. Find the slope of the line through $(4, -5)$ and $(-12, -17)$.

31. Find the standard form of the equation of the line through $(-2, 10)$ and parallel to the line with equation $3x + y = 7$.

32. Consider the set of ordered pairs.

$$\{(-3, 2), (-2, 6), (0, 4), (1, 2), (2, 6)\}$$

(a) Is this a function?   **(b)** What is its domain?   **(c)** What is its range?

Solve each system of equations.

33. $y = 5x + 3$
$2x + 3y = -8$

34. $x + 2y + z = 8$
$2x - y + 3z = 15$
$-x + 3y - 3z = -11$

35. $xy = -5$
$2x + y = 3$

36. Nuts worth $3 per lb are to be mixed with 8 lb of nuts worth $4.25 per lb to obtain a mixture that will be sold for $4 per lb. How many pounds of the $3 nuts should be used?

Graph.

37. $x - 3y = 6$

38. $4x - y < 4$

39. $f(x) = 2(x - 2)^2 - 3$

40. $\dfrac{x^2}{9} + \dfrac{y^2}{25} = 1$

41. $x^2 - y^2 = 9$

42. $g(x) = \left(\dfrac{1}{3}\right)^x$

43. $y = \log_{1/3} x$

44. Find $f^{-1}(x)$ if $f(x) = 9x + 5$.

45. Find the equation of a circle with center at $(-5, 12)$ and radius 9.

46. Write the first five terms of the sequence defined by $a_n = 5n - 12$.

47. Find each sum.

(a) The sum of the first six terms of the arithmetic sequence with $a_1 = 8$ and $d = 2$

(b) The sum of the geometric series $15 - 6 + \frac{12}{5} - \frac{24}{25} + \cdots$

48. Find the sum $\displaystyle\sum_{i=1}^{4} 3i$.

49. Use the binomial theorem to expand $(2a - 1)^5$.

50. What is the fourth term in the expansion of $\left(3x^4 - \frac{1}{2}y^2\right)^5$?

Sets

OBJECTIVES

1 Learn the vocabulary and symbols used to discuss sets.

2 Decide whether a set is finite or infinite.

3 Decide whether a given set is a subset of another set.

4 Find the complement of a set.

5 Find the union and the intersection of two sets.

OBJECTIVE 1 **Learn the vocabulary and symbols used to discuss sets.** A **set** is a collection of objects. These objects are called the **elements** of the set. A set is represented by listing its elements between **braces,** { }.* The order in which the elements of a set are listed is unimportant.

Capital letters are used to name sets. To state that 5 is an element of

$$S = \{1, 2, 3, 4, 5\},$$

write $5 \in S$. The statement $6 \notin S$ means that 6 is not an element of S.

The set with no elements is called the **empty set,** or the **null set.** The symbol $\emptyset$ or { } is used for the empty set. If we let A be the set of all negative natural numbers, then A is the empty set.

$$A = \emptyset \quad \text{or} \quad A = \{ \ \}$$

⚠ **CAUTION** Do not make the common error of writing the empty set as $\{\emptyset\}$.

EXAMPLE 1 Listing the Elements of Sets

Represent each set by listing its elements.

(a) The set of states in the United States that border the Pacific Ocean is

{California, Oregon, Washington, Hawaii, Alaska}.

(b) The set of all counting numbers less than $6 = \{1, 2, 3, 4, 5\}$.

(c) The set of all counting numbers less than $0 = \emptyset$ NOW TRY

In any discussion of sets, there is some set that includes all the elements under consideration. This set is called the **universal set** for that situation. For example, if the discussion is about presidents of the United States, then the set of all presidents of the United States is the universal set. The universal set is denoted U.

OBJECTIVE 2 **Decide whether a set is finite or infinite.** In **Example 1,** there are five elements in the set in part (a) and five in part (b). If the number of elements in a set is either 0 or a counting number, then the set is **finite.** By contrast, the set of natural numbers is an **infinite** set, because there is no final natural number. We can list the elements of the set of natural numbers as

$$N = \{1, 2, 3, 4, \ldots\},$$

where the three dots indicate that the set continues indefinitely. Not all infinite sets can be listed in this way. For example, there is no way to list the elements in the set of all real numbers between 1 and 2.

NOW TRY
EXERCISE 1

List the elements of the set of odd natural numbers less than 13.

NOW TRY ANSWER
1. {1, 3, 5, 7, 9, 11}

---

*Some people refer to this convention as *roster notation*.

893

NOW TRY
EXERCISE 2

List the elements of each set if possible. Decide whether each set is finite or infinite.

(a) The set of negative integers

(b) The set of even natural numbers between 11 and 19

EXAMPLE 2 Distinguishing between Finite and Infinite Sets

List the elements of each set if possible. Decide whether each set is finite or infinite.

(a) The set of all integers

One way to list the elements is $\{ \ldots, -2, -1, 0, 1, 2, \ldots \}$. The set is infinite.

(b) The set of all natural numbers between 0 and 5

$\{1, 2, 3, 4\}$ The set is finite.

(c) The set of all irrational numbers

This is an infinite set whose elements cannot be listed.   NOW TRY

Two sets are equal if they have exactly the same elements. Thus, the set of natural numbers and the set of positive integers are equal sets. Also, the sets

$$\{1, 2, 4, 7\} \quad \text{and} \quad \{4, 2, 7, 1\} \quad \text{are equal.}$$

The order of the elements does not make a difference.

OBJECTIVE 3 **Decide whether a given set is a subset of another set.** If all elements of a set A are also elements of another set B, then we say that A is a **subset** of B, written $A \subseteq B$. We use the symbol $A \nsubseteq B$ to mean that A is not a subset of B.

NOW TRY
EXERCISE 3

Let

$A = \{1, 3, 5, 7, 9, 11\}$,
$B = \{1, 5, 7, 9\}$, and
$C = \{1, 9, 11\}$.

Tell whether each statement is *true* or *false*.

(a) $B \subseteq A$ **(b)** $C \subseteq B$

(c) $C \nsubseteq A$

EXAMPLE 3 Using Subset Notation

Let $A = \{1, 2, 3, 4\}$, $B = \{1, 4\}$, and $C = \{1\}$. Then

$$B \subseteq A, \qquad C \subseteq A, \qquad \text{and} \qquad C \subseteq B,$$

but

$$A \nsubseteq B, \qquad A \nsubseteq C, \qquad \text{and} \qquad B \nsubseteq C. \qquad \text{NOW TRY}$$

The empty set is defined to be a subset of any set. Thus, the set $M = \{a, b\}$ has four subsets:

$$\{a, b\}, \quad \{a\}, \quad \{b\}, \quad \text{and} \quad \emptyset.$$

How many subsets does $N = \{a, b, c\}$ have? There is one subset with three elements: $\{a, b, c\}$. There are three subsets with two elements:

$$\{a, b\}, \quad \{a, c\}, \quad \text{and} \quad \{b, c\}.$$

There are three subsets with one element:

$$\{a\}, \quad \{b\}, \quad \text{and} \quad \{c\}.$$

There is one subset with no elements: $\emptyset$. Thus, set N has eight subsets.

The following generalization can be made and proved in more advanced courses.

Number of Subsets of a Set

A set with n elements has 2^n subsets.

NOW TRY ANSWERS
2. (a) $\{-1, -2, -3, -4, \ldots\}$; infinite
(b) $\{12, 14, 16, 18\}$; finite
3. (a) true   **(b)** false   **(c)** false

To illustrate the relationships between sets, **Venn diagrams** are often used. A rectangle represents the universal set, U. The sets under discussion are represented by regions within the rectangle. The Venn diagram in **FIGURE 1** on the next page shows that $B \subseteq A$.

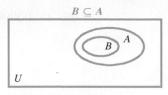

FIGURE 1

OBJECTIVE 4 Find the complement of a set. For every set A, there is a set A', the **complement** of A, that contains all the elements of U that are not in A. The shaded region in the Venn diagram in **FIGURE 2** represents A'.

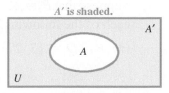

FIGURE 2

⟳ *NOW TRY*
EXERCISE 4

Let

$U = \{2, 4, 6, 8, 10, 12, 14\}$
and $M = \{2, 10, 12, 14\}$.
List the elements in M'.

EXAMPLE 4 Determining Complements of a Set

Given $U = \{a, b, c, d, e, f, g\}$, $A = \{a, b, c\}$, $B = \{a, d, f, g\}$, and $C = \{d, e\}$, list the elements of A', B', and C'.

$A' = \{d, e, f, g\}$, $B' = \{b, c, e\}$,   and $C' = \{a, b, c, f, g\}$.   *NOW TRY* ⟳

OBJECTIVE 5 Find the union and the intersection of two sets. The **union** of two sets A and B, written $A \cup B$, is the set of all elements of A together with all elements of B. Thus, for the sets in **Example 4,**

$$A \cup B = \{a, b, c, d, f, g\}   \text{ and }   A \cup C = \{a, b, c, d, e\}.$$

In **FIGURE 3**, the shaded region is the union of sets A and B.

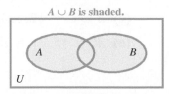

FIGURE 3

⟳ *NOW TRY*
EXERCISE 5

If $M = \{1, 3, 5, 7, 9\}$ and
$N = \{0, 3, 6, 9\}$, find $M \cup N$.

EXAMPLE 5 Finding the Union of Two Sets

If $M = \{2, 5, 7\}$ and $N = \{1, 2, 3, 4, 5\}$, find $M \cup N$.

$$M \cup N = \{1, 2, 3, 4, 5, 7\}$$ *NOW TRY* ⟳

The **intersection** of two sets A and B, written $A \cap B$, is the set of all elements that belong to both A and B. For example, if

$$A = \{\text{José, Ellen, Marge, Kevin}\}$$

and

$$B = \{\text{José, Patrick, Ellen, Sue}\},$$

then

$$A \cap B = \{\text{José, Ellen}\}.$$

NOW TRY ANSWERS
4. $\{4, 6, 8\}$
5. $\{0, 1, 3, 5, 6, 7, 9\}$

The shaded region in **FIGURE 4** represents the intersection of the two sets A and B.

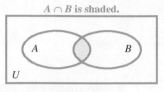

$A \cap B$ is shaded.

FIGURE 4

NOW TRY
EXERCISE 6

If $M = \{1, 3, 5, 7, 9\}$ and $N = \{0, 3, 6, 9\}$, find $M \cap N$.

EXAMPLE 6 Finding the Intersection of Two Sets

Suppose that $P = \{3, 9, 27\}$, $Q = \{2, 3, 10, 18, 27, 28\}$, and $R = \{2, 10, 28\}$. Find each of the following.

(a) $P \cap Q = \{3, 27\}$ **(b)** $Q \cap R = \{2, 10, 28\} = R$ **(c)** $P \cap R = \emptyset$

NOW TRY

Sets like P and R in **Example 6** that have no elements in common are called **disjoint sets.** The Venn diagram in **FIGURE 5** shows a pair of disjoint sets.

NOW TRY
EXERCISE 7

Let

$U = \{1, 2, 4, 5, 7, 8, 9, 10\}$,
$A = \{1, 4, 7, 9, 10\}$,
$B = \{2, 5, 8\}$, and
$C = \{5\}$.

Find each of the following.

(a) $B \cup C$ **(b)** $A \cap B$ **(c)** C'

NOW TRY ANSWERS
6. $\{3, 9\}$
7. (a) $\{2, 5, 8\} = B$ **(b)** $\emptyset$
  (c) $\{1, 2, 4, 7, 8, 9, 10\}$

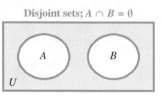

Disjoint sets; $A \cap B = \emptyset$

FIGURE 5

EXAMPLE 7 Using Set Operations

Let $U = \{2, 5, 7, 10, 14, 20\}$, $A = \{2, 10, 14, 20\}$, $B = \{5, 7\}$, and $C = \{2, 5, 7\}$. Find each of the following.

(a) $A \cup B = \{2, 5, 7, 10, 14, 20\} = U$ **(b)** $A \cap B = \emptyset$

(c) $B \cup C = \{2, 5, 7\} = C$ **(d)** $B \cap C = \{5, 7\} = B$

(e) $A' = \{5, 7\} = B$

NOW TRY

EXERCISES   **MyMathLab**
PRACTICE   WATCH   DOWNLOAD   READ   REVIEW

List the elements of each set. ***See Examples 1 and 2.***

1. The set of all natural numbers less than 8

2. The set of all integers between 4 and 10

3. The set of seasons

4. The set of months of the year

5. The set of women presidents of the United States before 2008

6. The set of all living humans who are more than 200 years old

7. The set of letters of the alphabet between K and M

8. The set of letters of the alphabet between D and H

9. The set of positive even integers

10. The set of all multiples of 5

11. Which of the sets described in **Exercises 1–10** are infinite sets?

12. Which of the sets described in **Exercises 1–10** are finite sets?

Concept Check *Tell whether each statement is* true *or* false.

13. $5 \in \{1, 2, 5, 8\}$ **14.** $6 \in \{1, 2, 3, 4, 5\}$

15. $2 \in \{1, 3, 5, 7, 9\}$ **16.** $1 \in \{6, 2, 5, 1\}$

17. $7 \notin \{2, 4, 6, 8\}$ **18.** $7 \notin \{1, 3, 5, 7\}$

19. $\{2, 4, 9, 12, 13\} = \{13, 12, 9, 4, 2\}$ **20.** $\{7, 11, 4\} = \{7, 11, 4, 0\}$

Let

$$A = \{1, 3, 4, 5, 7, 8\}, \quad B = \{2, 4, 6, 8\}, \quad C = \{1, 3, 5, 7\}, \quad D = \{1, 2, 3\},$$
$$E = \{3, 7\}, \quad \text{and} \quad U = \{1, 2, 3, 4, 5, 6, 7, 8, 9, 10\}.$$

Tell whether each statement is true *or* false. ***See Examples 3, 5, 6, and 7.***

21. $A \subseteq U$ **22.** $D \subseteq A$ **23.** $\emptyset \subseteq A$ **24.** $\{1, 2\} \subseteq D$ **25.** $C \subseteq A$

26. $A \subseteq C$ **27.** $D \subseteq B$ **28.** $E \subseteq C$ **29.** $D \not\subseteq E$ **30.** $E \not\subseteq A$

31. There are exactly 4 subsets of E.   **32.** There are exactly 8 subsets of D.

33. There are exactly 12 subsets of C.   **34.** There are exactly 16 subsets of B.

35. $\{4, 6, 8, 12\} \cap \{6, 8, 14, 17\} = \{6, 8\}$ **36.** $\{2, 5, 9\} \cap \{1, 2, 3, 4, 5\} = \{2, 5\}$

37. $\{3, 1, 0\} \cap \{0, 2, 4\} = \{0\}$ **38.** $\{4, 2, 1\} \cap \{1, 2, 3, 4\} = \{1, 2, 3\}$

39. $\{3, 9, 12\} \cap \emptyset = \{3, 9, 12\}$ **40.** $\{3, 9, 12\} \cup \emptyset = \emptyset$

41. $\{3, 5, 7, 9\} \cup \{4, 6, 8\} = \emptyset$ **42.** $\{1, 2, 3\} \cup \{1, 2, 3\} = \{1, 2, 3\}$

43. $\{4, 9, 11, 7, 3\} \cup \{1, 2, 3, 4, 5\} = \{1, 2, 3, 4, 5, 7, 9, 11\}$

44. $\{5, 10, 15, 20\} \cup \{5, 15, 30\} = \{5, 15\}$

Let

$$U = \{a, b, c, d, e, f, g, h\}, \quad A = \{a, b, c, d, e, f\},$$
$$B = \{a, c, e\}, \quad C = \{a, f\}, \quad \text{and} \quad D = \{d\}.$$

List the elements in each set. ***See Examples 4–7.***

45. A' **46.** B' **47.** C' **48.** D'

49. $A \cap B$ **50.** $B \cap A$ **51.** $A \cap D$ **52.** $B \cap D$

53. $B \cap C$ **54.** $A \cup B$ **55.** $B \cup D$ **56.** $B \cup C$

57. $C \cup B$ **58.** $C \cup D$ **59.** $A \cap \emptyset$ **60.** $B \cup \emptyset$

61. Name every pair of disjoint sets among sets A–D in the directions for **Exercises 45–60**.

62. Show that for sets B and D in the directions for **Exercises 45–60**,

$$(B \cup D)' = B' \cap D'.$$

Review of Exponents, Polynomials, and Factoring

(Transition from Beginning to Intermediate Algebra)

OBJECTIVES

1 Review the basic rules for exponents.

2 Review addition, subtraction, and multiplication of polynomials.

3 Review factoring techniques.

OBJECTIVE 1 **Review the basic rules for exponents.** In **Sections 4.1 and 4.2,** we introduced the following definitions and rules for working with exponents.

Definitions and Rules for Exponents

If no denominators are 0, the following are true for any integers m and n.

		Examples
Product rule	$a^m \cdot a^n = a^{m+n}$	$7^4 \cdot 7^5 = 7^9$
Zero exponent	$a^0 = 1$	$(-3)^0 = 1$
Negative exponent	$a^{-n} = \dfrac{1}{a^n}$	$5^{-3} = \dfrac{1}{5^3}$
Quotient rule	$\dfrac{a^m}{a^n} = a^{m-n}$	$\dfrac{2^2}{2^5} = 2^{-3} = \dfrac{1}{2^3}$
Power rules (a)	$(a^m)^n = a^{mn}$	$(4^2)^3 = 4^6$
(b)	$(ab)^m = a^m b^m$	$(3k)^4 = 3^4 k^4$
(c)	$\left(\dfrac{a}{b}\right)^m = \dfrac{a^m}{b^m}$	$\left(\dfrac{2}{3}\right)^2 = \dfrac{2^2}{3^2}$
Negative-to-positive rules	$\dfrac{a^{-m}}{b^{-n}} = \dfrac{b^n}{a^m}$	$\dfrac{2^{-4}}{5^{-3}} = \dfrac{5^3}{2^4}$
	$\left(\dfrac{a}{b}\right)^{-m} = \left(\dfrac{b}{a}\right)^m$	$\left(\dfrac{4}{7}\right)^{-2} = \left(\dfrac{7}{4}\right)^2$

EXAMPLE 1 Applying Definitions and Rules for Exponents

Simplify. Write answers using only positive exponents. Assume that all variables represent nonzero real numbers.

(a) $(x^2 y^{-3})(x^{-5} y^7)$

$= (x^{2+(-5)})(y^{-3+7})$ Product rule

$= x^{-3} y^4$ Add exponents.

$= \dfrac{1}{x^3} y^4$,   or $\dfrac{y^4}{x^3}$ Definition of negative exponent; $\frac{1}{x^3} y^4 = \frac{1}{x^3} \cdot \frac{y^4}{1} = \frac{y^4}{x^3}$

899

NOW TRY
EXERCISE 1

Simplify. Write answers using only positive exponents. Assume that all variables represent nonzero real numbers.

(a) $(m^{-8}n^4)(m^4n^{-3})$

(b) $-8^0 + 8^0$

(c) $\dfrac{(p^{-3}q)^4}{(p^2q^5)^2}$

(d) $\left(\dfrac{2x^{-2}y}{x^2y^{-4}}\right)^{-4}$

(b) $(-5)^0 + (-5^0)$

$= 1 + (-1) \qquad (-5^0) = -1 \cdot 5^0 = -1 \cdot 1 = -1$

$= 0 \qquad\qquad$ Add.

(c) $\dfrac{(t^5s^{-4})^2}{(t^{-3}s^5)^3}$

$= \dfrac{t^{10}s^{-8}}{t^{-9}s^{15}} \qquad$ Power rule (b)

$= \dfrac{t^{10}t^9}{s^{15}s^8} \qquad$ Negative-to-positive rule

$= \dfrac{t^{10+9}}{s^{15+8}}, \quad \text{or} \quad \dfrac{t^{19}}{s^{23}} \qquad$ Product rule

(d) $\left(\dfrac{-3x^{-4}y}{x^5y^{-4}}\right)^{-2}$

$= \left(\dfrac{x^5y^{-4}}{-3x^{-4}y}\right)^2 \qquad$ Negative-to-positive rule

$= \dfrac{x^{10}y^{-8}}{9x^{-8}y^2} \qquad$ Power rules (b) and (c)

$= \dfrac{x^{18}}{9y^{10}} \qquad$ Quotient rule

(e) $(2x^2y^3z)^2(x^4y^2)^3$

$= (4x^4y^6z^2)(x^{12}y^6) \qquad$ Power rule (b)

$= 4x^{16}y^{12}z^2 \qquad$ Product rule $\qquad$ NOW TRY

OBJECTIVE 2 Review addition, subtraction, and multiplication of polynomials. These arithmetic operations with polynomials were covered in **Sections 4.4–4.6.**

Adding and Subtracting Polynomials

To add polynomials, add like terms.

To subtract polynomials, change all signs in the second polynomial and add the result to the first polynomial.

NOW TRY
EXERCISE 2

Add or subtract as indicated.

(a) $(3x^3 + x^2 - 5x - 6) +$
$(-6x^3 + 2x^2 + 4x - 1)$

(b) Subtract.

$\quad 4x^2 + 7x - 5$
$\underline{-5x^2 - 2x + 3}$

EXAMPLE 2 Adding and Subtracting Polynomials

Add or subtract as indicated.

(a) $(-4x^3 + 3x^2 - 8x + 2) + (5x^3 - 8x^2 + 12x - 3)$

$= (-4x^3 + 5x^3) + (3x^2 - 8x^2) + (-8x + 12x) + (2 - 3)$
$\qquad\qquad$ Commutative and associative properties

$= (-4 + 5)x^3 + (3 - 8)x^2 + (-8 + 12)x + (2 - 3)$
$\qquad\qquad$ Distributive property

$= x^3 - 5x^2 + 4x - 1 \qquad$ Simplify.

(b) $-4(x^2 + 3x - 6) - (2x^2 - 3x + 7)$

$= -4x^2 - 12x + 24 - 2x^2 + 3x - 7 \qquad$ Distributive property; definition of subtraction

$= -6x^2 - 9x + 17 \qquad$ Combine like terms.

NOW TRY ANSWERS

1. (a) $\dfrac{n}{m^4}$ (b) 0

(c) $\dfrac{1}{p^{16}q^6}$ (d) $\dfrac{x^{16}}{16y^{20}}$

2. (a) $-3x^3 + 3x^2 - x - 7$
(b) $9x^2 + 9x - 8$

(c) Subtract.

$\begin{array}{l} 2t^2 - 3t - 4 \\ \underline{-8t^2 + 4t - 1} \end{array}$ Change the sign of each term in $-8t^2 + 4t - 1$, and add. $\qquad \begin{array}{l} 2t^2 - 3t - 4 \\ \underline{8t^2 - 4t + 1} \\ 10t^2 - 7t - 3 \end{array}$ Change signs. Add.

NOW TRY

Multiplying Polynomials

To multiply two polynomials, multiply each term of the second polynomial by each term of the first polynomial and add the products. In particular, when multiplying two binomials, use the FOIL method. (See **Section 4.5**.)

The special product rules are useful when multiplying binomials.

Special Product Rules

For x and y, the following are true.

$$(x + y)^2 = x^2 + 2xy + y^2$$
$$(x - y)^2 = x^2 - 2xy + y^2$$
Square of a binomial

$$(x + y)(x - y) = x^2 - y^2$$
Product of the sum and difference of two terms

NOW TRY
EXERCISE 3

Find each product.

(a) $(6x - 5)(2x - 3)$

(b) $(4m - 3n)(4m + 3n)$

(c) $(7z + 1)^2$

(d) $(r + 3)(r^2 - 3r + 9)$

EXAMPLE 3   Multiplying Polynomials

Find each product.

(a) $(4y - 1)(3y + 2)$

First terms   Outer terms   Inner terms   Last terms

$= 4y(3y) + 4y(2) - 1(3y) - 1(2)$ FOIL method

$= 12y^2 + 8y - 3y - 2$ Multiply.

$= 12y^2 + 5y - 2$ Combine like terms.

(b) $(3x + 5y)(3x - 5y)$ $(ab)^2 = a^2b^2$, **not** ab^2.

$= (3x)^2 - (5y)^2$ $(x + y)(x - y) = x^2 - y^2$

$= 9x^2 - 25y^2$ Power rule (b)

(c) $(2t + 3)^2$

$= (2t)^2 + 2(2t)(3) + 3^2$ $(x + y)^2 = x^2 + 2xy + y^2$

$= 4t^2 + 12t + 9$ Remember the middle term.

(d) $(5x - 1)^2$

$= (5x)^2 - 2(5x)(1) + 1^2$ $(x - y)^2 = x^2 - 2xy + y^2$

$= 25x^2 - 10x + 1$ $(5x)^2 = 5^2x^2 = 25x^2$

(e) $(3x + 2)(9x^2 - 6x + 4)$

$$9x^2 - 6x + 4$$
Multiply vertically.
$$3x + 2$$
$$\overline{18x^2 - 12x + 8}$$ ← $2(9x^2 - 6x + 4)$
Be sure to write like terms in columns.
$$\underline{27x^3 - 18x^2 + 12x}$$ ← $3x(9x^2 - 6x + 4)$
$$27x^3 \qquad\qquad + 8$$ Add.

The product is the sum of cubes, $27x^3 + 8$.

NOW TRY ANSWERS

3. (a) $12x^2 - 28x + 15$

(b) $16m^2 - 9n^2$

(c) $49z^2 + 14z + 1$

(d) $r^3 + 27$

NOW TRY

OBJECTIVE 3 **Review factoring techniques.** Factoring, which involves writing a polynomial as a product, was covered in **Chapter 5.** Here are some general guidelines to use when factoring.

Factoring a Polynomial

1. **Is there a common factor?** If so, factor it out.

2. **How many terms are in the polynomial?**

   Two terms: Check to see whether it is a difference of squares or the sum or difference of cubes. If so, factor as in **Section 5.4.**

   $$x^2 - y^2 = (x + y)(x - y) \qquad \text{Difference of squares}$$
   $$x^3 - y^3 = (x - y)(x^2 + xy + y^2) \qquad \text{Difference of cubes}$$
   $$x^3 + y^3 = (x + y)(x^2 - xy + y^2) \qquad \text{Sum of cubes}$$

   Three terms: Is it a perfect square trinomial?

   $$x^2 + 2xy + y^2 = (x + y)^2$$
   $$x^2 - 2xy + y^2 = (x - y)^2 \qquad \text{Perfect square trinomials}$$

   If the trinomial is not a perfect square, check to see whether the coefficient of the second-degree term is 1. If so, use the method of **Section 5.2.** If the coefficient of the second-degree term of the trinomial is not 1, use the general factoring methods of **Section 5.3.**

   Four terms: Try to factor the polynomial by grouping, as in **Section 5.1.**

3. **Can any factors be factored further?** If so, factor them.

EXAMPLE 4 Factoring Polynomials

Factor each polynomial completely.

(a) $6x^2y^3 - 12x^3y^2$

$$= 6x^2y^2 \cdot y - 6x^2y^2 \cdot 2x \qquad 6x^2y^2 \text{ is the greatest common factor.}$$
$$= 6x^2y^2(y - 2x) \qquad \text{Distributive property}$$

(b) $3x^2 - x - 2$

To find the factors, find two terms that multiply to give $3x^2$ (here $3x$ and x) and two terms that multiply to give -2 (here $+2$ and -1). Make sure that the sum of the outer and inner products in the factored form is $-x$.

$$3x^2 - x - 2 \quad \text{factors as} \quad (3x + 2)(x - 1).$$

CHECK To check, multiply the factors using the FOIL method.

(c) $3x^2 - 27x + 42$

$$= 3(x^2 - 9x + 14) \qquad \text{Factor out the common factor.}$$
$$= 3(x - 7)(x - 2) \qquad \text{Factor the trinomial.}$$

(d) $100t^2 - 81$

$$= (10t)^2 - 9^2 \qquad \text{Difference of squares}$$
$$= (10t + 9)(10t - 9) \qquad x^2 - y^2 = (x + y)(x - y)$$

NOW TRY
EXERCISE 4
Factor each polynomial completely.

(a) $5x^2 - 20x - 60$

(b) $10t^2 + 13t - 3$

(c) $49x^2 + 42x + 9$

(d) $mn - 2n + 5m - 10$

(e) $27x^3 - 1000$

(e) $4x^2 + 20xy + 25y^2$

The terms $4x^2$ and $25y^2$ are both perfect squares, so this trinomial might factor as a perfect square trinomial.

Try to factor $4x^2 + 20xy + 25y^2$ as $(2x + 5y)^2$.

CHECK Take twice the product of the two terms in the squared binomial.

$$2 \cdot 2x \cdot 5y = 20xy \longleftarrow \text{Middle term of } 4x^2 + 20xy + 25y^2$$

Twice —— First term —— Last term

Since $20xy$ is the middle term of the trinomial, the trinomial is a perfect square.

$$4x^2 + 20xy + 25y^2 \quad \text{factors as} \quad (2x + 5y)^2.$$

(f) $1000x^3 - 27$

$$= (10x)^3 - 3^3 \qquad \text{Difference of cubes}$$

$$= (10x - 3)[(10x)^2 + 10x(3) + 3^2] \quad x^3 - y^3 = (x - y)(x^2 + xy + y^2)$$

$$= (10x - 3)(100x^2 + 30x + 9) \qquad (10x)^2 = 10^2x^2$$

(g) $6xy - 3x + 4y - 2$

Since there are four terms, try factoring by grouping.

$$6xy - 3x + 4y - 2$$

$$= (6xy - 3x) + (4y - 2) \qquad \text{Group the terms.}$$

$$= 3x(2y - 1) + 2(2y - 1) \qquad \text{Factor each group.}$$

$$= (2y - 1)(3x + 2) \qquad \text{Factor out } 2y - 1.$$

In the final step, factor out the greatest common factor, the binomial $2y - 1$.

NOW TRY

NOW TRY ANSWERS

4. (a) $5(x - 6)(x + 2)$

(b) $(5t - 1)(2t + 3)$

(c) $(7x + 3)^2$

(d) $(n + 5)(m - 2)$

(e) $(3x - 10)(9x^2 + 30x + 100)$

EXERCISES MyMathLab Math XL PRACTICE WATCH DOWNLOAD READ REVIEW

Simplify each expression. Write the answers using only positive exponents. Assume that all variables represent positive real numbers. **See Example 1.**

1. $(a^4b^{-3})(a^{-6}b^2)$

2. $(t^{-3}s^{-5})(t^8s^{-2})$

3. $(5x^{-2}y)^2(2xy^4)^2$

4. $(7x^{-3}y^4)^3(2x^{-1}y^{-4})^2$

5. $-6^0 + (-6)^0$

6. $(-12)^0 - 12^0$

7. $\dfrac{(2w^{-1}x^2y^{-1})^3}{(4w^5x^{-2}y)^2}$

8. $\dfrac{(5p^{-3}q^2r^{-4})^2}{(10p^4q^{-1}r^5)^{-1}}$

9. $\left(\dfrac{-4a^{-2}b^4}{a^3b^{-1}}\right)^{-3}$

10. $\left(\dfrac{r^{-3}s^{-8}}{-6r^2s^{-4}}\right)^{-2}$

11. $(7x^{-4}y^2z^{-2})^{-2}(7x^4y^{-1}z^3)^2$

12. $(3m^{-5}n^2p^{-4})^3(3m^4n^{-3}p^5)^{-2}$

Add or subtract as indicated. **See Example 2.**

13. $(2a^4 + 3a^3 - 6a^2 + 5a - 12) + (-8a^4 + 8a^3 - 14a^2 + 21a - 3)$

14. $(-6r^4 - 3r^3 + 12r^2 - 9r + 9) + (8r^4 - 13r^3 - 14r^2 - 10r - 3)$

15. $(6x^3 - 12x^2 + 3x - 4) - (-2x^3 + 6x^2 - 3x + 12)$

16. $(10y^3 - 4y^2 + 8y + 7) - (7y^3 + 5y^2 - 2y - 13)$

17. Add.

$$5x^2y + 2xy^2 + y^3$$
$$\underline{-4x^2y - 3xy^2 + 5y^3}$$

18. Add.

$$6ab^3 - 2a^2b^2 + 3b^5$$
$$\underline{8ab^3 + 12a^2b^2 - 8b^5}$$

19. $3(5x^2 - 12x + 4) - 2(9x^2 + 13x - 10)$

20. $-4(2t^3 - 3t^2 + 4t - 1) - 3(-8t^3 + 3t^2 - 2t + 9)$

21. Subtract.

$$6x^3 - 2x^2 + 3x - 1$$
$$\underline{-4x^3 + 2x^2 - 6x + 3}$$

22. Subtract.

$$-9y^3 - 2y^2 + 3y - 8$$
$$\underline{-8y^3 + 4y^2 + 3y + 1}$$

Find each product. **See Example 3.**

23. $(3x + 1)(2x - 7)$ **24.** $(5z + 3)(2z - 3)$ **25.** $(4x - 1)(x - 2)$

26. $(7t - 3)(t - 4)$ **27.** $(4t + 3)(4t - 3)$ **28.** $(6x + 1)(6x - 1)$

29. $(2y^2 + 4)(2y^2 - 4)$ **30.** $(3b^3 + 2t)(3b^3 - 2t)$ **31.** $(4x - 3)^2$

32. $(9t + 2)^2$ **33.** $(6r + 5y)^2$ **34.** $(8m - 3n)^2$

35. $(c + 2d)(c^2 - 2cd + 4d^2)$ **36.** $(f + 3g)(f^2 - 3fg + 9g^2)$

37. $(4x - 1)(16x^2 + 4x + 1)$ **38.** $(5r - 2)(25r^2 + 10r + 4)$

39. $(7t + 5s)(2t^2 + 5st - s^2)$ **40.** $(8p + 3q)(2p^2 - 4pq + q^2)$

Factor each polynomial completely. **See Example 4.**

41. $8x^3y^4 + 12x^2y^3 + 36xy^4$ **42.** $10m^5n + 4m^2n^3 + 18m^3n^2$

43. $x^2 - 2x - 15$ **44.** $x^2 + x - 12$

45. $2x^2 - 9x - 18$ **46.** $3x^2 + 2x - 8$

47. $36t^2 - 25$ **48.** $49r^2 - 9$

49. $16t^2 + 24t + 9$ **50.** $25t^2 + 90t + 81$

51. $4m^2p - 12mnp + 9n^2p$ **52.** $16p^2r - 40pqr + 25q^2r$

53. $x^3 + 1$ **54.** $x^3 + 27$

55. $8t^3 + 125$ **56.** $27s^3 + 64$

57. $t^6 - 125$ **58.** $w^6 - 27$

59. $5xt + 15xr + 2yt + 6yr$ **60.** $3am + 18mb + 2an + 12nb$

61. $6ar + 12br - 5as - 10bs$ **62.** $7mt + 35ms - 2nt - 10ns$

63. $t^4 - 1$ **64.** $r^4 - 81$

65. $4x^2 + 12xy + 9y^2 - 1$ **66.** $81t^2 + 36ty + 4y^2 - 9$

67. $4x^2 - 28x + 40$ **68.** $2x^2 - 18x + 36$

Synthetic Division

OBJECTIVES

1. Use synthetic division to divide by a polynomial of the form $x - k$.
2. Use the remainder theorem to evaluate a polynomial.
3. Decide whether a given number is a solution of an equation.

OBJECTIVE 1 **Use synthetic division to divide by a polynomial of the form** $x - k$**.** If a polynomial in x is divided by a binomial of the form $x - k$, a shortcut method can be used. For an illustration, look at the division on the left below.

$$
\begin{array}{r}
3x^2 + 9x + 25 \\
x - 3\overline{)3x^3 + 0x^2 - 2x + 5} \\
3x^3 - 9x^2 \\
\hline
9x^2 - 2x \\
9x^2 - 27x \\
\hline
25x + 5 \\
25x - 75 \\
\hline
80
\end{array}
$$

$$
\begin{array}{r}
\quad 3 \quad 9 \quad 25 \\
1 - 3\overline{)3 \quad 0 \quad -2 \quad 5} \\
3 \quad -9 \\
\hline
9 \quad -2 \\
9 \quad -27 \\
\hline
25 \quad 5 \\
25 \quad -75 \\
\hline
80
\end{array}
$$

On the right above, exactly the same division is shown written without the variables. This is why it is *essential* to use 0 as a placeholder in synthetic division. All the numbers in color on the right are repetitions of the numbers directly above them, so we omit them, as shown on the left below.

$$
\begin{array}{r}
\quad 3 \quad 9 \quad 25 \\
1 - 3\overline{)3 \quad 0 \quad -2 \quad 5} \\
-9 \\
\hline
9 \quad -2 \\
-27 \\
\hline
25 \quad 5 \\
-75 \\
\hline
80
\end{array}
$$

$$
\begin{array}{r}
\quad 3 \quad 9 \quad 25 \\
1 - 3\overline{)3 \quad 0 \quad -2 \quad 5} \\
-9 \\
\hline
9 \\
-27 \\
\hline
25 \\
-75 \\
\hline
80
\end{array}
$$

The numbers in color on the left are again repetitions of the numbers directly above them. They too are omitted, as shown on the right above. If we bring the 3 in the dividend down to the beginning of the bottom row, the top row can be omitted, since it duplicates the bottom row.

$$
\begin{array}{r}
1 - 3\overline{)3 \quad 0 \quad -2 \quad 5} \\
-9 \quad -27 \quad -75 \\
\hline
3 \quad 9 \quad 25 \quad 80
\end{array}
$$

We omit the 1 at the upper left, since it represents $1x$, which will always be the first term in the divisor. Also, to simplify the arithmetic, we replace subtraction in the second row by addition. To compensate for this, we change the -3 at the upper left to its additive inverse, 3.

Additive inverse $\longrightarrow$

$$3\overline{)\begin{array}{cccc} 3 & 0 & -2 & 5 \\ & 9 & 27 & 75 \\ \hline 3 & 9 & 25 & 80 \end{array}}$$ $\leftarrow$ Signs changed
$\leftarrow$ Remainder

The quotient is read from the bottom row.

$$3x^2 + 9x + 25 + \frac{80}{x - 3}$$

The first three numbers in the bottom row are the coefficients of the quotient polynomial with degree 1 less than the degree of the dividend. The last number gives the remainder.

This shortcut procedure is called **synthetic division.** *It is used only when dividing a polynomial by a binomial of the form $x - k$.*

NOW TRY
EXERCISE 1
Use synthetic division to divide.

$$\frac{4x^3 + 18x^2 + 19x + 7}{x + 3}$$

EXAMPLE 1 Using Synthetic Division

Use synthetic division to divide $5x^2 + 16x + 15$ by $x + 2$.

We change $x + 2$ into the form $x - k$ by writing it as

$$x + 2 = x - (-2), \quad \text{where } k = -2.$$

Now write the coefficients of $5x^2 + 16x + 15$, placing -2 to the left.

$x + 2$ leads to -2. $\longrightarrow$ $-2\overline{)5 \quad 16 \quad 15}$ $\leftarrow$ Coefficients

$$-2\overline{)\begin{array}{ccc} 5 & 16 & 15 \\ & -10 & \\ \hline 5 & & \end{array}}$$

Bring down the 5, and multiply: $-2 \cdot 5 = -10$.

$$-2\overline{)\begin{array}{ccc} 5 & 16 & 15 \\ & -10 & -12 \\ \hline 5 & 6 & \end{array}}$$

Add 16 and -10, getting 6, and multiply 6 and -2 to get -12.

$$-2\overline{)\begin{array}{ccc} 5 & 16 & 15 \\ & -10 & -12 \\ \hline 5 & 6 & 3 \end{array}}$$

Add 15 and -12, getting 3.

$\leftarrow$ Remainder

The result is read from the bottom row.

$$\frac{5x^2 + 16x + 15}{x + 2} = 5x + 6 + \frac{3}{x + 2}$$

NOW TRY

NOW TRY
EXERCISE 2
Use synthetic division to divide.

$$\frac{-3x^4 + 13x^3 - 6x^2 + 31}{x - 4}$$

EXAMPLE 2 Using Synthetic Division with a Missing Term

Use synthetic division to find $(-4x^5 + x^4 + 6x^3 + 2x^2 + 50) \div (x - 2)$.

$$2\overline{)\begin{array}{cccccc} -4 & 1 & 6 & 2 & 0 & 50 \\ & -8 & -14 & -16 & -28 & -56 \\ \hline -4 & -7 & -8 & -14 & -28 & -6 \end{array}}$$

Use the steps given above, first inserting a 0 for the missing x-term.

Read the result from the bottom row.

$$\frac{-4x^5 + x^4 + 6x^3 + 2x^2 + 50}{x - 2} = -4x^4 - 7x^3 - 8x^2 - 14x - 28 + \frac{-6}{x - 2}$$

NOW TRY

NOW TRY ANSWERS

1. $4x^2 + 6x + 1 + \frac{4}{x + 3}$
2. $-3x^3 + x^2 - 2x - 8 + \frac{-1}{x - 4}$

OBJECTIVE 2 **Use the remainder theorem to evaluate a polynomial.** We can use synthetic division to evaluate polynomials. For example, in the synthetic division of **Example 2,** where the polynomial was divided by $x - 2$, the remainder was -6.

Replacing x in the polynomial with 2 gives

$$-4x^5 + x^4 + 6x^3 + 2x^2 + 50$$

$$= -4 \cdot 2^5 + 2^4 + 6 \cdot 2^3 + 2 \cdot 2^2 + 50 \qquad \text{Replace } x \text{ with 2.}$$

$$= -4 \cdot 32 + 16 + 6 \cdot 8 + 2 \cdot 4 + 50 \qquad \text{Evaluate the powers.}$$

$$= -128 + 16 + 48 + 8 + 50 \qquad \text{Multiply.}$$

$$= -6, \qquad \text{Add.}$$

the same number as the remainder. Dividing by $x - 2$ produced a remainder equal to the result when x is replaced with 2. This always happens, as the following **remainder theorem** states. This result is proved in more advanced courses.

> **Remainder Theorem**
>
> If the polynomial $P(x)$ is divided by $x - k$, then the remainder is equal to $P(k)$.

**NOW TRY
EXERCISE 3**

Let $P(x) = 3x^3 - 2x^2 + 5x + 30$. Use synthetic division to evaluate $P(-2)$.

EXAMPLE 3 Using the Remainder Theorem

Let $P(x) = 2x^3 - 5x^2 - 3x + 11$. Use synthetic division to evaluate $P(-2)$.

Use the remainder theorem, and divide $P(x)$ by $x - (-2)$.

$$\text{Value of } k \rightarrow -2)\overline{\begin{array}{rrrr} 2 & -5 & -3 & 11 \\ & -4 & 18 & -30 \\ \hline 2 & -9 & 15 & -19 \end{array}} \leftarrow \text{Remainder}$$

Thus, $P(-2) = -19$.   NOW TRY

OBJECTIVE 3 **Decide whether a given number is a solution of an equation.**
We can also use the remainder theorem to do this.

**NOW TRY
EXERCISE 4**

Use synthetic division to decide whether -4 is a solution of the equation.

$$5x^3 + 19x^2 - 2x + 8 = 0$$

EXAMPLE 4 Using the Remainder Theorem

Use synthetic division to decide whether -5 is a solution of the equation.

$$2x^4 + 12x^3 + 6x^2 - 5x + 75 = 0$$

If synthetic division gives a remainder of 0, then -5 is a solution. Otherwise, it is not.

$$\text{Proposed solution} \rightarrow -5)\overline{\begin{array}{rrrrr} 2 & 12 & 6 & -5 & 75 \\ & -10 & -10 & 20 & -75 \\ \hline 2 & 2 & -4 & 15 & 0 \end{array}} \leftarrow \text{Remainder}$$

Since the remainder is 0, the polynomial has value 0 when $k = -5$. So -5 is a solution of the given equation.   NOW TRY

The synthetic division in **Example 4** shows that $x - (-5)$ divides the polynomial with 0 remainder. Thus $x - (-5) = x + 5$ is a *factor* of the polynomial and

$$2x^4 + 12x^3 + 6x^2 - 5x + 75 \quad \text{factors as} \quad (x + 5)(2x^3 + 2x^2 - 4x + 15).$$

The second factor is the quotient polynomial found in the last row of the synthetic division.

NOW TRY ANSWERS
3. -12 **4.** yes

EXERCISES

Use synthetic division to find each quotient. **See Examples 1 and 2.**

1. $\dfrac{x^2 - 6x + 5}{x - 1}$

2. $\dfrac{x^2 - 4x - 21}{x + 3}$

3. $\dfrac{4m^2 + 19m - 5}{m + 5}$

4. $\dfrac{3x^2 - 5x - 12}{x - 3}$

5. $\dfrac{2a^2 + 8a + 13}{a + 2}$

6. $\dfrac{4y^2 - 5y - 20}{y - 4}$

7. $(p^2 - 3p + 5) \div (p + 1)$

8. $(z^2 + 4z - 6) \div (z - 5)$

9. $\dfrac{4a^3 - 3a^2 + 2a - 3}{a - 1}$

10. $\dfrac{5p^3 - 6p^2 + 3p + 14}{p + 1}$

11. $(x^5 - 2x^3 + 3x^2 - 4x - 2) \div (x - 2)$

12. $(2y^5 - 5y^4 - 3y^2 - 6y - 23) \div (y - 3)$

13. $(-4r^6 - 3r^5 - 3r^4 + 5r^3 - 6r^2 + 3r + 3) \div (r - 1)$

14. $(2t^6 - 3t^5 + 2t^4 - 5t^3 + 6t^2 - 3t - 2) \div (t - 2)$

15. $(-3y^5 + 2y^4 - 5y^3 - 6y^2 - 1) \div (y + 2)$

16. $(m^6 + 2m^4 - 5m + 11) \div (m - 2)$

Use the remainder theorem to find $P(k)$. **See Example 3.**

17. $P(x) = 2x^3 - 4x^2 + 5x - 3; k = 2$

18. $P(x) = x^3 + 3x^2 - x + 5; k = -1$

19. $P(x) = -x^3 - 5x^2 - 4x - 2; k = -4$

20. $P(x) = -x^3 + 5x^2 - 3x + 4; k = 3$

21. $P(x) = 2x^3 - 4x^2 + 5x - 33; k = 3$

22. $P(x) = x^3 - 3x^2 + 4x - 4; k = 2$

23. Explain why a 0 remainder in synthetic division of $P(x)$ by $x - k$ indicates that k is a solution of the equation $P(x) = 0$.

24. Explain why it is important to insert 0s as placeholders for missing terms before performing synthetic division.

Use synthetic division to decide whether the given number is a solution of the equation. **See Example 4.**

25. $x^3 - 2x^2 - 3x + 10 = 0; x = -2$

26. $x^3 - 3x^2 - x + 10 = 0; x = -2$

27. $3x^3 + 2x^2 - 2x + 11 = 0; x = -2$

28. $3x^3 + 10x^2 + 3x - 9 = 0; x = -2$

29. $2x^3 - x^2 - 13x + 24 = 0; x = -3$

30. $5x^3 + 22x^2 + x - 28 = 0; x = -4$

31. $x^4 + 2x^3 - 3x^2 + 8x - 8 = 0; x = -2$

32. $x^4 - x^3 - 6x^2 + 5x + 10 = 0; x = -2$

RELATING CONCEPTS EXERCISES 33–38

FOR INDIVIDUAL OR GROUP WORK

We can show a connection between dividing one polynomial by another and factoring the first polynomial. Let $P(x) = 2x^2 + 5x - 12$. **Work Exercises 33–38 in order.**

33. Factor $P(x)$.

34. Solve $P(x) = 0$.

35. Evaluate $P(-4)$.

36. Evaluate $P\left(\frac{3}{2}\right)$.

37. Complete the following sentence: If $P(a) = 0$, then $x -$ _____ is a factor of $P(x)$.

38. Use the conclusion reached in **Exercise 37** to decide whether $x - 3$ is a factor of $Q(x) = 3x^3 - 4x^2 - 17x + 6$. Factor $Q(x)$ completely.

An Introduction to Calculators

There is little doubt that the appearance of handheld calculators more than three decades ago and the later development of scientific and graphing calculators have changed the methods of learning and studying mathematics forever. For example, computations with tables of logarithms and slide rules made up an important part of mathematics courses prior to 1970. Today, with the widespread availability of calculators, these topics are studied only for their historical significance.

Calculators come in a large array of different types, sizes, and prices. *For the course for which this textbook is intended, the most appropriate type is the scientific calculator,* which costs $10–$20.

In this introduction, we explain some of the features of scientific and graphing calculators. However, remember that calculators vary among manufacturers and models and that, while the methods explained here apply to many of them, they may not apply to your specific calculator. *This introduction is only a guide and is not intended to take the place of your owner's manual.* Always refer to the manual whenever you need an explanation of how to perform a particular operation.

Scientific Calculators

Scientific calculators are capable of much more than the typical four-function calculator that you might use for balancing your checkbook. Most scientific calculators use *algebraic logic.* (Models sold by Texas Instruments, Sharp, Casio, and Radio Shack, for example, use algebraic logic.) A notable exception is Hewlett-Packard, a company whose calculators use *Reverse Polish Notation* (RPN). In this introduction, we explain the use of calculators with algebraic logic.

Arithmetic Operations   To perform an operation of arithmetic, simply enter the first number, press the operation key $+$, $-$, $\times$, or $\div$, enter the second number, and then press the $=$ key. For example, to add 4 and 3, use the following keystrokes.

$$\boxed{4}\ \boxed{+}\ \boxed{3}\ \boxed{=}\ \boxed{\qquad 7}$$

Change Sign Key   The key marked $+/-$ allows you to change the sign of a display. This is particularly useful when you wish to enter a negative number. For example, to enter -3, use the following keystrokes.

$$\boxed{3}\ \boxed{+/-}\ \boxed{\quad -3}$$

Memory Key Scientific calculators can hold a number in memory for later use. The label of the memory key varies among models; two of these are (M) and (STO). The (M+) and (M−) keys allow you to add to or subtract from the value currently in memory. The memory recall key, labeled (MR), (RM), or (RCL), allows you to retrieve the value stored in memory.

Suppose that you wish to store the number 5 in memory. Enter 5, and then press the key for memory. You can then perform other calculations. When you need to retrieve the 5, press the key for memory recall.

If a calculator has a constant memory feature, the value in memory will be retained even after the power is turned off. Some advanced calculators have more than one memory. Read the owner's manual for your model to see exactly how memory is activated.

Clearing/Clear Entry Keys The key (C) or (CE) allows you to clear the display or clear the last entry entered into the display. In some models, pressing the (C) key once will clear the last entry, while pressing it twice will clear the entire operation in progress.

Second Function Key This key, usually marked (2nd), is used in conjunction with another key to activate a function that is printed *above* an operation key (and not on the key itself). For example, suppose you wish to find the square of a number, and the squaring function (explained in more detail later) is printed above another key. You would need to press (2nd) before the desired squaring function can be activated.

Square Root Key Pressing (√) or (√x) will give the square root (or an approximation of the square root) of the number in the display. On some scientific calculators, the square root key is pressed *before* entering the number, while other calculators use the opposite order. Experiment with your calculator to see which method it uses. For example, to find the square root of 36, use the following keystrokes.

$$(√) \quad (3) \quad (6) \quad (\ \ 6\ \ ) \qquad \text{or} \qquad (3) \quad (6) \quad (√) \quad (\ \ 6\ \ )$$

The square root of 2 is an example of an irrational number (**Chapter 10**). The calculator will give an approximation of its value, since the decimal for $\sqrt{2}$ never terminates and never repeats. The number of digits shown will vary among models. To find an approximation for $\sqrt{2}$, use the following keystrokes.

$$(√) \quad (2) \quad (\ 1.4142136\ ) \qquad \text{or} \qquad (2) \quad (√) \quad (\ 1.4142136\ )$$

An approximation for $\sqrt{2}$

Squaring Key The (x^2) key allows you to square the entry in the display. For example, to square 35.7, use the following keystrokes.

$$(3) \quad (5) \quad (.) \quad (7) \quad (x^2) \quad (\ 1274.49\ )$$

The squaring key and the square root key are often found together, with one of them being a second function (that is, activated by the second function key previously described).

Reciprocal Key The key marked $(1/x)$ is the reciprocal key. (When two numbers have a product of 1, they are called *reciprocals*. See **Chapter 1**.) Suppose that you wish to find the reciprocal of 5. Use the following keystrokes.

$$(5) \quad (1/x) \quad (\ \ 0.2\ \ )$$

Inverse Key Some calculators have an inverse key, marked $\boxed{\text{INV}}$. Inverse operations are operations that "undo" each other. For example, the operations of squaring and taking the square root are inverse operations. The use of the $\boxed{\text{INV}}$ key varies among different models of calculators, so read your owner's manual carefully.

Exponential Key The key marked $\boxed{x^y}$ or $\boxed{y^x}$ allows you to raise a number to a power. For example, if you wish to raise 4 to the fifth power (that is, find 4^5, as explained in **Chapter 1**), use the following keystrokes.

$$\boxed{4} \quad \boxed{x^y} \quad \boxed{5} \quad \boxed{=} \quad \boxed{1024}$$

Root Key Some calculators have a key specifically marked $\boxed{\sqrt[x]{x}}$ or $\boxed{\sqrt[x]{y}}$; with others, the operation of taking roots is accomplished by using the inverse key in conjunction with the exponential key. Suppose, for example, your calculator is of the latter type and you wish to find the fifth root of 1024. Use the following keystrokes.

$$\boxed{1} \quad \boxed{0} \quad \boxed{2} \quad \boxed{4} \quad \boxed{\text{INV}} \quad \boxed{x^y} \quad \boxed{5} \quad \boxed{=} \quad \boxed{4}$$

Notice how this "undoes" the operation explained in the discussion of the exponential key.

Pi Key The number π is an important number in mathematics. It occurs, for example, in the area and circumference formulas for a circle. One popular model gives the following display when the $\boxed{\pi}$ key is pressed. (Because π is irrational, the display shows only an approximation.)

$$\boxed{3.1415927} \quad \text{An approximation for } \pi$$

Methods of Display When decimal approximations are shown on scientific calculators, they are either *truncated* or *rounded*. To see how a particular model is programmed, evaluate 1/18 as an example. If the display shows 0.0555555 (last digit 5), the calculator truncates the display. If the display shows 0.0555556 (last digit 6), the calculator rounds the display.

When very large or very small numbers are obtained as answers, scientific calculators often express these numbers in scientific notation (**Chapter 4**). For example, if you multiply 6,265,804 by 8,980,591, the display might look like this:

$$\boxed{5.6270623 \ 13}$$

The 13 at the far right means that the number on the left is multiplied by 10^{13}. This means that the decimal point must be moved 13 places to the right if the answer is to be expressed in its usual form. Even then, the value obtained will only be an approximation: 56,270,623,000,000.

Graphing Calculators

While you are not expected to have a graphing calculator to study from this book, we include the following as background information and reference should your course or future courses require the use of graphing calculators.

Basic Features In addition to possessing the typical keys found on scientific calculators, graphing calculators have keys that can be used to create graphs, make tables, analyze data, and change settings. One of the major differences between graphing and scientific calculators is that a graphing calculator has a larger viewing screen with graphing capabilities. The following screens illustrate the graphs of $Y = X$ and $Y = X^2$. (We use screens from a Texas Instruments calculator in our illustrations.)

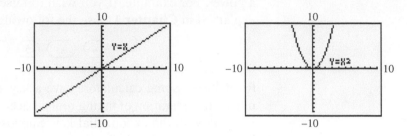

If you look closely at the screens, you will see that the graphs appear to be jagged rather than smooth. The reason for this is that graphing calculators have much lower resolution than computer screens. Because of this, graphs generated by graphing calculators must be interpreted carefully.

Editing Input The screen of a graphing calculator can display several lines of text at a time. This feature allows you to view both previous and current expressions. If an incorrect expression is entered, an error message is displayed. The erroneous expression can be viewed and corrected by using various editing keys, much like a word-processing program. You do not need to enter the entire expression again. Many graphing calculators can also recall past expressions for editing or updating. The screen on the left shows how two expressions are evaluated. The final line is entered incorrectly, and the resulting error message is shown in the screen on the right.

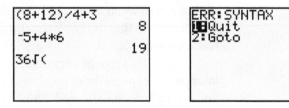

Order of Operations Arithmetic operations on graphing calculators are usually entered as they are written in mathematical expressions. For example, to evaluate $\sqrt{36}$ you would first press the square root key and then enter 36. See the left screen below. The order of operations on a graphing calculator is also important, and current models assist the user by inserting parentheses when typical errors might occur. The open parenthesis that follows the square root symbol is automatically entered by the calculator so that an expression such as $\sqrt{2 \times 8}$ will not be calculated incorrectly as $\sqrt{2} \times 8$. Compare the two entries and their results in the screen on the right.

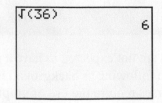

Viewing Windows   The viewing window for a graphing calculator is similar to the viewfinder in a camera. A camera usually cannot take a photograph of an entire view of a scene. The camera must be centered on some object and can capture only a portion of the available scenery. A camera with a zoom lens can photograph different views of the same scene by zooming in and out. Graphing calculators have similar capabilities. The xy-coordinate plane is infinite. The calculator screen can show only a finite, rectangular region in the plane, and it must be specified before the graph can be drawn. This is done by setting both minimum and maximum values for the x- and y-axes. The scale (distance between tick marks) is usually specified as well. Determining an appropriate viewing window for a graph is often a challenge, and many times it will take a few attempts before a satisfactory window is found.

The screen on the left shows a standard viewing window, and the graph of $Y = 2X + 1$ is shown on the right. Using a different window would give a different view of the line.

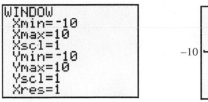

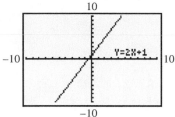

Locating Points on a Graph: Tracing and Tables   Graphing calculators allow you to trace along the graph of an equation and display the coordinates of points on the graph. For example, the screen on the left below indicates that the point $(2, 5)$ lies on the graph of $Y = 2X + 1$. Tables for equations can also be displayed. The screen on the right shows a partial table for this same equation. Note the middle of the screen, which indicates that when $X = 2$, $Y = 5$.

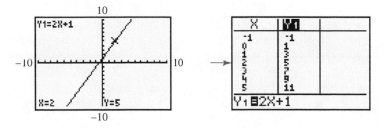

Additional Features   There are many features of graphing calculators that go far beyond the scope of this book. These calculators can be programmed, much like computers. Many of them can solve equations at the stroke of a key, analyze statistical data, and perform symbolic algebraic manipulations. Calculators also provide the opportunity to ask "What if . . . ?" more easily. Values in algebraic expressions can be altered and conjectures tested quickly.

Final Comments   Despite the power of today's calculators, they cannot replace human thought. ***In the entire problem-solving process, your brain is the most important component.*** Calculators are only tools, and like any tool, they must be used appropriately in order to enhance our ability to understand mathematics. Mathematical insight may often be the quickest and easiest way to solve a problem; a calculator may be neither needed nor appropriate. By applying mathematical concepts, you can make the decision whether to use a calculator.

Answers to Selected Exercises

In this section we provide the answers that we think most students will obtain when they work the exercises using the methods explained in the text. If your answer does not look exactly like the one given here, it is not necessarily wrong. In many cases, there are equivalent forms of the answer that are correct. For example, if the answer section shows $\frac{3}{4}$ and your answer is 0.75, you have obtained the right answer, but written it in a different (yet equivalent) form. Unless the directions specify otherwise, 0.75 is just as valid an answer as $\frac{3}{4}$.

In general, if your answer does not agree with the one given in the text, see whether it can be transformed into the other form. If it can, then it is the correct answer. If you still have doubts, talk with your instructor. You might also want to obtain a copy of the *Student's Solutions Manual* that goes with this book. Your college bookstore either has this manual or can order it for you.

5   FACTORING AND APPLICATIONS

Section 5.1 (pages 301–303)

1. 4   **3.** 6   **5.** 1   **7.** 8   **9.** $10x^3$ **11.** xy^2 **13.** $6m^3n^2$ **15.** factored **17.** not factored   **19.** $3m^2$ **21.** $2z^4$ **23.** $2mn^4$ **25.** $y + 2$ **27.** $a - 2$ **29.** $2 + 3xy$ **31.** First, verify that you have factored completely. Then multiply the factors. The product should be the original polynomial.   **33.** $x(x - 4)$ **35.** $3t(2t + 5)$ **37.** $9m(3m^2 - 1)$ **39.** $8z^2(2z^2 + 3)$ **41.** $6x^2(2x + 1)$ **43.** $5y^6(13y^1 + 7)$ **45.** in factored form   **47.** $8mn^3(1 + 3m)$ **49.** $13y^2(y^6 + 2y^2 - 3)$ **51.** $9p^3q(4p^3 + 5p^2q^3 + 9q)$ **53.** $a^3(a^2 + 2b^2 - 3a^2b^2 + 4ab^3)$ **55.** $(x + 2)(c - d)$ **57.** $(m + 2n)(m + n)$ **59.** $(p - 4)(q^2 + 1)$ **61.** not in factored form; $(7t + 4)(8 + x)$ **63.** in factored form **65.** not in factored form   **67.** The quantities in parentheses are not the same, so there is no common factor of the two terms $18x^2(y + 4)$ and $7(y - 4)$.   **69.** $(p + 4)(p + q)$ **71.** $(a - 2)(a + b)$ **73.** $(z + 2)(7z - a)$ **75.** $(3r + 2y)(6r - x)$ **77.** $(a^2 + b^2)(3a + 2b)$ **79.** $(3 - a)(4 - b)$ **81.** $(4m - p^2)(4m^2 - p)$ **83.** $(y + 3)(y + x)$ **85.** $(5 - 2p)(m + 3)$ **87.** $(3r + 2y)(6r - t)$ **89.** $(1 + 2b)(a^5 - 3)$ **91.** commutative property **92.** $2x(y - 4) - 3(y - 4)$ **93.** No, because it is not a product. It is the difference between $2x(y - 4)$ and $3(y - 4)$. **94.** $(2x - 3)(y - 4)$; yes   **95.** $x^2 - 3x - 54$ **97.** $x^2 + 9x + 14$ **99.** $2x^4 + 6x^3 + 10x^2$

Section 5.2 (pages 307–309)

1. 1 and 48, -1 and -48, 2 and 24, -2 and -24, 3 and 16, -3 and -16, 4 and 12, -4 and -12, 6 and 8, -6 and -8; The pair with a sum of -19 is -3 and -16.   **3.** 1 and -24, -1 and 24, 2 and -12, -2 and 12,

3 and -8, -3 and 8, 4 and -6, -4 and 6; The pair with a sum of -5 is 3 and -8.   **5.** a and b must have different signs, one positive and one negative.   **7.** A prime polynomial is a polynomial that cannot be factored by using only integers in the factors.   **9.** C   **11.** $a^2 + 13a + 36$ **13.** $p + 6$ **15.** $x + 11$ **17.** $x - 8$ **19.** $y - 5$ **21.** $x + 11$ **23.** $y - 9$ **25.** $(y + 8)(y + 1)$ **27.** $(b + 3)(b + 5)$ **29.** $(m + 5)(m - 4)$ **31.** $(y - 5)(y - 3)$ **33.** prime **35.** $(z - 7)(z - 8)$ **37.** $(r - 6)(r + 5)$ **39.** $(a + 4)(a - 12)$ **41.** prime   **43.** $(x + 16)(x - 2)$ **45.** $(r + 2a)(r + a)$ **47.** $(t + 2z)(t - 3z)$ **49.** $(x + y)(x + 3y)$ **51.** $(v - 5w)(v - 6w)$ **53.** $4(x + 5)(x - 2)$ **55.** $2t(t + 1)(t + 3)$ **57.** $2x^4(x - 3)(x + 7)$ **59.** $5m^2(m^3 + 5m^2 - 8)$ **61.** $mn(m - 6n)(m - 4n)$ **63.** $a^3(a + 4b)(a - b)$ **65.** $yz(y + 3z)(y - 2z)$ **67.** $z^8(z - 7y)(z + 3y)$ **69.** $(a + b)(x + 4)(x - 3)$ **71.** $(2p + q)(r - 9)(r - 3)$ **73.** $2y^2 + y - 28$ **75.** $15z^2 - 4z - 4$

Section 5.3 (pages 314–316)

1. $(2t + 1)(5t + 2)$ **3.** $(3z - 2)(5z - 3)$ **5.** $(2s - t)(4s + 3t)$ **7.** **(a)** 2, 12, 24, 11   **(b)** 3, 8 (Order is irrelevant.)   **(c)** $3m, 8m$ **(d)** $2m^2 + 3m + 8m + 12$ **(e)** $(2m + 3)(m + 4)$ **(f)** $(2m + 3)(m + 4) = 2m^2 + 11m + 12$ **9.** B   **11.** B   **13.** A **15.** $2a + 5b$ **17.** $x^2 + 3x - 4; x + 4, x - 1$, or $x - 1, x + 4$ **19.** $2z^2 - 5z - 3; 2z + 1, z - 3$, or $z - 3, 2z + 1$ **21.** The binomial $2x - 6$ cannot be a factor because its terms have a common factor of 2, which the polynomial terms do not have. **23.** $(3a + 7)(a + 1)$ **25.** $(2y + 3)(y + 2)$ **27.** $(3m - 1)(5m + 2)$ **29.** $(3s - 1)(4s + 5)$ **31.** $(5m - 4)(2m - 3)$ **33.** $(4w - 1)(2w - 3)$ **35.** $(4y + 1)(5y - 11)$ **37.** prime   **39.** $2(5x + 3)(2x + 1)$ **41.** $3(4x - 1)(2x - 3)$ **43.** $q(5m + 2)(8m - 3)$ **45.** $3n^2(5n - 3)(n - 2)$ **47.** $y^2(5x - 4)(3x + 1)$ **49.** $(5a + 3b)(a - 2b)$ **51.** $(4s + 5t)(3s - t)$ **53.** $m^4n(3m + 2n)(2m + n)$ **55.** $(x - 5)(x - 1)$ **57.** $(3x + 4)(x + 4)$ **59.** $-5x(2x + 7)(x - 4)$ **61.** $(12x + 1)(x - 4)$ **63.** $(24y + 7x)(y - 2x)$ **65.** $(18x^2 - 5y)(2x^2 - 3y)$ **67.** $2(24a + b)(a - 2b)$ **69.** $x^2y^5(10x - 1)(x + 4)$ **71.** $4ab^2(9a + 1)(a - 3)$ **73.** $(12x - 5)(2x - 3)$ **75.** $(8x^2 - 3)(3x^2 + 8)$ **77.** $(4x + 3y)(6x + 5y)$ **79.** $-1(x + 7)(x - 3)$ **81.** $-1(3x + 4)(x - 1)$ **83.** $-1(a + 2b)(2a + b)$ **85.** $(m + 1)^3(5q - 2)(5q + 1)$ **87.** $(r + 3)^3(3x + 2y)^2$ **89.** $-4, 4$ **91.** $-11, -7, 7, 11$ **93.** $49p^2 - 9$ **95.** $x^2 + 12x + 36$

Section 5.4 (pages 323–325)

1. 1; 4; 9; 16; 25; 36; 49; 64; 81; 100; 121; 144; 169; 196; 225; 256; 289; 324; 361; 400   **3.** 1; 8; 27; 64; 125; 216; 343; 512; 729; 1000
5. (a) both of these   **(b)** perfect cube   **(c)** perfect square
(d) perfect square   **7.** $(y + 5)(y - 5)$ **9.** $(x + 12)(x - 12)$
11. prime   **13.** $4(m^2 + 4)$ **15.** $(3r + 2)(3r - 2)$
17. $4(3x + 2)(3x - 2)$ **19.** $(14p + 15)(14p - 15)$
21. $(4r + 5a)(4r - 5a)$ **23.** prime   **25.** $(p^2 + 7)(p^2 - 7)$
27. $(x^2 + 1)(x + 1)(x - 1)$ **29.** $(p^2 + 16)(p + 4)(p - 4)$
31. $k^2 - 9$ can be factored as $(k + 3)(k - 3)$. The completely factored
form is $(k^2 + 9)(k + 3)(k - 3)$.   **33.** 10   **35.** 9   **37.** $(w + 1)^2$
39. $(x - 4)^2$ **41.** $2(x + 6)^2$ **43.** $(4x - 5)^2$ **45.** $(7x - 2y)^2$
47. $(8x + 3y)^2$ **49.** $2(5h - 2y)^2$ **51.** $k(4k^2 - 4k + 9)$
53. $z^2(25z^2 + 5z + 1)$ **55.** $(a - 1)(a^2 + a + 1)$
57. $(m + 2)(m^2 - 2m + 4)$ **59.** $(k + 10)(k^2 - 10k + 100)$
61. $(3x - 4)(9x^2 + 12x + 16)$ **63.** $6(p + 1)(p^2 - p + 1)$
65. $5(x + 2)(x^2 - 2x + 4)$ **67.** $(y - 2x)(y^2 + 2yx + 4x^2)$
69. $2(x - 2y)(x^2 + 2xy + 4y^2)$
71. $(2p + 9q)(4p^2 - 18pq + 81q^2)$
73. $(3a + 4b)(9a^2 - 12ab + 16b^2)$
75. $(5t + 2s)(25t^2 - 10ts + 4s^2)$
77. $(2x - 5y^2)(4x^2 + 10xy^2 + 25y^4)$
79. $(3m^2 + 2n)(9m^4 - 6m^2n + 4n^2)$
81. $(x + y)(x^2 - xy + y^2)(x^6 - x^3y^3 + y^6)$ **83.** $\left(p + \frac{1}{3}\right)\left(p - \frac{1}{3}\right)$
85. $\left(6m + \frac{4}{5}\right)\left(6m - \frac{4}{5}\right)$ **87.** $(x + 0.8)(x - 0.8)$ **89.** $\left(t + \frac{1}{2}\right)^2$
91. $(x - 0.5)^2$ **93.** $\left(x + \frac{1}{2}\right)\left(x^2 - \frac{1}{2}x + \frac{1}{4}\right)$ **95.** $4mn$
97. $(m - p + 2)(m + p)$ **99.** $\{4\}$ **101.** $\{-5\}$

Summary Exercises on Factoring (pages 326–327)

1. G   **2.** H   **3.** A   **4.** B   **5.** E   **6.** I   **7.** C   **8.** F   **9.** I   **10.** E
11. $(a - 6)(a + 2)$ **12.** $(a + 8)(a + 9)$ **13.** $6(y - 2)(y + 1)$
14. $7y^4(y + 6)(y - 4)$ **15.** $6(a + 2b + 3c)$
16. $(m - 4n)(m + n)$ **17.** $(p - 11)(p - 6)$ **18.** $(z + 7)(z - 6)$
19. $(5z - 6)(2z + 1)$ **20.** $2(m - 8)(m + 3)$ **21.** $17xy(x^2y + 3)$
22. $5(3y + 1)$ **23.** $8a^3(a - 3)(a + 2)$ **24.** $(4k + 1)(2k - 3)$
25. $(z - 5a)(z + 2a)$ **26.** $50(z^2 - 2)$ **27.** $(x - 5)(x - 4)$
28. $10nr(10nr + 3r^2 - 5n)$ **29.** $(3n - 2)(2n - 5)$
30. $(3y - 1)(3y + 5)$ **31.** $4(4x + 5)$ **32.** $(m + 5)(m - 3)$
33. $(3y - 4)(2y + 1)$ **34.** $(m + 9)(m - 9)$ **35.** $(6z + 1)(z + 5)$
36. $(12x - 1)(x + 4)$ **37.** $(2k - 3)^2$ **38.** $(8p - 1)(p + 3)$
39. $6(3m + 2z)(3m - 2z)$ **40.** $(4m - 3)(2m + 1)$
41. $(3k - 2)(k + 2)$ **42.** $15a^3b^2(3b^3 - 4a + 5a^3b^2)$
43. $7k(2k + 5)(k - 2)$ **44.** $(5 + r)(1 - s)$
45. $(y^2 + 4)(y + 2)(y - 2)$ **46.** $10y^4(2y - 3)$ **47.** $8m(1 - 2m)$
48. $(k + 4)(k - 4)$ **49.** $(z - 2)(z^2 + 2z + 4)$
50. $(y - 8)(y + 7)$ **51.** prime   **52.** $9p^8(3p + 7)(p - 4)$
53. $8m^3(4m^6 + 2m^2 + 3)$ **54.** $(2m + 5)(4m^2 - 10m + 25)$
55. $(4r + 3m)^2$ **56.** $(z - 6)^2$ **57.** $(5h + 7g)(3h - 2g)$
58. $5z(z - 7)(z - 2)$ **59.** $(k - 5)(k - 6)$
60. $4(4p - 5m)(4p + 5m)$ **61.** $3k(k - 5)(k + 1)$
62. $(y - 6k)(y + 2k)$ **63.** $(10p + 3)(100p^2 - 30p + 9)$

64. $(4r - 7)(16r^2 + 28r + 49)$ **65.** $(2 + m)(3 + p)$
66. $(2m - 3n)(m + 5n)$ **67.** $(4z - 1)^2$
68. $5m^2(5m - 3n)(5m - 13n)$ **69.** $3(6m - 1)^2$
70. $(10a + 9y)(10a - 9y)$ **71.** prime   **72.** $(2y + 5)(2y - 5)$
73. $8z(4z - 1)(z + 2)$ **74.** $5(2m - 3)(m + 4)$
75. $(4 + m)(5 + 3n)$ **76.** $(2 - q)(2 - 3p)$
77. $2(3a - 1)(a + 2)$ **78.** $6y^4(3y + 4)(2y - 5)$
79. $(a - b)(a^2 + ab + b^2)$ **80.** $4(2k - 3)^2$
81. $(8m - 5n)^2$ **82.** $12y^2(6yz^2 + 1 - 2y^2z^2)$
83. $(4k - 3h)(2k + h)$ **84.** $(2a + 5)(a - 6)$
85. $2(x + 4)(x^2 - 4x + 16)$ **86.** $(2a - 3)(4a^2 + 6a + 9)$
87. $(5y - 6z)(2y + z)$ **88.** $(m - 2)^2$ **89.** $(8a - b)(a + 3b)$
90. $(a^2 + 25)(a + 5)(a - 5)$ **91.** $(x^3 - 1)(x^3 + 1)$
92. $(x - 1)(x^2 + x + 1)(x + 1)(x^2 - x + 1)$
93. $(x^2 - 1)(x^4 + x^2 + 1)$ **94.** $(x - 1)(x + 1)(x^4 + x^2 + 1)$
95. The result in **Exercise 92** is factored completely.   **96.** Show that
$x^4 + x^2 + 1 = (x^2 + x + 1)(x^2 - x + 1)$.   **97.** difference of squares
98. $(x - 3)(x^2 + 3x + 9)(x + 3)(x^2 - 3x + 9)$

Section 5.5 (pages 334–337)

1. $ax^2 + bx + c$ **3.** factor   **5.** $0; x$ **7.** To solve $2x(3x - 4) = 0$, set
each *variable* factor equal to 0 to get $x = 0$ or $3x - 4 = 0$. The *constant*
factor 2 does not introduce solutions into the equation. The solution set is
$\left\{0, \frac{4}{3}\right\}$.   **9.** The variable x is another factor to set equal to 0, so the
solution set is $\left\{0, \frac{1}{7}\right\}$.   **11.** $\{-5, 2\}$ **13.** $\left\{3, \frac{7}{2}\right\}$ **15.** $\left\{-\frac{1}{2}, \frac{1}{6}\right\}$
17. $\left\{-\frac{5}{6}, 0\right\}$ **19.** $\left\{0, \frac{4}{3}\right\}$ **21.** $\{6\}$ **23.** $\{-2, -1\}$ **25.** $\{1, 2\}$
27. $\{-8, 3\}$ **29.** $\{-1, 3\}$ **31.** $\{-2, -1\}$ **33.** $\{-4\}$ **35.** $\left\{-2, \frac{1}{3}\right\}$
37. $\left\{-\frac{4}{3}, \frac{1}{2}\right\}$ **39.** $\left\{-\frac{2}{3}\right\}$ **41.** $\{-3, 3\}$ **43.** $\left\{-\frac{7}{4}, \frac{7}{4}\right\}$
45. $\{-11, 11\}$ **47.** $\{0, 7\}$ **49.** $\left\{0, \frac{1}{2}\right\}$ **51.** $\{2, 5\}$ **53.** $\left\{-4, \frac{1}{2}\right\}$
55. $\{-17, 4\}$ **57.** $\left\{-\frac{5}{2}, \frac{1}{3}, 5\right\}$ **59.** $\left\{-\frac{7}{2}, -3, 1\right\}$ **61.** $\left\{-\frac{7}{3}, 0, \frac{7}{3}\right\}$
63. $\{-2, 0, 4\}$ **65.** $\{-5, 0, 4\}$ **67.** $\{-3, 0, 5\}$ **69.** $\{-1, 3\}$
71. $\{-1, 3\}$ **73.** $\{3\}$ **75.** $\left\{-\frac{2}{3}, 4\right\}$ **77.** $\left\{-\frac{4}{3}, -1, \frac{1}{2}\right\}$
79. (a) 64; 144; 4; 6   **(b)** No time has elapsed, so the object hasn't
fallen (been released) yet.   **81.** $\{-0.5, 0.1\}$ **83.** 1845   **85.** 9, 10

Section 5.6 (pages 342–347)

1. Read; variable; equation; Solve; answer; Check, original
3. *Step 3:* $45 = (2x + 1)(x + 1)$; *Step 4:* $x = 4$ or $x = -\frac{11}{2}$;
Step 5: base: 9 units; height: 5 units; *Step 6:* $9 \cdot 5 = 45$
5. *Step 3:* $80 = (x + 8)(x - 8)$; *Step 4:* $x = 12$ or $x = -12$;
Step 5: length: 20 units; width: 4 units; *Step 6:* $20 \cdot 4 = 80$
7. length: 14 cm; width: 12 cm   **9.** base: 12 in.; height: 5 in.
11. height: 13 in.; width: 10 in.   **13.** length: 15 in.; width: 12 in.
15. mirror: 7 ft; painting: 9 ft   **17.** 20, 21   **19.** 0, 1, 2 or 7, 8, 9
21. 7, 9, 11   **23.** $-2, 0, 2$ or 6, 8, 10   **25.** 12 cm   **27.** 12 mi   **29.** 8 ft
31. 112 ft   **33.** 256 ft   **35. (a)** 1 sec   **(b)** $\frac{1}{2}$ sec and $1\frac{1}{2}$ sec   **(c)** 3 sec
(d) The negative solution, -1, does not make sense, since t represents
time, which cannot be negative.   **37. (a)** 104.4 million; The result obtained from the model is less than 109 million, the actual number for 2000.
(b) 18   **(c)** 272.7 million; The result is more than 263 million.
(d) 326.6 million   **39.** $\frac{25}{36}$ **41.** $\frac{16}{-9}$, or $-\frac{16}{9}$

Chapter 5 Review Exercises (pages 350–352)

1. $7(t + 2)$ **2.** $30z(2z^2 + 1)$ **3.** $(2y + 3)(x - 4)$
4. $(3y + 2x)(2y + 3)$ **5.** $(x + 3)(x + 2)$ **6.** $(y - 5)(y - 8)$
7. $(q + 9)(q - 3)$ **8.** $(r - 8)(r + 7)$ **9.** $(r + 8s)(r - 12s)$
10. $(p + 12q)(p - 10q)$ **11.** $8p(p + 2)(p - 5)$
12. $3x^2(x + 2)(x + 8)$ **13.** $p^5(p - 2q)(p + q)$
14. $3r^3(r + 3s)(r - 5s)$ **15.** $9x^2y(x + 2)(x - 3)$
16. $2x^5(x - 2y)(x + 3y)$ **17.** r and $6r$, $2r$ and $3r$ **18.** Factor out z.
19. $(2k - 1)(k - 2)$ **20.** $(3r - 1)(r + 4)$ **21.** $(3r + 2)(2r - 3)$
22. $(5z + 1)(2z - 1)$ **23.** $(v + 3)(8v - 7)$
24. $4x^3(3x - 1)(2x - 1)$ **25.** $-3(x + 2)(2x - 5)$
26. $rs(5r + 6s)(2r + s)$ **27.** $4x^2y(3x + y)(4x - y)$ **28.** The
student stopped too soon. He needs to factor out the common factor
$4x - 1$ to get $(4x - 1)(4x - 5)$ as the correct answer. **29.** B
30. D **31.** $(n + 7)(n - 7)$ **32.** $(5b + 11)(5b - 11)$
33. $(7y + 5w)(7y - 5w)$ **34.** $36(2p + q)(2p - q)$ **35.** prime
36. $(r - 6)^2$ **37.** $(3t - 7)^2$ **38.** $(m + 10)(m^2 - 10m + 100)$
39. $(5k + 4x)(25k^2 - 20kx + 16x^2)$
40. $(7x - 4)(49x^2 + 28x + 16)$
41. $(10 - 3x^2)(100 + 30x^2 + 9x^4)$
42. $(x - y)(x + y)(x^2 + xy + y^2)(x^2 - xy + y^2)$
43. $\left\{-\frac{3}{4}, 1\right\}$ **44.** $\{-7, -3, 4\}$ **45.** $\left\{0, \frac{5}{2}\right\}$ **46.** $\{-3, -1\}$
47. $\{1, 4\}$ **48.** $\{3, 5\}$ **49.** $\left\{-\frac{4}{3}, 5\right\}$ **50.** $\left\{-\frac{8}{9}, \frac{8}{9}\right\}$ **51.** $\{0, 8\}$
52. $\{-1, 6\}$ **53.** $\{7\}$ **54.** $\{6\}$ **55.** $\left\{-2, -1, -\frac{2}{5}\right\}$ **56.** $\{-3, 3\}$
57. length: 10 ft; width: 4 ft **58.** 5 ft **59.** 6, 7 or $-5, -4$ **60.** 26 mi
61. (a) 256 ft **(b)** 1024 ft **62. (a)** 601,000 vehicles; The result is
slightly higher than the actual number for 2005. **(b)** 655,000 vehicles
(c) The estimate may be unreliable because the conditions that prevailed
in the years 2001–2006 may have changed, causing either a greater increase
or a decrease predicted by the model for the number of alternative-
fueled vehicles. **63.** D **64.** The factor $(2x + 8)$ has a factor of 2.
The completely factored form is $2(x + 4)(3x - 4)$.
65. $(3k + 5)(k + 2)$ **66.** $(z - x)(z - 10x)$
67. $(y^2 + 25)(y + 5)(y - 5)$ **68.** $(3m + 4)(5m - 4p)$
69. $8abc(3b^2c - 7ac^2 + 9ab)$ **70.** $3m(2m + 3)(m - 5)$
71. $6xyz(2xz^2 + 2y - 5x^2yz^3)$ **72.** prime **73.** $(2r + 3q)(6r - 5)$
74. $2a^3(a + 2)(a - 6)$ **75.** $(7t + 4)^2$
76. $(10a + 3)(100a^2 - 30a + 9)$ **77.** $\{0, 7\}$ **78.** $\{-5, 2\}$
79. $\left\{-\frac{2}{5}\right\}$ **80.** $-5, -4, -3$ or $5, 6, 7$ **81.** length: 6 m; width: 4 m
82. 15 m, 36 m, 39 m **83.** 6 m **84.** width: 10 m; length: 17 m

Chapter 5 Test (page 353)

[5.1–5.4] **1.** D **2.** $6x(2x - 5)$ **3.** $m^2n(2mn + 3m - 5n)$
4. $(2x + y)(a - b)$ **5.** $(x + 3)(x - 8)$ **6.** $(2x + 3)(x - 1)$
7. $(5z - 1)(2z - 3)$ **8.** prime **9.** prime **10.** $(2 - a)(6 + b)$
11. $(3y + 8)(3y - 8)$ **12.** $(2x - 7y)^2$ **13.** $-2(x + 1)^2$
14. $3t^2(2t + 9)(t - 4)$ **15.** $(r - 5)(r^2 + 5r + 25)$
16. $8(k + 2)(k^2 - 2k + 4)$ **17.** $(x^2 + 9)(x + 3)(x - 3)$
18. $(3x + 2y)(3x - 2y)(9x^2 + 4y^2)$ **19.** $(3x^3y^2 + 2)^2$
[5.5] **20.** $\left\{\frac{1}{2}, 6\right\}$ **21.** $\left\{-\frac{2}{5}, \frac{2}{5}\right\}$ **22.** $\{0, 9\}$ **23.** $\{10\}$

24. $\left\{-8, -\frac{5}{2}, \frac{1}{3}\right\}$ [5.6] **25.** 6 ft by 9 ft **26.** $-2, -1$ **27.** 17 ft
28. $8493 billion

Chapter 1-5 Cumulative Review Exercises (pages 354–355)

[2.1–2.3] **1.** $\{0\}$ **2.** $\{0.05\}$ **3.** $\{6\}$ [2.5] **4.** $P = \dfrac{A}{1 + rt}$
5. $110°$ and $70°$ [2.4] **6.** gold: 11; silver: 12; bronze: 6
[2.6] **7.** 230; 205; 38%; 12% [3.1] **8. (a)** negative, positive
(b) negative, negative
[3.2, 3.3] **9. (a)** $\left(-\frac{1}{4}, 0\right), (0, 3)$ **(b)** 12 **(c)**

[3.3, 3.4] **10. (a)** 16; A slope of (approximately) 16 means that retail
sales of prescription drugs increased by about $16 billion per year.
(b) (2005, 230) [4.1, 4.2] **11.** $\frac{16}{9}$ **12.** 256 **13.** $\dfrac{1}{p^2}$ **14.** $\dfrac{1}{m^6}$
[4.4] **15.** $-4k^2 - 4k + 8$ [4.5] **16.** $45x^2 + 3x - 18$
[4.6] **17.** $9p^2 + 12p + 4$ [4.7] **18.** $4x^3 + 6x^2 - 3x + 10$
[4.3] **19.** 5.5×10^4; 2.0×10^6 [5.2, 5.3] **20.** $(2a - 1)(a + 4)$
21. $(2m + 3)(5m + 2)$ **22.** $(4t + 3v)(2t + v)$
[5.4] **23.** $(2p - 3)^2$ **24.** $(5r + 9t)(5r - 9t)$
[5.3] **25.** $2pq(3p + 1)(p + 1)$ [5.5] **26.** $\left\{-\frac{2}{3}, \frac{1}{2}\right\}$ **27.** $\{0, 8\}$
[5.6] **28.** 5 m, 12 m, 13 m

6 RATIONAL EXPRESSIONS AND APPLICATIONS

Connections **(page 363)** **1.** $3x^2 + 11x + 8$ cannot be factored, so
this quotient cannot be simplified. By long division, the quotient is
$3x + 5 + \dfrac{-2}{x + 2}$. **2.** The numerator factors as $(x - 2)(x^2 + 2x + 4)$,
so, after simplification, the quotient is $x - 2$. Long division gives the
same quotient.

Section 6.1 (pages 364–366)

1. (a) $\frac{7}{10}$ **(b)** $\frac{8}{15}$ **3. (a)** 0 **(b)** -1 **5. (a)** $-\frac{64}{15}$ **(b)** undefined
7. (a) undefined **(b)** $\frac{8}{25}$ **9. (a)** 0 **(b)** 0 **11. (a)** 0 **(b)** undefined
13. A rational expression is a quotient of two polynomials, such as
$\dfrac{x^2 + 3x - 6}{x + 4}$. One can think of this as an algebraic fraction. **15.** Division
by 0 is undefined. If the denominator of a rational expression equals 0,
the expression is undefined. **17.** $y \neq 0$ **19.** $x \neq 6$
21. $x \neq -\frac{5}{3}$ **23.** $m \neq -3, m \neq 2$ **25.** It is never undefined.
27. It is never undefined. **29. (a)** numerator: x^2, $4x$; denominator: x, 4
(b) First factor the numerator, getting $x(x + 4)$. Then divide the
numerator and denominator by the common factor $x + 4$ to get $\frac{x}{1}$, or x.

31. $3r^2$ **33.** $\frac{2}{5}$ **35.** $\dfrac{x - 1}{x + 1}$ **37.** $\frac{7}{5}$ **39.** $\frac{6}{7}$ **41.** $m - n$ **43.** $\dfrac{2}{t - 3}$
45. $\dfrac{3(2m + 1)}{4}$ **47.** $\dfrac{3m}{5}$ **49.** $\dfrac{3r - 2s}{3}$ **51.** $k - 3$ **53.** $\dfrac{x - 3}{x + 1}$

55. $\dfrac{x+1}{x-1}$ **57.** $\dfrac{x+2}{x-4}$ **59.** $-\dfrac{3}{7t}$ **61.** $\dfrac{z-3}{z+5}$ **63.** $\dfrac{r+s}{r-s}$ **65.** $\dfrac{a+b}{a-b}$

67. $\dfrac{m+n}{2}$ **69.** $\dfrac{x^2+1}{x}$ **71.** $1-p+p^2$ **73.** x^2+3x+9

75. $-\dfrac{b^2+ba+a^2}{a+b}$ **77.** $\dfrac{k^2-2k+4}{k-2}$ **79.** $\dfrac{z+3}{z}$ **81.** $\dfrac{1-2r}{2}$

83. B, D   **85.** -1 **87.** $-(m+1)$ **89.** -1 **91.** It is already in lowest terms.   **93.** B

Answers may vary in Exercises 95, 97, and 99.   **95.** $\dfrac{-(x+4)}{x-3}, \dfrac{-x-4}{x-3},$

$\dfrac{x+4}{-(x-3)}, \dfrac{x+4}{-x+3}$ **97.** $\dfrac{-(2x-3)}{x+3}, \dfrac{-2x+3}{x+3}, \dfrac{2x-3}{-(x+3)}, \dfrac{2x-3}{-x-3}$

99. $\dfrac{-(3x-1)}{5x-6}, \dfrac{-3x+1}{5x-6}, \dfrac{3x-1}{-(5x-6)}, \dfrac{3x-1}{-5x+6}$

101. x^2+3 **103. (a)** 0   **(b)** 1.6   **(c)** 4.1   **(d)** The waiting time also increases.   **105.** $\dfrac{5}{9}$ **107.** 4

Section 6.2 (pages 371–372)

1. (a) B   **(b)** D   **(c)** C   **(d)** A   **3.** $\dfrac{3a}{2}$ **5.** $-\dfrac{4x^4}{3}$ **7.** $\dfrac{2}{c+d}$

9. $4(x-y)$ **11.** $\dfrac{t^2}{2}$ **13.** $\dfrac{x+3}{2x}$ **15.** 5   **17.** $-\dfrac{3}{2t^4}$ **19.** $\dfrac{1}{4}$

21. $-\dfrac{35}{8}$ **23.** $\dfrac{2(x+2)}{x(x-1)}$ **25.** $\dfrac{x(x-3)}{6}$ **27.** $\dfrac{10}{9}$ **29.** $-\dfrac{3}{4}$ **31.** $-\dfrac{9}{2}$

33. $\dfrac{p+4}{p+2}$ **35.** -1 **37.** $\dfrac{(2x-1)(x+2)}{x-1}$ **39.** $\dfrac{(k-1)^2}{(k+1)(2k-1)}$

41. $\dfrac{4k-1}{3k-2}$ **43.** $\dfrac{m+4p}{m+p}$ **45.** $\dfrac{m+6}{m+3}$ **47.** $\dfrac{y+3}{y+4}$ **49.** $\dfrac{m}{m+5}$

51. $\dfrac{r+6s}{r+s}$ **53.** $\dfrac{(q-3)^2(q+2)^2}{q+1}$ **55.** $\dfrac{x+10}{10}$ **57.** $\dfrac{3-a-b}{2a-b}$

59. $-\dfrac{(x+y)^2(x^2-xy+y^2)}{3y(y-x)(x-y)}$, or $\dfrac{(x+y)^2(x^2-xy+y^2)}{3y(x-y)^2}$ **61.** $\dfrac{5xy^2}{4q}$

63. $2\cdot 3^2$ **65.** $2^2\cdot 3^3$ **67.** 6   **69.** $6q^3$

Section 6.3 (pages 376–378)

1. C   **3.** C   **5.** 60   **7.** 1800   **9.** x^5 **11.** $30p$ **13.** $180y^4$ **15.** $84r^5$

17. $15a^5b^3$ **19.** $12p(p-2)$ **21.** $28m^2(3m-5)$ **23.** $30(b-2)$

25. $18(r-2)$ **27.** $12p(p+5)^2$ **29.** $8(y+2)(y+1)$

31. $c-d$ or $d-c$ **33.** $m-3$ or $3-m$ **35.** $p-q$ or $q-p$

37. $k(k+5)(k-2)$ **39.** $a(a+6)(a-3)$

41. $(p+3)(p+5)(p-6)$ **43.** $(k+3)(k-5)(k+7)(k+8)$

45. 7   **46.** 1   **47.** identity property of multiplication

48. 7   **49.** 1   **50.** identity property of multiplication

51. $\dfrac{20}{55}$ **53.** $\dfrac{-45}{9k}$ **55.** $\dfrac{60m^2k^3}{32k^4}$ **57.** $\dfrac{57z}{6z-18}$ **59.** $\dfrac{-4a}{18a-36}$

61. $\dfrac{6(k+1)}{k(k-4)(k+1)}$ **63.** $\dfrac{36r(r+1)}{(r-3)(r+2)(r+1)}$

65. $\dfrac{ab(a+2b)}{2a^3b+a^2b^2-ab^3}$ **67.** $\dfrac{(t-r)(4r-t)}{t^3-r^3}$

69. $\dfrac{2y(z-y)(y-z)}{y^4-z^3y}$, or $\dfrac{-2y(y-z)^2}{y^4-z^3y}$ **71.** $\dfrac{11}{8}$ **73.** $\dfrac{13}{20}$

Section 6.4 (pages 383–386)

1. E   **3.** C   **5.** B   **7.** G   **9.** $\dfrac{11}{m}$ **11.** $\dfrac{4}{y+4}$ **13.** 1   **15.** $\dfrac{m-1}{m+1}$

17. b **19.** x **21.** $y-6$ **23.** $\dfrac{1}{x-3}$ **25.** $\dfrac{3z+5}{15}$ **27.** $\dfrac{10-7r}{14}$

29. $\dfrac{-3x-2}{4x}$ **31.** $\dfrac{57}{10x}$ **33.** $\dfrac{x+1}{2}$ **35.** $\dfrac{5x+9}{6x}$ **37.** $\dfrac{7-6p}{3p^2}$

39. $\dfrac{-k-8}{k(k+4)}$ **41.** $\dfrac{x+4}{x+2}$ **43.** $\dfrac{6m^2+23m-2}{(m+2)(m+1)(m+5)}$

45. $\dfrac{4y^2-y+5}{(y+1)^2(y-1)}$ **47.** $\dfrac{3}{t}$ **49.** $m-2$ or $2-m$

51. $\dfrac{-2}{x-5}$, or $\dfrac{2}{5-x}$ **53.** -4 **55.** $\dfrac{-5}{x-y^2}$, or $\dfrac{5}{y^2-x}$

57. $\dfrac{x+y}{5x-3y}$, or $\dfrac{-x-y}{3y-5x}$ **59.** $\dfrac{-6}{4p-5}$, or $\dfrac{6}{5-4p}$

61. $\dfrac{-m-n}{2(m-n)}$ **63.** $\dfrac{-x^2+6x+11}{(x+3)(x-3)(x+1)}$

65. $\dfrac{-5q^2-13q+7}{(3q-2)(q+4)(2q-3)}$ **67.** $\dfrac{9r+2}{r(r+2)(r-1)}$

69. $\dfrac{2(x^2+3xy+4y^2)}{(x+y)(x+y)(x+3y)}$, or $\dfrac{2(x^2+3xy+4y^2)}{(x+y)^2(x+3y)}$

71. $\dfrac{15r^2+10ry-y^2}{(3r+2y)(6r-y)(6r+y)}$ **73. (a)** $\dfrac{9k^2+6k+26}{5(3k+1)}$ **(b)** $\dfrac{1}{4}$

75. $\dfrac{10x}{49(101-x)}$ **77.** $\dfrac{5}{4}$ **79.** $\dfrac{6}{7}$

Section 6.5 (pages 392–394)

1. (a) $6; \dfrac{1}{6}$ **(b)** $12; -\dfrac{1}{4}$ **(c)** $\dfrac{1}{6} \div \left(-\dfrac{1}{4}\right)$ **(d)** $-\dfrac{2}{3}$ **3.** Choice D is correct, because every sign has been changed in the fraction. This means it was multiplied by $\dfrac{-1}{-1} = 1$.   **5.** -6 **7.** $\dfrac{1}{xy}$ **9.** $\dfrac{2a^2b}{3}$

11. $\dfrac{m(m+2)}{3(m-4)}$ **13.** $\dfrac{2}{x}$ **15.** $\dfrac{8}{x}$ **17.** $\dfrac{a^2-5}{a^2+1}$ **19.** $\dfrac{31}{50}$ **21.** $\dfrac{y^2+x^2}{xy(y-x)}$

23. $\dfrac{40-12p}{85p}$ **25.** $\dfrac{5y-2x}{3+4xy}$ **27.** $\dfrac{a-2}{2a}$ **29.** $\dfrac{z-5}{4}$ **31.** $\dfrac{-m}{m+2}$

33. $\dfrac{3m(m-3)}{(m-1)(m-8)}$ **35.** $\dfrac{2x-7}{3x+1}$ **37.** $\dfrac{y+4}{y-8}$ **39.** $\dfrac{x^2y^2}{y^2+x^2}$

41. $\dfrac{y^2+x^2}{xy^2+x^2y}$, or $\dfrac{y^2+x^2}{xy(y+x)}$ **43.** $\dfrac{1}{2xy}$ **45.** $\dfrac{x-3}{x-5}$ **47.** division

49. $\dfrac{\frac{3}{8}+\frac{5}{6}}{2}$ **50.** $\dfrac{29}{48}$ **51.** $\dfrac{29}{48}$ **52.** Answers will vary.   **53.** $\dfrac{5}{3}$ **55.** $\dfrac{13}{2}$

57. $\dfrac{19r}{15}$ **59.** $12x+2$ **61.** $-44p^2+27p$ **63.** $\left\{\dfrac{1}{2}\right\}$ **65.** $\{-5\}$

Section 6.6 (pages 401–404)

1. expression; $\dfrac{43}{40}x$ **3.** equation; $\left\{\dfrac{40}{43}\right\}$ **5.** expression; $-\dfrac{1}{10}x$

7. equation; $\{-10\}$ **9.** equation; $\{0\}$ **11.** $x \neq -2, 0$

13. $x \neq -3, 4, -\dfrac{1}{2}$ **15.** $x \neq -9, 1, -2, 2$ **17.** $\dfrac{2}{3x}+\dfrac{1}{5x}$ is an expression, not an equation. Only equations and inequalities are "solved."

19. $\left\{\frac{1}{4}\right\}$ **21.** $\left\{-\frac{3}{4}\right\}$ **23.** $\{-15\}$ **25.** $\{7\}$ **27.** $\{-15\}$ **29.** $\{-5\}$
31. $\{-6\}$ **33.** $\varnothing$ **35.** $\{5\}$ **37.** $\{4\}$ **39.** $\{5\}$ **41.** $\left\{x \mid x \neq \pm\frac{4}{3}\right\}$
43. $\{1\}$ **45.** $\{4\}$ **47.** $\{5\}$ **49.** $\{-4\}$ **51.** $\{-2, 12\}$ **53.** $\varnothing$
55. $\{3\}$ **57.** $\{3\}$ **59.** $\{-3\}$ **61.** $\left\{-\frac{1}{5}, 3\right\}$ **63.** $\left\{-\frac{1}{2}, 5\right\}$ **65.** $\{3\}$
67. $\left\{-\frac{1}{3}, 3\right\}$ **69.** $\{-1\}$ **71.** $\{-6\}$ **73.** $\left\{-6, \frac{1}{2}\right\}$ **75.** $\{6\}$
77. Transform so that the terms with k are on one side and the remaining
term is on the other.   **79.** $F = \dfrac{ma}{k}$ **81.** $a = \dfrac{kF}{m}$ **83.** $R = \dfrac{E - Ir}{I}$, or
$R = \dfrac{E}{I} - r$ **85.** $\mathcal{A} = \dfrac{h(B + b)}{2}$ **87.** $a = \dfrac{2S - ndL}{nd}$, or $a = \dfrac{2S}{nd} - L$
89. $y = \dfrac{xz}{x + z}$ **91.** $t = \dfrac{rs}{rs - 2s - 3r}$, or $t = \dfrac{-rs}{-rs + 2s + 3r}$
93. $z = \dfrac{3y}{5 - 9xy}$, or $z = \dfrac{-3y}{9xy - 5}$ **95.** $t = \dfrac{2x - 1}{x + 1}$, or $t = \dfrac{-2x + 1}{-x - 1}$
97. $\dfrac{288}{t}$ mph   **99.** $\dfrac{289}{z}$ hr

Summary Exercises on Rational Expressions and Equations (pages 405–406)

1. expression; $\dfrac{10}{p}$ **2.** expression; $\dfrac{y^3}{x^3}$ **3.** expression; $\dfrac{1}{2x^2(x + 2)}$

4. equation; $\{9\}$ **5.** expression; $\dfrac{y + 2}{y - 1}$ **6.** expression;

$\dfrac{5k + 8}{k(k - 4)(k + 4)}$ **7.** equation; $\{39\}$ **8.** expression; $\dfrac{t - 5}{3(2t + 1)}$

9. expression; $\dfrac{13}{3(p + 2)}$ **10.** equation; $\left\{-1, \frac{12}{5}\right\}$ **11.** equation;

$\left\{\frac{1}{7}, 2\right\}$ **12.** expression; $\dfrac{16}{3k}$ **13.** expression; $\dfrac{7}{12z}$ **14.** equation; $\{13\}$

15. expression; $\dfrac{3m + 5}{(m + 3)(m + 2)(m + 1)}$ **16.** expression; $\dfrac{k + 3}{5(k - 1)}$

17. equation; $\varnothing$ **18.** equation; $\varnothing$ **19.** expression; $\dfrac{t + 2}{2(2t + 1)}$

20. equation; $\{-7\}$

Section 6.7 (pages 410–414)

1. (a) the amount   **(b)** $5 + x$ **(c)** $\dfrac{5 + x}{6} = \dfrac{13}{3}$ **3.** $\dfrac{12}{18}$ **5.** $\dfrac{12}{3}$ **7.** 12
9. $\dfrac{1386}{97}$ **11.** 18.809 min   **13.** 314.248 m per min   **15.** 3.275 hr
17. $\dfrac{D}{R} = \dfrac{d}{r}$ **19.** $\dfrac{500}{x - 10} = \dfrac{600}{x + 10}$ **21.** 8 mph   **23.** 32 mph
25. 165 mph   **27.** 3 mph   **29.** 18.5 mph   **31.** $\dfrac{1}{10}$ job per hr
33. $\dfrac{1}{8}t + \dfrac{1}{6}t = 1$, or $\dfrac{1}{8} + \dfrac{1}{6} = \dfrac{1}{t}$ **35.** $2\frac{2}{5}$ hr   **37.** $5\frac{5}{11}$ hr   **39.** 3 hr
41. $2\frac{7}{10}$ hr   **43.** $9\frac{1}{11}$ min   **45.** 2   **47.** $\dfrac{5}{2}$ **49.** 0   **51.** $y = -\frac{3}{2}x + 4$

Chapter 6 Review Exercises (pages 419–421)

1. (a) $\dfrac{11}{8}$ **(b)** $\dfrac{13}{22}$ **2. (a)** undefined   **(b)** 1   **3.** $x \neq 3$ **4.** $y \neq 0$
5. $k \neq -5, -\frac{2}{3}$ **6.** Set the denominator equal to 0 and solve the
equation. Any solutions are values for which the rational expression is

undefined.   **7.** $\dfrac{b}{3a}$ **8.** -1 **9.** $\dfrac{-(2x + 3)}{2}$ **10.** $\dfrac{2p + 5q}{5p + q}$

Answers may vary in Exercises 11 and 12.   **11.** $\dfrac{-(4x - 9)}{2x + 3}, \dfrac{-4x + 9}{2x + 3},$
$\dfrac{4x - 9}{-(2x + 3)}, \dfrac{4x - 9}{-2x - 3}$ **12.** $\dfrac{-(8 - 3x)}{3 - 6x}, \dfrac{-8 + 3x}{3 - 6x}, \dfrac{8 - 3x}{-(3 - 6x)},$
$\dfrac{8 - 3x}{-3 + 6x}$ **13.** $\dfrac{72}{p}$ **14.** 2   **15.** $\dfrac{5}{8}$ **16.** $\dfrac{r + 4}{3}$ **17.** $\dfrac{3a - 1}{a + 5}$
18. $\dfrac{y - 2}{y - 3}$ **19.** $\dfrac{p + 5}{p + 1}$ **20.** $\dfrac{3z + 1}{z + 3}$ **21.** $108y^4$
22. $(x + 3)(x + 1)(x + 4)$ **23.** $\dfrac{15a}{10a^4}$ **24.** $\dfrac{-54}{18 - 6x}$ **25.** $\dfrac{15y}{50 - 10y}$
26. $\dfrac{4b(b + 2)}{(b + 3)(b - 1)(b + 2)}$ **27.** $\dfrac{15}{x}$ **28.** $-\dfrac{2}{p}$ **29.** $\dfrac{4k - 45}{k(k - 5)}$
30. $\dfrac{28 + 11y}{y(7 + y)}$ **31.** $\dfrac{-2 - 3m}{6}$ **32.** $\dfrac{3(16 - x)}{4x^2}$
33. $\dfrac{7u + 6b}{(a - 2b)(a + 2b)}$ **34.** $\dfrac{-k^2 - 6k + 3}{3(k + 3)(k - 3)}$ **35.** $\dfrac{5z - 16}{z(z + 6)(z - 2)}$
36. $\dfrac{-13p + 33}{p(p - 2)(p - 3)}$ **37.** $\dfrac{4(y - 3)}{y + 3}$ **38.** $\dfrac{10}{13}$ **39.** $\dfrac{xw + 1}{xw - 1}$
40. $\dfrac{(q - p)^2}{pq}$ **41.** $(x - 5)(x - 3)$, or $x^2 - 8x + 15$ **42.** $\dfrac{y + x}{xy}$
43. $\varnothing$ **44.** $\{-16\}$ **45.** $\{0\}$ **46.** $\{3\}$ **47.** $t = \dfrac{Ry}{m}$
48. $y = \dfrac{4x + 5}{3}$ **49.** $m = \dfrac{4 + p^2q}{3p^2}$ **50.** $\dfrac{20}{15}$ **51.** $\dfrac{3}{18}$ **52.** 10 mph
53. $3\frac{1}{13}$ hr   **54.** 2 hr   **55.** $\dfrac{m + 7}{(m - 1)(m + 1)}$ **56.** $8p^2$ **57.** $\dfrac{1}{6}$
58. $\dfrac{s^3 + t^3}{st(s - t)}$ **59.** 3   **60.** $\dfrac{z + 7}{(z + 1)(z - 1)^2}$ **61.** $\dfrac{-t - 1}{(t + 2)(t - 2)}$, or
$\dfrac{t + 1}{(2 + t)(2 - t)}$ **62.** $\{-2, 3\}$ **63.** $v = at + w$ **64.** 150 km per hr
65. $5\frac{1}{11}$ hr   **66. (a)** -3 **(b)** -1 **(c)** $-3, -1$ **67.** $\dfrac{15}{2x}$
68. If $x = 0$, the divisor R is equal to 0, and division by 0 is undefined.
69. $(x + 3)(x + 1)$ **70.** $\dfrac{7}{x + 1}$ **71.** $\dfrac{11x + 21}{4x}$ **72.** $\varnothing$
73. We know that -3 is not allowed, because P and R are undefined for
$x = -3$.   **74.** Rate is equal to distance divided by time. Here, distance
is 6 miles and time is $(x + 3)$ minutes, so rate $= \dfrac{6}{x + 3}$, which is the
expression for P.   **75.** $\dfrac{6}{5}, \dfrac{5}{2}$

Chapter 6 Test (page 422)

[6.1] **1. (a)** $\dfrac{11}{6}$ **(b)** undefined   **2.** $x \neq -2, 4$ **3.** (Answers may
vary.) $\dfrac{-(6x - 5)}{2x + 3}, \dfrac{-6x + 5}{2x + 3}, \dfrac{6x - 5}{-(2x + 3)}, \dfrac{6x - 5}{-2x - 3}$ **4.** $-3x^2y^3$
5. $\dfrac{3a + 2}{a - 1}$ [6.2] **6.** $\dfrac{25}{27}$ **7.** $\dfrac{3k - 2}{3k + 2}$ **8.** $\dfrac{a - 1}{a + 4}$ **9.** $\dfrac{x - 5}{3 - x}$
[6.3] **10.** $150p^5$ **11.** $(2r + 3)(r + 2)(r - 5)$ **12.** $\dfrac{240p^2}{64p^3}$
13. $\dfrac{21}{42m - 84}$ [6.4] **14.** 2   **15.** $\dfrac{-14}{5(y + 2)}$ **16.** $\dfrac{-x^2 + x + 1}{3 - x}$, or

$\dfrac{x^2 - x - 1}{x - 3}$ **17.** $\dfrac{-m^2 + 7m + 2}{(2m + 1)(m - 5)(m - 1)}$ [6.5] **18.** $\dfrac{2k}{3p}$

19. $\dfrac{-2 - x}{4 + x}$ **20.** $\dfrac{2y^2 + x^2}{xy(y - x)}$ [6.6] **21.** $\left\{-\frac{1}{2}, 1\right\}$ **22.** $\left\{-\frac{1}{2}\right\}$

23. $D = \dfrac{dF - k}{F}$, or $D = d - \dfrac{k}{F}$ [6.7] **24.** 3 mph **25.** $2\frac{2}{9}$ hr

Chapters 1–6 Cumulative Review Exercises (pages 423–424)

[1.2, 1.5, 1.6] **1.** 2 [2.3] **2.** $\{17\}$ [2.5] **3.** $b = \dfrac{2\mathscr{A}}{h}$ [2.6] **4.** $\left\{-\frac{2}{7}\right\}$

[2.8] **5.** $[-8, \infty)$ [3.1, 3.2] **6. (a)** $(-3, 0)$ **(b)** $(0, -4)$

7.   [4.4] **8.**

[4.1, 4.2] **9.** $\dfrac{1}{2^4 x^7}$ **10.** $\dfrac{1}{m^6}$ [4.4] **11.** $k^2 + 2k + 1$

[4.6] **12.** $4a^2 - 4ab + b^2$ [4.5] **13.** $3y^3 + 8y^2 + 12y - 5$

[4.7] **14.** $6p^2 + 7p + 1 + \dfrac{3}{p - 1}$ [5.3] **15.** $(4t + 3v)(2t + v)$

16. prime [5.4] **17.** $(4x^2 + 1)(2x + 1)(2x - 1)$ [5.5] **18.** $\{-3, 5\}$

19. $\left\{5, -\frac{1}{2}, \frac{2}{3}\right\}$ [5.6] **20.** -2 or -1 **21.** 6 m [6.1] **22.** A **23.** D

[6.4] **24.** $\dfrac{4}{q}$ **25.** $\dfrac{3r + 28}{7r}$ **26.** $\dfrac{7}{15(q - 4)}$ **27.** $\dfrac{-k - 5}{k(k + 1)(k - 1)}$

[6.2] **28.** $\dfrac{7(2z + 1)}{24}$ [6.5] **29.** $\dfrac{195}{29}$ [6.6] **30.** $\left\{\frac{21}{2}\right\}$ **31.** $\{-2, 1\}$

[6.7] **32.** $1\frac{1}{5}$ hr

---

7 GRAPHS, LINEAR EQUATIONS, AND FUNCTIONS

Connections **(page 432)** **1.** x-intercept: $(-2, 0)$; y-intercept: $(0, 3)$
For Problems 2 and 3, we give each equation solved for y. Graphs are not included. **2.** $y = 4x + 3$ **3.** $y = -0.5x$

Section 7.1 (pages 438–443)

1. (a) I **(b)** III **(c)** II **(d)** IV **(e)** none **(f)** none

3.   **5. (a)** $-3; 3; 2; -1$ **7. (a)** $3; 1; -1; 3$
(b)   **(b)**

9. $(6, 0); (0, 4)$ **11.** $(6, 0); (0, -2)$ **13.** $(-2, 0); \left(0, -\frac{5}{3}\right)$

15. none; $(0, 5)$ **17.** $(2, 0)$; none **19.** $(-4, 0)$; none

21. none; $(0, -2)$ **23.** $(0, 0); (0, 0)$ **25.** $(0, 0); (0, 0)$

27. $(-5, -1)$ **29.** $\left(\frac{9}{2}, -\frac{3}{2}\right)$ **31.** $\left(0, \frac{11}{2}\right)$ **33.** $(2.1, 0.9)$ **35.** $(1, 1)$
37. $\left(-\frac{5}{12}, \frac{5}{28}\right)$ **39.** B **41.** A, B, D, G **43. (a)** C **(b)** A **(c)** D
(d) B **45. (a)** 2 **(b)** 0 **(c)** undefined **(d)** $-\frac{1}{3}$ **(e)** 1 **(f)** -4
47. (a) 8 **(b)** rises **49. (a)** $\frac{5}{6}$ **(b)** rises **51. (a)** 0 **(b)** horizontal
53. (a) $-\frac{1}{2}$ **(b)** falls **55. (a)** undefined **(b)** vertical **57. (a)** -1
(b) falls **59.** 6 **61.** -3 **63.** $-\frac{5}{2}$ **65.** undefined
67. $-\frac{1}{2}$ 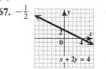 **69.** $\frac{5}{2}$

71. 4   **73.** undefined

75. 0   **77.**   **79.**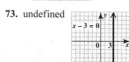

81. **83.** **85.**

87. $-\frac{4}{9}; \frac{9}{4}$ **89.** parallel **91.** perpendicular **93.** neither **95.** parallel
97. neither **99.** perpendicular **101.** $-\$4000$ per yr; The value of the
machine is decreasing \$4000 each year during these years. **103.** 0%
per yr (or no change); The percent of pay raise is not changing—
it is 3% each year during these years. **105. (a)** 21.2 **(b)** The number
of subscribers increased by an average of 21.2 million each year from
2005 to 2008. **107. (a)** -5 theaters per yr **(b)** The negative slope
means that the number of drive-in theaters decreased by an average of
5 each year from 2000 to 2007. **109.** \$1371.67 million per yr; Sales of
plasma TVs increased by an average of \$1371.67 million each year from
2003 to 2006. **111.** $3x - 2y = 19$

Section 7.2 (pages 451–455)

1. A **3.** A **5.** $3x + y = 10$ **7.** A **9.** C **11.** H **13.** B
15. $y = 5x + 15$ **17.** $y = -\frac{2}{3}x + \frac{4}{5}$ **19.** $y = x - 1$
21. $y = \frac{2}{5}x + 5$ **23.** $y = \frac{2}{3}x + 1$ **25.** $y = -x - 2$
27. (a) $y = x + 4$ **(b)** 1 **(c)** $(0, 4)$ **(d)**

29. (a) $y = -\frac{6}{5}x + 6$ **(b)** $-\frac{6}{5}$ **(c)** $(0, 6)$ **(d)**

31. (a) $y = \frac{4}{5}x - 4$ **(b)** $\frac{4}{5}$ **(c)** $(0, -4)$ **(d)**

33. (a) $y = -\frac{1}{2}x - 2$ **(b)** $-\frac{1}{2}$ **(c)** $(0, -2)$ **(d)**

35. (a) $2x + y = 18$ **(b)** $y = -2x + 18$ **37. (a)** $3x + 4y = 10$
(b) $y = -\frac{3}{4}x + \frac{5}{2}$ **39. (a)** $x - 2y = -13$ **(b)** $y = \frac{1}{2}x + \frac{13}{2}$
41. (a) $4x - y = 12$ **(b)** $y = 4x - 12$ **43. (a)** $7x - 5y = -20$
(b) $y = 1.4x + 4$ **45.** $y = 5$ **47.** $x = 9$ **49.** $y = -\frac{3}{2}$ **51.** $y = 8$
53. $x = 0.5$ **55. (a)** $2x - y = 2$ **(b)** $y = 2x - 2$
57. (a) $x + 2y = 8$ **(b)** $y = -\frac{1}{2}x + 4$ **59. (a)** $y = 5$ **(b)** $y = 5$
61. (a) $x = 7$ **(b)** not possible **63. (a)** $y = -3$ **(b)** $y = -3$
65. (a) $2x - 13y = -6$ **(b)** $y = \frac{2}{13}x + \frac{6}{13}$ **67. (a)** $y = 3x - 19$
(b) $3x - y = 19$ **69. (a)** $y = \frac{1}{2}x - 1$ **(b)** $x - 2y = 2$
71. (a) $y = -\frac{1}{2}x + 9$ **(b)** $x + 2y = 18$ **73. (a)** $y = 7$ **(b)** $y = 7$
75. $y = 45x;\ (0, 0),\ (5, 225),\ (10, 450)$ **77.** $y = 3.10x;\ (0, 0)$,
$(5, 15.50),\ (10, 31.00)$ **79.** $y = 111x;\ (0, 0),\ (5, 555),\ (10, 1110)$
81. (a) $y = 112.50x + 12$ **(b)** $(5, 574.50)$; The cost for 5 tickets
and a parking pass is $574.50. **(c)** $237 **83. (a)** $y = 41x + 99$
(b) $(5, 304)$; The cost for a 5-month membership is $304. **(c)** $591
85. (a) $y = 60x + 36$ **(b)** $(5, 336)$; The cost of the plan for 5 months
is $336. **(c)** $756 **87. (a)** $y = 6x + 30$ **(b)** $(5, 60)$; It costs $60
to rent the saw for 5 days. **(c)** 18 days **89. (a)** $y = 1294.7x + 3921$;
Sales of digital cameras in the United States increased by
$1294.7 million per yr from 2003 to 2006. **(b)** $9099.8 million
91. (a) $y = 5.25x + 22.25$ **(b)** $48.5 billion; It is greater than the
actual value. **93.** 32; 212 **94.** $(0, 32)$ and $(100, 212)$ **95.** $\frac{9}{5}$
96. $F = \frac{9}{5}C + 32$ **97.** $C = \frac{5}{9}(F - 32)$ **98.** $86°$ **99.** $10°$
100. $-40°$ **101.** $[0, \infty)$ **103.** $[-4, 4]$

Summary Exercises on Slopes and Equations of Lines (page 456)

1. $-\frac{3}{5}$ **2.** $-\frac{4}{7}$ **3.** 2 **4.** $\frac{5}{2}$ **5.** undefined **6.** 0 **7. (a)** $y = -\frac{5}{6}x + \frac{13}{3}$
(b) $5x + 6y = 26$ **8. (a)** $y = 3x + 11$ **(b)** $3x - y = -11$
9. (a) $y = -\frac{5}{2}x$ **(b)** $5x + 2y = 0$ **10. (a)** $y = -8$ **(b)** $y = -8$

11. (a) $y = -\frac{7}{9}$ **(b)** $9y = -7$ **12. (a)** $y = -3x + 10$
(b) $3x + y = 10$ **13. (a)** $y = \frac{2}{3}x + \frac{14}{3}$ **(b)** $2x - 3y = -14$
14. (a) $y = 2x - 10$ **(b)** $2x - y = 10$ **15. (a)** $y = -\frac{5}{2}x + 2$
(b) $5x + 2y = 4$ **16. (a)** $y = \frac{2}{3}x + 8$ **(b)** $2x - 3y = -24$
17. (a) $y = -7x + 3$ **(b)** $7x + y = 3$ **18. (a)** B **(b)** D **(c)** A
(d) C **(e)** E

Section 7.3 (pages 462–464)

1. Answers will vary. A function is a set of ordered pairs in which
each first component corresponds to exactly one second component.
For example, $\{(0, 1), (1, 2), (2, 3), (3, 4)\}$ is a function.

3. independent variable

In Exercises 5 and 7, answers will vary.

5.

7.

x	y
-3	-4
-3	1
2	0

9. function; domain: $\{5, 3, 4, 7\}$; range: $\{1, 2, 9, 6\}$ **11.** not a
function; domain: $\{2, 0\}$; range: $\{4, 2, 5\}$ **13.** function; domain:
$\{-3, 4, -2\}$; range: $\{1, 7\}$ **15.** not a function; domain: $\{1, 0, 2\}$;
range: $\{1, -1, 0, 4, -4\}$ **17.** function; domain: $\{2, 5, 11, 17, 3\}$;
range: $\{1, 7, 20\}$ **19.** not a function; domain: $\{1\}$; range: $\{5, 2, -1, -4\}$
21. function; domain: $\{4, 2, 0, -2\}$; range: $\{-3\}$ **23.** function;
domain: $\{-2, 0, 3\}$; range: $\{2, 3\}$ **25.** function; domain: $(-\infty, \infty)$;
range: $(-\infty, \infty)$ **27.** not a function; domain: $(-\infty, 0]$; range: $(-\infty, \infty)$
29. function; domain: $(-\infty, \infty)$; range: $(-\infty, 4]$ **31.** not a function;
domain: $[-4, 4]$; range: $[-3, 3]$ **33.** function, $(-\infty, \infty)$
35. function; $(-\infty, \infty)$ **37.** function; $(-\infty, \infty)$ **39.** not a function;
$[0, \infty)$ **41.** function; $(-\infty, \infty)$ **43.** function; $(-\infty, 0) \cup (0, \infty)$
45. function; $(-\infty, 4) \cup (4, \infty)$ **47.** function; $\left(-\infty, -\frac{3}{4}\right) \cup \left(-\frac{3}{4}, \infty\right)$
49. not a function; $[1, \infty)$ **51.** function; $(-\infty, 0) \cup (0, \infty)$
53. (a) yes **(b)** domain: $\{2004, 2005, 2006, 2007, 2008\}$; range:
$\{42.3, 42.8, 43.7, 43.8\}$ **(c)** Answers will vary. Two possible answers
are $(2005, 42.3)$ and $(2008, 43.8)$. **55.** -9 **57.** 1 **59.** $y = \frac{1}{2}x - \frac{7}{4}$

Section 7.4 (pages 468–472)

1. B **3.** 4 **5.** -11 **7.** 3 **9.** 2.75 **11.** $-3p + 4$ **13.** $3x + 4$
15. $-3x - 2$ **17.** $-\pi^2 + 4\pi + 1$ **19.** $-3x - 3h + 4$ **21.** -9
23. (a) -1 **(b)** -1 **25. (a)** 2 **(b)** 3 **27. (a)** 15 **(b)** 10
29. (a) 4 **(b)** 1 **31. (a)** 3 **(b)** -3 **33. (a)** -3 **(b)** 2
35. (a) 2 **(b)** 0 **(c)** -1 **37. (a)** $f(x) = -\frac{1}{3}x + 4$ **(b)** 3
39. (a) $f(x) = 3 - 2x^2$ **(b)** -15 **41. (a)** $f(x) = \frac{4}{3}x - \frac{8}{3}$ **(b)** $\frac{4}{3}$
43. line; -2; $-2x + 4$; -2; 3; -2
45. domain: $(-\infty, \infty)$; **47.** domain: $(-\infty, \infty)$;
range: $(-\infty, \infty)$ range: $(-\infty, \infty)$

49. domain: $(-\infty, \infty)$; range: $(-\infty, \infty)$

51. domain: $(-\infty, \infty)$; range: $\{-4\}$

53. domain: $(-\infty, \infty)$; range: $\{0\}$

55. x-axis **57. (a)** $11.25 **(b)** 3 is the value of the independent variable, which represents a package weight of 3 lb; $f(3)$ is the value of the dependent variable, representing the cost to mail a 3-lb package. **(c)** $18.75; $f(5) = 18.75$

59. (a) 194.53 cm **(b)** 177.29 cm **(c)** 177.41 cm **(d)** 163.65 cm
61. (a) $f(x) = 12x + 100$ **(b)** 1600; The cost to print 125 t-shirts is $1600. **(c)** 75; $f(75) = 1000$; The cost to print 75 t-shirts is $1000.
63. (a) 1.1 **(b)** 5 **(c)** -1.2 **(d)** $(0, 3.5)$ **(e)** $f(x) = -1.2x + 3.5$
65. (a) $[0, 100]$; $[0, 3000]$ **(b)** 25 hr; 25 hr **(c)** 2000 gal
(d) $f(0) = 0$; The pool is empty at time 0. **(e)** $f(25) = 3000$; After 25 hr, there are 3000 gal of water in the pool. **67.** $15x^2 - x - 4$
69. $12x^2 - 11x - 5$ **71.** $3x^2 - 2x$

Section 7.5 (pages 478–480)

1. (a) -10 **(b)** 8 **3. (a)** 8 **(b)** 2 **5. (a)** 8 **(b)** 74
7. (a) -11 **(b)** 4 **9. (a)** $8x - 3$ **(b)** $2x - 17$
11. (a) $-x^2 + 12x - 12$ **(b)** $9x^2 + 4x + 6$ **13.** $x^2 + 2x - 9$
15. 6 **17.** $x^2 - x - 6$ **19.** 6 **21.** -33 **23.** 0 **25.** $-\frac{9}{4}$ **27.** $-\frac{9}{2}$
29. For example, let $f(x) = 2x^3 + 3x^2 + x + 4$ and $g(x) = 2x^4 + 3x^3 - 9x^2 + 2x - 4$. For these functions, $(f - g)(x) = -2x^4 - x^3 + 12x^2 - x + 8$, and $(g - f)(x) = 2x^4 + x^3 - 12x^2 + x - 8$.
Because the two differences are not equal, subtraction of functions is not commutative. **31.** $10x^2 - 2x$ **33.** $2x^2 - x - 3$ **35.** $8x^3 - 27$
37. $2x^3 - 18x$ **39.** -20 **41.** $2x^2 - 6x$ **43.** 36 **45.** $\frac{35}{4}$ **47.** $\frac{1859}{64}$
49. $5x - 1$; 0 **51.** $2x - 3$; -1 **53.** $4x^2 + 6x + 9$; $\frac{3}{2}$
55. $\frac{x^2 - 9}{2x}$, $x \neq 0$ **57.** $-\frac{5}{4}$ **59.** $\frac{x - 3}{2x}$, $x \neq 0$ **61.** 0 **63.** $-\frac{35}{4}$
65. $\frac{7}{2}$ **67.** 6 **69.** 83 **71.** 53 **73.** 13 **75.** $2x^2 + 11$ **77.** $2x - 2$
79. $\frac{97}{4}$ **81.** 8 **83.** $(f \circ g)(x) = 63{,}360x$; It computes the number of inches in x miles. **85.** $(\mathcal{A} \circ r)(t) = 4\pi t^2$; This is the area of the circular layer as a function of time. **87.** $\frac{1}{3}$ **89.** 3

Section 7.6 (pages 486–489)

1. direct **3.** direct **5.** inverse **7.** inverse **9.** inverse **11.** direct
13. joint **15.** combined **17.** increases; decreases **19.** The perimeter of a square varies directly as the length of its side. **21.** The surface area of a sphere varies directly as the square of its radius.
23. The area of a triangle varies jointly as the length of its base and height. **25.** 4; 2; 4π; $\frac{4}{3}\pi$; $\frac{1}{2}$; $\frac{1}{3}\pi$ **27.** 36 **29.** $\frac{16}{9}$ **31.** 0.625 **33.** $\frac{16}{5}$
35. $222\frac{2}{9}$ **37.** $2.919, or $2.91\frac{9}{10}$ **39.** 8 lb **41.** about 450 cm³
43. 256 ft **45.** $106\frac{2}{3}$ mph **47.** 100 cycles per sec **49.** $21\frac{1}{3}$ foot-candles **51.** $420 **53.** about 11.8 lb **55.** about 448.1 lb

57. about 68,600 calls **59.** Answers will vary.

61. **63.**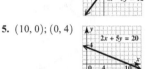

Chapter 7 Review Exercises (pages 493–496)

1.

x	y
0	5
$\frac{10}{3}$	0
2	2
$\frac{14}{3}$	-2

2.

x	y
2	-6
5	-3
3	-5
6	-2

3. $(3, 0)$; $(0, -4)$
4. $\left(\frac{28}{5}, 0\right)$; $(0, 4)$
5. $(10, 0)$; $(0, 4)$
6. $(8, 0)$; $(0, -2)$

7. $(0, 2)$ **8.** $\left(-\frac{9}{2}, \frac{3}{2}\right)$ **9.** $-\frac{7}{5}$ **10.** $-\frac{1}{2}$ **11.** 2 **12.** $\frac{3}{4}$ **13.** undefined
14. $\frac{2}{3}$ **15.** $-\frac{1}{3}$ **16.** undefined **17.** $-\frac{1}{3}$ **18.** -1 **19.** positive
20. negative **21.** undefined **22.** 0 **23.** 12 ft **24.** $1496 per yr
25. (a) $y = -\frac{1}{3}x - 1$ **(b)** $x + 3y = -3$ **26. (a)** $y = -2$
(b) $y = -2$ **27. (a)** $y = -\frac{4}{3}x + \frac{29}{3}$ **(b)** $4x + 3y = 29$
28. (a) $y = 3x + 7$ **(b)** $3x - y = -7$ **29. (a)** not possible
(b) $x = 2$ **30. (a)** $y = -9x + 13$ **(b)** $9x + y = 13$
31. (a) $y = \frac{7}{5}x + \frac{16}{5}$ **(b)** $7x - 5y = -16$ **32. (a)** $y = -x + 2$
(b) $x + y = 2$ **33. (a)** $y = 4x - 29$ **(b)** $4x - y = 29$
34. (a) $y = -\frac{5}{2}x + 13$ **(b)** $5x + 2y = 26$ **35. (a)** $y = 57x + 159$;
$843 **(b)** $y = 47x + 159$; $723 **36. (a)** $y = 143.75x + 1407.75$;
The revenue from skiing facilities increased by an average of
$143.75 million each year from 2003 to 2007. **(b)** $2558 million
37. domain: $\{-4, 1\}$; range: $\{2, -2, 5, -5\}$; not a function
38. domain: $\{9, 11, 4, 17, 25\}$; range: $\{32, 47, 69, 14\}$; function
39. domain: $[-4, 4]$; range: $[0, 2]$; function **40.** domain: $(-\infty, 0]$;
range: $(-\infty, \infty)$; not a function **41.** function; domain: $(-\infty, \infty)$;
linear function **42.** not a function; domain: $[0, \infty)$ **43.** function;
domain: $(-\infty, 6) \cup (6, \infty)$ **44.** -6 **45.** -8.52 **46.** -8
47. $-2k^2 + 3k - 6$ **48.** $f(x) = 2x^2$; 18 **49.** C **50. (a)** yes
(b) domain: $\{1960, 1970, 1980, 1990, 2000, 2009\}$; range: $\{69.7,$
$70.8, 73.7, 75.4, 76.8, 78.1\}$ **(c)** Answers will vary. Two possible
answers are $(1960, 69.7)$ and $(2009, 78.1)$. **(d)** 73.7; In 1980, life
expectancy at birth was 73.7 yr. **(e)** 2000 **51. (a)** -11 **(b)** 4
52. (a) $5x^2 - x + 5$ **(b)** $-5x^2 + 5x + 1$ **(c)** 11 **(d)** -9
53. (a) $36x^3 - 9x^2$ **(b)** $4x - 1$, $x \neq 0$ **(c)** -45 **(d)** 7
54. (a) 167 **(b)** 1495 **(c)** 20 **(d)** 42 **(e)** $75x^2 + 220x + 160$
(f) $15x^2 + 10x + 2$ **55.** C **56.** 430 mm **57.** 5.59 vibrations
per sec **58.** 22.5 ft³

Chapter 7 Test (pages 496–497)

[7.1] **1.** $-\frac{10}{3}$; -2; 0 **2.** $\left(\frac{20}{3}, 0\right)$; $(0, -10)$

3. none; $(0, 5)$ 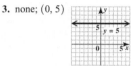 **4.** $(2, 0)$; none

5. $\frac{1}{2}$ **6.** It is a vertical line. **7.** perpendicular **8.** neither
9. -929 farms per yr; The number of farms decreased, on the average,
by about 929 each year from 1980 to 2008. [7.2] **10. (a)** $y = -5x + 19$
(b) $5x + y = 19$ **11. (a)** $y = 14$ **(b)** $y = 14$ **12. (a)** $y = -\frac{1}{2}x + 2$
(b) $x + 2y = 4$ **13. (a)** not possible **(b)** $x = 5$
14. (a) $y = -\frac{3}{5}x - \frac{11}{5}$ **(b)** $3x + 5y = -11$ **15. (a)** $y = -\frac{1}{2}x - \frac{3}{2}$
(b) $x + 2y = -3$ **16.** B **17. (a)** $y = 2078x + 51{,}557$
(b) $\$61{,}947$; It is more than the actual value. [7.3] **18.** D **19.** D
20. (a) domain: $[0, \infty)$; range: $(-\infty, \infty)$ **(b)** domain: $\{0, -2, 4\}$;
range: $\{1, 3, 8\}$ [7.4] **21. (a)** 0 **(b)** $-a^2 + 2a - 1$
22. domain: $(-\infty, \infty)$;   [7.5] **23. (a)** -18 **(b)** $-2x^2 + 12x - 9$
range: $(-\infty, \infty)$ **(c)** $-2x^2 - 2x - 3$ **(d)** -7
          24. (a) $x^3 + 4x^2 + 5x + 2$ **(b)** 0
25. (a) $x + 2$, $x \ne -1$ **(b)** 0
26. (a) 23 **(b)** $3x^2 + 11$
(c) $9x^2 + 30x + 27$

[7.6] **27.** 200 amps **28.** 0.8 lb

Chapters 1–7 Cumulative Review Exercises (pages 498–499)

[1.4, 1.5] **1.** always true **2.** never true **3.** sometimes true; For example,
$3 + (-3) = 0$, but $3 + (-1) = 2 \ne 0$. **4.** 4 [1.7] **5.** $4m - 3$
[1.6] **6.** $-\frac{19}{2}$ [1.5, 1.6] **7.** -39 **8.** undefined [2.3] **9.** $\left\{\frac{7}{6}\right\}$
10. $\{-1\}$ [2.5] **11.** 6 in. [2.7] **12.** 2 hr

[2.8] **13.** $\left(-3, \frac{7}{2}\right)$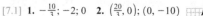

14. $(-\infty, 1]$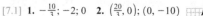

[3.2, 7.1] **15.** x-intercept: $(4, 0)$; y-intercept: $\left(0, \frac{12}{5}\right)$

[3.3, 7.1] **16. (a)** $-\frac{6}{5}$ **(b)** $\frac{5}{6}$ [3.4, 7.2] **17. (a)** $y = -\frac{3}{4}x - 1$
(b) $3x + 4y = -4$ **18. (a)** $y = -\frac{4}{3}x + \frac{7}{3}$ **(b)** $4x + 3y = 7$
[4.1, 4.2] **19.** $\dfrac{y}{18x}$ [4.6] **20.** $49x^2 + 42xy + 9y^2$
[4.4] **21.** $x^3 + 12x^2 - 3x - 7$ [4.7] **22.** $m^2 - 2m + 3$
[5.1–5.4] **23.** $(2w + 7z)(8w - 3z)$ **24.** $(2x - 1 + y)(2x - 1 - y)$
25. $(2p + 3)(4p^2 - 6p + 9)$ [5.5] **26.** $\left\{\frac{1}{3}\right\}$ [5.6] **27.** 4 ft

28. longer sides: 18 in.; distance between: 16 in.
[6.4] **29.** $\dfrac{6x + 22}{(x + 1)(x + 3)}$ [6.2] **30.** $\dfrac{(x + 3)^2}{3x}$ [6.5] **31.** 6
[6.6] **32.** $\{5\}$ [7.3] **33.** domain: $\{14, 91, 75, 23\}$; range: $\{9, 70, 56, 5\}$;
not a function; 75 in the domain is paired with two different values, 70 and
56, in the range.
[7.4] **34. (a)** domain: $(-\infty, \infty)$; range: $(-\infty, \infty)$ **(b)** 22 **(c)** 1
[7.2] **35.** -2.02; The per capita consumption of potatoes in the United
States decreased by an average of 2.02 lb per yr from 2003 to 2008.

8 SYSTEMS OF LINEAR EQUATIONS

Connections **(page 507)** **1.** $\{(-1, 5)\}$ **2.** $\{(0.25, -0.5)\}$
3. $\{(1.5, -1.5)\}$

Section 8.1 (pages 507–511)

1. A; The ordered-pair solution must be in quadrant II, and
$(-4, -4)$ is in quadrant III. **3.** no **5.** yes **7.** yes **9.** no
11. yes **13. (a)** B **(b)** C **(c)** D **(d)** A
15. $\{(4, 2)\}$ **17.** $\{(0, 4)\}$ **19.** $\{(4, -1)\}$

In Exercises 21–31, we do not show the graphs.
21. $\{(1, 3)\}$ **23.** $\{(0, 2)\}$ **25.** $\emptyset$ (inconsistent system)
27. $\{(x, y) \mid 3x + y = 5\}$ (dependent equations) **29.** $\{(4, -3)\}$
31. $\emptyset$ (inconsistent system) **33.** It is difficult to read the exact
coordinates of the solution. Thus, the solution cannot be checked.
35. (a) neither **(b)** intersecting lines **(c)** one solution
37. (a) dependent **(b)** one line **(c)** infinite number of solutions
39. (a) neither **(b)** intersecting lines **(c)** one solution
41. (a) inconsistent **(b)** parallel lines **(c)** no solution
43. (a) 1980–2000 **(b)** 2001; about 750 newspapers
45. (a) 1997–2002 **(b)** 2001 **(c)** 2002 **(d)** $(1998, 30)$ (The y-value
is approximate.) **47.** 30 **49.** B **51.** A **53.** $y = -3x + 4$
55. $y = \frac{9}{2}x - 2$ **57.** $\{2\}$ **59.** $\left\{\frac{4}{5}\right\}$

Section 8.2 (pages 516–518)

1. The student must find the value of y and write the solution as an
ordered pair. The solution set is $\{(3, 0)\}$. **3.** $\{(3, 9)\}$ **5.** $\{(7, 3)\}$
7. $\{(-4, 8)\}$ **9.** $\{(3, -2)\}$ **11.** $\{(0, 5)\}$ **13.** $\{(x, y) \mid 3x - y = 5\}$
15. $\left\{\left(\frac{1}{4}, -\frac{1}{2}\right)\right\}$ **17.** $\emptyset$ **19.** $\{(x, y) \mid 2x - y = -12\}$ **21.** $\{(2, 6)\}$
23. $\{(2, -4)\}$ **25.** $\{(-2, 1)\}$ **27.** $\{(x, y) \mid x + 2y = 48\}$
29. $\{(10, 4)\}$ **31.** $\{(4, -9)\}$ **33.** To find the total cost, multiply the
number of bicycles (x) by the cost per bicycle $(\$400)$, and add the fixed cost
$(\$5000)$. Thus, $y_1 = 400x + 5000$ gives this total cost (in dollars).
34. $y_2 = 600x$ **35.** $y_1 = 400x + 5000$, $y_2 = 600x$; solution
set: $\{(25, 15{,}000)\}$ **36.** 25; 15,000; 15,000

37. $\{(2, 4)\}$

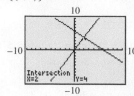

39. $\{(1, 5)\}$

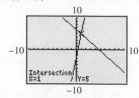

41. $\{(5, -3)\}$; The equations to input are $Y_1 = \dfrac{5 - 4X}{5}$ and $Y_2 = \dfrac{1 - 2X}{3}$.

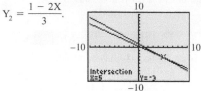

43. $16x$ **45.** $10y$ **47.** $4x$ **49.** -2

Section 8.3 (pages 522–524)

1. false; The solution set is $\emptyset$. **3.** $\{(4, 6)\}$ **5.** $\{(-1, -3)\}$
7. $\{(-2, 3)\}$ **9.** $\left\{\left(\tfrac{1}{2}, 4\right)\right\}$ **11.** $\{(3, -6)\}$ **13.** $\{(0, 4)\}$
15. $\{(0, 0)\}$ **17.** $\{(7, 4)\}$ **19.** $\{(0, 3)\}$ **21.** $\{(3, 0)\}$
23. $\{(x, y)\,|\,x - 3y = -4\}$ **25.** $\emptyset$ **27.** $\{(-3, 2)\}$ **29.** $\{(11, 15)\}$
31. $\left\{\left(13, -\tfrac{7}{5}\right)\right\}$ **33.** $\{(6, -4)\}$ **35.** $\{(x, y)\,|\,x + 3y = 6\}$ **37.** $\emptyset$
39. $\left\{\left(-\tfrac{5}{7}, -\tfrac{2}{7}\right)\right\}$ **41.** $\left\{\left(\tfrac{1}{8}, -\tfrac{5}{6}\right)\right\}$ **43.** $5.39 = 2000a + b$
44. $7.18 = 2008a + b$ **45.** $2000a + b = 5.39, 2008a + b = 7.18$;
solution set: $\{(0.22375, -442.11)\}$ **46. (a)** $y = 0.22375x - 442.11$
(b) 6.96 ($\$6.96$); This is a bit more ($\$0.08$) than the actual figure.
47. $8x - 12y + 4z = 20$ **49.** 4 **51.** -3

Summary Exercises on Solving Systems of Linear Equations (page 525)

1. (a) Use substitution, since the second equation is solved for y.
(b) Use elimination, since the coefficients of the y-terms are opposites.
(c) Use elimination, since the equations are in standard form with no
coefficients of 1 or -1. Solving by substitution would involve fractions.
2. System B is easier to solve by substitution because the second equation
is already solved for y. **3. (a)** $\{(1, 4)\}$ **(b)** $\{(1, 4)\}$ **(c)** Answers
will vary. **4. (a)** $\{(-5, 2)\}$ **(b)** $\{(-5, 2)\}$ **(c)** Answers will vary.
5. $\{(3, 12)\}$ **6.** $\{(-3, 2)\}$ **7.** $\left\{\left(\tfrac{1}{3}, \tfrac{1}{2}\right)\right\}$ **8.** $\emptyset$ **9.** $\{(3, -2)\}$
10. $\{(-1, -11)\}$ **11.** $\{(x, y)\,|\,2x - 3y = 5\}$ **12.** $\{(9, 4)\}$
13. $\left\{\left(\tfrac{45}{31}, \tfrac{4}{31}\right)\right\}$ **14.** $\{(4, -5)\}$ **15.** $\emptyset$ **16.** $\{(-4, 6)\}$
17. $\{(-3, 2)\}$ **18.** $\left\{\left(\tfrac{22}{13}, -\tfrac{23}{13}\right)\right\}$ **19.** $\{(0, 0)\}$ **20.** $\{(2, -3)\}$
21. $\{(24, -12)\}$ **22.** $\{(3, 2)\}$ **23.** $\{(10, -12)\}$
24. $\{(-4, 2)\}$ **25.** $\{(5, 3)\}$

Section 8.4 (pages 531–533)

1. B **3.** $\{(3, 2, 1)\}$ **5.** $\{(1, 4, -3)\}$ **7.** $\{(0, 2, -5)\}$
9. $\{(1, 0, 3)\}$ **11.** $\left\{\left(1, \tfrac{3}{10}, \tfrac{2}{5}\right)\right\}$ **13.** $\left\{\left(-\tfrac{7}{3}, \tfrac{22}{3}, 7\right)\right\}$
15. $\{(-12, 18, 0)\}$ **17.** $\{(0.8, -1.5, 2.3)\}$ **19.** $\{(4, 5, 3)\}$
21. $\{(2, 2, 2)\}$ **23.** $\left\{\left(\tfrac{8}{3}, \tfrac{2}{3}, 3\right)\right\}$ **25.** $\{(-1, 0, 0)\}$

27. $\{(-4, 6, 2)\}$ **29.** $\{(-3, 5, -6)\}$ **31.** $\emptyset$; inconsistent system
33. $\{(x, y, z)\,|\,x - y + 4z = 8\}$; dependent equations **35.** $\{(3, 0, 2)\}$
37. $\{(x, y, z)\,|\,2x + y - z = 6\}$; dependent equations **39.** $\{(0, 0, 0)\}$
41. $\emptyset$; inconsistent system **43.** $\{(2, 1, 5, 3)\}$ **45.** $\{(-2, 0, 1, 4)\}$
47. 100 in., 103 in., 120 in. **49.** $-4, 8, 12$

Section 8.5 (pages 541–546)

1. wins: 95; losses: 67 **3.** length: 78 ft; width: 36 ft **5.** AT&T:
$\$124.0$ billion; Verizon: $\$97.4$ billion **7.** $x = 40$ and $y = 50$, so the
angles measure $40°$ and $50°$. **9.** NHL: $\$288.23$; NBA: $\$291.93$
11. Junior Roast Beef: $\$2.09$; Big Montana: $\$4.39$ **13. (a)** 6 oz
(b) 15 oz **(c)** 24 oz **(d)** 30 oz **15.** $\$2.29x$ **17.** 6 gal of 25%;
14 gal of 35% **19.** pure acid: 6 L; 10% acid: 48 L **21.** nuts: 14 kg;
cereal: 16 kg **23.** $\$1000$ at 2%; $\$2000$ at 4% **25. (a)** $(10 - x)$ mph
(b) $(10 + x)$ mph **27.** train: 60 km per hr; plane: 160 km per hr
29. boat: 21 mph; current: 3 mph **31.** $\$0.75$-per-lb candy: 5.22 lb;
$\$1.25$-per-lb candy: 3.78 lb **33.** general admission: 76; with student
ID: 108 **35.** 8 for a citron; 5 for a wood apple **37.** $x + y + z = 180$;
angle measures: $70°, 30°, 80°$ **39.** first: $20°$; second: $70°$; third: $90°$
41. shortest: 12 cm; middle: 25 cm; longest: 33 cm **43.** gold: 23;
silver: 21; bronze: 28 **45.** $\$16$ tickets: 1170; $\$23$ tickets: 985;
$\$40$ tickets: 130 **47.** bookstore A: 140; bookstore B: 280;
bookstore C: 380 **49.** first chemical: 50 kg; second chemical: 400 kg;
third chemical: 300 kg **51.** wins: 53; losses: 19; overtime losses: 10
53. (a) 6 **(b)** $-\tfrac{1}{6}$ **55. (a)** $-\tfrac{7}{8}$ **(b)** $\tfrac{8}{7}$

Section 8.6 (pages 552–553)

1. (a) $0, 5, -3$ **(b)** $1, -3, 8$ **(c)** yes; The number of rows is
the same as the number of columns (three). **(d)** $\begin{bmatrix} 1 & 4 & 8 \\ 0 & 5 & -3 \\ -2 & 3 & 1 \end{bmatrix}$

(e) $\begin{bmatrix} 1 & -\tfrac{3}{2} & -\tfrac{1}{2} \\ 0 & 5 & -3 \\ 1 & 4 & 8 \end{bmatrix}$ **(f)** $\begin{bmatrix} 1 & 15 & 25 \\ 0 & 5 & -3 \\ 1 & 4 & 8 \end{bmatrix}$ **3.** 3×2 **5.** 4×2

7. $\{(4, 1)\}$ **9.** $\{(1, 1)\}$ **11.** $\{(-1, 4)\}$ **13.** $\emptyset$
15. $\{(x, y)\,|\,2x + y = 4\}$ **17.** $\{(0, 0)\}$ **19.** $\{(4, 0, 1)\}$
21. $\{(-1, 23, 16)\}$ **23.** $\{(3, 2, -4)\}$
25. $\{(x, y, z)\,|\,x - 2y + z = 4\}$ **27.** $\emptyset$ **29.** $\{(1, 1)\}$
31. $\{(-1, 2, 1)\}$ **33.** $\{(1, 7, -4)\}$
35. $[16, \infty)$ **37.** $(-\infty, 4)$

Chapter 8 Review Exercises (pages 557–559)

1. yes **2.** no **3.** $\{(3, 1)\}$ **4.** $\{(0, -2)\}$ **5.** $\emptyset$
6. $\{(x, y)\,|\,x - 2y = 2\}$ **7.** It would be easiest to solve for x in the
second equation because its coefficient is -1. No fractions would be
involved. **8.** The true statement $0 = 0$ is an indication that the system
has an infinite number of solutions. Write the solution set using set-builder
notation and the equation of the system that is in standard form with
integer coefficients having greatest common factor 1. **9.** $\{(2, 1)\}$
10. $\{(3, 5)\}$ **11.** $\{(6, 4)\}$ **12.** $\{(x, y)\,|\,x + 3y = 6\}$ **13.** C
14. (a) 2 **(b)** 9 **15.** $\{(7, 1)\}$ **16.** $\{(-4, 3)\}$

17. $\{(x, y) \mid 3x - 4y = 9\}$ **18.** $\emptyset$ **19.** $\{(-4, 1)\}$
20. $\{(x, y) \mid 2x - 3y = 0\}$ **21.** $\{(9, 2)\}$ **22.** $\{(8, 9)\}$
23. $\{(2, 1)\}$ **24.** $\{(-3, 2)\}$ **25.** $\{(1, -5, 3)\}$ **26.** $\{(1, 2, 3)\}$
27. $\emptyset$; inconsistent system **28.** length: 200 ft; width: 85 ft **29.** New
York Yankees: $72.97; Boston Red Sox: $50.24 **30.** plane: 300 mph;
wind: 20 mph **31.** $2-per-lb nuts: 30 lb; $1-per-lb candy: 70 lb
32. $85°, 60°, 35°$ **33.** $40,000 at 10%; $100,000 at 6%; $140,000 at 5%
34. 5 L of 8%; 3 L of 20%; none of 10% **35.** Mantle: 54; Maris: 61;
Berra: 22 **36.** $\{(3, -2)\}$ **37.** $\{(-1, 5)\}$ **38.** $\{(0, 0, -1)\}$
39. $\{(1, 2, -1)\}$ **40.** B; The second equation is already solved for y.
41. $\{(12, 9)\}$ **42.** $\emptyset$ **43.** $\{(3, -1)\}$ **44.** $\{(5, 3)\}$ **45.** $\{(0, 4)\}$
46. $\left\{\left(\frac{82}{23}, -\frac{4}{23}\right)\right\}$ **47.** 20 L **48.** U.S.: 37; Germany: 30; Canada: 26

Chapter 8 Test (pages 560–561)

[8.1] **1.** $x = 8$, or 800 items; $3000 **2.** about $400 **3. (a)** no
(b) no **(c)** yes **4.** $\{(6, 1)\}$ [8.2, 8.3] **5.** $\{(6, -4)\}$

6. $\left\{\left(-\frac{9}{4}, \frac{5}{4}\right)\right\}$ **7.** $\{(x, y) \mid 12x - 5y = 8\}$; dependent equations
8. $\{(3, 3)\}$ **9.** $\{(0, -2)\}$ **10.** $\emptyset$; inconsistent system **11.** $\{(-15, 6)\}$
[8.4] **12.** $\left\{\left(-\frac{2}{3}, \frac{4}{5}, 0\right)\right\}$ **13.** $\{(3, -2, 1)\}$ [8.5] **14.** *Star Wars*
Episode IV: A New Hope: $461.0 million; *Indiana Jones and the*
Kingdom of the Crystal Skull: $317.0 million **15.** 45 mph, 75 mph
16. 20% solution: 4 L; 50% solution: 8 L **17.** AC adaptor: $8;
rechargeable flashlight: $15 **18.** Orange Pekoe: 60 oz; Irish Breakfast:
30 oz; Earl Grey: 10 oz [8.6] **19.** $\left\{\left(\frac{2}{5}, \frac{7}{5}\right)\right\}$ **20.** $\{(-1, 2, 3)\}$

Chapters 1–8 Cumulative Review Exercises (pages 561–563)

[1.6] **1.** $-1, 1, -2, 2, -4, 4, -5, 5, -8, 8, -10, 10, -20, 20, -40, 40$
2. 46 [1.3] **3.** 1 [1.7] **4.** distributive property [2.3] **5.** $\left\{-\frac{13}{11}\right\}$
6. $\left\{\frac{9}{11}\right\}$ [2.5] **7.** $T = \dfrac{PV}{k}$ [2.8] **8.** $(-18, \infty)$ **9.** $\left(-\frac{11}{2}, \infty\right)$
[2.6] **10.** 2010; 1813; 62.8%; 57.2% [2.4] **11.** in favor: 68; against: 31
[2.5] **12.** $46°, 46°, 88°$
[3.2, 7.1] **13.**   **14.**

[3.3, 7.1] **15.** $-\frac{4}{3}$ **16.** $-\frac{1}{4}$ [3.4, 7.2] **17.** $y = \frac{1}{2}x + 3$
18. $y = 2x + 1$ **19. (a)** $x = 9$ **(b)** $y = -1$ [4.1] **20.** $\dfrac{m}{n}$
[4.4] **21.** $4y^2 - 7y - 6$ [4.5] **22.** $12f^2 + 5f - 3$
[4.6] **23.** $\frac{1}{16}x^2 + \frac{5}{2}x + 25$ [4.7] **24.** $x^2 + 4x - 7$
[5.2, 5.3] **25.** $(2x + 5)(x - 9)$ [5.4] **26.** $25(2t^2 + 1)(2t^2 - 1)$
27. $(2p + 5)(4p^2 - 10p + 25)$ [5.5] **28.** $\left\{-\frac{7}{3}, 1\right\}$ [6.1] **29.** $\dfrac{y + 4}{y - 4}$
[6.2] **30.** $\dfrac{a(a - b)}{2(a + b)}$ [6.4] **31.** 3 [6.6] **32.** $\{-4\}$

[7.4] **33. (a)** $\dfrac{5x - 8}{3}$, or $\dfrac{5}{3}x - \dfrac{8}{3}$ **(b)** -1
[7.5] **34. (a)** $2x^3 - 2x^2 + 6x - 4$ **(b)** $2x^3 - 4x^2 + 2x + 2$
(c) -14 **(d)** $x^4 + 2x^2 - 3$ [8.1–8.3, 8.6] **35.** $\{(3, -3)\}$
36. $\{(x, y) \mid x - 3y = 7\}$ [8.4] **37.** $\{(5, 3, 2)\}$ [8.5] **38.** Tickle
Me Elmo: $27.63; T.M.X.: $40.00

9 INEQUALITIES AND ABSOLUTE VALUE

Section 9.1 (pages 571–573)

1. true **3.** false; The union is $(-\infty, 7) \cup (7, \infty)$. **5.** false;
The intersection is $\emptyset$. **7.** $\{1, 3, 5\}$, or B **9.** $\{4\}$, or D **11.** $\emptyset$
13. $\{1, 2, 3, 4, 5, 6\}$, or A **15.**
17.   **19.** $(-3, 2)$
21. $(-\infty, 2]$ **23.** $\emptyset$
25. $[5, 9]$ **27.** $(-3, -1)$
29. $(-\infty, 4]$ **31.**
33.   **35.** $(-\infty, 8]$
37. $[-2, \infty)$
39. $(-\infty, \infty)$
41. $(-\infty, -5) \cup (5, \infty)$
43. $(-\infty, -1) \cup (2, \infty)$
45. $(-\infty, \infty)$ **47.** $[-4, -1]$ **49.** $[-9, -6]$
51. $(-\infty, 3)$ **53.** $[3, 9)$
55. intersection; $(-5, -1)$
57. union; $(-\infty, 4)$
59. union; $(-\infty, 0] \cup [2, \infty)$
61. intersection; $[4, 12]$ **63.** {Tuition and fees}
65. {Tuition and fees, Board rates, Dormitory charges} **67.** Maria, Joe
68. none of them **69.** none of them **70.** Luigi, Than **71.** Maria, Joe
72. all of them **73.** $(-3, 2)$ **75.** -21 **77.** false

Connections **(page 579)** The filled carton may contain between
30.4 and 33.6 oz, inclusive.

Section 9.2 (pages 580–582)

1. E; C; D; B; A **3. (a)** one **(b)** two **(c)** none **5.** $\{-12, 12\}$
7. $\{-5, 5\}$ **9.** $\{-6, 12\}$ **11.** $\{-5, 6\}$ **13.** $\left\{-3, \frac{11}{2}\right\}$

15. $\left\{-\frac{19}{2}, \frac{9}{2}\right\}$ **17.** $\{-10, -2\}$ **19.** $\left\{-\frac{32}{3}, 8\right\}$ **21.** $\{-75, 175\}$

23. $(-\infty, -3) \cup (3, \infty)$

25. $(-\infty, -4] \cup [4, \infty)$

27. $(-\infty, -25] \cup [15, \infty)$

29. $(-\infty, -12) \cup (8, \infty)$

31. $(-\infty, -2) \cup (8, \infty)$

33. $\left(-\infty, -\frac{9}{5}\right] \cup [3, \infty)$

35. (a) **(b)**

37. $[-3, 3]$ **39.** $(-4, 4)$

41. $(-25, 15)$

43. $[-12, 8]$

45. $[-2, 8]$ **47.** $\left(-\frac{9}{5}, 3\right)$

49. $(-\infty, -5) \cup (13, \infty)$

51. $(-\infty, -25) \cup (15, \infty)$

53. $\{-6, -1\}$

55. $\left[-\frac{10}{3}, 4\right]$

57. $\left[-\frac{7}{6}, -\frac{5}{6}\right]$

59. $(-\infty, -3] \cup [4, \infty)$ **61.** $\{-5, 1\}$

63. $\{3, 9\}$ **65.** $\{0, 20\}$ **67.** $\{-5, 5\}$ **69.** $\{-5, -3\}$

71. $(-\infty, -3) \cup (2, \infty)$ **73.** $[-10, 0]$ **75.** $\left\{-\frac{5}{3}, \frac{1}{3}\right\}$

77. $(-\infty, 20] \cup [30, \infty)$ **79.** $\{-1, 3\}$ **81.** $\left\{-3, \frac{5}{3}\right\}$ **83.** $\left\{-\frac{1}{3}, -\frac{1}{15}\right\}$

85. $\left\{-\frac{5}{4}\right\}$ **87.** $(-\infty, \infty)$ **89.** $\emptyset$ **91.** $\left\{-\frac{1}{4}\right\}$ **93.** $\emptyset$ **95.** $(-\infty, \infty)$

97. $\left\{-\frac{3}{7}\right\}$ **99.** $\left\{\frac{2}{5}\right\}$ **101.** $(-\infty, \infty)$ **103.** $\emptyset$

105. $|x - 1000| \leq 100$; $900 \leq x \leq 1100$ **107.** 810.5 ft

108. Bank of America Center, Texaco Heritage Plaza **109.** Williams Tower, Bank of America Center, Texaco Heritage Plaza, Enterprise Plaza, Centerpoint Energy Plaza, Continental Center I, Fulbright Tower

110. $|x - 810.5| \geq 95$; $x \geq 905.5$ or $x \leq 715.5$

(b) JPMorgan Chase Tower, Wells Fargo Plaza, One Shell Plaza; It makes sense because it includes all buildings *not* listed in the answer to **Exercise 109.**

111.   **113.** no

Summary Exercises on Solving Linear and Absolute Value Equations and Inequalities (page 583)

1. $\{12\}$ **2.** $\{-5, 7\}$ **3.** $\{7\}$ **4.** $\left\{-\frac{2}{5}\right\}$ **5.** $\emptyset$ **6.** $(-\infty, -1]$

7. $\left[-\frac{2}{3}, \infty\right)$ **8.** $\{-1\}$ **9.** $\{-3\}$ **10.** $\left\{1, \frac{11}{3}\right\}$ **11.** $(-\infty, 5]$

12. $(-\infty, \infty)$ **13.** $\{2\}$ **14.** $(-\infty, -8] \cup [8, \infty)$ **15.** $\emptyset$ **16.** $(-\infty, \infty)$

17. $(-5.5, 5.5)$ **18.** $\left\{\frac{13}{3}\right\}$ **19.** $\left\{-\frac{96}{5}\right\}$ **20.** $(-\infty, 32]$

21. $(-\infty, -24)$ **22.** $\left\{\frac{3}{8}\right\}$ **23.** $\left\{\frac{7}{2}\right\}$ **24.** $(-6, 8)$

25. {all real numbers} **26.** $(-\infty, 5)$ **27.** $(-\infty, -4) \cup (7, \infty)$

28. $\{24\}$ **29.** $\left\{-\frac{1}{5}\right\}$ **30.** $\left(-\infty, -\frac{5}{2}\right]$ **31.** $\left[-\frac{1}{3}, 3\right]$ **32.** $[1, 7]$

33. $\left\{-\frac{1}{6}, 2\right\}$ **34.** $\{-3\}$ **35.** $(-\infty, -1] \cup \left[\frac{5}{3}, \infty\right)$ **36.** $\left[\frac{3}{4}, \frac{15}{8}\right]$

37. $\left\{-\frac{5}{2}\right\}$ **38.** $\{60\}$ **39.** $\left[-\frac{9}{2}, \frac{15}{2}\right]$ **40.** $(1, 9)$ **41.** $(-\infty, \infty)$

42. $\left\{\frac{1}{3}, 9\right\}$ **43.** {all real numbers} **44.** $\left\{-\frac{10}{9}\right\}$ **45.** $\{-2\}$ **46.** $\emptyset$

47. $(-\infty, -1) \cup (2, \infty)$ **48.** $[-3, -2]$

Connections **(page 589)** We include a calculator graph and supporting explanation only with the answer to Problem 1.

1. (a) $\{-0.6\}$; The graph of $y_1 = 5x + 3$ has x-intercept $(-0.6, 0)$.

(b) $(-0.6, \infty)$; The graph of y_1 lies *above* the x-axis for values of x greater than -0.6.

(c) $(-\infty, -0.6)$; The graph of y_1 lies *below* the x-axis for values of x less than -0.6.

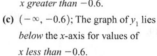

2. (a) $\{-0.5\}$ **(b)** $(-0.5, \infty)$ **(c)** $(-\infty, -0.5)$ **3. (a)** $\{-1.2\}$ **(b)** $(-\infty, -1.2]$ **(c)** $[-1.2, \infty)$ **4. (a)** $\{-3\}$ **(b)** $(-\infty, -3]$ **(c)** $[-3, \infty)$

Section 9.3 (pages 589–592)

1. solid; below **3.** dashed; above

5.   **7.** **9.**

11. Use a dashed line if the symbol is $<$ or $>$. Use a solid line if the symbol is $\leq$ or $\geq$.

13.   **15.** **17.**

19. **21.** **23.**

31. **32.** **33.**

25. **27.** **29.**

34. **35.** **36.** D   **37.** $[-2, 3)$

38. $(-\infty, \infty)$ **39.** $\left\{-\frac{7}{3}, 1\right\}$

40. $[-16, 10]$

41. $\left(-\infty, -\frac{13}{5}\right) \cup (3, \infty)$

31. **33.** **35.**

42. $(-\infty, \infty)$ **43.** $\left\{-4, -\frac{2}{3}\right\}$ **44.** $[-4, -2]$ **45.** $\left\{1, \frac{11}{3}\right\}$

46. (a) $\emptyset$ **(b)** $\emptyset$ **(c)** $(-\infty, \infty)$ **47.** $(6, 8)$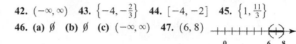

48. $(-\infty, -2] \cup [7, \infty)$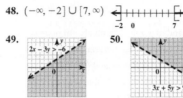

37. **39.** $-3 < x < 3$ **41.** $-2 < x + 1 < 2$

49. **50.**

43. **45.** 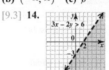 **47.**

51. (a) {Illinois}   **(b)** {Illinois, Maine, North Carolina, Oregon, Utah}

(c) $\emptyset$ **52. (a)** $\left(-\infty, -\frac{11}{3}\right] \cup [1, \infty)$ **(b)** $\left[-\frac{11}{3}, 1\right]$

Chapter 9 Test (page 596)

[9.1] **1.** $\emptyset$ **2.** Managerial/Professional, Technical/Sales/Administrative

Support, Service, Operators/Fabricators/Laborers

3. $\{1, 5\}$ **4.** $\{1, 2, 5, 7, 9, 12\}$

5. $[2, 9)$

6. $(-\infty, 3) \cup [6, \infty)$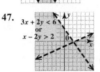

49. C   **51.** A   **53. (a)** $\{-4\}$ **(b)** $(-\infty, -4)$ **(c)** $(-4, \infty)$

55. (a) $\{3.5\}$ **(b)** $(3.5, \infty)$ **(c)** $(-\infty, 3.5)$

57. $x \le 200, x \ge 100, y \ge 3000$

58.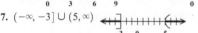

59. $C = 50x + 100y$

60. Some examples are $(100, 5000)$, $(150, 3000)$, and $(150, 5000)$. The corner points are $(100, 3000)$ and $(200, 3000)$.

[9.2] **7.** $\left\{-1, \frac{5}{2}\right\}$ **8.** $\left(-\infty, -\frac{7}{6}\right) \cup \left(\frac{17}{6}, \infty\right)$

9. $\emptyset$ **10.** $\left\{-\frac{5}{7}, \frac{11}{3}\right\}$ **11.** $\left(\frac{1}{3}, \frac{7}{3}\right)$ **12.** $(-\infty, \infty)$ **13. (a)** $\emptyset$

(b) $(-\infty, \infty)$ **(c)** $\emptyset$

61. The least value occurs when $x = 100$ and $y = 3000$.

62. The company should use 100 workers and manufacture 3000 units to achieve the least possible cost.   **63.** 64   **65.** -144

[9.3] **14.** 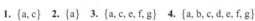 **15.**

16. **17.**

Chapter 9 Review Exercises (pages 594–595)

1. $\{a, c\}$ **2.** $\{a\}$ **3.** $\{a, c, e, f, g\}$ **4.** $\{a, b, c, d, e, f, g\}$

5. $(6, 9)$

6. $(8, 14)$

7. $(-\infty, -3] \cup (5, \infty)$

8. $(-\infty, \infty)$ **9.** $\emptyset$

10. $(-\infty, -2] \cup [7, \infty)$

Chapters 1–9 Cumulative Review Exercises (pages 596–598)

[1.4] **1. (a)** A, B, C, D, F   **(b)** B, C, D, F   **(c)** D, F   **(d)** C, D, F

(e) E, F   **(f)** D, F   [1.2] **2.** 32   [1.4, 1.5] **3.** 0   [2.3] **4.** $\{-65\}$

5. {all real numbers}   [2.5] **6.** $t = \dfrac{A - p}{pr}$ [2.8] **7.** $(-\infty, 6)$

[2.6] **8.** 32%; 390; 270; 10%   [2.4] **9.** 15°, 35°, 130°

11. $(-3, 4)$ **12.** $(-\infty, 2)$ **13.** $(4, \infty)$ **14.** $(1, \infty)$ **15.** $\{-7, 7\}$

16. $\{-11, 7\}$ **17.** $\left\{-\frac{1}{3}, 5\right\}$ **18.** $\emptyset$ **19.** $\{0, 7\}$ **20.** $\left\{-\frac{3}{2}, \frac{1}{2}\right\}$

21. $\left\{-\frac{3}{4}, \frac{1}{2}\right\}$ **22.** $\left\{-\frac{1}{2}\right\}$ **23.** $(-14, 14)$ **24.** $[-1, 13]$

25. $[-3, -2]$ **26.** $(-\infty, \infty)$ **27.** $\left(-\infty, -\frac{8}{5}\right) \cup (2, \infty)$ **28.** $\emptyset$

29. $(-\infty, \infty)$ **30.** $\left\{\frac{3}{11}\right\}$

[3.3, 7.1] **10.** $-\frac{4}{3}$ **11.** 0 [3.4, 7.2] **12. (a)** $y = -4x + 15$
(b) $4x + y = 15$ **13. (a)** $y = 4x$ **(b)** $4x - y = 0$
[3.2, 7.1] **14.**

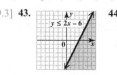

[4.1, 4.2] **15.** $\dfrac{8m^9n^3}{p^6}$ **16.** $\dfrac{y^7}{x^{13}z^2}$

[4.4] **17.** $2x^2 - 5x + 10$

[4.5] **18.** $x^3 + 8y^3$

19. $15x^2 + 7xy - 2y^2$ [4.7] **20.** $4xy^4 - 2y + \dfrac{1}{x^2y}$

[5.2, 5.3] **21.** $(m + 8)(m + 4)$ [5.4] **22.** $(5t^2 + 6)(5t^2 - 6)$
23. $(9z + 4)^2$ [5.5] **24.** $\{-2, -1\}$ [6.1] **25.** $x \neq -7, 2$

[6.2] **26.** $\dfrac{x + 1}{x}$ **27.** $(t + 5)(t + 3)$, or $t^2 + 8t + 15$

[6.4] **28.** $\dfrac{-2x - 14}{(x + 3)(x - 1)}$ [6.5] **29.** -21 [6.6] **30.** $\{19\}$

[7.1, 7.2] **31. (a)** $-12,272.8$ thousand lb per yr; The number of pounds of shrimp caught decreased an average of 12,272.8 thousand lb per yr.
(b) $y = -12,272.8x + 322,486$ **(c)** 285,668 thousand lb
[7.3] **32.** domain: $\{-4, -1, 2, 5\}$; range: $\{-2, 0, 2\}$; function
[7.4] **33.** -9 [8.1–8.3, 8.6] **34.** $\{(3, 2)\}$ **35.** $\emptyset$
[8.4, 8.6] **36.** $\{(1, 0, -1)\}$ [8.5] **37.** length: 42 ft; width: 30 ft
38. 15% solution: 6 L; 30% solution: 3 L [9.1] **39.** $(-4, 4)$
40. $(-\infty, 0] \cup (2, \infty)$ [9.2] **41.** $\left\{-\frac{1}{3}, 1\right\}$ **42.** $\left(-\infty, -\frac{8}{3}\right] \cup [2, \infty)$
[9.3] **43.**

44.

---

10 **ROOTS, RADICALS, AND ROOT FUNCTIONS**

Section 10.1 (pages 607–611)

1. true **3.** false; Zero has only one square root. **5.** true **7.** $-3, 3$
9. $-8, 8$ **11.** $-13, 13$ **13.** $-\frac{5}{14}, \frac{5}{14}$ **15.** $-30, 30$ **17.** 1 **19.** 7
21. -16 **23.** $-\frac{12}{11}$ **25.** 0.8 **27.** It is not a real number. **29.** It is not
a real number. **31.** 19 **33.** 19 **35.** $\frac{2}{3}$ **37.** $3x^2 + 4$ **39.** a must be
positive. **41.** a must be negative. **43.** rational; 5 **45.** irrational;
5.385 **47.** rational; -8 **49.** irrational; -17.321 **51.** It is not a real
number. **53.** irrational; 34.641 **55.** 9 and 10 **57.** 7 and 8
59. -7 and -6 **61.** 4 and 5 **63.** 1; 8; 27; 64; 125; 216; 343; 512;
729; 1000 **65. (a)** E **(b)** F **(c)** D **(d)** B **(e)** A **(f)** C
67. -9 **69.** 6 **71.** -4 **73.** -8 **75.** 6 **77.** -2 **79.** It is not a
real number. **81.** 2 **83.** It is not a real number. **85.** $\frac{8}{9}$ **87.** $\frac{4}{3}$
89. $-\frac{1}{2}$ **91.** 3 **93.** 0.5 **95.** -0.7 **97.** 0.1
In Exercises 99–105, we give the domain and then the range.

99. $[-3, \infty)$; $[0, \infty)$

101. $[0, \infty)$; $[-2, \infty)$

103. $(-\infty, \infty)$; $(-\infty, \infty)$ **105.** $(-\infty, \infty)$; $(-\infty, \infty)$

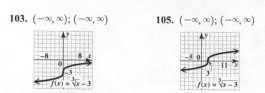

107. 12 **109.** 10 **111.** 2 **113.** -9 **115.** -5 **117.** $|x|$
119. $|z|$ **121.** x **123.** x^5 **125.** $|x|^5$ (or $|x^5|$) **127.** C **129.** 97.381
131. 16.863 **133.** -9.055 **135.** 7.507 **137.** 3.162 **139.** 1.885
141. A **143.** 1,183,000 cycles per sec **145.** 10 mi **147.** 392,000 mi²
149. (a) 1.732 amps **(b)** 2.236 amps **151.** x^1, or x **153.** $\dfrac{3^3}{2^3}$, or $\dfrac{27}{8}$

Section 10.2 (pages 617–619)

1. C **3.** A **5.** H **7.** B **9.** D **11.** 13 **13.** 9 **15.** 2 **17.** $\frac{8}{9}$
19. -3 **21.** It is not a real number. **23.** 1000 **25.** 27 **27.** -1024
29. 16 **31.** $\frac{1}{8}$ **33.** $\frac{1}{512}$ **35.** $\frac{9}{25}$ **37.** $\frac{27}{8}$ **39.** $\sqrt{10}$ **41.** $\left(\sqrt[4]{8}\right)^3$
43. $\left(\sqrt[8]{9q}\right)^5 - \left(\sqrt[3]{2x}\right)^2$ **45.** $\dfrac{1}{\left(\sqrt{2m}\right)^3}$ **47.** $\left(\sqrt[3]{2y + x}\right)^2$
49. $\dfrac{1}{\left(\sqrt[3]{3m^4 + 2k^2}\right)^2}$ **51.** 64 **53.** 64 **55.** x^{10} **57.** $\sqrt[6]{x^5}$
59. $\sqrt[15]{t^8}$ **61.** 9 **63.** 4 **65.** y **67.** $x^{5/12}$ **69.** $k^{2/3}$
71. x^3y^8 **73.** $\dfrac{1}{x^{10/3}}$ **75.** $\dfrac{1}{m^{1/4}n^{3/4}}$ **77.** p^2 **79.** $\dfrac{c^{11/3}}{b^{11/4}}$ **81.** $\dfrac{q^{5/3}}{9p^{7/2}}$
83. $p + 2p^2$ **85.** $k^{7/4} - k^{3/4}$ **87.** $6 + 18a$ **89.** $-5x^2 + 5x$
91. $x^{17/20}$ **93.** $\dfrac{1}{x^{3/2}}$ **95.** $y^{5/6}z^{1/3}$ **97.** $m^{1/12}$ **99.** $x^{1/8}$ **101.** $x^{1/24}$
103. $\sqrt{a^2 + b^2} = \sqrt{3^2 + 4^2} = 5; a + b = 3 + 4 = 7; 5 \neq 7$
105. 4.5 hr **107.** 19.0°; The table gives 19°. **109.** 4.2°; The table
gives 4°. **111.** 30; 30; They are the same.

Section 10.3 (pages 626–629)

1. $\sqrt{9}$, or 3 **3.** $\sqrt{36}$, or 6 **5.** $\sqrt{30}$ **7.** $\sqrt{14x}$ **9.** $\sqrt{42pqr}$
11. $\sqrt[3]{10}$ **13.** $\sqrt[3]{14xy}$ **15.** $\sqrt[4]{33}$ **17.** $\sqrt[4]{6x^3}$ **19.** This expression
cannot be simplified by the product rule. **21.** $\frac{8}{11}$ **23.** $\dfrac{\sqrt{3}}{5}$ **25.** $\dfrac{\sqrt{x}}{5}$
27. $\dfrac{p^3}{9}$ **29.** $-\frac{3}{4}$ **31.** $\dfrac{\sqrt[3]{r^2}}{2}$ **33.** $-\dfrac{3}{x}$ **35.** $\dfrac{1}{x^3}$ **37.** $2\sqrt{3}$ **39.** $12\sqrt{2}$
41. $-4\sqrt{2}$ **43.** $-2\sqrt{7}$ **45.** This radical cannot be simplified further.
47. $4\sqrt[3]{2}$ **49.** $-2\sqrt[3]{2}$ **51.** $2\sqrt[3]{5}$ **53.** $-4\sqrt[3]{2}$ **55.** $2\sqrt[5]{2}$
57. $-3\sqrt[5]{2}$ **59.** $2\sqrt[6]{2}$ **61.** His reasoning was incorrect. Here, 8 is a
term, not a factor. **63.** $6k\sqrt{2}$ **65.** $12xy^4\sqrt{xy}$ **67.** $11x^3$ **69.** $-3t^4$
71. $-10m^4z^2$ **73.** $5a^2b^3c^4$ **75.** $\frac{1}{2}r^2t^5$ **77.** $5x\sqrt{2x}$ **79.** $-10r^5\sqrt{5r}$
81. $x^3y^4\sqrt{13x}$ **83.** $2z^2w^3$ **85.** $-2zt^2\sqrt[3]{2z^2t}$ **87.** $3x^3y^4$
89. $-3r^3s^2\sqrt[4]{2r^3s^2}$ **91.** $\dfrac{y^5\sqrt{y}}{6}$ **93.** $\dfrac{x^5\sqrt[3]{x}}{3}$ **95.** $4\sqrt{3}$
97. $\sqrt{5}$ **99.** $x^2\sqrt{x}$ **101.** $\sqrt[6]{432}$ **103.** $\sqrt[12]{6912}$ **105.** $\sqrt[9]{x^5}$
107. 5 **109.** $8\sqrt{2}$ **111.** $2\sqrt{14}$ **113.** 13 **115.** $9\sqrt{2}$
117. $\sqrt{17}$ **119.** 5 **121.** $6\sqrt{2}$ **123.** $\sqrt{5y^2 - 2xy + x^2}$

125. $2\sqrt{106} + 4\sqrt{2}$ **127.** 15.3 mi   **129.** 27.0 in.   **131.** 581
133. $\sqrt{9} + \sqrt{9} = 3 + 3 = 6$, and $\sqrt{4} = 2$; $6 \neq 2$, so the statement
is false.   **135.** MSX-77: 18.4 in.; MSX-83: 17.0 in.; MSX-60: 14.1 in.
137. $22x^4 - 10x^3$ **139.** $8q^2 - 3q$

Section 10.4 (pages 632–633)

1. -4 **3.** $7\sqrt{3}$ **5.** $14\sqrt[3]{2}$ **7.** $5\sqrt[4]{2}$ **9.** $24\sqrt{2}$ **11.** The expression
cannot be simplified further.   **13.** $20\sqrt{5}$ **15.** $4\sqrt{2x}$
17. $-11m\sqrt{2}$ **19.** $7\sqrt[3]{2}$ **21.** $2\sqrt[3]{x}$ **23.** $-7\sqrt[3]{x^2y}$ **25.** $-x\sqrt[3]{xy^2}$
27. $19\sqrt[4]{2}$ **29.** $x\sqrt[4]{xy}$ **31.** $9\sqrt[4]{2a^3}$ **33.** $(4 + 3xy)\sqrt[3]{xy^2}$
35. $4t\sqrt[3]{3st} - 3s\sqrt{3st}$ **37.** $4x\sqrt[3]{x} + 6x\sqrt[4]{x}$ **39.** $2\sqrt{2} - 2$
41. $\dfrac{5\sqrt{5}}{6}$ **43.** $\dfrac{7\sqrt{2}}{6}$ **45.** $\dfrac{5\sqrt{2}}{3}$ **47.** $5\sqrt{2} + 4$ **49.** $\dfrac{5 + 3x}{x^4}$
51. $\dfrac{m\sqrt[3]{m^2}}{2}$ **53.** $\dfrac{3x\sqrt[3]{2} - 4\sqrt[3]{5}}{x^3}$ **55.** B
57. 15; Each radical expression simplifies to a whole number.
59. A; 42 m   **61.** $\left(12\sqrt{5} + 5\sqrt{3}\right)$ in.   **63.** $\left(24\sqrt{2} + 12\sqrt{3}\right)$ in.
65. $10x^3y^4 - 20x^2y$ **67.** $a^4 - b^2$ **69.** $64x^9 + 144x^6 + 108x^3 + 27$
71. $\dfrac{4x - 5}{3x}$

Connections   (page 639)   1. $\dfrac{319}{6\left(8\sqrt{5} + 1\right)}$ **2.** $\dfrac{9a - b}{b\left(3\sqrt{a} - \sqrt{b}\right)}$
3. $\dfrac{9a - b}{\left(\sqrt{b} - \sqrt{a}\right)\left(3\sqrt{a} - \sqrt{b}\right)}$ **4.** $\dfrac{\left(3\sqrt{a} + \sqrt{b}\right)\left(\sqrt{b} + \sqrt{a}\right)}{b - a}$;
Instead of multiplying by the conjugate of the numerator, we use the conjugate of the denominator.

Section 10.5 (pages 640–642)

1. E   **3.** A   **5.** D   **7.** $3\sqrt{6} + 2\sqrt{3}$ **9.** $20\sqrt{2}$ **11.** -2
13. -1 **15.** 6   **17.** $\sqrt{6} - \sqrt{2} + \sqrt{3} - 1$
19. $\sqrt{22} + \sqrt{55} - \sqrt{14} - \sqrt{35}$ **21.** $8 - \sqrt{15}$ **23.** $9 + 4\sqrt{5}$
25. $26 - 2\sqrt{105}$ **27.** $4 - \sqrt[3]{36}$ **29.** 10
31. $6x + 3\sqrt{x} - 2\sqrt{5x} - \sqrt{5}$ **33.** $9r - s$
35. $4\sqrt[3]{4y^2} - 19\sqrt[3]{2y} - 5$ **37.** $3x - 4$ **39.** $4x - y$ **41.** $2\sqrt{6} - 1$
43. $\sqrt{7}$ **45.** $5\sqrt{3}$ **47.** $\dfrac{\sqrt{6}}{2}$ **49.** $\dfrac{9\sqrt{15}}{5}$ **51.** $-\dfrac{7\sqrt{3}}{12}$ **53.** $\dfrac{\sqrt{14}}{2}$
55. $-\dfrac{\sqrt{14}}{10}$ **57.** $\dfrac{2\sqrt{6x}}{x}$ **59.** $\dfrac{-8\sqrt{3k}}{k}$ **61.** $\dfrac{-5m^2\sqrt{6mn}}{n^2}$
63. $\dfrac{12x^3\sqrt{2xy}}{y^5}$ **65.** $\dfrac{5\sqrt{2my}}{y^2}$ **67.** $-\dfrac{4k\sqrt{3z}}{z}$ **69.** $\dfrac{\sqrt[3]{18}}{3}$ **71.** $\dfrac{\sqrt[3]{12}}{3}$
73. $\dfrac{\sqrt[4]{18}}{4}$ **75.** $-\dfrac{\sqrt[3]{2pr}}{r}$ **77.** $\dfrac{x^2\sqrt[3]{y^2}}{y}$ **79.** $\dfrac{2\sqrt[4]{x^3}}{x}$ **81.** $\dfrac{\sqrt[4]{2yz^3}}{z}$
83. $\dfrac{3\left(4 - \sqrt{5}\right)}{11}$ **85.** $\dfrac{6\sqrt{2} + 4}{7}$ **87.** $\dfrac{2\left(3\sqrt{5} - 2\sqrt{3}\right)}{33}$
89. $2\sqrt{3} + \sqrt{10} - 3\sqrt{2} - \sqrt{15}$ **91.** $\sqrt{m} - 2$
93. $\dfrac{4\left(\sqrt{x} + 2\sqrt{y}\right)}{x - 4y}$ **95.** $\dfrac{x - 2\sqrt{xy} + y}{x - y}$ **97.** $\dfrac{5\sqrt{k}\left(2\sqrt{k} - \sqrt{q}\right)}{4k - q}$

99. $3 - 2\sqrt{6}$ **101.** $1 - \sqrt{5}$ **103.** $\dfrac{4 - 2\sqrt{2}}{3}$ **105.** $\dfrac{6 + 2\sqrt{6p}}{3}$
107. $\dfrac{3\sqrt{x + y}}{x + y}$ **109.** $\dfrac{p\sqrt{p + 2}}{p + 2}$ **111.** Each expression is approximately
equal to 0.2588190451.   **113.** $\dfrac{33}{8\left(6 + \sqrt{3}\right)}$ **115.** $\dfrac{4x - y}{3x\left(2\sqrt{x} + \sqrt{y}\right)}$
117. $\left\{\frac{3}{8}\right\}$ **119.** $\left\{-\frac{1}{3}, \frac{3}{2}\right\}$

Summary Exercises on Operations with Radicals and Rational Exponents (pages 642–643)

1. $-6\sqrt{10}$ **2.** $7 - \sqrt{14}$ **3.** $2 + \sqrt{6} - 2\sqrt{3} - 3\sqrt{2}$ **4.** $4\sqrt{2}$
5. $73 + 12\sqrt{35}$ **6.** $\dfrac{-\sqrt{6}}{2}$ **7.** $4\left(\sqrt{7} - \sqrt{5}\right)$ **8.** $-3 + 2\sqrt{2}$
9. -44 **10.** $\dfrac{\sqrt{x} + \sqrt{5}}{x - 5}$ **11.** $2abc^3\sqrt[3]{b^2}$ **12.** $5\sqrt[3]{3}$
13. $3\left(\sqrt{5} - 2\right)$ **14.** $\dfrac{\sqrt{15x}}{5x}$ **15.** $\dfrac{8}{5}$ **16.** $\dfrac{\sqrt{2}}{8}$ **17.** $-\sqrt[3]{100}$
18. $11 + 2\sqrt{30}$ **19.** $-3\sqrt{3x}$ **20.** $52 - 30\sqrt{3}$ **21.** $\dfrac{\sqrt[3]{117}}{9}$
22. $3\sqrt{2} + \sqrt{15} + \sqrt{42} + \sqrt{35}$ **23.** $2\sqrt[4]{27}$ **24.** $\dfrac{1 + \sqrt[3]{3} + \sqrt[3]{9}}{-2}$
25. $\dfrac{x\sqrt[3]{x^2}}{y}$ **26.** $-4\sqrt{3} - 3$ **27.** $xy^{6/5}$ **28.** $x^{10}y$ **29.** $\dfrac{1}{25x^2}$
30. $7 + 4 \cdot 3^{1/2}$, or $7 + 4\sqrt{3}$ **31.** $3\sqrt[3]{2x^2}$ **32.** -2
33. (a) 8   (b) $\{-8, 8\}$ **34.** (a) 10   (b) $\{-10, 10\}$
35. (a) $\{-4, 4\}$ (b) -4 **36.** (a) $\{-5, 5\}$ (b) -5
37. (a) $-\frac{9}{11}$ (b) $\left\{-\frac{9}{11}, \frac{9}{11}\right\}$ **38.** (a) $-\frac{7}{10}$ (b) $\left\{-\frac{7}{10}, \frac{7}{10}\right\}$
39. (a) $\{-0.2, 0.2\}$ (b) 0.2   **40.** (a) $\{-0.3, 0.3\}$ (b) 0.3

Section 10.6 (pages 648–650)

1. (a) yes   (b) no   **3.** (a) yes   (b) no   **5.** No. There is no solution.
The radical expression, which is positive, cannot equal a negative number.
7. $\{11\}$ **9.** $\left\{\frac{1}{3}\right\}$ **11.** $\emptyset$ **13.** $\{5\}$ **15.** $\{18\}$ **17.** $\{5\}$ **19.** $\{4\}$
21. $\{17\}$ **23.** $\{5\}$ **25.** $\emptyset$ **27.** $\{0\}$ **29.** $\{0\}$ **31.** $\emptyset$ **33.** $\{1\}$
35. It is incorrect to just square each term. The right side should be
$(8 - x)^2 = 64 - 16x + x^2$. The correct first step is $3x + 4 =$
$64 - 16x + x^2$, and the solution set is $\{4\}$.   **37.** $\{1\}$ **39.** $\{-1\}$
41. $\{14\}$ **43.** $\{8\}$ **45.** $\{0\}$ **47.** $\emptyset$ **49.** $\{7\}$ **51.** $\{7\}$
53. $\{4, 20\}$ **55.** $\emptyset$ **57.** $\left\{\frac{5}{4}\right\}$ **59.** $\{9, 17\}$ **61.** $\left\{\frac{1}{4}, 1\right\}$
63. $L = CZ^2$ **65.** $K = \dfrac{V^2m}{2}$ **67.** $M = \dfrac{r^2F}{m}$ **69.** $r = \dfrac{a}{4\pi^2N^2}$
71. $1 + x$ **73.** $2x^2 + x - 15$ **75.** $\dfrac{-7\left(5 + \sqrt{2}\right)}{23}$

Section 10.7 (pages 655–657)

1. i **3.** -1 **5.** $-i$ **7.** $13i$ **9.** $-12i$ **11.** $i\sqrt{5}$ **13.** $4i\sqrt{3}$
15. $-\sqrt{105}$ **17.** -10 **19.** $i\sqrt{33}$ **21.** $\sqrt{3}$ **23.** $5i$ **25.** -2
27. Any real number a can be written as $a + 0i$, a complex number with
imaginary part 0.   **29.** $-1 + 7i$ **31.** 0   **33.** $7 + 3i$ **35.** -2

37. $1 + 13i$ **39.** $6 + 6i$ **41.** $4 + 2i$ **43.** -81 **45.** -16
47. $-10 - 30i$ **49.** $10 - 5i$ **51.** $-9 + 40i$ **53.** $-16 + 30i$
55. 153 **57.** 97 **59.** 4 **61.** $a - bi$ **63.** $1 + i$ **65.** $2 + 2i$
67. $-1 + 2i$ **69.** $-\frac{5}{13} - \frac{12}{13}i$ **71.** $1 - 3i$ **73.** $1 + 3i$ **75.** -1
77. i **79.** -1 **81.** $-i$ **83.** $-i$ **85.** Since $i^{20} = (i^4)^5 = 1^5 = 1$,
the student multiplied by 1, which is justified by the identity property for
multiplication. **87.** $\frac{1}{2} + \frac{1}{2}i$ **89.** Substitute both $1 + 5i$ and $1 - 5i$
for x, and show that the result is $0 = 0$ in each case. **91.** $\frac{37}{10} - \frac{19}{10}i$
93. $-\frac{13}{10} + \frac{11}{10}i$ **95.** $\left\{-\frac{13}{6}\right\}$ **97.** $\{-8, 5\}$ **99.** $\left\{-\frac{2}{5}, 1\right\}$

Chapter 10 Review Exercises (pages 662–665)

1. 42 **2.** -17 **3.** 6 **4.** -5 **5.** -3 **6.** -2 **7.** $\sqrt[n]{a}$ is not a real
number if n is even and a is negative. **8. (a)** $|x|$ **(b)** $-|x|$ **(c)** x
9. -6.856 **10.** -5.053 **11.** 4.960 **12.** 0.009 **13.** -3968.503
14. -0.189

15. 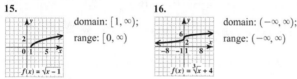 domain: $[1, \infty)$;
range: $[0, \infty)$
$f(x) = \sqrt{x - 1}$

16. domain: $(-\infty, \infty)$;
range: $(-\infty, \infty)$
$f(x) = \sqrt[3]{x + 4}$

17. B **18.** cube (third); 8; 2; second; 4; 4 **19.** A **20. (a)** m must be
even. **(b)** m must be odd. **21.** no **22.** 7 **23.** -11 **24.** 32
25. -4 **26.** $-\frac{216}{125}$ **27.** -32 **28.** $\frac{1000}{27}$ **29.** It is not a real number.
30. $\left(\sqrt[3]{8}\right)^2$; $\sqrt[3]{8^2}$ **31.** The radical $\sqrt[n]{a^m}$ is equivalent to $a^{m/n}$.
For example, $\sqrt[3]{8^2} = \sqrt[3]{64} = 4$, and $8^{2/3} = (8^{1/3})^2 = 2^2 = 4$.
32. $\sqrt{m + 3n}$ **33.** $\frac{1}{\left(\sqrt[3]{3a + b}\right)^5}$, or $\frac{1}{\sqrt[3]{(3a + b)^5}}$ **34.** $7^{9/2}$
35. $p^{4/5}$ **36.** 5^2, or 25 **37.** 96 **38.** $a^{2/3}$ **39.** $\frac{1}{y^{1/2}}$ **40.** $\frac{z^{1/2}x^{8/5}}{4}$
41. $r^{1/2} + r$ **42.** $s^{1/2}$ **43.** $r^{3/2}$ **44.** $p^{1/2}$ **45.** $k^{9/4}$ **46.** $m^{13/3}$
47. $z^{1/12}$ **48.** $x^{1/8}$ **49.** $x^{1/15}$ **50.** $x^{1/36}$ **51.** The product rule for exponents applies only if the bases are the same. **52.** $\sqrt{66}$ **53.** $\sqrt{5r}$
54. $\sqrt[3]{30}$ **55.** $\sqrt[4]{21}$ **56.** $2\sqrt{5}$ **57.** $5\sqrt{3}$ **58.** $-5\sqrt{5}$
59. $-3\sqrt[3]{4}$ **60.** $10y^3\sqrt{y}$ **61.** $4pq^2\sqrt[3]{p}$ **62.** $3a^2b\sqrt[3]{4a^2b^2}$
63. $2r^2t\sqrt[3]{79r^2t}$ **64.** $\frac{y\sqrt{y}}{12}$ **65.** $\frac{m^5}{3}$ **66.** $\frac{\sqrt[3]{r^2}}{2}$ **67.** $\frac{a^2\sqrt[4]{a}}{3}$
68. $\sqrt{15}$ **69.** $p\sqrt{p}$ **70.** $\sqrt[12]{2000}$ **71.** $\sqrt[10]{x^7}$ **72.** 10 **73.** $\sqrt{197}$
74. $-11\sqrt{2}$ **75.** $23\sqrt{5}$ **76.** $7\sqrt{3y}$ **77.** $26m\sqrt{6m}$ **78.** $19\sqrt[3]{2}$
79. $-8\sqrt[4]{2}$ **80.** $\left(16\sqrt{2} + 24\sqrt{3}\right)$ ft **81.** $\left(12\sqrt{3} + 5\sqrt{2}\right)$ ft
82. $1 - \sqrt{3}$ **83.** 2 **84.** $9 - 7\sqrt{2}$ **85.** $15 - 2\sqrt{26}$ **86.** 29
87. $2\sqrt[3]{2y^2} + 2\sqrt[3]{4y} - 3$ **88.** $4.801960973 \neq 66.28725368$
89. The denominator would become $\sqrt[3]{6^2} = \sqrt[3]{36}$, which is not rational.
90. $\frac{\sqrt{30}}{5}$ **91.** $-3\sqrt{6}$ **92.** $\frac{3\sqrt{7py}}{y}$ **93.** $\frac{\sqrt{22}}{4}$ **94.** $-\frac{\sqrt[3]{45}}{5}$
95. $\frac{3m\sqrt[3]{4n}}{n^2}$ **96.** $\frac{\sqrt{2} - \sqrt{7}}{-5}$ **97.** $\frac{5\left(\sqrt{6} + 3\right)}{3}$ **98.** $\frac{1 - \sqrt{5}}{4}$
99. $\frac{1 - 4\sqrt{2}}{3}$ **100.** $\frac{-6 + \sqrt{3}}{2}$ **101.** $\{2\}$ **102.** $\{6\}$ **103.** $\emptyset$

104. $\{0, 5\}$ **105.** $\{9\}$ **106.** $\{3\}$ **107.** $\{7\}$ **108.** $\left\{-\frac{1}{2}\right\}$
109. $\{-13\}$ **110.** $\{-1\}$ **111.** $\{14\}$ **112.** $\{-4\}$ **113.** $\emptyset$
114. $\emptyset$ **115.** $\{7\}$ **116.** $\{4\}$ **117. (a)** $H = \sqrt{L^2 - W^2}$ **(b)** 7.9 ft
118. $5i$ **119.** $10i\sqrt{2}$ **120.** no **121.** $-10 - 2i$ **122.** $14 + 7i$
123. $-\sqrt{35}$ **124.** -45 **125.** 3 **126.** $5 + i$ **127.** $32 - 24i$
128. $1 - i$ **129.** $4 + i$ **130.** $-i$ **131.** 1 **132.** -1 **133.** 1
134. -4 **135.** $\frac{1}{100}$ **136.** $\frac{1}{z^{3/5}}$ **137.** k^6 **138.** $3z^3t^2\sqrt[3]{2t^2}$
139. $57\sqrt{2}$ **140.** $-\frac{\sqrt{3}}{6}$ **141.** $\frac{\sqrt[3]{60}}{5}$ **142.** 1 **143.** $7i$
144. $3 - 7i$ **145.** $-5i$ **146.** $\frac{1 + \sqrt{6}}{2}$ **147.** $5 + 12i$ **148.** $6x\sqrt[3]{y^2}$
149. The expression cannot be simplified further.
150. $\sqrt{35} + \sqrt{15} - \sqrt{21} - 3$ **151.** $\{5\}$ **152.** $\{-4\}$ **153.** $\left\{\frac{3}{2}\right\}$
154. $\{2\}$ **155.** $\{1\}$ **156.** $\{2\}$ **157.** $\{9\}$ **158.** $\{4\}$ **159.** $\{7\}$
160. $\{6\}$

Chapter 10 Test (pages 665–666)

[10.1] **1.** -29 **2.** -8 [10.2] **3.** 5 [10.1] **4.** C **5.** 21.863
6. -9.405 **7.** domain: $[-6, \infty)$;
range: $[0, \infty)$
$f(x) = \sqrt{x + 6}$

[10.2] **8.** $\frac{125}{64}$ **9.** $\frac{1}{256}$ **10.** $\frac{9y^{3/10}}{x^2}$ **11.** $x^{4/3}y^6$ **12.** $7^{1/2}$, or $\sqrt{7}$
[10.3] **13.** $a^3\sqrt[3]{a^2}$, or $a^{11/3}$ **14.** $\sqrt{145}$ **15.** 10 **16.** $3x^2y^3\sqrt{6x}$
17. $2ab^3\sqrt[4]{2a^3b}$ **18.** $\sqrt[6]{200}$ [10.4] **19.** $26\sqrt{5}$ **20.** $(2ts - 3t^2)\sqrt[3]{2s^2}$
[10.5] **21.** $66 + \sqrt{5}$ **22.** $23 - 4\sqrt{15}$ **23.** $-\frac{\sqrt{10}}{4}$ **24.** $\frac{2\sqrt[3]{25}}{5}$
25. $-2\left(\sqrt{7} - \sqrt{5}\right)$ **26.** $3 + \sqrt{6}$ [10.6] **27. (a)** 59.8
(b) $T = \frac{V_0^2 - V^2}{-V^2k}$, or $T = \frac{V^2 - V_0^2}{V^2k}$ **28.** $\{-1\}$ **29.** $\{3\}$
30. $\{-3\}$ [10.7] **31.** $-5 - 8i$ **32.** $-2 + 16i$ **33.** $3 + 4i$ **34.** i
35. (a) true **(b)** true **(c)** false **(d)** true

Chapters 1–10 Cumulative Review Exercises (pages 667–668)

[1.4–1.6] **1.** 1 **2.** $-\frac{14}{9}$ [2.3] **3.** $\{-4\}$ **4.** $\{-12\}$ **5.** $\{6\}$
[2.8] **6.** $(-6, \infty)$ [2.7] **7.** 36 nickels; 64 quarters
8. $2\frac{2}{39}$ L [3.2, 7.1] **9.**
[3.3, 3.4, 7.1, 7.2]
$4x - 3y = 12$
10. $-\frac{3}{2}$; $y = -\frac{3}{2}x$
[4.4] **11.** $-k^3 - 3k^2 - 8k - 9$
[4.5] **12.** $8x^2 + 17x - 21$
[4.7] **13.** $3y^3 - 3y^2 + 4y + 1 + \frac{-10}{2y + 1}$
[5.2, 5.3] **14.** $(2p - 3q)(p - q)$
[5.4] **15.** $(3k^2 + 4)(k - 1)(k + 1)$
16. $(x + 8)(x^2 - 8x + 64)$ [5.5] **17.** $\left\{-3, -\frac{5}{2}\right\}$ **18.** $\left\{-\frac{2}{5}, 1\right\}$

[6.1] **19.** $x \ne -3, x \ne 3$ [6.2] **20.** $\dfrac{y}{y+5}$ [6.4] **21.** $\dfrac{4x+2y}{(x+y)(x-y)}$

[6.5] **22.** $-\dfrac{9}{4}$ **23.** $\dfrac{1}{xy-1}$ [6.6] **24.** $\varnothing$ [6.7] **25.** Danielle: 8 mph;

Richard: 4 mph   [7.4] **26.** -37 [7.6] **27.** \$9.92

[8.1–8.3, 8.6] **28.** $\{(7, -2)\}$ [8.4, 8.6] **29.** $\{(-1, 1, 1)\}$

[8.5] **30.** 2-oz letter: \$0.61; 3-oz letter: \$0.78   [9.1] **31.** $(2, 3)$

32. $(-\infty, 2) \cup (3, \infty)$ [9.2] **33.** $\left\{-\dfrac{10}{3}, 1\right\}$ **34.** $(-\infty, -2] \cup [7, \infty)$

[10.3] **35.** $2x\sqrt[3]{6x^2y^2}$ [10.4] **36.** $7\sqrt{2}$ [10.5] **37.** $\dfrac{\sqrt{10}+2\sqrt{2}}{2}$

[10.3] **38.** $\sqrt{29}$ [10.6] **39.** $\{3, 4\}$ [10.7] **40.** $4 + 2i$

11 QUADRATIC EQUATIONS, INEQUALITIES, AND FUNCTIONS

Section 11.1 (pages 674–675)

1. B, C   **3.** The zero-factor property requires a product equal to 0. The first step should have been to rewrite the equation with 0 on one side.

5. $\{-7, 8\}$ **7.** $\{-11, 11\}$, or $\{\pm 11\}$ **9.** $\left\{-\dfrac{5}{3}, 6\right\}$ **11.** $\{\pm 9\}$

13. $\left\{\pm\sqrt{14}\right\}$ **15.** $\left\{\pm 4\sqrt{3}\right\}$ **17.** $\left\{\pm\dfrac{5}{2}\right\}$ **19.** $\{\pm 1.5\}$

21. $\left\{\pm\sqrt{3}\right\}$ **23.** $\left\{\pm 2\sqrt{5}\right\}$ **25.** $\left\{\pm\dfrac{2\sqrt{7}}{7}\right\}$ **27.** $\left\{\pm 2\sqrt{6}\right\}$

29. $\left\{\pm\dfrac{2\sqrt{5}}{5}\right\}$ **31.** $\left\{\pm 3\sqrt{3}\right\}$ **33.** $\left\{\pm 2\sqrt{2}\right\}$ **35.** $\{-2, 8\}$

37. $\left\{4 \pm \sqrt{3}\right\}$ **39.** $\left\{8 \pm 3\sqrt{3}\right\}$ **41.** $\left\{-3, \dfrac{5}{3}\right\}$ **43.** $\left\{0, \dfrac{3}{2}\right\}$

45. $\left\{\dfrac{1 \pm \sqrt{7}}{3}\right\}$ **47.** $\left\{\dfrac{-1 \pm 3\sqrt{2}}{3}\right\}$ **49.** $\left\{\dfrac{5 \pm \sqrt{30}}{2}\right\}$

51. $\left\{-10 \pm 4\sqrt{3}\right\}$ **53.** $\left\{\dfrac{1 \pm 4\sqrt{3}}{4}\right\}$ **55.** $\{-4.48, 0.20\}$

57. $\{-3.09, -0.15\}$ **59.** $\left\{\pm 2i\sqrt{3}\right\}$ **61.** $\{5 \pm 2i\}$

63. $\left\{\dfrac{1}{6} \pm \dfrac{\sqrt{2}}{3}i\right\}$ **65.** 5.6 sec   **67.** 9 in.   **69.** 2%   **71.** $\dfrac{4 + 4\sqrt{3}}{5}$

73. $\dfrac{3 + \sqrt{6}}{4}$ **75.** $(x - 5)^2$

Section 11.2 (pages 681–683)

1. Solve $(2x + 1)^2 = 5$ by the square root property. Solve $x^2 + 4x = 12$ by completing the square.   **3.** 9; $(x + 3)^2$

5. 36; $(p - 6)^2$ **7.** $\dfrac{81}{4}$; $\left(q + \dfrac{9}{2}\right)^2$ **9.** $\dfrac{1}{64}$; $\left(x + \dfrac{1}{8}\right)^2$

11. 0.16; $(x - 0.4)^2$ **13.** 4   **15.** 25   **17.** $\dfrac{1}{36}$ **19.** $\{1, 3\}$

21. $\left\{-1 \pm \sqrt{6}\right\}$ **23.** $\left\{-2 \pm \sqrt{6}\right\}$ **25.** $\left\{-5 \pm \sqrt{7}\right\}$

27. $\left\{4 \pm 2\sqrt{3}\right\}$ **29.** $\left\{\dfrac{-7 \pm \sqrt{53}}{2}\right\}$ **31.** $\left\{-\dfrac{3}{2}, \dfrac{1}{2}\right\}$ **33.** $\left\{-\dfrac{8}{3}, 3\right\}$

35. $\left\{\dfrac{-5 \pm \sqrt{41}}{4}\right\}$ **37.** $\left\{\dfrac{5 \pm \sqrt{15}}{5}\right\}$ **39.** $\left\{\dfrac{4 \pm \sqrt{3}}{3}\right\}$

41. $\{-4, 2\}$ **43.** $\left\{4 \pm \sqrt{3}\right\}$ **45.** $\left\{1 \pm \sqrt{6}\right\}$ **47.** $\left\{\dfrac{2 \pm \sqrt{3}}{3}\right\}$

49. $\left\{1 \pm \sqrt{2}\right\}$ **51. (a)** $\left\{\dfrac{3 \pm 2\sqrt{6}}{3}\right\}$ **(b)** $\{-0.633, 2.633\}$

53. (a) $\left\{-2 \pm \sqrt{3}\right\}$ **(b)** $\{-3.732, -0.268\}$ **55.** $\{-2 \pm 3i\}$

57. $\left\{-\dfrac{2}{3} \pm \dfrac{2\sqrt{2}}{3}i\right\}$ **59.** $\left\{-3 \pm i\sqrt{3}\right\}$ **61.** x^2 **62.** x **63.** $6x$

64. 1   **65.** 9   **66.** $(x + 3)^2$, or $x^2 + 6x + 9$ **67.** $\left\{\pm\sqrt{b}\right\}$

69. $\left\{\pm\dfrac{\sqrt{b^2 + 16}}{2}\right\}$ **71.** $\left\{\dfrac{2b \pm \sqrt{3a}}{5}\right\}$ **73.** $\sqrt{13}$ **75.** 1

Section 11.3 (pages 688–690)

1. The documentation was incorrect, since the fraction bar should extend under the term $-b$. The correct formula is $x = \dfrac{-b \pm \sqrt{b^2 - 4ac}}{2a}$.

3. The last step is wrong. Because 5 is not a common factor in the numerator, the fraction cannot be simplified. The solution set is

$\left\{\dfrac{5 \pm \sqrt{5}}{10}\right\}$.   **5.** $\{3, 5\}$ **7.** $\left\{\dfrac{-2 \pm \sqrt{2}}{2}\right\}$ **9.** $\left\{\dfrac{1 \pm \sqrt{3}}{2}\right\}$

11. $\left\{5 \pm \sqrt{7}\right\}$ **13.** $\left\{\dfrac{-1 \pm \sqrt{2}}{2}\right\}$ **15.** $\left\{\dfrac{-1 \pm \sqrt{7}}{3}\right\}$

17. $\left\{1 \pm \sqrt{5}\right\}$ **19.** $\left\{\dfrac{-2 \pm \sqrt{10}}{2}\right\}$ **21.** $\left\{-1 \pm 3\sqrt{2}\right\}$

23. $\left\{\dfrac{1 \pm \sqrt{29}}{2}\right\}$ **25.** $\left\{\dfrac{-4 \pm \sqrt{91}}{3}\right\}$ **27.** $\left\{\dfrac{-3 \pm \sqrt{57}}{8}\right\}$

29. $\left\{\dfrac{3}{2} \pm \dfrac{\sqrt{15}}{2}i\right\}$ **31.** $\left\{3 \pm i\sqrt{5}\right\}$ **33.** $\left\{\dfrac{1}{2} \pm \dfrac{\sqrt{6}}{2}i\right\}$

35. $\left\{-\dfrac{2}{3} \pm \dfrac{\sqrt{2}}{3}i\right\}$ **37.** $\left\{\dfrac{1}{2} \pm \dfrac{1}{4}i\right\}$ **39.** B; factoring

41. C; quadratic formula   **43.** A; factoring   **45.** D; quadratic formula

47. $\left\{-\dfrac{7}{5}\right\}$ **49.** $\left\{-\dfrac{1}{3}, 2\right\}$ **51. (a)** Discriminant is 25, or 5^2; solve by factoring; $\left\{-3, -\dfrac{4}{3}\right\}$ **(b)** Discriminant is 44; use the quadratic

formula; $\left\{\dfrac{7 \pm \sqrt{11}}{2}\right\}$ **53.** -10 or 10   **55.** 16   **57.** 25

59. $b = \dfrac{44}{5}; \dfrac{3}{10}$ **61.** $\{-8\}$ **63.** $\{5\}$

Section 11.4 (pages 697–700)

1. Multiply by the LCD, x.   **3.** Substitute a variable for $x^2 + x$.

5. The proposed solution -1 does not check. The solution set is $\{4\}$.

7. $\{-2, 7\}$ **9.** $\{-4, 7\}$ **11.** $\left\{-\dfrac{2}{3}, 1\right\}$ **13.** $\left\{-\dfrac{14}{17}, 5\right\}$

15. $\left\{-\dfrac{11}{7}, 0\right\}$ **17.** $\left\{\dfrac{-1 \pm \sqrt{13}}{2}\right\}$ **19.** $\left\{-\dfrac{8}{3}, -1\right\}$

21. $\left\{\dfrac{2 \pm \sqrt{22}}{3}\right\}$ **23.** $\left\{\dfrac{-1 \pm \sqrt{5}}{4}\right\}$ **25. (a)** $(20 - t)$ mph

(b) $(20 + t)$ mph   **27.** 25 mph   **29.** 50 mph   **31.** 3.6 hr   **33.** Rusty: 25.0 hr; Nancy: 23.0 hr   **35.** 3 hr; 6 hr   **37.** $\{2, 5\}$ **39.** $\{3\}$

41. $\left\{\frac{8}{9}\right\}$ **43.** $\{9\}$ **45.** $\left\{\frac{2}{5}\right\}$ **47.** $\{-2\}$ **49.** $\{\pm 2, \pm 5\}$

51. $\left\{\pm 1, \pm\frac{3}{2}\right\}$ **53.** $\left\{\pm 2, \pm 2\sqrt{3}\right\}$ **55.** $\{-6, -5\}$

57. $\left\{-\frac{16}{3}, -2\right\}$ **59.** $\{-8, 1\}$ **61.** $\{-64, 27\}$ **63.** $\left\{\pm 1, \pm\frac{27}{8}\right\}$

65. $\left\{-\frac{1}{3}, \frac{1}{6}\right\}$ **67.** $\left\{-\frac{1}{2}, 3\right\}$ **69.** $\left\{\pm\frac{\sqrt{6}}{3}, \pm\frac{1}{2}\right\}$ **71.** $\{3, 11\}$

73. $\{25\}$ **75.** $\left\{-\sqrt[3]{5}, -\frac{\sqrt[3]{4}}{2}\right\}$ **77.** $\left\{\frac{4}{3}, \frac{9}{4}\right\}$

79. $\left\{\pm\frac{\sqrt{9+\sqrt{65}}}{2}, \pm\frac{\sqrt{9-\sqrt{65}}}{2}\right\}$ **81.** $\left\{\pm 1, \pm\frac{\sqrt{6}}{2}i\right\}$

83. $W = \dfrac{P-2L}{2}$, or $W = \dfrac{P}{2} - L$ **85.** $C = \dfrac{5}{9}(F-32)$

Summary Exercises on Solving Quadratic Equations (page 700)

1. square root property **2.** factoring **3.** quadratic formula

4. quadratic formula **5.** factoring **6.** square root property

7. $\{\pm\sqrt{7}\}$ **8.** $\left\{-\frac{3}{2}, \frac{5}{3}\right\}$ **9.** $\{-3 \pm \sqrt{5}\}$ **10.** $\{-2, 8\}$

11. $\left\{-\frac{3}{2}, 4\right\}$ **12.** $\left\{-3, \frac{1}{3}\right\}$ **13.** $\left\{\frac{2 \pm \sqrt{2}}{2}\right\}$ **14.** $\{\pm 2i\sqrt{3}\}$

15. $\left\{\frac{1}{2}, 2\right\}$ **16.** $\{\pm 1, \pm 3\}$ **17.** $\left\{\frac{-3 \pm 2\sqrt{2}}{2}\right\}$ **18.** $\left\{\frac{4}{5}, 3\right\}$

19. $\{\pm\sqrt{2}, \pm\sqrt{7}\}$ **20.** $\left\{\frac{1 \pm \sqrt{5}}{4}\right\}$ **21.** $\left\{-\frac{1}{2} \pm \frac{\sqrt{3}}{2}i\right\}$

22. $\left\{-\frac{\sqrt[3]{175}}{5}, 1\right\}$ **23.** $\left\{\frac{3}{2}\right\}$ **24.** $\left\{\frac{2}{3}\right\}$ **25.** $\{\pm 6\sqrt{2}\}$

26. $\left\{-\frac{2}{3}, 2\right\}$ **27.** $\{-4, 9\}$ **28.** $\{\pm 13\}$ **29.** $\left\{1 \pm \frac{\sqrt{3}}{3}i\right\}$

30. $\{3\}$ **31.** $\left\{\frac{1}{6} \pm \frac{\sqrt{47}}{6}i\right\}$ **32.** $\left\{-\frac{1}{3}, \frac{1}{6}\right\}$

Section 11.5 (pages 705–709)

1. Find a common denominator, and then multiply both sides by the common denominator. **3.** Write it in standard form (with 0 on one side, in decreasing powers of w). **5.** $m = \sqrt{p^2 - n^2}$

7. $t = \dfrac{\pm\sqrt{dk}}{k}$ **9.** $d = \dfrac{\pm\sqrt{skl}}{l}$ **11.** $v = \dfrac{\pm\sqrt{kAF}}{F}$

13. $r = \dfrac{\pm\sqrt{3\pi Vh}}{\pi h}$ **15.** $t = \dfrac{-B \pm \sqrt{B^2 - 4AC}}{2A}$ **17.** $h = \dfrac{D^2}{k}$

19. $\ell = \dfrac{p^2 g}{k}$ **21.** $r = \dfrac{\pm\sqrt{S\pi}}{2\pi}$ **23.** $R = \dfrac{E^2 - 2pr \pm E\sqrt{E^2 - 4pr}}{2p}$

25. $r = \dfrac{5pc}{4}$ or $r = -\dfrac{2pc}{3}$ **27.** $I = \dfrac{-cR \pm \sqrt{c^2 R^2 - 4cL}}{2cL}$

29. 7.9, 8.9, 11.9 **31.** eastbound ship: 80 mi; southbound ship: 150 mi

33. 8 in., 15 in., 17 in. **35.** length: 24 ft; width: 10 ft **37.** 2 ft

39. 7 m by 12 m **41.** 20 in. by 12 in. **43.** 1 sec and 8 sec

45. 2.4 sec and 5.6 sec **47.** 9.2 sec **49.** It reaches its *maximum* height at 5 sec because this is the only time it reaches 400 ft. **51.** $0.80

53. 0.035, or 3.5% **55.** 5.5 m per sec **57.** 5 or 14

59. (a) $420 billion **(b)** $420 billion; They are the same.

61. 2004; The graph indicates that spending first exceeded $400 billion in 2005. **63.** 9 **65.** domain: $(-\infty, \infty)$; range: $[0, \infty)$

Section 11.6 (pages 715–718)

1. (a) B **(b)** C **(c)** A **(d)** D **3.** $(0, 0)$ **5.** $(0, 4)$ **7.** $(1, 0)$

9. $(-3, -4)$ **11.** $(5, 6)$ **13.** down; wider **15.** up; narrower

17. down; narrower **19. (a)** D **(b)** B **(c)** C **(d)** A

21.   **23.**   **25.**

27. vertex: $(4, 0)$; axis: $x = 4$; domain: $(-\infty, \infty)$; range: $[0, \infty)$

29. vertex: $(-2, -1)$; axis: $x = -2$; domain: $(-\infty, \infty)$; range: $[-1, \infty)$

31. vertex: $(2, -4)$; axis: $x = 2$; domain: $(-\infty, \infty)$; range: $[-4, \infty)$

 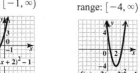

33. vertex: $(-1, 2)$; axis: $x = -1$; domain: $(-\infty, \infty)$; range: $(-\infty, 2]$

35. vertex: $(2, -3)$; axis: $x = 2$; domain: $(-\infty, \infty)$; range: $[-3, \infty)$

37. linear; positive

39. quadratic; positive

41. quadratic; negative

43. (a)

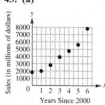

(b) quadratic; positive **(c)** $f(x) = 99.3x^2 + 400.7x + 1825$

(d) $9496 million **(e)** No. The number of digital cameras sold in 2007 is far below the number approximated by the model. Rather than continuing to increase, sales of digital cameras fell in 2007. **45. (a)** 6105

(b) The approximation using the model is low. **47.** $\{-4, 5\}$

49. -2 **51.** $\{-4, 1\}$ **53.** $\{-3 \pm 2\sqrt{3}\}$

Section 11.7 (pages 726–729)

1. If x is squared, it has a vertical axis. If y is squared, it has a horizontal axis. **3.** Use the discriminant of the function. If it is positive, there are two x-intercepts. If it is 0, there is one x-intercept (at the vertex), and if it is negative, there is no x-intercept. **5.** $(-4, -6)$ **7.** $(1, -3)$

9. $\left(-\frac{1}{2}, -\frac{29}{4}\right)$ **11.** $(-1, 3)$; up; narrower; no x-intercepts

13. $\left(\frac{5}{2}, \frac{37}{4}\right)$; down; same; two x-intercepts **15.** $(-3, -9)$; to the right; wider **17.** F **19.** C **21.** D

23. vertex: $(-4, -6)$; **25.** vertex: $(1, -3)$; **27.** vertex: $(1, -2)$;
axis: $x = -4$; axis: $x = 1$; axis: $y = -2$;
domain: $(-\infty, \infty)$; domain: $(-\infty, \infty)$; domain: $[1, \infty)$;
range: $[-6, \infty)$ range: $(-\infty, -3]$ range: $(-\infty, \infty)$

29. vertex: $(1, 5)$; axis: $y = 5$; **31.** vertex: $(-7, -2)$;
domain: $(-\infty, 1]$; axis: $y = -2$; domain: $[-7, \infty)$;
range: $(-\infty, \infty)$ range: $(-\infty, \infty)$

33. 20 and 20 **35.** 140 ft by 70 ft; 9800 ft^2 **37.** 16 ft; 2 sec
39. 2 sec; 65 ft **41.** 20 units; $210 **43. (a)** minimum
(b) 2003; $825.8 billion **45. (a)** The coefficient of x^2 is negative because a parabola that models the data must open down.
(b) $(18.45, 3860)$ **(c)** In 2018 Social Security assets will reach their maximum value of $3860 billion.
47. (a) $R(x) = (100 - x)(200 + 4x) = 20{,}000 + 200x - 4x^2$
(b) **(c)** 25 **(d)** $22,500

49. **51.**

53. $\left(-\frac{3}{2}, \infty\right)$

Section 11.8 (pages 735–736)

1. (a) $\{1, 3\}$ **(b)** $(-\infty, 1) \cup (3, \infty)$ **(c)** $(1, 3)$
3. (a) $\{-2, 5\}$ **(b)** $[-2, 5]$ **(c)** $(-\infty, -2] \cup [5, \infty)$
5. $(-\infty, -1) \cup (5, \infty)$
7. $(-4, 6)$
9. $(-\infty, 1] \cup [3, \infty)$
11. $\left(-\infty, -\frac{3}{2}\right] \cup \left[\frac{3}{5}, \infty\right)$
13. $\left[-\frac{3}{2}, \frac{3}{2}\right]$
15. $\left(-\infty, -\frac{1}{2}\right] \cup \left[\frac{1}{3}, \infty\right)$
17. $(-\infty, 0] \cup [4, \infty)$

19. $\left[0, \frac{5}{3}\right]$
21. $\left(-\infty, 3 - \sqrt{3}\right] \cup \left[3 + \sqrt{3}, \infty\right)$
23. $(-\infty, \infty)$ **25.** $\emptyset$ **27.** $(-\infty, 1) \cup (2, 4)$
29. $\left[-\frac{3}{2}, \frac{1}{3}\right] \cup [4, \infty)$
31. $(-\infty, 1) \cup (4, \infty)$
33. $\left[-\frac{3}{2}, 5\right)$ **35.** $(2, 6]$
37. $\left(-\infty, \frac{1}{2}\right) \cup \left(\frac{5}{4}, \infty\right)$
39. $[-7, -2)$
41. $(-\infty, 2) \cup (4, \infty)$
43. $\left(0, \frac{1}{2}\right) \cup \left(\frac{5}{2}, \infty\right)$
45. $\left[\frac{3}{2}, \infty\right)$
47. $\left(-2, \frac{5}{3}\right) \cup \left(\frac{5}{3}, \infty\right)$
49. domain: $\{0, 1, 2, 3\}$; range: $\{1, 2, 4, 8\}$ **51.** function

Chapter 11 Review Exercises (pages 740–744)

1. $\{\pm 11\}$ **2.** $\{\pm\sqrt{3}\}$ **3.** $\left\{-\frac{15}{2}, \frac{5}{2}\right\}$ **4.** $\left\{\frac{2}{3} \pm \frac{5}{3}i\right\}$
5. By the square root property, the first step should be $x = \sqrt{12}$ or $x = -\sqrt{12}$. The solution set is $\{\pm 2\sqrt{3}\}$. **6.** 5.8 sec
7. $\{-2 \pm \sqrt{19}\}$ **8.** $\left\{\frac{1}{2}, 1\right\}$ **9.** $\left\{\frac{-4 \pm \sqrt{22}}{2}\right\}$
10. $\left\{\frac{3}{8} \pm \frac{\sqrt{87}}{8}i\right\}$ **11.** $\left\{-\frac{7}{2}, 3\right\}$ **12.** $\left\{\frac{-5 \pm \sqrt{53}}{2}\right\}$
13. $\left\{\frac{1 \pm \sqrt{41}}{2}\right\}$ **14.** $\left\{-\frac{3}{4} \pm \frac{\sqrt{23}}{4}i\right\}$ **15.** $\left\{\frac{2}{3} \pm \frac{\sqrt{2}}{3}i\right\}$
16. $\left\{\frac{-7 \pm \sqrt{37}}{2}\right\}$ **17. (a)** C **(b)** A **18. (a)** D **(b)** B
19. $\left\{-\frac{5}{2}, 3\right\}$ **20.** $\left\{-\frac{1}{2}, 1\right\}$ **21.** $\{-4\}$ **22.** $\left\{-\frac{11}{6}, -\frac{19}{12}\right\}$
23. $\left\{-\frac{343}{8}, 64\right\}$ **24.** $\{\pm 1, \pm 3\}$ **25.** 7 mph **26.** 40 mph **27.** 4.6 hr
28. Zoran: 2.6 hr; Claude: 3.6 hr **29.** $v = \dfrac{\pm\sqrt{rFkw}}{kw}$ **30.** $y = \dfrac{6p^2}{z}$
31. $t = \dfrac{3m \pm \sqrt{9m^2 + 24m}}{2m}$ **32.** 9 ft, 12 ft, 15 ft
33. 12 cm by 20 cm **34.** 1 in. **35.** 18 in. **36.** 5.2 sec **37.** 3 min

38. (a) $15,511 million; It is close to the number suggested by the graph. **(b)** $x = 6$, which represents 2006; Based on the graph, the revenue in 2006 was closer to $13,000 million than $14,000 million. **39.** $(1, 0)$
40. $(3, 7)$ **41.** $(-4, 3)$ **42.** $\left(\frac{2}{3}, -\frac{2}{3}\right)$

43. vertex: $(2, -3)$;   **44.** vertex: $(2, 3)$;   **45.** vertex: $(-4, -3)$;
axis: $x = 2$;   axis: $x = 2$;   axis: $y = -3$;
domain: $(-\infty, \infty)$;   domain: $(-\infty, \infty)$;   domain: $[-4, \infty)$;
range: $[-3, \infty)$ range: $(-\infty, 3]$ range: $(-\infty, \infty)$

$$y = 2(x - 2)^2 - 3$$

$$f(x) = -2x^2 + 8x - 5$$

$$x = 2(y + 3)^2 - 4$$

46. vertex: $(4, 6)$;   **47. (a)** $c = 2.9$
axis: $y = 6$; $100a + 10b + c = 24.3$
domain: $(-\infty, 4]$; $400a + 20b + c = 56.5$
range: $(-\infty, \infty)$ **(b)** $f(x) = 0.054x^2 + 1.6x + 2.9$
(c) $60.3 billion; The result using the model is close, but slightly low.

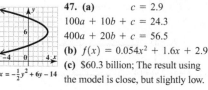
$$x = -\frac{1}{2}y^2 + 6y - 14$$

48. 5 sec; 400 ft   **49.** length: 50 m; width: 50 m; maximum area: 2500 m²

50. $\left(-\infty, -\frac{3}{2}\right) \cup (4, \infty)$

51. $[-4, 3]$

52. $(-\infty, -5] \cup [-2, 3]$ **53.** $\emptyset$

54. $\left(-\infty, \frac{1}{2}\right) \cup (2, \infty)$

55. $[-3, 2)$ **56.** $R = \dfrac{\pm\sqrt{Vh - r^2 h}}{h}$

57. $\left\{1 \pm \dfrac{\sqrt{3}}{3}i\right\}$ **58.** $\left\{\dfrac{-11 \pm \sqrt{7}}{3}\right\}$ **59.** $d = \dfrac{\pm\sqrt{Skl}}{l}$

60. $(-\infty, \infty)$ **61.** $\{4\}$ **62.** $\left\{\pm\sqrt{4 + \sqrt{15}}, \pm\sqrt{4 - \sqrt{15}}\right\}$

63. $\left(-5, -\frac{23}{5}\right]$ **64.** $\left\{-\frac{5}{3}, -\frac{3}{2}\right\}$ **65.** $\{-2, -1, 3, 4\}$

66. $(-\infty, -6) \cup \left(-\frac{3}{2}, 1\right)$ **67. (a)** F   **(b)** B   **(c)** C
(d) A   **(e)** E   **(f)** D
68. vertex: $\left(-\frac{1}{2}, -3\right)$; axis: $x = -\frac{1}{2}$;
domain: $(-\infty, \infty)$; range: $[-3, \infty)$

$$f(x) = 4x^2 + 4x - 2$$

69. 10 mph   **70.** length: 2 cm; width: 1.5 cm

Chapter 11 Test (pages 744–746)

$[11.1]$ **1.** $\{\pm 3\sqrt{6}\}$ **2.** $\left\{-\frac{8}{7}, \frac{2}{7}\right\}$ $[11.2]$ **3.** $\{-1 \pm \sqrt{5}\}$

$[11.3]$ **4.** $\left\{\dfrac{3 \pm \sqrt{17}}{4}\right\}$ **5.** $\left\{\dfrac{2}{3} \pm \dfrac{\sqrt{11}}{3}i\right\}$ $[11.1]$ **6.** A

$[11.3]$ **7.** discriminant: 88; There are two irrational solutions.

$[11.1–11.4]$ **8.** $\left\{\frac{2}{3}\right\}$ **9.** $\left\{-\frac{2}{3}, 6\right\}$ **10.** $\left\{\dfrac{-7 \pm \sqrt{97}}{8}\right\}$ **11.** $\left\{\pm\frac{1}{3}, \pm 2\right\}$

12. $\left\{-\frac{5}{2}, 1\right\}$ $[11.5]$ **13.** $r = \dfrac{\pm\sqrt{\pi S}}{2\pi}$ $[11.4]$ **14.** Terry: 11.1 hr;
Callie: 9.1 hr   **15.** 7 mph $[11.5]$ **16.** 2 ft   **17.** 16 m $[11.6]$ **18.** A
19. vertex: $(0, -2)$; axis: $x = 0$; $[11.7]$ **20.** vertex: $(2, 3)$; axis: $x = 2$;
domain: $(-\infty, \infty)$;   domain: $(-\infty, \infty)$;
range: $[-2, \infty)$ range: $(-\infty, 3]$

$$f(x) = \frac{1}{2}x^2 - 2$$

$$f(x) = -x^2 + 4x - 1$$

21. vertex: $(2, 2)$; axis: $y = 2$;   **22. (a)** 139 million   **(b)** 2007;
domain: $(-\infty, 2]$;   145 million   **23.** 160 ft by 320 ft
range: $(-\infty, \infty)$ $[11.8]$ **24.** $(-\infty, -5) \cup \left(\frac{3}{2}, \infty\right)$

$$x = -(y - 2)^2 + 2$$

25. $(-\infty, 4) \cup [9, \infty)$

Chapters 1–11 Cumulative Review Exercises (pages 746–747)

$[1.4, 10.7]$ **1. (a)** $-2, 0, 7$ **(b)** $-\frac{7}{3}, -2, 0, 0.7, 7, \frac{32}{3}$
(c) All are real except $\sqrt{-8}$.   **(c)** All are complex numbers.
$[2.3]$ **2.** $\left\{\frac{4}{5}\right\}$ $[9.2]$ **3.** $\left\{\frac{11}{10}, \frac{7}{2}\right\}$ $[10.6]$ **4.** $\left\{\frac{2}{3}\right\}$ $[6.6]$ **5.** $\emptyset$

$[11.2, 11.3]$ **6.** $\left\{\dfrac{7 \pm \sqrt{177}}{4}\right\}$ $[11.4]$ **7.** $\{\pm 1, \pm 2\}$ $[2.8]$ **8.** $[1, \infty)$

$[9.2]$ **9.** $\left[2, \frac{8}{3}\right]$ $[11.8]$ **10.** $(1, 3)$ **11.** $(-2, 1)$
$[3.2, 7.1, 7.3, 7.4]$ **12.** function;
          domain: $(-\infty, \infty)$; range: $(-\infty, \infty)$;
          $f(x) = \frac{4}{5}x - 3$

$$4x - 5y = 15$$

$[7.3, 9.3]$ **13.** not a function $[11.6]$ **14.** function;
                         domain: $(-\infty, \infty)$;
$$4x - 5y < 15$$ range: $(-\infty, 3]$;
                         $f(x) = -2(x - 1)^2 + 3$

$$y = -2(x - 1)^2 + 3$$

[3.2, 3.3, 7.1] **15.** $m = \frac{2}{7}$; x-intercept: $(-8, 0)$; y-intercept: $\left(0, \frac{16}{7}\right)$

[7.2] **16. (a)** $y = -\frac{5}{2}x + 2$ **(b)** $y = \frac{2}{5}x + \frac{13}{5}$ [4.1, 4.2] **17.** $\frac{x^8}{y^4}$

18. $\frac{4}{xy^2}$ [4.6] **19.** $\frac{4}{9}t^2 + 12t + 81$ [4.7] **20.** $4x^2 - 6x + 11 + \frac{4}{x+2}$

[5.1–5.4] **21.** $(4m - 3)(6m + 5)$ **22.** $(2x + 3y)(4x^2 - 6xy + 9y^2)$

23. $(3x - 5y)^2$ [6.2] **24.** $-\frac{5}{18}$ [6.4] **25.** $-\frac{8}{x}$ [6.5] **26.** $\frac{r-s}{r}$

[8.1–8.3, 8.6] **27.** $\{(1, -2)\}$ [8.4, 8.6] **28.** $\{(3, -4, 2)\}$

[8.5] **29.** Microsoft: $60.4 billion; Oracle: $22.4 billion

[10.3] **30.** $\frac{3\sqrt[3]{4}}{4}$ [10.5] **31.** $\sqrt{7} + \sqrt{5}$

[11.5] **32.** southbound car: 57 mi; eastbound car: 76 mi

---

12 INVERSE, EXPONENTIAL, AND LOGARITHMIC FUNCTIONS

Connections   (page 754)

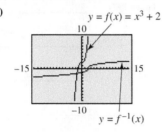
$y = f(x) = x^3 + 2$
$y = f^{-1}(x)$

Section 12.1 (pages 755–758)

1. This function is not one-to-one because both France and the United States are paired with the same trans fat percentage, 11.
3. Yes. By adding 1 to 1058, two distances would be the same, so the function would not be one-to-one. **5.** B **7.** A
9. $\{(6, 3), (10, 2), (12, 5)\}$ **11.** not one-to-one
13. $f^{-1}(x) = \frac{x-4}{2}$, or $f^{-1}(x) = \frac{1}{2}x - 2$ **15.** $g^{-1}(x) = x^2 + 3$,
$x \geq 0$ **17.** not one-to-one **19.** $f^{-1}(x) = \sqrt[3]{x + 4}$
21. (a) 8 **(b)** 3 **23. (a)** 1 **(b)** 0
25. (a) one-to-one **(b)**   **27. (a)** not one-to-one

29. (a) one-to-one **(b)**   **31.**

33.   **35.**

x	f(x)
0	0
1	1
4	2

37.

x	f(x)
-1	-3
0	-2
1	-1
2	6

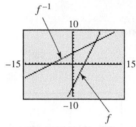

39. $f^{-1}(x) = \frac{x+5}{4}$, or $f^{-1}(x) = \frac{1}{4}x + \frac{5}{4}$

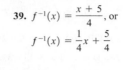

40. MY GRAPHING CALCULATOR IS THE GREATEST THING SINCE SLICED BREAD. **41.** If the function were not one-to-one, there would be ambiguity in some of the characters, as they could represent more than one letter. **42.** Answers will vary. For example, Jane Doe is 1004 5 2748 129 68 3379 129.

43. $f^{-1}(x) = \frac{x+7}{2}$, or $f^{-1}(x) = \frac{1}{2}x + \frac{7}{2}$ **45.** $f^{-1}(x) = \sqrt[3]{x} - 5$

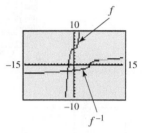

47. 64 **49.** $\frac{1}{2}$

Section 12.2 (pages 763–765)

1. C **3.** A **5.** 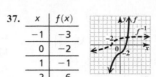 **7.**

$g(x) = \left(\frac{1}{3}\right)^x$

9.   **11.**   **13.** rises; falls
15. $\{2\}$ **17.** $\left\{\frac{3}{2}\right\}$
$y = 2^{2x-2}$ **19.** $\{7\}$ **21.** $\{-3\}$
23. $\{-1\}$ **25.** $\{-3\}$
27. 639.545 **29.** 0.066
31. 12.179 **33. (a)** 0.6°C **(b)** 0.3°C **35. (a)** 1.4°C **(b)** 0.5°C
37. (a) 5028 million tons **(b)** 6512 million tons
(c) It is less than what the model provides (7099 million tons).
39. (a) $5000 **(b)** $2973 **(c)** $1768
(d) 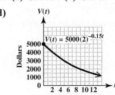 **41.** 6.67 yr after it was purchased
43. 4 **45.** 0

Section 12.3 (pages 770–773)

1. (a) B **(b)** E **(c)** D **(d)** F **(e)** A **(f)** C **3.** $\log_4 1024 = 5$
5. $\log_{1/2} 8 = -3$ **7.** $\log_{10} 0.001 = -3$ **9.** $\log_{625} 5 = \frac{1}{4}$
11. $\log_8 \frac{1}{4} = -\frac{2}{3}$ **13.** $\log_5 1 = 0$ **15.** $4^3 = 64$ **17.** $10^{-4} = \frac{1}{10,000}$

19. $6^0 = 1$ **21.** $9^{1/2} = 3$ **23.** $\left(\frac{1}{4}\right)^{1/2} = \frac{1}{2}$ **25.** $5^{-1} = 5^{-1}$

27. (a) C **(b)** B **(c)** B **(d)** C   **29.** $\left\{\frac{1}{3}\right\}$ **31.** $\{81\}$ **33.** $\left\{\frac{1}{5}\right\}$

35. $\{1\}$ **37.** $\{x \mid x > 0, x \neq 1\}$ **39.** $\{5\}$ **41.** $\left\{\frac{5}{3}\right\}$ **43.** $\{4\}$

45. $\left\{\frac{3}{2}\right\}$ **47.** $\{30\}$ **49.** 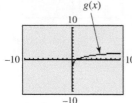   **51.**

53. Every power of 1 is equal to 1, and thus it cannot be used as a base.

55. $(0, \infty); (-\infty, \infty)$ **57.** 8   **59.** 24   **61. (a)** 4385 billion ft³

(b) 5555 billion ft³   **(c)** 6140 billion ft³   **63. (a)** 130 thousand units

(b) 190 thousand units   **(c)**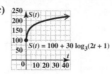

65. about 4 times as powerful

67. 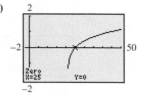   **69.**

71. 4^9 **73.** 7^{12}

Connections **(page 779)**   **1.**
$$\log_{10} 458.3 \approx 2.661149857$$
$$\underline{+\log_{10} 294.6 \approx 2.469232743}$$
$$\approx 5.130382600$$
$$10^{5.130382600} \approx 135{,}015.18$$
A calculator gives
$$(458.3)(294.6) = 135{,}015.18.$$

2. Answers will vary.

Section 12.4 (pages 780–781)

1. $\log_{10} 7 + \log_{10} 8$ **3.** 4   **5.** 9   **7.** $\log_7 4 + \log_7 5$

9. $\log_5 8 - \log_5 3$ **11.** $2 \log_4 6$ **13.** $\frac{1}{3}\log_3 4 - 2\log_3 x - \log_3 y$

15. $\frac{1}{2}\log_3 x + \frac{1}{2}\log_3 y - \frac{1}{2}\log_3 5$ **17.** $\frac{1}{3}\log_2 x + \frac{1}{5}\log_2 y - 2\log_2 r$

19. In the notation $\log_a (x + y)$, the parentheses do not indicate multiplication. They indicate that $x + y$ is the result of raising a to some power.

21. $\log_b xy$ **23.** $\log_a \frac{m}{n}$ **25.** $\log_a \frac{rt^3}{s}$ **27.** $\log_a \frac{125}{81}$

29. $\log_{10}(x^2 - 9)$ **31.** $\log_p \frac{x^3 y^{1/2}}{z^{3/2} a^3}$ **33.** 1.2552   **35.** -0.6532

37. 1.5562   **39.** 0.2386   **41.** 0.4771   **43.** 4.7710   **45.** false

47. true   **49.** true   **51.** false   **53.** The exponent of a quotient is the difference between the exponent of the numerator and the exponent of the denominator.   **55.** No number allowed as a logarithmic base can be raised to a power with a result of 0.   **57.** $\log_{10} 10{,}000 = 4$

59. $\log_{10} 0.01 = -2$ **61.** $10^0 = 1$

Section 12.5 (pages 787–790)

1. C   **3.** C   **5.** 31.6   **7.** 1.6335   **9.** 2.5164   **11.** -1.4868

13. 9.6776   **15.** 2.0592   **17.** -2.8896 **19.** 5.9613   **21.** 4.1506

23. 2.3026   **25. (a)** 2.552424846   **(b)** 1.552424846

(c) 0.552424846   **(d)** The whole number parts will vary, but the decimal parts are the same.   **27.** poor fen   **29.** bog   **31.** rich fen   **33.** 11.6

35. 4.3   **37.** 4.0×10^{-8} **39.** 4.0×10^{-6} **41. (a)** 107 dB

(b) 100 dB   **(c)** 98 dB   **43. (a)** 800 yr   **(b)** 5200 yr   **(c)** 11,500 yr

45. (a) 77%   **(b)** 1989   **47. (a)** \$54 per ton   **(b)** If $p = 0$, then $\ln(1 - p) = \ln 1 = 0$, so T would be negative. If $p = 1$, then $\ln(1 - p) = \ln 0$, but the domain of $\ln x$ is $(0, \infty)$.   **49.** 2.2619

51. 0.6826   **53.** 0.3155   **55.** 0.8736   **57.** 2.4849   **59.** Answers will vary. Suppose the name is Jeffery Cole, with $m = 7$ and $n = 4$.

(a) $\log_7 4$ is the exponent to which 7 must be raised to obtain 4.

(b) 0.7124143742   **(c)** 4   **61.** 6446 billion ft³   **63.** $\left\{-\frac{3}{5}\right\}$

65. $\{5\}$ **67.** $\{-3\}$ **69.** $\log(x + 2)(x + 3)$, or $\log(x^2 + 5x + 6)$

Connections   **(page 797)**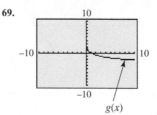

Section 12.6 (pages 797–800)

1. $\{0.827\}$ **3.** $\{0.833\}$ **5.** $\{1.201\}$ **7.** $\{2.269\}$ **9.** $\{15.967\}$

11. $\{-6.067\}$ **13.** $\{261.291\}$ **15.** $\{-10.718\}$ **17.** $\{3\}$

19. $\{5.879\}$ **21.** $\{-\pi\}$, or $\{-3.142\}$ **23.** $\{1\}$ **25.** Natural logarithms are a better choice because e is the base.   **27.** $\left\{\frac{2}{3}\right\}$

29. $\left\{\frac{33}{2}\right\}$ **31.** $\left\{-1 + \sqrt[3]{49}\right\}$ **33.** 2 cannot be a solution because $\log(2 - 3) = \log(-1)$, and -1 is not in the domain of $\log x$.

35. $\left\{\frac{1}{3}\right\}$ **37.** $\{2\}$ **39.** $\emptyset$ **41.** $\{8\}$ **43.** $\left\{\frac{4}{3}\right\}$ **45.** $\{8\}$

47. (a) \$2539.47   **(b)** 10.2 yr   **49. (a)** \$4934.71   **(b)** 19.8 yr

51. (a) \$11,260.96   **(b)** \$11,416.64   **(c)** \$11,497.99   **(d)** \$11,580.90

(e) \$11,581.83   **53.** \$137.41   **55. (a)** 15.9 million tons

(b) 30.7 million tons   **(c)** 59.2 million tons   **(d)** 93.7 million tons

57. \$143,598 million   **59. (a)** 1.62 g   **(b)** 1.18 g   **(c)** 0.69 g

(d) 2.00 g   **61. (a)** 179.73 g   **(b)** 21.66 yr   **63.** 2012   **65.** It means that after 250 yr, approximately 2.9 g of the original sample remain.

67.   **69.**

Chapter 12 Review Exercises (pages 804–808)

1. not one-to-one   **2.** one-to-one   **3.** $f^{-1}(x) = \frac{x - 7}{-3}$, or $f^{-1}(x) = -\frac{1}{3}x + \frac{7}{3}$ **4.** $f^{-1}(x) = \frac{x^3 + 4}{6}$ **5.** not one-to-one

6. This function is not one-to-one because two sodas in the list have 41 mg of caffeine.

7. 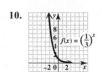 **8.**   **9.**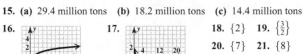

10.   **11.**   **12.** $\left\{\frac{1}{2}\right\}$ **13.** $\{4\}$

14. $\left\{\frac{3}{7}\right\}$

15. (a) 29.4 million tons **(b)** 18.2 million tons **(c)** 14.4 million tons

16. 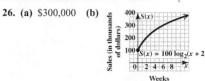 **17.** **18.** $\{2\}$ **19.** $\left\{\frac{3}{2}\right\}$

20. $\{7\}$ **21.** $\{8\}$

22. $\{4\}$

23. $\{b \mid b > 0, b \neq 1\}$ **24.** $\log_b a$ is the exponent to which b must be raised to obtain a. **25.** a

26. (a) \$300,000 **(b)**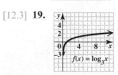

27. $\log_2 3 + \log_2 x + 2 \log_2 y$ **28.** $\frac{1}{2} \log_4 x + 2 \log_4 w - \log_4 z$

29. $\log_b \frac{3x}{y^2}$ **30.** $\log_3 \left(\frac{x + 7}{4x + 6} \right)$ **31.** 1.4609 **32.** -0.5901

33. 3.3638 **34.** -1.3587 **35.** 0.9251 **36.** 1.7925 **37.** 6.4

38. 8.4 **39.** 2.5×10^{-5} **40.** Magnitude 1 is about 6.3 times as intense as magnitude 3. **41. (a)** 18 yr **(b)** 12 yr **(c)** 7 yr **(d)** 6 yr **(e)** Each comparison shows approximately the same number. For example, in part (a) the doubling time is 18 yr (rounded) and $\frac{72}{4} = 18$. Thus, the formula $t = \frac{72}{100r}$ (called the *rule of 72*) is an excellent approximation of the doubling time formula. **42.** $\{2.042\}$

43. $\{4.907\}$ **44.** $\{18.310\}$ **45.** $\left\{\frac{1}{9}\right\}$ **46.** $\left\{-6 + \sqrt[3]{25}\right\}$

47. $\{2\}$ **48.** $\left\{\frac{3}{8}\right\}$ **49.** $\{4\}$ **50.** $\{1\}$ **51.** When the power rule was applied in the second step, the domain was changed from $\{x \mid x \neq 0\}$ to $\{x \mid x > 0\}$. The valid solution -10 was "lost." The solution set is $\{\pm 10\}$. **52.** \$24,403.80 **53.** \$11,190.72 **54.** Plan A is better, since it would pay \$2.92 more. **55.** about 13.9 days **56. (a)** about \$4267 **(b)** about 11% **57.** about 67% **58.** D **59.** 7 **60.** 36 **61.** 4

62. e **63.** -5 **64.** 5.4 **65.** $\{72\}$ **66.** $\{3\}$ **67.** $\left\{\frac{1}{9}\right\}$ **68.** $\left\{\frac{4}{3}\right\}$

69. $\{3\}$ **70.** $\{0\}$ **71.** $\left\{\frac{1}{8}\right\}$ **72.** $\left\{\frac{11}{3}\right\}$ **73.** $\{-2, -1\}$ **74. (a)** $\left\{\frac{3}{8}\right\}$

(b) The x-value of the x-intercept is 0.375, the decimal equivalent of $\frac{3}{8}$.

75. about 32.28% **76. (a)** 0.325 **(c)** 0.673

Chapter 12 Test (pages 808–810)

[12.1] **1. (a)** not one-to-one **(b)** one-to-one **2.** $f^{-1}(x) = x^3 - 7$

3.   [12.2] **4.**   [12.3] **5.**

[12.1–12.3] **6.** Once the graph of $f(x) = 6^x$ is sketched, interchange the x- and y-values of its ordered pairs. The resulting points will be on the graph of $g(x) = \log_6 x$ since f and g are inverses. [12.2] **7.** $\{-4\}$

8. $\left\{-\frac{13}{3}\right\}$ [12.5] **9. (a)** 55.8 million **(b)** 80.8 million

[12.3] **10.** $\log_4 0.0625 = -2$ **11.** $7^2 = 49$ **12.** $\{32\}$ **13.** $\left\{\frac{1}{2}\right\}$

14. $\{2\}$ **15.** 5; 2; fifth; 32 [12.4] **16.** $2 \log_3 x + \log_3 y$

17. $\frac{1}{2} \log_5 x - \log_5 y - \log_5 z$ **18.** $\log_b \frac{s^3}{t}$ **19.** $\log_b \frac{r^{1/4} s^2}{t^{2/3}}$

[12.5] **20. (a)** 1.3636 **(b)** -0.1985 **21. (a)** $\dfrac{\log 19}{\log 3}$ **(b)** $\dfrac{\ln 19}{\ln 3}$

(c) 2.6801 [12.6] **22.** $\{3.966\}$ **23.** $\{3\}$ **24.** \$12,507.51

25. (a) \$19,260.38 **(b)** approximately 13.9 yr

Chapters 1–12 Cumulative Review Exercises (pages 810–811)

[1.4] **1.** $-2, 0, 6, \frac{30}{3}$ (or 10) **2.** $-\frac{9}{4}, -2, 0, 0.6, 6, \frac{30}{3}$ (or 10)

3. $-\sqrt{2}, \sqrt{11}$ [1.4–1.6] **4.** 16 **5.** -39 [2.3] **6.** $\left\{-\frac{2}{3}\right\}$

[2.8] **7.** $[1, \infty)$ [9.2] **8.** $\{-2, 7\}$ **9.** $(-\infty, -3) \cup (2, \infty)$

[10.6] **10.** $\{0, 4\}$ [11.1–11.3] **11.** $\left\{\dfrac{1 \pm \sqrt{13}}{6}\right\}$

[11.8] **12.** $(-\infty, -4) \cup (2, \infty)$ [11.4] **13.** $\{\pm 1, \pm 2\}$

[12.2] **14.** $\{-1\}$

[3.2, 7.1] **15.** 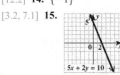 [9.3] **16.**

[11.6] **17.** $f(x) = \frac{1}{3}(x - 1)^2 + 2$ 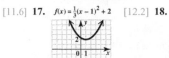 [12.2] **18.**

[12.3] **19.**

[3.3, 7.1, 7.3] **20. (a)** yes **(b)** 3346.2; The number of travelers increased by an average of 3346.2 thousand per year during 2003–2008.

[3.4, 7.2] **21.** $y = \frac{3}{4}x - \frac{19}{4}$ [4.5] **22.** $6p^2 + 7p - 3$

[4.6] **23.** $16k^2 - 24k + 9$ [4.4] **24.** $-5m^3 + 2m^2 - 7m + 4$

[4.7] **25.** $2t^3 + 5t^2 - 3t + 4$ [5.1] **26.** $x(8 + x^2)$

[5.2, 5.3] **27.** $(3y - 2)(8y + 3)$ **28.** $z(5z + 1)(z - 4)$

[5.4] **29.** $(4a + 5b^2)(4a - 5b^2)$ **30.** $(2c + d)(4c^2 - 2cd + d^2)$

31. $(4r + 7q)^2$ [4.1, 4.2] **32.** $-\dfrac{1875p^{13}}{8}$ [6.2] **33.** $\dfrac{x + 5}{x + 4}$

[6.4] **34.** $\dfrac{-3k - 19}{(k + 3)(k - 2)}$ [8.1–8.3, 8.6] **35.** $\{(4, 2)\}$

[8.4, 8.6] **36.** $\{(1, -1, 4)\}$ [8.5] **37.** 6 lb   [10.3] **38.** $12\sqrt{2}$

[10.4] **39.** $-27\sqrt{2}$ [10.7] **40.** 41

[12.4] **41.** $3 \log x + \frac{1}{2} \log y - \log z$

[12.6] **42.** **(a)** 25,000   **(b)** 30,500   **(c)** 37,300   **(d)** in about 3.5 hr, or at about 3:30 P.M.

---

13   **NONLINEAR FUNCTIONS, CONIC SECTIONS, AND NONLINEAR SYSTEMS**

Section 13.1 (pages 818–819)

1. E; 0; 0   **3.** A; $(-\infty, \infty)$; $\{\ldots, -2, -1, 0, 1, 2, \ldots\}$ **5.** B; It does not satisfy the conditions of the vertical line test.   **7.** B   **9.** A

11. domain: $(-\infty, \infty)$; range: $[0, \infty)$

13. domain: $(-\infty, 0) \cup (0, \infty)$; range: $(-\infty, 1) \cup (1, \infty)$

15. domain: $[2, \infty)$; range: $[0, \infty)$

17. domain: $(-\infty, 2) \cup (2, \infty)$; range: $(-\infty, 0) \cup (0, \infty)$

19. domain: $[-3, \infty)$; range: $[-3, \infty)$

21. domain: $(-\infty, \infty)$; range: $[1, \infty)$

23. Shift the graph of $g(x) = \dfrac{1}{x}$ to the right 3 units and up 2 units.

25. 3   **27.** 4   **29.** 0   **31.** -14 **33.** -11

35.

37.
$f(x) = \llbracket x - 3 \rrbracket$

39.

41. $\$2.75$ **43.** $2\sqrt{5}$ **45.** $\sqrt{(x - h)^2 + (y - k)^2}$

Connections   (page 824) $y_1 = -1 + \sqrt{36 - (x - 3)^2}$, $y_2 = -1 - \sqrt{36 - (x - 3)^2}$

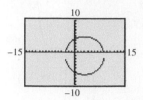

Section 13.2 (pages 825–828)

1. **(a)** $(0, 0)$ **(b)** 5   **(c)**

$x^2 + y^2 = 25$

3. B   **5.** D

7. $(x + 4)^2 + (y - 3)^2 = 4$ **9.** $(x + 8)^2 + (y + 5)^2 = 5$

11. center: $(-2, -3)$; $r = 2$ **13.** center: $(-5, 7)$; $r = 9$

15. center: $(2, 4)$; $r = 4$

17.

$x^2 + y^2 = 9$

19.

$2y^2 = 10 - 2x^2$

21. center: $(-3, 2)$

$(x + 3)^2 + (y - 2)^2 = 9$

23. center: $(2, 3)$

$x^2 + y^2 - 4x - 6y + 9 = 0$

25. center: $(-3, 3)$

$x^2 + y^2 + 6x - 6y + 9 = 0$

27. The thumbtack acts as the center and the length of the string acts as the radius.

29.

$\dfrac{x^2}{9} + \dfrac{y^2}{25} = 1$

31.
$\dfrac{x^2}{36} + \dfrac{y^2}{16} = 1$

33.
$\dfrac{x^2}{16} + \dfrac{y^2}{4} = 1$

35.
$\dfrac{y^2}{25} = 1 - \dfrac{x^2}{49}$

37.

$\dfrac{(x + 1)^2}{64} + \dfrac{(y - 2)^2}{49} = 1$

39.
$\dfrac{(x - 2)^2}{16} + \dfrac{(y - 1)^2}{9} = 1$

41. By the vertical line test the set is not a function, because a vertical line may intersect the graph of an ellipse in two points.

43. $y_1 = 4 + \sqrt{16 - (x + 2)^2}$, $y_2 = 4 - \sqrt{16 - (x + 2)^2}$

45.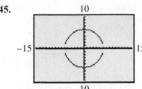

47.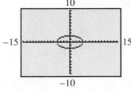

49. $3\sqrt{3}$ units   **51. (a)** 10 m   **(b)** 36 m

53. (a) 154.7 million mi   **(b)** 128.7 million mi (Answers are rounded.)

55.

57. $(3, 0)$; $(0, 4)$

Section 13.3 (pages 833–835)

1. C   **3.** D

5.
$$\frac{x^2}{16} - \frac{y^2}{9} = 1$$

7.
$$\frac{y^2}{4} - \frac{x^2}{25} = 1$$

9.
$$\frac{x^2}{25} - \frac{y^2}{36} = 1$$

11.
$$\frac{y^2}{16} - \frac{x^2}{16} = 1$$

13. hyperbola

15. ellipse
$$4x^2 + y^2 = 16$$

17. circle
$$y^2 = 36 - x^2$$

19. parabola
$$x^2 - 2y = 0$$

21. hyperbola
$$y^2 = 4 + x^2$$

23. domain: $[-4, 4]$; range: $[0, 4]$
$$f(x) = \sqrt{16 - x^2}$$

25. domain: $[-6, 6]$; range: $[-6, 0]$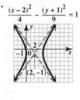
$$f(x) = -\sqrt{36 - x^2}$$

27. domain: $[-3, 3]$; range: $[-2, 0]$
$$y = -2\sqrt{1 - \frac{x^2}{9}}$$

29. domain: $(-\infty, \infty)$; range: $[3, \infty)$
$$\frac{y}{3} = \sqrt{1 + \frac{x^2}{9}}$$

31. $\dfrac{(x-2)^2}{4} - \dfrac{(y+1)^2}{9} = 1$

33. $\dfrac{y^2}{36} - \dfrac{(x-2)^2}{49} = 1$

35. (a) 50 m   **(b)** 69.3 m   **37.** $y_1 = \sqrt{\dfrac{x^2}{9} - 1}$, $y_2 = -\sqrt{\dfrac{x^2}{9} - 1}$

39.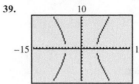

41.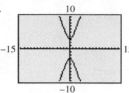

43. $\{(2, 9)\}$ **45.** $\{(-1, 2)\}$ **47.** $\left\{\pm\sqrt{3}, \pm\dfrac{\sqrt{2}}{2}i\right\}$

Section 13.4 (pages 840–841)

1. one   **3.** none

5.   **7.**   **9.** 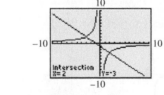   **11.**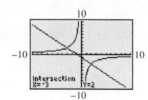

13. $\left\{(0, 0), \left(\tfrac{1}{2}, \tfrac{1}{2}\right)\right\}$ **15.** $\{(-6, 9), (-1, 4)\}$

17. $\left\{\left(-\tfrac{1}{5}, \tfrac{7}{5}\right), (1, -1)\right\}$ **19.** $\left\{(-2, -2), \left(-\tfrac{4}{3}, -3\right)\right\}$

21. $\{(-3, 1), (1, -3)\}$ **23.** $\left\{\left(-\tfrac{3}{2}, -\tfrac{9}{4}\right), (-2, 0)\right\}$

25. $\left\{\left(-\sqrt{3}, 0\right), \left(\sqrt{3}, 0\right), \left(-\sqrt{5}, 2\right), \left(\sqrt{5}, 2\right)\right\}$

27. $\left\{\left(\dfrac{\sqrt{3}}{3}i, -\dfrac{1}{2} + \dfrac{\sqrt{3}}{6}i\right), \left(-\dfrac{\sqrt{3}}{3}i, -\dfrac{1}{2} - \dfrac{\sqrt{3}}{6}i\right)\right\}$

29. $\{(-2, 0), (2, 0)\}$ **31.** $\left\{\left(\sqrt{3}, 0\right), \left(-\sqrt{3}, 0\right)\right\}$

33. $\left\{\left(-2\sqrt{3}, -2\right), \left(-2\sqrt{3}, 2\right), \left(2\sqrt{3}, -2\right), \left(2\sqrt{3}, 2\right)\right\}$

35. $\left\{\left(-2i\sqrt{2}, -2\sqrt{3}\right), \left(-2i\sqrt{2}, 2\sqrt{3}\right), \left(2i\sqrt{2}, -2\sqrt{3}\right),\right.$ $\left.\left(2i\sqrt{2}, 2\sqrt{3}\right)\right\}$ **37.** $\left\{\left(-\sqrt{5}, -\sqrt{5}\right), \left(\sqrt{5}, \sqrt{5}\right)\right\}$

39. $\{(i, 2i), (-i, -2i), (2, -1), (-2, 1)\}$

41. $\{(2, -3), (-3, 2)\}$

43. length: 12 ft; width: 7 ft   **45.** $20; \dfrac{4}{5}$ thousand or 800 calculators

47.
$$2x - y \le 4$$

Section 13.5 (pages 845–846)

1. C   **3.** B   **5.** A

7.
$$y^2 > 4 + x^2$$

9.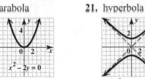
$$y \ge x^2 - 2$$

11.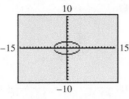
$$2y^2 \ge 8 - x^2$$

13.   **15.**   **17.**

12.   **13.**   **14.**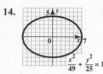

19.   **21.**   **23.**

15. $\dfrac{x^2}{65,286,400} + \dfrac{y^2}{2,560,000} = 1$ **16.** (a) 348.2 ft (b) 1787.6 ft

17.   **18.** 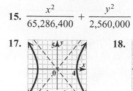 **19.**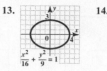

25. 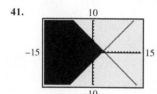 **27.**   **29.**

20. circle **21.** parabola **22.** hyperbola **23.** ellipse **24.** parabola

25. hyperbola **26.** $\dfrac{x^2}{625} - \dfrac{y^2}{1875} = 1$ **27.** $\{(6, -9), (-2, -5)\}$

31. 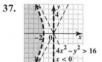 **33.**  **35.**

28. $\{(1, 2), (-5, 14)\}$ **29.** $\{(4, 2), (-1, -3)\}$

30. $\{(-2, -4), (8, 1)\}$ **31.** $\{(-\sqrt{2}, 2), (-\sqrt{2}, -2),$
$(\sqrt{2}, -2), (\sqrt{2}, 2)\}$ **32.** $\{(-\sqrt{6}, -\sqrt{3}), (-\sqrt{6}, \sqrt{3}),$
$(\sqrt{6}, -\sqrt{3}), (\sqrt{6}, \sqrt{3})\}$ **33.** 0, 1, or 2 **34.** 0, 1, 2, 3, or 4

37. 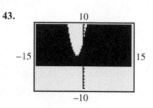 **39.**

35. 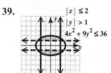 **36.**   **37.**

41. 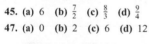 **43.**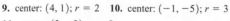

38.   **39.**   **40.**

45. (a) 6 (b) $\frac{7}{2}$ (c) $\frac{8}{3}$ (d) $\frac{9}{4}$
47. (a) 0 (b) 2 (c) 6 (d) 12

41.   **42.**   **43.**

Chapter 13 Review Exercises (pages 850–851)

1.   **2.** **3.**

44.   **45.** **46.**

4.   **5.** $(x + 2)^2 + (y - 4)^2 = 9$
6. $(x + 1)^2 + (y + 3)^2 = 25$
7. $(x - 4)^2 + (y - 2)^2 = 36$
8. center: $(-3, 2)$; $r = 4$

Chapter 13 Test (page 852)

[13.1] **1.** 0 **2.** $[0, \infty)$ **3.** $\{\ldots, -2, -1, 0, 1, 2, \ldots\}$
4. (a) C (b) A (c) D (d) B
5. domain: $(-\infty, \infty)$;   [13.2] **6.** center: $(2, -3)$;
    range: $[4, \infty)$ radius: 4

9. center: $(4, 1)$; $r = 2$ **10.** center: $(-1, -5)$; $r = 3$
11. center: $(3, -2)$; $r = 5$

7. center: $(-4, 1)$; radius: 5   [13.3] **8.**

[13.2] **9.**

[13.3] **10.**

11.

12. ellipse   **13.** hyperbola   **14.** circle
15. parabola   [13.4] **16.** $\left\{\left(-\frac{1}{2}, -10\right), (5, 1)\right\}$

17. $\left\{(-2, -2), \left(\frac{14}{5}, -\frac{2}{5}\right)\right\}$

18. $\left\{\left(-\sqrt{22}, -\sqrt{3}\right), \left(-\sqrt{22}, \sqrt{3}\right),\right.$
$\left.\left(\sqrt{22}, -\sqrt{3}\right), \left(\sqrt{22}, \sqrt{3}\right)\right\}$

[13.5] **19.**

20.

Chapters 1–13 Cumulative Review Exercises (pages 853–854)

[3.3, 7.1] **1.** $\frac{2}{3}$ [3.4, 7.2] **2.** $3x + 2y = -13$

[4.6] **3.** $25y^2 - 30y + 9$ [4.7] **4.** $4x^3 - 4x^2 + 3x + 5 + \dfrac{3}{2x + 1}$

[5.2, 5.3] **5.** $(3x + 2)(4x - 5)$ [5.4] **6.** $(z^2 + 1)(z + 1)(z - 1)$

7. $(a - 3b)(a^2 + 3ab + 9b^2)$ [6.2] **8.** $\dfrac{y - 1}{y(y - 3)}$

[6.4] **9.** $\dfrac{3c + 5}{(c + 5)(c + 3)}$ **10.** $\dfrac{1}{p}$ [6.7] **11.** $1\frac{1}{5}$ hr

[8.1–8.3, 8.6] **12.** $\{(3, -3)\}$ [8.4, 8.6] **13.** $\{(4, 1, -2)\}$

[13.4] **14.** $\left\{(-1, 5), \left(\frac{5}{2}, -2\right)\right\}$ [8.5] **15.** 40 mph

[4.1, 4.2] **16.** $\dfrac{a^5}{4}$ [10.4] **17.** $2\sqrt[3]{2}$ [10.5] **18.** $\dfrac{3\sqrt{10}}{2}$

[10.7] **19.** $\frac{7}{5} + \frac{11}{5}i$ [2.3] **20.** $\left\{\frac{2}{3}\right\}$ [2.8] **21.** $\left(-\infty, \frac{3}{5}\right]$

[9.2] **22.** $\{-4, 4\}$ **23.** $(-\infty, -5) \cup (10, \infty)$ [10.6] **24.** $\emptyset$

[5.5] **25.** $\left\{\frac{1}{5}, -\frac{3}{2}\right\}$ [11.2, 11.3] **26.** $\left\{\dfrac{3 \pm \sqrt{33}}{6}\right\}$

[11.4] **27.** $\left\{\pm\dfrac{\sqrt{6}}{2}, \pm\sqrt{7}\right\}$ [12.6] **28.** $\{3\}$

[11.5] **29.** $v = \dfrac{\pm\sqrt{rFkw}}{kw}$ [12.1] **30.** $f^{-1}(x) = \sqrt[3]{x - 4}$

[12.4, 12.5] **31. (a)** 4 **(b)** 7   [12.4] **32.** $\log \dfrac{(3x + 7)^2}{4}$

[12.2] **33. (a)** \$86.8 billion   **(b)** \$169.5 billion
[13.1] **34.** domain: $(-\infty, \infty)$; range: $[0, \infty)$

[7.4] **35.**

[11.6] **36.**

[13.5] **37.**

[13.1] **38.**

[13.3] **39.**

[12.2] **40.**

14   SEQUENCES AND SERIES

Section 14.1 (pages 860–862)

1. 2, 3, 4, 5, 6   **3.** $4, \frac{5}{2}, 2, \frac{7}{4}, \frac{8}{5}$ **5.** 3, 9, 27, 81, 243   **7.** $1, \frac{1}{4}, \frac{1}{9}, \frac{1}{16}, \frac{1}{25}$
9. $5, -5, 5, -5, 5$ **11.** $0, \frac{3}{2}, \frac{8}{3}, \frac{15}{4}, \frac{24}{5}$ **13.** -70 **15.** $\frac{49}{23}$ **17.** 171
19. $4n$ **21.** $-8n$ **23.** $\dfrac{1}{3^n}$ **25.** $\dfrac{n + 1}{n + 4}$ **27.** \$110, \$109, \$108, \$107,
\$106, \$105; \$400   **29.** \$6554   **31.** $4 + 5 + 6 + 7 + 8 = 30$
33. $3 + 6 + 11 = 20$ **35.** $-1 + 1 - 1 + 1 - 1 + 1 = 0$
37. $0 + 6 + 14 + 24 + 36 = 80$
Answers may vary for Exercises 39–43.
39. $\displaystyle\sum_{i=1}^{5}(i + 2)$ **41.** $\displaystyle\sum_{i=1}^{5} 2^i(-1)^i$ **43.** $\displaystyle\sum_{i=1}^{4} i^i$ **45.** A sequence is a list
of terms in a specific order, while a series is the indicated sum of the
terms of a sequence.   **47.** 9   **49.** $\frac{40}{9}$ **51.** 8036   **53.** $a = 6, d = 2$
55. 10

Section 14.2 (pages 867–869)

1. $d = 1$ **3.** not arithmetic   **5.** $d = -5$ **7.** 5, 9, 13, 17, 21
9. $-2, -6, -10, -14, -18$ **11.** $a_n = 5n - 3$ **13.** $a_n = \frac{3}{4}n + \frac{9}{4}$
15. $a_n = 3n - 6$ **17.** 76   **19.** 48   **21.** -1 **23.** 16   **25.** 6
27. n represents the number of terms.   **29.** 81   **31.** -3 **33.** 87
35. 390   **37.** 395   **39.** 31,375   **41.** \$465   **43.** \$2100 per month
45. 68; 1100   **47.** no; 3; 9   **49.** 18   **51.** $\frac{1}{2}$

Section 14.3 (pages 876–878)

1. $r = 2$ **3.** not geometric   **5.** $r = -3$ **7.** $r = -\frac{1}{2}$
There are alternative forms of the answers in Exercises 9–13.
9. $a_n = -5(2)^{n-1}$ **11.** $a_n = -2\left(-\frac{1}{3}\right)^{n-1}$ **13.** $a_n = 10\left(-\frac{1}{5}\right)^{n-1}$
15. $2(5)^9 = 3,906,250$ **17.** $\frac{1}{2}\left(\frac{1}{3}\right)^{11}$, or $\dfrac{1}{354,294}$ **19.** $2\left(\frac{1}{2}\right)^{24} = \dfrac{1}{2^{23}}$
21. 2, 6, 18, 54, 162   **23.** $5, -1, \frac{1}{5}, -\frac{1}{25}, \frac{1}{125}$ **25.** $\frac{121}{243}$ **27.** -1.997
29. 2.662   **31.** -2.982 **33.** \$33,410.84   **35.** \$104,273.05   **37.** 9

39. $\frac{10,000}{11}$ **41.** $-\frac{9}{20}$ **43.** The sum does not exist. **45.** $10\left(\frac{3}{5}\right)^4 \approx 1.3$ ft

47. 3 days; $\frac{1}{4}$ g **49. (a)** $1.1(1.06)^5 \approx 1.5$ billion units

(b) approximately 12 yr **51.** $\$50,000\left(\frac{3}{4}\right)^8 \approx \$5005.65$

53. $0.33333\ldots$ **54.** $0.66666\ldots$ **55.** $0.99999\ldots$

56. $\dfrac{a_1}{1-r} = \dfrac{0.9}{1-0.1} = \dfrac{0.9}{0.9} = 1$; Therefore, $0.99999\ldots = 1$

57. B **58.** $0.49999\ldots = 0.4 + 0.09999\ldots = \frac{4}{10} + \frac{1}{10}(0.9999\ldots) =$

$\frac{4}{10} + \frac{1}{10}(1) = \frac{5}{10} = \frac{1}{2}$ **59.** $9x^2 + 12xy + 4y^2$

61. $a^3 - 3a^2b + 3ab^2 - b^3$

Section 14.4 (page 883)

1. 720 **3.** 40,320 **5.** 15 **7.** 1 **9.** 120 **11.** 15 **13.** 78

15. $m^4 + 4m^3n + 6m^2n^2 + 4mn^3 + n^4$ **17.** $a^5 - 5a^4b + 10a^3b^2 -$

$10a^2b^3 + 5ab^4 - b^5$ **19.** $8x^3 + 36x^2 + 54x + 27$

21. $\dfrac{x^4}{16} - \dfrac{x^3y}{2} + \dfrac{3x^2y^2}{2} - 2xy^3 + y^4$ **23.** $x^8 + 4x^6 + 6x^4 + 4x^2 + 1$

25. $27x^6 - 27x^4y^2 + 9x^2y^4 - y^6$ **27.** $r^{12} + 24r^{11}s + 264r^{10}s^2 +$

$1760r^9s^3$ **29.** $3^{14}x^{14} - 14(3^{13})x^{13}y + 91(3^{12})x^{12}y^2 - 364(3^{11})x^{11}y^3$

31. $t^{20} + 10t^{18}u^2 + 45t^{16}u^4 + 120t^{14}u^6$ **33.** $120(2^7)m^7n^3$

35. $\dfrac{7x^2y^6}{16}$ **37.** $36k^7$ **39.** $160x^6y^3$ **41.** $4320x^9y^4$

Chapter 14 Review Exercises (pages 887–888)

1. $-1, 1, 3, 5$ **2.** $0, \frac{1}{2}, \frac{2}{3}, \frac{3}{4}$ **3.** $1, 4, 9, 16$ **4.** $\frac{1}{2}, \frac{1}{4}, \frac{1}{8}, \frac{1}{16}$

5. $0, 3, 8, 15$ **6.** $1, -2, 3, -4$ **7.** $1 + 4 + 9 + 16 + 25$

8. $2 + 3 + 4 + 5 + 6 + 7$ **9.** $11 + 16 + 21 + 26$ **10.** 18

11. 126 **12.** $\frac{2827}{840}$ **13.** \$15,444 billion **14.** arithmetic; $d = 3$

15. arithmetic; $d = 4$ **16.** geometric; $r = -\frac{1}{2}$ **17.** geometric; $r = -1$

18. neither **19.** geometric; $r = \frac{1}{2}$ **20.** 89 **21.** 73 **22.** 69

23. $a_n = -5n + 1$ **24.** $a_n = -3n + 9$ **25.** 15 **26.** 22 **27.** 152

28. 164 **29.** $a_n = -1(4)^{n-1}$ **30.** $a_n = \dfrac{2}{3}\left(\dfrac{1}{5}\right)^{n-1}$

31. $2(-3)^{10} = 118,098$ **32.** $5(2)^9 = 2560$ or $5(-2)^9 = -2560$

33. $\frac{341}{1024}$ **34.** 0 **35.** 1 **36.** The sum does not exist.

37. $32p^5 - 80p^4q + 80p^3q^2 - 40p^2q^3 + 10pq^4 - q^5$

38. $x^8 + 12x^6y + 54x^4y^2 + 108x^2y^3 + 81y^4$

39. $81t^{12} - 108t^9s^2 + 54t^6s^4 - 12t^3s^6 + s^8$ **40.** $7752(3)^{16}a^{16}b^3$

41. $a_{10} = 1536; S_{10} = 1023$ **42.** $a_{40} = 235; S_{10} = 280$

43. $a_{15} = 38; S_{10} = 95$ **44.** $a_9 = 6561; S_{10} = -14,762$

45. $a_n = 2(4)^{n-1}$ **46.** $a_n = 5n - 3$ **47.** $a_n = -3n + 15$

48. $a_n = 27\left(\dfrac{1}{3}\right)^{n-1}$ **49.** 10 sec **50.** \$21,973.00

51. approximately 42,000 **52.** $\frac{1}{128}$ **53. (a)** $\dfrac{5}{10} + \dfrac{5}{10}\left(\dfrac{1}{10}\right) +$

$\dfrac{5}{10}\left(\dfrac{1}{10}\right)^2 + \dfrac{5}{10}\left(\dfrac{1}{10}\right)^3 + \cdots$ **(b)** $\frac{1}{10}$ **(c)** $\frac{5}{9}$

54. No, the sum cannot be found, because $r = 2$. This value of r does not satisfy $|r| < 1$.

Chapter 14 Test (page 889)

[14.1] **1.** 0, 2, 0, 2, 0 [14.2] **2.** 4, 6, 8, 10, 12 [14.3] **3.** 48, 24, 12, 6, 3 [14.2] **4.** 0 [14.3] **5.** $\frac{64}{3}$ or $-\frac{64}{3}$ [14.2] **6.** 75

[14.3] **7.** 124 or 44 [14.1] **8.** 85,311 [14.3] **9.** \$137,925.91

10. It has a sum if $|r| < 1$. [14.2] **11.** 70 **12.** 33 **13.** 125,250

[14.3] **14.** 42 **15.** $\frac{1}{3}$ **16.** The sum does not exist. [14.4] **17.** 40,320

18. 1 **19.** 15 **20.** 66 **21.** $81k^4 - 540k^3 + 1350k^2 - 1500k + 625$

22. $\dfrac{14,080x^8y^4}{9}$ [14.1] **23.** \$324 [14.3] **24.** $20(3^{11}) = 3,542,940$

Chapters 1–14 Cumulative Review Exercises (pages 890–891)

[1.4–1.6] **1.** 8 **2.** -55 [1.4] **3.** $-\frac{8}{3}, 10, 0, \frac{45}{15}$ (or 3), 0.82, -3

4. $\sqrt{13}, -\sqrt{3}$ [2.3] **5.** $\left\{\frac{1}{6}\right\}$ [2.8] **6.** $[10, \infty)$ [9.2] **7.** $\left\{-\frac{9}{2}, 6\right\}$

[2.3] **8.** $\{9\}$ [9.1] **9.** $(-\infty, -3) \cup (4, \infty)$

[9.2] **10.** $(-\infty, -3] \cup [8, \infty)$ [5.5] **11.** $\left\{-\frac{5}{2}, 2\right\}$ [11.8] **12.** $[-2, 3]$

[6.6] **13.** $\emptyset$ [11.2, 11.3] **14.** $\left\{\dfrac{-5 \pm \sqrt{217}}{12}\right\}$ [12.2] **15.** $\left\{\frac{5}{2}\right\}$

[12.6] **16.** $\{2\}$ [4.5] **17.** $20p^2 - 2p - 6$

[4.6] **18.** $9k^2 - 42k + 49$ [4.4] **19.** $-5m^3 - 3m^2 + 3m + 8$

[4.7] **20.** $2t^3 + 3t^2 - 4t + 2 + \dfrac{3}{3t - 2}$

[5.2, 5.3] **21.** $z(3z + 4)(2z - 1)$ [5.4] **22.** $(7a^2 + 3b)(7a^2 - 3b)$

23. $(c + 3d)(c^2 - 3cd + 9d^2)$ [4.1, 4.2] **24.** $\frac{9}{4}$ **25.** $-\dfrac{27p^2}{10}$

[6.2] **26.** $\dfrac{x + 7}{x - 2}$ [6.4] **27.** $\dfrac{3p - 26}{p(p + 3)(p - 4)}$ [10.4] **28.** $10\sqrt{2}$

[10.7] **29.** 73 [3.3, 7.1] **30.** $\frac{3}{4}$ [3.4, 7.2] **31.** $3x + y = 4$

[7.3] **32. (a)** yes **(b)** $\{-3, -2, 0, 1, 2\}$ **(c)** $\{2, 6, 4\}$

[8.1–8.3, 8.6] **33.** $\{(-1, -2)\}$ [8.4, 8.6] **34.** $\{(2, 1, 4)\}$

[13.4] **35.** $\left\{(-1, 5), \left(\frac{5}{2}, -2\right)\right\}$ [8.5] **36.** 2 lb

[3.2, 7.1] **37.**   [9.3] **38.**

[11.6] **39.**   [13.2] **40.**

$f(x) = 2(x - 2)^2 - 3$

$\dfrac{x^2}{9} + \dfrac{y^2}{25} = 1$

[13.3] **41.**   [12.2] **42.**

$x^2 - y^2 = 9$

$g(x) = \left(\frac{1}{3}\right)^x$

[12.3] **43.**

[12.1] **44.** $f^{-1}(x) = \dfrac{x - 5}{9}$,

or $f^{-1}(x) = \dfrac{1}{9}x - \dfrac{5}{9}$

[13.2] **45.** $(x + 5)^2 + (y - 12)^2 = 81$ [14.1] **46.** $-7, -2, 3, 8, 13$

[14.2, 14.3] **47. (a)** 78   **(b)** $\frac{75}{7}$ [14.2] **48.** 30

[14.4] **49.** $32a^5 - 80a^4 + 80a^3 - 40a^2 + 10a - 1$ **50.** $-\dfrac{45x^8y^6}{4}$

APPENDICES

Appendix A (pages 896–897)

1. $\{1, 2, 3, 4, 5, 6, 7\}$ **3.** $\{$winter, spring, summer, fall$\}$ **5.** $\emptyset$
7. $\{L\}$ **9.** $\{2, 4, 6, 8, 10, \dots\}$ **11.** The sets in **Exercises 9 and 10**
are infinite sets.   **13.** true   **15.** false   **17.** true   **19.** true   **21.** true
23. true   **25.** true   **27.** false   **29.** true   **31.** true   **33.** false
35. true   **37.** true   **39.** false   **41.** false   **43.** true   **45.** $\{g, h\}$
47. $\{b, c, d, e, g, h\}$ **49.** $\{a, c, e\} = B$ **51.** $\{d\} = D$ **53.** $\{a\}$
55. $\{a, c, d, e\}$ **57.** $\{a, c, e, f\}$ **59.** $\emptyset$ **61.** B and D; C and D

Appendix B (pages 903–904)

1. $\dfrac{1}{a^2 b}$ **3.** $\dfrac{100y^{10}}{x^2}$ **5.** 0   **7.** $\dfrac{x^{10}}{2w^{13}y^5}$ **9.** $\dfrac{a^{15}}{-64b^{15}}$ **11.** $\dfrac{x^{16}z^{10}}{y^6}$
13. $-6a^4 + 11a^3 - 20a^2 + 26a - 15$ **15.** $8x^3 - 18x^2 + 6x - 16$

17. $x^2 y - xy^2 + 6y^3$ **19.** $-3x^2 - 62x + 32$
21. $10x^3 - 4x^2 + 9x - 4$ **23.** $6x^2 - 19x - 7$ **25.** $4x^2 - 9x + 2$
27. $16t^2 - 9$ **29.** $4y^4 - 16$ **31.** $16x^2 - 24x + 9$
33. $36r^2 + 60ry + 25y^2$ **35.** $c^3 + 8d^3$ **37.** $64x^3 - 1$
39. $14t^3 + 45st^2 + 18s^2t - 5s^3$ **41.** $4xy^3(2x^2y + 3x + 9y)$
43. $(x + 3)(x - 5)$ **45.** $(2x + 3)(x - 6)$ **47.** $(6t + 5)(6t - 5)$
49. $(4t + 3)^2$ **51.** $p(2m - 3n)^2$ **53.** $(x + 1)(x^2 - x + 1)$
55. $(2t + 5)(4t^2 - 10t + 25)$ **57.** $(t^2 - 5)(t^4 + 5t^2 + 25)$
59. $(5x + 2y)(t + 3r)$ **61.** $(6r - 5s)(a + 2b)$
63. $(t^2 + 1)(t + 1)(t - 1)$ **65.** $(2x + 3y - 1)(2x + 3y + 1)$
67. $4(x - 5)(x - 2)$

Appendix C (page 908)

1. $x - 5$ **3.** $4m - 1$ **5.** $2a + 4 + \dfrac{5}{a + 2}$ **7.** $p - 4 + \dfrac{9}{p + 1}$
9. $4a^2 + a + 3$ **11.** $x^4 + 2x^3 + 2x^2 + 7x + 10 + \dfrac{18}{x - 2}$
13. $-4r^5 - 7r^4 - 10r^3 - 5r^2 - 11r - 8 + \dfrac{-5}{r - 1}$
15. $-3y^4 + 8y^3 - 21y^2 + 36y - 72 + \dfrac{143}{y + 2}$ **17.** 7   **19.** -2
21. 0   **23.** By the remainder theorem, a 0 remainder means that $P(k) = 0$.
That is, k is a number that makes $P(x) = 0$.   **25.** yes   **27.** no   **29.** yes
31. no   **33.** $(2x - 3)(x + 4)$ **34.** $\left\{-4, \frac{3}{2}\right\}$ **35.** 0   **36.** 0   **37.** a
38. Yes, $x - 3$ is a factor. $Q(x) = (x - 3)(3x - 1)(x + 2)$

Glossary

For a more complete discussion, see the section(s) in parentheses.

A

absolute value The absolute value of a number is the distance between 0 and the number on a number line. (Section 1.4)

absolute value equation An absolute value equation is an equation that involves the absolute value of a variable expression. (Section 9.2)

absolute value function The function defined by $f(x) = |x|$ with a graph that includes portions of two lines is called the absolute value function. (Section 13.1)

absolute value inequality An absolute value inequality is an inequality that involves the absolute value of a variable expression. (Section 9.2)

addition property of equality The addition property of equality states that the same number can be added to (or subtracted from) both sides of an equation to obtain an equivalent equation. (Section 2.1)

addition property of inequality The addition property of inequality states that the same number can be added to (or subtracted from) both sides of an inequality without changing the solution set. (Section 2.8)

additive inverse (opposite) The additive inverse of a number x, symbolized $-x$, is the number that is the same distance from 0 on the number line as x, but on the opposite side of 0. The number 0 is its own additive inverse. For all real numbers x, $x + (-x) = (-x) + x = 0$. (Section 1.4)

algebraic expression An algebraic expression is a sequence of numbers, variables, operation symbols, and/or grouping symbols (such as parentheses) formed according to the rules of algebra. (Section 1.3)

annuity An annuity is a sequence of equal payments made at equal periods of time. (Section 14.3)

area Area is a measure of the surface covered by a two-dimensional (flat) figure. (Section 2.5)

arithmetic mean (average) The arithmetic mean of a group of numbers is the sum of all the numbers divided by the number of numbers. (Section 14.1)

arithmetic sequence (arithmetic progression) An arithmetic sequence is a sequence in which each term after the first differs from the preceding term by a constant difference. (Section 14.2)

associative property of addition The associative property of addition states that the grouping of terms in a sum does not affect the sum. (Section 1.7)

associative property of multiplication The associative property of multiplication states that the grouping of factors in a product does not affect the product. (Section 1.7)

asymptote A line that a graph more and more closely approaches as the graph gets farther away from the origin is called an asymptote of the graph. (Sections 12.2, 13.1)

asymptotes of a hyperbola The two intersecting straight lines that the branches of a hyperbola approach are called asymptotes of the hyperbola. (Section 13.3)

augmented matrix An augmented matrix is a matrix that has a vertical bar that separates the columns of the matrix into two groups, separating the coefficients from the constants of the corresponding system of equations. (Section 8.6)

axis (axis of symmetry) The axis of a parabola is the vertical or horizontal line (depending on the orientation of the graph) through the vertex of the parabola. (Sections 4.4, 11.6, 11.7)

B

base The base in an exponential expression is the expression that is the repeated factor. In b^x, b is the base. (Sections 1.2, 4.1)

binomial A binomial is a polynomial consisting of exactly two terms. (Section 4.4)

binomial theorem (general binomial expansion) The binomial theorem provides a formula used to expand a binomial raised to a power. (Section 14.4)

boundary line In the graph of an inequality, the boundary line separates the region that satisfies the inequality from the region that does not satisfy the inequality. (Sections 9.3, 13.5)

C

center of a circle The fixed point that is a fixed distance from all the points that form a circle is the center of the circle. (Section 13.2)

center of an ellipse The center of an ellipse is the fixed point located exactly halfway between the two foci. (Section 13.2)

center-radius form of the equation of a circle The center-radius form of the equation of a circle with center (h, k) and radius r is $(x - h)^2 + (y - k)^2 = r^2$. (Section 13.2)

circle A circle is the set of all points in a plane that lie a fixed distance from a fixed point. (Section 13.2)

circle graph (pie chart) A circle graph (or pie chart) is a circle divided into sectors, or wedges, whose sizes show the relative magnitudes of the categories of data being represented. (Section 1.1)

coefficient (See **numerical coefficient.**)

column of a matrix A column of a matrix is a group of elements that are read vertically. (Section 8.6)

combined variation A relationship among variables that involves both direct and inverse variation is called combined variation. (Section 7.6)

combining like terms Combining like terms is a method of adding or subtracting terms having exactly the same variable factors by using the properties of real numbers. (Section 1.8)

common difference The common difference d is the difference between any two adjacent terms of an arithmetic sequence. (Section 14.2)

common factor An integer that is a factor of two or more integers is called a common factor of those integers. (Section 5.1)

common logarithm A common logarithm is a logarithm having base 10. (Section 12.5)

common ratio The common ratio r is the constant multiplier between adjacent terms in a geometric sequence. (Section 14.3)

commutative property of addition The commutative property of addition states that the order of terms in a sum does not affect the sum. (Section 1.7)

commutative property of multiplication The commutative property of multiplication states that the order of factors in a product does not affect the product. (Section 1.7)

complement of a set The set of elements in the universal set that are not in a set A is the complement of A, written A'. (Appendix A)

complementary angles (complements) Complementary angles are two angles whose measures have a sum of $90°$. (Section 2.4)

completing the square The process of adding to a binomial the expression that makes it a perfect square trinomial is called completing the square. (Section 11.2)

complex conjugate The complex conjugate of $a + bi$ is $a - bi$. (Section 10.7)

complex fraction A complex fraction is a quotient with one or more fractions in the numerator, denominator, or both. (Section 6.5)

complex number A complex number is any number that can be written in the form $a + bi$, where a and b are real numbers and i is the imaginary unit. (Section 10.7)

components In an ordered pair (x, y), x and y are called the components of the ordered pair. (Section 7.1)

composite function If g is a function of x, and f is a function of $g(x)$, then $f(g(x))$ defines the composite function of f and g. It is symbolized $(f \circ g)(x)$. (Section 7.5)

composite number A natural number greater than 1 that is not prime is a composite number. It is composed of prime factors represented in one and only one way. (Section 1.1)

composition of functions The process of finding a composite function is called composition of functions. (Section 7.5)

compound inequality A compound inequality consists of two inequalities linked by a connective word such as *and* or *or*. (Section 9.1)

conditional equation A conditional equation is true for some replacements of the variable and false for others. (Section 2.3)

conic section When a plane intersects an infinite cone at different angles, the figures formed by the intersections are called conic sections. (Section 13.2)

conjugate The conjugate of $a + b$ is $a - b$. (Section 10.5)

consecutive integers Two integers that differ by 1 are called consecutive integers. (Sections 2.4, 5.6)

consistent system A system of equations with a solution is called a consistent system. (Section 8.1)

constant function A linear function of the form $f(x) = b$, where b is a constant, is called a constant function. (Section 7.4)

constant of variation In the variation equations $y = kx$, $y = \frac{k}{x}$, or $y = kxz$, the nonzero real number k is called the constant of variation. (Section 7.6)

contradiction A contradiction is an equation that is never true. It has no solution. (Section 2.3)

coordinate on a number line Every point on a number line is associated with a unique real number, called the coordinate of the point. (Section 1.4)

coordinates of a point The numbers in an ordered pair are called the coordinates of the corresponding point in the plane. (Sections 3.1, 7.1)

cross products The cross products in the proportion $\frac{a}{b} = \frac{c}{d}$ are ad and bc. (Section 2.6)

cube root A number b is a cube root of a if $b^3 = a$ is true. (Section 10.1)

cube root function The function defined by $f(x) = \sqrt[3]{x}$ is called the cube root function. (Section 10.1)

D

degree A degree is a basic unit of measure for angles in which one degree ($1°$) is $\frac{1}{360}$ of a complete revolution. (Section 2.4)

degree of a polynomial The degree of a polynomial is the greatest degree of any of the terms in the polynomial. (Section 4.4)

degree of a term The degree of a term is the sum of the exponents on the variables in the term. (Section 4.4)

denominator The number below the fraction bar in a fraction is called the denominator. It indicates the number of equal parts in a whole. (Section 1.1)

dependent equations Equations of a system that have the same graph (because they are different forms of the same equation) are called dependent equations. (Section 8.1)

dependent variable In an equation relating x and y, if the value of the variable y depends on the value of the variable x, then y is called the dependent variable. (Section 7.3)

descending powers A polynomial in one variable is written in descending powers of the variable if the exponents on the variables of the terms of the polynomial decrease from left to right. (Section 4.4)

difference The answer to a subtraction problem is called the difference. (Section 1.1)

difference of cubes The difference of cubes, $x^3 - y^3$, can be factored as $x^3 - y^3 = (x - y)(x^2 + xy + y^2)$. (Section 5.4)

difference of squares The difference of squares, $x^2 - y^2$, can be factored as $x^2 - y^2 = (x + y)(x - y)$. (Section 5.4)

direct variation y varies directly as x if there exists a nonzero real number (constant) k such that $y = kx$. (Section 7.6)

discriminant The discriminant of the quadratic equation $ax^2 + bx + c = 0$ is the quantity $b^2 - 4ac$ under the radical in the quadratic formula. (Section 11.3)

disjoint sets Sets that have no elements in common are disjoint sets. (Appendix A)

distributive property of multiplication with respect to addition (distributive property) For any real numbers a, b, and c, the distributive property states that $a(b + c) = ab + ac$ and $(b + c)a = ba + ca$. (Section 1.7)

domain The set of all first components (x-values) in the ordered pairs of a relation is called the domain. (Section 7.3)

E

element of a matrix The numbers in a matrix are called the elements of the matrix. (Section 8.6)

elements (members) The elements (members) of a set are the objects that belong to the set. (Section 1.3, Appendix A)

elimination method The elimination method is an algebraic method used to solve a system of equations in which the equations of the system are combined so that one or more variables is eliminated. (Section 8.3)

ellipse An ellipse is the set of all points in a plane such that the sum of the distances from two fixed points is constant. (Section 13.2)

empty set (null set) The empty set, denoted by $\{\ \}$ or $\emptyset$, is the set containing no elements. (Section 2.3, Appendix A)

equation An equation is a statement that two algebraic expressions are equal. (Section 1.3)

equivalent equations Equivalent equations are equations that have the same solution set. (Section 2.1)

equivalent inequalities Equivalent inequalities are inequalities that have the same solution set. (Section 2.8)

exponent (power) An exponent, or power, is a number that indicates how many times its base is used as a factor. In b^x, x is the exponent (power). (Sections 1.2, 4.1)

exponential equation An exponential equation is an equation that has a variable in at least one exponent. (Section 12.2)

exponential expression A number or letter (variable) written with an exponent is an exponential expression. (Sections 1.2, 4.1)

exponential function with base a An exponential function with base a is a function of the form $f(x) = a^x$, where $a > 0$ and $a \neq 1$ for all real numbers x. (Section 12.2)

extraneous solution (extraneous value) A proposed solution to an equation, following any of several procedures in the solution process, that does not satisfy the original equation is called an extraneous solution. (Sections 7.6, 10.6)

extremes of a proportion In the proportion $\frac{a}{b} = \frac{c}{d}$, the a- and d-terms are called the extremes. (Section 2.6)

F

factor If a, b, and c represent numbers and $a \cdot b = c$, then a and b are factors of c. (Sections 1.1, 5.1)

factored A number is factored by writing it as the product of two or more numbers. (Section 1.1)

factored form An expression is in factored form when it is written as a product. (Section 5.1)

factoring Writing a polynomial as the product of two or more simpler polynomials is called factoring. (Section 5.1)

factoring by grouping Factoring by grouping is a method for grouping the terms of a polynomial in such a way that the polynomial can be factored. It is used when the greatest common factor of the terms of the polynomial is 1. (Section 5.1)

factoring out the greatest common factor Factoring out the greatest common factor is the process of using the distributive property to write a polynomial as a product of the greatest common factor and a simpler polynomial. (Section 5.1)

finite sequence A finite sequence has a domain that includes only the first n positive integers. (Section 14.1)

first-degree equation A first-degree (linear) equation has no term with the variable to a power other than 1. (Section 7.1)

foci (singular, **focus**) Foci are fixed points used to determine the points that form a parabola, an ellipse, or a hyperbola. (Sections 13.2, 13.3)

FOIL FOIL is a mnemonic device which represents a method for multiplying two binomials $(a + b)(c + d)$. Multiply **F**irst terms ac, **O**uter terms ad, **I**nner terms bc, and **L**ast terms bd. Then combine like terms. (Section 4.5)

formula A formula is an equation in which variables are used to describe a relationship among several quantities. (Section 2.5)

fourth root A number b is a fourth root of a if $b^4 = a$ is true. (Section 10.1)

function A function is a set of ordered pairs (x, y) in which each value of the first component x corresponds to exactly one value of the second component y. (Section 7.3)

function notation If a function is denoted by f, the notation $y = f(x)$ is called function notation. Here y, or $f(x)$, represents the value of the function at x. (Section 7.4)

fundamental rectangle The asymptotes of a hyperbola are the extended diagonals of its fundamental rectangle, with corners at the points (a, b), $(-a, b)$, $(-a, -b)$, and $(a, -b)$. (Section 13.3)

future value of an annuity The future value of an annuity is the sum of the compound amounts of all the payments, compounded to the end of the term. (Section 14.3)

G

general term of a sequence The expression a_n, which defines a sequence, is called the general term of the sequence. (Section 14.1)

geometric sequence (geometric progression) A geometric sequence is a sequence in which each term after the first is a constant multiple of the preceding term. (Section 14.3)

graph of a number The point on a number line that corresponds to a number is its graph. (Section 1.4)

graph of an equation The graph of an equation in two variables is the set of all points that correspond to all of the ordered pairs that satisfy the equation. (Sections 3.2, 7.1)

graph of a relation The graph of a relation is the graph of its ordered pairs. (Section 7.3)

graphing method The graphing method for solving a system of equations requires graphing all equations of the system on the same axes and locating the ordered pair(s) of their intersection. (Section 8.1)

greatest common factor (GCF) The greatest common factor of a list of integers is the largest factor of all those integers. The greatest common factor of the terms of a polynomial is the largest factor of all the terms in the polynomial. (Sections 1.1, 5.1)

greatest integer function The function defined by $f(x) = [\![x]\!]$, where the symbol $[\![x]\!]$ is used to represent the greatest integer less than or equal to x, is called the greatest integer function. (Section 13.1)

grouping symbols Examples of grouping symbols are parentheses ( ), brackets [ ], and fraction bars. (Section 1.2)

H

horizontal line test The horizontal line test states that a function is one-to-one if every horizontal line intersects the graph of the function at most once. (Section 12.1)

hyperbola A hyperbola is the set of all points in a plane such that the absolute value of the difference of the distances from two fixed points is constant. (Section 13.3)

hypotenuse The side opposite the right angle in a right triangle is the longest side and is called the hypotenuse. (Sections 5.6, 10.3)

I

identity An identity is an equation that is true for all valid replacements of the variable. It has an infinite number of solutions. (Section 2.3)

identity element for addition For all real numbers a, $a + 0 = 0 + a = a$. The number 0 is called the identity element for addition. (Section 1.7)

identity element for multiplication For all real numbers a, $a \cdot 1 = 1 \cdot a = a$. The number 1 is called the identity element for multiplication. (Section 1.7)

identity property The identity property for addition states that the sum of 0 and any number equals the number. The identity property for multiplication states that the product of 1 and any number equals the number. (Section 1.7)

imaginary part   The imaginary part of the complex number $a + bi$ is b. (Section 10.7)

imaginary unit   The symbol i, which represents $\sqrt{-1}$, is called the imaginary unit. (Section 10.7)

inconsistent system   An inconsistent system of equations is a system with no solution. (Section 8.1)

independent equations   Equations of a system that have different graphs are called independent equations. (Section 8.1)

independent variable   In an equation relating x and y, if the value of the variable y depends on the value of the variable x, then x is called the independent variable. (Section 7.3)

index (order)   In a radical of the form $\sqrt[n]{a}$, n is called the index or order. (Section 10.1)

index of summation   When using summation notation, $\sum_{i=1}^{n} f(i)$, the letter i is called the index of summation. Other letters can be used. (Section 14.1)

inequality   An inequality is a statement that two expressions are not equal. (Section 1.2)

infinite sequence   An infinite sequence is a function with the set of all positive integers as the domain. (Section 14.1)

inner product   When using the FOIL method to multiply two binomials $(a + b)(c + d)$, the inner product is bc. (Section 4.5)

integers   The set of integers is $\{\ldots, -3, -2, -1, 0, 1, 2, 3, \ldots\}$. (Section 1.4)

intersection   The intersection of two sets A and B, written $A \cap B$, is the set of elements that belong to *both A and B*. (Section 9.1, Appendix A)

interval   An interval is a portion of a number line. (Section 2.8)

interval notation   Interval notation is a simplified notation that uses parentheses ( ) and/or brackets [ ] and/or the infinity symbol ∞ to describe an interval on a number line. (Section 2.8)

inverse of a function f If f is a one-to-one function, then the inverse of f is the set of all ordered pairs of the form (y, x) where (x, y) belongs to f. (Section 12.1)

inverse property   The inverse property for addition states that a number added to its opposite (additive inverse) is 0. The inverse property for multiplication states that a number multiplied by its reciprocal (multiplicative inverse) is 1. (Section 1.7)

inverse variation y varies inversely as x if there exists a nonzero real number (constant) k such that $y = \frac{k}{x}$. (Section 7.6)

irrational number   An irrational number cannot be written as the quotient of two integers, but can be represented by a point on a number line. (Sections 1.4, 10.1)

J

joint variation y varies jointly as x and z if there exists a nonzero real number (constant) k such that $y = kxz$. (Section 7.6)

L

least common denominator (LCD)   Given several denominators, the least multiple that is divisible by all the denominators is called the least common denominator. (Sections 1.1, 6.3)

legs of a right triangle   The two shorter perpendicular sides of a right triangle are called the legs. (Sections 5.6, 10.3)

like radicals   Like radicals are multiples of the same root of the same number or expression. (Section 10.3)

like terms   Terms with exactly the same variables raised to exactly the same powers are called like terms. (Sections 1.8, 4.4)

linear equation in one variable   A linear equation in one variable can be written in the form $Ax + B = C$, where A, B, and C are real numbers, with $A \neq 0$. (Section 2.1)

linear equation in two variables   A linear equation in two variables is an equation that can be written in the form $Ax + By = C$, where A, B, and C are real numbers, and A and B are not both 0. (Sections 3.1, 7.1)

linear function   A function defined by an equation of the form $f(x) = ax + b$, for real numbers a and b, is a linear function. The value of a is the slope m of the graph of the function. (Section 7.4)

linear inequality in one variable   A linear inequality in one variable can be written in the form $Ax + B < C$, $Ax + B \leq C$, $Ax + B > C$, or $Ax + B \geq C$, where A, B, and C are real numbers, with $A \neq 0$. (Section 2.8)

linear inequality in two variables   A linear inequality in two variables can be written in the form $Ax + By < C$, $Ax + By \leq C$, $Ax + By > C$, or $Ax + By \geq C$, where A, B, and C are real numbers, and A and B are not both 0. (Section 9.3)

linear system (system of linear equations)   Two or more linear equations in two or more variables form a linear system. (Section 8.1)

line graph   A line graph is a series of line segments in two dimensions that connect points representing data. (Section 3.1)

line of symmetry   The axis of a parabola is a line of symmetry for the graph. It is a line that can be drawn through the vertex of the graph in such a way that the part of the graph on one side of the line is an exact reflection of the part on the opposite side. (Sections 4.4, 11.6)

logarithm   A logarithm is an exponent. The expression $\log_a x$ represents the exponent to which the base a must be raised to obtain x. (Section 12.3)

logarithmic equation   A logarithmic equation is an equation with a logarithm of a variable expression in at least one term. (Section 12.3)

logarithmic function with base a If a and x are positive numbers with $a \neq 1$, then $f(x) = \log_a x$ defines the logarithmic function with base a. (Section 12.3)

lowest terms   A fraction is in lowest terms if the greatest common factor of the numerator and denominator is 1. (Sections 1.1, 6.1)

M

mathematical model   In a real-world problem, a mathematical model is one or more equations (or inequalities) that describe the situation. (Section 3.1)

matrix (plural, matrices)   A matrix is a rectangular array of numbers consisting of horizontal rows and vertical columns. (Section 8.6)

means of a proportion   In the proportion $\frac{a}{b} = \frac{c}{d}$, the b- and c-terms are called the means. (Section 2.6)

mixed number   A mixed number includes a whole number and a fraction written together and is understood to be the sum of the whole number and the fraction. (Section 1.1)

monomial   A monomial is a polynomial consisting of exactly one term. (Section 4.4)

multiplication property of equality   The multiplication property of equality states that the same nonzero number can be multiplied by (or divided into) both sides of an equation to obtain an equivalent equation. (Section 2.2)

multiplication property of inequality The multiplication property of inequality states that both sides of an inequality may be multiplied (or divided) by a positive number without changing the direction of the inequality symbol. Multiplying (or dividing) by a negative number reverses the direction of the inequality symbol. (Section 2.8)

multiplicative inverse (reciprocal) The multiplicative inverse (reciprocal) of a nonzero number x, symbolized $\frac{1}{x}$, is the real number which has the property that the product of the two numbers is 1. For all nonzero real numbers $x, \frac{1}{x} \cdot x = x \cdot \frac{1}{x} = 1$. (Section 1.6)

N

n-factorial ($n!$) For any positive integer n, $n(n-1)(n-2)(n-3)\cdots(2)(1) = n!$. By definition, $0! = 1$. (Section 14.4)

natural logarithm A natural logarithm is a logarithm having base e. (Section 12.5)

natural numbers The set of natural numbers is the set of numbers used for counting: $\{1, 2, 3, 4, \dots\}$. (Sections 1.1, 1.4)

negative number A negative number is located to the left of 0 on a number line. (Section 1.4)

nonlinear equation A nonlinear equation is an equation in which some terms have more than one variable or a variable of degree 2 or greater. (Section 13.4)

nonlinear system of equations A nonlinear system of equations consists of two or more equations to be considered at the same time, at least one of which is nonlinear. (Section 13.4)

nonlinear system of inequalities A nonlinear system of inequalities consists of two or more inequalities to be considered at the same time, at least one of which is nonlinear. (Section 13.5)

number line A line that has a point designated to correspond to the real number 0, and a standard unit chosen to represent the distance between 0 and 1, is a number line. All real numbers correspond to one and only one number on such a line. (Section 1.4)

numerator The number above the fraction bar in a fraction is called the numerator. It shows how many of the equivalent parts are being considered. (Section 1.1)

numerical coefficient (coefficient) The numerical factor in a term is called the numerical coefficient, or simply, the coefficient. (Sections 1.8, 4.4)

O

one-to-one function A one-to-one function is a function in which each x-value corresponds to only one y-value and each y-value corresponds to only one x-value. (Section 12.1)

ordered pair An ordered pair is a pair of numbers written within parentheses in the form (x, y). (Sections 3.1, 7.1)

ordered triple An ordered triple is a triple of numbers written within parentheses in the form (x, y, z). (Section 8.4)

ordinary annuity An ordinary annuity is an annuity in which the payments are made at the end of each time period, and the frequency of payments is the same as the frequency of compounding. (Section 14.3)

origin The point at which the x-axis and y-axis of a rectangular coordinate system intersect is called the origin. (Sections 3.1, 7.1)

outer product When using the FOIL method to multiply two binomials $(a + b)(c + d)$, the outer product is ad. (Section 4.5)

P

parabola The graph of a second-degree (quadratic) equation in two variables is called a parabola. (Sections 4.4, 11.6)

parallel lines Parallel lines are two lines in the same plane that never intersect. (Sections 3.3, 7.1)

Pascal's triangle Pascal's triangle is a triangular array of numbers that occur as coefficients in the expansion of $(x + y)^n$, using the binomial theorem. (Section 14.4)

payment period In an annuity, the time between payments is called the payment period. (Section 14.3)

percent Percent, written with the symbol %, means per one hundred. (Section 2.6)

percentage A percentage is a part of a whole. (Section 2.6)

perfect cube A perfect cube is a number with a rational cube root. (Section 10.1)

perfect square A perfect square is a number with a rational square root. (Section 10.1)

perfect square trinomial A perfect square trinomial is a trinomial that can be factored as the square of a binomial. (Section 5.4)

perimeter The perimeter of a two-dimensional figure is a measure of the distance around the outside edges of the figure—that is, the sum of the lengths of its sides. (Section 2.5)

perpendicular lines Perpendicular lines are two lines that intersect to form a right (90°) angle. (Sections 3.3, 7.1)

plot To plot an ordered pair is to locate it on a rectangular coordinate system. (Sections 3.1, 7.1)

point-slope form A linear equation is written in point-slope form if it is in the form $y - y_1 = m(x - x_1)$, where m is the slope and (x_1, y_1) is a point on the line. (Sections 3.4, 7.2)

polynomial A polynomial is a term or a finite sum of terms in which all coefficients are real, all variables have whole number exponents, and no variables appear in denominators. (Section 4.4)

polynomial function A function defined by a polynomial in one variable, consisting of one or more terms, is called a polynomial function. (Section 7.5)

polynomial in x A polynomial whose only variable is x is called a polynomial in x. (Section 4.4)

positive number A positive number is located to the right of 0 on a number line. (Section 1.4)

prime factor A prime factor of a number is a factor greater than 1 whose only factors are 1 and itself. For example, the prime factors of 12 are $2 \cdot 2 \cdot 3$. (Section 1.1)

prime number A natural number greater than 1 is prime if it has only 1 and itself as factors. (Section 1.1)

prime polynomial A prime polynomial is a polynomial that cannot be factored into factors having only integer coefficients. (Section 5.2)

principal root (principal nth root) For even indexes, the symbols $\sqrt{\ }$, $\sqrt[4]{\ }$, $\sqrt[6]{\ }, \dots, \sqrt[n]{\ }$ are used for nonnegative roots, which are called principal roots. (Section 10.1)

product The answer to a multiplication problem is called the product. (Section 1.1)

product of the sum and difference of two terms The product of the sum and difference of two terms is the difference of the squares of the terms, or $(x + y)(x - y) = x^2 - y^2$. (Section 4.6)

proportion A proportion is a statement that two ratios are equal. (Section 2.6)

proportional If y varies directly as x and there exists some nonzero real number (constant) k such that $y = kx$, then y is said to be proportional to x. (Section 7.6)

proposed solution A value that appears as an apparent solution after a rational, radical, or logarithmic equation has been solved according to standard methods is called a proposed solution for the original equation. It may or may not be an actual solution and must be checked. (Sections 6.6, 10.6, 12.6)

pure imaginary number If $a = 0$ and $b \neq 0$ in the complex number $a + bi$, the complex number is called a pure imaginary number. (Section 10.7)

Pythagorean theorem The Pythagorean theorem states that the square of the length of the hypotenuse of a right triangle equals the sum of the squares of the lengths of the two legs. (Sections 5.6, 10.3)

Q

quadrant A quadrant is one of the four regions in the plane determined by the axes in a rectangular coordinate system. (Sections 3.1, 7.1)

quadratic equation A quadratic equation is an equation that can be written in the form $ax^2 + bx + c = 0$, where a, b, and c are real numbers, with $a \neq 0$. (Sections 5.5, 11.1)

quadratic formula The quadratic formula is a general formula used to solve a quadratic equation of the form $ax^2 + bx + c = 0$, where $a \neq 0$. It is $x = \dfrac{-b \pm \sqrt{b^2 - 4ac}}{2a}$. (Section 11.3)

quadratic function A function defined by an equation of the form $f(x) = ax^2 + bx + c$, for real numbers a, b, and c, with $a \neq 0$, is a quadratic function. (Section 11.6)

quadratic inequality A quadratic inequality is an inequality that can be written in the form $ax^2 + bx + c < 0$ or $ax^2 + bx + c > 0$ (or with $\leq$ or $\geq$), where a, b, and c are real numbers, with $a \neq 0$. (Section 11.8)

quadratic in form An equation is quadratic in form if it can be written in the form $au^2 + bu + c = 0$, for $a \neq 0$ and an algebraic expression u. (Section 11.4)

quotient The answer to a division problem is called the quotient. (Section 1.1)

R

radical An expression consisting of a radical symbol, root index, and radicand is called a radical. (Section 10.1)

radical equation A radical equation is an equation with a variable in at least one radicand. (Section 10.6)

radical expression A radical expression is an algebraic expression that contains radicals. (Section 10.1)

radical symbol The symbol $\sqrt{}$ is called a radical symbol. (Section 10.1)

radicand The number or expression under a radical symbol is called the radicand. (Section 10.1)

radius The radius of a circle is the fixed distance between the center and any point on the circle. (Section 13.2)

range The set of all second components (y-values) in the ordered pairs of a relation is called the range. (Section 7.3)

ratio A ratio is a comparison of two quantities using a quotient. (Section 2.6)

rational expression The quotient of two polynomials with denominator not 0 is called a rational expression. (Section 6.1)

rational function A function that is defined by a quotient of polynomials is called a rational function. (Section 13.1)

rational inequality An inequality that involves rational expressions is called a rational inequality. (Section 11.8)

rationalizing the denominator The process of rewriting a radical expression so that the denominator contains no radicals is called rationalizing the denominator. (Section 10.5)

rational numbers Rational numbers can be written as the quotient of two integers, with denominator not 0. (Section 1.4)

real numbers Real numbers include all numbers that can be represented by points on the number line—that is, all rational and irrational numbers. (Section 1.4)

real part The real part of a complex number $a + bi$ is a. (Section 10.7)

reciprocal (See **multiplicative inverse**.)

reciprocal function The reciprocal function is defined by $f(x) = \frac{1}{x}$. (Section 13.1)

rectangular (Cartesian) coordinate system The x-axis and y-axis placed at a right angle at their zero points form a rectangular coordinate system. It is also called the Cartesian coordinate system. (Sections 3.1, 7.1)

relation A relation is a set of ordered pairs. (Section 7.3)

right angle A right angle measures 90°. (Section 2.4)

rise Rise refers to the vertical change between two points on a line—that is, the change in y-values. (Sections 3.3, 7.1)

row echelon form If a matrix is written with 1s on the diagonal from upper left to lower right and 0s below the 1s, it is said to be in row echelon form. (Section 8.6)

row of a matrix A row of a matrix is a group of elements that are read horizontally. (Section 8.6)

row operations Row operations are operations on a matrix that produce equivalent matrices, leading to systems that have the same solutions as the original system of equations. (Section 8.6)

run Run refers to the horizontal change between two points on a line—that is, the change in x-values. (Sections 3.3, 7.1)

S

scatter diagram A scatter diagram is a graph of ordered pairs of data. (Section 3.1)

scientific notation A number is written in scientific notation when it is expressed in the form $a \times 10^n$, where $1 \leq |a| < 10$ and n is an integer. (Section 4.3)

second-degree inequality A second-degree inequality is an inequality with at least one variable of degree 2 and no variable with degree greater than 2. (Section 13.5)

sequence A sequence is a function whose domain is the set of natural numbers or a set of the form $\{1, 2, 3, \ldots, n\}$. (Section 14.1)

series The indicated sum of the terms of a sequence is called a series. (Section 14.1)

set A set is a collection of objects. (Section 1.3, Appendix A)

set-builder notation The special symbolism $\{x \mid x$ has a certain property$\}$ is called set-builder notation. It is used to describe a set of numbers without actually having to list all of the elements. (Section 1.4)

signed numbers Signed numbers are numbers that can be written with a positive or negative sign. (Section 1.4)

simplified radical A simplified radical meets four conditions:

1. The radicand has no factor (except 1) that is a perfect square (if the radical is a square root), a perfect cube (if the radical is a cube root), and so on.

2. The radicand has no fractions.

3. No denominator contains a radical.

4. Exponents in the radicand and the index of the radical have greatest common factor 1.

(Section 10.3)

slope The ratio of the change in y to the change in x for any two points on a line is called the slope of the line. (Sections 3.3, 7.1)

slope-intercept form A linear equation is written in slope-intercept form if it is in the form $y = mx + b$, where m is the slope and $(0, b)$ is the y-intercept. (Sections 3.4, 7.2)

solution of an equation A solution of an equation is any replacement for the variable that makes the equation true. (Section 1.3)

solution of a system A solution of a system of equations is an ordered pair (x, y) that makes all equations true at the same time. (Section 8.1)

solution set The set of all solutions of an equation is called the solution set. (Section 2.1)

solution set of a linear system The set of all ordered pairs that satisfy all equations of a system at the same time is called the solution set. (Section 8.1)

solution set of a system of linear inequalities The set of all ordered pairs that make all inequalities of a linear system true at the same time is called the solution set of the system of linear inequalities. (Section 13.5)

square matrix A square matrix is a matrix that has the same number of rows as columns. (Section 8.6)

square of a binomial The square of a binomial is the sum of the square of the first term, twice the product of the two terms, and the square of the last term: $(x + y)^2 = x^2 + 2xy + y^2$ and $(x - y)^2 = x^2 - 2xy + y^2$. (Section 4.6)

square root The inverse of squaring a number is called taking its square root. That is, a number a is a square root of k if $a^2 = k$ is true. (Section 10.1)

square root function The function defined by $f(x) = \sqrt{x}$, with $x \geq 0$, is called the square root function. (Sections 10.1, 13.3)

square root property The square root property (for solving equations) states that if $x^2 = k$, with $k > 0$, then $x = \sqrt{k}$ or $x = -\sqrt{k}$. (Section 11.1)

squaring function The polynomial function defined by $f(x) = x^2$ is called the squaring function. (Section 13.1)

squaring property The squaring property (for solving equations) states that if each side of a given equation is squared, then all solutions of the given equation are *among* the solutions of the squared equation. (Section 10.6)

standard form of a complex number The standard form of a complex number is $a + bi$. (Section 10.7)

standard form of a linear equation A linear equation in two variables written in the form $Ax + By = C$, with A and B not both 0, is in standard form. (Sections 3.4, 7.2)

standard form of a quadratic equation A quadratic equation written in the form $ax^2 + bx + c = 0$, where a, b, and c are real numbers with $a \neq 0$, is in standard form. (Sections 5.5, 11.1)

step function A function that is defined using the greatest integer function and has a graph that resembles a series of steps is called a step function. (Section 13.1)

straight angle A straight angle measures $180°$. (Section 2.4)

subscript notation Subscript notation is a way of indicating nonspecific values. In x_1 and x_2, 1 and 2 are subscripts on the variable x. (Sections 3.3, 7.1)

subset If all elements of set A are in set B, then A is a subset of B, written $A \subseteq B$. (Appendix A)

substitution method The substitution method is an algebraic method for solving a system of equations in which one equation is solved for one of the variables, and then the result is substituted into the other equation. (Section 8.2)

sum The answer to an addition problem is called the sum. (Section 1.1)

sum of cubes The sum of cubes, $x^3 + y^3$, can be factored as $x^3 + y^3 = (x + y)(x^2 - xy + y^2)$. (Section 5.4)

summation (sigma) notation Summation notation is a compact way of writing a series using the general term of the corresponding sequence. It involves the use of the Greek letter sigma, Σ. (Section 14.1)

supplementary angles (supplements) Supplementary angles are two angles whose measures have a sum of $180°$. (Section 2.4)

synthetic division Synthetic division is a shortcut procedure for dividing a polynomial by a binomial of the form $x - k$. (Appendix C)

system of inequalities A system of inequalities consists of two or more inequalities to be solved at the same time. (Section 13.5)

system of linear equations (linear system) A system of linear equations consists of two or more linear equations to be solved at the same time. (Section 8.1)

T

table of values A table of values is an organized way of displaying ordered pairs. (Section 3.1)

term A term is a number, a variable, or the product or quotient of a number and one or more variables raised to powers. (Section 1.8)

term of an annuity The time from the beginning of the first payment period to the end of the last period is called the term of an annuity. (Section 14.3)

terms of a proportion The terms of the proportion $\frac{a}{b} = \frac{c}{d}$ are a, b, c, and d. (Section 2.6)

terms of a sequence The function values in a sequence, written in order, are called terms of the sequence. (Section 14.1)

three-part inequality An inequality that says that one number is between two other numbers is called a three-part inequality. (Section 2.8)

trinomial A trinomial is a polynomial consisting of exactly three terms. (Section 4.4)

U

union The union of two sets A and B, written $A \cup B$, is the set of elements that belong to *either A or B*, or both. (Section 9.1, Appendix A)

universal constant The number e is called a universal constant because of its importance in many areas of mathematics. (Section 12.5)

universal set The set that includes all elements under consideration is the universal set, symbolized U. (Appendix A)

unlike terms Unlike terms are terms that do not have the same variable, or terms with the same variables but whose variables are not raised to the same powers. (Section 1.8)

V

variable   A variable is a symbol, usually a letter, used to represent an unknown number. (Section 1.3)

vary directly (is proportional to) y varies directly as x if there exists a nonzero real number (constant) k such that $y = kx$. (Section 7.6)

vary inversely y varies inversely as x if there exists a nonzero real number (constant) k such that $y = \frac{k}{x}$. (Section 7.6)

vary jointly   If one variable varies as the product of several other variables (possibly raised to powers), then the first variable is said to vary jointly as the others. (Section 7.6)

Venn diagram   A Venn diagram consists of geometric figures, such as rectangles and circles, that illustrate the relationships among sets. (Appendix A)

vertex   The point on a parabola that has the least y-value (if the parabola opens up) or the greatest y-value (if the parabola opens down) is called the vertex of the parabola. (Sections 4.4, 11.6)

vertical angles   When two intersecting lines are drawn, the angles that lie opposite each other have the same measure and are called vertical angles. (Section 2.5)

vertical line test   The vertical line test states that any vertical line will intersect the graph of a function in at most one point. (Section 7.3)

volume   The volume of a three-dimensional figure is a measure of the space occupied by the figure. (Section 2.5)

W

whole numbers   The set of whole numbers is $\{0, 1, 2, 3, 4, \ldots\}$. (Sections 1.1, 1.4)

X

x-axis   The horizontal number line in a rectangular coordinate system is called the x-axis. (Sections 3.1, 7.1)

x-intercept   A point where a graph intersects the x-axis is called an x-intercept. (Sections 3.2, 7.1)

Y

y-axis   The vertical number line in a rectangular coordinate system is called the y-axis. (Sections 3.1, 7.1)

y-intercept   A point where a graph intersects the y-axis is called a y-intercept. (Sections 3.2, 7.2)

Z

zero-factor property   The zero-factor property states that if two numbers have a product of 0, then at least one of the numbers is 0. (Sections 5.5, 11.1)

A

Absolute value, 32–33
  definition of, 32
  distance definition of, 574
  evaluating, 33
  simplifying square roots, 605–606
Absolute value equations
  solution of, 575, 577–578
  steps to solve, 575
Absolute value function, 814
  graph of, 814
Absolute value inequalities
  solution of, 575–576, 578
  steps to solve, 575, 578
Addition
  associative property of, 61
  commutative property of, 60
  of complex numbers, 653
  of fractions, 6
  with grouping symbols, 40–41
  identity element for, 62
  identity property of, 62
  inverse for, 63
  of like terms, 256
  of multivariable polynomials, 260
  of negative numbers, 37
  on a number line, 37
  in order of operations, 16
  of polynomial functions, 474–475
  of polynomials, 258, 900
  properties of, 60–61
  of radical expressions, 629–630
  of rational expressions, 378–380
  of real numbers, 37, 59
  of signed numbers, 38, 59
  summary of properties of, 66
  word phrases for, 41
Addition property
  of equality, 87
  of inequality, 153
Additive identity element, 62
Additive inverse, 32, 63
  finding, 31–32
  in subtraction calculations, 40
Agreement on domain, 461
Algebraic expressions, 22
  distinguishing from equations, 25
  evaluating, 22–23, 54
  simplifying, 69–70
  from word phrases, 23–24, 72, 104
Angles
  complementary, 113
  measure of, 114, 122–123
  right, 113
  straight, 113, 122

supplementary, 113, 541
  vertical, 122, 541
Annuity
  definition of, 873
  ordinary, 873
  terms of, 873
Apogee, 484
  of an ellipse, 827
Approximately equal symbol, 606
Area of geometric figures, 120, 238,
  275–276
Area problem, 534, 703
Arithmetic mean, 859
Arithmetic progression, 862
Arithmetic sequence
  application of, 864
  common difference of, 862
  finding common difference of, 862
  general term of, 863
  specified term of, 864
  sum of terms of, 865–866
Associative properties
  definition of, 61
  distinguishing from commutative, 61–62
Asymptote, 814
Asymptotes
  of a hyperbola, 828
Augmented matrix, 547
  reduced row echelon form of, 553
Average, 58, 859
Average rate of change, 437–438
Axes of a coordinate system, 180
Axis
  of a coordinate system, 426
  of a parabola, 261, 709, 712
  transverse, 828

B

Babbage, Charles, 779
Base
  comparing percentage to, 134
  of an exponential expression, 15, 232
Basic principle of fractions, 3
Binomial coefficient formula, 880–881
Binomial expansion
  general, 881
  specified term of, 882
Binomial theorem, 879, 881
Binomials, 257
  conjugates of, 637
  greater powers of, 273
  multiplication by FOIL method, 267
  multiplication of, 634
  raising to a power, 879
  squares of, 271
  steps to multiply by FOIL method, 267

Boundary line, 584–587
Brackets, 16–17
Break-even point, 841

C

Calculator graphing
  of a circle, 824, 826
  for displaying binomial coefficients, 881
  of an ellipse, 824, 826
  to find inverse of a function, 754
  for generating quadratic models, 714
  of a hyperbola, 830
  of linear inequalities, 588
  of a root function, 832
  for solving exponential equations, 797
  for solving logarithmic equations, 797
  for solving nonlinear systems, 839
Cartesian coordinate system, 180, 426
  plotting points on, 181
Celsius-Fahrenheit relationship, 124, 455
Center
  of a circle, 820
  of an ellipse, 822
Center-radius form of a circle, 821
Change-of-base rule, 786
Circle, 820
  calculator graphing of, 824, 826
  center of, 820
  center-radius form of, 821
  equation of, 821
  graph, 9
  graph of, 820
  radius of, 820
Classifying polynomials, 257
Coefficient, 70, 256
  binomial, 880–881
Columns of a matrix, 547
Combinations, 880
Combined variation, 485
Combining like terms, 71, 256
Common denominator, 6
Common difference of an arithmetic
  sequence, 862
Common factor, 296
Common logarithms, 782
  applications of, 782
  evaluating, 782
Common ratio of a geometric
  sequence, 869
Commutative properties, 60
  distinguishing from associative, 61–62
Complement of a set, 895
  symbol for, 895
Complementary angles, 113
Completing the square, 677, 719
Complex conjugates, 654

Complex fractions, 386
  steps to simplify, 386, 388
Complex numbers, 652
  addition of, 653
  conjugates of, 654
  division of, 654
  imaginary part of, 652
  multiplication of, 653
  nonreal, 652
  real part of, 652
  standard form of, 652
  subtraction of, 653
Composite function, 476–477
Composite number, 3
Composition of functions,
    476–477
Compound inequalities, 566
  with *and,* 566
  with *or,* 569
Compound interest, 239, 794
  continuous, 795
  formula for, 708, 794
Concours d'elegance, 385
Conditional equation, 102–103
Conic sections, 813, 820
  geometric interpretation of,
    820
  identifying by equation, 831
  summary of, 830
Conjugate
  of a binomial, 637
  of a complex number, 654
Consecutive integers, 112, 338
  even, 113, 338
  odd, 113, 338
Consistent system, 505
Constant function, 468
Constant of variation, 481
Consumer Price Index (CPI), 704
Continuous compounding, 795
  formula for, 795
Contradiction, 103
Coordinate system, 180
  Cartesian, 180, 426
  origin of, 180
  quadrants of, 180
  rectangular, 180, 426
Coordinates of a point, 29, 180
  in a plane, 426
Cost, unit, 130
Cost-benefit equation, 789
Creating linear models, 449–451
Cross multiplication, 131
Cross products, 131–132
Cube(s)
  difference of, 320–321
  of a number, 15
  perfect, 603
  sum of, 322
Cube root, 602
  symbol for, 602

Cube root function, 604
  graph of, 604

D

Data, interpreting, 33
Data modeling, 449
Data set, 216
Decay
  applications of, 762–763
  exponential, 762–763, 796
Decibel, 784
Decimal numbers
  converting to percents, 134
  linear equations with, 102
  operations on, 134
  solving linear systems with, 516
Decimal numeration system, 283
Degree, 113
  of a polynomial, 257
  of a term, 257
Denominator(s), 2, 359
  common, 6
  least common, 6, 373
  rationalizing, 635
Dependent equations, 505
  elimination method for solving, 522
  substitution method for solving, 514
Dependent variable, 456–457
Depreciation, 197
Descartes, René, 180, 426
Descending powers, 257
Difference, 7, 39, 42
  of cubes, 320–321
  of squares, 317
Dimensions of a matrix, 547
Direct variation, 480
  as a power, 482
Discriminant, 686, 722
Distance, rate, and time relationship,
    143–144, 407, 537
Distance between points, formula for, 625
Distance formula for falling objects, 329
Distance to the horizon formula, 610, 628
Distributive property, 64
Dividend, 51
Divisibility tests for numbers, 58, 296
Division
  of complex numbers, 654
  of decimals, 134
  definition of, 51
  of fractions, 5
  long, 278–279
  in order of operations, 16
  of polynomial functions, 475–476
  of polynomials, 276–278
  of rational expressions, 368
  of real numbers, 51, 59
  of signed numbers, 52, 59
  synthetic, 905
  word phrases for, 54–55
  involving zero, 52

Divisor, 51
Domain
  agreement on, 461
  of a function, 459
  of a relation, 459
Double negative rule, 32
Double solution, 333
Doubling time, 788
Downward opening parabola, 712

E

e, 784
Earthquakes, intensity of, 251
Elements
  of a matrix, 547
  of a set, 25, 893
Elimination method
  for solving dependent equations, 522
  for solving inconsistent systems, 522
  for solving linear systems, 518
  for solving nonlinear systems, 837
  steps to solve by, 519
Ellipse
  apogee of, 827
  calculator graphing of, 824, 826
  center of, 822
  equation of, 822
  foci of, 822
  graph of, 823
  intercepts of, 822
  perigee of, 827
  perimeter of, 850
Empty set, 103, 893
  symbols for, 103, 893
Equal sets, 894
Equality
  addition property of, 87
  multiplication property of, 92
Equation(s), 24, 86
  absolute value, 575
  of a circle, 820–821
  conditional, 102–103
  dependent, 505
  for depreciation, 197
  distinguishing from expressions, 25, 395
  of an ellipse, 822
  equivalent, 86
  exponential, 760, 791
  first-degree, 427
  graph of, 188, 427
  of a horizontal line, 192, 429, 446–447
  of a hyperbola, 828
  independent, 505
  of an inverse function, 752
  linear in one variable, 86
  linear in three variables, 526
  linear in two variables, 177, 191, 427
  linear system of, 526
  literal, 123
  nonlinear, 835
  power rule for, 644

quadratic, 260, 329, 670
quadratic in form, 693
with radicals, 644
with rational expressions, 395
second-degree, 670
from sentences, 55–56
simplifying, 89, 95
slope of, 204
solution set of, 86
solutions of, 24, 86
square root property of, 670
of a vertical line, 193, 429, 446–447
Equation of a line, 211
point-slope form of, 213–214, 445
slope-intercept form of, 211, 444
standard form of, 215, 447
Equilibrium demand, 510
Equilibrium price, 841
Equilibrium supply, 510
Equivalent equations, 86
Equivalent forms for a rational expression, 362–363
Euler, Leonhard, 786
Even consecutive integers, 113, 338
Exponential decay, 762–763, 796
Exponential equations, 760, 791
applications of, 794
calculator graphing method for solving, 797
general method for solving, 792
properties for solving, 760, 791
steps to solve, 761
Exponential expressions, 15, 232
base of, 15, 232
evaluating, 15
Exponential functions, 758
applications of, 762
characteristics of graph of, 760
converting to logarithmic form, 766
graphs of, 758–760
properties of, 776
Exponential growth, 762, 796
Exponential notation, 611
Exponents, 15, 232
application of, 248
definitions and rules, 899
fractional, 611
integer, 239
negative, 239–240, 899
negative-to-positive rules, 241, 899
in order of operations, 16
positive, 241–242
power rules for, 234–235, 899
product rule for, 232–233, 899
quotient rule for, 242, 899
rational, 611
and scientific notation, 248
summary of rules for, 235, 243, 899
zero, 240, 899

Expressions
algebraic, 22
distinguishing from equations, 25, 395
exponential, 15, 232
quadratic, 329
radical, 600, 604, 629
rational, 358
simplifying, 69–70
terms of, 70–71, 256
from word phrases, 72
Extraneous solutions, 644
Extremes of a proportion, 131

F

Factorial notation, 880
Factoring, 296
difference of cubes, 320
difference of squares, 317
with four terms by grouping, 299–300
greatest common factor, 296
by grouping, 299
guidelines for, 306
perfect square trinomials, 318
polynomials, 325, 902
sum of cubes, 322
Factoring method for solving quadratic equations, 329, 670
Factoring trinomials, 304
by grouping, 309
in two variables, 313
using FOIL, 304, 311
Factors, 2, 296
common, 296
greatest common, 3, 296
of integers, 50
of a number, 2, 296
prime, 2
Fahrenheit-Celsius relationship, 124, 455
Farads, 607
Fibonacci, 600, 855
Finite sequence, 856
Finite set, 893
distinguishing from infinite, 894
First-degree equations, 427
graphs of, 427
Fixed cost, 220
Foci
of an ellipse, 822
of a hyperbola, 828
FOIL, 267, 304, 311, 634, 653
inner product of, 267
outer product of, 267
Formula(s), 701
binomial coefficient, 880–881
for compound interest, 794
distance, 625, 628
to evaluate variables, 120
Galileo's, 672
geometry, 120
Heron's, 610

midpoint, 430–431
of the Pythagorean theorem, 339, 624, 702
quadratic, 683–684
solving for a specified variable of, 701
with square roots, 701
vertex, 720
Fourth power(s)
perfect, 603
Fourth root, 602
symbol for, 602
Fraction(s), 2
basic principle of, 3
complex, 386
denominator of, 2
improper, 2
least common denominator of, 6, 373
linear equations with, 100–101
linear systems with, 515
lowest terms of, 3
mixed numbers, 7
numerator of, 2
operations on, 4–8
proper, 2
reciprocals of, 5, 51, 63
Fraction bar, 2, 16, 17
Fractional exponents, 611
radical form of, 614
Froude, William, 708
Froude number, 708
Function(s), 336, 457
absolute value, 814
coding information using, 757
composite, 476–477
composition of, 476–477
constant, 468
cube root, 604
definitions of, 457, 462
domain of, 459
equation of the inverse of, 752
exponential, 758
greatest integer, 816
inverse of, 750
linear, 467
logarithmic, 768
notation, 464
one-to-one, 750
operations on, 473–476
polynomial, 472–473
quadratic, 709–710
radical, 604
range of, 459
reciprocal, 814
root, 604
square root, 604, 814, 832
squaring, 814
step, 816
vertical line test for, 460
Fundamental property of rational expressions, 360

Fundamental rectangle of a hyperbola, 829
Future value of an ordinary annuity, 873
$f(x)$ notation, 464

G

Galilei, Galileo, 329, 336, 672
Galileo's formula, 672
General binomial expansion, 881
General term
  of an arithmetic sequence, 863
  of a geometric sequence, 870
  of a sequence, 856
Geometric progression, 869
Geometric sequence, 869
  common ratio of, 869
  general term of, 870
  specified term of, 871
  sum of terms of, 871–874
Geometry applications, 120
Geometry formulas, 120, 236–237, 238,
    275–276
Grade, 432
Graph(s), 425
  of absolute value functions, 814
  circle, 9
  of circles, 820
  of cube root functions, 604
  of ellipses, 823
  of equations, 188, 427
  of exponential functions, 758–760
  of first-degree equations, 427
  of a greatest integer function, 816–817
  of horizontal lines, 192, 429
  of hyperbolas, 828, 829
  of inequalities, 152
  of inverses, 753–754
  line, 176
  of linear equations, 188, 193, 427
  of linear inequalities, 152, 584
  of linear systems, 526
  of logarithmic functions, 768–769
  of numbers, 28
  of ordered pairs, 180, 426
  of parabolas, 261, 709, 724–725
  pie, 9
  of quadratic equations, 260
  of quadratic functions, 709
  of quadratic inequalities, 730
  of radical functions, 604
  of a rational number, 29
  of a reciprocal function, 814
  of second-degree inequalities, 842–843
  of square root functions, 604, 814, 831
  of systems of nonlinear inequalities,
    843
  of vertical lines, 193, 429
Graphical method
  for solving linear equations, 195
  for solving linear systems, 502–503
Graphing calculator method
  for scientific notation, 253

for solving linear equations, 195
for solving linear systems, 507
for solving quadratic equations,
    336
Greater powers of binomials, 273
Greater than, 18, 31, 151
  definition of, 31
Greater than or equal to, 18, 151
Greatest common factor, 3, 296
  factoring out, 298
  of numbers, 296
  steps to find, 296
  for variable terms, 297
Greatest integer function, 816
  graph of, 817
Grouping
  factoring by, 299
  factoring with four terms, 299–300
  factoring trinomials by, 309
Grouping symbols, 15–16
  addition with, 40–41
  subtraction with, 40–41
Growth
  applications of, 762
  exponential, 762, 796

H

Half-life, 796
Henrys, 607
Heron's formula, 610
Horizontal line, 192, 429
  equation of, 192–193, 216, 429,
    446–447, 449
  graph of, 192–193, 429
  slope of, 202–203, 434
Horizontal line test for a one-to-one
    function, 751
Horizontal parabola, 724–725
  graph of, 725
Horizontal shift, 815
  of a parabola, 711
Hyperbola, 828
  asymptotes of, 828
  equations of, 828
  foci of, 828
  fundamental rectangle of, 829
  graph of, 828, 829
  intercepts of, 828
  steps to graph, 829
Hypotenuse of a right triangle, 339,
    624

I

i, 650
  powers of, 655
Identity, 103
Identity element, 62
Identity properties, 62
Imaginary part of a complex number,
    652
Imaginary unit, 650

Improper fraction, 2
Incidence rate, 366
Inconsistent system, 505, 530, 551
  elimination method for solving, 522
  substitution method for solving, 513
Independent equations, 505
Independent variable, 456–457
Index
  of a radical, 603
  of summation, 858
Inequality(ies), 17–18, 151
  absolute value, 575
  addition property of, 153
  applied problems using, 157–158
  compound, 566
  graphs of, 152
  linear, 155–157
  linear in two variables, 584
  multiplication property of, 154
  nonlinear, 730
  nonlinear system of, 843
  polynomial, 733
  quadratic, 730
  rational, 733
  second-degree, 842
  solving linear, 151
  symbols of, 17–19, 151
  system of, 843
  three-part, 158
Infinite geometric sequence, 873–874
  sum of terms of, 874
Infinite sequence, 856
  terms of, 856
Infinite set, 893
  distinguishing from finite, 894
Infinity, 151
Inner product, 267
Integers, 28–29
  consecutive, 112, 338
  consecutive even, 113, 338
  consecutive odd, 113, 338
  as exponents, 239
  factors of, 50
Intensity of an earthquake, 251
Intercepts, 190, 211
  of an ellipse, 822
  of a hyperbola, 828
  of a linear equation, 190
  of a parabola, 722
  x, 428
  y, 428, 444–445
Interest
  compound, 239, 708, 794
  simple, 794
Interest problems, 139, 141–142
Interpreting graphs, 176
Intersection
  of linear inequalities, 587
  of sets, 566, 895
  symbol for, 566, 895
Interval notation, 151

Inverse
    additive, 31–32, 40, 63
    multiplicative, 51, 63
    of a one-to-one function, 750
Inverse of a function, 750
    calculator graphing method to find, 754
    definition of, 750
    equation of, 752
    graph of, 753–754
    steps to find the equation of, 752
    symbol for, 750
Inverse properties, 63
Inverse variation, 483
    as a power, 483
Irrational numbers, 30, 602
Isosceles triangle, 629

J

Joint variation, 484–485

L

Least common denominator, 6, 373
    steps to find, 373
Legs of a right triangle, 339, 624
Leonardo of Pisa, 600
Less than, 17, 31, 151
    definition of, 31
Less than or equal to, 18, 151
Like terms, 70, 256
    addition of, 256
    combining, 71, 256
Limit notation, 874
Line(s)
    equations of, 211
    horizontal, 192, 429
    intercepts of, 190, 211
    number, 28, 151
    parallel, 204
    perpendicular, 204
    slope of, 199, 432
    of symmetry, 261
    vertical, 193, 429
Line graph, 176, 427
    interpreting, 176
Line segment, midpoint of, 430
Linear equations in one variable, 86
    applications of, 108
    with decimal coefficients, 102
    with fractions, 100–101
    geometric applications of, 120
    with infinitely many solutions, 103
    with no solutions, 103
    solving, 97
    steps to solve, 97
Linear equations in three variables, 526
    graphs of, 526–527
Linear equations in two variables, 177, 191, 427
    calculator graphing of, 195
    graph of, 427

graphing calculator method for solving, 195
    graphing of, 188, 193
    intercepts of, 190
    point-slope form of, 213–214, 445–446
    slope-intercept form of, 211, 444
    slope of, 204
    solution of, 177
    standard form of, 215, 427, 447
    summary of forms of, 216, 449
    system of, 526
    systems of, 502
    use to model data, 194
    x-intercept of, 190, 428
    y-intercept of, 190, 428, 444–445
Linear functions, 467
    definition of, 467
Linear inequalities in one variable, 155–157
    graph of, 152
    solution of, 155–157
    steps to solve, 155
Linear inequalities in two variables, 584
    boundary line of graph, 584–587
    calculator graphing of, 588
    graph of, 584
    intersection of, 587
    region of solution, 584
    union of, 588
Linear models, creating, 449–451
Linear programming, 591
Literal equation, 123
Lithotripter, 827
Logarithmic equations, 767
    calculator graphing method for solving, 797
    properties for solving, 791
    solving, 792
    steps to solve, 794
Logarithmic functions, 766
    applications of, 770
    with base a, 768
    characteristics of graph of, 769
    converting to exponential form, 766
    graphs of, 768–769
    properties of, 776
Logarithms, 766
    alternative forms of, 777
    change-of-base rule for, 786
    common, 782
    definition of, 766
    evaluating, 782, 785
    exponential form of, 766
    natural, 784–785
    power rule for, 775
    product rule for, 773
    properties of, 768, 773, 777
    quotient rule for, 774
Long division, 278–279
LORAN, 851

Lowest terms
    of a fraction, 3
    of a rational expression, 359

M

Mapping of sets, 458
Mathematical model, 27
Matrix (matrices), 547
    augmented, 547
    calculator display of, 547
    columns of, 547
    dimensions of, 547
    elements of, 547
    reduced row echelon form of, 553
    row echelon form of, 548
    row operations on, 548
    rows of, 547
    square, 547
Matrix method for solving systems, 548, 551
Maximum value of a quadratic function, 723
Mean, 58
Mean, arithmetic, 859
Means of a proportion, 131
Measure of an angle, 114, 122–123
Midpoint of a line segment, 430–431
    formula for, 431
Minimum value of a quadratic function, 723
Minuend, 39
Mixed number, 2
Mixture problems, 111, 139–141, 536–537
Model(s), 449
    mathematical, 27
    quadratic, 340
    quadratic functions as, 704, 713
    using a linear equation to, 194
Money problems, 142–143, 535
Monomial, 70, 257
Motion problems, 144–145, 537–538, 691
Multiplication
    associative property of, 61
    of binomials, 267, 634
    commutative property of, 60
    of complex numbers, 653
    FOIL method of, 267, 634
    of fractions, 4
    identity element for, 62
    identity property of, 62
    inverse for, 51, 63
    of a monomial and a polynomial, 265
    in order of operations, 16
    of polynomial functions, 475
    of polynomials, 265, 901
    properties of, 60–61
    of radical expressions, 634
    of radicals, 619

Multiplication (*continued*)
  of radicals with different indexes, 623
  of rational expressions, 367
  of real numbers, 49, 59
  of signed numbers, 50, 59
  of sum and difference of two terms, 272
  summary of properties of, 66
  using logarithms, 773
  word phrases for, 54–55
  by zero, 49
Multiplication property
  of equality, 92
  of inequality, 154
Multiplicative identity element, 62
Multiplicative inverse, 51, 63
Multivariable polynomial, 256, 260
  addition of, 260
  subtraction of, 260

N

Napier, John, 779
Natural logarithms, 784
  applications of, 785
  evaluating, 785
Natural numbers, 2, 28
  negative of, 28
  opposite of, 28
Negative exponents, 239–240, 899
  changing to positive, 241–242
  in rational expressions, 391
Negative infinity, 151
  symbol for, 151
Negative numbers, 28
  addition of, 37
  as exponents, 240
Negative of a number, 28
Negative slope, 202, 435
Negative square roots, 600
Negative-to-positive rules, 241, 899
Newton, 481
n factorial, 880
Nonlinear equation, 835
Nonlinear system of equations, 835
  calculator graphing method for solving, 839
  elimination method for solving, 837
  substitution method for solving, 836
Nonlinear system of inequalities, 843
  graph of, 844
Nonreal complex number, 652
Not equal, 17
Notation
  exponential, 611
  factorial, 880
  function, 464
  interval, 151
  limit, 874
  scientific, 248
  set-builder, 29, 504

sigma, 858
subscript, 200, 431
summation, 858
*n*th root, 603
  exponential notation for, 611
Null set, 103, 893
  symbols for, 103, 893
Number(s)
  absolute value of, 32–33, 605–606
  additive inverse of, 31–32, 40, 63
  complex, 652
  composite, 3
  cube of, 15
  divisibility tests for, 58, 296
  factors of, 2, 296
  fractions, 2
  graph of, 28
  greatest common factor of, 296
  imaginary, 652
  integers, 28–29
  irrational, 30, 602
  mixed, 2
  natural, 2, 28
  negative, 28
  nonreal complex, 652
  opposite of, 28, 31–32, 40, 63
  ordered pair of, 426
  ordering of, 31
  perfect square, 602
  positive, 28
  prime, 2, 296
  prime factors of, 3
  pure imaginary, 652
  rational, 29
  real, 30
  reciprocal of, 5, 51
  signed, 28
  square of, 15, 600
  square roots of, 600
  whole, 2, 28
Number line, 28, 151
  addition on, 37
  graphing a number on, 28
  graphing intervals on, 151
  subtraction on, 39
Numerator, 2, 359
Numerator, rationalizing, 639
Numerical coefficient, 70, 256
Numerical expressions
  evaluating, 53
  from word phrases, 41–42, 54–55

O

Odd consecutive integers, 113, 338
Ohm's law, 657
One-to-one function, 750
  horizontal line test for, 751
  inverse of, 750
Operations
  on functions, 473–476
  on sets, 566, 568, 895–896

Opposite(s)
  of a number, 28, 31–32, 40, 63
  quotient of, 362
Order
  of operations, 15–16, 40–41
  of a radical, 603
Ordered pairs, 177, 426
  completing, 178
  components of, 426
  graph of, 180, 426
  plotting, 180
  table of, 179
Ordered triple, 526
Ordering of real numbers, 31
Ordinary annuity, 873
  future value of, 873
  payment period of, 873
Origin, 180, 426, 586–587
Outer product, 267

P

Pairs, ordered, 177, 426
Parabola, 261, 709
  applications of, 723–724
  axis of, 261, 709, 712, 724
  graph of, 261, 709–713, 724
  horizontal, 724
  horizontal shift of, 711
  intercepts of, 722
  line of symmetry of, 261
  summary of graphs of, 726
  symmetry of, 261, 709
  vertex formula for, 720
  vertex of, 261, 709, 712, 719, 724
  vertical, 710
  vertical shift of, 711
Parallel lines, 204
  slope of, 205, 436, 448
Parentheses, 15
Pascal, Blaise, 779, 879
Pascal's triangle, 879
Payment period of an ordinary annuity, 873
Percent(s), 133, 139
  applications of, 135
  converting to decimals, 134
  solving equations with, 134
  using to find percentages, 140
Percentage, 134
Perfect cube, 603
Perfect fourth power, 603
Perfect square, 602
Perfect square trinomial, 318, 676
  factoring of, 319, 323
Perigee, 484
  of an ellipse, 827
Perimeter
  of an ellipse, 850
  of a geometric figure, 12, 121
Perpendicular lines, 205
  slopes of, 205, 436, 448

pH, 782–783
    application of, 782–783
Pi (π), 30, 126, 602
Pie chart, 9
Pisa, Leonardo of, 600
Plane, 180, 526
    coordinates of points in, 426
    plotting points in, 426
Plotting points, 181
Plus or minus symbol, 671
Point-slope form, 213–214, 216, 445, 449
Points, coordinates in a plane, 180, 426
Polynomial(s)
    addition of, 258, 900
    binomial, 257
    classifying, 257
    degree of, 257
    of degree two, 260
    in descending powers, 257
    division by a monomial, 276
    division by a polynomial, 278–279
    evaluating, 258
    factoring summary, 325, 902
    graphing equations defined by, 260
    long division of, 278–282
    monomial, 257
    multiplication by a monomial, 265
    multiplication of, 265, 901
    multivariable, 256, 260
    numerical coefficients of, 256
    operations on, 258–260, 265–268, 276–282
    prime, 306
    subtraction of, 259, 900
    terms of, 257
    trinomial, 257
    in x, 257
Polynomial function(s), 472–473
    addition of, 474–475
    of degree n, 472
    division of, 475–476
    evaluating, 473
    multiplication of, 475
    subtraction of, 474–475
Polynomial inequality, 733
    third-degree, 733
Positive exponents, 241–242
Positive numbers, 28
Positive slope, 202, 435
Positive square roots, 600
Power rule(s)
    for exponents, 234–235, 899
    for logarithms, 775
    for radical equations, 644
Powers, 15, 232
    descending, 257
Powers of i, 655
    simplifying, 655
Price per unit, 130
Prime factors of a number, 3
Prime number, 2, 296
Prime polynomials, 306

Principal square root, 600
Product, 2, 49, 55
    of the sum and difference of two terms, 272
Product rule
    for exponents, 232–233, 899
    for logarithms, 773
    for radicals, 619
    special, 901
Progression
    arithmetic, 862
    geometric, 869
Proper fraction, 2
Properties of real numbers, 60–66
Proportional, 480
Proportion(s), 131
    applications of, 133
    cross products of, 131–132
    extremes of, 131
    means of, 131
    solving, 133
    terms of, 131
Pure imaginary number, 652
Pyramid, volume of, 127
Pythagorean theorem, 339, 624, 702

Q
Quadrants, 180, 426
Quadratic equations, 329, 670
    applications of, 337, 703
    completing the square method for
        solving, 677
    discriminant of, 686, 722
    factoring method for solving, 329, 331,
        670
    graphing of, 260
    with nonreal complex solutions, 673
    quadratic formula for solving, 684
    square root method for solving, 671
    standard form of, 329, 670
    steps to solve applied problems, 337
    steps to solve by completing the square,
        677
    substitution method for solving, 694,
        696
    summary of methods for solving, 700
    types of solutions, 686
    zero-factor property for solving, 331,
        670
Quadratic expression, 329
Quadratic formula, 683–684
    derivation of, 683–684
    solving quadratic equations using,
        684
Quadratic functions, 703, 710
    application using, 704, 713, 723
    general characteristics of, 712
    graphs of, 709
    maximum value of, 723
    minimum value of, 723
    steps to graph, 721

Quadratic in form equations, 694
Quadratic inequalities, 730
    graphs of, 730
    steps to solve, 732
Quadratic models, 340
Quotient, 5, 51, 55, 277
    of opposites, 362
Quotient rule
    for exponents, 242, 899
    for logarithms, 774
    for radicals, 620

R
Radical, 600
Radical equations, 644
    extraneous solutions of, 644
    power rule for solving, 644
    steps for solving, 645
Radical expressions, 600
    addition of, 629–631
    graphs of, 604
    multiplication of, 634
    rationalizing the denominator of, 635
    rationalizing the numerator of, 639
    simplifying, 619
    squaring of, 601
    subtraction of, 629–631
Radical symbol, 600
Radicals, 600
    conditions for simplified form, 621,
        642
    equations with, 644
    index of, 603
    multiplication of, 619
    order of, 603
    product rule for, 619
    quotient rule for, 620
    simplifying, 621, 642
Radicand, 600
Radius of a circle, 820
Range
    of a function, 459
    of a relation, 459
Rate of change, 209, 437–438
    average, 437–438
Rate of work, 408
Ratio, 130
    from word phrases, 130
Rational exponents, 611
    evaluating terms with, 613
    radical form of, 614
    rules for, 615
Rational expressions, 358
    applications of, 406
    with denominator zero, 359
    equations with, 395
    equivalent forms for, 362–363
    evaluating, 358
    fundamental property of, 360
    in lowest terms, 359
    with numerator zero, 359

Rational expressions (*continued*)
operations on, 370, 378–379, 381
simplifying with negative exponents, 391–392
solving an equation with, 397
steps for division of, 370
steps for multiplication of, 370
summary of operations on, 404–405
undefined values for, 359
Rational inequality, 733
steps to solve, 733
Rational numbers, 29–30
as exponents, 611
graph of, 29
Rationalizing a binomial denominator, 637
Rationalizing the denominator, 635
Rationalizing the numerator, 639
Reading graphs, 176
Real numbers, 30
absolute value of, 32–33
additive inverse of, 31–32
operations on, 37–40, 49–52
opposites of, 31–32
order of operations of, 40–41, 53
ordering of, 31
properties of, 60–66
sets of, 30
summary of operations on, 59
Real part of a complex number, 652
Reciprocal function, 814
graph of, 814
Reciprocals of fractions, 5, 51, 63
Rectangular box, volume of, 126
Rectangular coordinate system, 180, 426
plotting points in, 426
quadrants of, 426
Reduced row echelon form, 553
Regions in the real number plane, 584
Relation, 457
domain of, 459
range of, 459
Relative error, 579
Remainder theorem, 907
Richter, Charles F., 251
Richter scale, 251, 772
Right angle, 113
Right triangle, 339, 624
hypotenuse of, 339, 624
legs of, 339, 624
Rise, 199, 432
Root functions, 604
Roots
calculator approximation of, 606
cube, 602
fourth, 602
negative, 600, 603
*n*th, 603

positive, 600, 603
principal, 600, 603
square, 600, 602
Row echelon form, 548
Row operations on a matrix, 548
Rows of a matrix, 547
Rules for exponents, 243, 899
Run, 199, 432

S

Scale, 431
Scatter diagram, 182
Scientific notation, 248
on calculators, 253
and exponents, 248
steps to write a number in, 248
Second-degree equations, 670
Second-degree inequalities, 842
graphs of, 842
Semiperimeter, 610
Sequence, 856
arithmetic, 862
finite, 856
general term of, 856
geometric, 869
infinite, 856
terms of, 856
Series, 858
finite, 858
infinite, 858
Set(s), 25, 893
complement of, 895
elements of, 25, 893
empty, 103, 893
equal, 894
finite, 893
infinite, 893
intersection of, 566, 895
mapping of, 458
null, 103, 893
operations on, 566, 568, 895–896
of real numbers, 30
subset of, 894
union of, 568, 895
universal, 893
Set braces, 16, 25, 893
Set-builder notation, 29, 504
Set operations, 566, 568, 895–896
Sigma notation, 858
Signed numbers, 28
interpreting data with, 43
operations on, 39, 50, 52, 59
Similar triangles, 138
Simple interest, 794
Simple interest problems, 141–142
Simplified form of a radical, 621, 642
Simplifying algebraic expressions, 69–70
Six-step method for solving applied problems, 108

Slope(s), 199
from an equation, 204
formula for, 199, 201, 433
of horizontal lines, 202–203, 434
of a line, 199, 432
negative, 202, 435
of parallel lines, 205, 436, 448
of perpendicular lines, 205, 436, 448
positive, 202, 435
undefined, 203, 434, 436
of vertical lines, 203, 434
Slope-intercept form, 211, 216, 444, 449
Solution set
of an equation, 86
of a system of linear equations, 502
Solutions of an equation, 24, 86
Solving a literal equation, 123
Solving for a specified variable, 123, 400, 701
Special factorizations, summary of, 323
Sphere, volume of, 127
Square(s)
of a binomial, 271
completing, 677
difference of, 317
of a number, 15, 600
Square matrix, 547
Square root function, 604, 814
generalized, 832
graph of, 604, 814
Square root method for solving quadratic equations, 670, 672
Square root property, 671
Square roots, 600, 602
of *a*, 601
approximation of, 606
negative, 600
of a number, 600, 605–606
positive, 600
principal, 600
symbol for, 600
Square viewing window, 824
Squaring function, 814
Squaring of radical expressions, 601
Standard form
of a complex number, 652
of a linear equation, 177, 215–216, 427, 447, 449
of a quadratic equation, 329, 670
Standard viewing window, 431
Step function, 816
Straight angle, 113, 122
Study skills
analyzing test results, 223
managing time, 187
preparing for math final exam, 328
reading math textbook, 14
reviewing a chapter, 75
tackling homework, 36
taking lecture notes, 22
taking math tests, 164

using math textbook, xxii
using study cards, 48, 107
Subscript notation, 200, 431
Subset of a set, 894
  symbol for, 894
Substitution method
  for solving dependent equations, 514
  for solving inconsistent systems, 513
  for solving linear systems, 511
  for solving quadratic equations, 694, 696
  for solving systems, 836
  steps to solve by, 512
Subtraction
  of complex numbers, 653
  definition of, 40
  of fractions, 7
  with grouping symbols, 40–41
  of a multivariable polynomial, 260
  on a number line, 39
  in order of operations, 16
  of polynomial functions, 474–475
  of polynomials, 259, 900
  of radical expressions, 629–631
  of rational expressions, 381
  of real numbers, 40, 59
  of signed numbers, 40, 59
  word phrases for, 41–42
Subtrahend, 39
Sum, 6, 41
  of cubes, 322
  of an infinite geometric sequence, 874
  of terms of a geometric sequence, 871–872, 874
  of terms of an arithmetic sequence, 865–866
Sum of measures of angles of a triangle, 541, 545
Summation notation, 858
  index of, 858
Supplementary angles, 113, 541
Supply and demand, 510
Symbols of inequality, 17–19, 151
  statements with, 17–19
Symmetry about an axis, 261, 709
Synthetic division, 905
System of inequalities, 843
  graph of, 843
System of linear equations in three variables, 526
  applications of, 538–540
  with dependent equations, 530
  geometry of, 526–527
  graphs of, 526–527
  inconsistent, 530–531
  matrix method for solving, 550–551
  steps to solve, 527
System of linear equations in two variables, 502
  alternative method for solving, 521

applications of, 533–538
choosing a method to solve, 524
consistent, 505
with decimals, 516
with dependent equations, 505, 551
elimination method for solving, 518–522
with fractions, 515
graphical method for solving, 502–505
graphing calculator method for solving, 507
inconsistent, 505, 551
matrix method for solving, 548–549
with no solution, 504
solution of, 502
solution set of, 502
steps to solve applications of, 534
steps to solve by elimination, 519
steps to solve by graphing, 504
steps to solve by substitution, 512
substitution method for solving, 511–515
summary of outcomes, 505
System of nonlinear equations, 836
  elimination method for solving, 837
  substitution method for solving, 836

T

Table of data, 33
  interpreting, 33
Table of values, 179
Term(s), 70–71
  of an annuity, 873
  of a binomial expansion, 882
  combining, 71, 256
  degree of, 257
  of an expression, 70–71, 256
  like, 70, 256
  numerical coefficient of, 70, 256
  of a polynomial, 257
  of a proportion, 131
  of a sequence, 856
  unlike, 70, 256–257
Test point, 584
Tests for divisibility, 58–59, 296
Third-degree polynomial inequalities, 733
Three-part inequalities, 158
Threshold sound, 784
Threshold weight, 618
Traffic intensity, 366
Translating sentences into equations, 55–56
Transverse axis, 828
Triangle(s)
  isosceles, 629
  Pascal's, 879
  right, 339, 624
  similar, 138
  sum of angles of, 541, 545
Trinomials, 257
  factoring of, 304–307, 309–314
  perfect square, 318, 676
Triple, ordered, 526

U

Undefined rational expressions, 359
Undefined slope, 203, 434, 436
Union
  of linear inequalities, 588
  of sets, 568, 895
  symbol for, 568, 895
Unit cost, 130
Unit pricing, 130
Universal constant, 784
Universal set, 893
Unlike terms, 70, 256–257

V

Variable(s), 22
  dependent, 456–457
  formulas to evaluate, 120
  independent, 456–457
  solving for specified, 123, 400, 701
Variable cost, 220
Variation, 480
  combined, 485
  constant of, 480
  direct, 480
  inverse, 483
  joint, 484
  steps to solve problems with, 482
Venn diagrams, 894
Vertex of a parabola, 261, 709, 712, 719, 724
  formula for, 720
Vertical angles, 122, 541
Vertical line, 192–193, 429
  equation of, 193, 216, 429, 446–447, 449
  graph of, 192–193, 429
  slope of, 203, 434
Vertical line test for a function, 460
Vertical parabola, 710
  vertex of, 261, 709, 719
  x-intercepts of, 722
Vertical shift, 815
  of a parabola, 711
Volume, 126
  of a pyramid, 127
  of a rectangular box, 126
  of a sphere, 127

W

Whole numbers, 2, 28, 30
Windchill factor, 619
Word phrases
  for addition, 41–42
  to algebraic expressions, 23, 72, 104
  for division, 54–55
  to expressions, 72
  for multiplication, 54–55
  to numerical expressions, 41–42, 54–55
  to ratios, 130
  for subtraction, 41–42

Word statements to equations,
    55–56
Words to symbols conversions, 18–19,
    41–42, 54–55
Work problems, 408, 692–693

 X

x-axis, 180, 426
x-intercept, 190, 428
    of an ellipse, 822

of a hyperbola, 828
of a line, 428
of a parabola, 722

Y

y-axis, 180, 426
y-intercept, 190, 211–212, 428
    of an ellipse, 822
    of a hyperbola, 828
    of a line, 428, 444–445

Z

Zero
    division involving, 52
    multiplication by, 49
Zero denominator in a rational expression,
    359
Zero exponent, 240, 899
Zero-factor property, 329, 670
    solving an equation with, 331, 670

Triangles and Angles

Right Triangle
Triangle has one 90° (right) angle.

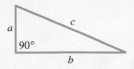

Pythagorean Theorem (for right triangles)
$a^2 + b^2 = c^2$

Right Angle
Measure is 90°.

Isosceles Triangle
Two sides are equal.

$AB = BC$

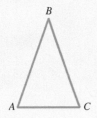

Straight Angle
Measure is 180°.

Equilateral Triangle
All sides are equal.

$AB = BC = CA$

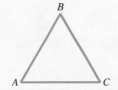

Complementary Angles
The sum of the measures of two complementary angles is 90°.

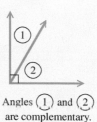

Angles ① and ② are complementary.

Sum of the Angles of Any Triangle
$A + B + C = 180°$

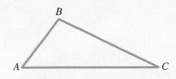

Supplementary Angles
The sum of the measures of two supplementary angles is 180°.

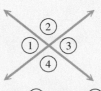

Angles ③ and ④ are supplementary.

Similar Triangles
Corresponding angles are equal. Corresponding sides are proportional.

$A = D, B = E, C = F$

$$\frac{AB}{DE} = \frac{AC}{DF} = \frac{BC}{EF}$$

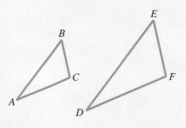

Vertical Angles
Vertical angles have equal measures.

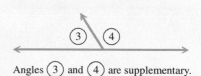

Angle ① = Angle ③

Angle ② = Angle ④

Formulas

Figure	Formulas	Illustration
Square	Perimeter: $P = 4s$ Area: $\mathcal{A} = s^2$	
Rectangle	Perimeter: $P = 2L + 2W$ Area: $\mathcal{A} = LW$	
Triangle	Perimeter: $P = a + b + c$ Area: $\mathcal{A} = \dfrac{1}{2}bh$	
Parallelogram	Perimeter: $P = 2a + 2b$ Area: $\mathcal{A} = bh$	
Trapezoid	Perimeter: $P = a + b + c + B$ Area: $\mathcal{A} = \dfrac{1}{2}h(b + B)$	
Circle	Diameter: $d = 2r$ Circumference: $C = 2\pi r$ $C = \pi d$ Area: $\mathcal{A} = \pi r^2$	